Complete Solut
to Accompany

Calculus
with Analytic Geometry
FOURTH EDITION

HOWARD ANTON
DREXEL UNIVERSITY

Prepared by

Albert Herr
Drexel University

JOHN WILEY & SONS, INC.
New York   Chichester   Brisbane   Toronto   Singapore

Printed and bound by Malloy Lithographing, Inc.

10 9 8 7 6 5 4 3 2 1

Preface

This supplement to the *fourth edition* of **Calculus with Analytic Geometry** by Howard Anton is designed to serve as a handy reference for teachers, tutors, and instructional services. It contains answers and, where appropriate, detailed solutions to the more than 7000 exercises in the text. For each exercise, the level of difficulty, the mathematical skills needed, and a method of solution can be quickly determined. The solutions show intermediate algebraic steps and manipulations that are a frequent cause of trouble for students, and also show details in the use of the various formulas that are encountered in calculus. Diagrams are used throughout the manual to assist in the visualization of problems and to suggest strategies for their solutions. High quality computer-generated figures ensure accuracy where a graph is needed in a solution or answer.

The **Student's Solutions Manual** consists of all of the odd-numbered exercises that are contained in the Complete Solutions Manual.

Special thanks are due to everyone at **Techsetters Incorporated** for the outstanding technical assistance that was provided for the production of this manual – typing, generation of art, and many other services that facilitated its preparation.

Contents

CHAPTER 1
Coordinates, Graphs, Lines

EXERCISE SET 1.1

1. **(a)** rational   **(b)** integer, rational   **(c)** integer, rational
   (d) rational   **(e)** integer, rational   **(f)** irrational
   (g) rational   **(h)** integer, rational

2. **(a)** irrational   **(b)** rational   **(c)** rational   **(d)** rational

3. **(a)**
$$x = 0.123123123\cdots$$
$$1000x = 123.123123123\cdots$$
$$999x = 123$$
$$x = \frac{123}{999} = \frac{41}{333}$$

   (b)
$$x = 12.7777\cdots$$
$$10x = 127.7777\cdots$$
$$9x = 115$$
$$x = \frac{115}{9}$$

   (c)
$$x = 38.07818181\cdots$$
$$100x = 3807.81818181\cdots$$
$$99x = 3769.74 = \frac{3769.74}{99}$$
$$= \frac{376974}{9900} = \frac{20943}{550}$$

   (d)
$$0.4296000\cdots = 0.4296$$
$$= \frac{4296}{10000}$$
$$= \frac{537}{1250}$$

4. $x = 0.99999\cdots$, $10x = 9.99999\cdots$, $9x = 9$, $x = 1$

5. **(a)** If r is the radius, then $D = 2r$ so $\left(\dfrac{8}{9}D\right)^2 = \left(\dfrac{16}{9}r\right)^2 = \dfrac{256}{81}r^2$. The area of a circle of radius r is πr^2 so 256/81 was the approximation used for π.
   (b) $256/81 \approx 3.16049$, $22/7 \approx 3.14268$, and $\pi \approx 3.14159$ so 256/81 is worse than 22/7.

6. **(a)** $\dfrac{223}{71} < \dfrac{333}{106} < \dfrac{63}{25}\dfrac{(17 + 15\sqrt{5})}{(7 + 15\sqrt{5})} < \dfrac{355}{113} < \dfrac{22}{7}$
   (b) Ramanujan's   **(c)** Athoniszoon's   **(d)** Ramanujan's

7. line 2: blocks 3, 4; line 3: blocks 1, 2
   line 4: blocks 3, 4; line 5: blocks 2, 4, 5
   line 6: blocks 1, 2; line 7: blocks 3, 4

8.   line 1: all blocks; line 2: none
     line 3: blocks 2, 4; line 4: block 2
     line 5: blocks 2, 3

9.   **(a)** always correct (add -3 to both sides of $a \leq b$)
     (b) not always correct (correct only if $a = b = 0$)
     (c) not always correct (correct only if $a = b = 0$)
     (d) always correct (multiply both sides of $a \leq b$ by 6)
     (e) not always correct (correct only if $a \geq 0$)
     (f) always correct (multiply both sides of $a \leq b$ by the nonnegative quantity a^2)

10. **(a)** always correct
     (b) not always correct (for example let $a = b = 0$, $c = 1$, $d = 2$)
     (c) not always correct (for example let $a = 1$, $b = 2$, $c = d = 0$)

11. **(a)** all values because $a = a$ is always valid   **(b)** none

12. $a = b$, because if $a \neq b$ then $a < b$ and $b < a$ are contradictory

13. **(a)** yes, because $a \leq b$ is true if $a < b$ **(b)** no, because $a < b$ is false if $a = b$ is true

14. **(a)** $x^2 - 5x = 0$, $x(x - 5) = 0$ so $x = 0$ or $x = 5$
     (b) $-1, 0, 1, 2$ are the only integers that satisfy $-2 < x < 3$

15. **(a)** $\{x : x$ is a positive odd integer$\}$ **(b)** $\{x : x$ is an even integer$\}$
     (c) $\{x : x$ is irrational$\}$ **(d)** $\{x : x$ is an integer and $7 \leq x \leq 10\}$

16. **(a)** not equal to A because 0 is not in A **(b)** equal to A
     (c) equal to A because $(x - 3)(x^2 - 3x + 2) = 0$, $(x - 3)(x - 2)(x - 1) = 0$ so $x = 1, 2,$ or 3

17. **(a)** false, there are points inside the triangle that are not inside the circle
     (b) true, all points inside the triangle are also inside the square
     (c) true   **(d)** false   **(e)** true
     (f) true, a is inside the circle   **(g)** true

18. **(a)** ϕ, $\{a_1\}$, $\{a_2\}$, $\{a_3\}$, $\{a_1, a_2\}$, $\{a_1, a_3\}$, $\{a_2, a_3\}$, $\{a_1, a_2, a_3\}$ **(b)** ϕ

19. **(a)**

(b)

(c)

(d)

(e)

(f)

20. **(a)**

(b)

(c)

(d) none

21. **(a)** $[-2, 2]$

(b) $(-\infty, -2) \cup (2, +\infty)$

22. **(a)**

(b)

(c)

(d)

(e)

(f)

(g)

(h)

23. $3x - 2 < 8$
$$3x < 10$$
$$x < \frac{10}{3}$$
$$S = (-\infty, 10/3)$$

24. $\frac{1}{5}x + 6 \geq 14$
$$\frac{1}{5}x \geq 8$$
$$x \geq 40$$
$$S = [40, +\infty)$$

25. $4 + 5x \le 3x - 7$

$2x \le -11$

$x \le -\dfrac{11}{2}$

$S = (-\infty, -11/2]$

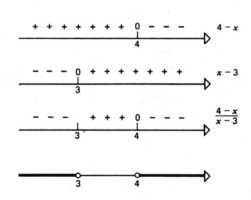

26. $2x - 1 > 11x + 9$

$-9x > 10$

$x < -\dfrac{10}{9}$

$S = (-\infty, -10/9)$

27. $3 \le 4 - 2x < 7$

$-1 \le -2x < 3$

$\dfrac{1}{2} \ge x > -\dfrac{3}{2}$

$S = (-3/2, 1/2]$

28. $-2 \ge 3 - 8x \ge -11$

$-5 \ge -8x \ge -14$

$\dfrac{5}{8} \le x \le \dfrac{7}{4}$

$S = [5/8, 7/4]$

29. $\dfrac{x}{x-3} < 4$

$\dfrac{x}{x-3} - 4 < 0$

$\dfrac{x - 4(x-3)}{x-3} < 0$

$\dfrac{12 - 3x}{x-3} < 0$

$\dfrac{4 - x}{x-3} < 0$

$S = (-\infty, 3) \cup (4, +\infty)$

30.
$$\frac{x}{8-x} \geq -2$$

$$\frac{x}{8-x} + 2 \geq 0$$

$$\frac{x + 2(8-x)}{8-x} \geq 0$$

$$\frac{16-x}{8-x} \geq 0$$

$$S = (-\infty, 8) \cup [16, +\infty)$$

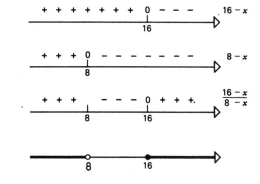

31.
$$\frac{3x+1}{x-2} < 1$$

$$\frac{3x+1}{x-2} - 1 < 0$$

$$\frac{3x+1-(x-2)}{x-2} < 0$$

$$\frac{2x+3}{x-2} < 0$$

$$\frac{x+3/2}{x-2} < 0$$

$$S = (-3/2, 2)$$

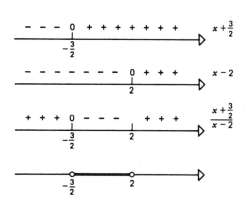

32.
$$\frac{(1/2)x - 3}{4+x} > 1$$

$$\frac{(1/2)x - 3}{4+x} - 1 > 0$$

$$\frac{(1/2)x - 3 - (4+x)}{4+x} > 0$$

$$\frac{(-1/2)x - 7}{4+x} > 0$$

$$\frac{x+14}{x+4} < 0$$

$$S = (-14, -4)$$

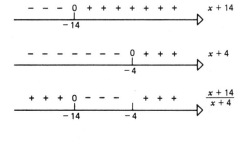

33.

$$\frac{4}{2-x} \le 1$$

$$\frac{4-(2-x)}{2-x} \le 0$$

$$\frac{x+2}{2-x} \le 0$$

$$S = (-\infty, -2] \cup (2, +\infty)$$

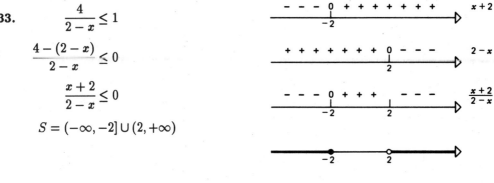

34.

$$\frac{3}{x-5} \le 2$$

$$\frac{3-2(x-5)}{x-5} \le 0$$

$$\frac{13-2x}{x-5} \le 0$$

$$\frac{13/2-x}{x-5} \le 0$$

$$S = (-\infty, 5) \cup [13/2, +\infty)$$

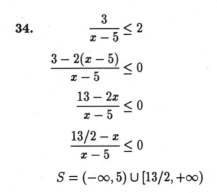
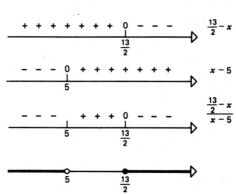

35.

$$x^2 > 9$$

$$x^2 - 9 > 0$$

$$(x+3)(x-3) > 0$$

$$S = (-\infty, -3) \cup (3, +\infty)$$

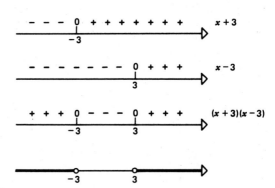

36.

$$x^2 \leq 5$$
$$x^2 - 5 \leq 0$$
$$(x + \sqrt{5})(x - \sqrt{5}) \leq 0$$
$$S = [-\sqrt{5}, \sqrt{5}]$$

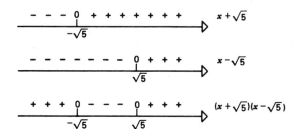

37. $(x - 4)(x + 2) > 0$

$$S = (-\infty, -2) \cup (4, +\infty)$$

38. $(x - 3)(x + 4) < 0$

$$S = (-4, 3)$$

39. $x^2 - 9x + 20 \leq 0$

       $(x-4)(x-5) \leq 0$

         $S = [4, 5]$

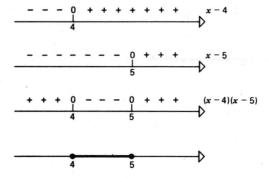

40. $2 - 3x + x^2 \geq 0$

       $(x-1)(x-2) \geq 0$

       $S = (-\infty, 1] \cup [2, +\infty)$

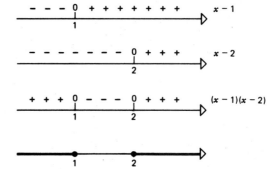

41. $\dfrac{2}{x} < \dfrac{3}{x-4}$

       $\dfrac{2}{x} - \dfrac{3}{x-4} < 0$

     $\dfrac{2(x-4) - 3x}{x(x-4)} < 0$

        $\dfrac{-x-8}{x(x-4)} < 0$

         $\dfrac{x+8}{x(x-4)} > 0$

    $S = (-8, 0) \cup (4, +\infty)$

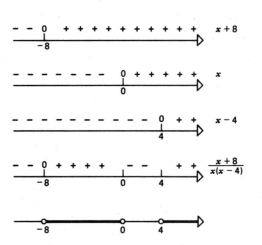

42.

$$\frac{1}{x+1} \geq \frac{3}{x-2}$$

$$\frac{1}{x+1} - \frac{3}{x-2} \geq 0$$

$$\frac{x-2-3(x+1)}{(x+1)(x-2)} \geq 0$$

$$\frac{-2x-5}{(x+1)(x-2)} \geq 0$$

$$\frac{x+5/2}{(x+1)(x-2)} \leq 0$$

$$S = (-\infty, -5/2] \cup (-1, 2)$$

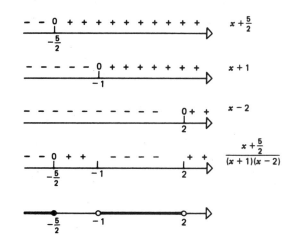

43. By trial-and-error we find that $x = 2$ is a root of the equation $x^3 - x^2 - x - 2 = 0$ so $x - 2$ is a factor of $x^3 - x^2 - x - 2$. By long division we find that $x^2 + x + 1$ is another factor so $x^3 - x^2 - x - 2 = (x-2)(x^2 + x + 1)$. The linear factors of $x^2 + x + 1$ can be determined by first finding the roots of $x^2 + x + 1 = 0$ by the quadratic formula. These roots are complex numbers so $x^2 + x + 1 \neq 0$ for all real x; thus $x^2 + x + 1$ must be always positive or always negative. Since $x^2 + x + 1$ is positive when $x = 0$, it follows that $x^2 + x + 1 > 0$ for all real x. Hence $x^3 - x^2 - x - 2 > 0$, $(x-2)(x^2 + x + 1) > 0$, $x - 2 > 0$, $x > 2$, so $S = (2, +\infty)$.

44. By trial-and-error we find that $x = 1$ is a root of the equation $x^3 - 3x + 2 = 0$ so $x - 1$ is a factor of $x^3 - 3x + 2$. By long division we find that $x^2 + x - 2$ is another factor so $x^3 - 3x + 2 = (x-1)(x^2 + x - 2) = (x-1)(x-1)(x+2) = (x-1)^2(x+2)$. Therefore we want to solve $(x-1)^2(x+2) \leq 0$. Now if $x \neq 1$, then $(x-1)^2 > 0$ and so $x + 2 \leq 0$, $x \leq -2$. By inspection, $x = 1$ is also a solution so $S = (-\infty, -2] \cup \{1\}$.

45. $\sqrt{x^2 + x - 6}$ is real if $x^2 + x - 6 \geq 0$. Factor to get $(x+3)(x-2) \geq 0$ which has as its solution $x \leq -3$ or $x \geq 2$.

46. $\sqrt{\dfrac{x+2}{x-1}}$ is real if $\dfrac{x+2}{x-1} \geq 0$, which is true for $x \leq -2$ or $x > 1$.

47. $25 \leq \dfrac{5}{9}(F - 32) \leq 40$, $45 \leq F - 32 \leq 72$, $77 \leq F \leq 104$.

48. (a) $n = 2k$, $n^2 = 4k^2 = 2(2k^2)$ where $2k^2$ is an integer.
(b) $n = 2k + 1$, $n^2 = 4k^2 + 4k + 1 = 2(2k^2 + 2k) + 1$ where $2k^2 + 2k$ is an integer.

49. **(a)** Assume m and n are rational, then $m = \dfrac{p}{q}$ and $n = \dfrac{r}{s}$ where p, q, r, and s are integers

    so $m + n = \dfrac{p}{q} + \dfrac{r}{s} = \dfrac{ps + rq}{qs}$ which is rational because $ps + rq$ and qs are integers.

    (b) (proof by contradiction)   Assume m is rational and n is irrational, then $m = \dfrac{p}{q}$ where

    p and q are integers. Suppose that $m + n$ is rational, then $m + n = \dfrac{r}{s}$ where r and s

    are integers so $n = \dfrac{r}{s} - m = \dfrac{r}{s} - \dfrac{p}{q} = \dfrac{rq - ps}{sq}$. But $rq - ps$ and sq are integers, so n is

    rational which contradicts the assumption that n is irrational.

50. **(a)** Assume m and n are rational, then $m = \dfrac{p}{q}$ and $n = \dfrac{r}{s}$ where p, q, r, and s are integers

    so $mn = \dfrac{p}{q} \cdot \dfrac{r}{s} = \dfrac{pr}{qs}$ which is rational because pr and qs are integers.

    (b) (proof by contradiction)   Assume m is rational and nonzero and that n is irrational,

    then $m = \dfrac{p}{q}$ where p and q are integers and $p \neq 0$. Suppose that mn is rational, then

    $mn = \dfrac{r}{s}$ where r and s are integers so $n = \dfrac{r/s}{m} = \dfrac{r/s}{p/q} = \dfrac{rq}{ps}$. But rq and ps are integers,

    so n is rational which contradicts the assumption that n is irrational.

51. (by example)   Given that $\sqrt{2}$ is irrational, then

    $\qquad (-1)\sqrt{2} = -\sqrt{2}$ is irrational (Exercise 50, part (b))

    but $\sqrt{2} + (-\sqrt{2}) = 0$, which is rational;

    $\qquad \sqrt{2} + \sqrt{2} = 2\sqrt{2}$, which is irrational (Exercise 50, part (b));

    $\qquad (\sqrt{2})(\sqrt{2}) = 2$, which is rational;

    $\qquad 1 + \sqrt{2}$ is irrational (Exercise 49, part (b))

    and so $\sqrt{2}(1 + \sqrt{2}) = \sqrt{2} + 2$, which is irrational (Exercise 49, part (b)).

52. **(a)** irrational (Exercise 49, part (b))   **(b)** irrational (Exercise 50, part (b))
    (c) rational (because $\sqrt{8}\sqrt{2} = \sqrt{16} = 4$)
    (d) irrational (by contradiction: suppose that $\sqrt{\pi}$ is rational, then from Exercise 50, part
    (a), $\sqrt{\pi}\sqrt{\pi}$ is rational; but $\sqrt{\pi}\sqrt{\pi} = \pi$, which is irrational).

53. **(I)** The average of two rational numbers is rational:
    Assume m and n are rational; then $m = \dfrac{p}{q}$ and $n = \dfrac{r}{s}$ where p, q, r, and s are integers.
    The average of m and n is

    $$\frac{1}{2}(m + n) = \frac{1}{2}(p/q + r/s) = \frac{ps + rq}{2qs}$$

    which is rational because $ps + rq$ and $2qs$ are integers.

(II) The average of two irrational numbers can be rational or irrational:

By example,

$\sqrt{2}$, and $-\sqrt{2}$ are irrational and their average is $\frac{1}{2}(\sqrt{2}+(-\sqrt{2})) = \frac{1}{2}(0) = 0$, which is rational;

$\sqrt{2}$ and $\sqrt{2}$ are irrational and their average is $\frac{1}{2}(\sqrt{2}+\sqrt{2}) = \sqrt{2}$, which is irrational.

54. If $10^x = 3$, then $x > 0$ because $10^x \leq 1$ for $x \leq 0$. Suppose that $x = p/q$ where p and q are positive integers, then $10^{p/q} = 3$ so $10^p = 3^q$. But positive integer powers of 3 are always divisible by 3, and positive integer powers of 10 are never divisible by 3 thus there are no positive integer values of p and q for which $10^p = 3^q$ so x cannot be rational.

55. $8x^3 - 4x^2 - 2x + 1$ can be factored by grouping terms:

$(8x^3 - 4x^2) - (2x - 1) = 4x^2(2x - 1) - (2x - 1) = (2x - 1)(4x^2 - 1) = (2x - 1)^2(2x + 1)$. The problem, then, is to solve $(2x - 1)^2(2x + 1) < 0$. By inspection, $x = 1/2$ is not a solution. If $x \neq 1/2$, then $(2x - 1)^2 > 0$ and it follows that $2x + 1 < 0$, $2x < -1$, $x < -1/2$, so $S = (-\infty, -1/2)$.

56. First, rewrite the inequality as $12x^3 - 20x^2 + 11x - 2 \geq 0$. Now, if a polynomial in x with integer coefficients has a rational zero $\dfrac{p}{q}$, then p will be a factor of the constant term and q will be a factor of the coefficient of the highest power of x. By trial-and-error we find that $x = 1/2$ is a zero, thus $(x - 1/2)$ is a factor so

$$12x^3 - 20x^2 + 11x - 2 = (x - 1/2)\left(12x^2 - 14x + 4\right)$$
$$= 2(x - 1/2)\left(6x^2 - 7x + 2\right)$$
$$= 2(x - 1/2)(2x - 1)(3x - 2) = (2x - 1)^2(3x - 2).$$

Now to solve $(2x - 1)^2(3x - 2) \geq 0$ we first note that $x = 1/2$ is a solution. If $x \neq 1/2$ then $(2x - 1)^2 > 0$ and $3x - 2 \geq 0$, $3x \geq 2$, $x \geq 2/3$ so $S = [2/3, +\infty) \cup \{1/2\}$.

57. If $a < b$, then $ac < bc$ because c is positive; if $c < d$, then $bc < bd$ because b is positive, so $ac < bd$ (part (a), Theorem 1.1.3.)

58. Consider the long division process as applied to $\dfrac{m}{n}$ where m and n are positive integers with no common factors, and $0 < \dfrac{m}{n} < 1$. Note: We only need to work with positive fractions because the proper sign can be affixed after the decimal representation is obtained, moreover, it is sufficient to suppose that the fraction is less than 1 because if p is an integer that does not have n as a factor and $\dfrac{p}{n} > 1$, then $\dfrac{p}{n} = q + \dfrac{m}{n}$ where q is a positive integer and $0 < \dfrac{m}{n} < 1$.

At each stage of the division process there is an integer remainder that is between 0 and $n - 1$ inclusive. After at most $n - 1$ steps either a remainder of zero will occur and the decimal will terminate, or a remainder equal to either m or some previous remainder will occur and the decimal representation will repeat in regular cycles. Three examples follow.

Examples: (for emphasis, the remainder at each step is shown underscored)

$$
\begin{array}{r}
0.375 \\
8\,\overline{\smash{)}\,3.000} \\
\underline{2\ 4} \\
6\,0 \\
\underline{5\,6} \\
4\,0 \\
\underline{4\,0} \\
0
\end{array}
\qquad
\begin{array}{r}
0.428571\cdots \\
7\,\overline{\smash{)}\,3.000000} \\
\underline{2\ 8} \\
2\,0 \\
\underline{1\,4} \\
6\,0 \\
\underline{5\,6} \\
4\,0 \\
\underline{3\,5} \\
5\,0 \\
\underline{4\,9} \\
1\,0 \\
\underline{7} \\
3
\end{array}
\qquad
\begin{array}{r}
0.427\cdots \\
110\,\overline{\smash{)}\,47.000} \\
\underline{44\ 0} \\
3\ 00 \\
\underline{2\ 20} \\
800 \\
\underline{770} \\
30
\end{array}
$$

process
terminates

$\dfrac{3}{8} = 0.375$

$\dfrac{3}{7} = 0.428571428571\cdots$

$\dfrac{47}{110} = 0.42727\cdots$

EXERCISE SET 1.2

1. **(a)** 7   **(b)** $\sqrt{2}$ **(c)** k^2 **(d)** k^2

2. $\sqrt{(x-6)^2} = x - 6$ if $x \geq 6$, $\sqrt{(x-6)^2} = -(x-6) = -x + 6$ if $x < 6$.

3. $|x - 3| = |3 - x| = 3 - x$ if $3 - x \geq 0$, which is true if $x \leq 3$.

4. $|x + 2| = x + 2$ if $x + 2 \geq 0$ so $x \geq -2$.   **5.** All real values of x because $x^2 + 9 > 0$.

6. $|x^2 + 5x| = x^2 + 5x$ if $x^2 + 5x \geq 0$ so $x(x + 5) \geq 0$ which is true for $x \leq -5$ or $x \geq 0$.

7. $|3x^2 + 2x| = |x(3x + 2)| = |x||3x + 2|$. If $|x||3x + 2| = x|3x + 2|$, then $|x||3x + 2| - x|3x + 2| = 0$, $(|x| - x)|3x + 2| = 0$, so either $|x| - x = 0$ or $|3x + 2| = 0$. If $|x| - x = 0$, then $|x| = x$, which is true for $x \geq 0$. If $|3x + 2| = 0$, then $x = -2/3$. The statement is true for $x \geq 0$ or $x = -2/3$.

8. $|6 - 2x| = |2(3 - x)| = |2||3 - x| = 2|x - 3|$ for all real values of x.

9. $\sqrt{(x + 5)^2} = |x + 5| = x + 5$ if $x + 5 \geq 0$, which is true if $x \geq -5$.

10. $\sqrt{(3x-2)^2} = |3x-2| = |2-3x| = 2-3x$ if $2-3x \geq 0$ so $x \leq 2/3$.

13.   **(a)** $|7-9| = |-2| = 2$ **(b)** $|3-2| = |1| = 1$
        (c) $|6-(-8)| = |14| = 14$ **(d)** $|-3-\sqrt{2}| = |-(3+\sqrt{2})| = 3+\sqrt{2}$
        (e) $|-4-(-11)| = |7| = 7$ **(f)** $|-5-0| = |-5| = 5$

14. $\sqrt{a^4} = \sqrt{(a^2)^2} = |a^2|$, but $|a^2| = a^2$ because $a^2 \geq 0$ so it is valid for all values of a.

15.   **(a)** B is 6 units to the left of A; $b = a - 6 = -3 - 6 = -9$.
       (b) B is 9 units to the right of A; $b = a + 9 = -2 + 9 = 7$.
       (c) B is 7 units from A; either $b = a + 7 = 5 + 7 = 12$ or $b = a - 7 = 5 - 7 = -2$. Since it is
            given that $b > 0$, it follows that $b = 12$.

16.   In each case we solve for e in terms of f:
       (a) $e = f - 4$; e is to the left of f.   **(b)** $e = f + 4$; e is to the right of f.
       (c) $e = f + 6$; e is to the right of f.   **(d)** $e = f - 7$; e is to the left of f.

17. $|6x - 2| = 7$ **18.** $|3 + 2x| = 11$

Case 1:	Case 2:		Case 1:	Case 2:
$6x - 2 = 7$	$6x - 2 = -7$		$3 + 2x = 11$	$3 + 2x7 = -11$
$6x = 9$	$6x = -5$		$2x = 8$	$2x = -14$
$x = 3/2$	$x = -5/6$		$x = 4$	$x = -7$

19. $|6x - 7| = |3 + 2x|$ **20.** $|4x + 5| = |8x - 3|$

Case 1:	Case 2:		Case 1:	Case 2:
$6x - 7 = 3 + 2x$	$6x - 7 = -(3 + 2x)$		$4x + 5 = 8x - 3$	$4x + 5 = -(8x - 3)$
$4x = 10$	$8x = 4$		$-4x = -8$	$12x = -2$
$x = 5/2$	$x = 1/2$		$x = 2$	$x = -1/6$

21. $|9x| - 11 = x$ **22.** $2x - 7 = |x + 1|$

Case 1:	Case 2:		Case 1:	Case 2:
$9x - 11 = x$	$-9x - 11 = x$		$2x - 7 = x + 1$	$2x - 7 = -(x + 1)$
$8x = 11$	$-10x = 11$		$x = 8$	$3x = 6$
$x = 11/8$	$x = -11/10$			$x = 2$; not a solution
				because x must also
				satisfy $x < -1$

23. $\left|\dfrac{x+5}{2-x}\right| = 6$

Case 1:

$\dfrac{x+5}{2-x} = 6$

$x+5 = 12-6x$

$7x = 7$

$x = 1$

Case 2:

$\dfrac{x+5}{2-x} = -6$

$x+5 = -12+6x$

$-5x = -17$

$x = 17/5$

24. $\left|\dfrac{x-3}{x+4}\right| = 5$

Case 1:

$\dfrac{x-3}{x+4} = 5$

$x-3 = 5x+20$

$-4x = 23$

$x = -23/4$

Case 2:

$\dfrac{x-3}{x+4} = -5$

$x-3 = -5x-20$

$6x = -17$

$x = -17/6$

25. $|x+6| < 3$

$-3 < x+6 < 3$

$-9 < x < -3$

$S = (-9, -3)$

26. $|7-x| \le 5$

$-5 \le 7-x \le 5$

$-12 \le -x \le -2$

$12 \ge x \ge 2$

$S = [2, 12]$

27. $|2x-3| \le 6$

$-6 \le 2x-3 \le 6$

$-3 \le 2x \le 9$

$-3/2 \le x \le 9/2$

$S = [-3/2, 9/2]$

28. $|3x+1| < 4$

$-4 < 3x+17 < 4$

$-5 < 3x < 3$

$-5/3 < x < 1$

$S = (-5/3, 1)$

29. $|x+2| > 1$

Case 1:

$x+2 > 1$

$x > -1$

Case 2:

$x+2 < -1$

$x < -3$

$S = (-\infty, -3) \cup (-1, +\infty)$

30. $\left|\dfrac{1}{2}x - 1\right| \ge 2$

Case 1:

$\dfrac{1}{2}x - 1 \ge 2$

$\dfrac{1}{2}x \ge 3$

$x \ge 6$

Case 2:

$\dfrac{1}{2}x - 1 \le -2$

$\dfrac{1}{2}x \le -1$

$x \le -2$

$S = (-\infty, -2] \cup [6, +\infty)$

31. $|5-2x| \ge 4$

Case 1:

$5-2x \ge 4$

$-2x \ge -1$

$x \le 1/2$

Case 2:

$5-2x \le -4$

$-2x \le -9$

$x \ge 9/2$

$S = (-\infty, 1/2] \cup [9/2, +\infty)$

32. $|7x+1| > 3$

Case 1:

$7x+1 > 3$

$7x > 2$

$x > 2/7$

Case 2:

$7x+1 < -3$

$7x < -4$

$x < -4/7$

$S = (-\infty, -4/7) \cup (2/7, +\infty)$

33. $\dfrac{1}{|x-1|} < 2, x \neq 1$

$|x-1| > 1/2$

Case 1:   Case 2:

$x-1 > 1/2$ $x-1 < -1/2$

$x > 3/2$ $x < 1/2$

$S = (-\infty, 1/2) \cup (3/2, +\infty)$

34. $\dfrac{1}{|3x+1|} \geq 5, x \neq -1/3$

$|3x+1| \leq 1/5$

$-1/5 \leq 3x+1 \leq 1/5$

$-6/5 \leq 3x \leq -4/5$

$-2/5 \leq x \leq -4/15$

$S = [-2/5, -1/3) \cup (-1/3, -4/15]$

35. $\dfrac{3}{|2x-1|} \geq 4, x \neq 1/2$

$\dfrac{|2x-1|}{3} \leq \dfrac{1}{4}$

$|2x-1| \leq 3/4$

$-3/4 \leq 2x-1 \leq 3/4$

$1/4 \leq 2x \leq 7/4$

$1/8 \leq x \leq 7/8$

$S = [1/8, 1/2) \cup (1/2, 7/8]$

36. $\dfrac{2}{|x+3|} < 1, x \neq -3$

$\dfrac{|x+3|}{2} > 1$

$|x+3| > 2$

Case 1:   Case 2:

$x+3 > 2$ $x+3 < -2$

$x > -1$ $x < -5$

$S = (-\infty, -5) \cup (-1, +\infty)$

37. $|x+3| < |x-8|$

$(x+3)^2 < (x-8)^2$

$x^2 + 6x + 9 < x^2 - 16x + 64$

$22x < 55$

$x < 5/2$

$S = (-\infty, 5/2)$

38. $|3x| \leq |2x-5|$

$(3x)^2 \leq (2x-5)^2$

$9x^2 \leq 4x^2 - 20x + 25$

$5x^2 + 20x - 25 \leq 0$

$(x+5)(x-1) \leq 0$

$S = [-5, 1]$

39.

$$|4x| \geq |7 - 6x|$$
$$(4x)^2 \geq (7 - 6x)^2$$
$$16x^2 \geq 49 - 84x + 36x^2$$
$$-20x^2 + 84x - 49 \geq 0$$
$$20x^2 - 84x + 49 \leq 0$$
$$(2x - 7)(10x - 7) \leq 0$$
$$(x - 7/2)(x - 7/10) \leq 0$$
$$S = [7/10, 7/2]$$

40.

$$|2x + 1| > |x - 5|$$
$$(2x + 1)^2 > (x - 5)^2$$
$$4x^2 + 4x + 1 > x^2 - 10x + 26$$
$$3x^2 + 14x - 24 > 0$$
$$(x + 6)(3x - 4) > 0$$
$$(x + 6)(x - 4/3) > 0$$
$$S = (-\infty, -6) \cup (4/3, +\infty)$$

41.

$$\left|\frac{x - 1/2}{x + 1/2}\right| < 1, \quad x \neq -1/2$$
$$|x - 1/2| < |x + 1/2|$$
$$(x - 1/2)^2 < (x + 1/2)^2$$
$$x^2 - x + 1/4 < x^2 + x + 1/4$$
$$-2x < 0$$
$$x > 0$$
$$S = (0, +\infty)$$

42.

$$\left|\frac{3 - 2x}{1 + x}\right| \leq 4, \quad x \neq -1$$
$$|3 - 2x| \leq 4|1 + x|$$
$$9 - 12x + 4x^2 \leq 16(1 + 2x + x^2)$$
$$-12x^2 - 44x - 7 \leq 0$$
$$12x^2 + 44x + 7 \geq 0$$
$$(2x + 7)(6x + 1) \geq 0$$
$$(x + 7/2)(x + 1/6) \geq 0$$
$$S = (-\infty, -7/2] \cup [-1/6, +\infty)$$

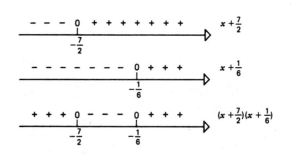

43.
$$\frac{1}{|x-4|} < \frac{1}{|x+7|}, \quad x \neq 4 \text{ or } -7$$
$$|x+7| < |x-4|$$
$$x^2 + 14x + 49 < x^2 - 8x + 16$$
$$22x < -33$$
$$x < -3/2;$$
but $x = -7$ is excluded
so $S = (-\infty, -7) \cup (-7, -3/2)$

44.
$$\frac{1}{|x-3|} - \frac{1}{|x+4|} \geq 0, \quad x \neq 3 \text{ or } -4$$
$$\frac{1}{|x+4|} \leq \frac{1}{|x-3|}$$
$$|x+4| \geq |x-3|$$
$$x^2 + 8x + 16 \geq x^2 - 6x + 9$$
$$14x \geq -7$$
$$x \geq -1/2;$$
but $x = 3$ is excluded so
$$S = [-1/2, 3) \cup (3, +\infty)$$

45. $\sqrt{(x^2 - 5x + 6)^2} = x^2 - 5x + 6$ if $x^2 - 5x + 6 \geq 0$ or, equivalently, if $(x-2)(x-3) \geq 0$; $x \in (-\infty, 2] \cup [3, +\infty)$.

46. If $x \geq 2$ then $3 \leq x - 2 \leq 7$ so $5 \leq x \leq 9$; if $x < 2$ then $3 \leq 2 - x \leq 7$ so $-5 \leq x \leq -1$. $S = [-5, -1] \cup [5, 9]$.

47. If $u = |x - 3|$ then $u^2 - 4u = 12$, $u^2 - 4u - 12 = 0$, $(u - 6)(u + 2) = 0$, so $u = 6$ or $u = -2$. If $u = 6$ then $|x - 3| = 6$, so $x = 9$ or $x = -3$. If $u = -2$ then $|x - 3| = -2$ which is impossible. The solutions are -3 and 9.

48. If $|x + 2| < 2$ then $-2 < x + 2 < 2$, $-4 < x < 0$, $-12 < 3x < 0$, $-14 < 3x - 2 < -2$, so $|3x - 2| < 14$.

49. If $|3x - 4| < 5$ then $-5 < 3x - 4 < 5$, $-1 < 3x < 9$, $-1/3 < x < 3$, $-2/3 < x - 1/3 < 8/3$, so $|x - 1/3| < 8/3$.

51. $|a - b| = |a + (-b)|$
$$\leq |a| + |-b| \text{ (triangle inequality)}$$
$$= |a| + |b|.$$

52. $a = (a - b) + b$
$$|a| = |(a - b) + b|$$
$$|a| \leq |a - b| + |b| \text{ (triangle inequality)}$$
$$|a| - |b| \leq |a - b|.$$

53. From Exercise 52

(i) $|a| - |b| \leq |a - b|$; but $|b| - |a| \leq |b - a| = |a - b|$, so (ii) $|a| - |b| \geq -|a - b|$. Combining (i) and (ii): $-|a - b| \leq |a| - |b| \leq |a - b|$, so $||a| - |b|| \leq |a - b|$.

54. If $2 \leq x \leq 7$ then $\dfrac{1}{2} \geq \dfrac{1}{x} \geq \dfrac{1}{7}$ but $\dfrac{1}{x} = \left|\dfrac{1}{x}\right|$ because $\dfrac{1}{x} > 0$, thus $\left|\dfrac{1}{x}\right| \leq \dfrac{1}{2}$ so $M = \dfrac{1}{2}$.

55. $-4 < x < 2, 3 < x + 7 < 9,$

$1/3 > \dfrac{1}{x+7} > 1/9,$ but $\dfrac{1}{x+7} = \left|\dfrac{1}{x+7}\right|$ because $\dfrac{1}{x+7} > 0,$ thus $\left|\dfrac{1}{x+7}\right| < \dfrac{1}{3}$ so $M = \dfrac{1}{3}.$

56. $|x^3 - 2x + 1| = |x^3 + (-2x) + 1|$

$\qquad \leq |x^3| + |(-2x) + 1| \quad$ (triangle inequality)

$\qquad \leq |x^3| + |-2x| + 1 = |x|^3 + |-2||x| + 1 = |x|^3 + 2|x| + 1;$

if $-2 < x < 3,$ then $|x| < 3$ and $2|x| < 6$ and $|x|^3 < 27$ thus $|x^3 - 2x + 1| < 27 + 6 + 1 = 34$ so $M = 34.$

57. $\left|\dfrac{x+3}{x-3}\right| = \dfrac{|x+3|}{|x-3|};$ if $-\dfrac{3}{4} \leq x \leq \dfrac{1}{4},$ then

$-\dfrac{15}{4} \leq x - 3 \leq -\dfrac{11}{4}, |x-3| \geq \dfrac{11}{4}, \dfrac{1}{|x-3|} \leq \dfrac{4}{11}$ so (i) $\dfrac{|x+3|}{|x-3|} \leq \dfrac{4}{11}|x+3|.$

But $\dfrac{9}{4} \leq x + 3 \leq \dfrac{13}{4}, |x+3| \leq \dfrac{13}{4}, \dfrac{4}{11}|x+3| \leq \dfrac{4}{11} \cdot \dfrac{13}{4} = \dfrac{13}{11},$ thus from (i) it follows that

$\dfrac{|x+3|}{|x-3|} \leq \dfrac{13}{11}$ so $M = \dfrac{13}{11}.$

EXERCISE SET 1.3

1.

2. **(a)** $x = 0$

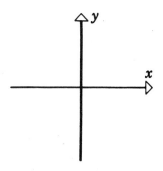

(b) $y = 0$

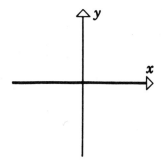

(c) $y < 0$

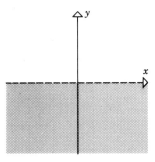

(d) $x \geq 1$ and $y \leq 2$

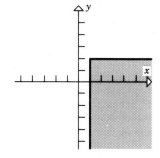

(e) $x = 3$

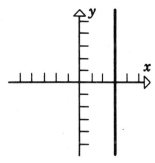

(f) $|x| = 5$

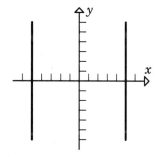

3. **(a)** $x = 2$

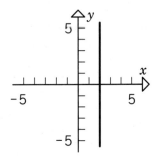

(b) $y = -3$

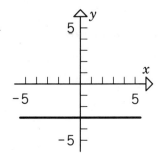

(c) $x \geq 0$

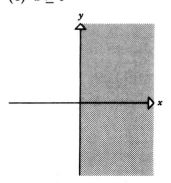

(d) $y = x$

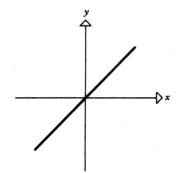

(e) $y \geq x$

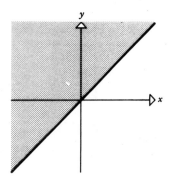

(f) $|x| \geq 1$

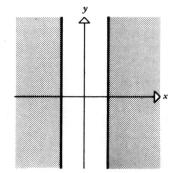

4. **(a)** horizontal   **(b)** horizontal   **(c)** vertical

5. **(a)** vertical   **(b)** horizontal   **(c)** vertical

6. Let $A(-1,4)$, $B(6,4)$, and $C(-1,9)$ be the given vertices. Line segment AB is horizontal (A and B have the same ordinate) and line segment AC is vertical (A and C have the same abscissa). Thus AB and AC form a right angle and so AB and AC are sides of the rectangle. The fourth vertex must lie on the vertical line through B and the horizontal line through C, which identifies it as the point $(6,9)$.

7. **(a)** $0^2 - 2(0) + 4 = 4$, yes   **(b)** $(-3)^2 - 2(-3) + 7 = 22$, no

     (c) $(1/2)^2 - 2(1/2) + 19/4 = 1/4 - 1 + 19/4$, yes

     (d) $(1 + \sqrt{5-t})^2 - 2(1 + \sqrt{5-t}) + t = 1 + 2\sqrt{5-t} + (5-t) - 2 - 2\sqrt{5-t} + t = 4$, yes

8. **(a)**   **(b)**   **(c)**

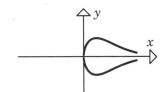 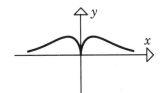 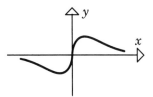

9. **(a)** origin   **(b)** x-axis   **(c)** none   **(d)** y-axis

10. The test in part (c) of Theorem 1.3.2 is satisfied if both of the tests in parts (a) and (b) are satisfied. Consider $y = x^3$ to see that the converse is not true; it is symmetric about the origin but it is not symmetric about the x-axis or the y-axis.

11. **(a)** $x = y^2$, $x = -y^2$ **(b)** $y = x^2$, $y = -x^2$, $y = 1/x^2$, $y = -1/x^2$

     (c) $y = x^3$, $y = \sqrt[3]{x}$, $y = 1/x$, $y = -1/x$

12. **(a)** x-axis, because $x = 5(-y)^2 + 9$ gives $x = 5y^2 + 9$.
     (b) x-axis, y-axis, and origin, because $x^2 - 2(-y)^2 = 3$, $(-x)^2 - 2y^2 = 3$, and
         $(-x)^2 - 2(-y)^2 = 3$ all give $x^2 - 2y^2 = 3$.
     (c) origin, because $(-x)(-y) = 5$ gives $xy = 5$.

13. **(a)** y-axis, because $(-x)^4 = 2y^3 + y$ gives $x^4 = 2y^3 + y$.
     (b) origin, because $(-y) = \dfrac{(-x)}{3 + (-x)^2}$ gives $y = \dfrac{x}{3 + x^2}$.
     (c) x-axis, y-axis, and origin because $(-y)^2 = |x| - 5$, $y^2 = |-x| - 5$, and $(-y)^2 = |-x| - 5$ all give $y^2 = |x| - 5$.

14. $y = 2x - 3$

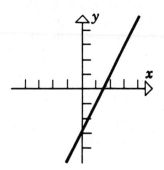

15. $y = 6 - x$

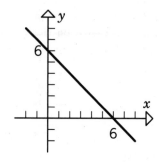

16. $y = 1 + x^2$

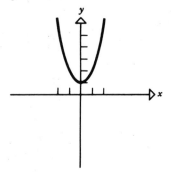

17. $y = 4 - x^2$

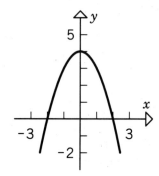

18. $y = -\sqrt{x + 1}$

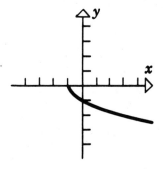

19. $y = \sqrt{x - 4}$

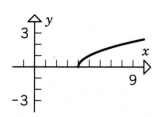

20. $y = |x|$

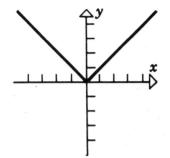

21. $y = |x - 3|$

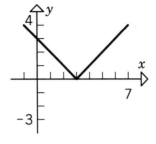

22. $xy = -1$

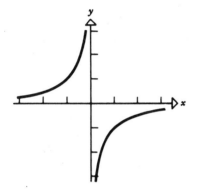

23. $x^2 y = 2$

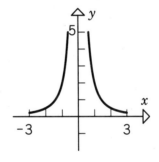

24. $9x^2 + 4y^2 = 36$

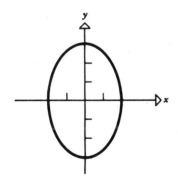

25. $4x^2 + 16y^2 = 16$

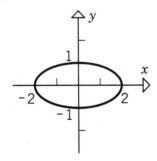

26. $y^2 = 3x$

The union of the graphs of

$y = \sqrt{3x}$ and $y = -\sqrt{3x}$.

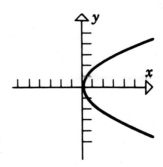

27. $(x - y)(x + y) = 0$
The union of the graphs of
$x - y = 0$ and $x + y = 0$.

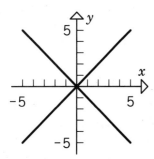

28. $F = \dfrac{9}{5}C + 32$

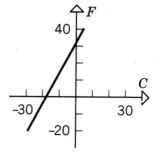

29. $u = 3v^2$

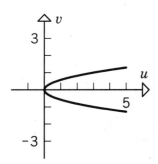

30. $Y = 4X + 5$

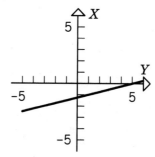

EXERCISE SET 1.4

1. **(a)** $m = \dfrac{4-2}{3-(-1)} = \dfrac{1}{2}$ **(b)** $m = \dfrac{1-3}{7-5} = -1$

   (c) $m = \dfrac{\sqrt{2}-\sqrt{2}}{-3-4} = 0$ **(d)** $m = \dfrac{12-(-6)}{-2-(-2)} = \dfrac{18}{0}$, not defined

2. $m_1 = \dfrac{5-2}{6-(-1)} = \dfrac{3}{7},\ m_2 = \dfrac{7-2}{2-(-1)} = \dfrac{5}{3},\ m_3 = \dfrac{7-5}{2-6} = -\dfrac{1}{2}$

3. **(a)** The line through $(1,1)$ and $(-2,-5)$ has slope $m_1 = \dfrac{-5-1}{-2-1} = 2$, the line through $(1,1)$

   and $(0,-1)$ has slope $m_2 = \dfrac{-1-1}{0-1} = 2$. The given points lie on a line because $m_1 = m_2$.

   (b) The line through $(-2,4)$ and $(0,2)$ has slope $m_1 = \dfrac{2-4}{0+2} = -1$, the line through $(-2,4)$

   and $(1,5)$ has slope $m_2 = \dfrac{5-4}{1+2} = \dfrac{1}{3}$. The given points do not lie on a line because

   $m_1 \neq m_2$.

4.   5.

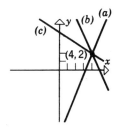   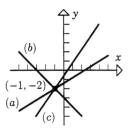

6. (b), (a), (d), (c)   7. (c), (b), (d), (a)

8. **(a)** $m = (0-2)/(2-0) = -1$ **(b)** $m = [1-(-1)]/[2-(-1)] = 2/3$

9. **(a)** $m = [0-(-3)]/(2-0) = 3/2$ **(b)** $m = (-2-1)/[3-(-1)] = -3/4$

10. $27°C = 80.6°F$, $15°C = 59°F$, and 40 cm $= 1.3124$ ft so
    $m = (59-80.6)/(1.3124-0) = -16.46°F/\text{ft}$.

11. slope $\approx 2.4/10 = 0.24$ N/mm $= 240$ N/m.

12. $m \approx (13.35 - 13.6)/(100 - 0) = -0.0025$ g/cm^3/°C; the mass density decreases at the rate of 0.0025 g/cm^3 per °C.

13. slope $\approx (354 - 330)/(40 - 0) = 0.6$ m/sec/°C; the speed of sound increases at the rate of 0.6 m/sec per °C.

14. Use $(7,5)$ and (x,y) to calculate the slope: $(y - 5)/(x - 7) = -2$
 (a) if $x = 9$, then $(y - 5)/(9 - 7) = -2$, $y - 5 = -4$, $y = 1$
 (b) if $y = 12$, then $(12 - 5)/(x - 7) = -2$, $x - 7 = -7/2$, $x = 7/2$

15. Use the points $(1,2)$ and (x,y) to calculate the slope: $(y - 2)/(x - 1) = 3$
 (a) if $x = 5$, then $(y - 2)/(5 - 1) = 3$, $y - 2 = 12$, $y = 14$
 (b) if $y = -2$, then $(-2 - 2)/(x - 1) = 3$, $x - 1 = -4/3$, $x = -1/3$

16. The slope obtained by using the points $(1,5)$ and $(k,4)$ must be the same as that obtained from the points $(1,5)$ and $(2,-3)$ so $\dfrac{4 - 5}{k - 1} = \dfrac{-3 - 5}{2 - 1}$, $-\dfrac{1}{k - 1} = -8$, $k - 1 = 1/8$, $k = 9/8$.

17. Using $(3,k)$ and $(-2,4)$ to calculate the slope, we find $\dfrac{k - 4}{3 - (-2)} = 5$, $k - 4 = 25$, $k = 29$.

18. Use $(0,0)$ and (x,y) to get $\dfrac{y - 0}{x - 0} = \dfrac{1}{2}$, $y = \dfrac{1}{2}x$. Use $(7,5)$ and (x,y) to get $\dfrac{y - 5}{x - 7} = 2$, $y - 5 = 2(x - 7)$, $y = 2x - 9$. Solve the system of equations $y = \dfrac{1}{2}x$ and $y = 2x - 9$ to get $x = 6$, $y = 3$.

19. $(0 - 2)/(x - 1) = -(0 - 5)/(x - 4)$, $-2x + 8 = 5x - 5$, $7x = 13$, $x = 13/7$.

20. (a) $\tan 45° = 1$ (b) $\tan \dfrac{2\pi}{3} = -\sqrt{3}$ (c) $\tan 30° = 1/\sqrt{3}$

21. (a) $\tan \dfrac{\pi}{6} = 1/\sqrt{3}$ (b) $\tan 135° = -1$ (c) $\tan 60° = \sqrt{3}$

22. (a) 27°   (b) 135°   (c) 63°   (d) 91°

23. (a) 153°   (b) 45°   (c) 117°   (d) 89°

24. Let m' be the slope of line L'.
 (a) $m' = (8 - 4)/(4 - 2) = 2$, $m' = m$ so L' is parallel to L.
 (b) $m' = (2 - 4)/(6 - 2) = -1/2$, $mm' = -1$ so L' is perpendicular to L.

(c) $m' = (-3 - 5)/(2 - 1) = -8$, $m' \neq m$ and $mm' \neq -1$ so L' is neither parallel nor perpendicular to L.

25. Let m' be the slope of line L'.
    (a) $m' = (5 - 8)/(2 - 1) = -3$, $m' = m$ so L' is parallel to L.
    (b) $m' = (4 - 5)/(3 - 6) = 1/3$, $mm' = -1$ so L' is perpendicular to L.
    (c) $m' = (1 - 0)/(-2 - 1) = -1/3$, $m' \neq m$ and $mm' \neq -1$ so L' is neither parallel nor perpendicular to L.

26. The triangle is equiangular because it is equilateral. The angles of inclination of the sides are $0°$, $60°$, and $120°$ (see figure), thus the slopes of its sides are $\tan 0° = 0$, $\tan 60° = \sqrt{3}$, and $\tan 120° = -\sqrt{3}$.

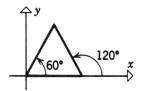

27. Let $P(x, 0)$ be a point on the x-axis. If AP is perpendicular to BP then $m_{AP}m_{BP} = -1$, so
$$\frac{0 - 2}{x - 1} \cdot \frac{0 - 3}{x - 8} = -1,$$ thus $x^2 - 9x + 14 = 0$, $(x - 7)(x - 2) = 0$, thus $x = 2$ or $x = 7$.

28. The line through $(3, 1)$ and $(6, 3)$ has slope $m_1 = 2/3$, the line through $(3, 1)$ and $(2, 9)$ has slope $m_2 = -8$, the line through $(6, 3)$ and $(2, 9)$ has slope $m_3 = -3/2$. Because $m_1 m_3 = -1$, the corresponding lines are perpendicular so the given points are vertices of a right triangle.

29. Show that opposite sides are parallel by showing that they have the same slope:

    using $(3, -1)$ and $(6, 4)$, $m_1 = 5/3$; using $(6, 4)$ and $(-3, 2)$, $m_2 = 2/9$;

    using $(-3, 2)$ and $(-6, -3)$, $m_3 = 5/3$; using $(-6, -3)$ and $(3, -1)$, $m_4 = 2/9$.

    Opposite sides are parallel because $m_1 = m_3$ and $m_2 = m_4$.

30. The slope of the radius from the center to P is $[3 - (-1)]/(2 - 4) = -2$. The tangent is perpendicular to the radius at P, so its slope is $-1/(-2) = 1/2$.

31. (a) Draw the line through the point of intersection of L_1 and L_2, parallel to the x-axis (see figure). Based on the figure we see that $\phi_2 = \theta + \phi_1$, so $\theta = \phi_2 - \phi_1$.
    (b) if neither L_1 nor L_2 is vertical, then their slopes m_1 and m_2 both exist and are given by
    $$m_1 = \tan \phi_1 \text{ and } m_2 = \tan \phi_2$$

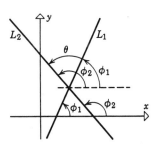

so $\tan \theta = \tan(\phi_2 - \phi_1)$

$$= \frac{\tan \phi_2 - \tan \phi_1}{1 + \tan \phi_2 \tan \phi_1} \quad \text{(trig identity)}$$

$$= \frac{m_2 - m_1}{1 + m_1 m_2} \quad \text{if } m_1 m_2 \neq -1$$

(that is, if L_1 and L_2 are not perpendicular).

32. (a) $m_1 = 1, m_2 = 3$; $\tan \theta = \dfrac{3 - 1}{1 + (1)(3)} = \dfrac{1}{2}$

(b) $m_1 = 4, m_2 = -2$; $\tan \theta = \dfrac{-2 - 4}{1 + (4)(-2)} = \dfrac{6}{7}$

(c) $m_1 = -\dfrac{2}{3}, m_2 = -\dfrac{1}{2}$, $\tan \theta = \dfrac{-1/2 - (-2/3)}{1 + (-2/3)(-1/2)} = \dfrac{1}{8}$

33. (a) $m_1 = \dfrac{1}{3}, m_2 = \dfrac{4}{5}$; $\tan \theta = \dfrac{4/5 - 1/3}{1 + (1/3)(4/5)} = \dfrac{7}{19}$

(b) $m_1 = 5, m_2 = -0.7$; $\tan \theta = \dfrac{-0.7 - 5}{1 + (5)(-0.7)} = \dfrac{5.7}{2.5} = \dfrac{57}{25}$

(c) $m_1 = -6, m_2 = -2$; $\tan \theta = \dfrac{-2 - (-6)}{1 + (-6)(-2)} = \dfrac{4}{13}$

34. (a) $27°$ (b) $41°$ (c) $7°$

35. (a) $20°$ (b) $66°$ (c) $17°$

36. Let $A(4, -3)$, $B(-3, -1)$ and $C(6, 6)$ be the given vertices (see figure). The line through

A and B has slope $m_1 = -2/7$,

A and C has slope $m_2 = 9/2$,

B and C has slope $m_3 = 7/9$.

Using the result of Exercise 31,

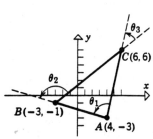

$$\tan \theta_1 = \frac{m_1 - m_2}{1 + m_1 m_2} = \frac{-2/7 - 9/2}{1 - 9/7} = \frac{67}{4}, \theta_1 = 87° \text{ so}$$

angle $A = 87°$; $\tan \theta_2 = \dfrac{m_1 - m_3}{1 + m_1 m_3} = \dfrac{-2/7 - 7/9}{1 - 2/9} = -\dfrac{67}{49}$,

$\theta_2 = 126°$ so $B = 180° - 126° = 54°$ because θ_2 is the exterior angle at B;

$$\tan \theta_3 = \frac{m_2 - m_3}{1 + m_2 m_3} = \frac{9/2 - 7/9}{1 + 7/2} = \frac{67}{81}, \theta_3 = 40° \text{ so } C = 40°. \text{ As a check,}$$

$A + B + C = 87° + 54° + 40° = 181°$ which is close enough to $180°$, considering that each angle was only calculated to the nearest degree.

37. The slope of the line through A and B is $m_1 = -3/4$ and that through A and C is $m_2 = 1/2$. Let m denote the slope of the line L that bisects the angle A (see figure). Then

$$\theta_1 = \theta_2$$

$$\tan \theta_1 = \tan \theta_2$$

$$\frac{m_1 - m}{1 + m_1 m} = \frac{m - m_2}{1 + m_2 m}$$

$$\frac{-\dfrac{3}{4} - m}{1 - \dfrac{3}{4}m} = \frac{m - \dfrac{1}{2}}{1 + \dfrac{1}{2}m}$$

$$\frac{-3 - 4m}{4 - 3m} = \frac{2m - 1}{2 + m}$$

$$(-3 - 4m)(2 + m) = (2m - 1)(4 - 3m)$$

$$-4m^2 - 11m - 6 = -6m^2 + 11m - 4$$

$$2m^2 - 22m - 2 = 0$$

$$m^2 - 11m - 1 = 0$$

and from the quadratic formula $m = \dfrac{11 \pm \sqrt{121 + 4}}{2} = \dfrac{11 \pm \sqrt{125}}{2}$, $m \approx 11.09$ or -0.09, of which only the line with a slope of 11.09 is consistent with the figure.

38. Let k be the slope of a line K. If the angle between K and L is $45°$ and the angle of inclination of K is

smaller than L, then $\dfrac{-2 - k}{1 - 2k} = \tan 45° = 1$, $-2 - k = 1 - 2k$, $k = 3$;

larger than L, then $\dfrac{k + 2}{1 - 2k} = \tan 45° = 1$, $k + 2 = 1 - 2k$, $3k = -1$, $k = -\dfrac{1}{3}$.

39. Let L_3 be a line that is perpendicular to L_1, then $m_3 = -1/m_1$. But $m_2 = -1/m_1$, so L_2 is parallel to L_3 because they have the same slope. If L_3 is perpendicular to L_1, then so is L_2.

EXERCISE SET 1.5

1. (a)

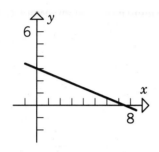

(b)

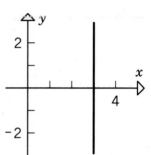

(c)

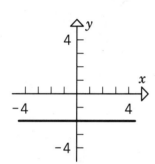

(d)

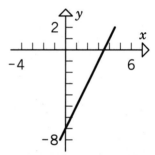

2. (a)

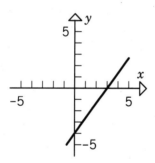

(b)

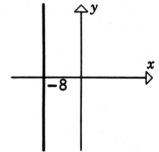

(c)

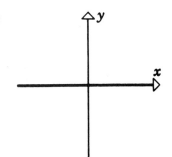

(d)

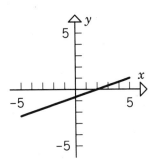

3. (a)

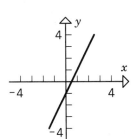

(b)

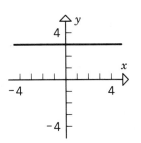

(c)

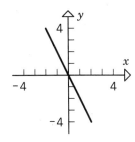

4. (a)

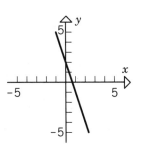

(b)

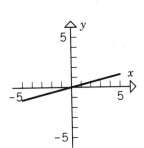

(c)

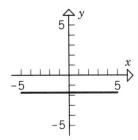

5. (a) $m = 3, b = 2$

(b) $m = -\dfrac{1}{4}, b = 3$

(c) $y = -\dfrac{3}{5}x + \dfrac{8}{5}$ so $m = -\dfrac{3}{5}, b = \dfrac{8}{5}$

(d) $m = 0, b = 1$

(e) $y = -\dfrac{b}{a}x + b$ so $m = -\dfrac{b}{a}$, y-intercept b

6. (a) $m = -4, b = 2$

(b) $y = \dfrac{1}{3}x - \dfrac{2}{3}$ so $m = \dfrac{1}{3}, b = -\dfrac{2}{3}$

(c) $y = -\dfrac{3}{2}x + 3$ so $m = -\dfrac{3}{2}, b = 3$

(d) $y = 3$ so $m = 0, b = 3$

(e) $y = -\dfrac{a_0}{a_1}x$ so $m = -\dfrac{a_0}{a_1}$, $b = 0$

7. (a) $m = \tan\phi = \sqrt{3}$, $\phi = 60°$ (b) $m = \tan\phi = -2$, $\phi = 117°$

8. (a) $m = \tan\phi = -\sqrt{3}/3$, $\phi = 150°$ (b) $m = \tan\phi = 4$, $\phi = 76°$

9. $y = -2x + 4$ **10.** $y = 5x - 3$

11. The slope m of the line must equal the slope of $y = 4x - 2$, thus $m = 4$ so the equation is $y = 4x + 7$.

12. The slope of the line $3x + 2y = 5$ is $-3/2$ so the line through $(-1, 2)$ with this slope is
$y - 2 = -\dfrac{3}{2}(x + 1);\ y = -\dfrac{3}{2}x + \dfrac{1}{2}.$

13. The slope m of the line must be the negative reciprocal of the slope of $y = 5x + 9$, thus $m = -1/5$ and the equation is $y = -x/5 + 6$.

14. The slope of the line $x - 4y = 7$ is $1/4$ so a line perpendicular to it must have a slope of -4; $y + 4 = -4(x - 3);\ y = -4x + 8.$

15. $y - 4 = \dfrac{-7 - 4}{1 - 2}(x - 2) = 11(x - 2),\ y = 11x - 18.$

16. $y - 6 = \dfrac{1 - 6}{-2 - (-3)}(x - (-3)),\ y - 6 = -5(x + 3),\ y = -5x - 9.$

17. $m = \tan\dfrac{\pi}{6} = \dfrac{1}{\sqrt{3}}$ so $y = \dfrac{1}{\sqrt{3}}x - 3.$

18. $m = \tan\dfrac{2\pi}{3} = -\sqrt{3}$ so $y - 2 = -\sqrt{3}(x - 1),\ y = -\sqrt{3}x + 2 + \sqrt{3}.$

19. The line passes through $(0, 2)$ and $(-4, 0)$, thus $m = \dfrac{0 - 2}{-4 - 0} = \dfrac{1}{2}$ so $y = \dfrac{1}{2}x + 2.$

20. The line passes through $(0, b)$ and $(a, 0)$, thus $m = \dfrac{0 - b}{a - 0} = -\dfrac{b}{a}$, so the equation is $y = -\dfrac{b}{a}x + b.$

21. $y = 1$ **22.** $y = -8$

23. The line is vertical because $\phi = \dfrac{\pi}{2}$, so $x = 5.$

24. $x = 0$

25. (a) $m_1 = 4$, $m_2 = 4$; parallel because $m_1 = m_2$.
    (b) $m_1 = 2$, $m_2 = -1/2$; perpendicular because $m_1 m_2 = -1$.
    (c) $m_1 = 5/3$, $m_2 = 5/3$; parallel because $m_1 = m_2$.
    (d) If $A \neq 0$ and $B \neq 0$, then $m_1 = -A/B$, $m_2 = B/A$ and the lines are perpendicular because $m_1 m_2 = -1$. If either A or B (but not both) is zero, then the lines are perpendicular because one is horizontal and the other is vertical.
    (e) $m_1 = 4$, $m_2 = 1/4$; neither.

26. (a) $m_1 = -5$, $m_2 = -5$; parallel because $m_1 = m_2$.
    (b) $m_1 = 2$, $m_2 = -1/2$; perpendicular because $m_1 m_2 = -1$.
    (c) $m_1 = -4/5$, $m_2 = 5/4$; perpendicular because $m_1 m_2 = -1$.
    (d) If $B \neq 0$, then $m_1 = m_2 = -A/B$ and the lines are parallel because $m_1 = m_2$. If $B = 0$ (and $A \neq 0$), then the lines are parallel because they are both perpendicular to the x-axis.
    (e) $m_1 = 1/2$, $m_2 = 2$; neither.

27. $y = (-3/k)x + 4/k$, $k \neq 0$
    (a) $-3/k = 2$, $k = -3/2$.   (b) $4/k = 5$, $k = 4/5$.
    (c) $3(-2) + k(4) = 4$, $k = 5/2$.
    (d) The slope of $2x - 5y = 1$ is $2/5$ so $-3/k = 2/5$, $k = -15/2$.
    (e) The slope of $4x + 3y = 2$ is $-4/3$ so the slope of the line perpendicular to it is $3/4$; $-3/k = 3/4$, $k = -4$.

28. (a)
    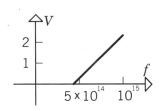

    (b) $V = 4.1 \times 10^{-15} f - 1.77$, $V = 0$
    if $f = 1.77/4.1 \times 10^{-15}$
    $\approx 4.3 \times 10^{14}$ Hz

29. (a) If we plot T_C along the horizontal axis and T_F along the vertical axis, then any point on the line relating T_C and T_F can be denoted by (T_C, T_F). From the fact that $(0, 32)$ and $(100, 212)$ are on the line, it follows that the slope is $\dfrac{212 - 32}{100 - 0} = \dfrac{180}{100} = \dfrac{9}{5}$ and that the T_F-intercept is 32. An equation of the line is $T_F = \dfrac{9}{5} T_C + 32$.
    (b) Solving $T_F = \dfrac{9}{5} T_C + 32$ for T_C we get $T_C = \dfrac{5}{9} T_F - \dfrac{160}{9}$, which identifies the slope as $\dfrac{5}{9}$.

   (c) If $T_C = T_F = T$, then $T = \dfrac{9}{5}T + 32$, $T = -40°F = -40°C$.

   (d) $T_C = \dfrac{5}{9}(98.6) - \dfrac{160}{9} = 37°C$

30. **(a)** The slope of the line relating T_C to T_K is 1 because the size of a degree is the same on both scales. $T_C = 0.01$ when $T_K = 273.16$ so $T_C - 0.01 = (1)(T_K - 273.16)$, $T_C = T_K - 273.15$

   (b) If $T_K = 0$, then $T_C = -273.15°C$

31. **(a)** slope $= (5.9 - 1)/(50 - 0) = 0.098$ atm/m, $p = 0.098h + 1$.

   (b) If $p = 2$, then $h = 1/0.098 \approx 10.2$ m.

32. **(a)** $m = (133.9 - 123.4)/(45 - 20) = 0.42$, $R - 133.9 = 0.42(T - 20)$, $R = 0.42T + 115$.

   (b) $128.6 = 0.42T + 115$, $T = 32.4°C$.

33. **(a)** $m = (0.75 - 0.80)/4 = -0.0125$ mm/day, $r = -0.0125t + 0.8$.

   (b) If $r = 0$, then $t = 0.8/0.0125 = 64$ days

34. **(a)** yes   **(b)** yes   **(c)** no   **(d)** yes   **(e)** yes   **(f)** yes   **(g)** no

35. Solve $x = 5t + 2$ for t to get $t = \dfrac{1}{5}x - \dfrac{2}{5}$, so $y = \left(\dfrac{1}{5}x - \dfrac{2}{5}\right) - 3 = \dfrac{1}{5}x - \dfrac{17}{5}$, which is a line.

36. Solve $x = 1 + 3t^2$ for t^2 to get $t^2 = \dfrac{1}{3}x - \dfrac{1}{3}$, so $y = 2 - \left(\dfrac{1}{3}x - \dfrac{1}{3}\right) = -\dfrac{1}{3}x + \dfrac{7}{3}$, which is a line; $1 + 3t^2 \geq 1$ for all t so $x \geq 1$.

37. An equation of the line through $(1,4)$ and $(2,1)$ is $y = -3x + 7$. It crosses the y-axis at $y = 7$, and the x-axis at $x = 7/3$, so the area of the triangle is $\dfrac{1}{2}(7)(7/3) = 49/6$.

38. $(2x - 3y)(2x + 3y) = 0$

   so $2x - 3y = 0$, $y = \dfrac{2}{3}x$

   or $2x + 3y = 0$, $y = -\dfrac{2}{3}x$.

   The graph consists of the

   lines $y = \pm\dfrac{2}{3}x$.

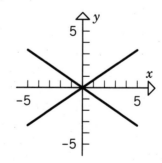

39. **(a)** Replace y by -1 in the first equation to get $2x - 3 = 5$, $2x = 8$, $x = 4$, so the point is $(4, -1)$.

(b) Multiply the first equation through by 2 and the second by 3 to get the equations $8x + 6y = -4$ and $15x - 6y = 27$; then, by adding these equations, $23x = 23$, $x = 1$, and substitution of this into the first of the original equations gives $4 + 3y = -2$, $3y = -6$, $y = -2$ so the point is $(1, -2)$.

40. **(a)** If $6x - 9y = 7$ and $x = -2/3$, then substitution yields $6(-2/3) - 9y = 7$, $-4 - 9y = 7$, $y = -11/9$ so the point is $(-2/3, -11/9)$.

(b) Multiply the first equation by 3 and the second by 2 to get $18x - 6y = -9$ and $-16x + 6y = 10$; then, by adding these equations, $2x = 1$, $x = 1/2$; next, using the first of the original equations, $6(1/2) - 2y = -3$, $3 - 2y = -3$, $y = 3$ so the point is $(1/2, 3)$.

41. Any line parallel to $y = x - 2$ can be written as $y = x + b$ which intersects $y = x^2$ where $x + b = x^2$, $x^2 - x - b = 0$. Solve, using the quadratic formula, to get $x = (1 \pm \sqrt{1 + 4b})/2$, which has real solutions only if $1 + 4b \geq 0$ so $b \geq -1/4$. The line $y = x + b$ intersects $y = x^2$ and is closest to $y = x - 2$ if $b = -1/4$, so $x = 1/2$ and $y = 1/4$. The point $(1/2, 1/4)$ is closest to $y = x - 2$.

42. If $x = x_1$, then from (1) $y = y_1$ so (x_1, y_1) satisfies (1). If $x \neq x_1$ and (x, y) satisfies (1), then it follows that $\dfrac{y - y_1}{x - x_1} = m$, that is, (x, y) lies on the line of slope m passing through $P_1(x_1, y_1)$.

43. To prove that the graph of $Ax + By + C = 0$ is a straight line consider two cases, $B = 0$ and $B \neq 0$. If $B \neq 0$, solve for y to get $y = -\dfrac{A}{B}x - \dfrac{C}{B}$ which is the slope-intercept form of a line with $m = -A/B$ and $b = -C/B$. If $B = 0$, then $A \neq 0$ because A and B cannot both be zero. Thus we get $Ax + C = 0$, or $x = -C/A$ which is an equation of a line parallel to the y-axis. In either case the graph of $Ax + By + C = 0$ is a straight line.

Conversely, consider any straight line in the xy-plane. If it is vertical, then it has an equation of the form $x = a$, or $x - a = 0$ which is like $Ax + By + C = 0$ with $A = 1$, $B = 0$, and $C = -a$. If the line is not vertical, then it can be written in slope-intercept form as $y = mx + b$, or $mx - y + b = 0$ which is like $Ax + By + C = 0$ with $A = m$, $B = -1$, and $C = b$.

EXERCISE SET 1.6

1. In the proof of Theorem 1.6.1.

2. **(a)** $d = \sqrt{(-1 - 2)^2 + (1 - 5)^2} = \sqrt{9 + 16} = \sqrt{25} = 5$

(b) $\left(\dfrac{2 + (-1)}{2}, \dfrac{5 + 1}{2}\right) = (1/2, 3)$

3. (a) $d = \sqrt{(1-7)^2 + (9-1)^2} = \sqrt{36 + 64} = \sqrt{100} = 10$

    (b) $\left(\dfrac{7+1}{2}, \dfrac{1+9}{2}\right) = (4, 5)$

4. (a) $d = \sqrt{(-3-2)^2 + (6-0)^2} = \sqrt{25 + 36} = \sqrt{61}$

    (b) $\left(\dfrac{2+(-3)}{2}, \dfrac{0+6}{2}\right) = (-1/2, 3)$

5. (a) $d = \sqrt{[-7-(-2)]^2 + [-4-(-6)]^2} = \sqrt{25 + 4} = \sqrt{29}$

    (b) $\left(\dfrac{-2+(-7)}{2}, \dfrac{-6+(-4)}{2}\right) = (-9/5, -5)$

6. Let $A(1, 1)$, $B(-2, -8)$, and $C(4, 10)$ be
    the given points (see diagram). A, B,
    and C lie on a straight line if and only
    if $d_1 + d_2 = d_3$, where d_1, d_2, and d_3
    are the lengths of the line segments
    AB, AC, and BC. But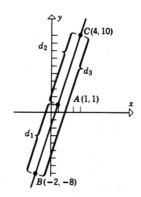

    $d_1 = \sqrt{(-2-1)^2 + (-8-1)^2} = 3\sqrt{10}$

    $d_2 = \sqrt{(4-1)^2 + (10-1)^2} = 3\sqrt{10}$

    $d_3 = \sqrt{(4+2)^2 + (10+8)^2} = 6\sqrt{10}$

    Because $d_1 + d_2 = d_3$, it follows that A, B, and C lie on a straight line.

7. Let $A(5, -2)$, $B(6, 5)$, and $C(2, 2)$ be the given vertices and a, b, and c the lengths of the sides
    opposite these vertices; then

    $a = \sqrt{(2-6)^2 + (2-5)^2} = \sqrt{25} = 5$ and $b = \sqrt{(2-5)^2 + (2+2)^2} = \sqrt{25} = 5$.

    Triangle ABC is isosceles because it has two equal sides ($a = b$).

8. A triangle is a right triangle if and only if the square of the longest side is equal to the sum of the
    squares of the other two sides (Pythagorean theorem). With $A(1, 3)$, $B(4, 2)$, and $C(-2, -6)$
    as vertices and s_1, s_2, and s_3 the lengths of the sides opposite these vertices we find that
    $s_1^2 = (-2-4)^2 + (-6-2)^2 = 100$, $s_2^2 = (-2-1)^2 + (-6-3)^2 = 90$, $s_3^2 = (4-1)^2 + (2-3)^2 = 10$,
    and that $s_1^2 = s_2^2 + s_3^2$, so ABC is a right triangle.

9. $P_1(0, -2)$, $P_2(-4, 8)$, and $P_3(3, 1)$ all lie on a circle whose center is $C(-2, 3)$ if the points P_1,
    P_2 and P_3 are equidistant from C. Denoting the distances between P_1, P_2, P_3 and C by d_1,
    d_2 and d_3 we find that $d_1 = \sqrt{(0+2)^2 + (-2-3)^2} = \sqrt{29}$,

    $d_2 = \sqrt{(-4+2)^2 + (8-3)^2} = \sqrt{29}$, and $d_3 = \sqrt{(3+2)^2 + (1-3)^2} = \sqrt{29}$.

    So P_1, P_2 and P_3 lie on a circle whose center is $C(-2, 3)$ because $d_1 = d_2 = d_3$.

10. The distance between $(t, 2t - 6)$ and $(0, 4)$ is
$$\sqrt{(t - 0)^2 + (2t - 6 - 4)^2} = \sqrt{t^2 + (2t - 10)^2} = \sqrt{5t^2 - 40t + 100};$$
the distance between $(t, 2t - 6)$ and $(8, 0)$ is $\sqrt{(t - 8)^2 + (2t - 6)^2} = \sqrt{5t^2 - 40t + 100}$, so $(t, 2t - 6)$ is equidistant from $(0, 4)$ and $(8, 0)$.

11. If $(2, k)$ is equidistant from $(3,7)$ and $(9,1)$, then
$$\sqrt{(2 - 3)^2 + (k - 7)^2} = \sqrt{(2 - 9)^2 + (k - 1)^2}, \ 1 + (k - 7)^2 = 49 + (k - 1)^2,$$
$$1 + k^2 - 14k + 49 = 49 + k^2 - 2k + 1, \ -12k = 0, \ k = 0.$$

12. $(x - 3)/2 = 4$ and $(y + 2)/2 = -5$ so $x = 11$ and $y = -12$.

13. The slope of the line segment joining $(2,8)$ and $(-4,6)$ is $\dfrac{6 - 8}{-4 - 2} = \dfrac{1}{3}$ so the slope of the perpendicular bisector is -3. The midpoint of the line segment is $(-1, 7)$ so an equation of the bisector is $y - 7 = -3(x + 1); \ y = -3x + 4$.

14. The slope of the line segment joining $(5, -1)$ and $(4, 8)$ is $\dfrac{8 - (-1)}{4 - 5} = -9$ so the slope of the perpendicular bisector is $\dfrac{1}{9}$. The midpoint of the line segment is $(9/2, 7/2)$ so an equation of the bisector is $y - \dfrac{7}{2} = \dfrac{1}{9}\left(x - \dfrac{9}{2}\right); \ y = \dfrac{1}{9}x + 3$.

15. Method (see figure): Find an equation of the perpendicular bisector of the line segment joining $A(3, 3)$ and $B(7, -3)$. All points on this perpendicular bisector are equidistant from A and B, thus find where it intersects the given line. The midpoint of AB is $(5, 0)$, the slope of AB is $-3/2$ thus the slope of the perpendicular bisector is $2/3$ so an equation is

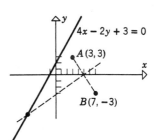

$$
\begin{aligned}
y - 0 &= \frac{2}{3}(x - 5) \\
3y &= 2x - 10 \\
2x - 3y - 10 &= 0.
\end{aligned}
$$

The solution of the system

$$\begin{cases} 4x - 2y + 3 &= 0 \\ 2x - 3y - 10 &= 0 \end{cases}$$

gives the point $(-29/8, -23/4)$.

16. **(a)** $y = 4$ is a horizontal line, so the vertical distance is $|4 - (-2)| = |6| = 6$.

    (b) $x = -1$ is a vertical line, so the horizontal distance is $|-1 - 3| = |-4| = 4$.

17. Method (see figure): write an equation of the line that goes through the given point and that is perpendicular to the given line; find the point P where this line intersects the given line; find the distance between P and the given point.

    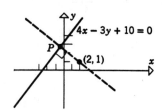

    The slope of the given line is $4/3$, so the slope of a line perpendicular to it is $-3/4$.

    The line through $(2,1)$ having a slope of $-3/4$ is $y - 1 = -\dfrac{3}{4}(x - 2)$ or, after simplification,

    $3x + 4y = 10$ which when solved simultaneously with $4x - 3y + 10 = 0$ yields $(-2/5, 14/5)$ as the point of intersection. The distance d between $(-2/5, 14/5)$ and $(2,1)$ is

    $$d = \sqrt{(2 + 2/5)^2 + (1 - 14/5)^2} = 3.$$

18. (See the solution to Exercise 17 for a description of the method.) The slope of the line $5x + 12y - 36 = 0$ is $-5/12$. The line through $(8,4)$ and perpendicular to the given line is $y - 4 = \dfrac{12}{5}(x - 8)$ or, after simplification, $12x - 5y = 76$. The point of intersection of this line with the given line is found to be $\left(\dfrac{84}{13}, \dfrac{4}{13}\right)$ and the distance between it and $(8,4)$ is 4.

19. If $B = 0$, then the line $Ax + C = 0$ is vertical and $x = -C/A$ for each point on the line. The line through (x_0, y_0) and perpendicular to the given line is horizontal and intersects the given line at the point $(-C/A, y_0)$. The distance d between $(-C/A, y_0)$ and (x_0, y_0) is

    $$d = \sqrt{(x_0 + C/A)^2 + (y_0 - y_0)^2} = \sqrt{\dfrac{(Ax_0 + C)^2}{A^2}} = \dfrac{|Ax_0 + C|}{\sqrt{A^2}}$$

    which is the value of $\dfrac{|Ax_0 + By_0 + C|}{\sqrt{A^2 + B^2}}$ for $B = 0$.

    If $B \neq 0$, then the slope of the given line is $-A/B$ and the line through (x_0, y_0) and perpendicular to the given line is

    $$y - y_0 = \dfrac{B}{A}(x - x_0), \quad Ay - Ay_0 = Bx - Bx_0, \quad Bx - Ay = Bx_0 - Ay_0.$$

    The point of intersection of this line and the given line is obtained by solving

$Ax + By = -C$ and $Bx - Ay = Bx_0 - Ay_0$.

Multiply the first equation through by A and the second by B and add the results to get

$(A^2 + B^2)x = B^2x_0 - ABy_0 - AC$ so $x = \dfrac{B^2x_0 - ABy_0 - AC}{A^2 + B^2}$

Similarly, by multiplying by B and $-A$, we get $y = \dfrac{-ABx_0 + A^2y_0 - BC}{A^2 + B^2}$.

The square of the distance d between (x, y) and (x_0, y_0) is

$$d^2 = \left[x_0 - \frac{B^2x_0 - ABy_0 - AC}{A^2 + B^2}\right]^2 + \left[y_0 - \frac{-ABx_0 + A^2y_0 - BC}{A^2 + B^2}\right]^2$$

$$= \frac{(A^2x_0 + ABy_0 + AC)^2}{(A^2 + B^2)^2} + \frac{(ABx_0 + B^2y_0 + BC)^2}{(A^2 + B^2)^2}$$

$$= \frac{A^2(Ax_0 + By_0 + C)^2 + B^2(Ax_0 + By_0 + C)^2}{(A^2 + B^2)^2}$$

$$= \frac{(Ax_0 + By_0 + C)^2(A^2 + B^2)}{(A^2 + B^2)^2} = \frac{(Ax_0 + By_0 + C)^2}{A^2 + B^2}$$

so $d = \dfrac{|Ax_0 + By_0 + C|}{\sqrt{A^2 + B^2}}$.

20. $d = \dfrac{|4(2) - 3(1) + 10|}{\sqrt{4^2 + (-3)^2}} = \dfrac{|15|}{\sqrt{25}} = \dfrac{15}{5} = 3.$

21. $d = \dfrac{|5(8) + 12(4) - 36|}{\sqrt{5^2 + 12^2}} = \dfrac{|52|}{\sqrt{169}} = \dfrac{52}{13} = 4.$

22. Method (see figure): Let $A(0, a)$, $B(b, 0)$, and $C(c, 0)$ be the given vertices; find equations for the perpendicular bisectors L_1, L_2, and L_3 and show that they all intersect at the same point.

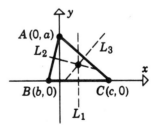

line L_1 : The midpoint of BC is $\left(\dfrac{b+c}{2}, 0\right)$ and since L_1 is vertical, an equation for L_1 is

$x = \dfrac{b+c}{2}$;

line L_2 : The midpoint of AB is $\left(\dfrac{b}{2}, \dfrac{a}{2}\right)$; the slope of AB is $-\dfrac{a}{b}$ (if $b \neq 0$) so the slope of L_2

is $\dfrac{b}{a}$ (even if $b = 0$) and an equation of L_2 is $y - \dfrac{a}{2} = \dfrac{b}{a}\left(x - \dfrac{b}{2}\right)$;

line L_3 : The midpoint of AC is $\left(\frac{c}{2}, \frac{a}{2}\right)$; the slope of AC is $-\frac{a}{c}$ (if $c \neq 0$) so the slope of L_3 is $\frac{c}{a}$ (even if $c = 0$) and an equation of L_3 is $y - \frac{a}{2} = \frac{c}{a}\left(x - \frac{c}{2}\right)$.

For the point of intersection of L_1 and L_2, solve $x = \frac{b+c}{2}$ and $y - \frac{a}{2} = \frac{b}{a}\left(x - \frac{b}{2}\right)$.

The point is found to be $\left(\frac{b+c}{2}, \frac{a^2+bc}{2}\right)$. The point of intersection of L_1 and L_3 is obtained by solving the system $x = \frac{b+c}{2}$ and $y - \frac{a}{2} = \frac{c}{a}\left(x - \frac{c}{2}\right)$, its solution yields the point $\left(\frac{b+c}{2}, \frac{a^2+bc}{2}\right)$. So $L_1 L_2$, and L_3 all intersect at the same point.

23. (a) center $(0,0)$, radius 5 (b) center $(1,4)$, radius 4
  (c) center $(-1,-3)$, radius $\sqrt{5}$ (d) center $(0,-2)$, radius 1

24. (a) center $(0,0)$, radius 3 (b) center $(3,5)$, radius 6
  (c) center $(-4,-1)$, radius $\sqrt{8}$ (d) center $(-1,0)$, radius 1

25. $(x-3)^2 + (y-(-2))^2 = 4^2$, $(x-3)^2 + (y+2)^2 = 16$

26. $(x-1)^2 + (y-0)^2 = (\sqrt{8}/2)^2$, $(x-1)^2 + y^2 = 2$

27. $r = 8$ because the circle is tangent to the x-axis, so $(x+4)^2 + (y-8)^2 = 64$.

28. $r = 5$ because the circle is tangent to the y-axis, so $(x-5)^2 + (y-8)^2 = 25$.

29. $(0,0)$ is on the circle, so $r = \sqrt{(-3-0)^2 + (-4-0)^2} = 5$; $(x+3)^2 + (y+4)^2 = 25$.

30. $r = \sqrt{(4-1)^2 + (-5-3)^2} = \sqrt{73}$; $(x-4)^2 + (y+5)^2 = 73$.

31. The center is the midpoint of the line segment joining $(2,0)$ and $(0,2)$ so the center is at $(1,1)$. The radius is $r = \sqrt{(2-1)^2 + (0-1)^2} = \sqrt{2}$, so $(x-1)^2 + (y-1)^2 = 2$.

32. The center is the midpoint of the line segment joining $(6,1)$ and $(-2,3)$, so the center is at $(2,2)$. The radius is $r = \sqrt{(6-2)^2 + (1-2)^2} = \sqrt{17}$, so $(x-2)^2 + (y-2)^2 = 17$.

33. $(x^2 - 2x) + (y^2 - 4y) = 11$, $(x^2 - 2x + 1) + (y^2 - 4y + 4) = 11 + 1 + 4$, $(x-1)^2 + (y-2)^2 = 16$; center $(1,2)$ and radius 4.

34. $(x^2 + 8x) + y^2 = -8$, $(x^2 + 8x + 16) + y^2 = -8 + 16$, $(x+4)^2 + y^2 = 8$; center $(-4,0)$ and radius $2\sqrt{2}$.

35. $2(x^2 + 2x) + 2(y^2 - 2y) = 0,\ 2(x^2 + 2x + 1) + 2(y^2 - 2y + 1) = 2 + 2,\ (x + 1)^2 + (y - 1)^2 = 2$; center $(-1, 1)$ and radius $\sqrt{2}$.

36. $6(x^2 - x) + 6(y^2 + y) = 3,\ 6(x^2 - x + 1/4) + 6(y^2 + y + 1/4) = 3 + 6/4 + 6/4,$
$(x - 1/2)^2 + (y + 1/2)^2 = 1$; center $(1/2, -1/2)$ and radius 1.

37. $(x^2 + 2x) + (y^2 + 2y) = -2,\ (x^2 + 2x + 1) + (y^2 + 2y + 1) = -2 + 1 + 1,\ (x + 1)^2 + (y + 1)^2 = 0$;
the point $(-1, -1)$.

38. $(x^2 - 4x) + (y^2 - 6y) = -13,\ (x^2 - 4x + 4) + (y^2 - 6y + 9) = -13 + 4 + 9,\ (x - 2)^2 + (y - 3)^2 = 0$;
the point $(2, 3)$.

39. $x^2 + y^2 = 1/9$; center $(0, 0)$ and radius $1/3$.

40. $x^2 + y^2 = 4$; center $(0,0)$ and radius 2.

41. $x^2 + (y^2 + 10y) = -26,\ x^2 + (y^2 + 10y + 25) = -26 + 25,\ x^2 + (y + 5)^2 = -1$; no graph

42. $(x^2 - 10x) + (y^2 - 2y) = -29,\ (x^2 - 10x + 25) + (y^2 - 2y + 1) = -29 + 25 + 1,\ (x - 5)^2 + (y - 1)^2 = -3$;
no graph

43. $16\left(x^2 + \dfrac{5}{2}x\right) + 16(y^2 + y) = 7,\ 16\left(x^2 + \dfrac{5}{2}x + \dfrac{25}{16}\right) + 16\left(y^2 + y + \dfrac{1}{4}\right) = 7 + 25 + 4,$
$(x + 5/4)^2 + (y + 1/2)^2 = 9/4$; center $(-5/4, -1/2)$ and radius $3/2$.

44. $4(x^2 - 4x) + 4(y^2 - 6y) = 9,\ 4(x^2 - 4x + 4) + 4(y^2 - 6y + 9) = 9 + 16 + 36,$
$(x - 2)^2 + (y - 3)^2 = 61/4$; center $(2, 3)$ and radius $\sqrt{61}/2$.

45.   **(a)** $y^2 = 16 - x^2$, so $y = \pm\sqrt{16 - x^2}$. The bottom half is $y = -\sqrt{16 - x^2}$.
      (b) Complete the square in y to get $(y - 2)^2 = 3 - 2x - x^2$, so $y - 2 = \pm\sqrt{3 - 2x - x^2}$, or
         $y = 2 \pm \sqrt{3 - 2x - x^2}$. The top half is $y = 2 + \sqrt{3 - 2x - x^2}$.

46.   **(a)** $x^2 = 9 - y^2$ so $x = \pm\sqrt{9 - y^2}$. The right half is $x = \sqrt{9 - y^2}$.
      (b) Complete the square in x to get $(x - 2)^2 = 1 - y^2$ so $x - 2 = \pm\sqrt{1 - y^2}$, $x = 2 \pm \sqrt{1 - y^2}$.
         The left half is $x = 2 - \sqrt{1 - y^2}$.

47. (a)

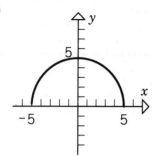

   (b) y $= \sqrt{5 + 4x - x^2}$

               $= \sqrt{5 - (x^2 - 4x)}$

               $= \sqrt{5 + 4 - (x^2 - 4x + 4)}$

               $= \sqrt{9 - (x - 2)^2}$

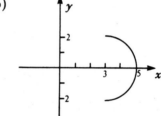

48. (a)

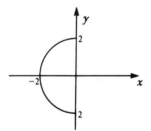

   (b)

49. The tangent line is perpendicular to the radius at the point. The slope of the radius is $4/3$, so the slope of the perpendicular *is* $- 3/4$. An equation of the tangent line is $y - 4 = -\dfrac{3}{4}(x - 3)$, or $y = -\dfrac{3}{4}x + \dfrac{25}{4}$.

50. (a) $(x + 1)^2 + y^2 = 10$, center at $C(-1,0)$. The slope of CP is $-1/3$ so the slope of the tangent is 3; $y + 1 = 3(x - 2)$, $y = 3x - 7$.

   (b) $(x - 3)^2 + (y + 2)^2 = 26$, center at $C(3,-2)$. The slope of CP is 5 so the slope of the tangent is $-\dfrac{1}{5}$; $y - 3 = -\dfrac{1}{5}(x - 4)$, $y = -\dfrac{1}{5}x + \dfrac{19}{5}$.

51. (a) The center of the circle is at $(0,0)$ and its radius is $\sqrt{20} = 2\sqrt{5}$. The distance between P and the center is $\sqrt{(-1)^2 + (2)^2} = \sqrt{5}$ which is less than $2\sqrt{5}$, so P is inside the circle.

   (b) Draw the diameter of the circle that passes through P, then the shorter segment of the diameter is the shortest line that can be drawn from P to the circle, and the longer segment is the longest line that can be drawn from P to the circle (can you prove it?). Thus, the smallest distance is $2\sqrt{5} - \sqrt{5} = \sqrt{5}$, and the largest is $2\sqrt{5} + \sqrt{5} = 3\sqrt{5}$.

52. **(a)** $x^2 + (y-1)^2 = 5$, center at $C(0,1)$ and radius $\sqrt{5}$. The distance between P and C is $3\sqrt{5}/2$ so P is outside the circle.

    (b) The smallest distance is $\dfrac{3}{2}\sqrt{5} - \sqrt{5} = \dfrac{1}{2}\sqrt{5}$, the largest distance is $\dfrac{3}{2}\sqrt{5} + \sqrt{5} = \dfrac{5}{2}\sqrt{5}$.

53. Let (a, b) be the coordinates of T (or T'). The radius from $(0,0)$ to T (or T') will be perpendicular to L (or L') so, using slopes, $b/a = -(a-3)/b$, $a^2 + b^2 = 3a$. But (a, b) is on the circle so $a^2 + b^2 = 1$, thus $3a = 1$, $a = 1/3$. Let $a = 1/3$ in $a^2 + b^2 = 1$ to get $b^2 = 8/9$, $b = \pm\sqrt{8}/3$. The coordinates of T and T' are $(1/3, \sqrt{8}/3)$ and $(1/3, -\sqrt{8}/3)$.

54. **(a)** $\sqrt{(x-2)^2 + (y-0)^2} = \sqrt{2}\sqrt{(x-0)^2 + (y-1)^2}$; square both sides and expand to get $x^2 - 4x + 4 + y^2 = 2(x^2 + y^2 - 2y + 1)$, $x^2 + y^2 + 4x - 4y - 2 = 0$, which is a circle.

    (b) $(x^2 + 4x) + (y^2 - 4y) = 2$, $(x^2 + 4x + 4) + (y^2 - 4y + 4) = 2 + 4 + 4$, $(x+2)^2 + (y-2)^2 = 10$; center $(-2, 2)$, radius $\sqrt{10}$.

55. **(a)** $[(x-4)^2 + (y-1)^2] + [(x-2)^2 + (y+5)^2] = 45$
       $x^2 - 8x + 16 + y^2 - 2y + 1 + x^2 - 4x + 4 + y^2 + 10y + 25 = 45$
       $2x^2 + 2y^2 - 12x + 8y + 1 = 0$, which is a circle.

    (b) $2(x^2 - 6x) + 2(y^2 + 4y) = -1$, $2(x^2 - 6x + 9) + 2(y^2 + 4y + 4) = -1 + 18 + 8$,
       $(x-3)^2 + (y+2)^2 = 25/2$; center $(3, -2)$, radius $5/\sqrt{2}$.

56. If $x^2 - y^2 = 0$, then $y^2 = x^2$ so $y = x$ or $y = -x$. The graph of $x^2 - y^2 = 0$ consists of the graphs of the two lines $y = \pm x$. The graph of $(x - c)^2 + y^2 = 1$ is a circle of radius 1 with center at $(c, 0)$. Examine the figure to see that the system cannot have just one solution, and has 0 solutions if $|c| > \sqrt{2}$, 2 solutions if $|c| = \sqrt{2}$, 3 solutions if $|c| = 1$, and 4 solutions if $|c| < \sqrt{2}$, $|c| \neq 1$.

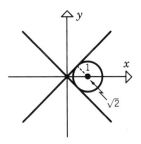

2 solutions

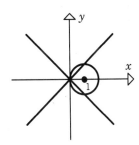

3 solutions

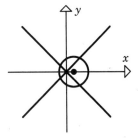

4 solutions

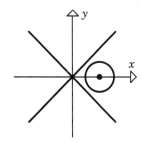

0 solutions

57. $y = x^2 + 2$

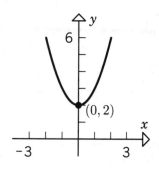

58. $y = x^2 - 3$

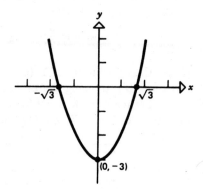

59. $y = x^2 + 2x - 3$

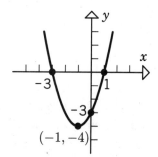

60. $y = x^2 - 3x - 4$

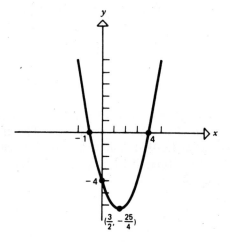

61. $y = -x^2 + 4x + 5$

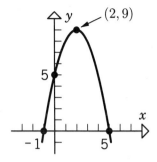

62. $y = -x^2 + x$

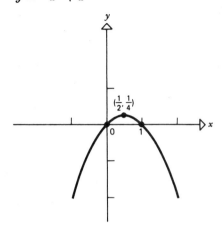

63. $y = (x - 2)^2$

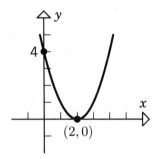

64. $y = (3 + x)^2$

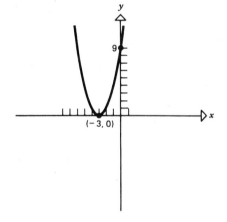

65. $x^2 - 2x + y = 0$

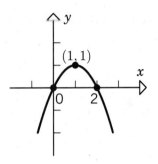

66. $x^2 + 8x + 8y = 0$

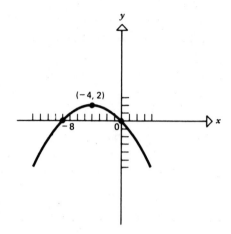

67. $y = 3x^2 - 2x + 1$

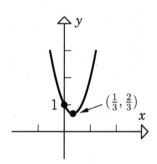

68. $y = x^2 + x + 2$

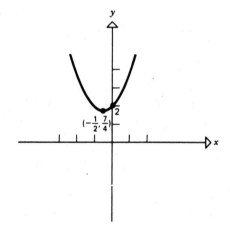

69. $x = -y^2 + 2y + 2$

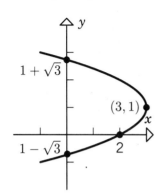

70. $x = y^2 - 4y + 5$

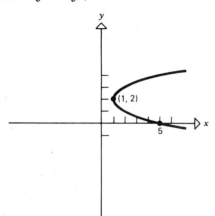

71.   **(a)** $x^2 = 3 - y$, $x = \pm\sqrt{3-y}$. The right half is $x = \sqrt{3-y}$.

     (b)   Complete the square in x to get $(x-1)^2 = y+1$, $x = 1 \pm \sqrt{y+1}$. The left half is $x = 1 - \sqrt{y+1}$.

72.   **(a)** $y^2 = x + 5$, $y = \pm\sqrt{x+5}$. The upper half is $y = \sqrt{x+5}$.

     (b)   Complete the square in y to get $(y-1/2)^2 = x + 9/4$, $y - 1/2 = \pm\sqrt{x+9/4}$,

      $y = 1/2 \pm \sqrt{x+9/4}$. The lower half is $y = 1/2 - \sqrt{x+9/4}$.

73.   **(a)**   **(b)**

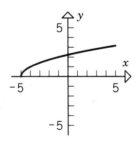   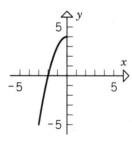

74.   **(a)**   **(b)**

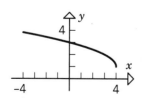   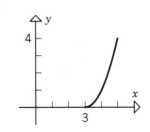

75. **(a)** $s = 32t - 16t^2$

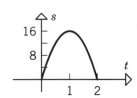

(b) The ball will be at its highest point when $t = 1$ sec; it will rise 16 ft.

76. **(a)** $2x + y = 500$, $y = 500 - 2x$.   **(b)** $A = xy = x(500 - 2x) = 500x - 2x^2$.

  (c) The graph of A versus x is a parabola with its vertex (high point) at $x = -b/(2a) = -500/(-4) = 125$, so the maximum value of A is $A = 500(125) - 2(125)^2 = 31{,}250 \text{ ft}^2$.

77. **(a)** $(3)(2x) + (2)(2y) = 600$, $6x + 4y = 600$, $y = 150 - 3x/2$.

  (b) $A = xy = x(150 - 3x/2) = 150x - 3x^2/2$.

  (c) The graph of A versus x is a parabola with its vertex (high point) at $x = -b/(2a) = -150/(-3) = 50$, so the maximum value of A is $A = 150(50) - 3(50)^2/2 = 3{,}750 \text{ ft}^2$.

78. **(a)** $y = ax^2 + bx + c = a\left(x^2 + \dfrac{b}{a}x\right) + c$

$$= a\left(x^2 + \frac{b}{a}x + \frac{b^2}{4a^2}\right) + c - \frac{b^2}{4a} = a\left(x + \frac{b}{2a}\right)^2 + \left(c - \frac{b^2}{4a}\right)$$

  (b) If $a < 0$ then y is always less than $c - \dfrac{b^2}{4a}$ except when $x = -\dfrac{b}{2a}$, so the graph has its high point there. If $a > 0$ then y is always greater than $c - \dfrac{b^2}{4a}$ except when $x = -\dfrac{b}{2a}$, so the graph has its low point there.

SUPPLEMENTARY EXERCISES, CHAPTER 1

1. **(a)** $(-3, 5]$

  (b) $-1 < 0 \leq x^2$ for all x, thus $-1 < x^2 \leq 9$ is equivalent to $x^2 \leq 9$, so $|x| \leq 3$. The interval is $[-3, 3]$.

  (c) $x^2 \geq \dfrac{1}{4}$ is equivalent to $|x| \geq \dfrac{1}{2}$, which in interval notation is $(-\infty, -1/2] \cup [1/2, +\infty)$.

2. (a) $|2x + 1| > 5$; <u>Case 1</u>: $2x + 1 > 5$, $x > 2$,
        <u>Case 2</u>: $2x + 1 < -5$, $x < -3$ so $S = (-\infty, -3) \cup (2, +\infty)$

    (b) $|x^2 - 9| \geq 7$
        <u>Case 1</u>: $x^2 - 9 \geq 7$, $x^2 \geq 16$, $|x| \geq 4$; $S_1 = (-\infty, -4] \cup [4, +\infty)$
        <u>Case 2</u>: $x^2 - 9 \leq -7$, $x^2 \leq 2$, $|x| \leq \sqrt{2}$; $S_2 = [-\sqrt{2}, \sqrt{2}]$
        so $S = S_1 \cup S_2 = (-\infty, -4] \cup [-\sqrt{2}, \sqrt{2}] \cup [4, +\infty)$

    (c) <u>Case 1</u>: If $x \geq 0$ then $1 \leq x \leq 3$,
        <u>Case 2</u>: If $x < 0$ then $1 \leq -x \leq 3$, $-1 \geq x \geq -3$ so $S = [-3, -1] \cup [1, 3]$

3. (a) $2x^2 - 5x > 3$
                $2x^2 - 5x - 3 > 0$
                $(2x + 1)(x - 3) > 0$
                $(x + 1/2)(x - 3) > 0$
                $S = (-\infty, -1/2) \cup (3, +\infty)$

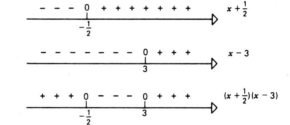

    (b) $x^2 - 5x + 4 \leq 0$
            $(x - 1)(x - 4) \leq 0$
            $S = [1, 4]$

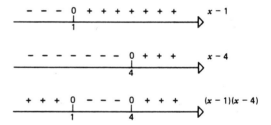

4. (a) $\dfrac{x}{1 - x} \geq 3$

              $\dfrac{x - 3(1 - x)}{1 - x} \geq 0$

                $\dfrac{4x - 3}{1 - x} \geq 0$

                $\dfrac{x - 3/4}{1 - x} \geq 0$

            $S = [3/4, 1)$

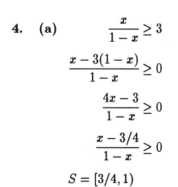
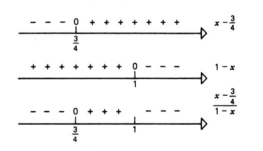

(b)
$$\frac{2x+3}{x} \geq x$$

$$\frac{2x+3-x^2}{x} \geq 0$$

$$\frac{x^2-2x-3}{x} \leq 0$$

$$\frac{(x+1)(x-3)}{x} \leq 0$$

$$S = (-\infty, -1] \cup (0, 3]$$

5. (a) $\dfrac{|x|-1}{|x|-2} \leq 0$

<u>Case 1:</u> $x \geq 0$,

$$\frac{x-1}{x-2} \leq 0$$

<u>Case 2:</u> $x < 0$,

$$\frac{-x-1}{-x-2} \leq 0; \frac{x+1}{x+2} \leq 0$$

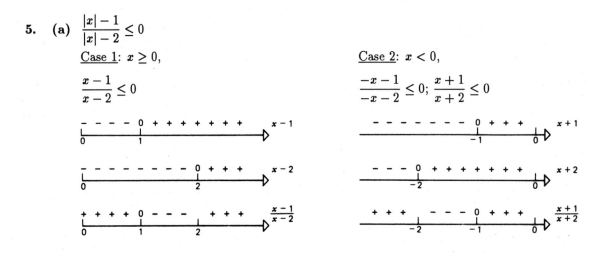

$$S_1 = [1, 2) \qquad\qquad S_2 = (-2, -1]$$

$$S = S_1 \cup S_2 = (-2, -1] \cup [1, 2)$$

(b)
$$|x-1| \leq 2|x+2|$$
$$x^2 - 2x + 1 \leq 4(x^2 + 4x + 4)$$
$$-3x^2 - 18x - 15 \leq 0$$
$$x^2 + 6x + 5 \geq 0$$
$$(x+1)(x+5) \geq 0$$
$$S = (-\infty, -5] \cup [-1, +\infty)$$

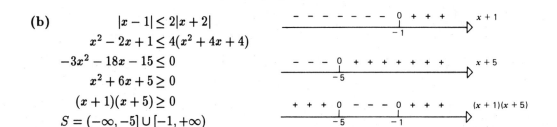

6. (a) rational

(b) rational

(c) irrational

(d) rational

(e) integer, rational

(f) irrational

(g) rational

(h) integer, rational

7. (a) $a = -2$ and $b = 1$

   (b) $a^2 < b^2$, $a^2 - b^2 < 0$, $(a+b)(a-b) < 0$; if $a < b$ then $a - b < 0$ so $(a+b)(a-b) < 0$ if
        $a + b > 0$

8. (b), (c), (d), (e)

9. $x^2 \leq x^2 + y^2$ because $y^2 \geq 0$, thus $\sqrt{x^2} \leq \sqrt{x^2 + y^2}$ and so $|x| \leq \sqrt{x^2 + y^2}$.

   Similarly, $|y| \leq \sqrt{x^2 + y^2}$. The right triangle with vertices $(0,0)$, (x,y), and $(x,0)$ has legs
   of lengths $|x|$ and $|y|$, and a hypotenuse of length $\sqrt{x^2 + y^2}$. The lengths of the legs cannot
   exceed the length of the hypotenuse.

10. (a)

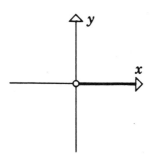

    (b)

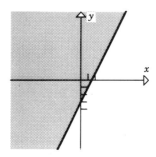

11. (a) $xy = x^2$

              $xy - x^2 = 0$

              $x(y - x) = 0$,

         so $x = 0$ or $y - x = 0$

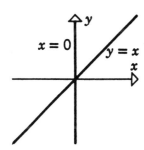

    (b) $y(x - 1) = x^2 - 1$

                  $y(x - 1) - (x^2 - 1) = 0$

                  $y(x - 1) - (x - 1)(x + 1) = 0$

                  $(x - 1)(y - x - 1) = 0$,

           so $x - 1 = 0$ or $y - x - 1 = 0$

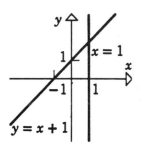

12.   **(a)** $y = \dfrac{x^3 - 1}{x - 1}$

$\qquad = \dfrac{(x-1)(x^2 + x + 1)}{x - 1}$

$\qquad = x^2 + x + 1 \text{ if } x \neq 1$

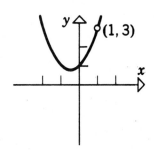

(b)

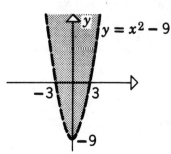

13.   **(a)** Complete the square:
$(x^2 - 2x + 1) + (y^2 - 6y + 9) \geq 6 + 1 + 9$
$(x - 1)^2 + (y - 3)^2 \geq 16,$
all points on or outside the circle
with center $(1, 3)$ and radius 4.

(b) $x + |y - 2| = 1$
If $y \geq 2$, then
$x + y - 2 = 1$
$\qquad y = -x + 3.$
If $y < 2$, then $x - (y - 2) = 1$
$\qquad\qquad y = x + 1.$

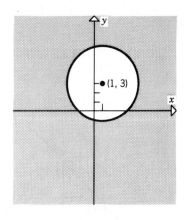

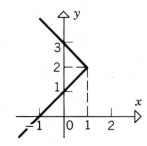

14.   **(a)** $x + y = 4$ if $x \geq 0$ and $y \geq 0,$
$\qquad -x + y = 4$ if $x < 0$ and $y \geq 0,$
$\qquad -x - y = 4$ if $x < 0$ and $y < 0,$
$\qquad x - y = 4$ if $x \geq 0$ and $y < 0.$

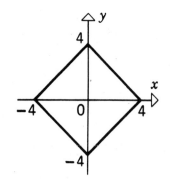

(b) $x - y = 4$ if $x \geq 0$ and $y \geq 0$,
        $-x - y = 4$ if $x < 0$ and $y \geq 0$,
        $-x + y = 4$ if $x < 0$ and $y < 0$,
        $x + y = 4$ if $x \geq 0$ and $y < 0$.

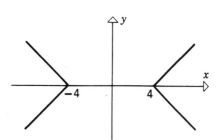

15. The curves intersect at (x, y) where $y = x^2$ and $y = x + 2$, so $x^2 = x + 2$, $x^2 - x - 2 = 0$, $(x + 1)(x - 2) = 0$, $x = -1$ or $x = 2$. The points of intersection are $(-1, 1)$ and $(2, 4)$.

16.

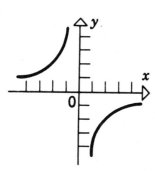

17. If $x \geq 2$, then $y = x - 2$;
         if $x < 2$, then $y = -x + 2$.

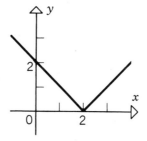

18.

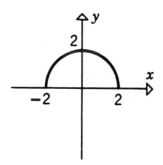

19.

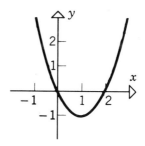

20. Because the point $(3, 1)$ is on the circle, the radius is $r = |1 - (-2)| = 3$, so the equation is $(x - 3)^2 + (y + 2)^2 = 9$.

21. The radius is $r = \sqrt{(4 - 1)^2 + (-2 - 2)^2} = 5$, so $(x - 1)^2 + (y - 2)^2 = 25$.

22. Let $(2, k)$ be the center, and r the radius. Then $(x - 2)^2 + (y - k)^2 = r^2$. But $(1,3)$ is on the circle, so $(1 - 2)^2 + (3 - k)^2 = r^2$, $10 - 6k + k^2 = r^2$ (i), and $(3, -11)$ is on the circle so $(3 - 2)^2 + (-11 - k)^2 = r^2$, $122 + 22k + k^2 = r^2$ (ii). Eliminate r^2 from (i) and (ii) to get $122 + 22k + k^2 = 10 - 6k + k^2$, $28k = -112$, $k = -4$, thus, from (i), $r^2 = 10 - 6(-4) + (-4)^2 = 50$, so $(x - 2)^2 + (y + 4)^2 = 50$.

23. Let $C(h, k)$ be the center, then $|h - 6| = 5$ and $|k - 7| = 5$, so $h = 6 \pm 5$ and $k = 7 \pm 5$. There are four circles, $(x - h)^2 + (y - k)^2 = 25$, where $h = 1$ or 11 and $k = 2$ or 12.

24. Let $C(h, k)$ be the center, then $(x - h)^2 + (y - k)^2 = 169$. But $(0, 0)$ is on the circle, so $(0 - h)^2 + (0 - k)^2 = 169$, $h^2 + k^2 = 169$ (i), also $(0, -24)$ is on the circle so $(0 - h)^2 + (-24 - k)^2 = 169$, $h^2 + 576 + 48k + k^2 = 169$ (ii). Subtract (i) from (ii) to get $48k + 576 = 0$, $k = -12$, and then, from (i), $h^2 + (-12)^2 = 169$, $h^2 = 25$, $h = \pm 5$. There are two circles, $(x \pm 5)^2 + (y + 12)^2 = 169$.

25. $(x^2 + 4x + 4) + (y^2 + 2y + 1) = -5 + 4 + 1$, $(x + 2)^2 + (y + 1)^2 = 0$; the point $(-2, -1)$.

26. $4(x^2 - x + 1/4) + 4(y^2 + 2y + 1) = -1 + 1 + 4$,

$(x - 1/2)^2 + (y + 1)^2 = 1$; circle, center $(1/2, -1)$, radius 1.

27. $(x^2 - 3x + 9/4) + (y^2 + 2y + 1) = -4 + 9/4 + 1$, $(x - 3/2)^2 + (y + 1)^2 = -3/4$; no graph

28. $3\left(x^2 - \dfrac{5}{3}x + \dfrac{25}{36}\right) + 3\left(y^2 + \dfrac{7}{3}y + \dfrac{49}{36}\right) = -3 + \dfrac{25}{12} + \dfrac{49}{12}$,

$(x - 5/6)^2 + (y + 7/6)^2 = 19/18$; circle, center $(5/6, -7/6)$, radius $\sqrt{38}/6$

29. **(a)** $m = \dfrac{-4 - 4}{-3 - 3} = \dfrac{4}{3}$, so $y - 4 = \frac{4}{3}(x - 3)$, $y = \dfrac{4}{3}x$; $d = \sqrt{(-6)^2 + (-8)^2} = 10$;
midpoint: $(0, 0)$.

(b) $m = \dfrac{-4 - 4}{3 - 3} = \dfrac{-8}{0}$ which is not defined, so the vertical line $x = 3$; $d = |-4 - 4| = 8$;
midpoint: $(3, 0)$.

(c) $m = \dfrac{4 - 4}{-3 - 3} = 0$, so $y = 4$; $d = |-3 - 3| = 6$; midpoint: $(0, 4)$.

(d) $m = \dfrac{3 - 4}{4 - 3} = -1$, so $y - 4 = -(x - 3)$, $y = -x + 7$; $d = \sqrt{(1)^2 + (-1)^2} = \sqrt{2}$;
midpoint: $(7/2, 7/2)$.

30. $x - 4y = 5$ is an equation of the line through $(-3, -2)$ and $(1, -1)$, but $(8, 1)$ does not satisfy it.

31. Equation of circle is $x^2 + y^2 = 25$, equation of line is $y = -\dfrac{3}{4}x$.

Eliminate $y : x^2 + \left(-\dfrac{3}{4}x\right)^2 = 25$, $x^2 + \dfrac{9}{16}x^2 = 25$, $\dfrac{25}{16}x^2 = 25$, $x^2 = 16$, so $x = \pm 4$.

The points of intersection are $(-4, 3)$ and $(4, -3)$.

32. (a) $\tan 30° = 1/\sqrt{3}$ (b) $\tan 120° = -\sqrt{3}$ (c) $\tan 90°$ is not defined.

33. $m = \dfrac{-3 + 3}{4 - 2} = 0$, so $y = -3$.

34. $m = \tan 45° = 1$, and $(-2, 0)$ is on the line, so $y - 0 = (1)(x + 2)$, $y = x + 2$.

35. For $x + 2y = 3$, $m = -\dfrac{1}{2}$. A parallel line through the origin is $y - 0 = -\dfrac{1}{2}(x - 0)$, $y = -\dfrac{1}{2}x$.

36. The line segment joining $A(-2, -3)$ and $B(1, 1)$ has slope $m = \dfrac{4}{3}$ and midpoint $M\left(-\dfrac{1}{2}, -1\right)$.

The perpendicular bisector has slope $-\dfrac{3}{4}$ and goes through M, so $y + 1 = -\dfrac{3}{4}\left(x + \dfrac{1}{2}\right)$,

$y = -\dfrac{3}{4}x - \dfrac{11}{8}$.

37. $L : m = -2$, so $y = -2(x - 1)$; $L' : m = \dfrac{1}{2}$ because L' is perpendicular to L, so $y = \dfrac{1}{2}x - 3$. L meets L' when $-2(x - 1) = \dfrac{1}{2}x - 3$, which gives $x = 2$. But $y = -2$ when $x = 2$, so the point is $(2, -2)$.

38. $L :$ vertical line, so $x = -2$; $L' :$ horizontal line because L is vertical, so $y = 4$. L meets L' at the point $(-2, 4)$.

39. $L : y - 1 = \dfrac{2}{5}(x - 3)$, $y = \dfrac{2}{5}x - \dfrac{1}{5}$; $L' : \left(-\dfrac{8}{3}, 0\right)$ and $(0, -4)$ are on the line, so $m = -\dfrac{3}{2}$ and therefore $y = -\dfrac{3}{2}\left(x + \dfrac{8}{3}\right) = -\dfrac{3}{2}x - 4$. L meets L' when $\dfrac{2}{5}x - \dfrac{1}{5} = -\dfrac{3}{2}x - 4$, which gives $x = -2$. But $y = -1$ when $x = -2$, so the point is $(-2, -1)$.

40. (a) The median from C to AB is the line segment joining C and the midpoint of AB. The midpoint of AB is $M(3, -1/2)$, thus the slope of the line through C and M is $-3/4$, so $y - 4 = (-3/4)(x + 3)$.

(b) The altitude to AB is perpendicular to AB. The slope of AB is $5/4$, thus the slope of the line perpendicular to AB is $-4/5$, so $y - 4 = (-4/5)(x + 3)$.

41. Label the points as $A(5,6)$, $B(-4,3)$, $C(-3,-2)$, and $D(6,1)$. Then $m_{AB} = 1/3$, $m_{BC} = -5$, $m_{CD} = -1/3$, and $m_{DA} = -5$, so $ABCD$ is a parallelogram because opposite sides are parallel ($m_{AB} = m_{CD}$, $m_{BC} = m_{DA}$). It is not a rectangle because sides AB and BC do not form a right angle ($m_{AB} \neq -1/m_{BC}$).

42. **(a)** $y = -2x/k + 3$, if $k \neq 0$; $m = -2/k = 3$ if $k = -2/3$.

  (b) $k \neq 0$ (if $k = 0$, then the line coincides with the y-axis and does not have a unique y-intercept).

  (c) $-2/k = 0$ is impossible for any real value of k.

  (d) $(1,2)$ must satisfy $2x + ky = 3k$, so $2(1) + k(2) = 3k$ which gives $k = 2$.

CHAPTER 2
Functions and Limits

EXERCISE SET 2.1

1. (a) 14   (b) 50   (c) 2
    (d) 11   (e) $3a^2 + 6a + 5$ (f) $27t^2 + 2$

2. (a) 3   (b) 1/3   (c) $-5/3$
    (d) $\dfrac{\pi + 1}{\pi - 1}$ (e) $\dfrac{a}{a - 2}$ (f) $\dfrac{t + 1}{t}$

3. (a) $2(-4) = -8$ (b) 1/4   (c) $2(0) = 0$
    (d) $2(3) = 6$ (e) $2(2.9) = 5.8$ (f) $1/(t^2 + 5)$

4. (a) 1   (b) 3   (c) 2
    (d) 0   (e) 3   (f) $\sqrt{t^2} = |t|$

5. $(-\infty, 3) \cup (3, +\infty)$ 6. $(-\infty, -7/5) \cup (-7/5, +\infty)$

7. $(-\infty, -\sqrt{3}] \cup [\sqrt{3}, +\infty)$ 8. $(-\infty, +\infty)$

9. $\dfrac{x - 1}{x + 2} \geq 0$ if $x < -2$ or $x \geq 1$; domain: $(-\infty, -2) \cup [1, +\infty)$

10. $x - 3x^2 = x(1 - 3x) \geq 0$ if $0 \leq x \leq 1/3$; domain: $[0, 1/3]$

11. $(-\infty, +\infty)$

12. $\sqrt{x} \leq 3$ where $x \geq 0$, so $0 \leq x \leq 9$; domain: $[0, 9]$

13. $[5, +\infty) \cap (-\infty, 8] = [5, 8]$ 14. $[2, +\infty)$

15. $x^2 - 2x + 5 = 0$ has no real solutions so $x^2 - 2x + 5$ is always positive or always negative. If $x = 0$, then $x^2 - 2x + 5 = 5 > 0$; domain: $(-\infty, +\infty)$.

16. $\dfrac{x^2 - 4}{x - 4} \geq 0$ if $-2 \leq x \leq 2$ or $x > 4$; domain: $[-2, 2] \cup (4, +\infty)$

17. $(-\infty, 0) \cup (0, +\infty)$

18. $(-\infty, -1) \cup (-1, +\infty)$

19. $[0, +\infty)$

20. $(-\infty, 0) \cup (0, +\infty)$

21. all real values of x except those for which $\sin x = 1$; domain: all x except $x = \pi/2 + 2k\pi$, $k = 0, \pm 1, \pm 2, \cdots$

22. $(-\infty, +\infty)$

23. domain: $(-\infty, 3]$; range: $[0, +\infty)$

24. domain: $[2/3, +\infty)$; range: $[0, +\infty)$

25. domain: $[-2, 2]$; range: $[0, 2]$

26. domain: $[-3/2, 3/2]$; range: $[0, 3]$

27. domain: $[0, +\infty)$; range: $[3, +\infty)$

28. domain: $[0, +\infty)$; range: $(0, 1/3]$

29. domain: $(-\infty, +\infty)$; range: $[3, +\infty)$

30. domain: $(-\infty, +\infty)$; range: $(0, 2/3]$

31. domain: $(-\infty, +\infty)$; range: $(-\infty, +\infty)$

32. domain: $(-\infty, 0) \cup (0, +\infty)$; range: $(-\infty, 0) \cup (0, +\infty)$

33. domain: $(-\infty, +\infty)$; range: $[-3, 3]$

34. domain: $[0, +\infty)$; range: $[0, 1]$

35. domain: $(-\infty, +\infty)$; range: $[1, 3]$

36. domain: $(-\infty, +\infty)$; range: $[5/4, 5/2]$

37. If $x < 0$, then $|x| = -x$ so $f(x) = -x + 3x + 1 = 2x + 1$. If $x \geq 0$, then $|x| = x$ so $f(x) = x + 3x + 1 = 4x + 1$;

$$f(x) = \begin{cases} 2x + 1, & x < 0 \\ 4x + 1, & x \geq 0 \end{cases}$$

38. If $x < 5/2$, then $|2x - 5| = 5 - 2x$ so $f(x) = 3 + (5 - 2x) = 8 - 2x$. If $x \geq 5/2$, then $|2x - 5| = 2x - 5$ so $f(x) = 3 + (2x - 5) = 2x - 2$;

$$f(x) = \begin{cases} 8 - 2x, & x < 5/2 \\ 2x - 2, & x \geq 5/2. \end{cases}$$

39. If $x < 0$, then $|x| = -x$ and $|x - 1| = 1 - x$ so $g(x) = -x + 1 - x = 1 - 2x$. If $0 \leq x < 1$, then $|x| = x$ and $|x - 1| = 1 - x$ so $g(x) = x + 1 - x = 1$. If $x \geq 1$, then $|x| = x$ and $|x - 1| = x - 1$ so $g(x) = x + x - 1 = 2x - 1$;

$$g(x) = \begin{cases} 1 - 2x, & x < 0 \\ 1, & 0 \leq x < 1 \\ 2x - 1, & x \geq 1 \end{cases}.$$

40. If $x < -1$, then $|x - 2| = 2 - x$ and $|x + 1| = -x - 1$ so $g(x) = 3(2 - x) - (-x - 1) = 7 - 2x$.
If $-1 \le x < 2$, then $|x - 2| = 2 - x$ and $|x + 1| = x + 1$ so $g(x) = 3(2 - x) - (x + 1) = 5 - 4x$.
If $x \ge 2$, then $|x - 2| = x - 2$ and $|x + 1| = x + 1$ so $g(x) = 3(x - 2) - (x + 1) = 2x - 7$;

$$g(x) = \begin{cases} 7 - 2x, & x < -1 \\ 5 - 4x, & -1 \le x < 2 \\ 2x - 7, & x \ge 2 \end{cases}.$$

41. $\sqrt{3x - 2} = 6$, $3x - 2 = 36$, $3x = 38$, $x = 38/3$.

42. $\dfrac{1}{x + 3} = 5$, $x + 3 = \dfrac{1}{5}$, $x = -\dfrac{14}{5}$.   **43.** $x^2 + 5 = 7$, $x^2 = 2$, $x = \pm\sqrt{2}$.

44. $\dfrac{x}{x^2 + 3} = \dfrac{1}{4}$, $x^2 - 4x + 3 = 0$, $(x - 1)(x - 3) = 0$; $x = 1, 3$

45. $\cos x = 1$, $x = 2k\pi$, $k = 0, \pm 1, \pm 2, \cdots$

46. $\sin \dfrac{1}{x} = 1$, $\dfrac{1}{x} = \dfrac{\pi}{2} + 2k\pi$ for $k = 0, \pm 1, \pm 2, \cdots$
$x = 1/(\pi/2 + 2k\pi)$ for $k = 0, \pm 1, \pm 2, \cdots$

47. $\sin \sqrt{x} = 1/2$, $\sqrt{x} = \pi/6 + 2k\pi$ or $5\pi/6 + 2k\pi$ for $k = 0, 1, 2, \cdots$ so $x = (1/6 + 2k)^2 \pi^2$ or $(5/6 + 2k)^2 \pi^2$ for $k = 0, 1, 2, \cdots$

48. $3 \tan x = 3$, $\tan x = 1$, $x = \pi/4 + k\pi$ for $k = 0, \pm 1, \pm 2, \cdots$

49. $A = \pi r^2$, but $C = 2\pi r$ so $r = \dfrac{C}{2\pi}$; $A = \dfrac{C^2}{4\pi}$.

50. $A = \dfrac{1}{2}hs$, but $s^2 = h^2 + (s/2)^2$, $h^2 = \dfrac{3}{4}s^2$, $h = \dfrac{\sqrt{3}}{2}s$ so

    (a) $A = \dfrac{1}{4}\sqrt{3}s^2$ **(b)** $A = \dfrac{1}{3}\sqrt{3}h^2$

51. **(a)** $S = 6x^2$
    (b) $V = x^3$ so $x = V^{1/3}$; substitute into (a) to get $S = 6V^{2/3}$.

52. Let $h = $ height of cylinder, then $S = 2\pi r^2 + 2\pi rh$. But $V = \pi r^2 h$ so $h = V/(\pi r^2)$,
$S = 2\pi r^2 + 2V/r$.

53. $V = x(8 - 2x)(15 - 2x) = x(120 - 46x + 4x^2) = 4x^3 - 46x^2 + 120x$.

54. $x = 3000 \tan \theta$.

55. $h = L - L\cos\theta = L(1 - \cos\theta)$.

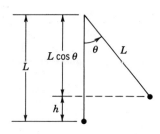

56. $L = 2[10\sin(\theta/2)]$
$\quad\; = 20\sin(\theta/2)$

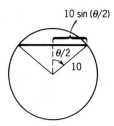

57. **(a)** $25°\mathrm{F}$　　　　　　　　　**(b)** $2°\mathrm{F}$　　　　　　　　　**(c)** $-15°\mathrm{F}$.

58. $1.6T - 55 = 60$, $T = -5/1.6 \approx -3°\mathrm{F}$.

59. $91.4 + (91.4 - T)[0.0203(8) - 0.304\sqrt{8} - 0.474] = -10$, solve for T to get $T \approx 5°\mathrm{F}$.

60. $91.4 + (91.4 - 20)(0.0203v - 0.304\sqrt{v} - 0.474) = 15$, $0.0203v - 0.304\sqrt{v} + 1.016 = 0$; use the quadratic formula to find $\sqrt{v}$, then square to get $v \approx 25$ or $v \approx 99$. But v must be between 4 and 45, so $v \approx 25$ mi/hr.

61. Multiplication of the numerator and denominator of a fraction by the same number is valid only if the number is not zero, so $(1 - 1/x)/(1 + 1/x) = (x - 1)/(x + 1)$ if $x \neq 0$.

62. $\dfrac{x^2 - 4}{x + 2} = \dfrac{(x + 2)(x - 2)}{x + 2} = x - 2$, $x \neq -2$

63. $\dfrac{(x + 2)(x^2 - 1)}{(x + 2)(x + 1)} = \dfrac{(x + 2)(x + 1)(x - 1)}{(x + 2)(x + 1)} = x - 1$, $x \neq -1$ or -2

64. $\dfrac{x^2 + x}{x} = \dfrac{x(x + 1)}{x} = x + 1$, $x \neq 0$

65. $\dfrac{x + 1 + \sqrt{x + 1}}{\sqrt{x + 1}} = \dfrac{\sqrt{x + 1}(\sqrt{x + 1} + 1)}{\sqrt{x + 1}} = \sqrt{x + 1} + 1$, $x \neq -1$

66. $\dfrac{x^2 - 9}{x - 3} = \dfrac{(x+3)(x-3)}{x-3} = x + 3, \ x \neq 3$

67. $\dfrac{x^3 + 2x^2 - 3x}{(x-1)(x+3)} = \dfrac{x(x^2 + 2x - 3)}{(x-1)(x+3)} = \dfrac{x(x-1)(x+3)}{(x-1)(x+3)} = x, \ x \neq -3 \text{ or } 1$

68. $\dfrac{x + \sqrt{x}}{\sqrt{x}} = \dfrac{\sqrt{x}(\sqrt{x}+1)}{\sqrt{x}} = \sqrt{x} + 1, \ x > 0$

EXERCISE SET 2.2

1. (a) $f(t) = t^2 + 1$
   (b) $f(t+2) = (t+2)^2 + 1 = t^2 + 4t + 5$
   (c) $f(x+2) = (x+2)^2 + 1 = x^2 + 4x + 5$
   (d) $f(1/x) = (1/x)^2 + 1 = 1/x^2 + 1$
   (e) $f(x+h) = (x+h)^2 + 1 = x^2 + 2hx + h^2 + 1$
   (f) $f(-x) = (-x)^2 + 1 = x^2 + 1$
   (g) $f(\sqrt{x}) = (\sqrt{x})^2 + 1 = x + 1, \ x \geq 0$
   (h) $f(3x) = (3x)^2 + 1 = 9x^2 + 1$

2. (a) $g(5s + 2) = \sqrt{5s + 2}$ (b) $g(\sqrt{x} + 2) = \sqrt{\sqrt{x} + 2}$
   (c) $3g(5x) = 3\sqrt{5x}$ (d) $1/g(x) = 1/\sqrt{x}$
   (e) $g(g(x)) = g(\sqrt{x}) = \sqrt{\sqrt{x}} = \sqrt[4]{x}$ (f) $g^2(x) = (\sqrt{x})^2 = x, x \geq 0$
   (g) $g(1/\sqrt{x}) = \sqrt{1/\sqrt{x}} = 1/\sqrt[4]{x}$ (h) $g((x-1)^2) = \sqrt{(x-1)^2} = |x-1|$

3. (a) $f(-1) - g(-1) = 4 - 3 = 1$ (b) $f(-1) \cdot g(-1) = (4)(3) = 12$
   (c) $f(2)/g(2) = 5/(-1) = -5$ (d) $f(g(2)) = f(-1) = 4$

4. (a) $\dfrac{3}{1/x} + \dfrac{1}{3/x} = 3x + \dfrac{1}{3}x = \dfrac{10}{3}x$ (b) $3/x^2 - (3/x)^2 = 3/x^2 - 9/x^2 = -6/x^2$

5. (a) $x^2 + 2x + 1$ (b) $-x^2 + 2x - 1$ (c) $2x(x^2 + 1)$
   (d) $\dfrac{2x}{x^2 + 1}$ (e) $2(x^2 + 1)$ (f) $4x^2 + 1$

6. (a) $3x - 2 + |x|$ (b) $3x - 2 - |x|$ (c) $(3x - 2)|x|$
   (d) $\dfrac{3x - 2}{|x|}$ (e) $3|x| - 2$ (f) $|3x - 2|$

7. **(a)** $\sqrt{x+1}+x-2$ **(b)** $\sqrt{x+1}-x+2$ **(c)** $(x-2)\sqrt{x+1}$

     (d) $\dfrac{\sqrt{x+1}}{x-2}$ **(e)** $\sqrt{x-1}$ **(f)** $\sqrt{x+1}-2$

8. **(a)** $\dfrac{2x^2+1}{x(1+x^2)}$ **(b)** $-\dfrac{1}{x(1+x^2)}$ **(c)** $\dfrac{1}{1+x^2},\ x\neq 0$

     (d) $\dfrac{x^2}{1+x^2},\ x\neq 0$ **(e)** $\dfrac{x}{x^2+1},\ x\neq 0$ **(f)** $\dfrac{1+x^2}{x}$

9. **(a)** $\sqrt{x-2}+\sqrt{x-3}$ **(b)** $\sqrt{x-2}-\sqrt{x-3}$ **(c)** $\sqrt{x-2}\sqrt{x-3}$

     (d) $\dfrac{\sqrt{x-2}}{\sqrt{x-3}}$ **(e)** $\sqrt{\sqrt{x-3}-2}$ **(f)** $\sqrt{\sqrt{x-2}-3}$

10. **(a)** $x^3+1/\sqrt[3]{x}$ **(b)** $x^3-1/\sqrt[3]{x}$ **(c)** $x^{8/3},\ x\neq 0$
     (d) $x^{10/3},\ x\neq 0$ **(e)** $1/x$ **(f)** $1/x$

11. **(a)** $\sqrt{1-x^2}+\sin 3x$ **(b)** $\sqrt{1-x^2}-\sin 3x$ **(c)** $\sqrt{1-x^2}\sin 3x$
     (d) $\sqrt{1-x^2}/\sin 3x$ **(e)** $\sqrt{1-\sin^2 3x}=\sqrt{\cos^2 3x}$ **(f)** $\sin 3\sqrt{1-x^2}$
                                                 $=|\cos 3x|$

12. **(a)** $\sin^2 x+\cos x$ **(b)** $\sin^2 x-\cos x$ **(c)** $\sin^2 x\cos x$
     (d) $\sin^2 x/\cos x$ **(e)** $\sin^2(\cos x)$ **(f)** $\cos(\sin^2 x)$

13. $(f\circ g)(x)=\dfrac{4}{x+5},\ x\geq 0;\ (g\circ f)(x)=\dfrac{2}{\sqrt{x^2+5}}$

14. $(f\circ g)(x)=\sqrt{2(8x^2+5)-10}=\sqrt{16x^2}=4|x|;$
     $(g\circ f)(x)=8(2x-10)+5=16x-75$ for $x\geq 5.$

15. **(a)** $4x-15$ **(b)** $4x^2-20x+25$

16. $f(g(x))=\begin{cases} 5x^3, & x\leq 0 \\ -x, & 0<x\leq 2 \\ \sqrt{x^3}, & x>2 \end{cases}$

17. **(a)** $f(g(x))=1/(x^2+1)$, which is defined for all x.
     (b) $g(x)=x^2+2$, for example
     (c) g must be defined for all x and $g(x)$ must never equal zero.

18. If $f(x) = x^2$ and $g(x) = 2x$, then $f(g(x)) = 4x^2$ and $g(f(x)) = 2x^2$, so $f \circ g \neq g \circ f$. Let $f(x) = x^2$ and $g(x) = x$, then $f(g(x)) = x^2 = g(f(x))$, so $f \circ g = g \circ f$.

19. Show that $(f \circ (g \circ h))(x) = ((f \circ g) \circ h)(x)$: $(f \circ (g \circ h))(x) = f((g \circ h)(x)) = f(g(h(x)))$, $((f \circ g) \circ h)(x) = (f \circ g)(h(x)) = f(g(h(x)))$. Thus $(f \circ (g \circ h))(x) = ((f \circ g) \circ h)(x)$ so $f \circ (g \circ h) = (f \circ g) \circ h$.

20. $g(x) = x + 1$, $h(x) = x^2$

21. $g(x) = \sqrt{x}$, $h(x) = x + 2$

22. $g(x) = \dfrac{1}{x}$, $h(x) = x - 3$

23. $g(x) = x^7$, $h(x) = x - 5$

24. $g(x) = a + x$, $h(x) = bx$

25. $g(x) = |x|$, $h(x) = x^2 - 3x + 5$

26. $g(x) = 3 \sin x$, $h(x) = x^2$

27. $g(x) = x^2$, $h(x) = \sin x$

28. $g(x) = x^3$, $h(x) = \cos 2x$

29. $g(x) = \dfrac{3}{5 + x}$, $h(x) = \cos x$

30. $g(x) = 3x^2 + 4x$, $h(x) = \sin x$

31. $g(x) = \dfrac{x}{3 + x}$, $h(x) = \tan x$

32. $f(x) = \sin x$, $g(x) = \sqrt{x}$, $h(x) = x^2 + 3x + 7$

33. $f(x) = \sqrt{x}$, $g(x) = 3 - x^2$, $h(x) = \sin x$

34. π is irrational so $f(f(\pi)) = f(0) = 1$

35. $u = x + 1$ so $x = u - 1$; $f(u) = (u - 1)^2 + 3(u - 1) + 5 = u^2 + u + 3$; $f(x) = x^2 + x + 3$.

36. $u = 3x$ so $x = u/3$; $f(u) = \dfrac{u/3}{(u/3)^2 + 1} = \dfrac{3u}{u^2 + 9}$; $f(x) = \dfrac{3x}{x^2 + 9}$.

37. $f(g(x)) = f(2x - 1) = 0$ only if $2x - 1 = -1$ or $2x - 1 = 2$, so $x = 0$ or $x = 3/2$.

38. $f(g(x)) = 2g(x) - 1 = x^2$, $g(x) = \dfrac{1}{2}(x^2 + 1)$.

39. $f(g(x)) = \sqrt{g(x) + 5} = 3|x|$, $g(x) + 5 = 9x^2$, $g(x) = 9x^2 - 5$.

40. **(a)** $f(g(0.3)) + f(h(0.3)) = f(\sin 0.3) + f(\cos 0.3) = \sin^2 0.3 + \cos^2 0.3 = 1$
    (b) $f(h(x)) - f(g(x)) = f(\cos x) - f(\sin x) = \cos^2 x - \sin^2 x = \cos 2x = h(2x)$

41. $f(x) = f(x/2 + x/2) = f(x/2) - f(x/2) = 0$

42. Let $x = 0$ to get $f(0) = -f(0)$, $2f(0) = 0$, $f(0) = 0$

43. **(a)** monomial, polynomial, rational, explicit algebraic
    (b) explicit algebraic
    (c) rational, explicit algebraic
    (d) polynomial, rational, explicit algebraic

44. **(a)** explicit algebraic
    (c) explicit algebraic

    (b) rational, explicit algebraic
    (d) polynomial, rational, explicit algebraic

45. **(a)** explicit algebraic
    (b) rational, explicit algebraic
    (c) monomial, polynomial, rational, explicit algebraic
    (d) explicit algebraic $\left(|x| = \sqrt{x^2}\right)$

46. **(a)** explicit algebraic
    (b) rational, explicit algebraic
    (c) monomial, polynomial, rational, explicit algebraic
    (d) explicit algebraic $\left(|x - 2| = \sqrt{(x - 2)^2}\right)$

EXERCISE SET 2.3

1. **(a)** $-4, -3, -2, 2, 3$
   (c) $-4 \le x \le -3, -2 \le x \le 2, x \ge 3$

   (b) $0, 4$
   (d) $x \le -4, -3 \le x \le -2, 2 \le x \le 3$

2.

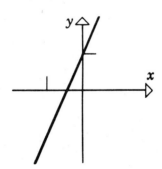

3.

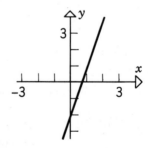

4.

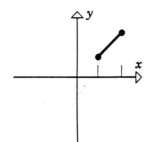

5.

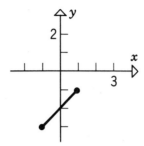

6.

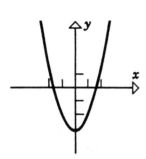

7.

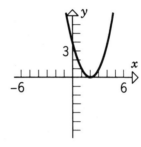

8.

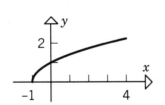

9.

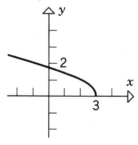

10.

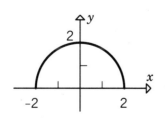

11.

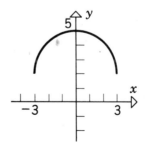

12.

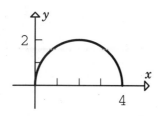

13.

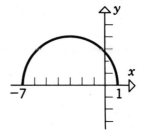

14.

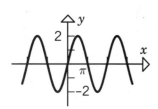

15.

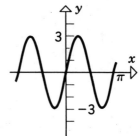

16.

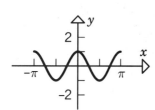

17.

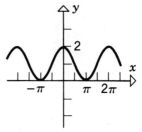

18.

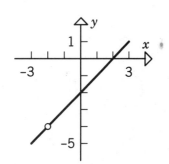

19.

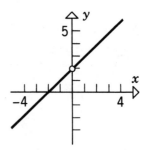

20.

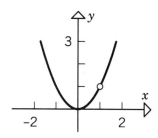

21.

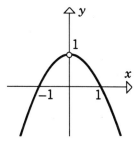

22.

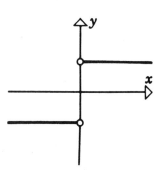

23.

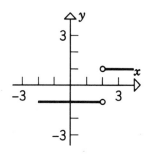

24.

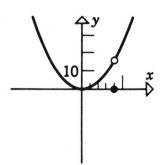

25.

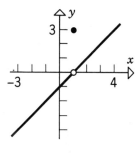

26.

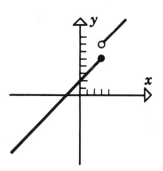

27.

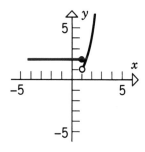

28.

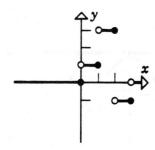

29.

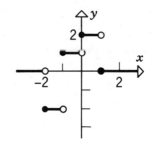

30. $x < 3 : f(x) = (3 - x) - x = 3 - 2x,$
$x \geq 3 : f(x) = (x - 3) - x = -3;$
$f(x) = \begin{cases} 3 - 2x, & x < 3 \\ -3, & x \geq 3 \end{cases}$

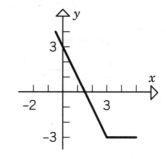

31. $x \leq 2 : f(x) = 2x + (2 - x) = x + 2,$
$x > 2 : f(x) = 2x + (x - 2) = 3x - 2;$
$f(x) = \begin{cases} x + 2, & x \leq 2 \\ 3x - 2, & x > 2 \end{cases}$

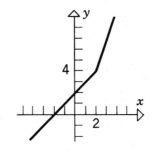

32. $x < 0 : g(x) = (-x) + (3 - x) = 3 - 2x,$
$0 \leq x < 3 : g(x) = x + (3 - x) = 3,$
$x \geq 3 : g(x) = x + (x - 3) = 2x - 3;$
$g(x) = \begin{cases} 3 - 2x, & x < 0 \\ 3, & 0 \leq x < 3 \\ 2x - 3, & x \geq 3 \end{cases}$

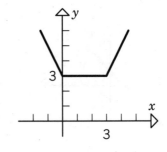

33. $x < 3 : g(x) = (5 - x) - (3 - x) = 2,$
$3 \le x < 5 : g(x) = (5 - x) - (x - 3) = 8 - 2x,$
$x \ge 5 : g(x) = (x - 5) - (x - 3) = -2;$

$$g(x) = \begin{cases} 2, & x < 3 \\ 8 - 2x, & 3 \le x < 5 \\ -2, & x \ge 5 \end{cases}$$

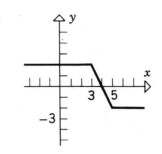

34. **(a)** $y = \begin{cases} f(x), & f(x) \ge 0 \\ 0, & f(x) < 0 \end{cases}$

$\quad\quad = \begin{cases} x^2 - 1, & |x| \ge 1 \\ 0, & |x| < 1 \end{cases}$

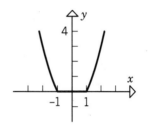

(b) $y = \begin{cases} 0, & f(x) \ge 0 \\ f(x), & f(x) < 0 \end{cases}$

$\quad\quad = \begin{cases} 0, & |x| \ge 1 \\ x^2 - 1, & |x| < 1 \end{cases}$

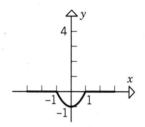

35. **(a)** $(f + g)(x) = \begin{cases} 0, & x < 0 \\ 2x, & x \ge 0 \end{cases}$ **(b)** $(f - g)(x) = \begin{cases} -2x, & x < 0 \\ 0, & x \ge 0 \end{cases}$

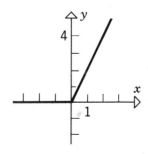

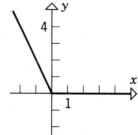

(c) $(f \cdot g)(x) = \begin{cases} -x^2, & x < 0 \\ x^2, & x \geq 0 \end{cases}$

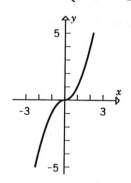

(d) $(f/g)(x) = \begin{cases} -1, & x < 0 \\ 1, & x > 0 \end{cases}$

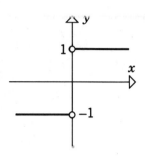

36. Let y be the distance of the top of the ladder from the ground, then $x^2 + y^2 = 10^2 = 100$ so

$y = \sqrt{100 - x^2}$ for $0 \leq x \leq 10$.

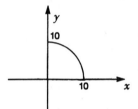

37. If $0 \leq x \leq 1$, $A = \frac{1}{2}(2x)(x) = x^2$;

if $x > 1$, $A = 1 + 2(x - 1) = 2x - 1$;

$A = \begin{cases} x^2, & 0 \leq x \leq 1 \\ 2x - 1, & x > 1 \end{cases}$

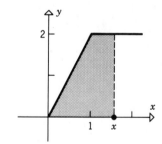

38. $f(x) = \begin{cases} x + 1, & x < 1 \\ 5 - 3x, & x \geq 1 \end{cases}$

39. $g(x) = \begin{cases} 2, & x < -1 \\ 1 - x, & -1 \leq x < 1 \\ \frac{1}{2}(x - 1), & x \geq 1 \end{cases}$

40. **(a)**

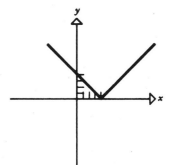

(b)

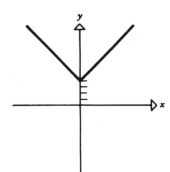

(c)

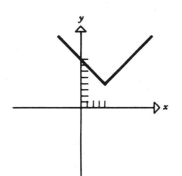

(d)

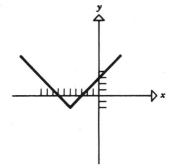

41. **(a)**

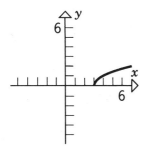

(b)

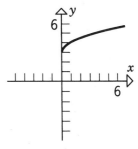

(c)

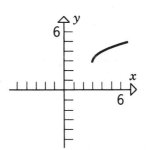

(d)

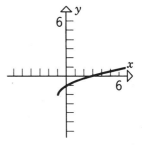

42. **(a)**

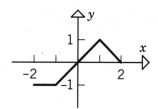

(b)

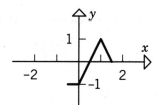

(c)

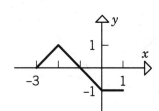

(d)

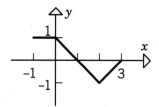

43.

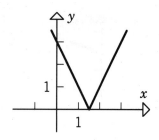

44.

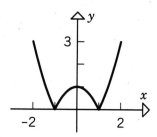

45. **(a)**

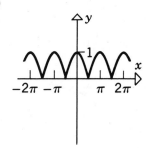

(b)

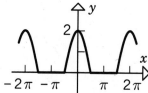

46.   **(a)**

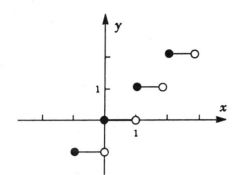

(b)

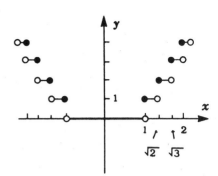

(c)

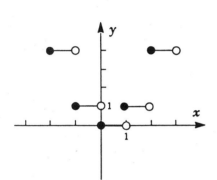

(d)

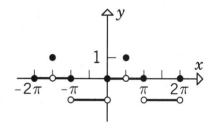

47.   **(a)** $f(-x) = (-x)^2 = x^2 = f(x)$, even   **(b)** $f(-x) = (-x)^3 = -x^3 = -f(x)$, odd
       (c) $f(-x) = |-x| = |x| = f(x)$, even   **(d)** $f(-x) = -x + 1$, neither

       (e) $f(-x) = \dfrac{(-x)^5 - (-x)}{1 + (-x)^2} = \dfrac{-x^5 + x}{1 + x^2} = -\dfrac{x^5 - x}{1 + x^2} = -f(x)$, odd

       (f) $f(-x) = 2 = f(x)$, even

48.   **(a)**

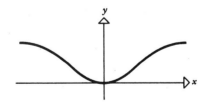

(b)

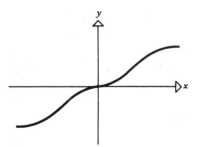

49.   **(a)** even   **(b)** odd   **(c)** odd   **(d)** neither

50. If f is both even and odd, then $f(-x) = f(x) = -f(x)$ so $2f(x) = 0$, $f(x) = 0$. The only function that is both even and odd is the constant function $f(x) = 0$.

51. (a) If f and g are even, then $(f \cdot g)(-x) = f(-x)g(-x) = f(x)g(x) = (f \cdot g)(x)$ so $f \cdot g$ is even.

(b) If f and g are odd, then
$(f \cdot g)(-x) = f(-x)g(-x) = [-f(x)][-g(x)] = f(x)g(x) = (f \cdot g)(x)$ so $f \cdot g$ is even.

(c) If f is even and g is odd, then
$(f \cdot g)(-x) = f(-x)g(-x) = f(x)[-g(x)] = -f(x)g(x) = -(f \cdot g)(x)$ so $f \cdot g$ is odd.

52. If a is constant and x is any real number, then $a - x$ lies $|x|$ units to one side of a and $a + x$ lies $|x|$ units to the other side of a. The condition $f(a - x) = f(a + x)$ implies symmetry of the graph of f about the vertical line at a.

53. (a) If $x_1 = 1.3$, then $x_2 = 1.320006122, x_3 = 1.323822354, \cdots, x_{12} = x_{13} = 1.324717957$

(b) If $x_1 = 1.3$, then $x_2 = 1.197000000, x_3 = 0.715072373, x_4 = -0.634363117, \cdots$
The graph of $y = x^3 - 1$ is steeper than that of the line $y = x$ at and near the solution.

54. Let $g(x) = \sqrt[5]{x + 2}$. On the calculator used to solve this problem, the successive approximations did not change after 1.267168305 was reached.

55. Let $g(x) = \cos x$. On the calculator used to solve this problem, the successive approximations did not change after 0.739085133 was reached.

56. (a) both; $y = \dfrac{3}{4}x - 3, x = \dfrac{4}{3}y + 4$ (b) x is a function of y; $x = 1/y^2$

(c) neither

(d) both; $y = \dfrac{1}{2}(1 - x)$ for $x \neq -1$, $x = 1 - 2y$ for $y \neq 1$

57. (a) both; $y = -2x - 4, x = -\dfrac{1}{2}y - 2$ (b) y is a function of x; $y = \dfrac{1}{x^{2/3}}$

(c) neither

(d) both; $y = \dfrac{1}{2x}, x = \dfrac{1}{2y}$

58. (a) $xy - x = 1$
$x(y - 1) = 1$

$x = \dfrac{1}{y - 1}$

(b) $y = \dfrac{x}{1 + x}$

$y + xy = x$
$xy - x = -y$
$x(y - 1) = -y$

$x = \dfrac{y}{1 - y}$

(c) $x^2 + 2xy + y^2 = 0$
$(x + y)^2 = 0$
$x + y = 0$
$x = -y$

59. **(a)** $y = 1/x^2$ **(b)** $x = \dfrac{1-y}{1+y}$ **(c)** $y^2 + 2xy + x^2 = 0$

$$x(1+y) = 1 - y$$
$$x + xy = 1 - y$$
$$xy + y = 1 - x$$
$$y(x+1) = 1 - x$$
$$y = \dfrac{1-x}{1+x}$$

$$(y+x)^2 = 0$$
$$y + x = 0$$
$$y = -x$$

60. Treat $y^2 + 3xy + x^2 = 0$ as a quadratic equation in y and use the quadratic formula to solve for y :

$$y = \frac{-3x \pm \sqrt{9x^2 - 4x^2}}{2} = \frac{-3x \pm \sqrt{5x^2}}{2} = \frac{-3x \pm \sqrt{5}|x|}{2}$$

With the exception of $x = 0$, there are two values of y for each value of x and so the original equation does not define y as a function of x.

61. Treat $y^2 + 4xy + 1 = 0$ as a quadratic equation in y and use the quadratic formula to solve for y :

$$y = \frac{-4x \pm \sqrt{16x^2 - 4}}{2} = -2x \pm \sqrt{4x^2 - 1}.$$

There are two real values of y for each x for which $|x| > 1/2$.

62. $-2x + \sqrt{4x^2 - 1}$ and $-2x - \sqrt{4x^2 - 1}$

63. **(a)** both   **(b)** a function of x
        (c) a function of y **(d)** neither

EXERCISE SET 2.4

1. **(a)** -1 **(b)** 3 **(c)** does not exist
        (d) 1 **(e)** -1 **(f)** 3

2. **(a)** 2 **(b)** 0 **(c)** does not exist
        (d) 2 **(e)** 0 **(f)** 2

3. **(a)** 1 **(b)** 1 **(c)** 1
        (d) 1 **(e)** $-\infty$ **(f)** $+\infty$

4. **(a)** 3   **(b)** 3   **(c)** 3
    (d) 3   **(e)** $+\infty$ **(f)** $+\infty$

5. **(a)** 0   **(b)** 0   **(c)** 0
    (d) 3   **(e)** $+\infty$ **(f)** $+\infty$

6. **(a)** 2   **(b)** 2   **(c)** 2
    (d) 3   **(e)** $-\infty$ **(f)** $+\infty$

7. **(a)** $-\infty$ **(b)** $+\infty$ **(c)** does not exist
    (d) not defined   **(e)** 2   **(f)** 0

8. **(a)** $+\infty$ **(b)** $+\infty$ **(c)** $+\infty$
    (d) not defined   **(e)** 0   **(f)** -1

9. **(a)** $-\infty$ **(b)** $-\infty$ **(c)** $-\infty$
    (d) 1   **(e)** 2   **(f)** 2

10. **(a)** 1   **(b)** $-\infty$ **(c)** does not exist
    (d) -2 **(e)** $+\infty$ **(f)** $+\infty$

11. **(a)** 0   **(b)** 0   **(c)** 0
    (d) 0   **(e)** does not exist   **(f)** does not exist

12. **(a)** 3   **(b)** 3   **(c)** 3
    (d) 3   **(e)** does not exist   **(f)** 0

13. all values except -4 14. all values except -6 and 3

EXERCISE SET 2.5

1. 7   2. -3 3. π 4. -6

5. 36   6. $-\infty$ 7. $\sqrt{109}$ 8. 2

9. 14   10. 3/4   11. 0   12. -3

13. $\lim\limits_{x\to 4} \dfrac{x^2-16}{x-4} = \lim\limits_{x\to 4} \dfrac{(x+4)(x-4)}{x-4} = \lim\limits_{x\to 4}(x+4) = 8$

14. $\lim\limits_{t\to -2} \dfrac{t^3+8}{t+2} = \lim\limits_{t\to -2} \dfrac{(t+2)(t^2-2t+4)}{t+2} = \lim\limits_{t\to -2}(t^2-2t+4) = 12$

15. $\lim\limits_{x\to 1+} \dfrac{x^4-1}{x-1} = \lim\limits_{x\to 1+} \dfrac{(x^2-1)(x^2+1)}{x-1}$

$\qquad\qquad = \lim\limits_{x\to 1+} \dfrac{(x-1)(x+1)(x^2+1)}{x-1} = \lim\limits_{x\to 1+}(x+1)(x^2+1) = 4$

16. $\lim\limits_{x\to 2} \dfrac{x^2-4x+4}{x^2+x-6} = \lim\limits_{x\to 2} \dfrac{(x-2)^2}{(x+3)(x-2)} = \lim\limits_{x\to 2} \dfrac{x-2}{x+3} = 0$

17. $\lim\limits_{x\to -1} \dfrac{x^2+6x+5}{x^2-3x-4} = \lim\limits_{x\to -1} \dfrac{(x+1)(x+5)}{(x+1)(x-4)} = \lim\limits_{x\to -1} \dfrac{x+5}{x-4} = -\dfrac{4}{5}$

18. $\lim\limits_{t\to 1} \dfrac{t^3+t^2-5t+3}{t^3-3t+2} = \lim\limits_{t\to 1} \dfrac{(t-1)^2(t+3)}{(t-1)^2(t+2)} = \lim\limits_{t\to 1} \dfrac{t+3}{t+2} = \dfrac{4}{3}$

19. $\lim\limits_{x\to +\infty} \dfrac{3x+1}{2x-5} = \lim\limits_{x\to +\infty} \dfrac{3+1/x}{2-5/x} = \dfrac{3}{2}$

20. 0 $\qquad\qquad\qquad\qquad\qquad\qquad\qquad$ **21.** 0

22. $\lim\limits_{x\to +\infty} \dfrac{5x^2+7}{3x^2-x} = \lim\limits_{x\to +\infty} \dfrac{5+7/x^2}{3-1/x} = \dfrac{5}{3}$

23. $\lim\limits_{x\to -\infty} \dfrac{x-2}{x^2+2x+1} = \lim\limits_{x\to -\infty} \dfrac{1/x-2/x^2}{1+2/x+1/x^2} = 0$

24. $\lim\limits_{s\to +\infty} \left[\dfrac{3s^7-4s^5}{2s^7+1}\right]^{1/3} = \lim\limits_{s\to +\infty} \left[\dfrac{3-4/s^2}{2+1/s^7}\right]^{1/3} = (3/2)^{1/3}$

25. $\lim\limits_{x\to -\infty} \sqrt{\dfrac{5x^2-2}{x+3}} = \lim\limits_{x\to -\infty} \dfrac{-\sqrt{5-2/x^2}}{1+3/x} = -\sqrt{5}$

26. $\lim\limits_{x\to +\infty} \dfrac{\sqrt{5x^2-2}}{x+3} = \lim\limits_{x\to +\infty} \dfrac{\sqrt{5-2/x^2}}{1+3/x} = \sqrt{5}$

27. $\lim\limits_{y\to -\infty} \dfrac{2-y}{\sqrt{7+6y^2}} = \lim\limits_{y\to -\infty} \dfrac{2/y-1}{-\sqrt{7/y^2+6}} = 1/\sqrt{6}$

28. $\displaystyle\lim_{y\to+\infty}\frac{2-y}{\sqrt{7+6y^2}}=\lim_{y\to+\infty}\frac{2/y-1}{\sqrt{7/y^2+6}}=-1/\sqrt{6}$

29. $\displaystyle\lim_{x\to-\infty}\frac{\sqrt{3x^4+x}}{x^2-8}=\lim_{x\to-\infty}\frac{\sqrt{3+1/x^3}}{1-8/x^2}=\sqrt{3}$

30. $\displaystyle\lim_{x\to+\infty}\frac{\sqrt{3x^4+x}}{x^2-8}=\lim_{x\to+\infty}\frac{\sqrt{3+1/x^3}}{1-8/x^2}=\sqrt{3}$

31. $+\infty$ **32.** $-\infty$ **33.** does not exist

34. $+\infty$ **35.** $-\infty$ **36.** does not exist

37. $+\infty$ **38.** $-\infty$ **39.** does not exist

40. $\displaystyle\lim_{x\to4^+}\frac{3-x}{x^2-2x-8}=\lim_{x\to4^+}\frac{3-x}{(x-4)(x+2)}=-\infty$

41. $\displaystyle\lim_{x\to4^-}\frac{3-x}{x^2-2x-8}=\lim_{x\to4^-}\frac{3-x}{(x-4)(x+2)}=+\infty$

42. does not exist (approaches $-\infty$ as $x\to4^+$, $+\infty$ as $x\to4^-$)

43. $\displaystyle\lim_{x\to+\infty}\frac{7-6x^5}{x+3}=\lim_{x\to+\infty}\frac{7/x-6x^4}{1+3/x}=-\infty$

44. $\displaystyle\lim_{t\to-\infty}\frac{5-2t^3}{t^2+1}=\lim_{t\to-\infty}\frac{5/t^2-2t}{1+1/t^2}=+\infty$

45. $\displaystyle\lim_{t\to+\infty}\frac{6-t^3}{7t^3+3}=\lim_{t\to+\infty}\frac{6/t^3-1}{7+3/t^3}=-1/7$

46. $\displaystyle\lim_{x\to0^+}\frac{x}{|x|}=\lim_{x\to0^+}\frac{x}{x}=\lim_{x\to0^+}1=1$

47. $\displaystyle\lim_{x\to0^-}\frac{x}{|x|}=\lim_{x\to0^-}\frac{x}{(-x)}=\lim_{x\to0^-}(-1)=-1$

48. $+\infty$

49. $\displaystyle\lim_{x\to9}\frac{x-9}{\sqrt{x}-3}=\lim_{x\to9}\frac{(\sqrt{x}-3)(\sqrt{x}+3)}{\sqrt{x}-3}=\lim_{x\to9}(\sqrt{x}+3)=6$

50. $\lim\limits_{y\to4}\dfrac{4-y}{2-\sqrt{y}} = \lim\limits_{y\to4}\dfrac{(2-\sqrt{y})(2+\sqrt{y})}{2-\sqrt{y}} = \lim\limits_{y\to4}(2+\sqrt{y}) = 4$

51. $+\infty$ **52.** $+\infty$ **53.** $+\infty$ **54.** $-\infty$ **55.** $-\infty$ **56.** $+\infty$

57. If $a\neq0$, then $\lim\limits_{x\to a}\dfrac{x}{x+a} = \lim\limits_{x\to a}\dfrac{a}{2a} = \dfrac{1}{2}$; if $a=0$, then $\lim\limits_{x\to0}\dfrac{x}{x} = \lim\limits_{x\to0}(1) = 1$.

58. $\dfrac{x^3-1}{x-1} = \dfrac{(x-1)(x^2+x+1)}{x-1} = x^2+x+1,\ x\neq1$;

    (a) $\lim\limits_{x\to1}\dfrac{x^3-1}{x-1} = \lim\limits_{x\to1}(x^2+x+1) = 3$ (b)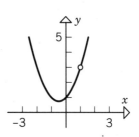

59. (a) $\lim\limits_{x\to3^-}f(x) = \lim\limits_{x\to3^-}(x-1) = 2$ (b) $\lim\limits_{x\to3^+}f(x) = \lim\limits_{x\to3^+}(3x-7) = 2$

    (c) 2

60. (a) $\lim\limits_{t\to0^-}g(t) = \lim\limits_{t\to0^-}(t-2) = -2$ (b) $\lim\limits_{t\to0^+}g(t) = \lim\limits_{t\to0^+}t^2 = 0$

    (c) does not exist, because $\lim\limits_{t\to0^-}g(t) \neq \lim\limits_{t\to0^+}g(t)$

61. $\lim\limits_{x\to3}h(x) = \lim\limits_{x\to3}(x^2-2x+1) = 4$

62. (a) $\lim\limits_{x\to-3}F(x) = \lim\limits_{x\to-3}\dfrac{x^2-9}{x+3} = \lim\limits_{x\to-3}(x-3) = -6$ and $F(-3) = k$ so $k = -6$.

    (b) $F(x) = x-3$ because $\dfrac{x^2-9}{x+3} = x-3$ if $x\neq-3$, and $x-3 = -6$ if $x = -3$.

63. (a) The limit of a difference is the difference of limits if the latter limits exist, in this problem these limits do not exist.

    (b) $\lim\limits_{x\to0^+}\left(\dfrac{1}{x}-\dfrac{1}{x^2}\right) = \lim\limits_{x\to0^+}\dfrac{x-1}{x^2} = -\infty$

64. $\lim\limits_{x\to0^-}\left(\dfrac{1}{x}+\dfrac{1}{x^2}\right) = \lim\limits_{x\to0^-}\dfrac{x+1}{x^2} = +\infty$

65. $\displaystyle\lim_{x\to 0}\frac{\sqrt{x+4}-2}{x}=\lim_{x\to 0}\frac{(x+4)-4}{x(\sqrt{x+4}+2)}=\lim_{x\to 0}\frac{1}{\sqrt{x+4}+2}=\frac{1}{4}$

66. $\displaystyle\lim_{x\to 0}\frac{\sqrt{x^2+4}-2}{x}=\lim_{x\to 0}\frac{x^2}{x(\sqrt{x^2+4}+2)}=\lim_{x\to 0}\frac{x}{\sqrt{x^2+4}+2}=0$

67. $\displaystyle\lim_{x\to 0}\frac{\sqrt{5x+9}-3}{x}=\lim_{x\to 0}\frac{5x}{x(\sqrt{5x+9}+3)}=\lim_{x\to 0}\frac{5}{\sqrt{5x+9}+3}=\frac{5}{6}$

68. $\displaystyle\lim_{x\to 3}\frac{1-\sqrt{x-2}}{x-3}=\lim_{x\to 3}\frac{3-x}{(x-3)(1+\sqrt{x-2})}=\lim_{x\to 3}\frac{-1}{1+\sqrt{x-2}}=-\frac{1}{2}$

69. $\displaystyle\lim_{x\to +\infty}\left(\sqrt{x^2+3}-x\right)=\lim_{x\to +\infty}\frac{(x^2+3)-x^2}{\sqrt{x^2+3}+x}=\lim_{x\to +\infty}\frac{3}{\sqrt{x^2+3}+x}=0$

70. $\displaystyle\lim_{x\to +\infty}\left(\sqrt{2x^2+5}-x\right)=\lim_{x\to +\infty}x\left(\sqrt{2+5/x^2}-1\right)=+\infty$

71. $\displaystyle\lim_{x\to +\infty}\left(\sqrt{x^2+5x}-x\right)=\lim_{x\to +\infty}\frac{5x}{\sqrt{x^2+5x}+x}=\lim_{x\to +\infty}\frac{5}{\sqrt{1+5/x}+1}=\frac{5}{2}$

72. $\displaystyle\lim_{x\to +\infty}\left(\sqrt{x^2-3x}-x\right)=\lim_{x\to +\infty}\frac{-3x}{\sqrt{x^2-3x}+x}=\lim_{x\to +\infty}\frac{-3}{\sqrt{1-3/x}+1}=-\frac{3}{2}$

73. $\displaystyle\lim_{x\to +\infty}\left(\sqrt{x^2+ax}-x\right)=\lim_{x\to +\infty}\frac{(x^2+ax)-x^2}{\sqrt{x^2+ax}+x}=\lim_{x\to +\infty}\frac{ax}{\sqrt{x^2+ax}+x}$

$\displaystyle\qquad\qquad =\lim_{x\to +\infty}\frac{a}{\sqrt{1+a/x}+1}=a/2$

74. $\displaystyle\lim_{x\to +\infty}\left(\sqrt{x^2+ax}-\sqrt{x^2+bx}\right)=\lim_{x\to +\infty}\frac{(a-b)x}{\sqrt{x^2+ax}+\sqrt{x^2+bx}}$

$\displaystyle\qquad\qquad =\lim_{x\to +\infty}\frac{a-b}{\sqrt{1+a/x}+\sqrt{1+b/x}}=\frac{1}{2}(a-b)$

75. $r(x)=p(x)/q(x)$ if $r(x)$ is a rational function, where $p(x)$ and $q(x)$ are polynomials. We know that $\displaystyle\lim_{x\to a}p(x)=p(a)$ and $\displaystyle\lim_{x\to a}q(x)=q(a)$ so if $q(a)\neq 0$ then

$$\lim_{x\to a}r(x)=\lim_{x\to a}\frac{p(x)}{q(x)}=\frac{\displaystyle\lim_{x\to a}p(x)}{\displaystyle\lim_{x\to a}q(x)}=\frac{p(a)}{q(a)}=r(a).\text{ If }q(a)=0,\text{ then }r(a)\text{ is not defined and}$$

thus cannot equal $\displaystyle\lim_{x\to a}r(x)$, so $\displaystyle\lim_{x\to a}r(x)=r(a)$ only if $r(a)$ is defined.

76. $\lim\limits_{x\to+\infty}\dfrac{c_0 + c_1 x + \cdots + c_n x^n}{d_0 + d_1 x + \cdots + d_m x^m} = \lim\limits_{x\to+\infty}\dfrac{x^n}{x^m}\dfrac{c_0/x^n + c_1/x^{n-1} + \cdots + c_n}{d_0/x^m + d_1/x^{m-1} + \cdots + d_m} = \lim\limits_{x\to+\infty} f(x)g(x),$

where $f(x) = \dfrac{x^n}{x^m} = x^{n-m}$ and $g(x) = \dfrac{c_0/x^n + c_1/x^{n-1} + \cdots + c_n}{d_0/x^m + d_1/x^{m-1} + \cdots + d_m}$. Note that

$g(x) \to c_n/d_m$ as $x \to +\infty$. If $m < n$, then $f(x) \to +\infty$ as $x \to +\infty$ because $n - m > 0$ so $f(x)g(x) \to +\infty$ when $c_n/d_m > 0$, and $f(x)g(x) \to -\infty$ when $c_n/d_m < 0$. If $m = n$, then $f(x) = 1$ so $f(x)g(x) \to c_n/d_m$ as $x \to +\infty$. If $m > n$, then $f(x) \to 0$ as $x \to +\infty$ because $n - m < 0$ so $f(x)g(x) \to 0$. The limit is $+\infty$ if $m < n$ and $c_n/d_m > 0$, $-\infty$ if $m < n$ and $c_n/d_m < 0$, c_n/d_m if $m = n$, 0 if $m > n$.

EXERCISE SET 2.6

1. $|2x - 8| < 0.1$
if $2|x - 4| < 0.1$
or if $|x - 4| < 0.05$,
so $\delta = 0.05$

2. $\left|\dfrac{1}{2}x - (-1)\right| < 0.1$

if $\dfrac{1}{2}|x + 2| < 0.1$

or if $|x + 2| < 0.2$,
so $\delta = 0.2$

3. $|(7x + 5) - (-2)| < 0.01$
if $|7x + 7| < 0.01$
or if $7|x + 1| < 0.01$
or if $|x + 1| < \dfrac{1}{700}$

so $\delta = \dfrac{1}{700}$.

4. $|(5x - 2) - 13| < 0.01$
if $|5x - 15| < 0.01$
or if $5|x - 3| < 0.01$
or if $|x - 3| < 0.002$,
so $\delta = 0.002$

5.   Suppose $x \neq 2$, then $\left|\dfrac{x^2 - 4}{x - 2} - 4\right| = |(x + 2) - 4| = |x - 2|$. Thus $\left|\dfrac{x^2 - 4}{x - 2} - 4\right| < 0.05$ if
$0 < |x - 2| < 0.05$, so $\delta = 0.05$.

6.   Suppose $x \neq -1$, then $\left|\dfrac{x^2 - 1}{x + 1} - (-2)\right| = |(x - 1) - (-2)| = |x + 1|$.

Thus $\left|\dfrac{x^2 - 1}{x + 1} - (-2)\right| < 0.05$ if $0 < |x + 1| < 0.05$, so $\delta = 0.05$.

7. $|x^2 - 16| = |(x+4)(x-4)| = |x+4| \, |x-4|$. If we restrict δ so that $\delta \leq 1$, then

$$|x - 4| < 1$$
$$3 < x < 5$$
$$7 < x + 4 < 9$$
$$|x + 4| < 9$$
$$|x + 4| \, |x - 4| \leq 9|x - 4|.$$

Thus $|x^2 - 16| < 0.001$ if $9|x - 4| < 0.001$, or if $|x - 4| < 1/9000$, so $\delta = 1/9000$.

8. $|\sqrt{x} - 3| = \left| \dfrac{\sqrt{x} - 3}{1} \, \dfrac{\sqrt{x} + 3}{\sqrt{x} + 3} \right| = \left| \dfrac{x - 9}{\sqrt{x} + 3} \right| = \dfrac{|x - 9|}{\sqrt{x} + 3}$. If we restrict δ so that $\delta \leq 9$, then

$$|x - 9| < 9$$
$$0 < x < 18$$
$$0 < \sqrt{x} < \sqrt{18}$$
$$3 < \sqrt{x} + 3 < \sqrt{18} + 3$$
$$\frac{1}{3} > \frac{1}{\sqrt{x} + 3} > \frac{1}{\sqrt{18} + 3}$$
$$\frac{1}{\sqrt{x} + 3} < \frac{1}{3}$$
$$\frac{|x - 9|}{\sqrt{x} + 3} \leq \frac{1}{3}|x - 9|.$$

Thus $|\sqrt{x} - 3| < 0.001$ if $\dfrac{1}{3}|x - 9| < 0.001$, or if $|x - 9| < 0.003$, so $\delta = 0.003$.

9. $\left| \dfrac{1}{x} - \dfrac{1}{5} \right| = \left| \dfrac{5 - x}{5x} \right| = \dfrac{|x - 5|}{|5x|}$. If we restrict δ so that $\delta \leq 1$, then

$$|x - 5| < 1$$
$$4 < x < 6$$
$$20 < 5x < 30$$
$$\frac{1}{20} > \frac{1}{5x} > \frac{1}{30}$$
$$\frac{1}{|5x|} < \frac{1}{20}$$
$$\frac{|x - 5|}{5|x|} \leq \frac{|x - 5|}{20}.$$

Thus $\left| \dfrac{1}{x} - \dfrac{1}{5} \right| < 0.05$ if $\dfrac{|x - 5|}{20} < 0.05$, or if $|x - 5| < 1$, so $\delta = 1$.

10. $||x| - 0| = |x|$. Thus $||x| - 0| < 0.05$ if $|x| < 0.05$, so $\delta = 0.05$.

11. $|3x - 15| = 3|x - 5| < \epsilon$, if $|x - 5| < \epsilon/3$, so $\delta = \epsilon/3$.

12. $|(4x - 5) - 7| = |4x - 12| = 4|x - 3| < \epsilon$ if $|x - 3| < \epsilon/4$, so $\delta = \epsilon/4$.

13. $|(2x - 7) + 3| = |2x - 4| = 2|x - 2| < \epsilon$ if $|x - 2| < \epsilon/2$, so $\delta = \epsilon/2$.

14. $|(2 - 3x) - 5| = |-3 - 3x| = 3|x + 1| < \epsilon$ if $|x + 1| < \epsilon/3$, so $\delta = \epsilon/3$.

15.   Suppose $x \neq 0$, then $\left| \dfrac{x^2 + x}{x} - 1 \right| = |(x + 1) - 1| = |x|$. Thus $\left| \dfrac{x^2 + 1}{x} - 1 \right| < \epsilon$ if $0 < |x| < \epsilon$,

      so $\delta = \epsilon$.

16.   Suppose $x \neq -3$, then $\left| \dfrac{x^2 - 9}{x + 3} - (-6) \right| = |(x - 3) - (-6)| = |x + 3|$. Thus $\left| \dfrac{x^2 - 9}{x - 3} - (-6) \right| < \epsilon$

      if $0 < |x + 3| < \epsilon$, so $\delta = \epsilon$.

17. $|2x^2 - 2| = 2|x + 1||x - 1|$. If we restrict δ so that $\delta \leq 1$, then

$$
\begin{aligned}
|x - 1| &< 1 \\
0 < x &< 2 \\
1 < x + 1 &< 3 \\
|x + 1| &< 3 \\
2|x + 1|\,|x - 1| &\leq 6|x - 1|.
\end{aligned}
$$

      Thus $|2x^2 - 2| < \epsilon$ if $6|x - 1| < \epsilon$, or if $|x - 1| < \epsilon/6$, so $\delta = \min(\epsilon/6, 1)$.

18. $|(x^2 - 5) - 4| = |x^2 - 9| = |x + 3||x - 3|$. If we restrict δ so that $\delta \leq 1$, then

$$
\begin{aligned}
|x - 3| &< 1 \\
2 < x &< 4 \\
5 < x + 3 &< 7 \\
|x + 3| &< 7 \\
|x + 3|\,|x - 3| &\leq 7|x - 3|.
\end{aligned}
$$

      Thus $|(x^2 - 5) - 4| < \epsilon$ if $7|x - 3| < \epsilon$, or if $|x - 3| < \epsilon/7$, so $\delta = \min(\epsilon/7, 1)$.

19. $\left| \dfrac{1}{x} - 3 \right| = \left| \dfrac{3}{x} \right| \left| \dfrac{1}{3} - x \right| = \left| \dfrac{3}{x} \right| \left| x - \dfrac{1}{3} \right|$. If we restrict δ so that $\delta \leq \dfrac{1}{4}$, then

$$
\left| x - \frac{1}{3} \right| < \frac{1}{4}
$$

$$
\frac{1}{12} < x < \frac{7}{12}
$$

$$12 > \frac{1}{x} > \frac{12}{7}$$

$$36 > \frac{3}{x} > \frac{36}{7}$$

$$\left|\frac{3}{x}\right| < 36$$

$$\left|\frac{3}{x}\right|\left|x - \frac{1}{3}\right| \le 36\left|x - \frac{1}{3}\right|.$$

Thus $\left|\frac{1}{x} - 3\right| < \epsilon$ if $36\left|x - \frac{1}{3}\right| < \epsilon$, or if $\left|x - \frac{1}{3}\right| < \frac{\epsilon}{36}$, so $\delta = \min(\epsilon/36, 1/4)$.

20. $\left|\frac{1}{x+1} - (-1)\right| = \left|\frac{x+2}{x+1}\right| = \frac{|x+2|}{|x+1|}$. If we restrict δ so that $\delta \le \frac{1}{2}$, then

$$|x+2| < \frac{1}{2}$$

$$-\frac{5}{2} < x < -\frac{3}{2}$$

$$-\frac{3}{2} < x+1 < -\frac{1}{2}$$

$$-\frac{2}{3} > \frac{1}{x+1} > -2$$

$$\frac{1}{|x+1|} < 2$$

$$\frac{|x+2|}{|x+1|} \le 2|x+2|.$$

Thus $\left|\frac{1}{x+1} - (-1)\right| < \epsilon$ if $2|x+2| < \epsilon$, or if $|x+2| < \epsilon/2$, so $\delta = \min(\epsilon/2, 1/2)$.

21. $|\sqrt{x} - 2| = \left|\frac{\sqrt{x}-2}{1}\frac{\sqrt{x}+2}{\sqrt{x}+2}\right| = \frac{|x-4|}{\sqrt{x}+2}$. If we restrict δ so that $\delta \le 4$, then

$$|x-4| < 4$$
$$0 < x < 8$$
$$0 < \sqrt{x} < \sqrt{8}$$
$$2 < \sqrt{x} + 2 < \sqrt{8} + 2$$
$$\frac{1}{2} > \frac{1}{\sqrt{x}+2} > \frac{1}{\sqrt{8}+2}$$

$$\frac{1}{\sqrt{x}+2} < \frac{1}{2}$$

$$\frac{|x-4|}{\sqrt{x}+2} \leq \frac{1}{2}|x-4|$$

Thus $|\sqrt{x}-2| < \epsilon$ if $\frac{1}{2}|x-4| < \epsilon$, or if $|x-4| < 2\epsilon$, so $\delta = \min(2\epsilon, 4)$.

22. $|\sqrt{x+3}-3| = \left|\frac{\sqrt{x+3}-3}{1}\frac{\sqrt{x+3}+3}{\sqrt{x+3}+3}\right| = \left|\frac{(x+3)-9}{\sqrt{x+3}+3}\right| = \frac{|x-6|}{\sqrt{x+3}+3}$. If we restrict δ so that $\delta \leq 9$, then

$$|x-6| < 9$$
$$-3 < x < 15$$
$$0 < x+3 < 18$$
$$0 < \sqrt{x+3} < \sqrt{18}$$
$$3 < \sqrt{x+3}+3 < \sqrt{18}+3$$
$$\frac{1}{\sqrt{x+3}+3} < \frac{1}{3}$$
$$\frac{|x-6|}{\sqrt{x+3}+3} \leq \frac{1}{3}|x-6|$$

Thus $|\sqrt{x+3}-3| < \epsilon$ if $\frac{1}{3}|x-6| < \epsilon$, or if $|x-6| < 3\epsilon$ so $\delta = \min(3\epsilon, 9)$.

23. If $x \neq 1$, then $|f(x)-3| = |(x+2)-3| = |x-1|$. Thus $|f(x)-3| < \epsilon$ if $0 < |x-1| < \epsilon$ so $\delta = \epsilon$.

24. $|(x^2+3x-1)-9| = |x^2+3x-10| = |x+5||x-2|$. If we restrict δ so that $\delta \leq 1$, then

$$|x-2| < 1$$
$$1 < x < 3$$
$$6 < x+5 < 8$$
$$|x+5| < 8$$
$$|x+5||x-2| \leq 8|x-2|.$$

Thus $|(x^2+3x-1)-9| < \epsilon$ if $8|x-2| < \epsilon$, or if $|x-2| < \epsilon/8$, so $\delta = \min(\epsilon/8, 1)$.

25. Assume there is a number L such that $\lim_{x \to 0} f(x) = L$. Then there exists a number $\delta > 0$ such that $|f(x)-L| < \frac{1}{8}$ whenever $0 < |x-0| < \delta$; in particular, $x = \frac{\delta}{2}$ and $x = -\frac{\delta}{2}$ are two

such values of x. But $f(\delta/2) = \dfrac{1}{8}$ and $f(-\delta/2) = -\dfrac{1}{8}$ so $\left|\dfrac{1}{8} - L\right| < \dfrac{1}{8}$ and $\left|-\dfrac{1}{8} - L\right| < \dfrac{1}{8}$ or, equivalently, $0 < L < \dfrac{1}{4}$ and $-\dfrac{1}{4} < L < 0$, which is impossible.

26. Assume there is a number L such that $\lim\limits_{x \to 0} g(x) = L$. Then there exists a number $\delta > 0$ such that $|g(x) - L| < 1$ whenever $0 < |x - 0| < \delta$; in particular, $x = \dfrac{\delta}{2}$ and $x = -\dfrac{\delta}{2}$ are two such values of x. But $g\left(\dfrac{\delta}{2}\right) = 1 + \dfrac{\delta}{2}$ and $g\left(-\dfrac{\delta}{2}\right) = -\dfrac{\delta}{2} - 1$, so $\left|1 + \dfrac{\delta}{2} - L\right| < 1$ and $\left|-\dfrac{\delta}{2} - 1 - L\right| < 1$ or, equivalently, $\dfrac{\delta}{2} < L < \dfrac{\delta}{2} + 2$ and $-2 - \dfrac{\delta}{2} < L < -\dfrac{\delta}{2}$, which is impossible.

27. Assume there is a number L such that $\lim\limits_{x \to 1} \dfrac{1}{x - 1} = L$. Then there exists a number $\delta > 0$ such that $\left|\dfrac{1}{x - 1} - L\right| < 1$ whenever $0 < |x - 1| < \delta$; in particular, $x = 1 + \dfrac{\delta}{\delta + 1}$ and $x = 1 - \dfrac{\delta}{\delta + 1}$ are two such values of x. So $\left|\dfrac{\delta + 1}{\delta} - L\right| < 1$ and $\left|-\dfrac{\delta + 1}{\delta} - L\right| < 1$ or equivalently, $\dfrac{1}{\delta} < L < \dfrac{1}{\delta} + 2$ and $-2 - \dfrac{1}{\delta} < L < -\dfrac{1}{\delta}$, which is impossible.

28. (a) to assure that we can allow x to approach a from both sides of a.
     (b) because $\sqrt{x}$ is not defined (not a real number) for $x < 0$.
     (c) yes, because $\sqrt{x}$ is defined on an open interval containing 0.01, for example $(0, 0.02)$.

29. $|x^2 - 9| = |x + 3||x - 3|$. If $\delta \leq 2$, then

$$|x - 3| < 2$$
$$1 < x < 5$$
$$4 < x + 3 < 8$$
$$|x + 3| < 8$$
$$|x + 3|\,|x - 3| \leq 8|x - 3|.$$

Thus $|x^2 - 9| < \epsilon$ if $8|x - 3| < \epsilon$, or if $|x - 3| < \epsilon/8$, so $\delta = \min(\epsilon/8, 2)$

EXERCISE SET 2.7

1. continuous on (d), (e), (f); discontinuous at $x = 2$ on (a), (b), (c)

2. continuous on (d), (f); discontinuous at $x = 2$ on (a), (b), (c), (e)

3. continuous on (b), (d), (f); discontinuous at $x = 1, 3$ on (a), $x = 1$ on (c), $x = 3$ on (e)

4. continuous on (b), (d), (e), (f); discontinuous at $x = 1$ on (a), (c)

5. none   **6.** none   **7.** none   **8.** $x = \pm 1$ **9.** $x = \pm 4$

10. f is discontinuous at x if $x^2 + 7x - 2 = 0$; by the quadratic formula
$x = (-7 \pm \sqrt{49 - 4(1)(-2)})/2 = (-7 \pm \sqrt{57})/2$.

11. $x = \pm 3$ **12.** $x = 0, -4$ **13.** none   **14.** $x = 0, -3$

15. none   **16.** $x = 1$ because $\lim\limits_{x \to 1} \dfrac{3}{x - 1}$ does not exist.

17. **(a)** f is continuous everywhere for any k, except perhaps at $x = 1$;
$\lim\limits_{x \to 1^-} f(x) = \lim\limits_{x \to 1^-} (7x - 2) = 5$, $\lim\limits_{x \to 1^+} f(x) = \lim\limits_{x \to 1^+} kx^2 = k$, and $f(1) = 5$ thus
$\lim\limits_{x \to 1} f(x) = f(1)$ if $k = 5$, so f is continuous everywhere if $k = 5$.

   (b) $\lim\limits_{x \to 2^-} f(x) = \lim\limits_{x \to 2^-} kx^2 = 4k$, $\lim\limits_{x \to 2^+} f(x) = \lim\limits_{x \to 2^+} (2x + k) = 4 + k$, and $f(2) = 4k$,
   so $\lim\limits_{x \to 2} f(x) = f(2)$ if $4k = 4 + k$, $k = 4/3$.

18. **(c)**

19. **(a)** If $c > 0$, then $\lim\limits_{x \to c} f(x) = \lim\limits_{x \to c} \sqrt{x} = \sqrt{c} = f(c)$; also $\lim\limits_{x \to 0^+} f(x) = \lim\limits_{x \to 0^+} \sqrt{x} = 0 = f(0)$ so
   $f(x)$ is continuous on $[0, +\infty)$.

   (b) $\sqrt{g(x)}$ is continuous by Theorem 2.7.6 because it is the composition of $\sqrt{x}$ with $g(x)$
   where $\sqrt{x}$ is continuous on $[0, +\infty)$ and $g(x)$ is continuous and nonnegative.

20. $|x|$ is continuous so $|g(x)|$ is continuous by Theorem 2.7.6.

21. $x = 0, \pm 1, \pm 2, \cdots$

22. **(a)** $\lim\limits_{x \to 1} f(x) = \lim\limits_{x \to 1} \dfrac{x^2 - 1}{x - 1} = \lim\limits_{x \to 1} (x + 1) = 2$, so removable; $\lim\limits_{x \to 1} g(x) = \lim\limits_{x \to 1} (1) = 1$, so
   removable

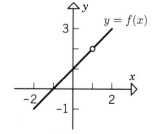
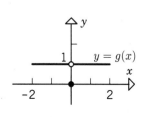

(b) define $f(1) = 2$; redefine $g(1) = 1$

23. **(a)** $x = 0$; not removable because $\lim\limits_{x \to 0} \dfrac{|x|}{x}$ does not exist.

(b) $x = -3$; removable because $\lim\limits_{x \to -3} \dfrac{x^2 + 3x}{x + 3} = -3$.

(c) $x = \pm 2$; removable at $x = 2$ because $\lim\limits_{x \to 2} \dfrac{x - 2}{|x| - 2} = 1$, not removable at $x = -2$ because

$\lim\limits_{x \to -2} \dfrac{x - 2}{|x| - 2}$ does not exist.

24. **(a)** $x = 2$; removable because $\lim\limits_{x \to 2} \dfrac{x^2 - 4}{x^3 - 8} = \dfrac{1}{3}$.

(b) $x = 2$; not removable because $\lim\limits_{x \to 2^-} f(x) \neq \lim\limits_{x \to 2^+} f(x)$.

(c) $x = 1$; removable because $\lim\limits_{x \to 1} f(x) = 8$.

25. If f and g are continuous at c, then $\lim\limits_{x \to c} f(x) = f(c)$ and $\lim\limits_{x \to c} g(x) = g(c)$, so

(a) $\lim\limits_{x \to c} (f + g)(x) = \lim\limits_{x \to c} [f(x) + g(x)] = \lim\limits_{x \to c} f(x) + \lim\limits_{x \to c} g(x) = f(c) + g(c) = (f + g)(c)$
therefore $f + g$ is continuous at c.

(b) Similar to part (a) with $+$ replaced by $-$.

(c) $\lim\limits_{x \to c} (f \cdot g)(x) = \lim\limits_{x \to c} [f(x)g(x)] = \left[\lim\limits_{x \to c} f(x) \right] \left[\lim\limits_{x \to c} g(x) \right] = f(c)g(c) = (f \cdot g)(c)$
therefore $f \cdot g$ is continuous at c.

26. A rational function is one of the form p/q where p and q are polynomials. But p and q are continuous everywhere by Theorem 2.7.2, so by part (d) of Theorem 2.7.3 p/q is continuous everywhere except at the points where the denominator is zero.

27. **(a)** Let $f(x) = \begin{cases} 0, & x < 2 \\ 1, & x \geq 2 \end{cases}$ and $g(x) = \begin{cases} 1, & x < 2 \\ 0, & x \geq 2 \end{cases}$; f and g are discontinuous at $x = 2$,

but $f + g$ is continuous at $x = 2$. If $f(x) = \begin{cases} 0, & x < 2 \\ 1, & x \geq 2 \end{cases}$ and $g(x) = \begin{cases} 1, & x < 2 \\ 2, & x \geq 2 \end{cases}$;

then f, g, and $f + g$ are discontinuous at $x = 2$.

(b) Replace $f + g$ by $f \cdot g$ everywhere in part (a).

28. If f is continuous at c, then $\lim\limits_{x \to c} f(x) = f(c)$ so for every $\epsilon > 0$ there exists a $\delta > 0$ such that $|f(x) - f(c)| < \epsilon$ whenever $0 < |x - c| < \delta$. But $|f(x) - f(c)| < \epsilon$ if $x = c$ as well, so $|f(x) - f(c)| < \epsilon$ whenever $|x - c| < \delta$. Conversely, if $|f(x) - f(c)| < \epsilon$ whenever $|x - c| < \delta$, then $|f(x) - f(c)| < \epsilon$ whenever $0 < |x - c| < \delta$, which shows that $\lim\limits_{x \to c} f(x) = f(c)$ and hence that f is continuous at c.

29. If $f(a)$ and $f(b)$ have opposite signs then 0 is between $f(a)$ and $f(b)$. From Theorem 2.7.9 there is at least one number x in $[a, b]$ such that $f(x) = 0$. But $f(a) \neq 0$ and $f(b) \neq 0$ by assumption, so there is at least one solution of $f(x) = 0$ in the interval (a, b).

30. $f(x) = x^3 - 4x + 1$ is continuous on $[1, 2]$, $f(1) = -2$ and $f(2) = 1$ have opposite signs so Theorem 2.7.10 applies.

31. $f(x) = x^3 + x^2 - 2x - 1$ is continuous on $[-1, 1]$, $f(-1) = 1$ and $f(1) = -1$ have opposite signs so Theorem 2.7.10 applies.

32. From the graph there are two real solutions, one in $(-1.5, -1)$ and the other in $(-.5, 1)$. For the one in $(-1.5, -1)$ we find

x	-1.5	-1.4	-1.3	-1.2
y	2.56	1.44	0.56	-0.13

so one solution is in $(-1.3, -1.2)$; use -1.25 to approximate it. For the one in $(0.5, 1)$ we find

x	0.5	0.6	0.7	0.8
y	-0.44	-0.27	-0.06	0.21

so this solution is in $(0.7, 0.8)$; use 0.75 to approximate it.

33. From the graph there are two real solutions, one in $(-2, -1.5)$ and the other in $(1, 1.5)$. For the one in $(-2, -1.5)$ we find

x	-2.0	-1.9	-1.8	-1.7	-1.6
y	$-9.$	-6.13	-3.70	-1.65	0.05

so one solution is in $(-1.7, -1.6)$; use -1.65 to approximate it. For the one in $(1, 1.5)$ we find

x	1.0	1.1	1.2	1.3	1.4
y	3.	2.44	1.73	0.84	-0.24

so this solution is in $(1.3, 1.4)$; use 1.35 to approximate it.

34. $f(x) = x^3 - x - 1$, $f(1.32) = -0.02$ and $f(1.33) = 0.02$ have opposite signs so the solution is approximately 1.325 with an error of at most 0.005.

35. If $f(x) = x^2 - 5$, then $f(2) = -1$ and $f(3) = 4$ have opposite signs so $\sqrt{5}$ is in $(2, 3)$.
    (a) $f(2.2) = -0.16$ and $f(2.3) = 0.29$ so $\sqrt{5}$ is in $(2.2, 2.3)$; use 2.25 to approximate it with an error of at most 0.05.

(b) $f(2.23) = -0.03$ and $f(2.24) = 0.02$ so $\sqrt{5}$ is in $(2.23, 2.24)$; use 2.235 to approximate it with an error of at most 0.005.

36. If $h(x) = f(x) - g(x)$, then h is continuous on $[a, b]$, and $h(a)$ and $h(b)$ have opposite signs so by Theorem 2.7.10 there is at least one solution of $h(x) = 0$ in the interval (a, b).

37. $f(x) = \begin{cases} x + 1, & 0 \le x \le 1 \\ x - 3, & 1 < x \le 2 \end{cases}$, for example.

38. Let $f(x) = \dfrac{a}{x - 1} + \dfrac{b}{x - 3}$, then $\lim\limits_{x \to 1^+} f(x) = +\infty$ and $\lim\limits_{x \to 3^-} f(x) = -\infty$, moreover f is continuous on $(1, 3)$. There exist numbers x_1 and x_2 where $1 < x_1 < x_2 < 3$ such that f is continuous on $[x_1, x_2]$, and $f(x_1)$ and $f(x_2)$ have opposite signs so by Theorem 2.7.10 $f(x) = 0$ has at least one solution in (x_1, x_2), and hence in $(1, 3)$.

39. If $p(x) = a_n x^n + a_{n-1} x^{n-1} + \cdots + a_1 x + a_0$ where $a_n \ne 0$ and n is odd, then either
$$\lim\limits_{x \to +\infty} p(x) = +\infty \text{ and } \lim\limits_{x \to -\infty} p(x) = -\infty, \text{ or } \lim\limits_{x \to -\infty} p(x) = -\infty \text{ and } \lim\limits_{x \to +\infty} p(x) = +\infty,$$
depending on whether $a_n > 0$ or $a_n < 0$, respectively. In either case, there are numbers a and b with $p(x)$ continuous on $[a, b]$ where $p(a)$ and $p(b)$ have opposite signs so that $p(x) = 0$ has at least one real solution in (a, b).

EXERCISE SET 2.8

1. none

2. $x = \pi$

3. $x = n\pi$; $n = 0, \pm 1, \pm 2, \cdots$

4. $x = \pi/2 + n\pi$, $n = 0, \pm 1, \pm 2, \cdots$

5. $x = n\pi$; $n = 0, \pm 1, \pm 2, \cdots$

6. none

7. none

8. $x = \pi/2 + n\pi$, $n = 0, \pm 1, \pm 2, \cdots$

9. discontinuous if $\sin x = 1/2$, so $x = \pi/6 + 2n\pi$ or $x = 5\pi/6 + 2n\pi$; $n = 0, \pm 1, \pm 2, \cdots$

10. none

11. $\sin(g(x))$ is the composition of $\sin x$ with $g(x)$; $\sin x$ is continuous, so by Theorem 2.7.6 $\sin(g(x))$ is continuous at every point where $g(x)$ is continuous.

12. **(a)** $f(x) = \sin x$ and $g(x) = x^3 + 7x + 1$ are continuous everywhere so $f(g(x))$ is also continuous.

(b) $f(x) = |x|$ and $g(x) = \sin x$ are continuous everywhere so $f(g(x))$ is also continuous.

(c) $f(x) = x^3$, $g(x) = \cos x$, and $h(x) = x + 1$ are continuous everywhere so $f(g(h(x)))$ is also continuous.

(d) $f(x) = 3 + x$, $g(x) = \sin x$, and $h(x) = 2x$ are continuous everywhere so $f(g(h(x))) = 3 + \sin 2x$ is also continuous; $\sqrt{x}$ is continuous for $x \geq 0$ so $\sqrt{3 + \sin 2x}$ is continuous because $3 + \sin 2x > 0$.

13. $\lim\limits_{x \to +\infty} \cos(1/x) = \cos(0) = 1$

14. $\lim\limits_{x \to +\infty} \sin(2/x) = \sin(0) = 0$

15. $\lim\limits_{x \to +\infty} \sin\left(\dfrac{\pi x}{2 - 3x}\right) = \sin\left(\lim\limits_{x \to +\infty} \dfrac{\pi x}{2 - 3x}\right) = \sin(-\pi/3) = -\sqrt{3}/2$

16. $\lim\limits_{h \to 0} \dfrac{\sin h}{2h} = \dfrac{1}{2} \lim\limits_{h \to 0} \dfrac{\sin h}{h} = \dfrac{1}{2}(1) = \dfrac{1}{2}$.

17. $\lim\limits_{\theta \to 0} \dfrac{\sin 3\theta}{\theta} = \lim\limits_{\theta \to 0} 3\dfrac{\sin 3\theta}{3\theta} = 3 \lim\limits_{\theta \to 0} \dfrac{\sin 3\theta}{3\theta} = 3(1) = 3$.

18. $\lim\limits_{\theta \to 0^+} \dfrac{\sin \theta}{\theta^2} = \lim\limits_{\theta \to 0^+} \dfrac{(\sin \theta)/\theta}{\theta} = +\infty$

19. $\lim\limits_{x \to 0^-} \dfrac{\sin x}{|x|} = \lim\limits_{x \to 0^-} \left(-\dfrac{\sin x}{x}\right) = -1$

20. $\lim\limits_{x \to 0} \dfrac{\sin^2 x}{3x^2} = \dfrac{1}{3} \lim\limits_{x \to 1} \left(\dfrac{\sin x}{x}\right)^2 = \dfrac{1}{3}(1)^2 = \dfrac{1}{3}$

21. $\lim\limits_{x \to 0^+} \dfrac{\sin x}{5\sqrt{x}} = \dfrac{1}{5} \lim\limits_{x \to 0^+} \sqrt{x} \left(\dfrac{\sin x}{x}\right) = 0$

22. $\lim\limits_{x \to 0} \dfrac{\sin 6x}{\sin 8x} = \lim\limits_{x \to 0} \dfrac{\dfrac{\sin 6x}{x}}{\dfrac{\sin 8x}{x}} = \lim\limits_{x \to 0} \dfrac{6\dfrac{\sin 6x}{6x}}{8\dfrac{\sin 8x}{8x}} = \dfrac{6(1)}{8(1)} = \dfrac{3}{4}$

23. $\lim\limits_{x \to 0} \dfrac{\tan 7x}{\sin 3x} = \lim\limits_{x \to 0} \dfrac{\dfrac{\sin 7x}{\cos 7x}}{\sin 3x} = \lim\limits_{x \to 0} \dfrac{1}{\cos 7x} \dfrac{\sin 7x}{\sin 3x} = \lim\limits_{x \to 0} \dfrac{1}{\cos 7x} \dfrac{7\dfrac{\sin 7x}{7x}}{3\dfrac{\sin 3x}{3x}}$

$= \dfrac{7}{3} \lim\limits_{x \to 0} \dfrac{1}{\cos 7x} \dfrac{\lim\limits_{x \to 0} \dfrac{\sin 7x}{7x}}{\lim\limits_{x \to 0} \dfrac{\sin 3x}{3x}} = \dfrac{7}{3}(1)\dfrac{(1)}{(1)} = \dfrac{7}{3}$.

24. $\displaystyle\lim_{\theta\to 0}\frac{\sin^2\theta}{\theta}=\lim_{\theta\to 0}(\sin\theta)\left(\frac{\sin\theta}{\theta}\right)=(0)(1)=0$

25. $\displaystyle\lim_{h\to 0}\frac{h}{\tan h}=\lim_{h\to 0}\frac{h}{\dfrac{\sin h}{\cos h}}=\lim_{h\to 0}\frac{h\cos h}{\sin h}=\lim_{h\to 0}\frac{\cos h}{\dfrac{\sin h}{h}}=\frac{\displaystyle\lim_{h\to 0}\cos h}{\displaystyle\lim_{h\to 0}\frac{\sin h}{h}}=\frac{1}{1}=1.$

26. $\displaystyle\lim_{h\to 0}\frac{\sin h}{1-\cos h}=\lim_{h\to 0}\frac{\sin h}{1-\cos h}\frac{1+\cos h}{1+\cos h}=\lim_{h\to 0}\frac{\sin h(1+\cos h)}{1-\cos^2 h}$

$$=\lim_{h\to 0}\frac{\sin h(1+\cos h)}{\sin^2 h}=\lim_{h\to 0}\frac{1+\cos h}{\sin h}$$

but $\displaystyle\lim_{h\to 0^-}\frac{1+\cos h}{\sin h}=-\infty$ and $\displaystyle\lim_{h\to 0^+}\frac{1+\cos h}{\sin h}=+\infty$, so $\displaystyle\lim_{h\to 0}\frac{\sin h}{1-\cos h}$ does not exist.

27. $\displaystyle\lim_{\theta\to 0}\frac{\theta^2}{1-\cos\theta}=\lim_{\theta\to 0}\frac{\theta^2}{1-\cos\theta}\frac{1+\cos\theta}{1+\cos\theta}=\lim_{\theta\to 0}\frac{\theta^2(1+\cos\theta)}{1-\cos^2\theta}$

$$=\lim_{\theta\to 0}\frac{\theta^2(1+\cos\theta)}{\sin^2\theta}=\lim_{\theta\to 0}\frac{1+\cos\theta}{\dfrac{\sin^2\theta}{\theta^2}}=\frac{\displaystyle\lim_{\theta\to 0}(1+\cos\theta)}{\displaystyle\lim_{\theta\to 0}\left(\frac{\sin\theta}{\theta}\right)^2}=\frac{1+1}{1^2}=2.$$

28. $\displaystyle\lim_{x\to 0}\frac{x}{\cos\left(\dfrac{\pi}{2}-x\right)}=\lim_{x\to 0}\frac{x}{\sin x}=\lim_{x\to 0}\frac{1}{\dfrac{\sin x}{x}}=\frac{1}{1}=1.$

29. $\displaystyle\lim_{\theta\to 0}\frac{\theta}{\cos\theta}=\frac{\displaystyle\lim_{\theta\to 0}\theta}{\displaystyle\lim_{\theta\to 0}\cos\theta}=\frac{0}{1}=0.$

30. $\displaystyle\lim_{t\to 0}\frac{t^2}{1-\cos^2 t}=\lim_{t\to 0}\frac{t^2}{\sin^2 t}=\lim_{t\to 0}\frac{1}{\left(\dfrac{\sin t}{t}\right)^2}=\frac{1}{1^2}=1.$

31. Use the identity $1 - \cos\theta = 2\sin^2\dfrac{\theta}{2}$:

$$\lim_{h\to 0}\frac{1-\cos 5h}{\cos 7h - 1} = \lim_{h\to 0}\frac{2\sin^2(5h/2)}{-2\sin^2(7h/2)} = -\lim_{h\to 0}\frac{(5/2)^2\dfrac{\sin^2(5h/2)}{(5h/2)^2}}{(7/2)^2\dfrac{\sin^2(7h/2)}{(7h/2)^2}}$$

$$= -\frac{25}{49}\frac{\displaystyle\lim_{h\to 0}\left[\frac{\sin(5h/2)}{5h/2}\right]^2}{\displaystyle\lim_{h\to 0}\left[\frac{\sin(7h/2)}{7h/2}\right]^2} = -\frac{25}{49}\cdot\frac{1^2}{1^2} = -\frac{25}{49}.$$

32. $\displaystyle\lim_{x\to 0^+}\sin(1/x)$ does not exist due to oscillation

33. $\displaystyle\lim_{x\to 0^+}\cos(1/x)$ does not exist due to oscillation

34. $\displaystyle\lim_{x\to 0}\frac{x^2 - 3\sin x}{x} = \lim_{x\to 0}\left(x - 3\frac{\sin x}{x}\right) = 0 - 3 = -3$

35. $\displaystyle\lim_{x\to 0}\frac{2x + \sin x}{x} = \lim_{x\to 0}\left(2 + \frac{\sin x}{x}\right) = 2 + 1 = 3$

36. $\displaystyle\lim_{x\to 0}\frac{\sin 3x}{x} = \lim_{x\to 0}3\frac{\sin 3x}{3x} = 3$ so $k = 3$.

37. $\displaystyle\lim_{x\to 0^-}f(x) = \lim_{x\to 0^-}\frac{\tan kx}{x} = \lim_{x\to 0^-}\frac{k}{\cos kx}\frac{\sin kx}{kx} = k;\ \lim_{x\to 0^+}f(x) = \lim_{x\to 0^+}(3x + 2k^2) = 2k^2;$
$f(0) = 2k^2;$ so $\displaystyle\lim_{x\to 0}f(x) = f(0)$ if $2k^2 = k,\ 2k^2 - k = 0,\ k(2k - 1) = 0;\ k = 1/2.$

38. $\displaystyle\lim_{x\to 0^-}f(x) = \lim_{x\to 0^-}\frac{\sin x}{-x} = -\lim_{x\to 0^-}\frac{\sin x}{x} = -1$, so f is not continuous at $x = 0$.

39. (a) If $t = \dfrac{1}{x}$, then $x = \dfrac{1}{t}$ and $x \to +\infty$ as $t \to 0^+$ so $\displaystyle\lim_{x\to +\infty}x\sin\frac{1}{x} = \lim_{t\to 0^+}\frac{\sin t}{t} = 1.$

(b) If $t = \dfrac{1}{x}$, then $x = \dfrac{1}{t}$ and $x \to -\infty$ as $t \to 0^-$ so $\displaystyle\lim_{x\to -\infty}\left(1 - \cos\frac{1}{x}\right) = \lim_{t\to 0^-}\frac{1 - \cos t}{t} = 0.$

(c) If $t = \pi - x$, then $x = \pi - t$ and $x \to \pi$ as $t \to 0$

so $\displaystyle\lim_{x\to\pi}\frac{\pi - x}{\sin x} = \lim_{t\to 0}\frac{t}{\sin(\pi - t)} = \lim_{t\to 0}\frac{t}{\sin t} = 1.$

40. Let $t = \dfrac{\pi}{2} - \dfrac{\pi}{x}$, then $x = \dfrac{2\pi}{\pi - 2t}$ and $x \to 2$ as $t \to 0$

so $\displaystyle\lim_{x \to 2} \frac{\cos(\pi/x)}{x - 2} = \lim_{t \to 0} \frac{\cos(\pi/2 - t)}{4t/(\pi - 2t)} = \lim_{t \to 0} \frac{(\pi - 2t)\sin t}{4t} = \lim_{t \to 0} \frac{\pi - 2t}{4} \cdot \frac{\sin t}{t} = \pi/4.$

41. Let $t = x - 1$, then $x = t + 1$ and

$\displaystyle\lim_{x \to 1} \frac{\sin(\pi x)}{x - 1} = \lim_{t \to 0} \frac{\sin(\pi t + \pi)}{t} = \lim_{t \to 0} \frac{-\sin \pi t}{t} = -\pi \lim_{t \to 0} \frac{\sin \pi t}{\pi t} = -\pi$

42. Let $t = x - \pi/4$, then $x = t + \pi/4$ and $x \to \pi/4$ as $t \to 0$

so $\displaystyle\lim_{x \to \pi/4} \frac{\tan x - 1}{x - \pi/4} = \lim_{t \to 0} \frac{\tan(t + \pi/4) - 1}{t},$

but $\tan(t + \pi/4) = \dfrac{\tan t + \tan \pi/4}{1 - \tan t \tan \pi/4} = \dfrac{\tan t + 1}{1 - \tan t}$

thus $\tan(t + \pi/4) - 1 = \dfrac{\tan t + 1}{1 - \tan t} - 1 = \dfrac{2\tan t}{1 - \tan t} = \dfrac{2\sin t}{\cos t - \sin t}$

and $\dfrac{\tan(t + \pi/4) - 1}{t} = \dfrac{2\sin t}{(\cos t - \sin t)t} = \dfrac{2}{\cos t - \sin t} \cdot \dfrac{\sin t}{t}$

so $\displaystyle\lim_{t \to 0} \frac{\tan(t + \pi/4) - 1}{t} = \lim_{t \to 0} \left(\frac{2}{\cos t - \sin t}\right)\left(\frac{\sin t}{t}\right) = \frac{2}{1 - 0} \cdot (1) = 2.$

43. **(a)** $-1 \le \sin x \le 1$ so $-\dfrac{1}{x} \le \dfrac{\sin x}{x} \le \dfrac{1}{x}$ if $x > 0$.

But $-1/x$ and $1/x \to 0$ as $x \to +\infty$, thus $\displaystyle\lim_{x \to +\infty} \frac{\sin x}{x} = 0.$

(b) Replace $\sin x$ by $\cos x$ in part (a).

44. $-1 \le \sin(1/x) \le 1$ so $-x \le x\sin(1/x) \le x$. But $-x$ and $x \to 0$ as $x \to 0^+$, thus $\displaystyle\lim_{x \to 0^+} x\sin(1/x) = 0.$

45. $\displaystyle\lim_{x \to 0}(1 - x^2) = 1$ and $\displaystyle\lim_{x \to 0} \cos x = 1$ so $\displaystyle\lim_{x \to 0} f(x) = 1.$

46. $xf(x) = x$ if x is rational, $xf(x) = 0$ if x is irrational. If $x > 0$, then $0 < xf(x) \le x$ so $\displaystyle\lim_{x \to 0^+} xf(x) = 0$ because $\displaystyle\lim_{x \to 0^+} 0 = 0$ and $\displaystyle\lim_{x \to 0^+} x = 0$. Similarly if $x < 0$, then $x \le xf(x) \le 0$ so $\displaystyle\lim_{x \to 0^-} xf(x) = 0$, thus $\displaystyle\lim_{x \to 0} xf(x) = 0.$

47. If $x > 0$, then $xL \le xf(x) \le xM$; if $x < 0$, then $xL \ge xf(x) \ge xM$. So $\displaystyle\lim_{x \to 0} xf(x) = 0$ because $\displaystyle\lim_{x \to 0^+} xL = \lim_{x \to 0^+} xM = 0$ and $\displaystyle\lim_{x \to 0^-} xL = \lim_{x \to 0^-} xM = 0.$

48.

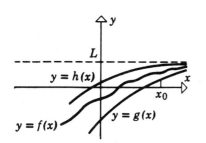 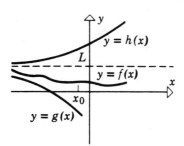

49. If $h < 0$, then $-h > 0$ so from (7) $\cos(-h) < \dfrac{\sin(-h)}{-h} < 1, \cos h < \dfrac{-\sin h}{-h} < 1,$

$\cos h < \dfrac{\sin h}{h} < 1.$

50. Let t be the radian equivalent of θ, then

$\theta = \dfrac{180}{\pi} t$ and $\displaystyle\lim_{\theta \to 0} \dfrac{\sin \theta}{\theta} = \lim_{t \to 0} \dfrac{\sin t}{\dfrac{180}{\pi} t} = \dfrac{\pi}{180} \lim_{t \to 0} \dfrac{\sin t}{t} = \dfrac{\pi}{180}.$

51. **(a)** $\sin 10° \approx 0.17365$ **(b)** $\pi/18 \approx 0.17453$

52. **(a)** $\cos \theta = 1 - 2\sin^2(\theta/2)$, but if θ is small and in radians then $\sin(\theta/2) \approx \theta/2$, so $\cos \theta \approx 1 - 2(\theta/2)^2 = 1 - \theta^2/2$.

     (b) $\cos 10° \approx 0.98481$ **(c)** $1 - \dfrac{1}{2}(\pi/18)^2 \approx 0.98477$

53. **(a)** $\tan 5° \approx 0.08749$ **(b)** $\pi/36 \approx 0.08727$

54. **(a)** $h = 500 \tan 6° \approx 52.55$ ft

     (b) If L is large compared to h, then α is small. From Exercise 53, $\tan \alpha \approx \pi\alpha/180$ so $h \approx \pi L\alpha/180$.

     (c) $h \approx \pi(500)(6)/180 \approx 52.36$ ft

55. $f(x) = x - \cos x$ is continuous on $[0, \pi/2]$; $f(0) = -1$ and $f(\pi/2) = \pi/2$ have opposite signs so Theorem 2.7.10 applies.

56. $f(x) = x + \sin x - 1$ is continuous on $[0, \pi/6]$; $f(0) = -1$ and $f(\pi/6) = \pi/6 - 1/2$ have opposite signs so Theorem 2.7.10 applies.

SUPPLEMENTARY EXERCISES CHAPTER 2

1. $\sqrt{4-x^2}$ is real if and only if $4-x^2 \geq 0$, thus $4 \geq x^2$, so the domain is $|x| \leq 2$; $f(-\sqrt{2}) = \sqrt{2}$, $f(0) = 2$, $f(\sqrt{3}) = 1$.

2. domain: $x > 1$; $f(0)$ and $f(1)$ are not defined, $f(2) = 1$.

3. $f(x) = \dfrac{(x-1)}{(x+2)(x-1)}$, domain: all x except -2 and 1; $f(0) = 1/2$, $f(1)$ is not defined, $f(2) = 1/4$.

4. domain: $|x| \geq 2$; $f(-3) = 1$, $f(0)$ is not a real number, $f(2) = 0$.

5. domain: all x; $f(0) = -1$, $f(2) = 3$, $f(4) = \sqrt{3}$.

6. **(a)** $f(x^2) - (f(x))^2 = \sqrt{3-x^2} - (3-x)$
    (b) $f(x+3) - [f(x) + f(3)] = \sqrt{3-(x+3)} - [\sqrt{3-x} + \sqrt{3-3}] = \sqrt{-x} - \sqrt{3-x}$
    (c) $f(1/x) - 1/f(x) = \sqrt{3 - 1/x} - 1/\sqrt{3-x}$
    (d) $f(f(x)) = \sqrt{3 - \sqrt{3-x}}$

7. **(a)** $f(x^2) - (f(x))^2 = \dfrac{3-x^2}{x^2} - \left(\dfrac{3-x}{x}\right)^2 = \dfrac{3-x^2}{x^2} - \dfrac{9-6x+x^2}{x^2} = \dfrac{-2x^2+6x-6}{x^2}$

    (b) $f(x+3) - [f(x) + f(3)] = \dfrac{3-(x+3)}{x+3} - \left[\dfrac{3-x}{x} + \dfrac{3-3}{3}\right] = -\dfrac{9}{x(x+3)}$

    (c) $f(1/x) - 1/f(x) = \dfrac{3-1/x}{1/x} - \dfrac{x}{3-x} = 3x - 1 - \dfrac{x}{3-x} = \dfrac{3x^2-9x+3}{x-3}$

    (d) $f(f(x)) = f\left(\dfrac{3-x}{x}\right) = \dfrac{3 - \dfrac{3-x}{x}}{\dfrac{3-x}{x}} = \dfrac{4x-3}{3-x}$

8.

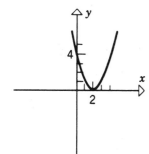

domain: all x
range: $y \geq 0$

9.

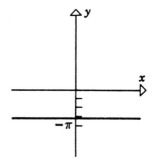

domain: all x
range: $y = -\pi$

10.

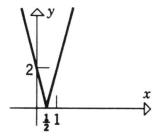

domain: all x
range: $y \geq 0$

11.

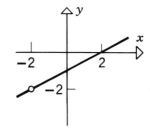

$$f(x) = \frac{x^2 - 4}{2x + 4} = \frac{1}{2}(x - 2).$$

$x \neq -2$
domain: all x except -2
range: all y except -2

12.

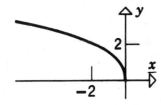

domain: $x \leq 0$
range: $y \geq 0$

13.

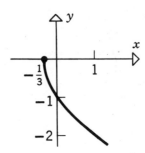

domain: $x \geq -1/3$
range: $y \leq 0$

14.

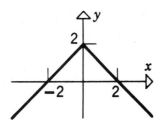

domain: all x
range: $y \leq 2$

15.

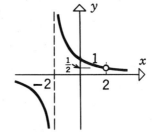

$$f(x) = \frac{2x-4}{x^2-4} = \frac{2}{x+2}, x \neq 2$$

domain: all x except $-2, 2$
range: all y except $0, 1/2$

16. **(a)** $y = f(x) = \left(x^2 - 5x + \dfrac{25}{4}\right) + 6 - \dfrac{25}{4} = \left(x - \dfrac{5}{2}\right)^2 - \dfrac{1}{4}$; range: $y \geq -\dfrac{1}{4}$.

  (b) $y = f(x) = -3(x^2 - 4x + 4) - 7 + 12 = -3(x-2)^2 + 5$; range: $y \leq 5$.

17. Some possible answers are:

  (a) $h(x) = x^3$, $g(x) = x^2 + 3$; $h(x) = x^6$, $g(x) = x + 3$

  (b) $h(x) = x^2 + 1$, $g(x) = \sqrt{x}$; $h(x) = x^2$, $g(x) = \sqrt{x+1}$

  (c) $h(x) = 3x + 2$, $g(x) = \sin x$; $h(x) = 3x$, $g(x) = \sin(x+2)$

18. $\displaystyle \lim_{x \to k} \frac{x^3 - kx^2}{x^2 - k^2} = \lim_{x \to k} \frac{x^2(x-k)}{(x+k)(x-k)} = \lim_{x \to k} \frac{x^2}{x+k} = \frac{1}{2}k$

19. (a) -1
(b) does not exist
(c) 1
(d) 0
(e) $-\infty$ (does not exist)
(f) 0
(g) 0
(h) $-\infty$ (does not exist)

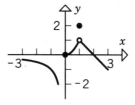

20. (a) 1
(b) 2
(c) does not exist
(d) 0
(e) 1
(f) $+\infty$ (does not exist)
(g) does not exist
(h) 2

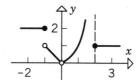

21. $f(x) = \sqrt{2-x}$ is defined for $x \le 2$ and $\lim\limits_{x \to a} f(x) = \sqrt{2-a}$ if $a < 2$, so $\lim\limits_{x \to a} f(x) = 2, 1, 0$ for $a = -2, 1, 2^-$. Because $f(x)$ is not defined for $x > 2$, $\lim\limits_{x \to 2+} f(x)$ and $\lim\limits_{x \to +\infty} f(x)$ do not exist. Finally, $\lim\limits_{x \to -\infty} f(x) = +\infty$, so this limit does not exist.

22. If $x \ne 2$, $f(x) = \dfrac{x-2}{|x-2|} = \begin{cases} 1, & x > 2 \\ -1, & x < 2 \end{cases}$, so $\lim\limits_{x \to a} f(x) = \lim\limits_{x \to a}(1) = 1$ for $a = 2^+$, $+\infty$ and $\lim\limits_{x \to a} f(x) = \lim\limits_{x \to a}(-1) = -1$ for $a = 0, 2^-, -\infty$. Because $\lim\limits_{x \to 2-} f(x) \ne \lim\limits_{x \to 2+} f(x)$, $\lim\limits_{x \to 2} f(x)$ does not exist.

23. $f(x) = \dfrac{x^2 - 25}{x - 5} = x + 5$, $x \ne 5$, so $\lim\limits_{x \to a} f(x) = \lim\limits_{x \to a}(x+5) = a+5 = 5, 10, 0, 10, 0$ for $a = 0, 5^+, -5^-, 5, -5$. Also, $\lim\limits_{x \to -\infty} f(x) = -\infty$ and $\lim\limits_{x \to +\infty} f(x) = +\infty$, so neither of these limits exist.

24. $f(x) = \dfrac{x+5}{x^2 - 25} = \dfrac{1}{x-5}$, $x \ne -5$, so $\lim\limits_{x \to a} f(x) = \lim\limits_{x \to a} \dfrac{1}{x-5} = \dfrac{1}{a-5} = -\dfrac{1}{5}, -\dfrac{1}{10}, -\dfrac{1}{10}$ for $a = 0, -5^-, -5$. Also, $\lim\limits_{x \to 5+} f(x) = +\infty$ and $\lim\limits_{x \to 5-} f(x) = -\infty$, so $\lim\limits_{x \to 5+} f(x)$ and $\lim\limits_{x \to 5} f(x)$ do not exist. Finally, $\lim\limits_{x \to a} f(x) = 0$ for $a = -\infty, +\infty$.

25. $\lim\limits_{x \to 0} \dfrac{\tan ax}{\sin bx} = \lim\limits_{x \to 0} \dfrac{\sin ax}{\sin bx} \dfrac{1}{\cos ax} = \lim\limits_{x \to 0} \dfrac{a[(\sin ax)/(ax)]}{b[(\sin bx)/(bx)]} \dfrac{1}{\cos ax} = \dfrac{a}{b}$.

26. $\displaystyle\lim_{x\to 0}\frac{\sin 3x}{\tan 3x} = \lim_{x\to 0}\cos 3x = 1$

27. $\displaystyle\lim_{\theta\to 0}\frac{\sin 2\theta}{\theta^2} = \lim_{\theta\to 0}\frac{\sin 2\theta}{2\theta}\frac{2}{\theta}$, but $\dfrac{\sin 2\theta}{2\theta} \to 1$ as $\theta \to 0$ and $\left|\dfrac{2}{\theta}\right| \to +\infty$ as $\theta \to 0$ so the limit does
not exist.

28. $\displaystyle\lim_{x\to 0}\frac{x\sin x}{1-\cos x} = \lim_{x\to 0}\frac{x\sin x}{1-\cos x}\cdot\frac{1+\cos x}{1+\cos x} = \lim_{x\to 0}\frac{x\sin x(1+\cos x)}{1-\cos^2 x}$

$$= \lim_{x\to 0}\frac{x\sin x(1+\cos x)}{\sin^2 x} = \lim_{x\to 0}\frac{1+\cos x}{[(\sin x)/x]} = \frac{1+1}{1} = 2.$$

29. $\displaystyle\lim_{x\to 0+}\frac{\sin x}{\sqrt{x}} = \lim_{x\to 0+}\sqrt{x}\left(\frac{\sin x}{x}\right) = (0)(1) = 0$

30. $\displaystyle\lim_{x\to 0}\frac{\sin^2(kx)}{x^2} = \lim_{x\to 0}k^2\left[\frac{\sin(kx)}{kx}\right]^2 = k^2$

31. $\displaystyle\lim_{x\to 0}\frac{3x-\sin(kx)}{x} = \lim_{x\to 0}\left[3 - k\frac{\sin(kx)}{kx}\right] = 3 - k$

32. $\displaystyle\lim_{x\to+\infty}\frac{2x+x\sin 3x}{5x^2-2x+1} = \lim_{x\to+\infty}\frac{2+\sin 3x}{5x-2+1/x} = 0.$

CHAPTER 3
Differentiation

EXERCISE SET 3.1

1. **(a)** $m_{\text{sec}} = \dfrac{f(4) - f(3)}{4 - 3} = \dfrac{\frac{1}{2}(4)^2 - \frac{1}{2}(3)^2}{1} = \dfrac{7}{2}$

   (b) $m_{\text{tan}} = \lim\limits_{h \to 0} \dfrac{f(3 + h) - f(3)}{h}$ **(c)**

   $\qquad = \lim\limits_{h \to 0} \dfrac{\frac{1}{2}(3 + h)^2 - \frac{9}{2}}{h}$

   $\qquad = \lim\limits_{h \to 0} \dfrac{3h + \frac{1}{2}h^2}{h}$

   $\qquad = \lim\limits_{h \to 0} \left(3 + \frac{1}{2}h\right) = 3;$

   tangent line: $y - 9/2 = 3(x - 3),$
   $\qquad\qquad\qquad y = 3x - 9/2.$

2. **(a)** $m_{\text{sec}} = \dfrac{f(2) - f(1)}{2 - 1} = \dfrac{2^3 - 1^3}{1} = 7$

   (b) $m_{\text{tan}} = \lim\limits_{h \to 0} \dfrac{f(1 + h) - f(1)}{h}$ **(c)**

   $\qquad = \lim\limits_{h \to 0} \dfrac{(1 + h)^3 - 1^3}{h}$

   $\qquad = \lim\limits_{h \to 0} \dfrac{3h + 3h^2 + h^3}{h}$

   $\qquad = \lim\limits_{h \to 0}(3 + 3h + h^2) = 3;$

   tangent line: $y - 1 = 3(x - 1),$
   $\qquad\qquad\qquad y = 3x - 2.$

3. **(a)** $m_{\text{sec}} = \dfrac{f(3) - f(2)}{3 - 2} = \dfrac{(1/3) - (1/2)}{1} = -\dfrac{1}{6}$

(b) $m_{\tan} = \lim\limits_{h \to 0} \dfrac{f(2+h) - f(2)}{h}$

$= \lim\limits_{h \to 0} \dfrac{\dfrac{1}{2+h} - \dfrac{1}{2}}{h}$

$= \lim\limits_{h \to 0} \dfrac{2 - (2+h)}{2h(2+h)}$

$= \lim\limits_{h \to 0} -\dfrac{1}{2(2+h)} = -\dfrac{1}{4};$

tangent line: $y - \dfrac{1}{2} = -\dfrac{1}{4}(x - 2),$

$y = -\dfrac{1}{4}x + 1.$

(c)

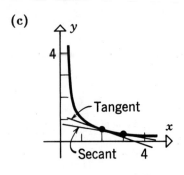

4. **(a)** $m_{\sec} = \dfrac{f(2) - f(1)}{2 - 1} = \dfrac{1/2^2 - 1/1^2}{1} = -\dfrac{3}{4}$

(b) $m_{\tan} = \lim\limits_{h \to 0} \dfrac{1/(1+h)^2 - 1/1^2}{h}$

$= \lim\limits_{h \to 0} \dfrac{1 - (1+h)^2}{h(1+h)^2}$

$= \lim\limits_{h \to 0} \dfrac{-2h - h^2}{h(1+h)^2}$

$= \lim\limits_{h \to 0} \dfrac{-2 - h}{(1+h)^2} = -2;$

tangent line: $y - 1 = -2(x - 1),$

$y = -2x + 3.$

(c)

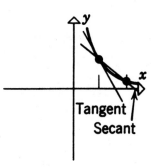

5. **(a)** $m_{\tan} = \lim\limits_{h \to 0} \dfrac{f(x_0 + h) - f(x_0)}{h} = \lim\limits_{h \to 0} \dfrac{(x_0 + h)^3 - x_0^3}{h}$

$= \lim\limits_{h \to 0} \dfrac{(x_0^3 + 3x_0^2 h + 3x_0 h^2 + h^3) - x_0^3}{h} = \lim\limits_{h \to 0} (3x_0^2 + 3x_0 h + h^2) = 3x_0^2.$

(b) $m_{\tan} = 3(5)^2 = 75$ at $(5, 5^3) = (5, 125)$, so $y - 125 = 75(x - 5)$, or $y = 75x - 250.$

(c) $y - x_0^3 = 3x_0^2(x - x_0)$, $y = 3x_0^2 x - 2x_0^3.$

6. **(a)** $m_{\tan} = \lim\limits_{h \to 0} \dfrac{f(x_0 + h) - f(x_0)}{h} = \lim\limits_{h \to 0} \dfrac{1/(x_0 + h) - 1/x_0}{h} = \lim\limits_{h \to 0} -\dfrac{1}{x_0(x_0 + h)} = -\dfrac{1}{x_0^2}.$

(b) $m_{\tan} = -\dfrac{1}{(-7)^2} = -\dfrac{1}{49}$ at $\left(-7, -\dfrac{1}{7}\right)$ so $y + \dfrac{1}{7} = -\dfrac{1}{49}(x + 7)$, or $y = -\dfrac{1}{49}x - \dfrac{2}{7}$.

(c) $y - \dfrac{1}{x_0} = -\dfrac{1}{x_0^2}(x - x_0)$, $y = -\dfrac{1}{x_0^2}x + \dfrac{2}{x_0}$.

7. **(a)** $m_{\tan} = \lim\limits_{h \to 0} \dfrac{f(x_0 + h) - f(x_0)}{h} = \lim\limits_{h \to 0} \dfrac{[(x_0 + h)^2 + (x_0 + h)] - (x_0^2 + x_0)}{h}$

$= \lim\limits_{h \to 0} \dfrac{2x_0 h + h^2 + h}{h} = \lim\limits_{h \to 0}(2x_0 + h + 1) = 2x_0 + 1.$

(b) $m_{\tan} = 2(2) + 1 = 5$ at $(2, 6)$ so $y - 6 = 5(x - 2)$, or $y = 5x - 4$.

(c) $y - (x_0^2 + x_0) = (2x_0 + 1)(x - x_0)$, $y = (2x_0 + 1)x - x_0^2$

8. **(a)** $m_{\tan} = \lim\limits_{h \to 0} \dfrac{f(x_0 + h) - f(x_0)}{h} = \lim\limits_{h \to 0} \dfrac{[(x_0 + h)^2 + 3(x_0 + h) + 2] - [x_0^2 + 3x_0 + 2]}{h}$

$= \lim\limits_{h \to 0}(2x_0 + h + 3) = 2x_0 + 3$

(b) $m_{\tan} = 2(2) + 3 = 7$ at $(2, 12)$ so $y - 12 = 7(x - 2)$, or $y = 7x - 2$.

(c) $y - (x_0^2 + 3x_0 + 2) = (2x_0 + 3)(x - x_0)$, $y = (2x_0 + 3)x - x_0^2 + 2$

9. **(a)** $m_{\tan} = (50 - 10)/(15 - 5)$
$= 40/10$
$= 4$ m/sec

(b)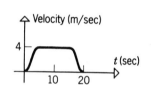

10. **(a)** $(10 - 10)/(3 - 0) = 0$ cm/sec
(b) $t = 0$, $t = 2$, and $t = 4.2$ (horizontal tangent line)
(c) maximum: $t = 1$ (largest positive slope) minimum: $t = 3$ (smallest negative slope)
(d) $(2 - 18)/(4 - 2) = -8$ cm/sec (slope of estimated tangent line to curve at $t = 3$)

11. From the figure:
(a) The particle is moving faster at time t_0 because the slope of the tangent to the curve at t_0 is greater than that at t_2.
(b) The initial velocity is 0 because the slope of a horizontal line is 0.
(c) The particle is speeding up because the slope increases as t increases from t_0 to t_1.

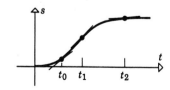

(d) The particle is slowing down because the slope decreases as t increases from t_1 to t_2.

12.

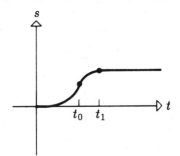

13. It is a straight line with slope equal to the velocity.

14. **(a)** decreasing (slope of tangent line decreases with increasing time)
(b) increasing (slope of tangent line increases with increasing time)
(c) increasing (slope of tangent line increases with increasing time)
(d) decreasing (slope of tangent line decreases with increasing time)

15. **(a)** 72°F at about 4:30 P.M.
(b) about $(66 - 42)/6 = 4°$F/hr
(c) decreasing most rapidly at about 9 P.M.; rate of change of temperature is about $-6°$F/hr (slope of estimated tangent line to curve at 9 P.M.)

16. For $V = 10$ the slope of the tangent line is about -0.25 atm/L, for $V = 25$ the slope is about -0.04 atm/L.

17. **(a)** during the first year after birth
(b) about 6 cm/year (slope of estimated tangent line at age 5)
(c) the growth rate is greatest at about age 14; about 10 cm/year
(d)

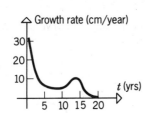

18. **(a)** The rock will hit the ground when $16t^2 = 576$, $t^2 = 36$, $t = 6$ seconds (only $t \geq 0$ is meaningful).

(b) average velocity $= \dfrac{16(6)^2 - 16(0)^2}{6 - 0} = 96$ ft/sec.

(c) average velocity $= \dfrac{16(3)^2 - 16(0)^2}{3 - 0} = 48$ ft/sec.

(d) $f'(6) = \lim\limits_{h \to 0} \dfrac{16(6 + h)^2 - 16(6)^2}{h} = \lim\limits_{h \to 0} \dfrac{16(12h + h^2)}{h} = \lim\limits_{h \to 0} 16(12 + h) = 192$ ft/sec.

19. **(a)** $5(40)^3 = 320{,}000$ ft.
    (b) average velocity $= 320{,}000/40 = 8{,}000$ ft/sec.
    (c) $5t^3 = 135$ when the rocket has gone 135 ft, so $t^3 = 27$, $t = 3$ sec;
    average velocity $= 135/3 = 45$ ft/sec.
    (d) $f'(40) = \lim\limits_{h \to 0} \dfrac{5(40 + h)^3 - 5(40)^3}{h} = \lim\limits_{h \to 0} \dfrac{5(4800h + 120h^2 + h^3)}{h}$

    $= \lim\limits_{h \to 0} 5(4800 + 120h + h^2) = 24{,}000$ ft/sec.

20. **(a)** average velocity $= \dfrac{[3(3)^2 + 3] - [3(1)^2 + 1]}{3 - 1} = 13$ mph.

    (b) $f'(1) = \lim\limits_{h \to 0} \dfrac{[3(1 + h)^2 + (1 + h)] - [3(1)^2 + (1)]}{h} = \lim\limits_{h \to 0} (7 + 3h) = 7$ mph

21. **(a)** average velocity $= \dfrac{6(4)^4 - 6(2)^4}{4 - 2} = 720$ ft/min.

    (b) $f'(2) = \lim\limits_{h \to 0} \dfrac{6(2 + h)^4 - 6(2)^4}{h} = \lim\limits_{h \to 0} \dfrac{6(32h + 24h^2 + 8h^3 + h^4)}{h}$

    $= \lim\limits_{h \to 0} 6(32 + 24h + 8h^2 + h^3) = 192$ ft/min.

22. If v is the velocity (assumed constant) for the final 20 miles, then it takes $20/v$ hrs to travel these 20 miles. It takes $100/50 = 2$ hrs to travel 100 miles at an average velocity of 50 mph, thus the time required for the entire trip is $2 + 20/v$ hrs, so the average velocity for the 120 miles is $\dfrac{120}{2 + 20/v} = \dfrac{60}{1 + 10/v}$, which is always less than 60 no matter how large v is.

23. **(a)** $x_0 = 1$, $x_1 = 4$; $y_0 = 2(1)^2 - 1 = 1$, $y_1 = 2(4)^2 - 1 = 31$, $\dfrac{y_1 - y_0}{x_1 - x_0} = \dfrac{31 - 1}{4 - 1} = 10$.

    (b) $y'(1) = \lim\limits_{h \to 0} \dfrac{[2(1 + h)^2 - 1] - [2(1)^2 - 1]}{h} = \lim\limits_{h \to 0} (4 + 2h) = 4$.

24. **(a)** $x_0 = -1$, $x_1 = 2$; $y_0 = 1/2$, $y_1 = 1/5$, $\dfrac{y_1 - y_0}{x_1 - x_0} = \dfrac{1/5 - 1/2}{2 - (-1)} = -1/10$.

(b) $y'(-1) = \lim\limits_{h \to 0} \dfrac{\dfrac{1}{(-1+h)^2 + 1} - \dfrac{1}{2}}{h} = \lim\limits_{h \to 0} \dfrac{2 - h}{2[(-1+h)^2 + 1]} = 1/2.$

25. **(a)** $r_0 = 1,\ r_1 = 2;\ A_0 = \pi(1)^2 = \pi,\ A_1 = \pi(2)^2 = 4\pi,\ \dfrac{A_1 - A_0}{r_1 - r_0} = \dfrac{4\pi - \pi}{2 - 1} = 3\pi.$

(b) $A'(2) = \lim\limits_{h \to 0} \dfrac{\pi(2+h)^2 - \pi(2)^2}{h} = \lim\limits_{h \to 0} \pi(4 + h) = 4\pi.$

26. **(a)** $\ell_0 = 2,\ \ell_1 = 4;\ V_0 = 2^3 = 8,\ V_1 = 4^3 = 64,\ \dfrac{V_1 - V_0}{\ell_1 - \ell_0} = \dfrac{64 - 8}{4 - 2} = 28.$

(b) $V'(s) = \lim\limits_{h \to 0} \dfrac{(5+h)^3 - 5^3}{h} = \lim\limits_{h \to 0} (75 + 15h + h^2) = 75.$

27. $m_{\sec} = \dfrac{f(x_1) - f(x_0)}{x_1 - x_0} = \dfrac{x_1^2 - x_0^2}{x_1 - x_0} = \dfrac{(x_1 + x_0)(x_1 - x_0)}{x_1 - x_0} = x_1 + x_0,\ x_1 \neq x_0$

$m_{\sec}$ approaches $2x_0$ as x_1 approaches x_0, thus $m_{\tan} = 2x_0$ so

$|m_{\tan} - m_{\sec}| = |2x_0 - (x_1 + x_0)| = |x_0 - x_1| = |x_1 - x_0|.$

EXERCISE SET 3.2

1. $f'(x) = \lim\limits_{h \to 0} \dfrac{3(x+h)^2 - 3x^2}{h} = \lim\limits_{h \to 0} \dfrac{3(x^2 + 2xh + h^2) - 3x^2}{h}$

$= \lim\limits_{h \to 0} \dfrac{6xh + 3h^2}{h} = \lim\limits_{h \to 0} (6x + 3h) = 6x.$

2. $f'(x) = \lim\limits_{h \to 0} \dfrac{[(x+h)^2 - (x+h)] - [x^2 - x]}{h}$

$= \lim\limits_{h \to 0} \dfrac{x^2 + 2xh + h^2 - x - h - x^2 + x}{h} = \lim\limits_{h \to 0} \dfrac{2xh + h^2 - h}{h}$

$= \lim\limits_{h \to 0} (2x + h - 1) = 2x - 1.$

3. $f'(x) = \lim\limits_{h \to 0} \dfrac{(x+h)^3 - x^3}{h} = \lim\limits_{h \to 0} \dfrac{x^3 + 3x^2 h + 3xh^2 + h^3 - x^3}{h}$

$= \lim\limits_{h \to 0} \dfrac{3x^2 h + 3xh^2 + h^3}{h} = \lim\limits_{h \to 0} (3x^2 + 3xh + h^2) = 3x^2.$

4. $f'(x) = \lim\limits_{h \to 0} \dfrac{[2(x+h)^3 + 1] - [2x^3 + 1]}{h}$

$\qquad = \lim\limits_{h \to 0} \dfrac{2(x^3 + 3x^2h + 3xh^2 + h^3) + 1 - 2x^3 - 1}{h}$

$\qquad = \lim\limits_{h \to 0} \dfrac{6x^2h + 6xh^2 + 2h^3}{h} = \lim\limits_{h \to 0}(6x^2 + 6xh + 2h^2) = 6x^2.$

5. $f'(x) = \lim\limits_{h \to 0} \dfrac{\sqrt{x+h+1} - \sqrt{x+1}}{h}$

$\qquad = \lim\limits_{h \to 0} \dfrac{\sqrt{x+h+1} - \sqrt{x+1}}{h} \dfrac{\sqrt{x+h+1} + \sqrt{x+1}}{\sqrt{x+h+1} + \sqrt{x+1}}$

$\qquad = \lim\limits_{h \to 0} \dfrac{(x+h+1) - (x+1)}{h(\sqrt{x+h+1} + \sqrt{x+1})} = \lim\limits_{h \to 0} \dfrac{h}{h(\sqrt{x+h+1} + \sqrt{x+1})}$

$\qquad = \lim\limits_{h \to 0} \dfrac{1}{\sqrt{x+h+1} + \sqrt{x+1}} = \dfrac{1}{2\sqrt{x+1}}.$

6. $f'(x) = \lim\limits_{h \to 0} \dfrac{(x+h)^4 - x^4}{h} = \lim\limits_{h \to 0} \dfrac{x^4 + 4x^3h + 6x^2h^2 + 4xh^3 + h^4 - x^4}{h}$

$\qquad = \lim\limits_{h \to 0} \dfrac{4x^3h + 6x^2h^2 + 4xh^3 + h^4}{h} = \lim\limits_{h \to 0}(4x^3 + 6x^2h + 4xh^2 + h^3) = 4x^3.$

7. $f'(x) = \lim\limits_{h \to 0} \dfrac{\dfrac{1}{x+h} - \dfrac{1}{x}}{h} = \lim\limits_{h \to 0} \dfrac{\dfrac{x - (x+h)}{x(x+h)}}{h}$

$\qquad = \lim\limits_{h \to 0} \dfrac{-h}{hx(x+h)} = \lim\limits_{h \to 0} -\dfrac{1}{x(x+h)} = -\dfrac{1}{x^2}.$

8. $f'(x) = \lim\limits_{h \to 0} \dfrac{\dfrac{1}{(x+h)^2} - \dfrac{1}{x^2}}{h} = \lim\limits_{h \to 0} \dfrac{\dfrac{x^2 - (x+h)^2}{x^2(x+h)^2}}{h}$

$\qquad = \lim\limits_{h \to 0} \dfrac{x^2 - x^2 - 2xh - h^2}{hx^2(x+h)^2} = \lim\limits_{h \to 0} \dfrac{-2xh - h^2}{hx^2(x+h)^2} = \lim\limits_{h \to 0} \dfrac{-2x - h}{x^2(x+h)^2} = -\dfrac{2}{x^3}.$

9. $f'(x) = \lim\limits_{h \to 0} \dfrac{[a(x+h)^2 + b] - [ax^2 + b]}{h} = \lim\limits_{h \to 0} \dfrac{ax^2 + 2axh + ah^2 + b - ax^2 - b}{h}$

$\qquad = \lim\limits_{h \to 0} \dfrac{2axh + ah^2}{h} = \lim\limits_{h \to 0}(2ax + ah) = 2ax.$

10. $f'(x) = \lim\limits_{h \to 0} \dfrac{\dfrac{1}{(x+h)+1} - \dfrac{1}{x+1}}{h} = \lim\limits_{h \to 0} \dfrac{\dfrac{(x+1)-(x+h+1)}{(x+1)(x+h+1)}}{h}$

$\quad = \lim\limits_{h \to 0} \dfrac{x+1-x-h-1}{h(x+1)(x+h+1)} = \lim\limits_{h \to 0} \dfrac{-h}{h(x+1)(x+h+1)}$

$\quad = \lim\limits_{h \to 0} \dfrac{-1}{(x+1)(x+h+1)} = -\dfrac{1}{(x+1)^2}.$

11. $f'(x) = \lim\limits_{h \to 0} \dfrac{\dfrac{1}{\sqrt{x+h}} - \dfrac{1}{\sqrt{x}}}{h} = \lim\limits_{h \to 0} \dfrac{\sqrt{x} - \sqrt{x+h}}{h\sqrt{x}\sqrt{x+h}}$

$\quad = \lim\limits_{h \to 0} \dfrac{x - (x+h)}{h\sqrt{x}\sqrt{x+h}(\sqrt{x} + \sqrt{x+h})} = \lim\limits_{h \to 0} \dfrac{-1}{\sqrt{x}\sqrt{x+h}(\sqrt{x} + \sqrt{x+h})} = -\dfrac{1}{2x^{3/2}}.$

12. $f'(x) = \lim\limits_{h \to 0} \dfrac{(x+h)^{1/3} - x^{1/3}}{h}$, but $a^3 - b^3 = (a-b)(a^2 + ab + b^2)$ so with $a = (x+h)^{1/3}$

and $b = x^{1/3}$

$f'(x) = \lim\limits_{h \to 0} \dfrac{(x+h) - x}{h[(x+h)^{2/3} + (x+h)^{1/3}x^{1/3} + x^{2/3}]}$

$\quad = \lim\limits_{h \to 0} \dfrac{1}{(x+h)^{2/3} + (x+h)^{1/3}x^{1/3} + x^{2/3}} = \dfrac{1}{3x^{2/3}}.$

13. $f'(3) = 6(3) = 18;\ f(3) = 3(3)^2 = 27$ so $y - 27 = 18(x - 3),\ y = 18x - 27.$

14. $f'(2) = 2(2) - 1 = 3;\ f(2) = 2^2 - 2 = 2$ so $y - 2 = 3(x - 2),\ y = 3x - 4.$

15. $f'(0) = 3(0)^2 = 0;\ f(0) = 0^3 = 0$ so $y - 0 = (0)(x - 0),\ y = 0.$

16. $f'(-1) = 6(-1)^2 = 6;\ f(-1) = 2(-1)^3 + 1 = -1$ so $y + 1 = 6(x + 1),\ y = 6x + 5.$

17. $f'(8) = \dfrac{1}{2\sqrt{8+1}} = \dfrac{1}{6};\ f(8) = \sqrt{8+1} = 3$ so $y - 3 = \dfrac{1}{6}(x - 8),\ y = \dfrac{1}{6}x + \dfrac{5}{3}.$

18. $f'(-2) = 4(-2)^3 = -32;\ f(-2) = (-2)^4 = 16$ so $y - 16 = -32(x + 2),\ y = -32x - 48.$

19. (a) $\dfrac{dy}{dx} = \lim\limits_{h \to 0} \dfrac{[4(x+h)^2 + 2] - [4x^2 + 2]}{h}$

$\quad = \lim\limits_{h \to 0} \dfrac{4x^2 + 8xh + 4h^2 + 2 - 4x^2 - 2}{h} = \lim\limits_{h \to 0} (8x + 4h) = 8x.$

(b) $\dfrac{dy}{dx}\bigg|_{x=1} = 8(1) = 8.$

20. **(a)** $\dfrac{dy}{dx} = \lim\limits_{h \to 0} \dfrac{\left(\dfrac{5}{x+h}+1\right) - \left(\dfrac{5}{x}+1\right)}{h} = \lim\limits_{h \to 0} \dfrac{\dfrac{5}{x+h} - \dfrac{5}{x}}{h}$

$$= \lim\limits_{h \to 0} \dfrac{\dfrac{5x - 5(x+h)}{(x+h)}}{h} = \lim\limits_{h \to 0} \dfrac{5x - 5x - 5h}{hx(x+h)} = \lim\limits_{h \to 0} \dfrac{-5}{x(x+h)} = -\dfrac{5}{x^2}.$$

(b) $\left.\dfrac{dy}{dx}\right|_{x=-2} = -\dfrac{5}{(-2)^2} = -\dfrac{5}{4}.$

21. $f'(t) = \lim\limits_{h \to 0} \dfrac{f(t+h) - f(t)}{h} = \lim\limits_{h \to 0} \dfrac{[4(t+h)^2 + (t+h)] - [4t^2 + t]}{h}$

$$= \lim\limits_{h \to 0} \dfrac{4t^2 + 8th + 4h^2 + t + h - 4t^2 - t}{h}$$

$$= \lim\limits_{h \to 0} \dfrac{8th + 4h^2 + h}{h} = \lim\limits_{h \to 0} (8t + 4h + 1) = 8t + 1.$$

22. $g'(u) = \lim\limits_{h \to 0} \dfrac{g(u+h) - g(u)}{h} = \lim\limits_{h \to 0} \dfrac{[5(u+h) + 3] - [5u + 3]}{h}$

$$= \lim\limits_{h \to 0} \dfrac{5u + 5h + 3 - 5u - 3}{h} = \lim\limits_{h \to 0} \dfrac{5h}{h} = \lim\limits_{h \to 0} 5 = 5.$$

23. $\dfrac{dA}{d\lambda} = \lim\limits_{h \to 0} \dfrac{[3(\lambda+h)^2 - (\lambda+h)] - [3\lambda^2 - \lambda]}{h} = \lim\limits_{h \to 0} \dfrac{3\lambda^2 + 6\lambda h + 3h^2 - \lambda - h - 3\lambda^2 + \lambda}{h}$

$$= \lim\limits_{h \to 0} \dfrac{6\lambda h + 3h^2 - h}{h} = \lim\limits_{h \to 0} (6\lambda + 3h - 1) = 6\lambda - 1.$$

24. $\dfrac{dV}{dr} = \lim\limits_{h \to 0} \dfrac{\dfrac{4}{3}\pi(r+h)^3 - \dfrac{4}{3}\pi r^3}{h} = \lim\limits_{h \to 0} \dfrac{\dfrac{4}{3}\pi(r^3 + 3r^2h + 3rh^2 + h^3 - r^3)}{h}$

$$= \lim\limits_{h \to 0} \dfrac{4}{3}\pi(3r^2 + 3rh + h^2) = 4\pi r^2.$$

25. **(a)** D   **(b)** F   **(c)** B   **(d)** C   **(e)** A   **(f)** E

26. $f'(1) = 2$, $f'(3) = 0$, $f'(5) = -2$, $f'(6) = -1/2$.

27. Estimate the slope of the tangent lines at $t = 0$ and $t = 15$ to get $\left.\dfrac{dc}{dt}\right|_{t=0} \approx 0.08$ mol/L per second and $\left.\dfrac{dc}{dt}\right|_{t=15} \approx 0.018$ mol/L per second.

28. **(a)** $dN/dt \approx 32$ million/year; in 1950 the world population was increasing at the rate of about 32 million per year.

   (b) $\dfrac{dN/dt}{N} \approx \dfrac{32}{2490} \approx 0.013 = 1.3\,\%/\text{year}$

29. **(a)** $F \approx 200$ lb, $dF/d\theta \approx 60$ lb/rad   **(b)** $\mu = (dF/d\theta)/F \approx 60/200 = 0.3$

30. **(a)** $T \approx 120°\mathrm{F}$, $dT/dt \approx -4.5°\mathrm{F}/\text{min}$

   (b) $k = (dT/dt)/(T - T_0) \approx (-4.5)/(120 - 75) = -0.1$

31.

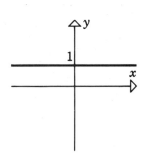

32.

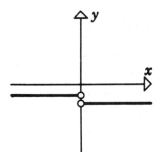

33.

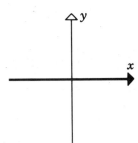

34.

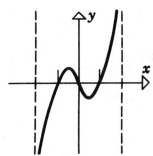

35.

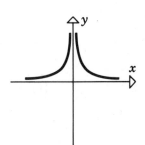

36.

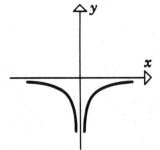

37.

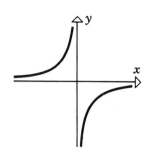

38.

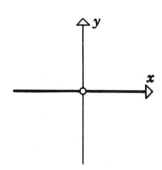

39. $\lim_{x \to 0} f(x) = \lim_{x \to 0} \sqrt[3]{x} = 0 = f(0)$,

so f is continuous at $x = 0$.

$$\lim_{h \to 0} \frac{f(0 + h) - f(0)}{h} = \lim_{h \to 0} \frac{\sqrt[3]{h} - 0}{h}$$

$$= \lim_{h \to 0} \frac{1}{h^{2/3}} = +\infty,$$

so $f'(0)$ does not exist.

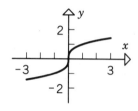

40. $\lim_{x \to 2} f(x) = \lim_{x \to 2} (x - 2)^{2/3} = 0 = f(2)$

so f is continuous at $x = 2$.

$$\lim_{h \to 0} \frac{f(2 + h) - f(2)}{h} = \lim_{h \to 0} \frac{h^{2/3} - 0}{h}$$

$$= \lim_{h \to 0} \frac{1}{h^{1/3}}$$

which does not exist so $f'(2)$ does not exist.

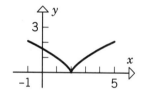

41. $\lim_{x \to 1^-} f(x) = \lim_{x \to 1^+} f(x) = f(1)$, so

f is continuous at $x = 1$.

$$\lim_{h \to 0^-} \frac{f(1 + h) - f(1)}{h} = \lim_{h \to 0^-} \frac{[(1 + h)^2 + 1] - 2}{h}$$

$$= \lim_{h \to 0^-} (2 + h) = 2;$$

$$\lim_{h \to 0^+} \frac{f(1 + h) - f(1)}{h} = \lim_{h \to 0^+} \frac{2(1 + h) - 2}{h}$$

$$= \lim_{h \to 0^+} 2 = 2,$$

so $f'(1) = 2$.

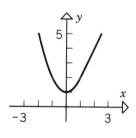

42. $\lim\limits_{x \to 1^-} f(x) = \lim\limits_{x \to 1^+} f(x) = f(1)$ so f is

continuous at $x = 1$.

$$\lim_{h \to 0^-} \frac{f(1+h) - f(1)}{h} = \lim_{h \to 0^-} \frac{[(1+h)^2 + 2] - 3}{h}$$

$$= \lim_{h \to 0^-} (2 + h) = 2;$$

$$\lim_{h \to 0^+} \frac{f(1+h) - f(1)}{h} = \lim_{h \to 0^+} \frac{[(1+h) + 2] - 3}{h}$$

$$= \lim_{h \to 0^+} 1 = 1,$$

so $f'(1)$ does not exist.

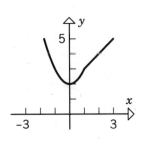

43. f is continuous at $x = 1$ because it is differentiable there, thus $\lim\limits_{h \to 0} f(1+h) = f(1)$ and so

$f(1) = 0$ because $\lim\limits_{h \to 0} \dfrac{f(1+h)}{h}$ exists; $f'(1) = \lim\limits_{h \to 0} \dfrac{f(1+h) - f(1)}{h} = \lim\limits_{h \to 0} \dfrac{f(1+h)}{h} = 5.$

44. Let $x = y = 0$ to get $f(0) = f(0) + f(0) + 0$ so $f(0) = 0$.

$f'(x) = \lim\limits_{h \to 0} \dfrac{f(x+h) - f(x)}{h}$, but (with $y = h$)

$f(x+h) = f(x) + f(h) + 5xh$ so $f(x+h) - f(x) = f(h) + 5xh$ and

$f'(x) = \lim\limits_{h \to 0} \dfrac{f(h) + 5xh}{h} = \lim\limits_{h \to 0} \left(\dfrac{f(h)}{h} + 5x\right) = 3 + 5x.$

45. $f'(x) = \lim\limits_{h \to 0} \dfrac{f(x+h) - f(x)}{h}$

$ = \lim\limits_{h \to 0} \dfrac{f(x)f(h) - f(x)}{h}$

$ = \lim\limits_{h \to 0} \dfrac{f(x)[f(h) - 1]}{h} = f(x) \lim\limits_{h \to 0} \dfrac{f(h) - f(0)}{h} = f(x)f'(0) = f(x)$

EXERCISE SET 3.3

1. $28x^6$

2. $-36x^{11}$

3. $24x^7 + 2$

4. $2x^3$

5. 0

6. $\sqrt{2}$

7. $-\dfrac{1}{3}(7x^6 + 2)$

8. $\dfrac{2}{5}x$

9. $3ax^2 + 2bx + c$

10. $\dfrac{1}{a}\left(2x + \dfrac{1}{b}\right)$ **11.** $24x^{-9} + 1/\sqrt{x}$ **12.** $-42x^{-7} - \dfrac{5}{2\sqrt{x}}$

13. $y = x^{-3} + x^{-7}$ so $\dfrac{dy}{dx} = -3x^{-4} - 7x^{-8}$

14. $\dfrac{1}{2\sqrt{x}} - \dfrac{1}{x^2}$

15. $\dfrac{dy}{dx} = (3x^2 + 6)\dfrac{d}{dx}\left(2x - \dfrac{1}{4}\right) + \left(2x - \dfrac{1}{4}\right)\dfrac{d}{dx}(3x^2 + 6)$

$= (3x^2 + 6)(2) + \left(2x - \dfrac{1}{4}\right)(6x) = 18x^2 - \dfrac{3}{2}x + 12$

16. $\dfrac{dy}{dx} = (2 - x - 3x^3)\dfrac{d}{dx}(7 + x^5) + (7 + x^5)\dfrac{d}{dx}(2 - x - 3x^3)$

$= (2 - x - 3x^3)(5x^4) + (7 + x^5)(-1 - 9x^2) = -24x^7 - 6x^5 + 10x^4 - 63x^2 - 7$

17. $\dfrac{dy}{dx} = (x^3 + 7x^2 - 8)\dfrac{d}{dx}(2x^{-3} + x^{-4}) + (2x^{-3} + x^{-4})\dfrac{d}{dx}(x^3 + 7x^2 - 8)$

$= (x^3 + 7x^2 - 8)(-6x^{-4} - 4x^{-5}) + (2x^{-3} + x^{-4})(3x^2 + 14x)$

$= -15x^{-2} - 14x^{-3} + 48x^{-4} + 32x^{-5}$

18. $\dfrac{dy}{dx} = (x^{-1} + x^{-2})\dfrac{d}{dx}(3x^3 + 27) + (3x^3 + 27)\dfrac{d}{dx}(x^{-1} + x^{-2})$

$= (x^{-1} + x^{-2})(9x^2) + (3x^3 + 27)(-x^{-2} - 2x^{-3}) = 3 + 6x - 27x^{-2} - 54x^{-3}$

19. $12x(3x^2 + 1)$

20. $y = x^{10} + 4x^6 + 4x^2,\ \dfrac{dy}{dx} = 10x^9 + 24x^5 + 8x$

21. $\dfrac{dy}{dx} = -\dfrac{1}{(5x - 3)^2}\dfrac{d}{dx}(5x - 3) = -\dfrac{5}{(5x - 3)^2}$

22. $\dfrac{dy}{dx} = -\dfrac{3}{(\sqrt{x} + 2)^2}\dfrac{d}{dx}(\sqrt{x} + 2) = -\dfrac{3}{2\sqrt{x}(\sqrt{x} + 2)^2}$

23. $\dfrac{dy}{dx} = \dfrac{(2x + 1)\dfrac{d}{dx}(3x) - (3x)\dfrac{d}{dx}(2x + 1)}{(2x + 1)^2} = \dfrac{(2x + 1)(3) - (3x)(2)}{(2x + 1)^2} = \dfrac{3}{(2x + 1)^2}$

24. $\dfrac{dy}{dx} = \dfrac{(3x)\dfrac{d}{dx}(x^2+1) - (x^2+1)\dfrac{d}{dx}(3x)}{(3x)^2} = \dfrac{(3x)(2x) - (x^2+1)(3)}{9x^2} = \dfrac{x^2-1}{3x^2}$

25. $\dfrac{dy}{dx} = \dfrac{(x+3)\dfrac{d}{dx}(2x-1) - (2x-1)\dfrac{d}{dx}(x+3)}{(x+3)^2} = \dfrac{(x+3)(2) - (2x-1)(1)}{(x+3)^2} = \dfrac{7}{(x+3)^2}$

26. $\dfrac{dy}{dx} = \dfrac{(x^2-5)\dfrac{d}{dx}(4x+1) - (4x+1)\dfrac{d}{dx}(x^2-5)}{(x^2-5)^2}$

$= \dfrac{(x^2-5)(4) - (4x+1)(2x)}{(x^2-5)^2} = -\dfrac{4x^2+2x+20}{(x^2-5)^2}$

27. $\dfrac{dy}{dx} = \left(\dfrac{3x+2}{x}\right)\dfrac{d}{dx}(x^{-5}+1) + (x^{-5}+1)\dfrac{d}{dx}\left(\dfrac{3x+2}{x}\right)$

$= \left(\dfrac{3x+2}{x}\right)(-5x^{-6}) + (x^{-5}+1)\left[\dfrac{x(3) - (3x+2)(1)}{x^2}\right]$

$= \left(\dfrac{3x+2}{x}\right)(-5x^{-6}) + (x^{-5}+1)\left(-\dfrac{2}{x^2}\right)$

28. $\dfrac{dy}{dx} = (2x^7 - x^2)\dfrac{d}{dx}\left(\dfrac{x-1}{x+1}\right) + \left(\dfrac{x-1}{x+1}\right)\dfrac{d}{dx}(2x^7 - x^2)$

$= (2x^7 - x^2)\left[\dfrac{(x+1)(1) - (x-1)(1)}{(x+1)^2}\right] + \left(\dfrac{x-1}{x+1}\right)(14x^6 - 2x)$

$= (2x^7 - x^2)\cdot\dfrac{2}{(x+1)^2} + \left(\dfrac{x-1}{x+1}\right)(14x^6 - 2x)$

29. **(a)** $g'(x) = \sqrt{x}f'(x) + \dfrac{1}{2\sqrt{x}}f(x), \ g'(4) = (2)(-5) + \dfrac{1}{4}(3) = -37/4$

(b) $g'(x) = \dfrac{xf'(x) - f(x)}{x^2}, \ g'(4) = \dfrac{(4)(-5) - 3}{16} = -23/16$

30. **(a)** $g'(x) = 6x - 5f'(x), \ g'(3) = 6(3) - 5(4) = -2$

(b) $g'(x) = \dfrac{2f(x) - (2x+1)f'(x)}{f^2(x)}, \ g'(3) = \dfrac{2(-2) - 7(4)}{(-2)^2} = -8$

31. $32t$ **32.** 2π **33.** $3\pi r^2$ **34.** $-2\alpha^{-2} + 1$

35. $\dfrac{ds}{dt} = \dfrac{(t^3+7)\dfrac{d}{dt}(t) - t\dfrac{d}{dt}(t^3+7)}{(t^3+7)^2} = \dfrac{(t^3+7)(1) - t(3t^2)}{(t^3+7)^2} = \dfrac{7 - 2t^3}{(t^3+7)^2}$

36. $\dfrac{d}{d\lambda}\left[\dfrac{\lambda\lambda_0 + \lambda^6}{2 - \lambda_0}\right] = \dfrac{1}{2 - \lambda_0}\dfrac{d}{d\lambda}(\lambda\lambda_0 + \lambda^6) = \dfrac{1}{2 - \lambda_0}(\lambda_0 + 6\lambda^5) = \dfrac{\lambda_0 + 6\lambda^5}{2 - \lambda_0}$

37. $F = GmMr^{-2}, \dfrac{dF}{dr} = -2GmMr^{-3} = -\dfrac{2GmM}{r^3}$

38. $\dfrac{dV}{dr} = 4\pi r^2$

39.   **(a)** $dy/dx = 21x^2 - 10x + 1, d^2y/dx^2 = 42x - 10$

     (b) $dy/dx = 24x - 2, d^2y/dx^2 = 24$

     (c) $dy/dx = -1/x^2, d^2y/dx^2 = 2/x^3$

     (d) $y = 35x^5 - 16x^3 - 3x, dy/dx = 175x^4 - 48x^2 - 3, d^2y/dx^2 = 700x^3 - 96x$

40.   **(a)** $y' = 28x^6 - 15x^2 + 2, y'' = 168x^5 - 30x$

     (b) $y' = 3, y'' = 0$

     (c) $y' = \dfrac{2}{5x^2}, y'' = -\dfrac{4}{5x^3}$

     (d) $y = 2x^4 + 3x^3 - 10x - 15, y' = 8x^3 + 9x^2 - 10, y'' = 24x^2 + 18x$

41.   **(a)** $y' = -5x^{-6} + 5x^4, y'' = 30x^{-7} + 20x^3, y''' = -210x^{-8} + 60x^2$

     (b) $y = x^{-1}, y' = -x^{-2}, y'' = 2x^{-3}, y''' = -6x^{-4}$

     (c) $y' = 3ax^2 + b, y'' = 6ax, y''' = 6a$

42.   **(a)** $dy/dx = 10x - 4, d^2y/dx^2 = 10, d^3y/dx^3 = 0$

     (b) $dy/dx = -6x^{-3} - 4x^{-2} + 1, d^2y/dx^2 = 18x^{-4} + 8x^{-3}, d^3y/dx^3 = -72x^{-5} - 24x^{-4}$

     (c) $dy/dx = 4ax^3 + 2bx, d^2y/dx^2 = 12ax^2 + 2b, d^3y/dx^3 = 24ax$

43.   **(a)** $f'(x) = 6x, f''(x) = 6, f'''(x) = 0, f'''(2) = 0$

     (b) $\dfrac{dy}{dx} = 30x^4 - 8x, \dfrac{d^2y}{dx^2} = 120x^3 - 8, \left.\dfrac{d^2y}{dx^2}\right|_{x=1} = 112$

     (c) $\dfrac{d}{dx}\left[x^{-3}\right] = -3x^{-4}, \dfrac{d^2}{dx^2}\left[x^{-3}\right] = 12x^{-5}, \dfrac{d^3}{dx^3}\left[x^{-3}\right] = -60x^{-6}, \dfrac{d^4}{dx^4}\left[x^{-3}\right] = 360x^{-7},$

        $\left.\dfrac{d^4}{dx^4}\left[x^{-3}\right]\right|_{x=1} = 360$

44.   **(a)** $y' = 16x^3 + 6x^2, y'' = 48x^2 + 12x, y''' = 96x + 12, y'''(0) = 12$

     (b) $y = 6x^{-4}, \dfrac{dy}{dx} = -24x^{-5}, \dfrac{d^2y}{dx^2} = 120x^{-6}, \dfrac{d^3y}{dx^3} = -720x^{-7}, \dfrac{d^4y}{dx^4} = 5040x^{-8},$

        $\left.\dfrac{d^4y}{dx^4}\right|_{x=1} = 5040$

45. $y' = 3x^2 + 3$, $y'' = 6x$, and $y''' = 6$ so

$y''' + xy'' - 2y' = 6 + x(6x) - 2(3x^2 + 3) = 6 + 6x^2 - 6x^2 - 6 = 0$.

46. $y = x^{-1}$, $y' = -x^{-2}$, $y'' = 2x^{-3}$ so

$x^3 y'' + x^2 y' - xy = x^3(2x^{-3}) + x^2(-x^{-2}) - x(x^{-1}) = 2 - 1 - 1 = 0$.

47. $F'(x) = xf'(x) + f(x)$, $F''(x) = xf''(x) + f'(x) + f'(x) = xf''(x) + 2f'(x)$

48. $dR/dT = 0.04124 - 3.558 \times 10^{-5} T$ which decreases as T increases from 0 to 700. When $T = 0$, $dR/dT = 0.04124\,\Omega/°C$; when $T = 700$, $dR/dT = 0.01633\,\Omega/°C$. The resistance is most sensitive to temperature changes at $T = 0°C$, least sensitive at $T = 700°C$.

49. The graph has a horizontal tangent at points where $\dfrac{dy}{dx} = 0$, but

$\dfrac{dy}{dx} = x^2 - 3x + 2 = (x-1)(x-2) = 0$ if $x = 1, 2$. The corresponding values of y are 5/6 and 2/3 so the tangent line is horizontal at $(1, 5/6)$ and $(2, 2/3)$.

50. $\dfrac{dy}{dx} = \dfrac{9 - x^2}{(x^2 + 9)^2}$; $\dfrac{dy}{dx} = 0$ when $x^2 = 9$ so $x = \pm 3$. The points are $(3, 1/6)$ and $(-3, -1/6)$.

51. $y - 2 = 5(x + 3)$, $y = 5x + 17$.

52. $\dfrac{dy}{dx} = \dfrac{(1+x)(-1) - (1-x)(1)}{(1+x)^2} = -\dfrac{2}{(1+x)^2}$, $\dfrac{dy}{dx}\Big|_{x=2} = -\dfrac{2}{9}$ and $y = -\dfrac{1}{3}$ for $x = 2$ so an

equation of the tangent line is $y - \left(-\dfrac{1}{3}\right) = -\dfrac{2}{9}(x - 2)$, or $y = -\dfrac{2}{9}x + \dfrac{1}{9}$.

53. $m_{\tan} = \dfrac{dy}{dx} = 2ax + b$ so $2a + b = 8$ when $x = 1$. Also $5 = a + b$ because $(1, 5)$ is on the curve. Solve the pair of equations $2a + b = 8$ and $a + b = 5$ to get $a = 3$ and $b = 2$.

54. $m_{\tan} = dy/dx = -2a/x^3$ so, for $x = 2$, $-a/4 = -2$, $a = 8$. The point $(2, 4)$ is on the curve so $4 = 8/(2)^2 + b$, $b = 2$.

55. If the y-intercept is -2, then the point $(0, -2)$ is on the graph so $-2 = a(0)^2 + b(0) + c$ so $c = -2$. If the x-intercept is 1, then the point $(1, 0)$ is on the graph so $0 = a + b - 2$. The slope is $dy/dx = 2ax + b$; at $x = 0$ the slope is b so $b = -1$, thus $a = 3$. The function is $y = 3x^2 - x - 2$.

56. Let $P(x_0, y_0)$ be the point where $y = x^2 + k$ is tangent to $y = 2x$. The slope of the curve is $\dfrac{dy}{dx} = 2x$ and the slope of the line is 2 thus at P, $2x_0 = 2$ so $x_0 = 1$. But P is on the line, so $y_0 = 2x_0 = 2$. Because P is also on the curve we get $y_0 = x_0^2 + k$ so $k = y_0 - x_0^2 = 2 - (1)^2 = 1$.

57. The points $(-1, 1)$ and $(2, 4)$ are on the secant line so its slope is $(4 - 1)/(2 + 1) = 1$. The slope of the tangent line to $y = x^2$ is $y' = 2x$ so $2x = 1$, $x = 1/2$.

58. The points $(1, 1)$ and $(4, 2)$ are on the secant line so its slope is $1/3$. The slope of the tangent line to $y = \sqrt{x}$ is $y' = 1/(2\sqrt{x})$ so $1/(2\sqrt{x}) = 1/3$, $2\sqrt{x} = 3$, $x = 9/4$.

59. $y' = -2x$, so at any point (x_0, y_0) on $y = 1 - x^2$ the tangent line is $y - y_0 = -2x_0(x - x_0)$, or $y = -2x_0 x + x_0^2 + 1$. The point $(2, 0)$ is to be on the line, so $0 = -4x_0 + x_0^2 + 1$, $x_0^2 - 4x_0 + 1 = 0$. Use the quadratic formula to get $x_0 = \dfrac{4 \pm \sqrt{16 - 4}}{2} = 2 \pm \sqrt{3}$.

60. Let $P_1(x_1, ax_1^2)$ and $P_2(x_2, ax_2^2)$ be the points of tangency. $y' = 2ax$ so the tangent lines at P_1 and P_2 are $y - ax_1^2 = 2ax_1(x - x_1)$ and $y - ax_2^2 = 2ax_2(x - x_2)$. Solve for x to get $x = \frac{1}{2}(x_1 + x_2)$ which is the x-coordinate of a point on the vertical line halfway between P_1 and P_2.

61. $y' = 3ax^2 + b$; the tangent line at $x = x_0$ is $y - y_0 = (3ax_0^2 + b)(x - x_0)$ where $y_0 = ax_0^3 + bx_0$. Solve with $y = ax^3 + bx$ to get

$$(ax^3 + bx) - (ax_0^3 + bx_0) = (3ax_0^2 + b)(x - x_0)$$
$$ax^3 + bx - ax_0^3 - bx_0 = 3ax_0^2 x - 3ax_0^3 + bx - bx_0$$
$$x^3 - 3x_0^2 x + 2x_0^3 = 0$$
$$(x - x_0)(x^2 + 2x_0 - 2x_0^2) = 0$$
$$(x - x_0)^2(x + 2x_0) = 0, \text{ so } x = -2x_0.$$

62. Let (x_0, y_0) be the point of tangency. Refer to the solution to Exercise 63 to see that the endpoints of the line segment are at $(2x_0, 0)$ and $(0, 2y_0)$, so (x_0, y_0) is the midpoint of the segment.

63. $y' = -\dfrac{1}{x^2}$; the tangent line at $x = x_0$ is $y - y_0 = -\dfrac{1}{x_0^2}(x - x_0)$, or $y = -\dfrac{x}{x_0^2} + \dfrac{2}{x_0}$. The tangent line crosses the x-axis at $2x_0$, the y-axis at $2/x_0$, so that the area of the triangle is $\dfrac{1}{2}(2/x_0)(2x_0) = 2$.

64. $f'(x) = 3ax^2 + 2bx + c$; there is a horizontal tangent where $f'(x) = 0$. Use the quadratic formula on $3ax^2 + 2bx + c = 0$ to get $x = (-b \pm \sqrt{b^2 - 3ac})/(3a)$ which gives two real solutions, one real solution, or none if

(a) $b^2 - 3ac > 0$ **(b)** $b^2 - 3ac = 0$ **(c)** $b^2 - 3ac < 0$

65. If the graphs of $f(x)$ and $g(x)$ have parallel tangent lines at $x = c$, then $f'(c) = g'(c)$. If $y = f(x) - g(x)$, then $dy/dx = f'(x) - g'(x)$ so at $x = c$, $dy/dx = f'(c) - g'(c) = 0$, hence $y = f(x) - g(x)$ has a horizontal tangent line at $x = c$.

66. **(a)** $(f \cdot g \cdot h)'(x) = [(f \cdot g) \cdot h]'(x)$
$$= (f \cdot g)(x)h'(x) + h(x)(f \cdot g)'(x)$$
$$= (f \cdot g)(x)h'(x) + h(x)[f(x)g'(x) + f'(x)g(x)]$$
$$= f(x)g(x)h'(x) + f(x)g'(x)h(x) + f'(x)g(x)h(x).$$

(b) $(f_1 f_2 \cdots f_n)' = (f_1' f_2 \cdots f_n) + (f_1 f_2' \cdots f_n) + \cdots + (f_1 f_2 \cdots f_n')$

67. **(a)** $2(1 + x^{-1})(x^{-3} + 7) + (2x + 1)(-x^{-2})(x^{-3} + 7) + (2x + 1)(1 + x^{-1})(-3x^{-4})$

(b) $-5x^{-6}(x^2 + 2x)(4 - 3x)(2x^9 + 1) + x^{-5}(2x + 2)(4 - 3x)(2x^9 + 1)$
$$+ x^{-5}(x^2 + 2x)(-3)(2x^9 + 1) + x^{-5}(x^2 + 2x)(4 - 3x)(18x^8)$$

(c) $(x^7 + 2x - 3)^3 = (x^7 + 2x - 3)(x^7 + 2x - 3)(x^7 + 2x - 3)$ so
$$\frac{d}{dx}(x^7 + 2x - 3)^3 = (7x^6 + 2)(x^7 + 2x - 3)(x^7 + 2x - 3)$$
$$+ (x^7 + 2x - 3)(7x^6 + 2)(x^7 + 2x - 3)$$
$$+ (x^7 + 2x - 3)(x^7 + 2x - 3)(7x^6 + 2)$$
$$= 3(7x^6 + 2)(x^7 + 2x - 3)^2$$

(d) $(x^2 + 1)^{50} = (x^2 + 1)(x^2 + 1) \cdots (x^2 + 1)$, where $(x^2 + 1)$ occurs 50 times so
$$\frac{d}{dx}(x^2 + 1)^{50} = [(2x)(x^2 + 1) \cdots (x^2 + 1)] + [(x^2 + 1)(2x) \cdots (x^2 + 1)]$$
$$+ \cdots + [(x^2 + 1)(x^2 + 1) \cdots (2x)]$$
$$= 2x(x^2 + 1)^{49} + 2x(x^2 + 1)^{49} + \cdots + 2x(x^2 + 1)^{49}$$
$$= 100x(x^2 + 1)^{49} \text{ because } 2x(x^2 + 1)^{49} \text{ occurs 50 times.}$$

68. $\frac{d}{dx}[f(x)f(x)] = f(x)f'(x) + f(x)f'(x) = 2f(x)f'(x).$

69. $2(2x^3 - 5x^2 + 7x - 2)(6x^2 - 10x + 7)$

70. $f^2(x) = x$ so $\frac{d}{dx}(x) = 2\sqrt{x}f'(x)$, $1 = 2\sqrt{x}f'(x)$, $f'(x) = \dfrac{1}{2\sqrt{x}}$.

71. f is continuous at 1 because $\lim\limits_{x \to 1^-} f(x) \lim\limits_{x \to 1^+} = f(x) = f(1)$, also $\lim\limits_{x \to 1^-} f'(x) = \lim\limits_{x \to 1^-} 2x = 2$
and $\lim\limits_{x \to 1^+} f'(x) = \lim\limits_{x \to 1^+} \dfrac{1}{2\sqrt{x}} = \dfrac{1}{2}$ so f is not differentiable at 1.

72. f is continuous at $1/2$ because $\lim\limits_{x \to 1/2^-} f(x) = \lim\limits_{x \to 1/2^+} f(x) = f(1/2)$, also

$\lim\limits_{x \to 1/2^-} f'(x) = \lim\limits_{x \to 1/2^-} 3x^2 = 3/4$ and $\lim\limits_{x \to 1/2^+} f'(x) = \lim\limits_{x \to 1/2^+} 3x/2 = 3/4$ so $f'(1/2) = 3/4.$

73. If f is differentiable at $x = 1$, then f is continuous there; $\lim\limits_{x \to 1^+} f(x) = \lim\limits_{x \to 1^-} f(x) = f(1) = 3,$
$a + b = 3; \lim_{x \to 1^+} f'(x) = a$ and $\lim\limits_{x \to 1^-} f'(x) = 6$ so $a = 6$ and $b = 3 - 6 = -3.$

74. **(a)** $\lim_{x \to 0^-} f'(x) = \lim_{x \to 0^-} 2x = 0$ and $\lim_{x \to 0^+} f'(x) = \lim_{x \to 0^+} 2x = 0$; $f'(0)$ does not exist because f is not continuous at $x = 0$.

(b) $\lim_{x \to 0^-} f'(x) = \lim_{x \to 0^+} f'(x) = 0$ and f is continuous at $x = 0$, so $f'(0) = 0$;

$\lim_{x \to 0^-} f''(x) = \lim_{x \to 0^-} (2) = 2$ and $\lim_{x \to 0^+} f''(x) = \lim_{x \to 0^+} 6x = 0$, so $f''(0)$ does not exist.

75. **(a)** $f(x) = 3x - 2$ if $x \geq 2/3$, $f(x) = -3x + 2$ if $x < 2/3$ so f is differentiable everywhere except perhaps at $2/3$. f is continuous at $2/3$, also $\lim_{x \to 2/3^-} f'(x) = \lim_{x \to 2/3^-} (-3) = -3$ and

$\lim_{x \to 2/3^+} f'(x) = \lim_{x \to 2/3^+} (3) = 3$ so f is not differentiable at $x = 2/3$.

(b) $f(x) = x^2 - 4$ if $|x| \geq 2$, $f(x) = -x^2 + 4$ if $|x| < 2$ so f is differentiable everywhere except perhaps at ± 2. f is continuous at -2 and 2, also $\lim_{x \to 2^-} f'(x) = \lim_{x \to 2^-} (-2x) = -4$

and $\lim_{x \to 2^+} f'(x) = \lim_{x \to 2^+} (2x) = 4$ so f is not differentiable at $x = 2$. Similarly, f is not differentiable at $x = -2$.

76. Use the Quotient Rule: $\dfrac{d}{dx}\left[\dfrac{1}{f(x)}\right] = \dfrac{f(x)(0) - (1)f'(x)}{[f(x)]^2} = -\dfrac{f'(x)}{[f(x)]^2}$

77. **(a)** $f'(x) = nx^{n-1}$, $f''(x) = n(n-1)x^{n-2}$, $f'''(x) = n(n-1)(n-2)x^{n-3}, \ldots,$

$f^{(n)}(x) = n(n-1)(n-2)\cdots 1$.

(b) From part (a), $f^{(k)}(x) = k(k-1)(k-2)\cdots 1$ so $f^{(k+1)}(x) = 0$ thus $f^{(n)}(x) = 0$ if $n > k$.

(c) From parts (a) and (b), $f^{(n)}(x) = a_n n(n-1)(n-2)\cdots 1$.

78. **(a)** $f'(x) = -(1)x^{-2}$, $f''(x) = (2 \cdot 2)x^{-3}$, $f'''(x) = -(3 \cdot 2 \cdot 1)x^{-4}$

$f^{(n)}(x) = (-1)^n \dfrac{n(n-1)(n-2)\cdots 1}{x^{n+1}}$

(b) $f'(x) = -2x^{-3}$, $f''(x) = (3 \cdot 2)x^{-4}$, $f'''(x) = -(4 \cdot 3 \cdot 2)x^{-5}$

$f^{(n)}(x) = (-1)^n \dfrac{(n+1)(n)(n-1)\cdots 2}{x^{n+2}}$

79. **(a)** $\dfrac{d^2}{dx^2}[cf(x)] = \dfrac{d}{dx}\left[\dfrac{d}{dx}[cf(x)]\right] = \dfrac{d}{dx}\left[c\dfrac{d}{dx}[f(x)]\right]$

$= c\dfrac{d}{dx}\left[\dfrac{d}{dx}[f(x)]\right] = c\dfrac{d^2}{dx^2}[f(x)]$

$$\frac{d^2}{dx^2}[f(x) + g(x)] = \frac{d}{dx}\left[\frac{d}{dx}[f(x) + g(x)]\right]$$

$$= \frac{d}{dx}\left[\frac{d}{dx}[f(x)] + \frac{d}{dx}[g(x)]\right]$$

$$= \frac{d^2}{dx^2}[f(x)] + \frac{d^2}{dx^2}[g(x)]$$

(b) yes, by repeated application of the procedure illustrated in part (a).

80. $(f \cdot g)'(x) = f(x)g'(x) + g(x)f'(x),$
    $(f \cdot g)''(x) = f(x)g''(x) + g'(x)f'(x) + g(x)f''(x) + f'(x)g'(x)$
    $\qquad = f''(x)g(x) + 2f'(x)g'(x) + f(x)g''(x)$

81. **(a)** The argument is based on the assumption that $\lim\limits_{h \to 0} f(x + h) = f(\lim\limits_{h \to 0}(x + h))$ which is not necessarily true.

    (b) If $h \neq 0$, then $1 + h \neq 1$ thus $f(1 + h) = 1 + h$ so $\lim\limits_{h \to 0} f(1 + h) = \lim\limits_{h \to 0}(1 + h) = 1$. But $f(1) = 3$ so $\lim\limits_{h \to 0} f(1 + h) \neq f(1)$.

82. $\lim\limits_{h \to 0} \dfrac{f'(x_0 + h) - f'(x_0)}{h} = f''(x_0);$

    $f'(x) = 8x^7 - 2,\ f''(x) = 56x^6,$ so $f''(2) = 56(2^6) = 3584.$

83. **(a)** If a function is differentiable at a point then it is continuous at that point, thus f' is continuous on (a, b) and consequently so is f.

    (b) f and all its derivatives up to $f^{(n-1)}(x)$ are continuous on (a, b).

EXERCISE SET 3.4

1. $f'(x) = -2\sin x - 3\cos x$

2. $f'(x) = \sin x(-\sin x) + \cos x(\cos x) = \cos^2 x - \sin^2 x = \cos 2x$

3. $f'(x) = \dfrac{x(\cos x) - \sin x(1)}{x^2} = \dfrac{x\cos x - \sin x}{x^2}$

4. $f'(x) = x^2(-\sin x) + (\cos x)(2x) = -x^2\sin x + 2x\cos x$

5. $f'(x) = x^3(\cos x) + (\sin x)(3x^2) - 5(-\sin x) = x^3\cos x + (3x^2 + 5)\sin x$

6. $f(x) = \dfrac{\cot x}{x}$ (because $\dfrac{\cos x}{\sin x} = \cot x$),

$f'(x) = \dfrac{x(-\csc^2 x) - (\cot x)(1)}{x^2} = -\dfrac{x\csc^2 x + \cot x}{x^2}$

7. $f'(x) = \sec x \tan x - \sqrt{2}\sec^2 x$

8. $f'(x) = (x^2 + 1)\sec x \tan x + (\sec x)(2x) = (x^2 + 1)\sec x \tan x + 2x \sec x$

9. $f'(x) = \sec x(\sec^2 x) + (\tan x)(\sec x \tan x) = \sec^3 x + \sec x \tan^2 x$

10. $f'(x) = \dfrac{(1 + \tan x)(\sec x \tan x) - (\sec x)(\sec^2 x)}{(1 + \tan x)^2}$

$= \dfrac{\sec x \tan x + \sec x \tan^2 x - \sec^3 x}{(1 + \tan x)^2}$

$= \dfrac{\sec x(\tan x + \tan^2 x - \sec^2 x)}{(1 + \tan x)^2} = \dfrac{\sec x(\tan x - 1)}{(1 + \tan x)^2}$

11. $f'(x) = 1 + 4\csc x \cot x - 2\csc^2 x$

12. $f'(x) = (\csc x)(-\csc^2 x) + (\cot x)(-\csc x \cot x) = -\csc^3 x - \csc x \cot^2 x$

13. $f'(x) = \dfrac{(1 + \csc x)(-\csc^2 x) - \cot x(0 - \csc x \cot x)}{(1 + \csc x)^2}$

$= \dfrac{\csc x(-\csc x - \csc^2 x + \cot^2 x)}{(1 + \csc x)^2}$

but $1 + \cot^2 x = \csc^2 x$ (identity) thus $\cot^2 x - \csc^2 x = -1$

so $f'(x) = \dfrac{\csc x(-\csc x - 1)}{(1 + \csc x)^2} = -\dfrac{\csc x}{1 + \csc x}$

14. $f'(x) = \dfrac{\tan x(-\csc x \cot x) - \csc x(\sec^2 x)}{\tan^2 x} = -\dfrac{\csc x(1 + \sec^2 x)}{\tan^2 x}$

15. $f(x) = \sin^2 x + \cos^2 x = 1$ (identity) so $f'(x) = 0$

16. $f'(x) = \dfrac{\cot x(0) - (1)(-\csc^2 x)}{\cot^2 x} = \dfrac{\csc^2 x}{\cot^2 x}$

17. $f(x) = \dfrac{\tan x}{1 + x \tan x}$ (because $\sin x \sec x = (\sin x)(1/\cos x) = \tan x$),

$$f'(x) = \frac{(1 + x \tan x)(\sec^2 x) - \tan x[x(\sec^2 x) + (\tan x)(1)]}{(1 + x \tan x)^2}$$

$$= \frac{\sec^2 x - \tan^2 x}{(1 + x \tan x)^2} = \frac{1}{(1 + x \tan x)^2} \text{ (because } \sec^2 x - \tan^2 x = 1)$$

18. $f(x) = \dfrac{(x^2 + 1) \cot x}{3 - \cot x}$ (because $\cos x \csc x = (\cos x)(1/\sin x) = \cot x$),

$$f'(x) = \frac{(3 - \cot x)[2x \cot x - (x^2 + 1) \csc^2 x] - (x^2 + 1) \cot x \csc^2 x}{(3 - \cot x)^2}$$

$$= \frac{6x \cot x - 2x \cot^2 x - 3(x^2 + 1) \csc^2 x}{(3 - \cot x)^2}$$

19. $dy/dx = -x \sin x + \cos x$,

$d^2y/dx^2 = -x \cos x - \sin x - \sin x = -x \cos x - 2 \sin x$

20. $dy/dx = -\csc x \cot x$,

$d^2y/dx^2 = -[(\csc x)(-\csc^2 x) + (\cot x)(-\csc x \cot x)] = \csc^3 x + \csc x \cot^2 x$

21. $dy/dx = x(\cos x) + (\sin x)(1) - 3(-\sin x) = x \cos x + 4 \sin x$,

$d^2y/dx^2 = x(-\sin x) + (\cos x)(1) + 4 \cos x = -x \sin x + 5 \cos x$

22. $dy/dx = x^2(-\sin x) + (\cos x)(2x) + 4 \cos x = -x^2 \sin x + 2x \cos x + 4 \cos x$,

$d^2y/dx^2 = -[x^2(\cos x) + (\sin x)(2x)] + 2[x(-\sin x) + \cos x] - 4 \sin x$

$= (2 - x^2) \cos x - 4(x + 1) \sin x$

23. $dy/dx = (\sin x)(-\sin x) + (\cos x)(\cos x) = \cos^2 x - \sin^2 x$,

$d^2y/dx^2 = (\cos x)(-\sin x) + (\cos x)(-\sin x) - [(\sin x)(\cos x) + (\sin x)(\cos x)]$

$= -4 \sin x \cos x$

24. **(a)** $f'(x) = \cos x$; $f'(x) = 0$ when $\cos x = 0$, $x = \dfrac{\pi}{2} + n\pi$, $n = 0, \pm1, \pm2, \cdots$.

(b) $f'(x) = \sec^2 x$; $f'(x) = 0$ when $\sec x = 0$, but $\sec x = 0$ has no solutions.

(c) $f'(x) = \sec x \tan x$; $f'(x) = 0$ when $\sec x \tan x = 0$, but $\sec x$ is never 0, thus $\tan x = 0$ so $x = n\pi$, $n = 0, \pm1, \pm2, \cdots$.

25. **(a)** $f'(x) = -\sin x$; $f'(x) = 0$ when $\sin x = 0$ so $x = n\pi$, $n = 0, \pm1, \pm2, \cdots$.

(b) $f'(x) = -\csc^2 x$; $f'(x) = 0$ when $\csc x = 0$, but $\csc x = 0$ has no solutions.

(c) $f'(x) = -\csc x \cot x$; $f'(x) = 0$ when $\cot x = 0$ so $x = \dfrac{\pi}{2} + n\pi$, $n = 0, \pm1, \pm2, \cdots$.

26. Let $f(x) = \sin x$, then $f'(x) = \cos x$.

    (a) $f(0) = 0$ and $f'(0) = 1$ so $y - 0 = (1)(x - 0)$, $y = x$.
    (b) $f(\pi) = 0$ and $f'(\pi) = -1$ so $y - 0 = (-1)(x - \pi)$, $y = -x + \pi$.
    (c) $f\left(\frac{\pi}{4}\right) = \frac{1}{\sqrt{2}}$ and $f'\left(\frac{\pi}{4}\right) = \frac{1}{\sqrt{2}}$ so $y - \frac{1}{\sqrt{2}} = \frac{1}{\sqrt{2}}\left(x - \frac{\pi}{4}\right)$, $y = \frac{1}{\sqrt{2}}x - \frac{\pi}{4\sqrt{2}} + \frac{1}{\sqrt{2}}$.

27. Let $f(x) = \tan x$, then $f'(x) = \sec^2 x$.

    (a) $f(0) = 0$ and $f'(0) = 1$ so $y - 0 = (1)(x - 0)$, $y = x$.
    (b) $f\left(\frac{\pi}{4}\right) = 1$ and $f'\left(\frac{\pi}{4}\right) = 2$ so $y - 1 = 2\left(x - \frac{\pi}{4}\right)$, $y = 2x - \frac{\pi}{2} + 1$.
    (c) $f\left(-\frac{\pi}{4}\right) = -1$ and $f'\left(-\frac{\pi}{4}\right) = 2$ so $y + 1 = 2\left(x + \frac{\pi}{4}\right)$, $y = 2x + \frac{\pi}{2} - 1$.

28. (a) If $y = \cos x$ then $y' = -\sin x$ and $y'' = -\cos x$ so $y'' + y = (-\cos x) + (\cos x) = 0$; if $y = \sin x$ then $y' = \cos x$ and $y'' = -\sin x$ so $y'' + y = (-\sin x) + (\sin x) = 0$.
    (b) $y' = A\cos x - B\sin x$, $y'' = -A\sin x - B\cos x$ so $y'' + y = (-A\sin x - B\cos x) + (A\sin x + B\cos x) = 0$.

29. $x = 10\sin\theta$, $dx/d\theta = 10\cos\theta$; if $\theta = 60°$, then
    $dx/d\theta = 10(1/2) = 5$ ft/rad $= \pi/36$ ft/° ≈ 0.087 ft/°.

30. $s = 3800\csc\theta$, $ds/d\theta = -3800\csc\theta\cot\theta$; if $\theta = 30°$, then
    $ds/d\theta = -3800(2)(\sqrt{3}) = -7600\sqrt{3}$ ft/rad $= -380\sqrt{3}\pi/9$ ft/° ≈ -230 ft/°.

31. $D = 50\tan\theta$, $dD/d\theta = 50\sec^2\theta$; if $\theta = 30°$, then
    $dD/d\theta = 50(\sqrt{2})^2 = 100$ m/rad $= 5\pi/9$ m/° ≈ 1.75 m/°.

32. (a) From the right triangle shown, $\sin\theta = r/(r + h)$ so $r + h = r\csc\theta$, $h = r(\csc\theta - 1)$.
    (b) $dh/d\theta = -r\csc\theta\cot\theta$; if $\theta = 30°$, then
    $dh/d\theta = -6378(2)(\sqrt{3}) \approx -22{,}094$ km/rad ≈ -386 km/°.

33. In each part, f is differentiable throughout its domain because f' can be determined there by use of the various derivative formulas that have been presented in the text; f is not differentiable elsewhere.

    (a) all x (b) all x
    (c) $x \neq \pi/2 + n\pi$, $n = 0, \pm 1, \pm 2, \cdots$ (d) $x \neq n\pi$, $n = 0, \pm 1, \pm 2, \cdots$
    (e) $x \neq \pi/2 + n\pi$, $n = 0, \pm 1, \pm 2, \cdots$ (f) $x \neq n\pi$, $n = 0, \pm 1, \pm 2, \cdots$
    (g) $x \neq \pi + 2n\pi$, $n = 0, \pm 1, \pm 2, \cdots$ (h) $x \neq n\pi/2$, $n = 0, \pm 1, \pm 2, \cdots$
    (i) all x

34. **(a)** $\dfrac{d}{dx}[\cot x] = \dfrac{d}{dx}\left[\dfrac{\cos x}{\sin x}\right] = \dfrac{\sin x(-\sin x) - \cos x(\cos x)}{\sin^2 x}$

$\qquad\qquad = \dfrac{-\sin^2 x - \cos^2 x}{\sin^2 x} = \dfrac{-1}{\sin^2 x} = -\csc^2 x.$

(b) $\dfrac{d}{dx}[\sec x] = \dfrac{d}{dx}\left[\dfrac{1}{\cos x}\right] = \dfrac{\cos x(0) - (1)(-\sin x)}{\cos^2 x} = \dfrac{\sin x}{\cos^2 x} = \sec x \tan x.$

(c) $\dfrac{d}{dx}[\csc x] = \dfrac{d}{dx}\left[\dfrac{1}{\sin x}\right] = \dfrac{\sin x(0) - (1)(\cos x)}{\sin^2 x} = -\dfrac{\cos x}{\sin^2 x} = -\csc x \cot x.$

35. $f'(x) = -\sin x$, $f''(x) = -\cos x$, $f'''(x) = \sin x$, and $f^{(4)}(x) = \cos x$ with higher order derivatives repeating this pattern, so $f^{(n)}(x) = \sin x$ for $n = 3, 7, 11, \cdots$

36. **(a)** $\displaystyle\lim_{h\to0}\dfrac{\tan h}{h} = \lim_{h\to0}\dfrac{\frac{\sin h}{\cos h}}{h} = \lim_{h\to0}\dfrac{\frac{\sin h}{h}}{\cos h} = \dfrac{1}{1} = 1.$

(b) $\dfrac{d}{dx}[\tan x] = \displaystyle\lim_{h\to0}\dfrac{\tan(x+h) - \tan x}{h} = \lim_{h\to0}\dfrac{\frac{\tan x + \tan h}{1 - \tan x \tan h} - \tan x}{h}$

$\qquad\qquad = \displaystyle\lim_{h\to0}\dfrac{\tan x + \tan h - \tan x + \tan^2 x \tan h}{h(1 - \tan x \tan h)} = \lim_{h\to0}\dfrac{\tan h(1 + \tan^2 x)}{h(1 - \tan x \tan h)}$

$\qquad\qquad = \displaystyle\lim_{h\to0}\dfrac{\tan h \sec^2 x}{h(1 - \tan x \tan h)} = \sec^2 x \lim_{h\to0}\dfrac{\frac{\tan h}{h}}{1 - \tan x \tan h}$

$\qquad\qquad = \sec^2 x \dfrac{\displaystyle\lim_{h\to0}\frac{\tan h}{h}}{\displaystyle\lim_{h\to0}(1 - \tan x \tan h)} = \sec^2 x.$

37. $\displaystyle\lim_{x\to0}\dfrac{\tan(x+y) - \tan y}{x} = \lim_{h\to0}\dfrac{\tan(y+h) - \tan y}{h} = \dfrac{d}{dy}(\tan y) = \sec^2 y$

39. Let t be the radian measure, then $h = \dfrac{180}{\pi}t$ and $\cos h = \cos t$, $\sin h = \sin t$.

(a) $\displaystyle\lim_{h\to0}\dfrac{\cos h - 1}{h} = \lim_{t\to0}\dfrac{\cos t - 1}{180t/\pi} = \dfrac{\pi}{180}\lim_{t\to0}\dfrac{\cos t - 1}{t} = 0.$

(b) $\displaystyle\lim_{h\to0}\dfrac{\sin h}{h} = \lim_{t\to0}\dfrac{\sin t}{180t/\pi} = \dfrac{\pi}{180}\lim_{t\to0}\dfrac{\sin t}{t} = \dfrac{\pi}{180}.$

(c) $\dfrac{d}{dx}[\sin x] = \sin x \displaystyle\lim_{h\to0}\dfrac{\cos h - 1}{h} + \cos x \lim_{h\to0}\dfrac{\sin h}{h}$

$\qquad\qquad = \sin x(0) + \cos x(\pi/180) = \dfrac{\pi}{180}\cos x.$

EXERCISE SET 3.5

1. $f'(x) = 37(x^3 + 2x)^{36}\dfrac{d}{dx}(x^3 + 2x) = 37(x^3 + 2x)^{36}(3x^2 + 2)$

2. $f'(x) = 6(3x^2 + 2x - 1)^5 \dfrac{d}{dx}(3x^2 + 2x - 1) = 6(3x^2 + 2x - 1)^5(6x + 2)$

   $= 12(3x^2 + 2x - 1)^5(3x + 1)$

3. $f'(x) = -2\left(x^3 - \dfrac{7}{x}\right)^{-3}\dfrac{d}{dx}\left(x^3 - \dfrac{7}{x}\right) = -2\left(x^3 - \dfrac{7}{x}\right)^{-3}\left(3x^2 + \dfrac{7}{x^2}\right)$

4. $f(x) = (x^5 - x + 1)^{-9}$,

   $f'(x) = -9(x^5 - x + 1)^{-10}\dfrac{d}{dx}(x^5 - x + 1) = -9(x^5 - x + 1)^{-10}(5x^4 - 1) = -\dfrac{9(5x^4 - 1)}{(x^5 - x + 1)^{10}}$

5. $f(x) = 4(3x^2 - 2x + 1)^{-3}$,

   $f'(x) = -12(3x^2 - 2x + 1)^{-4}\dfrac{d}{dx}(3x^2 - 2x + 1)$

   $= -12(3x^2 - 2x + 1)^{-4}(6x - 2) = \dfrac{24(1 - 3x)}{(3x^2 - 2x + 1)^4}$

6. $f'(x) = \dfrac{1}{2\sqrt{x^3 - 2x + 5}}\dfrac{d}{dx}(x^3 - 2x + 5) = \dfrac{3x^2 - 2}{2\sqrt{x^3 - 2x + 5}}.$

7. $f'(x) = \dfrac{1}{2\sqrt{4 + 3\sqrt{x}}}\dfrac{d}{dx}(4 + 3\sqrt{x}) = \dfrac{3}{4\sqrt{x}\sqrt{4 + 3\sqrt{x}}}$

8. $f'(x) = 3\sin^2 x\dfrac{d}{dx}(\sin x) = 3\sin^2 x \cos x$

9. $f'(x) = \cos(x^3)\dfrac{d}{dx}(x^3) = 3x^2 \cos(x^3)$

10. $f'(x) = 2\cos(3\sqrt{x})\dfrac{d}{dx}[\cos(3\sqrt{x})] = -2\cos(3\sqrt{x})\sin(3\sqrt{x})\dfrac{d}{dx}(3\sqrt{x})$

    $= -\dfrac{3\cos(3\sqrt{x})\sin(3\sqrt{x})}{\sqrt{x}}$

11. $f'(x) = \sec^2(4x^2)\dfrac{d}{dx}(4x^2) = 8x \sec^2(4x^2)$

12. $f'(x) = 12\cot^3 x \dfrac{d}{dx}(\cot x) = 12\cot^3 x(-\csc^2 x) = -12\cot^3 x \csc^2 x$

13. $f'(x) = 20\cos^4 x \dfrac{d}{dx}(\cos x) = 20\cos^4 x(-\sin x) = -20\cos^4 x \sin x$

14. $f'(x) = -\csc(x^3)\cot(x^3)\dfrac{d}{dx}(x^3) = -3x^2\csc(x^3)\cot(x^3)$

15. $f'(x) = \cos(1/x^2)\dfrac{d}{dx}(1/x^2) = -\dfrac{2}{x^3}\cos(1/x^2)$

16. $f'(x) = 4\tan^3(x^3)\dfrac{d}{dx}[\tan(x^3)] = 4\tan^3(x^3)\sec^2(x^3)\dfrac{d}{dx}(x^3) = 12x^2\tan^3(x^3)\sec^2(x^3)$

17. $f'(x) = 4\sec(x^7)\dfrac{d}{dx}[\sec(x^7)] = 4\sec(x^7)\sec(x^7)\tan(x^7)\dfrac{d}{dx}(x^7) = 28x^6\sec^2(x^7)\tan(x^7)$

18. $f'(x) = 3\cos^2\left(\dfrac{x}{x+1}\right)\dfrac{d}{dx}\cos\left(\dfrac{x}{x+1}\right)$

$\qquad = 3\cos^2\left(\dfrac{x}{x+1}\right)\left[-\sin\left(\dfrac{x}{x+1}\right)\right]\dfrac{(x+1)(1)-x(1)}{(x+1)^2}$

$\qquad = -\dfrac{3}{(x+1)^2}\cos^2\left(\dfrac{x}{x+1}\right)\sin\left(\dfrac{x}{x+1}\right)$

19. $f'(x) = \dfrac{1}{2\sqrt{\cos(5x)}}\dfrac{d}{dx}[\cos(5x)] = -\dfrac{5\sin(5x)}{2\sqrt{\cos(5x)}}$

20. $f'(x) = \dfrac{1}{2\sqrt{3x-\sin^2(4x)}}\dfrac{d}{dx}[3x-\sin^2(4x)] = \dfrac{3-8\sin(4x)\cos(4x)}{2\sqrt{3x-\sin^2(4x)}}$

21. $f'(x) = -3\left[x+\csc(x^3+3)\right]^{-4}\dfrac{d}{dx}\left[x+\csc(x^3+3)\right]$

$\qquad = -3\left[x+\csc(x^3+3)\right]^{-4}\left[1-\csc(x^3+3)\cot(x^3+3)\dfrac{d}{dx}(x^3+3)\right]$

$\qquad = -3\left[x+\csc(x^3+3)\right]^{-4}\left[1-3x^2\csc(x^3+3)\cot(x^3+3)\right]$

22. $f'(x) = -4\left[x^4 - \sec(4x^2 - 2)\right]^{-5}\dfrac{d}{dx}\left[x^4 - \sec(4x^2 - 2)\right]$

$\qquad = -4\left[x^4 - \sec(4x^2 - 2)\right]^{-5}\left[4x^3 - \sec(4x^2 - 2)\tan(4x^2 - 2)\dfrac{d}{dx}(4x^2 - 2)\right]$

$\qquad = -16x\left[x^4 - \sec(4x^2 - 2)\right]^{-5}\left[x^2 - 2\ \sec(4x^2 - 2)\tan(4x^2 - 2)\right]$

23. $f'(x) = x^2 \cdot \dfrac{-2x}{2\sqrt{5 - x^2}} + 2x\sqrt{5 - x^2} = \dfrac{x(10 - 3x^2)}{\sqrt{5 - x^2}}$

24. $f'(x) = \dfrac{\sqrt{1 - x^2}(1) - x(-x/\sqrt{1 - x^2})}{1 - x^2} = \dfrac{1}{(1 - x^2)^{3/2}}$

25. $f'(x) = x^3(2\sin 5x)\dfrac{d}{dx}(\sin 5x) + 3x^2\sin^2 5x = 10x^3\sin 5x\cos 5x + 3x^2\sin^2 5x$

26. $f'(x) = \sqrt{x}\left[3\tan^2(\sqrt{x})\sec^2(\sqrt{x})\dfrac{1}{2\sqrt{x}}\right] + \dfrac{1}{2\sqrt{x}}\tan^3(\sqrt{x})$

$\qquad = \dfrac{3}{2}\tan^2(\sqrt{x})\sec^2(\sqrt{x}) + \dfrac{1}{2\sqrt{x}}\tan^3(\sqrt{x})$

27. $f'(x) = x^5\sec\left(\dfrac{1}{x}\right)\tan\left(\dfrac{1}{x}\right)\dfrac{d}{dx}\left(\dfrac{1}{x}\right) + \sec\left(\dfrac{1}{x}\right)(5x^4)$

$\qquad = x^5\sec\left(\dfrac{1}{x}\right)\tan\left(\dfrac{1}{x}\right)\left(-\dfrac{1}{x^2}\right) + 5x^4\sec\left(\dfrac{1}{x}\right)$

$\qquad = -x^3\sec\left(\dfrac{1}{x}\right)\tan\left(\dfrac{1}{x}\right) + 5x^4\sec\left(\dfrac{1}{x}\right)$

28. $f'(x) = \dfrac{\sec(3x + 1)\cos x - 3\sin x\sec(3x + 1)\tan(3x + 1)}{\sec^2(3x + 1)}$

29. $f'(x) = -\sin(\cos x)\dfrac{d}{dx}(\cos x) = -\sin(\cos x)(-\sin x) = \sin(\cos x)\sin x$

30. $f'(x) = \cos(\tan 3x)\dfrac{d}{dx}(\tan 3x) = 3\sec^2 3x\cos(\tan 3x)$

31. $f'(x) = 3\cos^2(\sin 2x)\dfrac{d}{dx}[\cos(\sin 2x)]$

$\qquad = 3\cos^2(\sin 2x)[-\sin(\sin 2x)]\dfrac{d}{dx}(\sin 2x)$

$\qquad = -6\cos^2(\sin 2x)\sin(\sin 2x)\cos 2x$

32. $f'(x) = \dfrac{(1 - \cot x^2)(-2x \csc x^2 \cot x^2) - (1 + \csc x^2)(2x \csc^2 x^2)}{(1 - \cot x^2)^2}$

33. $f'(x) = (5x + 8)^{13}12(x^3 + 7x)^{11}\dfrac{d}{dx}(x^3 + 7x) + (x^3 + 7x)^{12}13(5x + 8)^{12}\dfrac{d}{dx}(5x + 8)$

$\quad = 12(5x + 8)^{13}(x^3 + 7x)^{11}(3x^2 + 7) + 65(x^3 + 7x)^{12}(5x + 8)^{12}$

34. $f'(x) = (2x - 5)^2 3(x^2 + 4)^2(2x) + (x^2 + 4)^3 2(2x - 5)(2)$

$\quad = 6x(2x - 5)^2(x^2 + 4)^2 + 4(2x - 5)(x^2 + 4)^3$

$\quad = 2(2x - 5)(x^2 + 4)^2(8x^2 - 15x + 8)$

35. $f'(x) = 3\left[\dfrac{x - 5}{2x + 1}\right]^2 \dfrac{d}{dx}\left[\dfrac{x - 5}{2x + 1}\right] = 3\left[\dfrac{x - 5}{2x + 1}\right]^2 \cdot \dfrac{11}{(2x + 1)^2} = \dfrac{33(x - 5)^2}{(2x + 1)^4}$

36. $f'(x) = 17\left(\dfrac{1 + x^2}{1 - x^2}\right)^{16} \dfrac{d}{dx}\left(\dfrac{1 + x^2}{1 - x^2}\right)$

$\quad = 17\left(\dfrac{1 + x^2}{1 - x^2}\right)^{16} \dfrac{(1 - x^2)(2x) - (1 + x^2)(-2x)}{(1 - x^2)^2}$

$\quad = 17\left(\dfrac{1 + x^2}{1 - x^2}\right)^{16} \dfrac{4x}{(1 - x^2)^2} = \dfrac{68x(1 + x^2)^{16}}{(1 - x^2)^{18}}$

37. $f'(x) = \dfrac{(4x^2 - 1)^8(3)(2x + 3)^2)(2) - (2x + 3)^3(8)(4x^2 - 1)^7(8x)}{(4x^2 - 1)^{16}}$

$\quad = \dfrac{2(2x + 3)^2(4x^2 - 1)^7[3(4x^2 - 1) - 32x(2x + 3)]}{(4x^2 - 1)^{16}}$

$\quad = -\dfrac{2(2x + 3)^2(52x^2 + 96x + 3)}{(4x^2 - 1)^9}$

38. $f'(x) = 12[1 + \sin^3(x^5)]^{11}\dfrac{d}{dx}[1 + \sin^3(x^5)]$

$\quad = 12[1 + \sin^3(x^5)]^{11}3\sin^2(x^5)\dfrac{d}{dx}\sin(x^5) = 180x^4[1 + \sin^3(x^5)]^{11}\sin^2(x^5)\cos(x^5)$

39. $f'(x) = 5\left[x \sin 2x \tan^4(x^7)\right]^4 \dfrac{d}{dx}\left[x \sin 2x \tan^4(x^7)\right]$

$\quad = 5\left[x \sin 2x \tan^4(x^7)\right]^4 \left[x \cos 2x \dfrac{d}{dx}(2x) + \sin 2x + 4\tan^3(x^7)\dfrac{d}{dx}\tan(x^7)\right]$

$\quad = 5\left[x \sin 2x \tan^4(x^7)\right]^4 \left[2x \cos 2x + \sin 2x + 28x^6 \tan^3(x^7)\sec^2(x^7)\right]$

40. $\dfrac{dy}{dx} = \cos(3x^2)\dfrac{d}{dx}(3x^2) = 6x\cos(3x^2),$

$\dfrac{d^2y}{dx^2} = 6x(-\sin(3x^2))\dfrac{d}{dx}(3x^2) + 6\cos(3x^2) = -36x^2\sin(3x^2) + 6\cos(3x^2)$

41. $\dfrac{dy}{dx} = x(-\sin(5x))\dfrac{d}{dx}(5x) + \cos(5x) - 2\sin x\dfrac{d}{dx}(\sin x)$

$\qquad = -5x\sin(5x) + \cos(5x) - 2\sin x\cos x = -5x\sin(5x) + \cos(5x) - \sin(2x),$

$\dfrac{d^2y}{dx^2} = -5x\cos(5x)\dfrac{d}{dx}(5x) - 5\sin(5x) - \sin(5x)\dfrac{d}{dx}(5x) - \cos(2x)\dfrac{d}{dx}(2x)$

$\qquad = -25x\cos(5x) - 10\sin(5x) - 2\cos(2x)$

42. $\dfrac{dy}{dx} = x\sec^2\left(\dfrac{1}{x}\right)\dfrac{d}{dx}\left(\dfrac{1}{x}\right) + \tan\left(\dfrac{1}{x}\right) = -\dfrac{1}{x}\sec^2\left(\dfrac{1}{x}\right) + \tan\left(\dfrac{1}{x}\right),$

$\dfrac{d^2y}{dx^2} = -\dfrac{2}{x}\sec\left(\dfrac{1}{x}\right)\dfrac{d}{dx}\sec\left(\dfrac{1}{x}\right) + \dfrac{1}{x^2}\sec^2\left(\dfrac{1}{x}\right) + \sec^2\left(\dfrac{1}{x}\right)\dfrac{d}{dx}\left(\dfrac{1}{x}\right) = \dfrac{2}{x^3}\sec^2\left(\dfrac{1}{x}\right)\tan\left(\dfrac{1}{x}\right)$

43. $\dfrac{dy}{dx} = -3x\sin 3x + \cos 3x;$ if $x = \pi$ then $y = -\pi$ and $\dfrac{dy}{dx} = -1$ so $y + \pi = -(x - \pi),\ y = -x.$

44. $\dfrac{dy}{dx} = 3x^2\cos(1 + x^3);$ if $x = -3$ then $y = \sin(-26) = -\sin 26$ and $\dfrac{dy}{dx} = 27\cos 26$

$\qquad$ so $y + \sin 26 = 27(\cos 26)(x + 3).$

45. $\dfrac{dy}{dx} = -3\sec^3(\pi/2 - x)\tan(\pi/2 - x);$ if $x = -\pi/2$ then $y = -1$ and $\dfrac{dy}{dx} = 0$

$\qquad$ so $y + 1 = (0)(x + \pi/2),\ y = -1.$

46. $\dfrac{dy}{dx} = 3(x - 1/x)^2(1 + 1/x^2);$ if $x = 2$ then $y = 27/8$ and $\dfrac{dy}{dx} = 135/16$

$\qquad$ so $y - \dfrac{27}{8} = \dfrac{135}{16}(x - 2),\ y = \dfrac{135}{16}x - \dfrac{27}{2}.$

47. $y = \cot^3(\pi - \theta) = -\cot^3\theta$ so $dy/dx = 3\cot^2\theta\csc^2\theta.$

48. $6\left(\dfrac{au + b}{cu + d}\right)^5\dfrac{ad - bc}{(cu + d)^2}$

49. $\dfrac{d}{d\omega}[a\cos^2\pi\omega + b\sin^2\pi\omega] = -2\pi a\cos\pi\omega\sin\pi\omega + 2\pi b\sin\pi\omega\cos\pi\omega$

$\qquad\qquad\qquad\qquad = \pi(b - a)(2\sin\pi\omega\cos\pi\omega) = \pi(b - a)\sin 2\pi\omega$

50. $2\csc^2(\pi/3 - y)\cot(\pi/3 - y)$

51. **(a)** $dy/dt = -A\omega \sin \omega t, d^2y/dt^2 = -A\omega^2 \cos \omega t = -\omega^2 y$

(b) One complete oscillation occurs when ωt increases over an interval of length 2π, or if t increases over an interval of length $2\pi/\omega$.

(c) $f = 1/T$

(d) amplitude $= 0.6$ cm, $T = 2\pi/15$ sec/oscillation, $f = 15/(2\pi)$ oscillations/sec.

52. $dy/dt = 3A \cos 3t, d^2y/dt^2 = -9A \sin 3t$, so $-9A \sin 3t + 2A \sin 3t = 4 \sin 3t$,

$-7A \sin 3t = 4 \sin 3t, -7A = 4, A = -4/7$.

53. **(a)** $p \approx 10$ lb/in^2, $dp/dh \approx -2$ lb/in^2 per mi

(b) $\dfrac{dp}{dt} = \dfrac{dp}{dh}\dfrac{dh}{dt} \approx (-2)(0.3) = -0.6$ lb/in^2 per sec

54. **(a)** $F = \dfrac{45}{\cos\theta + 0.3\sin\theta}$, $\dfrac{dF}{d\theta} = -\dfrac{45(-\sin\theta + 0.3\cos\theta)}{(\cos\theta + 0.3\sin\theta)^2}$;

if $\theta = 30°$, then $dF/d\theta \approx 10.5$ lb/rad ≈ 0.18 lb/°

(b) $\dfrac{dF}{dt} = \dfrac{dF}{d\theta}\dfrac{d\theta}{dt} \approx (0.18)(-0.5) = -0.09$ lb/sec

55. $3x^2y^2\dfrac{dy}{dx} + 2xy^3$

56. $\dfrac{y - 2x(dy/dx)}{y^3}$

57. $\left(x\dfrac{dy}{dx} + y\right)\cos(xy)$

58. $\dfrac{x + y(dy/dx)}{\sqrt{x^2 + y^2}}$

59. $2x\dfrac{dx}{dt} + 2y\dfrac{dy}{dt}$

60. $\left(3xy^2\dfrac{dy}{dt} + y^3\dfrac{dx}{dt}\right)\sec^2(xy^3)$

61. $\dfrac{x^2}{2\sqrt{y}}\dfrac{dy}{dt} + 2x\sqrt{y}\dfrac{dx}{dt}$

62. $\dfrac{2xy(dy/dt) - y^2(dx/dt)}{x^2}$

63. With $u = \sin x$, $\dfrac{d}{dx}(|\sin x|) = \dfrac{d}{dx}(|u|) = \dfrac{d}{du}(|u|)\dfrac{du}{dx} = \dfrac{d}{du}(|u|)\cos x = \begin{cases} \cos x, & u > 0 \\ -\cos x, & u < 0 \end{cases}$

$= \begin{cases} \cos x, & \sin x > 0 \\ -\cos x, & \sin x < 0 \end{cases} = \begin{cases} \cos x, & 0 < x < \pi \\ -\cos x, & -\pi < x < 0 \end{cases}$.

64. $\dfrac{d}{dx}(\cos x) = \dfrac{d}{dx}[\sin(\pi/2 - x)] = -\cos(\pi/2 - x) = -\sin x$.

65. **(a)** For $x \neq 0$, $f'(x) = x\left(\cos\dfrac{1}{x}\right)\left(-\dfrac{1}{x^2}\right) + \sin\dfrac{1}{x} = -\dfrac{1}{x}\cos\dfrac{1}{x} + \sin\dfrac{1}{x}$

(b) $\lim\limits_{x \to 0} x \sin \dfrac{1}{x} = 0 = f(0)$

(c) $\lim\limits_{h \to 0} \dfrac{f(0+h) - f(0)}{h} = \lim\limits_{h \to 0} \dfrac{h \sin \dfrac{1}{h}}{h} = \lim\limits_{h \to 0} \sin \dfrac{1}{h}$, which does not exist

66. **(a)** $f'(x) = x^2 \left(\cos \dfrac{1}{x} \right)\left(-\dfrac{1}{x^2} \right) + 2x \sin \dfrac{1}{x} = -\cos \dfrac{1}{x} + 2x \sin \dfrac{1}{x}$, $x \neq 0$

  (b) $\lim\limits_{x \to 0} x^2 \sin \dfrac{1}{x} = 0 = f(0)$

  (c) $f'(0) = \lim\limits_{h \to 0} \dfrac{f(0+h) - f(0)}{h} = \lim\limits_{h \to 0} \dfrac{h^2 \sin \dfrac{1}{h}}{h} = \lim\limits_{h \to 0} h \sin \dfrac{1}{h} = 0$

  (d) $\lim\limits_{x \to 0} f'(x)$ does not exist because $\cos \dfrac{1}{x}$ oscillates between 1 and -1.

67. **(a)** $g'(x) = 3[f(x)]^2 f'(x),$
  $g'(2) = 3[f(2)]^2 f'(2) = 3(1)^2(7) = 21$
  (b) $h'(x) = f'(x^3)(3x^2),$
  $h'(2) = f'(8)(12) = (-3)(12) = -36$

68. **(a)** $F'(x) = f'(g(x))g'(x),$
  $F'(-1) = f'(g(-1))g'(-1) = f'(2)(-3) = (4)(-3) = -12$
  (b) $G'(x) = g'(f(x))f'(x),$
  $G'(-1) = g'(f(-1))f'(-1) = g'(2)(3) = (-5)(3) = -15$

69. $(f \circ g)'(x) = f'(g(x))g'(x)$ so $(f \circ g)'(0) = f'(g(0))g'(0) = f'(0)(3) = (2)(3) = 6.$

70. $F'(x) = f'(g(x))g'(x) = \sqrt{3(x^2 - 1) + 4}(2x) = 2x\sqrt{3x^2 + 1}$

71. $F'(x) = f'(g(x))g'(x) = f'(\sqrt{3x - 1})\dfrac{3}{2\sqrt{3x - 1}} = \dfrac{\sqrt{3x - 1}}{(3x - 1) + 1}\dfrac{3}{2\sqrt{3x - 1}} = \dfrac{1}{2x}$

72. $\dfrac{d}{dx}[f(x^2)] = f'(x^2)(2x)$, thus $f'(x^2)(2x) = x^2$ so $f'(x^2) = x/2$ if $x \neq 0$.

73. $\dfrac{d}{dx}[f(3x)] = f'(3x)\dfrac{d}{dx}(3x) = 3f'(3x) = 6x$, so $f'(3x) = 2x$. Let $u = 3x$ to get $f'(u) = \dfrac{2}{3}u$;
  $\dfrac{d}{dx}[f(x)] = f'(x) = \dfrac{2}{3}x.$

74. **(a)** If $f(-x) = f(x)$, then $\dfrac{d}{dx}[f(-x)] = \dfrac{d}{dx}[f(x)]$, $f'(-x)(-1) = f'(x)$, $f'(-x) = -f'(x)$
  so f' is odd.

(b) If $f(-x) = -f(x)$, then $\dfrac{d}{dx}[f(-x)] = -\dfrac{d}{dx}[f(x)]$, $f'(-x)(-1) = -f'(x)$, $f'(-x) = f'(x)$ so f' is even.

75. $\dfrac{d}{dx}[f(g(h(x)))] = \dfrac{d}{dx}[f(g(u))], \quad u = h(x)$

$$= \dfrac{d}{du}[f(g(u))]\dfrac{du}{dx} = f'(g(u))g'(u)\dfrac{du}{dx} = f'(g(h(x)))g'(h(x))h'(x)$$

76. $\dfrac{dy}{dx} = \dfrac{dy}{du}\dfrac{du}{dv}\dfrac{dv}{dw}\dfrac{dw}{dx}$

EXERCISE SET 3.6

1. $y = (2x - 5)^{1/3}; \ dy/dx = \dfrac{2}{3}(2x - 5)^{-2/3}$

2. $dy/dx = \dfrac{1}{3}\left[2 + \tan(x^2)\right]^{-2/3}\sec^2(x^2)(2x) = \dfrac{2}{3}x\sec^2(x^2)\left[2 + \tan(x^2)\right]^{-2/3}$

3. $dy/dx = \dfrac{3}{2}\left[\dfrac{x-1}{x+2}\right]^{1/2}\dfrac{d}{dx}\left[\dfrac{x-1}{x+2}\right] = \dfrac{9}{2(x+2)^2}\left[\dfrac{x-1}{x+2}\right]^{1/2}$

4. $dy/dx = \dfrac{1}{2}\left[\dfrac{x^2+1}{x^2-5}\right]^{-1/2}\dfrac{d}{dx}\left[\dfrac{x^2+1}{x^2-5}\right] = \dfrac{1}{2}\left[\dfrac{x^2+1}{x^2-5}\right]^{-1/2}\dfrac{-12x}{(x^2-5)^2}$

$$= -\dfrac{6x}{(x^2-5)^2}\left[\dfrac{x^2+1}{x^2-5}\right]^{-1/2}$$

5. $dy/dx = x^3\left(-\dfrac{2}{3}\right)(5x^2+1)^{-5/3}(10x) + 3x^2(5x^2+1)^{-2/3} = \dfrac{1}{3}x^2(5x^2+1)^{-5/3}(25x^2+9)$

6. $dy/dx = \dfrac{x^2\dfrac{4}{3}(3-2x)^{1/3}(-2) - (3-2x)^{4/3}(2x)}{x^4} = \dfrac{2(3-2x)^{1/3}(2x-9)}{3x^3}$

7. $dy/dx = \dfrac{5}{2}[\sin(3/x)]^{3/2}[\cos(3/x)](-3/x^2) = -\dfrac{15[\sin(3/x)]^{3/2}\cos(3/x)}{2x^2}$

8. $dy/dx = -\dfrac{1}{2}\left[\cos(x^3)\right]^{-3/2}\left[-\sin(x^3)\right](3x^2) = \dfrac{3}{2}x^2\sin(x^3)\left[\cos(x^3)\right]^{-3/2}$

9. $dy/dx = \sec^2\left[(2x-1)^{-1/3}\right]\left(-\dfrac{1}{3}\right)(2x-1)^{-4/3}(2) = -\dfrac{2}{3}(2x-1)^{-4/3}\sec^2\left[(2x-1)^{-1/3}\right]$

10. $dy/dx = -\dfrac{1}{3}\left[\tan(2x-1)\right]^{-4/3}\sec^2(2x-1)(2) = -\dfrac{2}{3}\sec^2(2x-1)\left[\tan(2x-1)\right]^{-4/3}$

11. $y' = rx^{r-1}, y'' = r(r-1)x^{r-2}$ so $3x^2\left[r(r-1)x^{r-2}\right] + 4x\left(rx^{r-1}\right) - 2x^r = 0$,
    $3r(r-1)x^r + 4rx^r - 2x^r = 0, (3r^2 + r - 2)x^r = 0$,
    $3r^2 + r - 2 = 0, (3r-2)(r+1) = 0; r = -1, 2/3$.

12. $y' = rx^{r-1}, y'' = r(r-1)x^{r-2}$ so $16x^2\left[r(r-1)x^{r-2}\right] + 24x\left(rx^{r-1}\right) + x^r = 0$,
    $16r(r-1)x^r + 24rx^r + x^r = 0, (16r^2 + 8r + 1)x^r = 0$,
    $16r^2 + 8r + 1 = 0, (4r+1)^2 = 0; r = -1/4$.

13. $2x + 2y\dfrac{dy}{dx} = 0$ so $\dfrac{dy}{dx} = -\dfrac{x}{y}$

14. $3x^2 - 3y^2\dfrac{dy}{dx} = 6(x\dfrac{dy}{dx} + y), -(3y^2 + 6x)\dfrac{dy}{dx} = 6y - 3x^2$ so $\dfrac{dy}{dx} = \dfrac{x^2 - 2y}{y^2 + 2x}$

15. $x^2\dfrac{dy}{dx} + 2xy + 3x(3y^2)\dfrac{dy}{dx} + 3y^3 - 1 = 0$

    $(x^2 + 9xy^2)\dfrac{dy}{dx} = 1 - 2xy - 3y^3$ so $\dfrac{dy}{dx} = \dfrac{1 - 2xy - 3y^3}{x^2 + 9xy^2}$

16. $x^3(2y)\dfrac{dy}{dx} + 3x^2y^2 - 5x^2\dfrac{dy}{dx} - 10xy + 1 = 0$

    $(2x^3y - 5x^2)\dfrac{dy}{dx} = 10xy - 3x^2y^2 - 1$ so $\dfrac{dy}{dx} = \dfrac{10xy - 3x^2y^2 - 1}{2x^3y - 5x^2}$

17. $-\dfrac{1}{y^2}\dfrac{dy}{dx} - \dfrac{1}{x^2} = 0$ so $\dfrac{dy}{dx} = -\dfrac{y^2}{x^2}$

18. $2x = \dfrac{(x-y)(1+dy/dx) - (x+y)(1-dy/dx)}{(x-y)^2}$,

    $2x(x-y)^2 = -2y + 2x\dfrac{dy}{dx}$ so $\dfrac{dy}{dx} = \dfrac{x(x-y)^2 + y}{x}$

19. $\dfrac{1}{2\sqrt{x}} + \dfrac{1}{2\sqrt{y}}\dfrac{dy}{dx} = 0$ so $\dfrac{dy}{dx} = -\dfrac{\sqrt{y}}{\sqrt{x}}$

20. $\frac{1}{2}(xy)^{-1/2}\left(x\frac{dy}{dx} + y\right) = \frac{dy}{dx}$, $x\frac{dy}{dx} + y = 2\sqrt{xy}\frac{dy}{dx}$,

 $(x - 2\sqrt{xy})\frac{dy}{dx} = -y$ so $\frac{dy}{dx} = \frac{y}{2\sqrt{xy} - x}$

21. $35\left(x^2 + 3y^2\right)^{34}\left(2x + 6y\frac{dy}{dx}\right) = 1$,

 $70x(x^2 + 3y^2)^{34} + 210y(x^2 + 3y^2)^{34}\frac{dy}{dx} = 1$ so $\frac{dy}{dx} = \frac{1 - 70x(x^2 + 3y^2)^{34}}{210y(x^2 + 3y^2)^{34}}$

22. $\left(\frac{2}{3}xy^{-1/3}\frac{dy}{dx} + y^{2/3}\right) + \left(x^{2/3}\frac{dy}{dx} + \frac{2}{3}x^{-1/3}y\right) = 2x$, multiply through by $3x^{1/3}y^{1/3}$ to get

 $2x^{4/3}\frac{dy}{dx} + 3x^{1/3}y + 3xy^{1/3}\frac{dy}{dx} + 2y^{4/3} = 6x^{4/3}y^{1/3}$,

 $(2x^{4/3} + 3xy^{1/3})\frac{dy}{dx} = 6x^{4/3}y^{1/3} - 3x^{1/3}y - 2y^{4/3}$ so $\frac{dy}{dx} = \frac{6x^{4/3}y^{1/3} - 3x^{1/3}y - 2y^{4/3}}{2x^{4/3} + 3xy^{1/3}}$

23. $3x\frac{dy}{dx} + 3y = \frac{3}{2}\left(x^3 + y^2\right)^{1/2}\left(3x^2 + 2y\frac{dy}{dx}\right)$,

 $\left[3x - 3y(x^3 + y^2)^{1/2}\right]\frac{dy}{dx} = \frac{9}{2}x^2(x^3 + y^2)^{1/2} - 3y$ so $\frac{dy}{dx} = \frac{(3/2)x^2(x^3 + y^2)^{1/2} - y}{x - y(x^3 + y^2)^{1/2}}$

24. $(-\sin xy)\left(x\frac{dy}{dx} + y\right) = \frac{dy}{dx}$, $-(1 + x\sin xy)\frac{dy}{dx} = y\sin xy$ so $\frac{dy}{dx} = -\frac{y\sin xy}{1 + x\sin xy}$

25. $\cos(x^2y^2)\left[x^2(2y)\frac{dy}{dx} + 2xy^2\right] = 1$, $\frac{dy}{dx} = \frac{1 - 2xy^2\cos(x^2y^2)}{2x^2y\cos(x^2y^2)}$

26. $2x = \frac{(1 + \csc y)(-\csc^2 y)(dy/dx) - (\cot y)(-\csc y\cot y)(dy/dx)}{(1 + \csc y)^2}$,

 $2x(1 + \csc y)^2 = -\csc y(\csc y + \csc^2 y - \cot^2 y)\frac{dy}{dx}$,

 but $\csc^2 y - \cot^2 y = 1$, so $\frac{dy}{dx} = -\frac{2x(1 + \csc y)}{\csc y}$

27. $3\tan^2(xy^2 + y)\sec^2(xy^2 + y)\left(2xy\frac{dy}{dx} + y^2 + \frac{dy}{dx}\right) = 1$

 so $\frac{dy}{dx} = \frac{1 - 3y^2\tan^2(xy^2 + y)\sec^2(xy^2 + y)}{3(2xy + 1)\tan^2(xy^2 + y)\sec^2(xy^2 + y)}$

28. $\dfrac{(1+\sec y)[3xy^2(dy/dx)+y^3]-xy^3(\sec y\tan y)(dy/dx)}{(1+\sec y)^2}=4y^3\dfrac{dy}{dx}$,

   multiply through by $(1+\sec y)^2$ and solve for $\dfrac{dy}{dx}$

   to get $\dfrac{dy}{dx}=\dfrac{y(1+\sec y)}{4y(1+\sec y)^2-3x(1+\sec y)+xy\sec y\tan y}$

29. $\dfrac{1}{2}\left[1+\sin^3(xy^2)\right]^{-1/2}\left[3\sin^2(xy^2)\right]\left[\cos(xy^2)\right]\left(2xy\dfrac{dy}{dx}+y^2\right)=\dfrac{dy}{dx}$,

   multiply through by $2\sqrt{1+\sin^3(xy^2)}$ and solve for $\dfrac{dy}{dx}$

   to get $\dfrac{dy}{dx}=\dfrac{3y^2\sin^2(xy^2)\cos(xy^2)}{2\sqrt{1+\sin^3(xy^2)}-6xy\sin^2(xy^2)\cos(xy^2)}$

30. $\dfrac{dy}{dx}=\dfrac{5y^2-2xy}{x^2-10xy}$; $\left.\dfrac{dy}{dx}\right|_{(3,1)}=\dfrac{1}{21}$

31. $\dfrac{dy}{dx}=-\dfrac{3x^2y+y^3}{x^3+3y^2x}$; $\left.\dfrac{dy}{dx}\right|_{(1,2)}=-\dfrac{14}{13}$

32. $\dfrac{dy}{dx}=\dfrac{y\cos xy}{1-x\cos xy}$; $\left.\dfrac{dy}{dx}\right|_{(\pi/2,1)}=0$

33. $\dfrac{dy}{dx}=\dfrac{2y^{1/3}}{2x^{1/3}+3x^{1/3}y^{1/3}}$; $\left.\dfrac{dy}{dx}\right|_{(1,-1)}=2$

34. $\dfrac{dy}{dx}=-\dfrac{y}{x}$; $\left.\dfrac{dy}{dx}\right|_{(\pi/12,3)}=-\dfrac{36}{\pi}$

35. If $xy=8$, then $y=8/x$ so $dy/dx=-8/x^2$. By implicit differentiation we get $dy/dx=-y/x$. In both cases, $dy/dx|_{(2,4)}=-2$.

36. If $y^2-x+1=0$, then $y=\sqrt{x-1}$ goes through the point $(10,3)$ so $dy/dx=1/(2\sqrt{x-1})$. By implicit differentiation we get $dy/dx=1/(2y)$. In both cases, $dy/dx|_{(10,3)}=1/6$.

37. If $x^2+y^2=1$, then $y=-\sqrt{1-x^2}$ goes through the point $(1/\sqrt{2},\,-1/\sqrt{2})$ so $dy/dx=x/\sqrt{1-x^2}$. By implicit differentiation we get $dy/dx=-x/y$. In both cases, $dy/dx|_{(1/\sqrt{2},-1/\sqrt{2})}=1$.

38. If $(1-y)/(1+y)=x$, then $y=(1-x)/(1+x)$ so $dy/dx=-2/(1+x)^2$. By implicit differentiation we get $dy/dx=-(1+y)^2/2$. In both cases, $dy/dx|_{(0,1)}=-2$.

39. Apply the quadratic formula to $y^2-3xy+2x^2-4=0$ to get $y=(3x\pm\sqrt{9x^2-4(2x^2-4)})/2=(3x\pm\sqrt{x^2+16})/2$, of which only $y=(3x-\sqrt{x^2+16})/2$ contains the point $(3,2)$ so $dy/dx=[3-x(x^2+16)^{-1/2}]/2$. By implicit differentiation we get $dy/dx=(3y-4x)/(2y-3x)$. In both cases, $dy/dx|_{(3,2)}=6/5$.

40. $\dfrac{dy}{dx} = \dfrac{3x}{4y}$, $\dfrac{d^2y}{dx^2} = \dfrac{(4y)(3) - (3x)(4dy/dx)}{16y^2}$

$$= \dfrac{12y - 12x(3x/(4y))}{16y^2} = \dfrac{12y^2 - 9x^2}{16y^3} = \dfrac{-3(3x^2 - 4y^2)}{16y^3},$$

but $3x^2 - 4y^2 = 7$ so $\dfrac{d^2y}{dx^2} = \dfrac{-3(7)}{16y^3} = -\dfrac{21}{16y^3}$.

41. $\dfrac{dy}{dx} = -\dfrac{x^2}{y^2}$, $\dfrac{d^2y}{dx^2} = -\dfrac{y^2(2x) - x^2(2ydy/dx)}{y^4} = -\dfrac{2xy^2 - 2x^2y(-x^2/y^2)}{y^4} = -\dfrac{2x(y^3 + x^3)}{y^5}$,

but $x^3 + y^3 = 1$ so $\dfrac{d^2y}{dx^2} = -\dfrac{2x}{y^5}$.

42. $\dfrac{dy}{dx} = -\dfrac{y}{x}$, $\dfrac{d^2y}{dx^2} = -\dfrac{x(dy/dx) - y(1)}{x^2} = -\dfrac{x(-y/x) - y}{x^2} = \dfrac{2y}{x^2}$.

43. $\dfrac{dy}{dx} = \dfrac{y}{y - x}$,

$$\dfrac{d^2y}{dx^2} = \dfrac{(y - x)(dy/dx) - y(dy/dx - 1)}{(y - x)^2} = \dfrac{(y - x)\left(\dfrac{y}{y - x}\right) - y\left(\dfrac{y}{y - x} - 1\right)}{(y - x)^2}$$

$$= \dfrac{y^2 - 2xy}{(y - x)^3} \text{ but } y^2 - 2xy = -3, \text{ so } \dfrac{d^2y}{dx^2} = -\dfrac{3}{(y - x)^3}$$

44. $\dfrac{dy}{dx} = (1 + \cos y)^{-1}$, $\dfrac{d^2y}{dx^2} = -(1 + \cos y)^{-2}(-\sin y)\dfrac{dy}{dx} = \dfrac{\sin y}{(1 + \cos y)^3}$

45. $\dfrac{dy}{dx} = \dfrac{\cos y}{1 + x\sin y}$,

$$\dfrac{d^2y}{dx^2} = \dfrac{(1 + x\sin y)(-\sin y)(dy/dx) - (\cos y)[(x\cos y)(dy/dx) + \sin y]}{(1 + x\sin y)^2}$$

$$= -\dfrac{2\sin y\cos y + (x\cos y)(2\sin^2 y + \cos^2 y)}{(1 + x\sin y)^3},$$

but $x\cos y = y$, $2\sin y\cos y = \sin 2y$, and $\sin^2 y + \cos^2 y = 1$ so

$$\dfrac{d^2y}{dx^2} = -\dfrac{\sin 2y + y(\sin^2 y + 1)}{(1 + x\sin y)^3}.$$

46. $\dfrac{1}{2}u^{-1/2}\dfrac{du}{dv} + \dfrac{1}{2}v^{-1/2} = 0$ so $\dfrac{du}{dv} = -\dfrac{\sqrt{u}}{\sqrt{v}}$

47. $4a^3\dfrac{da}{dt} - 4t^3 = 6\left(a^2 + 2at\dfrac{da}{dt}\right)$, solve for $\dfrac{da}{dt}$ to get $\dfrac{da}{dt} = \dfrac{2t^3 + 3a^2}{2a^3 - 6at}$

48. $1 = (\cos x)\dfrac{dx}{dy}$ so $\dfrac{dx}{dy} = \dfrac{1}{\cos x} = \sec x$

49. $2a^2\omega\dfrac{d\omega}{d\lambda} + 2b^2\lambda = 0$ so $\dfrac{d\omega}{d\lambda} = -\dfrac{b^2\lambda}{a^2\omega}$

50. By implicit differentiation, $dy/dx = k/(2y)$ so the slope of the tangent to $y^2 = kx$ at (x_0, y_0) is $k/(2y_0)$ if $y_0 \neq 0$. The tangent line in this case is $y - y_0 = \dfrac{k}{2y_0}(x - x_0)$, or $2y_0 y - 2y_0^2 = kx - kx_0$. But $y_0^2 = kx_0$ because (x_0, y_0) is on the curve $y^2 = kx$, so the equation of the tangent line becomes $2y_0 y - 2kx_0 = kx - kx_0$ which gives $y_0 y = k(x + x_0)/2$. If $y_0 = 0$, then $x_0 = 0$; the graph of $y^2 = kx$ has a vertical tangent at $(0,0)$ so its equation is $x = 0$, but $y_0 y = k(x + x_2)/2$ gives the same result when $x_0 = y_0 = 0$.

51. By the chain rule, $\dfrac{dy}{dx} = \dfrac{dy}{dt}\dfrac{dt}{dx}$. Use implicit differentiation on $2y^3 t + t^3 y = 1$ to get $\dfrac{dy}{dt} = -\dfrac{2y^3 + 3t^2 y}{6ty^2 + t^3}$, but $\dfrac{dt}{dx} = \dfrac{1}{\cos t}$ so $\dfrac{dy}{dx} = -\dfrac{2y^3 + 3t^2 y}{(6ty^2 + t^3)\cos t}$.

52. $2x^3 y\dfrac{dy}{dt} + 3x^2 y^2\dfrac{dx}{dt} + \dfrac{dy}{dt} = 0$, $\dfrac{dy}{dt} = -\dfrac{3x^2 y^2}{2x^3 y + 1}\dfrac{dx}{dt}$

53. $2xy\dfrac{dy}{dt} = y^2\dfrac{dx}{dt} = 3(\cos 3x)\dfrac{dx}{dt}$, $\dfrac{dy}{dt} = \dfrac{3\cos 3x - y^2}{2xy}\dfrac{dx}{dt}$

54. Let $P(x_0, y_0)$ be the required point. The slope of the line $4x - 3y + 1 = 0$ is $4/3$ so the slope of the tangent to $y^2 = 2x^3$ at P must be $-3/4$. By implicit differentiation $dy/dx = 3x^2/y$, so at P, $3x_0^2/y_0 = -3/4$, or $y_0 = -4x_0^2$. But $y_0^2 = 2x_0^3$ because P is on the curve $y^2 = 2x^3$. Elimination of y_0 gives $16x_0^4 = 2x_0^3$, $x_0^3(8x_0 - 1) = 0$, so $x_0 = 0$ or $1/8$. From $y_0 = -4x_0^2$ it follows that $y_0 = 0$ when $x_0 = 0$, and $y_0 = -1/16$ when $x_0 = 1/8$. It does not follow, however, that $(0,0)$ is a solution because $dy/dx = 3x^2/y$ (the slope of the curve as determined by implicit differentiation) is valid only if $y \neq 0$. Further analysis shows that the curve is tangent to the x-axis at $(0,0)$, so the point $(1/8, -1/16)$ is the only solution.

55. The point $(1,1)$ is on the graph, so $1 + a = b$. The slope of the tangent line at $(1,1)$ is $-4/3$; use implicit differentiation to get $\dfrac{dy}{dx} = -\dfrac{2xy}{x^2 + 2ay}$ so at $(1,1)$, $-\dfrac{2}{1 + 2a} = -\dfrac{4}{3}$, $1 + 2a = 3/2$, $a = 1/4$ and hence $b = 1 + 1/4 = 5/4$.

56. Use implicit differentiation to get $dy/dx = (y - 3x^2)/(3y^2 - x)$, so $dy/dx = 0$ if $y = 3x^2$. Substitute this into $x^3 - xy + y^3 = 0$ to obtain $27x^6 - 2x^3 = 0$, $x^3 = 2/27$, $x = \sqrt[3]{2}/3$ and hence $y = \sqrt[3]{4}/3$.

57. Let $P(x_0, y_0)$ be a point where a line through the orgin is tangent to the curve $x^2 - 4x + y^2 + 3 = 0$. Implicit differentiation applied to the equation of the curve gives $dy/dx = (2 - x)/y$. At P the slope of the curve must equal the slope of the line so $(2 - x_0)/y_0 = y_0/x_0$, or $y_0^2 = 2x_0 - x_0^2$. But $x_0^2 - 4x_0 + y_0^2 + 3 = 0$ because (x_0, y_0) is on the curve, and elimination of y_0^2 in the latter two equations gives $x_0^2 - 4x_0 + (2x_0 - x_0^2) + 3 = 0$, $x_0 = 3/2$ which when substituted into $y_0^2 = 2x_0 - x_0^2$ yields $y_0^2 = 3/4$, so $y_0 = \pm\sqrt{3}/2$. The slopes of the lines are $(\pm\sqrt{3}/2)/(3/2) = \pm\sqrt{3}/3$ and their equations are $y = (\sqrt{3}/3)x$ and $y = -(\sqrt{3}/3)x$.

58. (a) $\dfrac{dy}{dx} = -\left(\dfrac{y}{x}\right)^{1/3}$ so $\dfrac{dy}{dx}\bigg|_{(-\frac{1}{4}\sqrt{2},\, \frac{1}{4}\sqrt{2})} = 1$

   (b) $y = (1 - x^{2/3})^{3/2}$ for $y \geq 0$,

   so $\dfrac{dy}{dx} = \dfrac{3}{2}(1 - x^{2/3})^{1/2}\left(-\dfrac{2}{3}x^{-1/3}\right) = -x^{-1/3}(1 - x^{2/3})^{1/2}$

   and for $x = -\dfrac{1}{4}\sqrt{2} = -2^{-3/2}$,

   $\dfrac{dy}{dx} = -(-2^{-3/2})^{-1/3}\left[1 - (-2^{-3/2})^{2/3}\right]^{1/2} = 2^{1/2}(1 - 2^{-1})^{1/2} = 2^{1/2}(1/2)^{1/2} = 1$

   (d) $(-1, 0)$ and $(1, 0)$

59. (a) The equation does not define y as an implicit function of x at the points where the curve crosses the x-axis. If $y = 0$ then $8x^4 = 100x^2$, $8x^2(x^2 - 25/2) = 0$ so $x = 0, \pm5/\sqrt{2}$. The points are $(0, 0)$, $(-5/\sqrt{2}, 0)$, and $(5/\sqrt{2}, 0)$.

   (b) $16(x^2 + y^2)\left(2x + 2y\dfrac{dy}{dx}\right) = 100\left(2x - 2y\dfrac{dy}{dx}\right)$,

   $\dfrac{dy}{dx} = \dfrac{x[25 - 4(x^2 + y^2)]}{y[25 + 4(x^2 + y^2)]}$; at $(3, 1)$ $\dfrac{dy}{dx} = -9/13$ so the equation of the tangent line is $y - 1 = (-9/13)(x - 3)$, $9x + 13y = 40$.

60. (a) $f'(x) = \dfrac{4}{3}x^{1/3}$, $f''(x) = \dfrac{4}{9}x^{-2/3}$

   (b) $f'(x) = \dfrac{7}{3}x^{4/3}$, $f''(x) = \dfrac{28}{9}x^{1/3}$, $f'''(x) = \dfrac{28}{27}x^{-2/3}$

   (c) generalize parts (a) and (b) with $k = (n - 1) + 1/3 = n - 2/3$

EXERCISE SET 3.7

1. **(a)** $\Delta y = (x + \Delta x)^2 - x^2$
$= (2 + 1)^2 - 2^2$
$= 9 - 4 = 5$

   (b) $dy = 2x\,dx$
$= 2(2)(1) = 4$

   (c)

   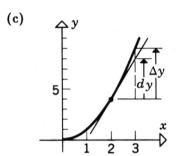

2. **(a)** $\Delta y = (x + \Delta x)^2 - x^2$
$= (2 - 1)^2 - 2^2$
$= -3$

   (b) $dy = 2x\,dx$
$= 2(2)(-1) = -4$

   (c)

   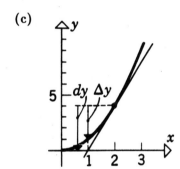

3. **(a)** $\Delta y = \dfrac{1}{x + \Delta x} - \dfrac{1}{x}$

$= \dfrac{1}{1 + 0.5} - \dfrac{1}{1}$

$= -\dfrac{1}{3}$

   (b) $dy = -\dfrac{1}{x^2}\,dx$

$= -\dfrac{1}{1^2}(0.5) = -0.5$

   (c)

   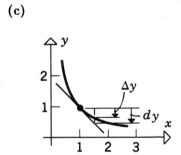

4. (a) $\Delta y = \dfrac{1}{x + \Delta x} - \dfrac{1}{x}$

   $= \dfrac{1}{1 - 0.5} - 1 = 1$

   (b) $dy = -\dfrac{1}{x^2} dx = 0.5$

   (c)

   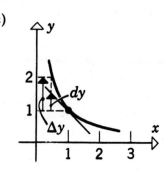

5. $dy = 3x^2 dx$;

   $\Delta y = (x + \Delta x)^3 - x^3 = x^3 3x^2 \Delta x + 3x(\Delta x)^2 + (\Delta x)^3 - x^3 = 3x^2 \Delta x + 3x(\Delta x)^2 + (\Delta x)^3$

6. $dy = 8dx$; $\Delta y = [8(x + \Delta x) - 4] - [8x - 4] = 8\Delta x$

7. $dy = (2x - 2)dx$;

   $\Delta y = [(x + \Delta x)^2 - 2(x + \Delta x) + 1] - [x^2 - 2x + 1]$
   $= x^2 + 2x \,\Delta x + (\Delta x)^2 - 2x - 2\Delta x + 1 - x^2 + 2x - 1 = 2x \,\Delta x + (\Delta x)^2 - 2\Delta x$

8. $dy = \cos x \, dx$; $\Delta y = \sin(x + \Delta x) - \sin x$

9. $dy = (12x^2 - 14x + 2)dx$

10. $dy = \dfrac{(x^3 - 1)d(0) - (1)d(x^3 - 1)}{(x^3 - 1)^2} = \dfrac{(x^3 - 1)(0) - (1)3x^2 dx}{(x^3 - 1)^2} = -\dfrac{3x^2}{(x^3 - 1)^2} dx$

11. $dy = x \, d(\cos x) + \cos x \, dx = x(-\sin x)dx + \cos x dx = (-x \sin x + \cos x)dx$

12. $dy = \dfrac{(2 - x)(-3x^2)dx - (1 - x^3)(-1)dx}{(2 - x)^2} = \dfrac{2x^3 - 6x^2 + 1}{(2 - x)^2} dx$

13. $\lim\limits_{\Delta x \to 0} \dfrac{(x + \Delta x)^2 - x^2}{\Delta x} = \dfrac{d}{dx}(x^2) = 2x$

14. $\lim\limits_{\Delta x \to 0} \dfrac{(3 + \Delta x)^2 - 3^2}{\Delta x} = \dfrac{d}{dx}(x^2)\Big|_{x=3} = 2(3) = 6$

15. $\lim\limits_{\Delta x \to 0} \dfrac{\sin(\pi + \Delta x) - \sin \pi}{\Delta x} = \dfrac{d}{dx}(\sin x)\Big|_{x=\pi} = \cos \pi = -1$

16. $\lim\limits_{\Delta x \to 0} \dfrac{5(2 + \Delta x)^4 - 5(2)^4}{\Delta x} = \dfrac{d}{dx}(5x^4)\Big|_{x=2} = 20(2)^3 = 160$

17. $f(x) = x^4$, $f'(x) = 4x^3$, $x_0 = 3$, $\Delta x = 0.02$; $(3.02)^4 \approx 3^4 + (108)(0.02) = 81 + 2.16 = 83.16$.

18. $f(x) = x^3$, $f'(x) = 3x^2$, $x_0 = 2$, $\Delta x = -0.03$; $(1.97)^3 \approx 2^3 + (12)(-0.03) = 8 - 0.36 = 7.64$.

19. $f(x) = \sqrt{x}$, $f'(x) = \dfrac{1}{2\sqrt{x}}$, $x_0 = 64$, $\Delta x = 1$; $\sqrt{65} \approx \sqrt{64} + \dfrac{1}{16}(1) = 8 + \dfrac{1}{16} = 8.0625$.

20. $f(x) = \sqrt{x}$, $f'(x) = \dfrac{1}{2\sqrt{x}}$, $x_0 = 25$, $\Delta x = -1$; $\sqrt{24} \approx \sqrt{25} + \dfrac{1}{10}(-1) = 5 - 0.1 = 4.9$.

21. $f(x) = \sqrt{x}$, $f'(x) = \dfrac{1}{2\sqrt{x}}$, $x_0 = 81$, $\Delta x = -0.1$; $\sqrt{80.9} \approx \sqrt{81} + \dfrac{1}{18}(-0.1) \approx 8.9944$.

22. $f(x) = \sqrt{x}$, $f'(x) = \dfrac{1}{2\sqrt{x}}$, $x_0 = 36$, $\Delta x = 0.03$;

    $\sqrt{36.03} \approx \sqrt{36} + \dfrac{1}{12}(0.03) = 6 + 0.0025 = 6.0025$.

23. $f(x) = \sqrt[3]{x}$, $f'(x) = \dfrac{1}{3}x^{-2/3}$, $x_0 = 8$, $\Delta x = 0.06$; $\sqrt[3]{8.06} \approx \sqrt[3]{8} + \dfrac{1}{12}(0.06) = 2.005$.

24. $f(x) = \sqrt[3]{x}$, $f'(x) = \dfrac{1}{3}x^{-2/3}$, $x_0 = 64$, $\Delta x = -0.3$;

    $\sqrt[3]{63.7} \approx \sqrt[3]{64} + \dfrac{1}{48}(-0.3) = 4 - 0.00625 = 3.99375$.

25. $f(x) = \cos x$, $f'(x) = -\sin x$, $x_0 = \pi/6$, $\Delta x = \pi/180$;

    $\cos 31° \approx \cos 30° + \left(-\dfrac{1}{2}\right)\left(\dfrac{\pi}{180}\right) = \dfrac{\sqrt{3}}{2} - \dfrac{\pi}{360} \approx 0.8573$.

26. $f(x) = \sin x$, $f'(x) = \cos x$, $x_0 = \pi/3$, $\Delta x = -\pi/180$;

    $\sin 59° \approx \sin 60° + \left(\dfrac{1}{2}\right)\left(-\dfrac{\pi}{180}\right) = \dfrac{\sqrt{3}}{2} - \dfrac{\pi}{360} \approx 0.8573$.

27. $f(x) = \sin x$, $f'(x) = \cos x$, $x_0 = \pi/4$, $\Delta x = -\pi/180$;

    $\sin 44° \approx \sin 45° + \dfrac{1}{\sqrt{2}}\left(-\dfrac{\pi}{180}\right) = \dfrac{1}{\sqrt{2}} - \dfrac{\pi}{180\sqrt{2}} \approx 0.6947$.

28. $f(x) = \tan x$, $f'(x) = \sec^2 x$, $x_0 = \pi/3$, $\Delta x = \pi/180$;

    $\tan 61° \approx \tan 60° + (4)(\pi/180) = \sqrt{3} + \pi/45 \approx 1.8019$.

29. $dy = \dfrac{3}{2\sqrt{3x-2}}dx$, $x = 2$, $dx = 0.03$; $\Delta y \approx dy = \dfrac{3}{4}(0.03) = 0.0225$.

30. $dy = \dfrac{x}{\sqrt{x^2+8}}dx,\ x=1,\ dx=-0.03;\ \Delta y \approx dy = (1/3)(-0.03) = -0.01.$

31. $dy = \dfrac{1-x^2}{(x^2+1)^2}dx,\ x=2,\ dx=-0.04;\ \Delta y \approx dy = \left(-\dfrac{3}{25}\right)(-0.04) = 0.0048.$

32. $dy = \left(\dfrac{4x}{\sqrt{8x+1}}+\sqrt{8x+1}\right)dx,\ x=3,\ dx=0.05;\ \Delta y \approx dy = (37/5)(0.05) = 0.37.$

33. **(a)** $A=x^2$ where x is the length of a side; $dA = 2x\,dx = 2(10)(\pm0.1) = \pm2$ ft^2.

  (b) relative error in $x \approx \dfrac{dx}{x} = \dfrac{\pm0.1}{10} = \pm0.01$ so percentage error in $x \approx \pm1\%$; relative error in $A \approx \dfrac{dA}{A} = \dfrac{2x\,dx}{x^2} = 2\dfrac{dx}{x} = 2(\pm0.01) = \pm0.02$ so percentage error in $A \approx \pm2\%$.

34. **(a)** $V=x^3$ where x is the length of a side; $dV = 3x^2dx = 3(25)^2(\pm1) = \pm1875$ cm^3.

  (b) relative error in $x \approx \dfrac{dx}{x} = \dfrac{\pm1}{25} = \pm0.04$ so percentage error in $x \approx \pm4\%$; relative error in $V \approx \dfrac{dV}{V} = \dfrac{3x^2dx}{x^3} = 3\dfrac{dx}{x} = 3(\pm0.04) = \pm0.12$ so percentage error in $V \approx \pm12\%$.

35. **(a)** $x=10\sin\theta,\ y=10\cos\theta$ (see figure), $dx = 10\cos\theta\,d\theta$

  $$= 10\left(\cos\dfrac{\pi}{6}\right)\left(\pm\dfrac{\pi}{180}\right)$$

  $$= 10\left(\dfrac{\sqrt{3}}{2}\right)\left(\pm\dfrac{\pi}{180}\right) \approx \pm0.151'',$$

  $$dy = -10(\sin\theta)d\theta = -10\left(\sin\dfrac{\pi}{6}\right)\left(\pm\dfrac{\pi}{180}\right) = -10\left(\dfrac{1}{2}\right)\left(\pm\dfrac{\pi}{180}\right) \approx \pm0.087''.$$

  (b) relative error in $x \approx \dfrac{dx}{x} = (\cot\theta)d\theta = \left(\cot\dfrac{\pi}{6}\right)\left(\pm\dfrac{\pi}{180}\right) = \sqrt{3}\left(\pm\dfrac{\pi}{180}\right) \approx \pm0.030$ so percentage error in $x \approx \pm3.0\%$; relative error in $y \approx \dfrac{dy}{y} = -\tan\theta\,d\theta = -\left(\tan\dfrac{\pi}{6}\right)\left(\pm\dfrac{\pi}{180}\right) = -\dfrac{1}{\sqrt{3}}\left(\pm\dfrac{\pi}{180}\right) \approx \pm0.010$ so percentage error in $y \approx \pm1.0\%$.

36.　(a) $x = 25\cot\theta$, $y = 25\csc\theta$ (see figure);

$dx = -25\csc^2\theta\,d\theta$

$= -25\left(\csc^2\dfrac{\pi}{3}\right)\left(\pm\dfrac{\pi}{360}\right)$

$= -25\left(\dfrac{4}{3}\right)\left(\pm\dfrac{\pi}{360}\right) \approx \pm 0.291$ cm,

$dy = -25\csc\theta\cot\theta\,d\theta$

$= -25\left(\csc\dfrac{\pi}{3}\right)\left(\cot\dfrac{\pi}{3}\right)\left(\pm\dfrac{\pi}{360}\right)$

$= -25\left(\dfrac{2}{\sqrt{3}}\right)\left(\dfrac{1}{\sqrt{3}}\right)\left(\pm\dfrac{\pi}{360}\right) \approx \pm 0.145$ cm.

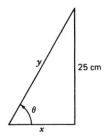

(b)　relative error in $x \approx \dfrac{dx}{x} = -\dfrac{\csc^2\theta}{\cot\theta}d\theta = -\dfrac{4/3}{1/\sqrt{3}}\left(\pm\dfrac{\pi}{360}\right) \approx \pm 0.020$ so percentage

error in $x \approx \pm 2.0\%$; relative error in $y \approx \dfrac{dy}{y} = -\cot\theta\,d\theta = -\dfrac{1}{\sqrt{3}}\left(\pm\dfrac{\pi}{360}\right) \approx \pm 0.005$

so percentage error in $y \approx \pm 0.5\%$.

37.　$\dfrac{dR}{R} = \dfrac{(-2k/r^3)dr}{(k/r^2)} = -2\dfrac{dr}{r}$, but $\dfrac{dr}{r} \approx \pm 0.05$ so $\dfrac{dR}{R} \approx -2(\pm 0.05) = \pm 0.10$; percentage error in $R \approx \pm 10\%$.

38.　$A = x^2$ where x is the length of a side; $\dfrac{dA}{A} = \dfrac{2x\,dx}{x^2} = 2\dfrac{dx}{x}$, but $\dfrac{dx}{x} \approx \pm 0.01$ so

$\dfrac{dA}{A} \approx 2(\pm 0.01) = \pm 0.02$; percentage error in $A \approx \pm 2\%$.

39.　$V = x^3$ where x is the length of a side; $\dfrac{dV}{V} = \dfrac{3x^2 dx}{x^3} = 3\dfrac{dx}{x}$, but $\dfrac{dx}{x} \approx \pm 0.02$

so $\dfrac{dV}{V} \approx 3(\pm 0.02) = \pm 0.06$; percentage error in $V \approx \pm 6\%$.

40.　$\dfrac{dV}{V} = \dfrac{4\pi r^2 dr}{4\pi r^3/3} = 3\dfrac{dr}{r}$, but $\dfrac{dV}{V} \approx \pm 0.03$ so $3\dfrac{dr}{r} \approx \pm 0.03$, $\dfrac{dr}{r} \approx \pm 0.01$; maximum permissible percentage error in $r \approx \pm 1\%$.

41.　$A = \dfrac{1}{4}\pi D^2$ where D is the diameter of the circle; $\dfrac{dA}{A} = \dfrac{(\pi D/2)dD}{\pi D^2/4} = 2\dfrac{dD}{D}$, but $\dfrac{dA}{A} \approx \pm 0.01$

so $2\dfrac{dD}{D} \approx \pm 0.01$, $\dfrac{dD}{D} \approx \pm 0.005$; maximum permissible percentage error in $D \approx \pm 0.5\%$.

42.　$V = x^3$ where x is the length of a side; approximate ΔV by dV if $x = 1$ and $dx = \Delta x = 0.02$,

$dV = 3x^2 dx = 3(1)^2(0.02) = 0.06$ in^3.

43. V = volume of cylindrical rod = $\pi r^2 h = \pi r^2(15) = 15\pi r^2$; approximate ΔV by dV if $r = 2.5$ and $dr = \Delta r = 0.001$. $dV = 30\pi r\, dr = 30\pi(2.5)(0.001) \approx 0.236$ cm^3.

44. $P = \dfrac{2\pi}{\sqrt{g}}\sqrt{L}$, $dP = \dfrac{2\pi}{\sqrt{g}}\dfrac{1}{2\sqrt{L}}dL = \dfrac{\pi}{\sqrt{g}\sqrt{L}}dL$, $\dfrac{dP}{P} = \dfrac{1}{2}\dfrac{dL}{L}$ so the relative error in $P \approx \dfrac{1}{2}$ the relative error in L. Thus the percentage error in $P \approx \dfrac{1}{2}$ the percentage error in L.

45. **(a)** $\alpha = \Delta L/(L\Delta T) = 0.006/(40 \times 10) = 1.5 \times 10^{-5}/°\text{C}$
   (b) $\Delta L = 2.3 \times 10^{-5}(180)(25) \approx 0.1$ cm, so the pole is about 180.1 cm long.

46. $\Delta V = 7.5 \times 10^{-4}(4000)(-20) = -60$ gallons; the truck delivers $4000 - 60 = 3940$ gallons.

47. $f(x) = \dfrac{1}{1+x}$, $f'(x) = -\dfrac{1}{(1+x)^2}$, $x_0 = 0$, $\Delta x = x$;
   $f(x_0 + \Delta x) \approx f(x_0) + f'(x_0)\Delta x$ so $f(x) \approx 1 - x$.
   $x = 0.1 : 1/(1+x) = 0.9091$, $1 - x = 0.9$
   $x = -0.02 : 1/(1+x) = 1.0204$, $1 - x = 1.02$

48. $f(x) = \sqrt{1+x}$, $f'(x) = \dfrac{1}{2\sqrt{1+x}}$, $x_0 = 0$, $\Delta x = x$;

   $f(x_0 + \Delta x) \approx f(x_0) + f'(x_0)\Delta x$ so $f(x) \approx 1 + \dfrac{1}{2}x$.

   $x = 0.1 : \sqrt{1+x} = 1.0488$, $1 + x/2 = 1.05$
   $x = -0.02 : \sqrt{1+x} = 0.9899$, $1 + x/2 = 0.99$.

49. $y = x^k$, $dy = kx^{k-1}dx$; $\dfrac{dy}{y} = \dfrac{kx^{k-1}dx}{x^k} = k\dfrac{dx}{x}$

SUPPLEMENTARY EXERCISES CHAPTER 3

1. $f'(x) = \lim\limits_{h \to 0} \dfrac{k(x+h) - kx}{h} = \lim\limits_{h \to 0} k = k$

2. $f'(x) = \lim\limits_{h \to 0} \dfrac{(x+h-a)^2 - (x-a)^2}{h} = \lim\limits_{h \to 0}[2(x-a) + h] = 2(x-a)$

3. $f'(x) = \lim\limits_{h \to 0} \dfrac{\sqrt{9 - 4(x+h)} - \sqrt{9 - 4x}}{h} = \lim\limits_{h \to 0} \dfrac{[9 - 4(x+h)] - [9 - 4x]}{h(\sqrt{9 - 4(x+h)} + \sqrt{9 - 4x})}$

   $= \lim\limits_{h \to 0} \dfrac{-4}{\sqrt{9 - 4(x+h)} + \sqrt{9 - 4x}} = -\dfrac{2}{\sqrt{9 - 4x}}$

4. $f'(x) = \lim\limits_{h \to 0} \dfrac{\dfrac{x+h}{x+h+1} - \dfrac{x}{x+1}}{h} = \lim\limits_{h \to 0} \dfrac{(x+h)(x+1) - x(x+h+1)}{h(x+1)(x+h+1)}$

$= \lim\limits_{h \to 0} \dfrac{1}{(x+1)(x+h+1)} = \dfrac{1}{(x+1)^2}$

5. $\dfrac{d}{dx}\left(|x|^3\right)\Big|_{x=0} = \lim\limits_{h \to 0} \dfrac{|0+h|^3 - |0|^3}{h} = \lim\limits_{h \to 0} \dfrac{|h|^3}{h} = \lim\limits_{h \to 0} h|h| = 0$

6. **(a)** f is continuous everywhere for all k, except perhaps at $x = 1$;

$\lim\limits_{x \to 1^-} f(x) = \lim\limits_{x \to 1^-} (x^2 - 1) = 0$, $\lim\limits_{x \to 1^+} f(x) = \lim\limits_{x \to 1^+} k(x-1) = 0$, and $f(1) = 0$ thus $\lim\limits_{x \to 1} f(x) = f(1)$ for all k, so f is continuous for all k.

(b) f is differentiable everywhere for all k, except perhaps at $x = 1$. Using the theorem that precedes Exercise 71, Section 3.3, $\lim\limits_{x \to 1^-} f'(x) = \lim\limits_{x \to 1^-} 2x = 2$ and

$\lim\limits_{x \to 1^+} f'(x) = \lim\limits_{x \to 1^+} k = k$; these limits are equal if $k = 2$, so f is differentiable if $k = 2$.

7. $y - (-1) = 5(x-3)$, $y = 5x - 16$.

8. $f'(x) = 2x$ so $m_{\tan} = f'\left(\dfrac{a+b}{2}\right) = a+b$, but $m_{\sec} = \dfrac{b^2 - a^2}{b - a} = b+a$ if $a \neq b$ so $m_{\tan} = m_{\sec}$.

9. **(a)** $2f(x)f'(x) - 3g'(x^2)(2x)\big|_{x=1} = 12$ **(b)** $f(x)g'(x) + f'(x)g(x)\big|_{x=1} = -7$

(c) $\dfrac{g(x)f'(x) - f(x)g'(x)}{g^2(x)}\bigg|_{x=-2} = 9$ **(d)** $\dfrac{f(x)g'(x) - g(x)f'(x)}{f^2(x)}\bigg|_{x=-2} = -\dfrac{9}{4}$

(e) $f'(g(x))g'(x)\big|_{x=1} = f'(g(1))g'(1) = f'(-2)(-1) = 5$

(f) $f'(g(x))g'(x)\big|_{x=-2} = f'(g(-2))g'(-2) = f'(1)(7) = 21$

(g) $g'(f(x))f'(x)\big|_{x=-2} = g'(f(-2))f'(-2) = g'(-2)(-5) = -35$

(h) $g'(g(x))g'(x)\big|_{x=-2} = g'(g(-2))g'(-2) = g'(1)(7) = -7$

(i) $f'(g(4-6x)g'(4-6x)(-6)\big|_{x=1} = f'(g(-2))g'(-2)(-6) = f'(1)(7)(-6) = -126$

(j) $3g^2(x)g'(x)\big|_{x=1} = 3(-2)^2(-1) = -12$

(k) $\dfrac{1}{2}[f(x)]^{-1/2}f'(x)\bigg|_{x=1} = \dfrac{1}{2}(1)^{-1/2}(3) = \dfrac{3}{2}$

(l) $f'(-x/2)(-1/2)\big|_{x=-2} = -\dfrac{3}{2}$

10. $f'(x) = (2x + 7)^6 5(x - 2)^4 + (x - 2)^5 6(2x + 7)^5 (2)$
$= (2x + 7)^5 (x - 2)^4 [5(2x + 7) + 12(x - 2)]$
$= (2x + 7)^5 (x - 2)^4 (22x + 11) - 11(2x + 7)^5 (x - 2)^4 (2x + 1)$

so $f'(x) = 0$ if $x = -7/2, 2, -1/2$.

11. $f'(x) = \dfrac{(x^2 + 2x)4(x - 3)^3 - (x - 3)^4 (2x + 2)}{(x^2 + 2x)^2}$

$= \dfrac{(x - 3)^3 [4(x^2 + 2x) - (x - 3)(2x + 2)]}{(x^2 + 2x)^2}$

$= \dfrac{(x - 3)^3 (2x^2 + 12x + 6)}{(x^2 + 2x)^2} = \dfrac{2(x - 3)^3 (x^2 + 6x + 3)}{(x^2 + 2x)^2}$

so $f'(x) = 0$ if $x - 3 = 0$ or if $x^2 + 6x + 3 = 0$; the solution of $x - 3 = 0$ is $x = 3$, and the solution of $x^2 + 6x + 3 = 0$ is $x = -3 \pm \sqrt{6}$.

12. $f'(x) = (3x + 1)^{1/2} 2(x - 1) + (x - 1)^2 \dfrac{1}{2}(3x + 1)^{-1/2}(3)$

$= \dfrac{1}{2}(3x + 1)^{-1/2}(x - 1)[4(3x + 1) + 3(x - 1)] = \dfrac{(x - 1)(15x + 1)}{2\sqrt{3x + 1}}$

so $f'(x) = 0$ if $x = -1/15, 1$.

13. $f'(x) = 3\left[\dfrac{3x + 1}{x^2}\right]^2 \dfrac{x^2(3) - (3x + 1)(2x)}{x^4} = -\dfrac{3(3x + 2)(3x + 1)^2}{x^7}$ so $f'(x) = 0$ if $x = -2/3, -1/3$.

14. $f'(x) = 3 \cdot \dfrac{(3x - 5)(1/3)(5x - 1)^{-2/3}(5) - (5x - 1)^{1/3}(3)}{(3x - 5)^2}$

$= \dfrac{(5x - 1)^{-2/3}[5(3x - 5) - 9(5x - 1)]}{(3x - 5)^2} = \dfrac{-2(15x + 8)}{(3x - 5)^2(5x - 1)^{2/3}}$

so $f'(x) = 0$ if $x = -8/15$.

15. $f'(x) = x^{1/2}(1/3)(x^2 + x + 1)^{-2/3}(2x + 1) + (x^2 + x + 1)^{1/3}(1/2)x^{-1/2}$

$= \dfrac{1}{6}x^{-1/2}(x^2 + x + 1)^{-2/3}[2x(2x + 1) + 3(x^2 + x + 1)]$

$= \dfrac{7x^2 + 5x + 3}{6x^{1/2}(x^2 + x + 1)^{2/3}}$

but $7x^2 + 5x + 3 = 0$ has no real solutions so there are no values of x for which $f'(x) = 0$.

16.   (a) by the chain rule;
$$\frac{d}{dx}[f(ax)] = f'(ax)\frac{d}{dx}(ax) = \frac{1}{ax}(a) = \frac{1}{x} = \frac{d}{dx}[f(x)]$$

(b) $\dfrac{dy}{dx} = f'(\sin x)\dfrac{d}{dx}(\sin x) = \dfrac{1}{\sin x}(\cos x) = \cot x;$

$\dfrac{dv}{dx} = f'(1/x)\dfrac{d}{dx}(1/x) = \dfrac{1}{(1/x)}(-1/x^2) = -1/x.$

17. $\dfrac{d}{dx}(\sqrt{2}x^{-2} - \dfrac{2}{5}x^{-1}) = -2\sqrt{2}x^{-3} + \dfrac{2}{5}x^{-2}$

18. $\dfrac{dy}{dx} = \dfrac{(x^2-1)(6x) - (3x^2+7)(2x)}{(x^2-1)^2} = -\dfrac{20x}{(x^2-1)^2}$

19. $z = (2\sin r \cos r)^2 = \sin^2 2r$ so $\dfrac{dz}{dr} = 2(\sin 2r)(\cos 2r)(2) = 2\sin 4r$

    and $\dfrac{dz}{dr}\bigg|_{r=\pi/6} = 2\sin(2\pi/3) = \sqrt{3}$

20. $g(x) = (2x)^{-1/2}$ so $g'(x) = -\dfrac{1}{2}(2x)^{-3/2}(2) = -1/(2x)^{3/2}$ and $g'(2) = -1/4^{3/2} = -1/8$

21. $u = \left[\dfrac{x-1}{x}\right]^2 = (1-x^{-1})^2$ so $\dfrac{du}{dx} = 2(1-x^{-1})(x^{-2}) = 2(x-1)/x^3.$

22. $w = \left(v^3 - v^{1/4}\right)^{1/5}$ so $\dfrac{dw}{dv} = \dfrac{1}{5}\left(v^3 - v^{1/4}\right)^{-4/5}\left(3v^2 - \dfrac{1}{4}v^{-3/4}\right)$

23. $\dfrac{d}{dx}(\sec^2 x - \tan^2 x) = \dfrac{d}{dx}(1) = 0$

24. $\dfrac{dy}{dx} = \dfrac{dy}{dt}\dfrac{dt}{dx} = \sec^2 t(-2\sin 2x)$, if $x = \pi/4$ then $t = \cos(\pi/2) = 0$

    so $\dfrac{dy}{dx}\bigg|_{x=\pi/4} = \sec^2(0)(-2\sin(\pi/2)) = -2$

25. $F(x) = \dfrac{2x + 4x^3}{1 + 2x^2} = \dfrac{2x(1+2x^2)}{1+2x^2} = 2x$ so $F'(x) = 2.$

26. $\Phi(x) = \left(x^{3/2} - 4x^{1/2}\right)/5$, $x \neq 0$ so $\Phi'(x) = \dfrac{1}{5}\left(\dfrac{3}{2}x^{1/2} - 2x^{-1/2}\right) = (1/10)(3x - 4)/\sqrt{x}$

27. $y' = 1 + x^{-2}$, and the slope of $2x - y = 5$ is 2 so we want $1 + x^{-2} = 2$ which gives $x^2 = 1$, $x = \pm 1.$

28. $y' = 6x^2 - 2x$, and the slope of $x + 4y = 10$ is $-1/4$ so we want $6x^2 - 2x = 4$ which results in $x = -2/3, 1.$

29. $y' = 2(x + 2)$ so at $(x_0, f(x_0))$ the tangent line is $y - f(x_0) = 2(x_0 + 2)(x - x_0)$, or
$y - (x_0+2)^2 = 2(x_0+2)(x-x_0)$. But if the line passes through the orgin then $x = 0$, $y = 0$ must
satisfy the latter equation thus $-(x_0 + 2)^2 = -2x_0(x_0 + 2)$ which leads to $(x_0 + 2)(x_0 - 2) = 0$
so $x_0 = -2, 2$.

30. $y' = 1 - 2\cos 2x$; the tangent is horizontal where $1 - 2\cos 2x = 0$ so $\cos 2x = 1/2$,
$2x = \pm\pi/3 + 2k\pi$, $x = \pm\pi/6 + k\pi$ where $k = 0, \pm1, \pm2 \cdots$.

31. $y' = 3 - \sec^2 x$, and the slope of $y - x = 2$ is 1 so we want $3 - \sec^2 x = 1$ which gives
$\sec^2 x = 2$, $\sec x = \pm\sqrt{2}$, $x = \pi/4 + k\pi/2$ where $k = 0, \pm1, \pm2, \cdots$.

32. $\Delta x = 1.5 - 2 = -0.5$, $\Delta y = y|_{x=1.5} - y|_{x=2} = 2 - 1 = 1$,

$dy = \dfrac{dy}{dx}\bigg|_{x=2} dx = -\dfrac{1}{(2-1)^2}(-0.5) = 0.5.$

33. $\Delta x = 0 - (-\pi/4) = \pi/4$, $\Delta y = y|_{x=0} - y|_{x=-\pi/4} = 0 - (-1) = 1$,

$dy = \sec^2(-\pi/4)(\pi/4) = \pi/2.$

34. $\Delta x = 3 - 0 = 3$, $\Delta y = y|_{x=3} - y|_{x=0} = \sqrt{16} - \sqrt{25} = -1$,

$dy = \dfrac{dy}{dx}\bigg|_{x=0} dx = -\dfrac{0}{\sqrt{25 - 0^2}}(3) = 0.$

35. **(a)** Consider $y = f(x) = \sqrt[3]{x}$ with $x = -8$ and $dx = -0.25 = -1/4$, then

$f(-8.25) \approx f(-8) + dy$, $\sqrt[3]{-8.25} \approx \sqrt[3]{-8} + \dfrac{1}{3}(-8)^{-2/3}(-1/4) = -2 - 1/48 = -97/48.$

   (b) Consider $y = f(x) = \cot x$ (x in radians) with $x = 45° = \pi/4$ radians and
   $dx = 1° = \pi/180$ radians, then $f(\pi/4 + 180/\pi) \approx f(\pi/4) + dy$,
   $\cot 46° \approx \cot 45° + (-\csc^2 45°)(\pi/180) = 1 - \pi/90.$

36. $A = \dfrac{1}{4}(4)^2 \sin 2\theta = 4\sin 2\theta$ thus $dA = 8\cos 2\theta d\theta$ so, with $\theta = 30° = \pi/6$ radians and

$d\theta = \pm15' = \pm1/4° = \pm\pi/720$ radians, $dA = 8\cos(\pi/3)(\pm\pi/720) = \pm\pi/180$ cm^2.

37. $h = 12\sin\theta$ thus $dh = 12\cos\theta d\theta$ so, with $\theta = 60° = \pi/3$ radians and $d\theta = -1° = -\pi/180$
radians, $dh = 12\cos(\pi/3)(-\pi/180) = -\pi/30$ ft.

38. $V = x^3$ and $S = 6x^2$ where x is the length of an edge thus $x = (S/6)^{1/2}$ so $V = (S/6)^{3/2}$ and
$dV/dS = (3/2)(S/6)^{1/2}(1/6) = \sqrt{S/6}/4.$

39. **(a)** $dW/dt|_{t=5} = 200(t - 15)|_{t=5} = -2000$ so water is running out at the rate of
   2000 gal/min.

(b) average rate of change of $W = (W|_{t=5} - W|_{t=0})/5 = (10,000 - 22,500)/5 = -2500$ so water flows out at an average rate of 2500 gal/min during the first 5 minutes.

40. $3(x+y)^2 \left(1 + \dfrac{dy}{dx}\right) + 3\left(x\dfrac{dy}{dx} + y\right) = 0$ so $\dfrac{dy}{dx} = -\dfrac{y + (x+y)^2}{x + (x+y)^2}$.

$\dfrac{dy}{dx}\bigg|_{(-2,1)} = 2$, the tangent line is $y - 1 = 2(x+2)$, $y = 2x + 5$.

41. $2xy\dfrac{dy}{dx} + y^2 = \cos(x+2y)\left(1 + 2\dfrac{dy}{dx}\right)$ so $\dfrac{dy}{dx} = \dfrac{\cos(x+2y) - y^2}{2xy - 2\cos(x+2y)}$.

$\dfrac{dy}{dx}\bigg|_{(0,0)} = -\dfrac{1}{2}$, the tangent line is $y = -x/2$.

42. $3(x+y)^2\left(1 + \dfrac{dy}{dx}\right) - 5 + \dfrac{dy}{dx} = 0$ so $\dfrac{dy}{dx} = \dfrac{5 - 3(x+y)^2}{1 + 3(x+y)^2}$. To find the points of intersection, replace $x + y$ by 1, and y by $1 - x$ in $(x+y)^3 - 5x + y = 1$ to get $1 - 5x + 1 - x = 1$, so $x = 1/6$ and $y = 1 - 1/6 = 5/6$. $\dfrac{dy}{dx}\bigg|_{(1/6,5/6)} = \dfrac{1}{2}$, the tangent line is $y - \dfrac{5}{6} = \dfrac{1}{2}\left(x - \dfrac{1}{6}\right)$.

43. $x = y = 1$ satisfies both equations so they intersect at the point $(1,1)$. For $2x^2 + 3y^2 = 5$, $\dfrac{dy}{dx} = -\dfrac{2x}{3y}$ so $\dfrac{dy}{dx}\bigg|_{(1,1)} = -\dfrac{2}{3}$. For $y^2 = x^3$, $\dfrac{dy}{dx} = \dfrac{3x^2}{2y}$ so $\dfrac{dy}{dx}\bigg|_{(1,1)} = \dfrac{3}{2}$. The tangent lines are perpendicular at $(1,1)$ because the slope of one curve is the negative reciprocal of the slope of the other curve.

44. If $x^2 + y^2 = r^2$, then $\dfrac{dy}{dx} = -\dfrac{x}{y}$ so $\dfrac{dy}{dx}\bigg|_{(x_0,y_0)} = -\dfrac{x_0}{y_0}$, $y_0 \neq 0$. The radius from the origin to P_0 has slope $\dfrac{y_0}{x_0}$, $x_0 \neq 0$. Thus, if $x_0 \neq 0$ and $y_0 \neq 0$, the slope of the tangent to the circle at P_0 is the negative reciprocal of the slope of the radius from the origin to P_0 so the tangent line is perpendicular to the radius at P_0. If $x_0 = 0$, then the tangent line is horizontal and the radius to P_0 is vertical. If $y_0 = 0$, then the circle has a vertical tangent at P_0 and the radius to P_0 is horizontal. Thus the tangent line at P_0 is perpendicular to the radius from the origin at P_0 for any point $P_0(x_0, y_0)$ on the circle.

45. $y = \cos x - 3\sin x$, $y' = -\sin x - 3\cos x$, $y'' = -\cos x + 3\sin x$, $y''' = \sin x + 3\cos x$ so $y''' + y'' + y' + y = (-3 - 1 + 3 + 1)\sin x + (1 - 3 - 1 + 3)\cos x = 0$.

46.   **(a)** $3y^2\dfrac{dy}{dx} + 6x = 4\dfrac{dy}{dx}, \ \dfrac{dy}{dx} = \dfrac{6x}{4 - 3y^2}$

$\dfrac{d^2y}{dx^2} = 6\dfrac{(4 - 3y^2)(1) - x(-6y\,dy/dx)}{(4 - 3y^2)^2} = 6\dfrac{4 - 3y^2 + 6xy[6x/(4 - 3y^2)]}{(4 - 3y^2)^2}$

$= 6\left[(4 - 3y^2)^2 + 36x^2y\right]/(4 - 3y^2)^3.$

(b) $\cos y\dfrac{dy}{dx} - \sin x = 0, \ \dfrac{dy}{dx} = \dfrac{\sin x}{\cos y}$

$\dfrac{d^2y}{dx^2} = \dfrac{\cos y\cos x - \sin x(-\sin y)dy/dx}{\cos^2 y} = (\cos^2 y\cos x + \sin^2 x\sin y)/\cos^3 y.$

CHAPTER 4
Applications of Differentiation

EXERCISE SET 4.1

1. **(a)** $A = x^2$, so $\dfrac{dA}{dt} = 2x\dfrac{dx}{dt}$

   (b) Find $\dfrac{dA}{dt}\Big|_{x=3}$ given that $\dfrac{dx}{dt}\Big|_{x=3} = 2$.

   From part (a), $\dfrac{dA}{dt}\Big|_{x=3} = 2(3)(2) = 12 \text{ ft}^2/\text{min}$.

2. **(a)** $A = \pi r^2$, so $\dfrac{dA}{dt} = 2\pi r\dfrac{dr}{dt}$.

   (b) Find $\dfrac{dA}{dt}\Big|_{r=5}$ given that $\dfrac{dr}{dt}\Big|_{r=5} = 2$.

   From part (a), $\dfrac{dA}{dt}\Big|_{r=5} = 2\pi(5)(2) = 20\pi \text{ in}^2/\text{sec}$.

3. **(a)** $V = \pi r^2 h$, so $\dfrac{dV}{dt} = \pi\left(r^2\dfrac{dh}{dt} + 2rh\dfrac{dr}{dt}\right)$.

   (b) Find $\dfrac{dV}{dt}\Big|_{\substack{h=6,\\r=10}}$ given that $\dfrac{dh}{dt}\Big|_{\substack{h=6,\\r=10}} = 1$ and $\dfrac{dr}{dt}\Big|_{\substack{h=6,\\r=10}} = -1$.

   From part (a), $\dfrac{dV}{dt}\Big|_{\substack{h=6,\\r=10}} = \pi[10^2(1) + 2(10)(6)(-1)] = -20\pi \text{ in}^3/\text{sec};$
   the volume is decreasing.

4. **(a)** $\ell^2 = x^2 + y^2$, so $\dfrac{d\ell}{dt} = \dfrac{1}{\ell}\left(x\dfrac{dx}{dt} + y\dfrac{dy}{dt}\right)$.

   (b) Find $\dfrac{d\ell}{dt}\Big|_{\substack{x=3,\\y=4}}$ given that $\dfrac{dx}{dt} = \dfrac{1}{2}$ and $\dfrac{dy}{dt} = -\dfrac{1}{4}$.

   From part (a) and the fact that $\ell = 5$, when $x = 3$ and $y = 4$,
   $\dfrac{d\ell}{dt}\Big|_{\substack{x=3,\\y=4}} = \dfrac{1}{5}\left[3\left(\dfrac{1}{2}\right) + 4\left(-\dfrac{1}{4}\right)\right] = \dfrac{1}{10}$ ft/sec; the diagonal is increasing.

5. **(a)** $\tan\theta = \dfrac{y}{x}$, so $\sec^2\theta\dfrac{d\theta}{dt} = \dfrac{x\dfrac{dy}{dt} - y\dfrac{dx}{dt}}{x^2}$, $\dfrac{d\theta}{dt} = \dfrac{\cos^2\theta}{x^2}\left(x\dfrac{dy}{dt} - y\dfrac{dx}{dt}\right)$.

(b) Find $\dfrac{d\theta}{dt}\Big|_{\substack{x=2,\\y=2}}$ given that $\dfrac{dx}{dt}\Big|_{\substack{x=2,\\y=2}} = 1$ and $\dfrac{dy}{dt}\Big|_{\substack{x=2,\\y=2}} = -\dfrac{1}{4}$.

When $x = 2$ and $y = 2$, $\tan\theta = 2/2 = 1$ so $\theta = \dfrac{\pi}{4}$ and $\cos\theta = \cos\dfrac{\pi}{4} - \dfrac{1}{\sqrt{2}}$. Thus

from part (a), $\dfrac{d\theta}{dt}\Big|_{\substack{x=2,\\y=2}} = \dfrac{(1/\sqrt{2})^2}{2^2}\left[2\left(-\dfrac{1}{4}\right) - 2(1)\right] = -\dfrac{5}{16}$ radians/sec; θ is decreasing.

6. Find $\dfrac{dz}{dt}\Big|_{\substack{x=1,\\y=2}}$ given that $\dfrac{dx}{dt}\Big|_{\substack{x=1,\\y=2}} = -2$ and $\dfrac{dy}{dt}\Big|_{\substack{x=1,\\y=2}} = 3$.

$\dfrac{dz}{dt} = 2x^3 y\dfrac{dy}{dt} + 3x^2 y^2\dfrac{dx}{dt}$, $\dfrac{dz}{dt}\Big|_{\substack{x=1,\\y=2}} = (4)(3) + (12)(-2) = -12$ units/sec; z is decreasing.

7. Let A be the area swept out, and θ the angle through which the minute hand has rotated. Find $\dfrac{dA}{dt}$ given that $\dfrac{d\theta}{dt} = \dfrac{\pi}{30}$ radians/min; $A = \dfrac{1}{2}r^2\theta = 80$, so $\dfrac{dA}{dt} = 8\dfrac{d\theta}{dt} = \dfrac{4\pi}{15}$ in^2/min.

8. Let r be the radius and A the area enclosed by the ripple. We want $\dfrac{dA}{dt}\Big|_{t=10}$ given that $\dfrac{dr}{dt} = 3$. We know that $A = \pi r^2$, so $\dfrac{dA}{dt} = 2\pi r\dfrac{dr}{dt}$. Because r is increasing at the constant rate of 3 ft/sec, it follows that $r = 30$ ft after 10 seconds so $\dfrac{dA}{dt}\Big|_{t=10} = 2\pi(30)(3) = 180\pi$ ft^2/sec.

9. Find $\dfrac{dr}{dt}\Big|_{A=9}$ given that $\dfrac{dA}{dt} = 6$. From $A = \pi r^2$ we get $\dfrac{dA}{dt} = 2\pi r\dfrac{dr}{dt}$ so $\dfrac{dr}{dt} = \dfrac{1}{2\pi r}\dfrac{dA}{dt}$. If $A = 9$ then $\pi r^2 = 9$, $r = 3/\sqrt{\pi}$ so $\dfrac{dr}{dt}\Big|_{A=9} = \dfrac{1}{2\pi(3/\sqrt{\pi})}(6) = 1/\sqrt{\pi}$ mph.

10. The volume V of a sphere of radius r is given by $V = \dfrac{4}{3}\pi r^3$ or, because $r = \dfrac{D}{2}$ where D is the diameter, $V = \dfrac{4}{3}\pi\left(\dfrac{D}{2}\right)^3 = \dfrac{1}{6}\pi D^3$. We want $\dfrac{dD}{dt}\Big|_{r=1}$ given that $\dfrac{dV}{dt} = 3$. From $V = \dfrac{1}{6}\pi D^3$ we get $\dfrac{dV}{dt} = \dfrac{1}{2}\pi D^2\dfrac{dD}{dt}$, $\dfrac{dD}{dt} = \dfrac{2}{\pi D^2}\dfrac{dV}{dt}$, so $\dfrac{dD}{dt}\Big|_{r=1} = \dfrac{2}{\pi(2)^2}(3) = \dfrac{3}{2\pi}$ ft/min.

11. Find $\dfrac{dV}{dt}\Big|_{r=9}$ given that $\dfrac{dr}{dt} = -15$. From $V = \dfrac{4}{3}\pi r^3$ we get $\dfrac{dV}{dt} = 4\pi r^2\dfrac{dr}{dt}$ so $\dfrac{dV}{dt}\Big|_{r=9} = 4\pi(9)^2(-15) = -4860\pi$. Air must be removed at the rate of 4860π cm^3/min.

12. Let x and y be the distances shown in the diagram.

We want to find $\dfrac{dy}{dt}\bigg|_{y=8}$ given that $\dfrac{dx}{dt}=5$. From

$x^2+y^2=17^2$ we get $2x\dfrac{dx}{dt}+2y\dfrac{dy}{dt}=0$, so

$\dfrac{dy}{dt}=-\dfrac{x}{y}\dfrac{dx}{dt}$. When $y=8$,

$x^2+8^2=17^2$, $x^2=289-64=225$, $x=15$

so $\dfrac{dy}{dt}\bigg|_{y=8}=-\dfrac{15}{8}(5)=-\dfrac{75}{8}$ ft/sec;

the top of the ladder is moving down the wall at a rate of 75/8 ft/sec.

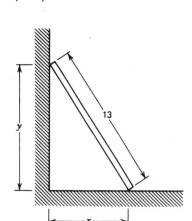

13. Find $\dfrac{dx}{dt}\bigg|_{y=5}$ given that $\dfrac{dy}{dt}=-2$. From

$x^2+y^2=13^2$ we get $2x\dfrac{dx}{dt}+2y\dfrac{dy}{dt}=0$ so

$\dfrac{dx}{dt}=-\dfrac{y}{x}\dfrac{dy}{dt}$. Use $x^2+y^2=169$ to find that

$x=12$ when $y=5$ so

$\dfrac{dx}{dt}\bigg|_{y=5}=-\dfrac{5}{12}(-2)=\dfrac{5}{6}$ ft/sec.

14. Let θ be the acute angle, and x the distance of the bottom of the plank from the wall. Find

$\dfrac{d\theta}{dt}\bigg|_{x=2}$ given that $\dfrac{dx}{dt}\bigg|_{x=2}=-\dfrac{1}{2}$ ft/sec. The variables θ and x are related by the equation

$\cos\theta=\dfrac{x}{10}$ so $-\sin\theta\dfrac{d\theta}{dt}=\dfrac{1}{10}\dfrac{dx}{dt}$, $\dfrac{d\theta}{dt}=-\dfrac{1}{10\sin\theta}\dfrac{dx}{dt}$. When $x=2$, the top of the plank is $\sqrt{10^2-2^2}=\sqrt{96}$ ft above the ground so $\sin\theta=\sqrt{96}/10$ and

$\dfrac{d\theta}{dt}\bigg|_{x=2}=-\dfrac{1}{\sqrt{96}}\left(-\dfrac{1}{2}\right)=\dfrac{1}{2\sqrt{96}}\approx 0.051$ radians/sec.

15. Let x be the length of each edge, S the surface area, and V the volume. Find $\dfrac{dS}{dt}\bigg|_{x=5}$ given

that $\dfrac{dV}{dt}\bigg|_{x=5}=2$. $S=6x^2$ and $V=x^3$, so $x=V^{1/3}$, $S=6V^{2/3}$,

$\dfrac{dS}{dt}=4V^{-1/3}\dfrac{dV}{dt}=\dfrac{4}{x}\dfrac{dV}{dt}=\dfrac{4}{5}(2)=8/5$ in^2/min.

16. Find $\left.\dfrac{dx}{dt}\right|_{x=4}$ given that $\left.\dfrac{dy}{dt}\right|_{x=4} = 2000.$

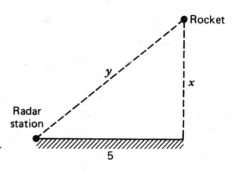

From $x^2 + 5^2 = y^2$ we get

$2x\dfrac{dx}{dt} = 2y\dfrac{dy}{dt}$ so $\dfrac{dx}{dt} = \dfrac{y}{x}\dfrac{dy}{dt}.$

Use $x^2 + 25 = y^2$ to find that $y = \sqrt{41}$

when $x = 4$ so $\left.\dfrac{dx}{dt}\right|_{x=4} = \dfrac{\sqrt{41}}{4}(2000) = 500\sqrt{41}$ mph.

17. With ϕ and x as shown in the figure,

find $\left.\dfrac{d\phi}{dt}\right|_{x=3000}$ given that

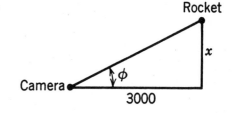

$\left.\dfrac{dx}{dt}\right|_{x=3000} = 500.$ But $\tan\phi = \dfrac{x}{3000}$

thus $\sec^2\phi\dfrac{d\phi}{dt} = \dfrac{1}{3000}\dfrac{dx}{dt}$

$\dfrac{d\phi}{dt} = \dfrac{\cos^2\phi}{3000}\dfrac{dx}{dt},$

$\phi = \pi/4$ when $x = 3000$ so $\cos\phi = 1/\sqrt{2}$ and $\left.\dfrac{d\phi}{dt}\right|_{x=3000} = \dfrac{1/2}{3000}(500) = 1/12$ radian/sec.

18. Find $\left.\dfrac{dx}{dt}\right|_{\phi=\pi/4}$ given that $\left.\dfrac{d\phi}{dt}\right|_{\phi=\pi/4} = 0.2$ (see figure accompanying Exercise 17).

But $x = 3000\tan\phi$ so $\dfrac{dx}{dt} = 3000(\sec^2\phi)\dfrac{d\phi}{dt}$, $\left.\dfrac{dx}{dt}\right|_{\phi=\pi/4} = 3000\left(\sec^2\dfrac{\pi}{4}\right)(0.2) = 1200$ ft/sec.

19. **(a)** $\theta = 0$ at perigee, so $r = 4995/1.12 \approx 4460$; the altitude is $4460 - 3960 = 500$ miles. $\theta = \pi$ at apogee, so $r = 4995/0.88 \approx 5676$; the altitude is $5676 - 3960 = 1716$ miles.

   (b) If $\theta = 120°$, then $r = 4995/0.94 \approx 5314$; the altitude is $5314 - 3960 = 1354$ miles. The rate of change of the altitude is given by

$$\dfrac{dr}{dt} = \dfrac{4995(0.12\sin\theta)}{(1 + 0.12\cos\theta)^2}\dfrac{d\theta}{dt}.$$

   Use $\theta = 120°$ and $d\theta/dt = 2.7°/\text{min} = (2.7)(\pi/180)$ rad/min to get $dr/dt \approx 27.7$ mi/min.

20. **(a)** Let x be the horizontal distance shown in the figure. Then $x = 4000\cot\theta$ and

$\dfrac{dx}{dt} = -4000\csc^2\theta\dfrac{d\theta}{dt}$, so $\dfrac{d\theta}{dt} = -\dfrac{\sin^2\theta}{4000}\dfrac{dx}{dt}$. Use $\theta = 30°$ and

$dx/dt = 300 \text{ mi/hr} = 300(5280/3600) \text{ ft/sec} = 440 \text{ ft/sec}$ to get
$d\theta/dt = -0.0275 \text{ rad/sec} \approx -1.6°/\text{sec}$; θ is decreasing at the rate of $1.6°/\text{sec}$.

(b) Let y be the distance between the observation point and the aircraft. Then $y = 4000 \csc \theta$
so $dy/dt = -4000(\csc \theta \cot \theta)(d\theta/dt)$. Use $\theta = 30°$ and $d\theta/dt = -0.0275 \text{ rad/sec}$ to get
$dy/dt \approx 381 \text{ ft/sec}$.

21. Find $\dfrac{dh}{dt}\bigg|_{h=16}$ given that $\dfrac{dV}{dt} = 20$. The volume

of water in the tank at a depth h is $V = \dfrac{1}{3}\pi r^2 h$.

Use similar triangles (see figure) to get $\dfrac{r}{h} = \dfrac{10}{24}$

so $r = \dfrac{5}{12}h$ thus $V = \dfrac{1}{3}\pi \left(\dfrac{5}{12}h\right)^2 h = \dfrac{25}{432}\pi h^3$,

$\dfrac{dV}{dt} = \dfrac{25}{144}\pi h^2 \dfrac{dh}{dt}; \dfrac{dh}{dt} = \dfrac{144}{25\pi h^2}\dfrac{dV}{dt}$,

$\dfrac{dh}{dt}\bigg|_{h=16} = \dfrac{144}{25\pi(16)^2}(20) = \dfrac{9}{20\pi} \text{ ft/min}.$

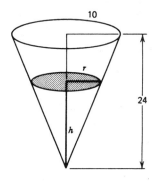

22. Find $\dfrac{dh}{dt}\bigg|_{h=6}$ given that $\dfrac{dV}{dt} = 8$. $V = \dfrac{1}{3}\pi r^2 h$, but

$r = \dfrac{1}{2}h$ so $V = \dfrac{1}{3}\pi \left(\dfrac{h}{2}\right)^2 h = \dfrac{1}{12}\pi h^3$,

$\dfrac{dV}{dt} = \dfrac{1}{4}\pi h^2 \dfrac{dh}{dt}, \dfrac{dh}{dt} = \dfrac{4}{\pi h^2}\dfrac{dV}{dt}$,

$\dfrac{dh}{dt}\bigg|_{h=6} = \dfrac{4}{\pi(6)^2}(8) = \dfrac{8}{9\pi} \text{ ft/min}.$

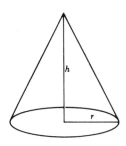

23. Find $\dfrac{dV}{dt}\bigg|_{h=10}$ given that $\dfrac{dh}{dt} = 5$. $V = \dfrac{1}{3}\pi r^2 h$,

but $r = \dfrac{1}{2}h$ so $V = \dfrac{1}{3}\pi \left(\dfrac{h}{2}\right)^2 h = \dfrac{1}{12}\pi h^3$,

$\dfrac{dV}{dt} = \dfrac{1}{4}\pi h^2 \dfrac{dh}{dt}, \dfrac{dV}{dt}\bigg|_{h=10}$

$= \dfrac{1}{4}\pi(10)^2(5) = 125\pi \text{ ft}^3/\text{min}.$

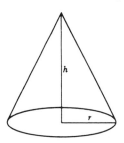

24.   Let r and h be as shown in the figure. If C is the circumference of the base, then we want to find $\dfrac{dC}{dt}\Big|_{h=8}$

given that $\dfrac{dV}{dt} = 10$. It is given that

$r = \dfrac{1}{2}h$, thus $C = 2\pi r = \pi h$

so $\dfrac{dC}{dt} = \pi\dfrac{dh}{dt}$ (1).

Use $V = \dfrac{1}{3}\pi r^2 h = \dfrac{1}{12}\pi h^3$ to get $\dfrac{dV}{dt} = \dfrac{1}{4}\pi h^2\dfrac{dh}{dt}$

$\dfrac{dh}{dt} = \dfrac{4}{\pi h^2}\dfrac{dV}{dt}$ (2).

Substitution of (2) into (1) gives $\dfrac{dC}{dt} = \dfrac{4}{h^2}\dfrac{dV}{dt}$ so $\dfrac{dC}{dt}\Big|_{h=8} = \dfrac{4}{64}(10) = \dfrac{5}{8}$ ft/min.

25.   With s and h as shown in the figure, we want to find $\dfrac{dh}{dt}$ given that

$\dfrac{ds}{dt} = 500$. From the figure, $h = s\sin 30° = \dfrac{1}{2}s$

so $\dfrac{dh}{dt} = \dfrac{1}{2}\dfrac{ds}{dt} = \dfrac{1}{2}(500) = 250$ mph.

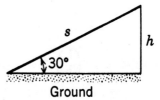

26.   Find $\dfrac{dx}{dt}\Big|_{y=125}$ given that $\dfrac{dy}{dt} = -20$.

From $x^2 + 10^2 = y^2$ we get

$2x\dfrac{dx}{dt} = 2y\dfrac{dy}{dt}$ so $\dfrac{dx}{dt} = \dfrac{y}{x}\dfrac{dy}{dt}$. Use

$x^2 + 100 = y^2$ to find that

$x = \sqrt{15,525} = 15\sqrt{69}$

when $y = 125$ so $\dfrac{dx}{dt}\Big|_{y=125} = \dfrac{125}{15\sqrt{69}}(-20) = -\dfrac{500}{3\sqrt{69}}$. The boat is approaching the dock at

the rate of $\dfrac{500}{3\sqrt{69}}$ ft/min.

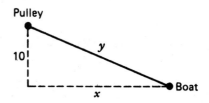

27. Find $\dfrac{dy}{dt}$ given that $\dfrac{dx}{dt}\Big|_{y=125} = -12.$

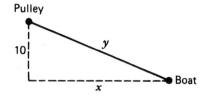

From $x^2 + 10^2 = y^2$ we get

$$2x\dfrac{dx}{dt} = 2y\dfrac{dy}{dt} \text{ so } \dfrac{dy}{dt} = \dfrac{x}{y}\dfrac{dx}{dt}.$$

Use $x^2 + 100 = y^2$ to find that

$x = \sqrt{15,525} = 15\sqrt{69}$ when $y = 125$ so $\dfrac{dy}{dt} = \dfrac{15\sqrt{69}}{125}(-12) = -\dfrac{36\sqrt{69}}{25}.$ The rope must be

pulled at the rate of $\dfrac{36\sqrt{69}}{25}$ ft/min.

28. (a) Let x and y be as shown in the figure. It is required to find $\dfrac{dx}{dt}$, given that $\dfrac{dy}{dt} = -3.$ By similar triangles, $\dfrac{x}{6} = \dfrac{x+y}{18},$

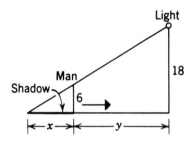

$18x = 6x + 6y,\ 12x = 6y,\ x = \dfrac{1}{2}y,$

so $\dfrac{dx}{dt} = \dfrac{1}{2}\dfrac{dy}{dt} = \dfrac{1}{2}(-3) = -\dfrac{3}{2}$ ft/sec.

   (b) The tip of the shadow is $z = x + y$ feet from the street light, thus the rate at which it is moving is given by $\dfrac{dz}{dt} = \dfrac{dx}{dt} + \dfrac{dy}{dt}.$ In part (a) we found that $\dfrac{dx}{dt} = -\dfrac{3}{2}$ when $\dfrac{dy}{dt} = -3$

so $\dfrac{dz}{dt} = (-3/2) + (-3) = -9/2$ ft/sec; the tip of the shadow is moving at the rate of 9/2 ft/sec toward the street light.

29. Find $\dfrac{dx}{dt}\Big|_{\theta=\pi/4}$ given that $\dfrac{d\theta}{dt} = \dfrac{2\pi}{10} = \dfrac{\pi}{5}$

radians/sec. $x = 4\tan\theta$ (see figure)

so $\dfrac{dx}{dt} = 4\sec^2\theta\dfrac{d\theta}{dt},$

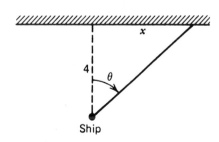

$\dfrac{dx}{dt}\Big|_{\theta=\pi/4} = 4\left(\sec^2\dfrac{\pi}{4}\right)\left(\dfrac{\pi}{5}\right) = 8\pi/5$ kilometers/sec.

30. If x, y, and z are as shown in the figure, then we want $\dfrac{dz}{dt}\Big|_{\substack{x=2,\\y=4}}$

given that $\dfrac{dx}{dt} = -600$ and $\dfrac{dy}{dt}\Big|_{\substack{x=2,\\y=4}} = -1200$.

But $z^2 = x^2 + y^2$ so $2z\dfrac{dz}{dt} = 2x\dfrac{dx}{dt} + 2y\dfrac{dy}{dt}$,

$\dfrac{dz}{dt} = \dfrac{1}{z}\left(x\dfrac{dx}{dt} + y\dfrac{dy}{dt}\right)$. When $x = 2$ and $y = 4$, $z^2 = 2^2 + 4^2 = 20$,

$z = \sqrt{20} = 2\sqrt{5}$ so $\dfrac{dz}{dt}\Big|_{\substack{x=2,\\y=4}} = \dfrac{1}{2\sqrt{5}}[2(-600) + 4(-1200)] = -\dfrac{3000}{\sqrt{5}} = -600\sqrt{5}$ mph; the

distance between missile and aircraft is decreasing at the rate of $600\sqrt{5}$ mph.

31. We wish to find $\dfrac{dz}{dt}\Big|_{\substack{x=2,\\y=4}}$ given that

$\dfrac{dx}{dt} = -600$ and $\dfrac{dy}{dt}\Big|_{\substack{x=2,\\y=4}} = -1200$

(see figure). From the law of cosines,

$z^2 = x^2 + y^2 - 2xy\cos 120°$
$\quad = x^2 + y^2 - 2xy(-1/2)$
$\quad = x^2 + y^2 + xy$,

so $2z\dfrac{dz}{dt} = 2x\dfrac{dx}{dt} + 2y\dfrac{dy}{dt} + x\dfrac{dy}{dt} + y\dfrac{dx}{dt}$,

$\dfrac{dz}{dt} = \dfrac{1}{2z}\left[(2x + y)\dfrac{dx}{dt} + (2y + x)\dfrac{dy}{dt}\right]$. When $x = 2$ and $y = 4$,

$z^2 = 2^2 + 4^2 + (2)(4) = 28$, so $z = \sqrt{28} = 2\sqrt{7}$, thus

$\dfrac{dz}{dt}\Big|_{\substack{x=2,\\y=4}} = \dfrac{1}{2(2\sqrt{7})}[(2(2) + 4)(-600) + (2(4) + 2)(-1200)] = -\dfrac{4200}{\sqrt{7}} = -600\sqrt{7}$ mph;

the distance between missile and aircraft is decreasing at the rate of $600\sqrt{7}$ mph.

32. (a) Let x, y, and z be the distances shown in the first figure.

Find $\dfrac{dz}{dt}\Big|_{\substack{x=2,\\y=0}}$ given that

$\dfrac{dx}{dt} = -75$ and $\dfrac{dy}{dt} = -100$.

In order to find an equation

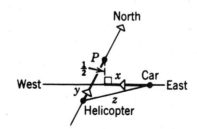

relating x, y, and z, first draw
the line segment that joins the
point P to the car, as shown in the
second figure. Because triangle
OPC is a right triangle, it
follows that PC has length
$\sqrt{x^2 + (1/2)^2}$; but triangle HPC is
also a right triangle so

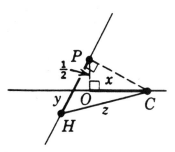

$$z^2 = \left(\sqrt{x^2 + (1/2)^2}\right)^2 + y^2 = x^2 + y^2 + 1/4$$

and $2z\dfrac{dz}{dt} = 2x\dfrac{dx}{dt} + 2y\dfrac{dy}{dt} + 0$, $\dfrac{dz}{dt} = \dfrac{1}{z}\left(x\dfrac{dx}{dt} + y\dfrac{dy}{dt}\right)$. Now, when

$x = 2$ and $y = 0$, $z^2 = (2)^2 + (0)^2 + 1/4 = 17/4$, $z = \sqrt{17}/2$

so $\dfrac{dz}{dt}\bigg|_{\substack{x=2, \\ y=0}} = \dfrac{1}{\sqrt{17}/2}[2(-75) + 0(-100)] = -300/\sqrt{17}$ mph

(b) decreasing, because $\dfrac{dz}{dt} < 0$.

33. **(a)** We want $\dfrac{dy}{dt}\bigg|_{\substack{x=1, \\ y=2}}$ given that $\dfrac{dx}{dt}\bigg|_{\substack{x=1, \\ y=2}} = 6$. For convenience, first rewrite the equation as

$xy^3 = \dfrac{8}{5} + \dfrac{8}{5}y^2$ then $3xy^2\dfrac{dy}{dt} + y^3\dfrac{dx}{dt} = \dfrac{16}{5}y\dfrac{dy}{dt}$, $\dfrac{dy}{dt} = \dfrac{y^3}{\frac{16}{5}y - 3xy^2}\dfrac{dx}{dt}$ so

$\dfrac{dy}{dt}\bigg|_{\substack{x=1, \\ y=2}} = \dfrac{2^3}{\frac{16}{5}(2) - 3(1)2^2}(6) = -60/7$ units/sec.

(b) falling, because $\dfrac{dy}{dt} < 0$.

34. Find $\dfrac{dx}{dt}\bigg|_{(2,5)}$ given that $\dfrac{dy}{dt}\bigg|_{(2,5)} = 2$. Square and rearrange to get $x^3 = y^2 - 17$

so $3x^2\dfrac{dx}{dt} = 2y\dfrac{dy}{dt}$, $\dfrac{dx}{dt} = \dfrac{2y}{3x^2}\dfrac{dy}{dt}$, $\dfrac{dx}{dt}\bigg|_{(2,5)} = \left(\dfrac{5}{6}\right)(2) = \dfrac{5}{3}$ units/sec.

35. The coordinates of P are $(x, 2x)$, so the distance between P and the point $(3,0)$ is

$$D = \sqrt{(x-3)^2 + (2x-0)^2} = \sqrt{5x^2 - 6x + 9}. \text{ Find } \dfrac{dD}{dt}\bigg|_{x=3} \text{ given that } \dfrac{dx}{dt}\bigg|_{x=3} = -2.$$

$\dfrac{dD}{dt} = \dfrac{5x-3}{\sqrt{5x^2 - 6x + 9}}\dfrac{dx}{dt}$, so $\dfrac{dD}{dt}\bigg|_{x=3} = \dfrac{12}{\sqrt{36}}(-2) = -4$ units/sec.

36.   **(a)**   Let D be the distance between P and $(2,0)$. Find $\left.\dfrac{dD}{dt}\right|_{x=3}$ given that $\left.\dfrac{dx}{dt}\right|_{x=3}=4$.

$$D=\sqrt{(x-2)^2+y^2}=\sqrt{(x-2)^2+x}=\sqrt{x^2-3x+4}\ \text{so}\ \frac{dD}{dt}=\frac{2x-3}{2\sqrt{x^2-3x+4}},$$

$$\left.\frac{dD}{dt}\right|_{x=3}=\frac{3}{2\sqrt{4}}=\frac{3}{4}\ \text{units/sec}.$$

  (b)   Let θ be the angle of inclination. Find $\left.\dfrac{d\theta}{dt}\right|_{x=3}$ given that $\left.\dfrac{dx}{dt}\right|_{x=3}=4$.

$$\tan\theta=\frac{y}{x-2}=\frac{\sqrt{x}}{x-2}\ \text{so}\ \sec^2\theta\,\frac{d\theta}{dt}=-\frac{x+2}{2\sqrt{x}(x-2)^2}\frac{dx}{dt},\ \frac{d\theta}{dt}=-\cos^2\theta\,\frac{x+2}{2\sqrt{x}(x-2)^2}\frac{dx}{dt}.$$

When $x=3$, $D=2$ so $\cos\theta=\dfrac{1}{2}$ and $\left.\dfrac{d\theta}{dt}\right|_{x=3}=-\dfrac{1}{4}\dfrac{5}{2\sqrt{3}}(4)=-\dfrac{5}{2\sqrt{3}}$ radians/sec.

37. $dy/dt=2x\,dx/dt$, but $dy/dt=3\,dx/dt$ so $3\,dx/dt=2x\,dx/dt$, $(3-2x)dx/dt=0$, $3-2x=0$, $x=3/2$.

38. $32x\,dx/dt+18y\,dy/dt=0$; if $dy/dt=dx/dt\neq0$, then $(32x+18y)dx/dt=0$, $32x+18y=0$, $y=-(16/9)x$ so $16x^2+9(256/81)x^2=144$, $(400/9)x^2=144$, $x^2=81/25$, $x=\pm9/5$. If $x=9/5$, then $y=-(16/9)(9/5)=-16/5$. Similarly, if $x=-9/5$, then $y=16/5$. The points are $(9/5,-16/5)$ and $(-9/5,16/5)$.

39.   Find $\left.\dfrac{dS}{dt}\right|_{s=10}$ given that $\left.\dfrac{ds}{dt}\right|_{s=10}=-2$. From $\dfrac{1}{s}+\dfrac{1}{S}=\dfrac{1}{6}$ we get $-\dfrac{1}{s^2}\dfrac{ds}{dt}-\dfrac{1}{S^2}\dfrac{dS}{dt}=0$, so $\dfrac{dS}{dt}=-\dfrac{S^2}{s^2}\dfrac{ds}{dt}$. If $s=10$, then $\dfrac{1}{10}+\dfrac{1}{S}=\dfrac{1}{6}$ which gives $S=15$. $\left.\dfrac{dS}{dt}\right|_{s=10}=-\dfrac{225}{100}(-2)=4.5$ cm/sec. The image is moving away from the lens.

40.   Suppose that the reservoir has height H and that the radius at the top is R. At any instant of time let h and r be the corresponding dimensions of the cone of water (see figure). We want to show that $\dfrac{dh}{dt}$ is constant and

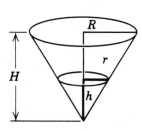

independent of H and R, given that $\dfrac{dV}{dt}=-kA$ where V is the volume of water, A is the area of a circle of radius r, and k is a positive constant. The volume of a cone of radius r and height h is $V=\dfrac{1}{3}\pi r^2h$. By similar triangles $\dfrac{r}{h}=\dfrac{R}{H}$, $r=\dfrac{R}{H}h$ thus

$$V=\frac{1}{3}\pi\left(\frac{R}{H}\right)^2h^3\ \text{so}\ \frac{dV}{dt}=\pi\left(\frac{R}{H}\right)^2h^2\frac{dh}{dt}\qquad(1)$$

But it is given that $\dfrac{dV}{dt} = -kA$ or, because $A = \pi r^2 = \pi \left(\dfrac{R}{H}\right)^2 h^2$, $\dfrac{dV}{dt} = -k\pi \left(\dfrac{R}{H}\right)^2 h^2$,

which when substituted into equation (1) gives $-k\pi \left(\dfrac{R}{H}\right)^2 h^2 = \pi \left(\dfrac{R}{H}\right)^2 h^2 \dfrac{dh}{dt}, \ \dfrac{dh}{dt} = -k.$

41. Let r be the radius, V the volume, and A the surface area of a sphere. Show that $\dfrac{dr}{dt}$ is a constant given that $\dfrac{dV}{dt} = -kA$, where k is a positive constant. Because $V = \dfrac{4}{3}\pi r^3$,

$$\frac{dV}{dt} = 4\pi r^2 \frac{dr}{dt} \qquad\qquad (1)$$

But it is given that $\dfrac{dV}{dt} = -kA$ or, because $A = 4\pi r^2$, $\dfrac{dV}{dt} = -4r^2 k$ which when substituted into equation (1) gives $-4\pi r^2 k = 4\pi r^2 \dfrac{dr}{dt}, \ \dfrac{dr}{dt} = -k.$

42. Let x be the distance between the tips of the minute and hour hands, and α and β the angles shown in the figure. Because the minute hand makes one revolution in 60 minutes,

$$\frac{d\alpha}{dt} = \frac{2\pi}{60} = \pi/30 \text{ radians/min}$$

the hour hand makes one revolution
in 12 hours (720 minutes), thus

$$\frac{d\beta}{dt} = \frac{2\pi}{720} = \pi/360 \text{ radians/min.}$$

We want to find $\dfrac{dx}{dt}\bigg|_{\substack{\alpha=2\pi, \\ \beta=3\pi/2}}$ given that

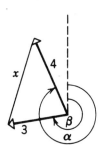

$\dfrac{d\alpha}{dt} = \pi/30$ and $\dfrac{d\beta}{dt} = \pi/360$. Using the
law of cosines on the triangle shown in the figure,

$x^2 = 3^2 + 4^2 - 2(3)(4)\cos(\alpha - \beta) = 25 - 24\cos(\alpha - \beta)$ so

$2x\dfrac{dx}{dt} = 0 + 24\sin(\alpha - \beta)\left(\dfrac{d\alpha}{dt} - \dfrac{d\beta}{dt}\right), \ \dfrac{dx}{dt} = \dfrac{12}{x}\left(\dfrac{d\alpha}{dt} - \dfrac{d\beta}{dt}\right)\sin(\alpha - \beta).$ When $\alpha = 2\pi$ and
$\beta = 3\pi/2$, $x^2 = 25 - 24\cos(2\pi - 3\pi/2) = 25$, $x = 5$ so

$$\frac{dx}{dt}\bigg|_{\substack{\alpha=2\pi, \\ \beta=3\pi/2}} = \frac{12}{5}(\pi/30 - \pi/360)\sin(2\pi - 3\pi/2) = 11\pi/150 \text{ in/min.}$$

43. Extend sides of cup to complete the cone and let V_0 be the volume of the portion added, then (see figure)

$V = \dfrac{1}{3}\pi r^2 h - V_0$ where

$\dfrac{r}{h} = \dfrac{4}{12} = \dfrac{1}{3}$ so $r = \dfrac{1}{3}h$ and

$V = \dfrac{1}{3}\pi \left(\dfrac{h}{3}\right)^2 h - V_0 = \dfrac{1}{27}\pi h^3 - V_0,$

$\dfrac{dV}{dt} = \dfrac{1}{9}\pi h^2 \dfrac{dh}{dt}, \quad \dfrac{dh}{dt} = \dfrac{9}{\pi h^2}\dfrac{dV}{dt},$

$\left.\dfrac{dh}{dt}\right|_{h=9} = \dfrac{9}{\pi(9)^2}(2) = \dfrac{2}{9\pi}$ cm/sec.

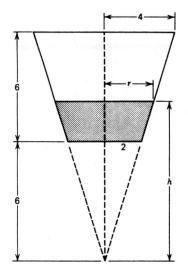

EXERCISE SET 4.2

1.   **(a)** (d, f) **(b)** $(a, d), (f, g)$ **(c)** $(a, b), (c, e)$ **(d)** $(b, c), (e, g)$

2. b, c, e

3.   A: $dy/dx < 0,\ d^2y/dx^2 > 0$
       B: $dy/dx > 0,\ d^2y/dx^2 < 0$
       C: $dy/dx < 0,\ d^2y/dx^2 < 0$

4.   **(a)** $<$ **(b)** $>$ **(c)** $>$ **(d)** $=$ **(e)** $<$ **(f)** $=$

5. $f'(x) = 2x - 5$
       $f''(x) = 2$

       (a) $[5/2, +\infty)$
       (b) $(-\infty, 5/2]$
       (c) $(-\infty, +\infty)$
       (d) none
       (e) none

6. $f'(x) = -2(x + 3/2)$
       $f''(x) = -2$

       (a) $(-\infty, -3/2]$
       (b) $[-3/2, +\infty)$
       (c) none
       (d) $(-\infty, +\infty)$
       (e) none

7. $f'(x) = 3(x + 2)^2$
    $f''(x) = 6(x + 2)$

    (a) $(-\infty, +\infty)$
    (b) none
    (c) $(-2, +\infty)$
    (d) $(-\infty, -2)$
    (e) -2

8. $f'(x) = 3(4 - x^2)$
    $f''(x) = -6x$

    (a) $[-2, 2]$
    (b) $(-\infty, -2], [2, +\infty)$
    (c) $(-\infty, 0)$
    (d) $(0, +\infty)$
    (e) 0

9. $f'(x) = 9(x^2 - 4/9)$
    $f''(x) = 18x$

    (a) $(-\infty, -2/3], [2/3, +\infty)$
    (b) $[-2/3, 2/3]$
    (c) $(0, +\infty)$
    (d) $(-\infty, 0)$
    (e) 0

10. $f'(x) = 4x(x^2 - 4)$
    $f''(x) = 12(x^2 - 4/3)$

    (a) $[-2, 0], [2, +\infty)$
    (b) $(-\infty, -2], [0, 2]$
    (c) $(-\infty, -2/\sqrt{3}), (2/\sqrt{3}, +\infty)$
    (d) $(-2/\sqrt{3}, 2/\sqrt{3})$
    (e) $-2/\sqrt{3}, 2/\sqrt{3}$

11. $f'(x) = 12x^2(x - 1)$

    $f''(x) = 36x(x - 2/3)$

    (a) $[1, +\infty)$
    (b) $(-\infty, 1]$
    (c) $(-\infty, 0), (2/3, +\infty)$
    (d) $(0, 2/3)$
    (e) $0, 2/3$

12. $f'(x) = \dfrac{2 - x^2}{(x^2 + 2)^2}$

    $f''(x) = \dfrac{2x(x^2 - 6)}{(x^2 + 2)^3}$

    (a) $[-\sqrt{2}, \sqrt{2}]$
    (b) $(-\infty, -\sqrt{2}], [\sqrt{2}, +\infty)$
    (c) $(-\sqrt{6}, 0), (\sqrt{6}, +\infty)$
    (d) $(-\infty, -\sqrt{6}), (0, \sqrt{6})$
    (e) $-\sqrt{6}, 0, \sqrt{6}$

13. $f'(x) = -\sin x$
    $f''(x) = -\cos x$

    (a) $[\pi, 2\pi)$
    (b) $(0, \pi]$
    (c) $(\pi/2, 3\pi/2)$
    (d) $(0, \pi/2), (3\pi/2, 2\pi)$
    (e) $\pi/2, 3\pi/2$

14. $f'(x) = 2\sin 4x$
    $f''(x) = 8\cos 4x$

    (a) $(0, \pi/4], [\pi/2, 3\pi/4]$
    (b) $[\pi/4, \pi/2], [3\pi/4, \pi)$
    (c) $(0, \pi/8), (3\pi/8, 5\pi/8), (7\pi/8, \pi)$
    (d) $(\pi/8, 3\pi/8), (5\pi/8, 7\pi/8)$
    (e) $\pi/8, 3\pi/8, 5\pi/8, 7\pi/8$

15. $f'(x) = \sec^2 x$

$f''(x) = 2\sec^2 x \tan x$

(a) $(-\pi/2, \pi/2)$
(b) none
(c) $(0, \pi/2)$
(d) $(-\pi/2, 0)$
(e) 0

16. $f'(x) = \frac{2}{3}x^{-1/3}$

$f''(x) = -\frac{2}{9}x^{-4/3}$

(a) $[0, +\infty)$
(b) $(-\infty, 0]$
(c) none
(d) $(-\infty, 0), (0, +\infty)$
(e) none

17. $f'(x) = \frac{1}{3}(x+2)^{-2/3}$

$f''(x) = -\frac{2}{9}(x+2)^{-5/3}$

(a) $(-\infty, +\infty)$
(b) none
(c) $(-\infty, -2)$
(d) $(-2, +\infty)$
(e) -2

18. $f'(x) = \frac{4(x - 1/4)}{3x^{2/3}}$

$f''(x) = \frac{4(x + 1/2)}{9x^{5/3}}$

(a) $[1/4, +\infty)$
(b) $(-\infty, 1/4]$
(c) $(-\infty, -1/2), (0, +\infty)$
(d) $(-1/2, 0)$
(e) $-1/2, 0$

19. $f'(x) = \frac{4(x+1)}{3x^{2/3}}$

$f''(x) = \frac{4(x - 2)}{9x^{5/3}}$

(a) $[-1, +\infty)$
(b) $(-\infty, -1]$
(c) $(-\infty, 0), (2, +\infty)$
(d) $(0, 2)$
(e) $0, 2$

20. $f'(x) = \begin{cases} x, & x \le 0 \\ -2x, & x > 0 \end{cases}$

$f''(x) = \begin{cases} 1, & x < 0 \\ -2, & x > 0 \end{cases}$

(a) none
(b) $(-\infty, +\infty)$
(c) $(-\infty, 0)$
(d) $(0, +\infty)$
(e) 0

21. $f'(x) = 1 + \cos x \ge 0$; $f'(x) = 0$ when $\cos x = -1$, $x = \pm\pi, \pm 3\pi, \pm 5\pi, \cdots$ so f is increasing on the intervals $\cdots [-3\pi, -\pi], [-\pi, \pi], [\pi, 3\pi], \cdots$ and putting all of these intervals together gives $(-\infty, +\infty)$.

22. Let $f(x) = x/(x^2+9)$, $f'(x) = (9-x^2)/(x^2+9)^2$ so f is decreasing on $[3, +\infty)$ thus $f(a) > f(b)$ if $3 \le a < b$.

23. $f'(x) = 1 - 1/x^2$ so f is increasing on $[1, +\infty)$ thus if $x > 1$, then $f(x) > f(1) = 2$, $x + 1/x > 2$.

24. $f'(x) = \sec^2 x - 1$ so f is increasing on $[0, \pi/2)$ thus if $0 < x < \pi/2$, then $f(x) > f(0) = 0$, $\tan x - x > 0$, $x < \tan x$.

25. $f'(x) = 1/3 - 1/[3(1+x)^{2/3}]$ so f is increasing on $[0, +\infty)$ thus if $x > 0$, then $f(x) > f(0) = 0$,
$1 + x/3 - \sqrt[3]{1+x} > 0$, $\sqrt[3]{1+x} < 1 + x/3$.

26. (a)
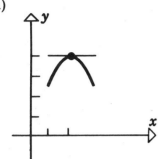

(b)
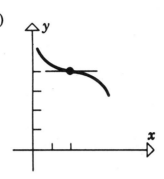

(c)
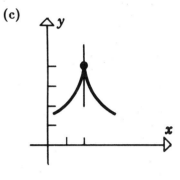

27. (a)
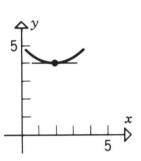

(b)
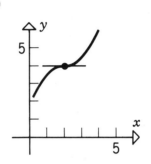

(c)
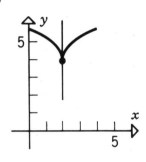

28. (a)
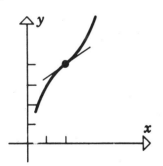

(b)
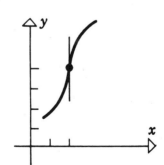

(c)
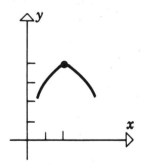

29. (a)

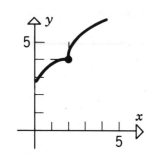

(b)

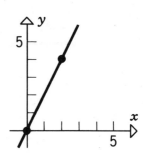

30. $f'(x) = 3(x-a)^2$, $f''(x) = 6(x-a)$; inflection point is $(a,0)$.

31. $f'(x) = 4(x-a)^3$, $f''(x) = 12(x-a)^2$; no inflection points.

32. $f'(x) = 2ax + b$, $f''(x) = 2a$; no inflection points.

33. $f(x_1) - f(x_2) = x_1^2 - x_2^2 = (x_1 + x_2)(x_1 - x_2) < 0$ if $x_1 < x_2$ for x_1, x_2 in $[0, +\infty)$, so $f(x_1) < f(x_2)$ and thus increasing.

34. $f(x_1) - f(x_2) = (x_1^2 - x_2^2) - 2(x_1 - x_2) = (x_1 - x_2)(x_1 + x_2 - 2) > 0$ if $x_1 < x_2$ for x_1, x_2 in $(-\infty, 1]$, so $f(x_1) > f(x_2)$ and thus decreasing.

35. $f(x_1) - f(x_2) = \sqrt{x_1} - \sqrt{x_2} = \dfrac{x_1 - x_2}{\sqrt{x_1} + \sqrt{x_2}} < 0$ if $x_1 < x_2$ for x_1, x_2 in $[0, +\infty)$, so

$f(x_1) < f(x_2)$ and thus increasing.

36. $f(x_1) - f(x_2) = \dfrac{1}{x_1} - \dfrac{1}{x_2} = \dfrac{x_2 - x_1}{x_1 x_2} > 0$ if $x_1 < x_2$ for x_1, x_2 in $(0, +\infty)$, so $f(x_1) > f(x_2)$
and thus decreasing.

37. If $x_1 < x_2$ where x_1 and x_2 are in I, then $f(x_1) < f(x_2)$ and $g(x_1) < g(x_2)$, so
$f(x_1) + g(x_1) < f(x_2) + g(x_2)$, $(f+g)(x_1) < (f+g)(x_2)$. Thus $f+g$ is increasing on I.

38. If $x_1 < x_2$ where x_1 and x_2 are in I, then $0 < f(x_1) < f(x_2)$ and $0 < g(x_1) < g(x_2)$, so
$f(x_1)g(x_1) < f(x_2)g(x_2)$, $(f \cdot g)(x_1) < (f \cdot g)(x_2)$. Thus $f \cdot g$ is increasing on I.

39. For example, $f(x) = x$ and $g(x) = 2x$ on $(-\infty, +\infty)$.

40. $f'(x) = 3ax^2 + 2bx + c$; $f'(x) > 0$ or $f'(x) < 0$ on $(-\infty, +\infty)$ if $f'(x) = 0$ has no real solutions
so from the quadratic formula $(2b)^2 - 4(3a)c < 0$, $4b^2 - 12ac < 0$, $b^2 - 3ac < 0$. If $b^2 - 3ac = 0$,
then $f'(x) = 0$ has only one real solution at, say, $x = c$ so f is always increasing or always
decreasing on both $(-\infty, c]$ and $[c, +\infty)$, and hence on $(-\infty, +\infty)$ because f is continuous
everywhere. Thus f is always increasing or decreasing if $b^2 - 3ac \le 0$.

41. $f''(x) = 6ax + 2b = 6a(x + \frac{b}{3a})$, $f''(x) = 0$ when $x = -\frac{b}{3a}$. f changes its direction of concavity at $x = -\frac{b}{3a}$ so $-\frac{b}{3a}$ is an inflection point.

42. $f''(x)$ is a polynomial of degree at most $n - 2$ so there are at most $n - 2$ real values of x for which it is 0.

43. **(a)** Let x_1 and x_2 be any points in (a, b) where $x_1 < x_2$. If x_1 and x_2 are both in $(a, c]$ or both in $[c, b)$, then $f(x_1) < f(x_2)$ because f is increasing on these intervals. If x_1 is in $(a, c]$ and x_2 is in (c, b), then $f(x_1) \leq f(c) < f(x_2)$ so $f(x_1) < f(x_2)$. Thus in all cases, $f(x_1) < f(x_2)$.

   (b) Similar to the proof in part (a).

EXERCISE SET 4.3

1. $f'(x) = 2x - 5$, $f'(x) = 0$ when $x = 5/2$ (stationary point).

2. $f'(x) = 8x + 2$, $f'(x) = 0$ when $x = -1/4$ (stationary point).

3. $f'(x) = 3x^2 + 6x - 9 = 3(x + 3)(x - 1)$, $f'(x) = 0$ when $x = -3, 1$ (stationary points).

4. $f'(x) = 6(x^2 - 1)$, $f'(x) = 0$ when $x = \pm 1$ (stationary points).

5. $f'(x) = 4x(x^2 - 3)$, $f'(x) = 0$ when $x = 0, \pm\sqrt{3}$ (stationary points).

6. $f'(x) = 12x^3 - 12x^2 = 12x^2(x - 1)$, $f'(x) = 0$ when $x = 0, 1$ (stationary points).

7. $f'(x) = (2 - x^2)/(x^2 + 2)^2$, $f'(x) = 0$ when $x = \pm\sqrt{2}$ (stationary points).

8. $f'(x) = 8x/(x^2 + 1)^2$, $f'(x) = 0$ when $x = 0$ (stationary point).

9. $f'(x) = \frac{2}{3}x^{-1/3} = 2/(3x^{1/3})$, $f'(x)$ does not exist when $x = 0$.

10. $f'(x) = \frac{1}{3}(x + 2)^{-2/3}$, $f'(x)$ does not exist when $x = -2$.

11. $f'(x) = -3\sin 3x$, $f'(x) = 0$ when $\sin 3x = 0$, $3x = n\pi$, $n = 0, \pm 1, \pm 2, \cdots$
    $x = n\pi/3$, $n = 0, \pm 1, \pm 2, \cdots$ (stationary points).

12. $f'(x) = x\sec^2 x + \tan x$, by inspection $f'(x) = 0$ when $x = 0$. If $-\pi/2 < x < 0$ then $f'(x) < 0$, and if $0 < x < \pi/2$ then $f'(x) > 0$ so $x = 0$ is the only stationary point.

13. $f'(x) = 4 \sin 2x \cos 2x = 2 \sin 4x$,

   $f'(x) = 0$ when $4x = n\pi$, $x = n\pi/4$, $n = 1, 2, 3, \cdots, 7$ (stationary points)

14. $f(x) = |\sin x| = \begin{cases} \sin x, & \sin x \geq 0 \\ -\sin x, & \sin x < 0 \end{cases}$ so $f'(x) = \begin{cases} \cos x, & \sin x > 0 \\ -\cos x, & \sin x < 0 \end{cases}$ and $f'(x)$ does

   not exist when $x = n\pi$, $n = 0, \pm1, \pm2, \cdots$ ($\sin x = 0$) because $\lim\limits_{x \to n\pi^-} f'(x) \neq \lim\limits_{x \to n\pi^+} f'(x)$

   (see Theorem preceding Exercise 71, Section 3.3). Now $f'(x) = 0$ when $\pm \cos x = 0$ provided

   $\sin x \neq 0$ so $x = \pi/2 + n\pi$, $n = 0, \pm1, \pm2, \cdots$ are stationary points.

15. $f'(x) = \dfrac{4(x+1)}{3x^{2/3}}$, $f'(x) = 0$ when $x = -1$ (stationary point), $f'(x)$ does not exist when $x = 0$.

16. $f'(x) = \dfrac{4(x - 3/2)}{3x^{2/3}}$, $f'(x) = 0$ when $x = 3/2$ (stationary point), $f'(x)$ does not exist when

   $x = 0$.

17.   (a) $x = 2$ because $f'(x)$ changes sign from $-$ to $+$ there.

   (b) $x = 0$ because $f'(x)$ changes sign from $+$ to $-$ there.

   (c) $x = 1, 3$ because $f''(x)$ (the slope of the graph of $f'(x)$) changes sign at these points.

18.   (a) $x = 1$ (b) $x = 5$ (c) $x = -1, 0, 3$

19.   critical points $x = 0, \pm\sqrt{5}$; $f'(x)$:

$$\begin{array}{ccccccc} - & 0 & + & 0 & - & 0 & + \\ \hline & -\sqrt{5} & & 0 & & \sqrt{5} & \end{array}$$

   $x = 0$: relative maximum; $x = \pm\sqrt{5}$: relative minimum.

20.   critical points $x = 0, -1/2, 1$; $f'(x)$:

$$\begin{array}{ccccccc} + & 0 & - & 0 & - & 0 & + \\ \hline & -1/2 & & 0 & & 1 & \end{array}$$

   $x = 0$: neither; $x = -1/2$: relative maximum; $x = 1$: relative minimum.

21.   critical points: $\pm 3/2, -1$; $f'(x)$:

$$\begin{array}{ccccccc} + & 0 & - & ? & + & 0 & - \\ \hline & -3/2 & & -1 & & 3/2 & \end{array}$$

   $x = \pm 3/2$: relative maximum; $x = -1$: relative minimum.

22. $f'(x) = \sin^2 x(2\sin x - 1)$, critical points $x = \pi, \pi/6, 5\pi/6$

$f'(x):$
$$\begin{array}{ccccc} - & 0 & + & 0 & - & 0 & - \\ & \text{\textbar} & & \text{\textbar} & & \text{\textbar} & \\ & \pi/6 & & 5\pi/6 & & \pi & \end{array}$$

$x = \pi$: neither; $x = \pi/6$: relative minimum; $x = 5\pi/6$: relative maximum.

23. $f'(x) = -2(x+2)$; critical point $x = -2$

(a) $f'(x):$
$$\begin{array}{ccc} +++ & 0 & --- \\ & \text{\textbar} & \\ & -2 & \end{array}$$

(b) $f''(x) = -2$; $f''(-2) < 0$, $f(-2) = 5$; relative max of 5 at $x = -2$

24. $f'(x) = 6(x-2)(x-1)$; critical points $x = 1, 2$

(a) $f'(x):$
$$\begin{array}{ccccc} +++0 & --- & 0+++ \\ & \text{\textbar} & & \text{\textbar} & \\ & 1 & & 2 & \end{array}$$

(b) $f''(x) = 12x - 18$; $f''(1) < 0$, $f''(2) > 0$, $f(1) = 5$, $f(2) = 4$; relative min of 4 at $x = 2$, relative max of 5 at $x = 1$

25. $f'(x) = 2\sin x \cos x = \sin 2x$; critical points $x = \pi/2, \pi, 3\pi/2$

(a) $f'(x):$
$$\begin{array}{ccccccc} +++ & 0 & --- & 0+++ & 0 & --- \\ & \text{\textbar} & & \text{\textbar} & & \text{\textbar} & \\ & \pi/2 & & \pi & & 3\pi/2 & \end{array}$$

(b) $f''(x) = 2\cos 2x$; $f''(\pi/2) < 0$, $f''(\pi) > 0$, $f''(3\pi/2) < 0$, $f(\pi/2) = f(3\pi/2) = 1$, $f(\pi) = 0$; relative min of 0 at $x = \pi$, relative max of 1 at $x = \pi/2, 3\pi/2$

26. $f'(x) = 1/2 - \cos x$; critical points $x = \pi/3, 5\pi/3$

(a) $f'(x):$
$$\begin{array}{ccccc} --- & 0 & +++ & 0 & --- \\ & \text{\textbar} & & \text{\textbar} & \\ & \pi/3 & & 5\pi/3 & \end{array}$$

(b) $f''(x) = -\sin x$; $f''(\pi/3) < 0$, $f''(5\pi/3) > 0$
$f(\pi/3) = \pi/6 - \sqrt{3}/2$, $f(5\pi/3) = 5\pi/6 + \sqrt{3}/2$;
relative min of $\pi/6 - \sqrt{3}/2$ at $x = \pi/3$, relative max of $5\pi/6 + \sqrt{3}/2$ at $x = 5\pi/3$

27. $f'(x) = 3x^2 + 5$; no relative extrema because there are no critical points.

28. $f'(x) = 4x(x^2 - 1)$; critical points $x = 0, 1, -1$
     $f''(x) = 12x^2 - 4$; $f''(0) < 0$, $f''(1) > 0$, $f''(-1) > 0$
     relative min of 6 at $x = 1, -1$, relative max of 7 at $x = 0$

29. $f'(x) = (x - 1)(3x - 1)$; critical points $x = 1, 1/3$
     $f''(x) = 6x - 4$; $f''(1) > 0$, $f''(1/3) < 0$
     relative min of 0 at $x = 1$, relative max of 4/27 at $x = 1/3$

30. $f'(x) = 2x^2(2x + 3)$; critical points $x = 0, -3/2$
     relative min of $-27/16$ at $x = -3/2$ (first derivative test)

31. $f'(x) = 4x(1 - x^2)$; critical points $x = 0, 1, -1$
     $f''(x) = 4 - 12x^2$; $f''(0) > 0$, $f''(1) < 0$, $f''(-1) < 0$
     relative min of 0 at $x = 0$, relative max of 1 at $x = 1, -1$

32. $f'(x) = 10(2x - 1)^4$; critical point $x = 1/2$; no relative extrema (first derivative test)

33. $f'(x) = \frac{4}{5}x^{-1/5}$; critical point $x = 0$; relative min of 0 at $x = 0$ (first derivative test)

34. $f'(x) = 2 + \frac{2}{3}x^{-1/3}$; critical points $x = 0, -1/27$
     relative min of 0 at $x = 0$, relative max of 1/27 at $x = -1/27$

35. $f'(x) = 2x/(x^2 + 1)^2$; critical point $x = 0$; relative min of 0 at $x = 0$

36. $f'(x) = 2/(x + 2)^2$; no critical points ($x = -2$ is not in the domain of f) no relative extrema

37. $f'(x) = 2x$ if $|x| > 2$, $f'(x) = -2x$ if $|x| < 2$,
     $f'(x)$ does not exist when $x = \pm 2$; critical points $x = 0, 2, -2$
     relative min of 0 at $x = 2, -2$, relative max of 4 at $x = 0$

38. $f'(x) = -1$ if $x < 3$, $f'(x) = 2x$ if $x > 3$, $f'(3)$ does not exist;
     critical point $x = 3$, relative min of 6 at $x = 3$

39. $f'(x) = -\sin 2x$; critical points $x = 0, \pm\pi/2, \pm\pi, \pm 3\pi/2, \cdots$
     relative min of 0 at $x = \pm\pi/2, \pm 3\pi/2, \cdots$; relative max of 1 at $x = 0, \pm\pi, \pm 2\pi, \cdots$

40. $f'(x) = \sqrt{3} + 2\cos x$; critical points $x = 5\pi/6, 7\pi/6$
     relative min of $7\sqrt{3}\pi/6 - 1$ at $x = 7\pi/6$; relative max of $5\sqrt{3}\pi/6 + 1$ at $x = 5\pi/6$

41. $f'(x) = 2x \sec^2(x^2 + 1)$; critical point $x = 0$; relative min of $\tan 1$ at $x = 0$

42. $f'(x) = (2 \cos x + 1)/(2 + \cos x)^2$; critical points $x = 2\pi/3, 4\pi/3$
relative min of $-\sqrt{3}/3$ at $x = 4\pi/3$, relative max of $\sqrt{3}/3$ at $x = 2\pi/3$

43. $f'(x) = 2 \cos 2x$ if $\sin 2x > 0$, $f'(x) = -2 \cos 2x$ if $\sin 2x < 0$,
$f'(x)$ does not exist when $x = \pi/2, \pi, 3\pi/2$;
critical points $x = \pi/4, 3\pi/4, 5\pi/4, 7\pi/4, \pi/2, \pi, 3\pi/2$
relative min of 0 at $x = \pi/2, \pi, 3\pi/2$; relative max of 1 at $x = \pi/4, 3\pi/4, 5\pi/4, 7\pi/4$

44. $f'(x) = -4 \sin 4x + 4 \cos 2x = -4(2 \sin 2x \cos 2x) + 4 \cos 2x = -4 \cos 2x(2 \sin 2x - 1)$;
critical points $x = \pi/4, 3\pi/4, \pi/12, 5\pi/12$; relative min of 1 at $x = \pi/4$, relative min of -3 at $x = 3\pi/4$, relative max of $3/2$ at $x = \pi/12, 5\pi/12$

45. Let $f(x) = x^2 + \dfrac{k}{x}$, then $f'(x) = 2x - \dfrac{k}{x^2} = \dfrac{2x^3 - k}{x^2}$. f has a relative extremum when $2x^3 - k = 0$, so $k = 2x^3 = 2(3)^3 = 54$.

46. Let $f(x) = \dfrac{x}{x^2 + k}$, then $f'(x) = \dfrac{k - x^2}{(x^2 + k)^2}$. f has a relative extremum when $k - x^2 = 0$, so $k = x^2 = 2.5^2 = 6.25$.

47. $f(x) = -x^4$ has a relative maximum at $x = 0$, $f(x) = x^4$ has a relative minimum at $x = 0$, $f(x) = x^3$ has neither at $x = 0$; $f'(0) = 0$ for all three functions.

48. (a) because h and g have relative maxima at x_0, $h(x) \leq h(x_0)$ for all x in I_1 and $g(x) \leq g(x_0)$ for all x in I_2, where I_1 and I_2 are open intervals containing x_0. If x is in $I_1 \cap I_2$ then both inequalities are true and by addition so is $h(x) + g(x) \leq h(x_0) + g(x_0)$ which shows that $h + g$ has a relative maximum at x_0.

(b) by counterexample, both $h(x) = -x^2$ and $g(x) = -2x^2$ have relative maxima at $x = 0$ but $h(x) - g(x) = x^2$ has a relative minimum at $x = 0$ so $h - g$ does not necessarily have a relative maximum at x_0.

49. **(a)**

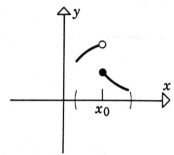

$f(x_0)$ is not an extreme value

(b)

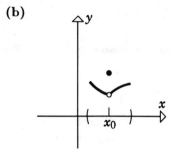

$f(x_0)$ is a relative
maximum.

(c)

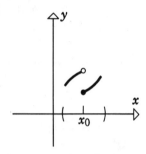

$f(x_0)$ is a relative
minimum.

50. Use the hint for the case where f changes its concavity from concave up to concave down at x_0. The other case is treated in a similar manner.

EXERCISE SET 4.4

1. $y = x^2 - 2x - 3$
$y' = 2(x - 1)$
$y'' = 2$

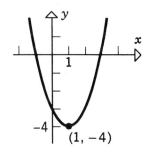

2. $y = 1 + x - x^2$
$y' = -2(x - 1/2)$
$y'' = -2$

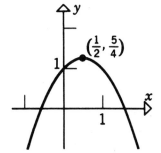

3. $y = x^3 - 3x + 1$
$y' = 3(x^2 - 1)$
$y'' = 6x$

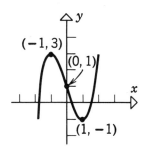

4. $y = 2x^3 - 6x + 4$
$y' = 6(x^2 - 1)$
$y'' = 12x$

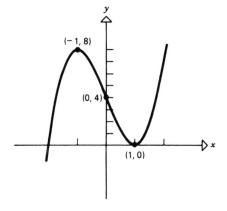

5. $y = x^3 + 3x^2 + 5$
    $y' = 3x(x + 2)$
    $y'' = 6(x + 1)$

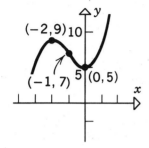

6. $y = x^2 - x^3$
    $y' = -3x(x - 2/3)$
    $y'' = -6(x - 1/3)$

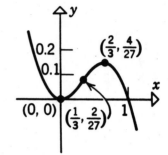

7. $y = 2x^3 - 3x^2 + 12x + 9$
    $y' = 6(x^2 - x + 2)$
    $y'' = 12(x - 1/2)$

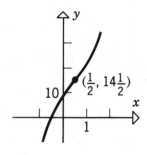

8. $y = x^3 - 3x^2 + 3$
    $y' = 3x(x - 2)$
    $y'' = 6(x - 1)$

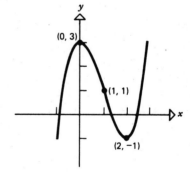

9. $y = (x - 1)^4$
       $y' = 4(x - 1)^3$
       $y'' = 12(x - 1)^2$

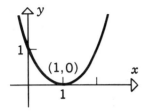

10. $y = (x - 1)^5$
        $y' = 5(x - 1)^4$
        $y'' = 20(x - 1)^3$

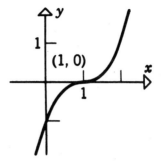

11. $y = x^4 + 2x^3 - 1$
       $y' = 4x^2(x + 3/2)$
       $y'' = 12x(x + 1)$

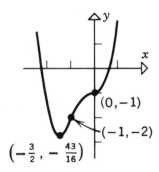

12. $y = x^4 - 2x^2 - 12$
        $y' = 4x(x^2 - 1)$
        $y'' = 12(x^2 - 1/3)$

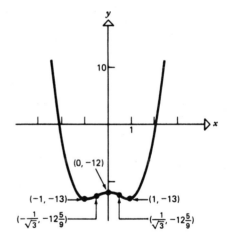

13. $y = x^4 - 3x^3 + 3x^2 + 1$
$y' = x(4x^2 - 9x + 6)$
$y'' = 12(x - 1/2)(x - 1)$

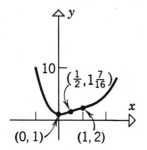

14. $y = x^5 - 4x^4 + 4x^3$
$y' = 5x^2(x - 6/5)(x - 2)$
$y'' = 4x(5x^2 - 12x + 6),$

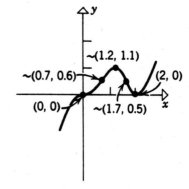

15. $y = x^3(3x^2 - 5)$
$y' = 15x^2(x^2 - 1)$
$y'' = 30x(2x^2 - 1)$

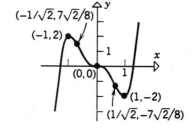

16. $y = 3x^3(x + 4/3)$
$y' = 12x^2(x + 1)$
$y'' = 36x(x + 2/3)$

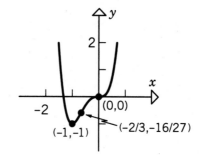

17. $y = x(x - 1)^3$
$y' = (4x - 1)(x - 1)^2$
$y'' = 6(2x - 1)(x - 1)$

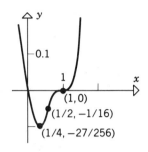

18. $y = x^4(x + 5)$
$y' = 5x^3(x + 4)$
$y'' = 20x^2(x + 3)$

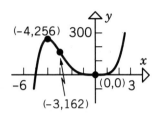

19. vertical: $x = 2$; horizontal: $y = 3$

20. vertical: $x = -2/3$; horizontal: $y = 4/3$

21. vertical: $x = -\sqrt{5}$, $x = \sqrt{5}$; horizontal: none

22. vertical: none; horizontal: $y = 0$

23. vertical: $x = -1$, $x = 3$; horizontal: $y = 1$

24. vertical: $x = -2$, $x = 0$; horizontal: $y = 2/3$

25. $x^2/(x^2 + 2x + 5) = 1$, $2x + 5 = 0$, $x = -5/2$.

26. $(x^2 - 3x + 2)/x^2 = 1$, $-3x + 2 = 0$, $x = 2/3$.

27. $(x^2 + 1)/(2x^2 - 6x) = 1/2$, $-3x = 1$, $x = -1/3$.

28. $(25 - 9x^2)/x^3 = 0$, $25 - 9x^2 = 0$, $x = \pm 5/3$.

29. $y = 2x/(x-3)$
$y' = -6(x-3)^2$
$y'' = 12/(x-3)^3$

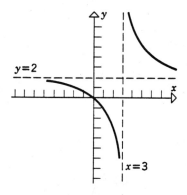

30. $y = \dfrac{x}{x^2-1}$

$y' = -\dfrac{x^2+1}{(x^2-1)^2}$

$y'' = \dfrac{2x(x^2+3)}{(x^2-1)^3}$

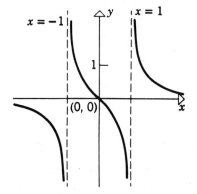

31. $y = \dfrac{x^2}{x^2-1}$

$y' = -\dfrac{2x}{(x^2-1)^2}$

$y'' = \dfrac{2(3x^2+1)}{(x^2-1)^3}$

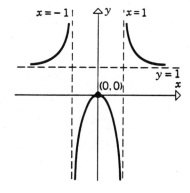

32. $y = 1/(x-1)^2$
$y' = -2/(x-1)^3$
$y'' = 6/(x-1)^4$

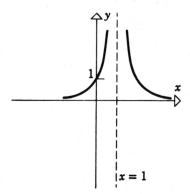

33. $y = \dfrac{x}{x^2 + 1}$

$y' = \dfrac{1 - x^2}{(x^2 + 1)^2}$

$y'' = \dfrac{2x(x^2 - 3)}{(x^2 + 1)^3}$

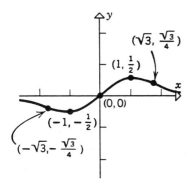

34. $y = 1 - 1/x$

$y' = 1/x^2$

$y'' = -2/x^3$

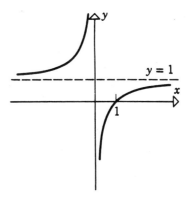

35. $y = (x - 1)/(x - 2)$

$y' = -1/(x - 2)^2$

$y'' = 2/(x - 2)^3$

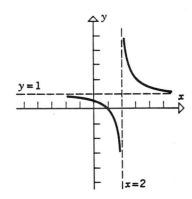

36. $y = \dfrac{1}{x^2 + 1}$

$y' = -\dfrac{2x}{(x^2 + 1)^2}$

$y'' = \dfrac{2(3x^2 - 1)}{(x^2 + 1)^3}$

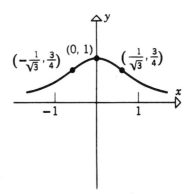

37. $y = x^2 - \dfrac{1}{x} = \dfrac{x^3 - 1}{x}$

$y' = \dfrac{2x^3 + 1}{x^2},$

$y' = 0$ when $x = -\sqrt[3]{\dfrac{1}{2}} \approx -0.8$

$y'' = \dfrac{2(x^3 - 1)}{x^3}$

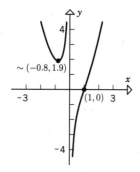

38. $y = \dfrac{2x^2 - 1}{x^2}$

$y' = \dfrac{2}{x^3}$

$y'' = -\dfrac{6}{x^4}$

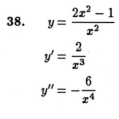

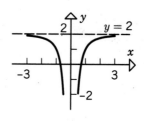

39. $y = \dfrac{1 - x}{x^2}$

$y' = \dfrac{x - 2}{x^3}$

$y'' = \dfrac{2(3 - x)}{x^4}$

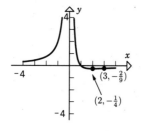

40. $y = \dfrac{8}{4 - x^2}$

$y' = \dfrac{16x}{(4 - x^2)^2}$

$y'' = \dfrac{16(3x^2 + 4)}{(4 - x^2)^3}$

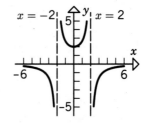

41. $y = \dfrac{x-1}{x^2-4}$

$y' = -\dfrac{x^2 - 2x + 4}{(x^2-4)^2}$

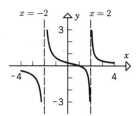

42. $y = \dfrac{8(x-2)}{x^2}$

$y' = \dfrac{8(4-x)}{x^3}$

$y'' = \dfrac{16(x-6)}{x^4}$

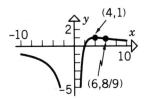

43. $y = \dfrac{(x-1)^2}{x^2}$

$y' = \dfrac{2(x-1)}{x^3}$

$y'' = \dfrac{2(3-2x)}{x^4}$

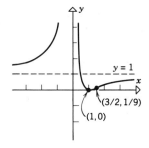

44. $y = 2 + \dfrac{3}{x} - \dfrac{1}{x^3}$

$y' = \dfrac{3(1-x^2)}{x^4}$

$y'' = \dfrac{6(x^2-2)}{x^5}$

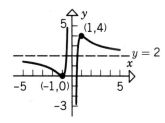

45. $y = 3 - \dfrac{4}{x} - \dfrac{4}{x^2}$

$y' = \dfrac{4(x+2)}{x^3}$

$y'' = -\dfrac{8(x+3)}{x^4}$

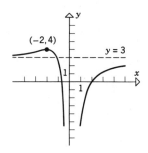

46. $y = \dfrac{x^2 - 1}{x^2 + 1}$

$y' = \dfrac{4x}{(x^2+1)^2}$

$y'' = \dfrac{4(1 - 3x^2)}{(x^2+1)^3}$

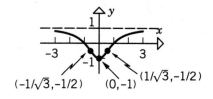

47. $y = \dfrac{x^3 - 1}{x^3 + 1}$

$y' = \dfrac{6x^2}{(x^3+1)^2}$

$y'' = \dfrac{12x(1 - 2x^3)}{(x^3+1)^3}$

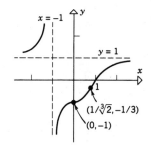

48. $\displaystyle\lim_{x \to \pm\infty} \left[\dfrac{P(x)}{Q(x)} - (ax + b) \right] = \lim_{x \to \pm\infty} \dfrac{R(x)}{Q(x)} = 0$ because the degree of $R(x)$ is less than the degree of $Q(x)$.

49. $y = \dfrac{x^2 - 2}{x} = x - \dfrac{2}{x}$

so $y = x$ is an oblique asymptote

$y' = \dfrac{x^2 + 2}{x^2}$

$y'' = -\dfrac{4}{x^3}$

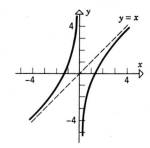

50. $y = \dfrac{x^2 - 2x - 3}{x + 2} = x - 4 + \dfrac{5}{x + 2}$

so $y = x - 4$ is an oblique asymptote

$y' = \dfrac{x^2 + 4x - 1}{(x + 2)^2}$,

$y'' = \dfrac{10}{(x + 2)^3}$

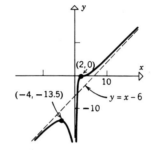

51. $y = \dfrac{(x - 2)^3}{x^2} = x - 6 + \dfrac{12x - 8}{x^2}$

so $y = x - 6$ is an oblique asymptote

$y' = \dfrac{(x - 2)^2(x + 4)}{x^3}$

$y'' = \dfrac{24(x - 2)}{x^4}$

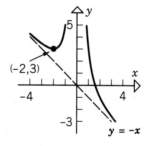

52. $y = \dfrac{4 - x^3}{x^2}$

$y' = -\dfrac{x^3 + 8}{x^3}$

$y'' = \dfrac{24}{x^4}$

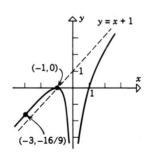

53. $y = x + 1 - \dfrac{1}{x} - \dfrac{1}{x^2} = \dfrac{(x - 1)(x + 1)^2}{x^2}$

$y = x + 1$ is an oblique asymptote

$y' = \dfrac{(x + 1)(x^2 - x + 2)}{x^3}$

$y'' = -\dfrac{2(x + 3)}{x^4}$

54. The oblique asymptote is $y = 2x$ so $(2x^3 - 3x + 4)/x^2 = 2x$, $-3x + 4 = 0$, $x = 4/3$.

55. $\lim\limits_{x \to \pm\infty} [f(x) - x^2] = \lim\limits_{x \to \pm\infty} (1/x) = 0$

$$y = x^2 + \frac{1}{x} = \frac{x^3 + 1}{x}$$

$$y' = 2x - \frac{1}{x^2} = \frac{2x^3 - 1}{x^2}$$

$$y'' = 2 + \frac{2}{x^3} = \frac{2(x^3 + 1)}{x^3}$$

$y' = 0$ when $x = 1/\sqrt[3]{2} \approx 0.8$,
$\qquad\qquad y = 3\sqrt[3]{2}/2 \approx 1.9$
$y'' = 0$ when $x = -1$, $y = 0$

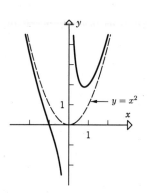

56. $\lim\limits_{x \to \pm\infty} [f(x) - (3 - x^2)] = \lim\limits_{x \to \pm\infty} (2/x) = 0$

$$y = 3 - x^2 + \frac{2}{x} = \frac{2 + 3x - x^3}{x}$$

$$y' = -2x - \frac{2}{x^2} = -\frac{2(x^3 + 1)}{x^2}$$

$$y'' = -2 + \frac{4}{x^3} = -\frac{2(x^3 - 2)}{x^3}$$

$y' = 0$ when $x = -1$, $y = 0$
$y'' = 0$ when $x = \sqrt[3]{2} \approx 1.3$,
$\qquad\qquad y = 3$

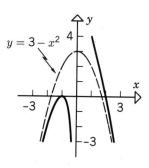

57. Let y be the length of the other side of the rectangle, then $L = 2x + 2y$ and $xy = 400$ so $y = 400/x$ and hence $L = 2x + 800/x$.

$L = 2x$ is an oblique asymptote

(see Exercise 48)

$$L = 2x + \frac{800}{x} = \frac{2(x^2 + 400)}{x}$$

$$L' = 2 - \frac{800}{x^2} = \frac{2(x^2 - 400)}{x^2}$$

$$L'' = \frac{1600}{x^3}$$

$L' = 0$ when $x = 20$, $L = 80$

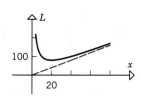

58. Let y be the height of the box, then $S = x^2 + 4xy$ and $x^2y = 500$ so $y = 500/x^2$ and hence $S = x^2 + 2000/x$.

The graph approaches the curve

$S = x^2$ asymptotically (see Exercise 55)

$$S = x^2 + \frac{2000}{x} = \frac{x^3 + 2000}{x}$$

$$S' = 2x - \frac{2000}{x^2} = \frac{2(x^3 - 1000)}{x^2}$$

$$S'' = 2 + \frac{4000}{x^3} = \frac{2(x^3 + 2000)}{x^3}$$

$S'' = 0$ when $x = 10$, $S = 300$

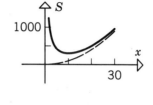

59. $y' = 0.1x^4(6x - 5)$

critical points: $x = 0$, $x = 5/6$

relative minimum at $x = 5/6$,

$y \approx -6.7 \times 10^{-3}$

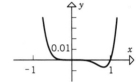

60. $y' = 0.1x^4(x + 1)(7x + 5)$

critical points: $x = 0$, $x = -1$, $x = -5/7$

relative maximum at $x = -1$, $y = 0$;

relative minimum at $x = -5/7$,

$y \approx -1.5 \times 10^{-3}$

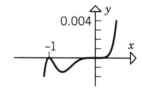

EXERCISE SET 4.5

1. $y = (x - 2)^{1/3}$

$y' = \dfrac{1}{3}(x - 2)^{-2/3}$

$y'' = -\dfrac{2}{9}(x - 2)^{-5/3}$

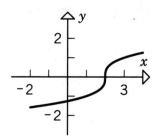

2. $y = x^{1/4}$

$y' = \dfrac{1}{4}x^{-3/4}$

$y'' = -\dfrac{3}{16}x^{-7/4}$

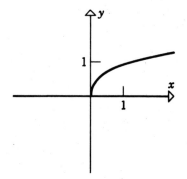

3. $y = x^{1/5}$

$y' = \dfrac{1}{5}x^{-4/5}$

$y'' = -\dfrac{4}{25}x^{-9/5}$

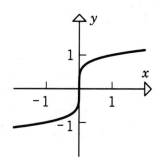

4. $y = x^{2/5}$

$y' = \dfrac{2}{5}x^{-3/5}$

$y'' = -\dfrac{6}{25}x^{-8/5}$

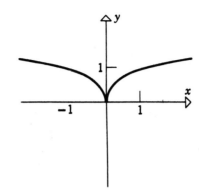

5. $y = x^{4/3}$

$y' = \dfrac{4}{3}x^{1/3}$

$y'' = \dfrac{4}{9}x^{-2/3}$

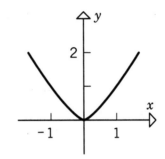

6. $y = x^{-1/3}$

$y' = -\dfrac{1}{3}x^{-4/3}$

$y'' = \dfrac{4}{9}x^{-7/3}$

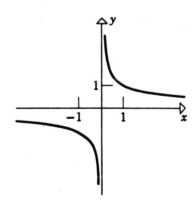

7. $y = 1 - x^{2/3}$

$y' = -\dfrac{2}{3}x^{-1/3}$

$y'' = \dfrac{2}{9}x^{-4/3}$

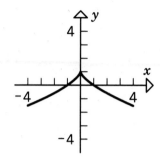

8. $y = \sqrt{x + 2}$

$y' = \dfrac{1}{2}(x + 2)^{-1/2}$

$y'' = -\dfrac{1}{4}(x + 2)^{-3/2}$

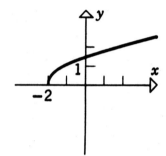

9. $y = \sqrt{x^2 - 1}$

$y' = \dfrac{x}{\sqrt{x^2 - 1}}$

$y'' = -\dfrac{1}{(x^2 - 1)^{3/2}}$

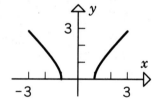

10. $y = \sqrt[3]{x^2 - 4}$

$y' = \dfrac{2x}{3(x^2 - 4)^{2/3}}$

$y'' = -\dfrac{2(3x^2 + 4)}{9(x^2 - 4)^{5/3}}$

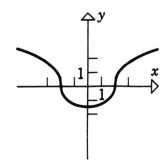

11. $y = 2x + 3x^{2/3}$

$y' = 2 + 2x^{-1/3}$,

$y'' = -\dfrac{2}{3}x^{-4/3}$

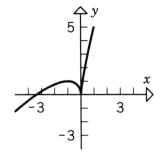

12. $y = 4x - 3x^{4/3}$

$y' = 4 - 4x^{1/3}$

$y'' = -\dfrac{4}{3}x^{-2/3}$

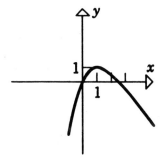

13. $y = x(3 - x)^{1/2}$

$y' = \dfrac{3(2 - x)}{2\sqrt{3 - x}}$

$y'' = \dfrac{3(x - 4)}{4(3 - x)^{3/2}}$

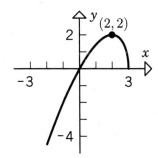

14. $y = x^{1/3}(4-x)$

$y' = \dfrac{4(1-x)}{3x^{2/3}}$

$y'' = -\dfrac{4(x+2)}{9x^{5/3}}$

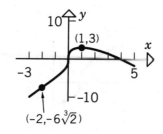

15. $y = \dfrac{8(\sqrt{x}-1)}{x}$

$y' = \dfrac{4(2-\sqrt{x})}{x^2}$

$y'' = \dfrac{2(3\sqrt{x}-8)}{x^3}$

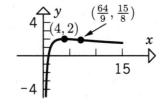

16. $y = \dfrac{1+\sqrt{x}}{1-\sqrt{x}}$

$y' = \dfrac{1}{\sqrt{x}(1-\sqrt{x})2}$

$y'' = \dfrac{3\sqrt{x}-1}{2x^{3/2}(1-\sqrt{x})^3}$

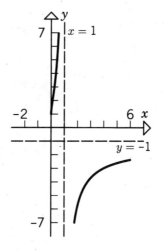

17. $y = \dfrac{\sqrt{x}}{x-3}$

$y' = -\dfrac{x+3}{2\sqrt{x}(x-3)^2}$

$y'' = \dfrac{3(x^2+6x-3)}{4x^{3/2}(x-3)^3}$

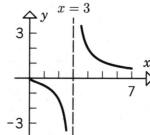

18. $y = x^{2/3}(x - 5)$

$y' = \dfrac{5(x - 2)}{3x^{1/3}}$

$y'' = \dfrac{10(x + 1)}{9x^{4/3}}$

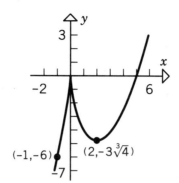

$(-1,-6)$ $(2,-3\sqrt[3]{4})$

19. $y = x - \cos x$
$y' = 1 + \sin x, \ y' = 0$
   when $x = -\pi/2 + 2n\pi$

$y'' = \cos x, \ y'' = 0$
   when $x = \pi/2 + n\pi$

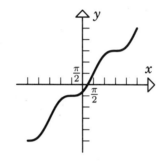

20. $y = x + \tan x$
$y' = 1 + \sec^2 x$
$y'' = 2\sec^2 x \tan x, \ y'' = 0$
   when $x = n\pi$

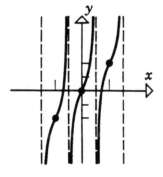

21. $y = \sin x + \cos x$
$y' = \cos x - \sin x, \ y' = 0$
   when $x = \pi/4 + n\pi$

$y'' = -\sin x - \cos x, \ y'' = 0$
   when $x = 3\pi/4 + n\pi$

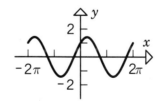

22. $y = \sqrt{3}\cos x + \sin x$
        $y' = -\sqrt{3}\sin x + \cos x,\ y' = 0$
            when $x = \pi/6 + n\pi$

        $y'' = -\sqrt{3}\cos x - \sin x,\ y'' = 0$
            when $x = 2\pi/3 + n\pi$

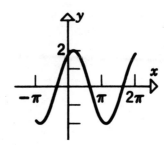

23. $y = \sin^2 x,\ 0 \le x \le 2\pi$
        $y' = 2\sin x \cos x = \sin 2x$
        $y'' = 2\cos 2x$

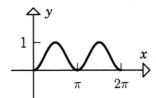

24. $y = x\tan x,\ -\pi/2 < x < \pi/2$
        $y' = x\sec^2 x + \tan x,\ y' = 0$
            when $x = 0$
        $y'' = 2\sec^2 x(x\tan x + 1)$,
            which is always positive
            for $-\pi/2 < x < \pi/2$

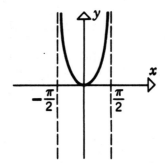

EXERCISE SET 4.6

1. $f'(x) = 8x - 4$, $f'(x) = 0$ when $x = 1/2$; $f(0) = 1$, $f(1/2) = 0$, $f(1) = 1$ so the maximum value is 1 at $x = 0, 1$ and the minimum value is 0 at $x = 1/2$.

2. $f'(x) = 8 - 2x$, $f'(x) = 0$ when $x = 4$; $f(0) = 0$, $f(4) = 16$, $f(6) = 12$ so the maximum value is 16 at $x = 4$ and the minimum value is 0 at $x = 0$.

3. $f'(x) = 3(x-1)^2$, $f'(x) = 0$ when $x = 1$; $f(0) = -1$, $f(1) = 0$, $f(4) = 27$ so the maximum value is 27 at $x = 4$ and the minimum value is -1 at $x = 0$.

4. $f'(x) = 6x^2 - 6x - 12 = 6(x+1)(x-2)$, $f'(x) = 0$ when $x = -1, 2$; $f(-2) = -4$, $f(-1) = 7$, $f(2) = -20$, $f(3) = -9$ so the maximum value is 7 at $x = -1$ and the minimum value is -20 at $x = 2$.

5. $f'(x) = 3/(4x^2 + 1)^{3/2}$, thus there are no critical points; $f(-1) = -3/\sqrt{5}$, $f(1) = 3/\sqrt{5}$ so the maximum value is $3/\sqrt{5}$ at $x = 1$ and the minimum value is $-3/\sqrt{5}$ at $x = -1$.

6. $f'(x) = (2-x^2)/(x^2+2)^2$, $f'(x) = 0$ for x in the interval $(-1, 4)$ when $x = \sqrt{2}$; $f(-1) = -1/3$, $f(\sqrt{2}) = \sqrt{2}/4$, $f(4) = 2/9$ so the maximum value is $\sqrt{2}/4$ at $x = \sqrt{2}$ and the minimum value is $-1/3$ at $x = -1$.

7. $f'(x) = \dfrac{5(8-x)}{3x^{1/3}}$, $f'(x) = 0$ when $x = 8$ and $f'(x)$ does not exist when $x = 0$; $f(-1) = 21$, $f(0) = 0$, $f(8) = 48$, $f(20) = 0$ so the maximum value is 48 at $x = 8$ and the minimum value is 0 at $x = 0, 20$.

8. $f'(x) = \dfrac{2(2x+1)}{3(x^2+x)^{1/3}}$, $f'(x) = 0$ when $x = -1/2$ and $f'(x)$ does not exist when $x = -1, 0$; $f(-2) = 2^{2/3}$, $f(-1) = 0$, $f(0) = 0$, $f(3) = 12^{2/3}$ so the maximum value is $12^{2/3}$ at $x = 3$ and the minimum value is 0 at $x = -1, 0$.

9. $f'(x) = 1 - \sec^2 x$, $f'(x) = 0$ for x in $(-\pi/4, \pi/4)$ when $x = 0$; $f(-\pi/4) = 1 - \pi/4$, $f(0) = 0$, $f(\pi/4) = \pi/4 - 1$ so the maximum value is $1 - \pi/4$ at $x = -\pi/4$ and the minimum value is $\pi/4 - 1$ at $x = \pi/4$.

10. $f'(x) = \cos x + \sin x$, $f'(x) = 0$ for x in $(0, \pi)$ when $x = 3\pi/4$; $f(0) = -1$, $f(3\pi/4) = \sqrt{2}$, $f(\pi) = 1$ so the maximum value is $\sqrt{2}$ at $x = 3\pi/4$ and the minimum value is -1 at $x = 0$.

11. $f'(x) = 2\sec x \tan x - \sec^2 x = (2\sin x - 1)/\cos^2 x$, $f'(x) = 0$ for x in $(0, \pi/4)$ when $x = \pi/6$; $f(0) = 2$, $f(\pi/6) = \sqrt{3}$, $f(\pi/4) = 2\sqrt{2} - 1$ so the maximum value is 2 at $x = 0$ and the minimum value is $\sqrt{3}$ at $x = \pi/6$.

12. $f'(x) = 2\sin x \cos x - \sin x = \sin x(2\cos x - 1)$, $f'(x) = 0$ for x in $(-\pi, \pi)$ when $x = 0, \pm\pi/3$; $f(-\pi) = -1$, $f(-\pi/3) = 5/4$, $f(0) = 1$, $f(\pi/3) = 5/4$, $f(\pi) = -1$ so the maximum value is $5/4$ at $x = \pm\pi/3$ and the minimum value is -1 at $x = \pm\pi$.

13. $f(x) = 1 + |9 - x^2| = \begin{cases} 10 - x^2, & |x| \le 3 \\ -8 + x^2, & |x| > 3 \end{cases}$, $f'(x) = \begin{cases} -2x, & |x| < 3 \\ 2x, & |x| > 3 \end{cases}$ thus $f'(x) = 0$ when $x = 0$, $f'(x)$ does not exist for x in $(-5, 1)$ when $x = -3$ because $\lim\limits_{x \to -3^-} f'(x) \ne \lim\limits_{x \to -3^+} f'(x)$ (see Theorem preceding Exercise 71, Section 3.3); $f(-5) = 17$, $f(-3) = 1$, $f(0) = 10$, $f(1) = 9$ so the maximum value is 17 at $x = -5$ and the minimum value is 1 at $x = -3$.

14. $f(x) = |6 - 4x| = \begin{cases} 6 - 4x, & x \le 3/2 \\ -6 + 4x, & x > 3/2 \end{cases}$, $f'(x) = \begin{cases} -4, & x < 3/2 \\ 4, & x > 3/2 \end{cases}$, $f'(x)$ does not exist
when $x = 3/2$ thus $3/2$ is the only critical point in $(-3, 3)$; $f(-3) = 18$, $f(3/2) = 0$, $f(3) = 6$
so the maximum value is 18 at $x = -3$ and the minimum value is 0 at $x = 3/2$.

15. $f'(x) = 2x - 3$; critical point $x = 3/2$. Minimum value $f(3/2) = -13/4$, no maximum.

16. $f'(x) = -4(x + 1)$; critical point $x = -1$. Maximum value $f(-1) = 5$, no minimum.

17. $f'(x) = 12x^2(1 - x)$; critical points $x = 0, 1$. Maximum value $f(1) = 1$, no minimum because
$\lim\limits_{x \to +\infty} f(x) = -\infty$.

18. $f'(x) = 4(x^3 + 1)$; critical point $x = -1$. Minimum value $f(-1) = -3$, no maximum.

19. $(x^2 - 1)^2$ can never be less than zero because it is the square of $x^2 - 1$; the minimum value is
0 for $x = \pm 1$, no maximum because $\lim\limits_{x \to +\infty} f(x) = +\infty$.

20. $(x - 1)^2(x + 2)^2$ can never be less than zero because it is the product of two squares; the
minimum value is 0 for $x = 1$ or -2, no maximum because $\lim\limits_{x \to +\infty} f(x) = +\infty$.

21. No maximum or minimum because $\lim\limits_{x \to +\infty} f(x) = +\infty$ and $\lim\limits_{x \to -\infty} f(x) = -\infty$.

22. No maximum or minimum because $\lim\limits_{x \to +\infty} f(x) = +\infty$ and $\lim\limits_{x \to -\infty} f(x) = -\infty$.

23. $f'(x) = -1/x^2$; no maximum or minimum because there are no critical points in $(0, +\infty)$.

24. $f'(x) = (1 - x^2)/(x^2 + 1)^2$; critical point $x = 1$. Maximum value $f(1) = 1/2$, minimum value
0 because $f(x)$ is never less than zero on $[0, +\infty)$ and $f(0) = 0$.

25. $f'(x) = x(x + 2)/(x + 1)^2$; critical point $x = -2$ in $(-5, -1)$. Maximum value $f(-2) = -4$,
no minimum.

26. $f'(x) = -6/(x - 3)^2$; no critical points in $[-5, 5]$ ($x = 3$ is not in the domain of f). No
maximum or minimum because $\lim\limits_{x \to 3^+} f(x) = +\infty$ and $\lim\limits_{x \to 3^-} f(x) = -\infty$.

27. $\sin 2x$ has a period of π, and $\sin 4x$ a period of $\pi/2$ so $f(x)$ is periodic with period π. Consider
the interval $[0, \pi]$. $f'(x) = 4\cos 2x + 4\cos 4x$, $f'(x) = 0$ when $\cos 2x + \cos 4x = 0$, but
$\cos 4x = 2\cos^2 2x - 1$ (trig identity) so

$$2\cos^2 2x + \cos 2x - 1 = 0$$
$$(2\cos 2x - 1)(\cos 2x + 1) = 0$$
$$\cos 2x = 1/2 \ \text{ or } \ \cos 2x = -1.$$

From $\cos 2x = 1/2$, $2x = \pi/3$ or $5\pi/3$ so $x = \pi/6$ or $5\pi/6$. From $\cos 2x = -1$, $2x = \pi$ so $x = \pi/2$. $f(0) = 0$, $f(\pi/6) = 3\sqrt{3}/2$, $f(\pi/2) = 0$, $f(5\pi/6) = -3\sqrt{3}/2$, $f(\pi) = 0$. The maximum value is $3\sqrt{3}/2$ at $x = \pi/6 + n\pi$ and the minimum value is $-3\sqrt{3}/2$ at $x = 5\pi/6 + n\pi$, $n = 0, \pm 1, \pm 2, \cdots$.

28. $\cos \dfrac{x}{3}$ has a period of 6π, and $\cos \dfrac{x}{2}$ a period of 4π, so $f(x)$ has a period of 12π. Consider the interval $[0, 12\pi]$. $f'(x) = -\sin \dfrac{x}{3} - \sin \dfrac{x}{2}$, $f'(x) = 0$ when $\sin \dfrac{x}{3} + \sin \dfrac{x}{2} = 0$ thus, by use of the trig identity $\sin a + \sin b = 2 \sin \dfrac{a+b}{2} \cos \dfrac{a-b}{2}$, $2 \sin\left(\dfrac{5x}{12}\right) \cos\left(-\dfrac{x}{12}\right) = 0$ so $\sin \dfrac{5x}{12} = 0$ or $\cos \dfrac{x}{12} = 0$. Solve $\sin \dfrac{5x}{12} = 0$ to get $x = 12\pi/5, 24\pi/5, 36\pi/5, 48\pi/5$ and then solve $\cos \dfrac{x}{12} = 0$ to get $x = 6\pi$. The corresponding values of $f(x)$ are $-4.0450, 1.5450, 1.5450, -4.0450, 1, 5, 5$ so the maximum value is 5 and the minimum value is -4.0450 (approximately).

29. $f'(x) = -[\cos(\cos x)] \sin x$; $f'(x) = 0$ if $\sin x = 0$ or if $\cos(\cos x) = 0$. If $\sin x = 0$, then $x = \pi$ is the critical point in $(0, 2\pi)$; $\cos(\cos x) = 0$ has no solutions because $-1 \le \cos x \le 1$. Thus $f(0) = \sin(1)$, $f(\pi) = \sin(-1) = -\sin(1)$, and $f(2\pi) = \sin(1)$ so the maximum value is $\sin(1) \approx 0.84147$ and the minimum value is $-\sin(1) \approx -0.84147$.

30. $f'(x) = -[\sin(\sin x)] \cos x$; $f'(x) = 0$ if $\cos x = 0$ or if $\sin(\sin x) = 0$. If $\cos x = 0$, then $x = \pi/2$ is the critical point in $(0, \pi)$; $\sin(\sin x) = 0$ if $\sin x = 0$, which gives no critical points in $(0, \pi)$. Thus $f(0) = 1$, $f(\pi/2) = \cos(1)$, and $f(\pi) = 1$ so the maximum value is 1 and the minimum value is $\cos(1) \approx 0.54030$.

31. $f'(x) = \begin{cases} 4, & x < 1 \\ 2x - 5, & x > 1 \end{cases}$ so $f'(x) = 0$ when $x = 5/2$, and $f'(x)$ does not exist when $x = 1$ because $\lim\limits_{x \to 1^-} f'(x) \ne \lim\limits_{x \to 1^+} f'(x)$ (see Theorem preceding Exercise 71, Section 3.3); $f(1/2) = 0$, $f(1) = 2$, $f(5/2) = -1/4$, $f(7/2) = 3/4$ so the maximum value is 2 and the minimum value is $-1/4$.

32. $f'(x) = 2x + p$ which exists throughout the interval $(0, 2)$ for all values of p so $f'(1) = 0$ because $f(1)$ is an extreme value, thus $2 + p = 0$, $p = -2$. $f(1) = 3$ so $1^2 + (-2)(1) + q = 3$, $q = 4$ thus $f(x) = x^2 - 2x + 4$ and $f(0) = 4$, $f(2) = 4$ so $f(1)$ is the minimum value.

33. $f'(x) = p(x-a)^{p-1}$; critical point $x = a$
     (a) if p is even then $p-1$ is odd and $f'(x) < 0$ when $x < a$, $f'(x) > 0$ when $x > a$ so $f(a) = 0$ is a relative minimum.
     (b) if p is odd then $p-1$ is even and $f'(x)$ does not change sign at $x = a$ so f does not have relative extrema.

34. Let m = slope at x, then $m = f'(x) = 3x^2 - 6x + 5$, $dm/dx = 6x - 6$; critical point for m is $x = 1$, minimum value of m is $f'(1) = 2$

35. **(a)** $f'(x) = -\dfrac{64\cos x}{\sin^2 x} + \dfrac{27\sin x}{\cos^2 x} = \dfrac{-64\cos^3 x + 27\sin^3 x}{\sin^2 x \cos^2 x}$, $f'(x) = 0$ when

$27\sin^3 x = 64\cos^3 x$, $\tan^3 x = 64/27$, $\tan x = 4/3$ so the critical point is $x = x_0$ where

$\tan x_0 = 4/3$ and $0 < x_0 < \pi/2$. To test x_0 first rewrite $f'(x)$ as

$$f'(x) = \frac{27\cos^3 x(\tan^3 x - 64/27)}{\sin^2 x \cos^2 x} = \frac{27\cos x(\tan^3 x - 64/27)}{\sin^2 x};$$

if $x < x_0$ then $\tan x < 4/3$ and $f'(x) < 0$, if $x > x_0$ then $\tan x > 4/3$ and $f'(x) > 0$ so

$f(x_0)$ is the minimum value. f has no maximum because $\displaystyle\lim_{x \to 0^+} f(x) = +\infty$.

(b) If $\tan x_0 = 4/3$ then (see figure)

$\sin x_0 = 4/5$ and $\cos x_0 = 3/5$

so $f(x_0) = 64/\sin x_0 + 27/\cos x_0$

          $= 64/(4/5) + 27/(3/5)$

          $= 80 + 45 = 125$

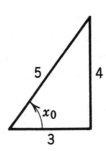

36. $f'(x) = 2x + \dfrac{256x}{(8-x)^3} = \dfrac{2x[(8-x)^3 + 128]}{(8-x)^3}$ and, for $x > 8$,

$f'(x) = 0$ when $(8-x)^3 = -128$, $8 - x = \sqrt[3]{-128} = -4\sqrt[3]{2}$,

$x = 8 + 4\sqrt[3]{2} = 4(2 + \sqrt[3]{2})$. $f''(x) = 2 + \dfrac{512(x+4)}{(8-x)^4} > 0$ for $x > 8$ so the minimum value occurs

at $x = 4(2 + \sqrt[3]{2})$.

37. $f(\theta) = \sin^2\theta\cos\theta$, $f'(\theta) = \sin\theta(2\cos^2\theta - \sin^2\theta) = \sin\theta(3\cos^2\theta - 1)$; $f'(\theta) = 0$ for θ in $(0, \pi/2)$

if $\cos\theta = 1/\sqrt{3}$. $f(0) = 0$ and $f(\pi/2) = 0$, so the maximum value occurs when $\cos\theta = 1/\sqrt{3}$

where $f(\theta) = \sin^2\theta\cos\theta = (1 - \cos^2\theta)\cos\theta = (1 - 1/3)(1/\sqrt{3}) = 2/(3\sqrt{3})$.

38. $f'(x) = (x^2 - t)/x^2$; critical point $x = \sqrt{t}$

$f''(x) = 2t/x^3$, $f''(\sqrt{t}) = 2/\sqrt{t} > 0$ so the minimum value is at $x = \sqrt{t}$.

$\displaystyle\lim_{x \to +\infty} f(x) = +\infty$ so there is no maximum value.

39. $(0, 9)$ is on the graph so $f(0) = a_0 + a_1(0) + a_2(0)^2 = 9$, $a_0 = 9$ thus $f(x) = 9 + a_1 x + a_2 x^2$.

$(2, 1)$ is on the graph so $f(2) = 9 + 2a_1 + 4a_2 = 1$,

$$a_1 + 2a_2 = -4 \tag{i}.$$

$f'(x) = a_1 + 2a_2 x$, but $f'(2) = 0$ because it is given that $f(2)$ is to be an extreme value, so

$$f'(2) = a_1 + 4a_2 = 0 \tag{ii}.$$

Solve (i) and (ii) to get $a_1 = -8$ and $a_2 = 2$, thus $f(x) = 9 - 8x + 2x^2$. As a check, we find

that $f''(x) = 4 > 0$ so $f(2)$ is a minimum.

40. Let $f(x) = x - \sin x$, then $f'(x) = 1 - \cos x$ and so $f'(x) = 0$ when $\cos x = 1$ which has no solution for $0 < x < 2\pi$ thus the minimum value of f must occur at 0 or 2π. $f(0) = 0$, $f(2\pi) = 2\pi$ so 0 is the minimum value on $[0, 2\pi]$ thus $x - \sin x \geq 0$, $\sin x \leq x$ for all x in $[0, 2\pi]$.

41. Let $f(x) = 1 - x^2/2 - \cos x$, then $f'(x) = -x + \sin x$ so $f'(x) = 0$ when $\sin x = x$ which has no solution for $0 < x < 2\pi$ thus the maximum and minimum values must occur at the endpoints of $[0, 2\pi]$. $f(0) = 0$, $f(2\pi) = -2\pi^2$, so 0 is the maximum value, thus $1 - x^2/2 - \cos x \leq 0$, $1 - x^2/2 \leq \cos x$ for all x in $[0, 2\pi]$.

42. **(a)**   **(b)**

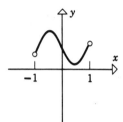   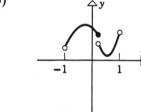

(c) No, because the theorem does not claim that a function cannot have both a maximum and a minimum value if the hypothesis is not satisfied.

43. By the quadratic formula, the roots are $x_1 = \dfrac{-b - \sqrt{b^2 - 4ac}}{2a}$ and $x_2 = \dfrac{-b + \sqrt{b^2 - 4ac}}{2a}$. The midpoint is $\dfrac{1}{2}(x_1 + x_2) = -\dfrac{b}{2a}$. But $f'(x) = 2ax + b$ so $f'\left(-\dfrac{b}{2a}\right) = 2a\left(-\dfrac{b}{2a}\right) + b = 0$.

44. Use the proof given in the text, replacing "maximum" by "minimum" and reversing the order of all inequality symbols.

45. $f'(x) = 2ax + b$; critical point is $x = -\dfrac{b}{2a}$

$f''(x) = 2a > 0$ so $f\left(-\dfrac{b}{2a}\right)$ is the minimum value of f, but

$f\left(-\dfrac{b}{2a}\right) = a\left(-\dfrac{b}{2a}\right)^2 + b\left(-\dfrac{b}{2a}\right) + c = \dfrac{-b^2 + 4ac}{4a}$ thus $f(x) \geq 0$ if and only if

$f\left(-\dfrac{b}{2a}\right) \geq 0$, $\dfrac{-b^2 + 4ac}{4a} \geq 0$, $-b^2 + 4ac \geq 0$, $b^2 - 4ac \leq 0$

46. Let $F(x)$ be the vertical distance between the line L and the curve $y = f(x)$ for each x in (a, b). Suppose that L is above the curve, then $F(x) = mx + b - f(x)$. If F has an extreme value on (a, b), then from Theorem 4.6.5 it must occur at a critical point of F, say $x = c$. But

$F'(x) = m - f'(x)$ so at $x = c$, $m - f'(c) = 0$, $f'(c) = m$, thus the tangent line to $y = f(x)$ at $x = c$ is parallel to L. (The case where L is below the curve is treated in a similar way, with $F(x) = f(x) - (mx + b)$.)

47. The slope of the line is -1, and the slope of the tangent to $y = -x^2$ is $-2x$ so $-2x = -1$, $x = 1/2$. The line lies above the curve so the vertical distance is given by $F(x) = 2 - x + x^2$; $F(-1) = 4$, $F(1/2) = 7/4$, $F(3/2) = 11/4$. The point $(1/2, -1/4)$ is closest, the point $(-1, -1)$ farthest.

48. The slope of the line is $4/3$; and the slope of the tangent to $y = x^3$ is $3x^2$ so $3x^2 = 4/3$, $x^2 = 4/9$, $x = \pm 2/3$. The line lies below the curve so the vertical distance is given by $F(x) = x^3 - 4x/3 + 1$; $F(-1) = 4/3$, $F(-2/3) = 43/27$, $F(2/3) = 11/27$, $F(1) = 2/3$. The closest point is $(2/3, 8/27)$, the farthest is $(-2/3, -8/27)$.

EXERCISE SET 4.7

1. Let $x =$ one number, $y =$ the other number, and $P = xy$ where $x + y = 10$. Thus $y = 10 - x$ so $P = x(10 - x) = 10x - x^2$ for x in $[0, 10]$. $dP/dx = 10 - 2x$, $dP/dx = 0$ when $x = 5$. If $x = 0, 5, 10$ then $P = 0, 25, 0$ so P is maximum when $x = 5$ and, from $y = 10 - x$, when $y = 5$.

2. Let x and y be nonnegative numbers and z the sum of their squares, then $z = x^2 + y^2$. But $x + y = 1$, $y = 1 - x$ so $z = x^2 + (1 - x)^2 = 2x^2 - 2x + 1$ for $0 \le x \le 1$. $dz/dx = 4x - 2$, $dz/dx = 0$ when $x = 1/2$. If $x = 0, 1/2, 1$ then $z = 1, 1/2, 1$ so

   (a) z is as large as possible when one number is 0 and the other is 1.

   (b) z is as small as possible when both numbers are $1/2$.

3. If $y = x + 1/x$ for $1/2 \le x \le 3/2$ then $dy/dx = 1 - 1/x^2 = (x^2 - 1)/x^2$, $dy/dx = 0$ when $x = 1$. If $x = 1/2, 1, 3/2$ then $y = 5/2, 2, 13/6$ so

   (a) y is as small as possible when $x = 1$.   (b) y is as large as possible when $x = 1/2$.

4. $A = xy$ where $x + 2y = 1000$ so $y = 500 - x/2$ and $A = 500x - x^2/2$ for x in $[0, 1000]$;

   $dA/dx = 500 - x$, $dA/dx = 0$ when $x = 500$.

   If $x = 0$ or 1000 then $A = 0$, if $x = 500$

   then $A = 125,000$ so the area is maximum

   when $x = 500$ ft and $y = 500 - 500/2 = 250$ ft.

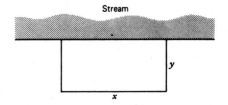

5. Let x and y be the dimensions shown
    in the figure and A the area, then
    $A = xy$ subject to the cost condition
    $3(2x) + 2(2y) = 6000$, or $y = 1500 - 3x/2$.
    Thus $A = x(1500 - 3x/2) = 1500x - 3x^2/2$
    for x in $[0, 1000]$. $dA/dx = 1500 - 3x$,

    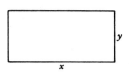

    Heavy-duty
    Standard

    $dA/dx = 0$ when $x = 500$. If $x = 0$ or 1000 then $A = 0$, if $x = 500$ then $A = 375,000$ so the
    area is greatest when $x = 500$ ft and (from $y = 1500 - 3x/2$) when $y = 750$ ft.

6. $A = xy$ where $2x + 2y = p$ so $y = p/2 - x$
    and $A = px/2 - x^2$ for x in $[0, p/2]$;
    $dA/dx = p/2 - 2x$, $dA/dx = 0$ when $x = p/4$.
    If $x = 0$ or $p/2$ then $A = 0$, if $x = p/4$
    then $A = p^2/16$ so the area is maximum
    when $x = p/4$ and $y = p/2 - p/4 = p/4$, which is a square.

    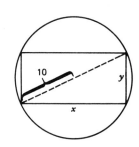

7. $A = xy$ where $x^2 + y^2 = 20^2 = 400$ so
    $y = \sqrt{400 - x^2}$ and $A = x\sqrt{400 - x^2}$ for
    $0 \le x \le 20$; $dA/dx = 2(200 - x^2)/\sqrt{400 - x^2}$,
    $dA/dx = 0$ when $x = \sqrt{200} = 10\sqrt{2}$. If
    $x = 0, 10\sqrt{2}, 20$ then $A = 0, 200, 0$ so
    the area is maximum when $x = 10\sqrt{2}$ and
    $y = \sqrt{400 - 200} = 10\sqrt{2}$.

    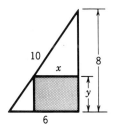

    10

8. Let x and y be the dimensions shown
    in the figure and A the area of the
    rectangle, then $A = xy$ and, by similar
    triangles, $x/6 = (8 - y)/8$, $y = 8 - 4x/3$
    so $A = x(8 - 4x/3) = 8x - 4x^2/3$ for x in
    $[0, 6]$. $dA/dx = 8 - 8x/3$, $dA/dx = 0$ when
    $x = 3$. If $x = 0, 3, 6$ then $A = 0, 12, 0$
    so the area is greatest when $x = 3$ in
    and (from $y = 8 - 4x/3$) $y = 4$ in.

    10
    8
    x
    6
    y

9. Let x, y, and z be as shown in the figure
    and A the area of the rectangle, then
    $A = xy$ and, by similar triangles, $z/10 = y/6$,
    $z = 5y/3$; also $x/10 = (8 - z)/8 = (8 - 5y/3)/8$
    thus $y = 24/5 - 12x/25$ so
    $A = x(24/5 - 12x/25) = 24x/5 - 12x^2/25$
    for x in $[0, 10]$. $dA/dx = 24/5 - 24x/25$,
    $dA/dx = 0$ when $x = 5$. If $x = 0, 5, 10$ then
    $A = 0, 12, 0$ so the area is greatest when $x = 5$ in. and $y = 12/5$ in.

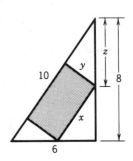

10. $A = (2x)y = 2xy$ where $y = 16 - x^2$ so
    $A = 32x - 2x^3$ for $0 \le x \le 4$;
    $dA/dx = 32 - 6x^2$, $dA/dx = 0$ when $x = 4/\sqrt{3}$.
    If $x = 0, 4/\sqrt{3}, 4$ then $A = 0, 256/(3\sqrt{3}), 0$
    so the area is largest when $x = 4/\sqrt{3}$
    and $y = 32/3$. The dimensions of the
    rectangle with largest area are $8/\sqrt{3}$ by $32/3$.

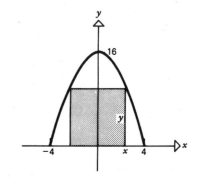

11. $V = x(12 - 2x)^2$ for $0 \le x \le 6$;
    $dV/dx = 12(x - 2)(x - 6)$, $dV/dx = 0$
    when $x = 2$ for $0 < x < 6$. If $x = 0, 2, 6$
    then $V = 0, 128, 0$ so the volume
    is largest when $x = 2$ in.

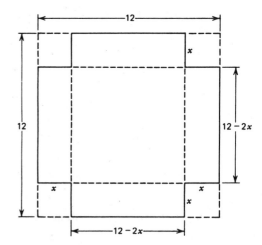

12. The dimensions of the box will be $(k-2x)$ by $(k-2x)$ by x so $V = (k-2x)^2 x = 4x^3 - 4kx^2 + k^2 x$
    for x in $[0, k/2]$. $dV/dx = 12x^2 - 8kx + k^2 = (6x - k)(2x - k)$, $dV/dx = 0$ for x in $(0, k/2)$
    when $x = k/6$. If $x = 0, k/6, k/2$ then $V = 0, 2k^3/27, 0$ so V is maximum when $x = k/6$. The
    squares should have dimensions $k/6$ by $k/6$.

13. Let x be the length of each side of a square, then $V = x(3 - 2x)(8 - 2x) = 4x^3 - 22x^2 + 24x$ for $0 \le x \le 3/2$; $dV/dx = 12x^2 - 44x + 24 = 4(3x - 2)(x - 3)$, $dV/dx = 0$ when $x = 2/3$ for $0 < x < 3/2$. If $x = 0, 2/3, 3/2$ then $V = 0, 200/27, 0$ so the maximum volume is $200/27$ ft^3.

14. Refer to the figure to see that

    $A = \dfrac{1}{2}hb$, but $h = L\sin\theta$ and $b = 2(L\cos\theta)$

    so $A = \dfrac{1}{2}L^2 2\sin\theta\cos\theta = \dfrac{1}{2}L^2\sin 2\theta$

    which is maximum when $\sin 2\theta = 1$,

    $2\theta = \pi/2$, $\theta = \pi/4$. Thus (without

    calculus) the area is maximum for

    an isosceles right triangle.

    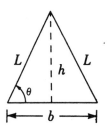

15. With x, y, r, and s as shown in the

    figure, the sum of the enclosed areas

    is $A = \pi r^2 + s^2$ where $r = \dfrac{x}{2\pi}$ and $s = \dfrac{y}{4}$

    because x is the circumference of the

    circle and y is the perimeter of the

    square, thus $A = \dfrac{x^2}{4\pi} + \dfrac{y^2}{16}$. But

    $x + y = 12$, so $y = 12 - x$ and

    $A = \dfrac{x^2}{4\pi} + \dfrac{(12 - x)^2}{16}$

    $= \dfrac{\pi + 4}{16\pi}x^2 - \dfrac{3}{2}x + 9$ for $0 \le x \le 12$. $\dfrac{dA}{dx} = \dfrac{\pi + 4}{8\pi}x - \dfrac{3}{2}$, $\dfrac{dA}{dx} = 0$ when $x = \dfrac{12\pi}{\pi + 4}$. If

    $x = 0, \dfrac{12\pi}{\pi + 4}, 12$ then $A = 9, \dfrac{36}{\pi + 4}, \dfrac{36}{\pi}$ so the sum of the enclosed areas is

    (a) a maximum when $x = 12$ in. (when all of the wire is used for the circle)

    (b) a minimum when $x = 12\pi/(\pi + 4)$ in.

16. Let $C =$ cost (in dollars) of the trip, so

    $C = $ (operating cost per mile) $\cdot$ (number of miles) $+$ (wage per hour) $\cdot$ (number of hours)

    $= (1/100)(12 + x/6)(400) + 6(400/x) = 48 + 2x/3 + 2400/x$ for x in $[40, 70]$.

    $dC/dx = 2/3 - 2400/x^2$, $dC/dx = 0$ when $x^2 = 3600$, $x = 60$. If $x = 40, 60, 70$ then

    $C = 134\dfrac{2}{3}, 128, 128\dfrac{20}{21}$ so the most economical speed is 60 mph.

17. The altitude of the triangle (see figure)

is $\sqrt{y^2 - x^2/4}$ so $A = \dfrac{1}{2}x\sqrt{y^2 - x^2/4}$

where $x + 2y = 12$ thus $y = 6 - x/2$ and

$A = \dfrac{1}{2}x\sqrt{(6 - x/2)^2 - x^2/4} = \dfrac{1}{2}x\sqrt{36 - 6x}$

for $0 \le x \le 6$; $dA/dx = 9(4 - x)/(2\sqrt{36 - 6x})$,

$dA/dx = 0$ when $x = 4$ for $0 < x < 6$. If

$x = 0, 4, 6$ then $A = 0, 4\sqrt{3}, 0$ so the area

is maximum when $x = 4$ and $y = 6 - 4/2 = 4$,

which is an equilateral triangle.

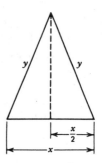

18. The area is (see figure)

$A\dfrac{1}{2}(2 \sin \theta)(4 + 4 \cos \theta)$

$\qquad = 4(\sin \theta + \sin \theta \cos \theta)$

for $0 \le \theta \le \pi/2$;

$dA/d\theta = 4(\cos \theta - \sin^2 \theta + \cos^2 \theta)$

$\qquad = 4(\cos \theta - [1 - \cos^2 \theta] + \cos^2 \theta)$

$\qquad = 4(2 \cos^2 \theta + \cos \theta - 1)$

$\qquad = 4(2 \cos \theta - 1)(\cos \theta + 1)$

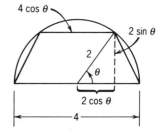

$dA/d\theta = 0$ when $\theta = \pi/3$ for $0 < \theta < \pi/2$. If $\theta = 0, \pi/3, \pi/2$ then $A = 0, 3\sqrt{3}, 4$ so the maximum area is $3\sqrt{3}$.

19. Let x be the length of each side of the squares and y the height of the frame, then the volume is $V = x^2 y$. The total length of the wire is L thus $8x + 4y = L$, $y = (L - 8x)/4$ so $V = x^2(L - 8x)/4 = (Lx^2 - 8x^3)/4$ for $0 \le x \le L/8$. $dV/dx = (2Lx - 24x^2)/4$, $dV/dx = 0$ for $0 < x < L/8$ when $x = L/12$. If $x = 0, L/12, L/8$ then $V = 0, L^3/1728, 0$ so the volume is greatest when $x = L/12$ and $y = L/12$.

20. Let $k = v_0^2/g$ then $R = k \sin 2\theta$ where we will assume that $0 \le \theta \le \pi/2$; $dR/d\theta = 2k \cos 2\theta$, $dR/d\theta = 0$ when $\cos 2\theta = 0$, $2\theta = \pi/2$, $\theta = \pi/4$. If $\theta = 0, \pi/4, \pi/2$ then $R = 0, k, 0$ so the maximum range is achieved when $\theta = \pi/4$ (or $45°$).

21. **(a)** The daily profit is

$\qquad P =$ (revenue) $-$ (production cost) $= 100x - (100,000 + 50x + 0.0025x^2)$

$\qquad\quad = -100,000 + 50x - 0.0025x^2$

for $0 \le x \le 7000$, so $dP/dx = 50 - 0.005x$ and $dP/dx = 0$ when $x = 10,000$. Because 10,000 is not in the interval $[0, 7000]$, the maximum profit must occur at an endpoint. When $x = 0$, $P = -100,000$; when $x = 7000$, $P = 127,500$ so 7000 units should be manufactured and sold daily.

(b) Yes, because $dP/dx > 0$ when $x = 7000$ so profit is increasing at this production level.

22. Let x and y be the dimensions shown in the figure, then the area of the rectangle is $A = xy$.

But $\left(\dfrac{x}{2}\right)^2 + y^2 = R^2$, thus

$y = \sqrt{R^2 - x^2/4} = \dfrac{1}{2}\sqrt{4R^2 - x^2}$

so $A = \dfrac{1}{2}x\sqrt{4R^2 - x^2}$ for $0 \le x \le 2R$.

$dA/dx = (2R^2 - x^2)/\sqrt{4R^2 - x^2}$,

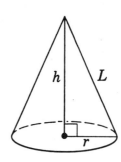

$dA/dx = 0$ when $x = \sqrt{2}R$. If $x = 0, \sqrt{2}R, 2R$ then $A = 0, R^2, 0$ so the greatest area occurs when $x = \sqrt{2}R$ and $y = \sqrt{2}R/2$.

23. Let h and r be the dimensions shown in the figure, then the volume is $V = \dfrac{1}{3}\pi r^2 h$.

But $r^2 + h^2 = L^2$ thus $r^2 = L^2 - h^2$ so

$V = \dfrac{1}{3}\pi(L^2 - h^2)h = \dfrac{1}{3}\pi(L^2 h - h^3)$

for $0 \le h \le L$. $\dfrac{dV}{dh} = \dfrac{1}{3}\pi(L^2 - 3h^2)$.

$\dfrac{dV}{dh} = 0$ when $h = L/\sqrt{3}$. If $h = 0, L/\sqrt{3}, 0$

then $V = 0, \dfrac{2\pi}{9\sqrt{3}}L^3, 0$ so the volume is as large as possible when $h = L/\sqrt{3}$ and $r = \sqrt{2/3}L$.

24. Let r and h be the dimensions shown in the figure, then the volume of the inscribed cylinder is $V = \pi r^2 h$. But

$r^2 + \left(\dfrac{h}{2}\right)^2 = R^2$ thus $r^2 = R^2 - \dfrac{h^2}{4}$

so $V = \pi\left(R^2 - \dfrac{h^2}{4}\right)h = \pi\left(R^2 h - \dfrac{h^3}{4}\right)$

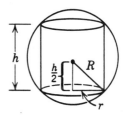

for $0 \le h \le 2R$. $\dfrac{dV}{dh} = \pi\left(R^2 - \dfrac{3}{4}h^2\right)$, $\dfrac{dV}{dh} = 0$

when $h = 2R/\sqrt{3}$. If $h = 0, 2R/\sqrt{3}, 2R$ then $V = 0, \dfrac{4\pi}{3\sqrt{3}}R^3, 0$ so the volume is largest when $h = 2R/\sqrt{3}$ and $r = \sqrt{2/3}R$.

25. Let r and h be the dimensions shown in the figure, then the surface area is $S = 2\pi rh + 2\pi r^2$.

But $r^2 + \left(\dfrac{h}{2}\right)^2 = R^2$ thus $h = 2\sqrt{R^2 - r^2}$ so

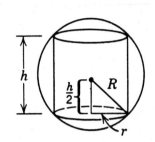

$S = 4\pi r\sqrt{R^2 - r^2} + 2\pi r^2$ for $0 \le r \le R$,

$\dfrac{dS}{dr} = \dfrac{4\pi(R^2 - 2r^2)}{\sqrt{R^2 - r^2}} + 4\pi r$. $\dfrac{dS}{dr} = 0$ when

$\dfrac{R^2 - 2r^2}{\sqrt{R^2 - r^2}} = -r$ \qquad (i)

$R^2 - 2r^2 = -r\sqrt{R^2 - r^2}$

$R^4 - 4R^2 r^2 + 4r^4 = r^2(R^2 - r^2)$

$5r^2 - 5R^2 r^2 + R^4 = 0$

and using the quadratic formula $r^2 = \dfrac{5R^2 \pm \sqrt{25R^4 - 20R^4}}{10} = \dfrac{5 \pm \sqrt{5}}{10}R^2$, $r = \sqrt{\dfrac{5 \pm \sqrt{5}}{10}}R$, of

which only $r = \sqrt{\dfrac{5 + \sqrt{5}}{10}}R$ satisfies (i). If $r = 0, \sqrt{\dfrac{5 + \sqrt{5}}{10}}R, 0$ then $S = 0, (5+\sqrt{5})\pi R^2, 2\pi R^2$

so the surface area is greatest when $r = \sqrt{\dfrac{5 + \sqrt{5}}{10}}R$ and, from $h = 2\sqrt{R^2 - r^2}$,

$h = 2\sqrt{\dfrac{5 - \sqrt{5}}{10}}R.$

26. Let R and H be the radius and height of the cone, and r and h the radius and height of the cylinder (see figure), then the volume of the cylinder is $V = \pi r^2 h$. By similar triangles (see figure) $\dfrac{H - h}{H} = \dfrac{r}{R}$ thus

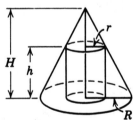

$h = \dfrac{H}{R}(R - r)$ so $V = \pi\dfrac{H}{R}(R - r)r^2 = \pi\dfrac{H}{R}(Rr^2 - r^3)$ for $0 \le r \le R$.

$\dfrac{dV}{dr} = \pi\dfrac{H}{R}(2Rr - 3r^2) = \pi\dfrac{H}{R}r(2R - 3r)$, $\dfrac{dV}{dr} = 0$ for $0 < r < R$ when $r = 2R/3$. If

$r = 0, 2R/3, R$ then $V = 0, 4\pi R^2 H/27, 0$ so the maximum volume is

$\dfrac{4\pi R^2 H}{27} = \dfrac{4}{9}\dfrac{1}{3}\pi R^2 H = \dfrac{4}{9} \cdot$ (volume of cone).

27. Let b and h be the dimensions shown in the figure, then the cross-sectional

area is $A = \dfrac{1}{2}h(5+b)$. But $h = 5\sin\theta$

and $b = 5 + 2(5\cos\theta) = 5 + 10\cos\theta$

so $A = \dfrac{5}{2}\sin\theta(10 + 10\cos\theta)$

$\qquad = 25\sin\theta(1 + \cos\theta)$ for $0 \le \theta \le \pi/2$.

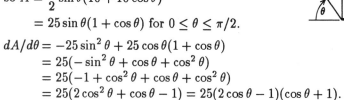

$dA/d\theta = -25\sin^2\theta + 25\cos\theta(1 + \cos\theta)$
$\qquad = 25(-\sin^2\theta + \cos\theta + \cos^2\theta)$
$\qquad = 25(-1 + \cos^2\theta + \cos\theta + \cos^2\theta)$
$\qquad = 25(2\cos^2\theta + \cos\theta - 1) = 25(2\cos\theta - 1)(\cos\theta + 1).$

$dA/d\theta = 0$ for $0 < \theta < \pi/2$ when $\cos\theta = 1/2$, $\theta = \pi/3$. If $\theta = 0, \pi/3, \pi/2$ then $A = 0, 75\sqrt{3}/4, 25$ so the cross-sectional area is greatest when $\theta = \pi/3$.

28. Let $x = $ number of steers per acre
     $\quad\;\; w = $ average market weight per steer
     $\quad\;\; T = $ total market weight per acre
     then $T = xw$ where $w = 2000 - 50(x - 20) = 3000 - 50x$
     so $T = x(3000 - 50x) = 3000x - 50x^2$ for $0 \le x \le 60$,

$dT/dx = 3000 - 100x$ and $dT/dx = 0$ when $x = 30$. If $x = 0, 30, 60$ then $T = 0, 45,000, 0$ so the total market weight per acre is largest when 30 steers per acre are allowed.

29. Let r and h be the radius and height of the cone (see figure). The slant height of any such cone will be R, the radius of the circular sheet. Refer to the solution of Exercise 23 to find that the largest volume is $\dfrac{2\pi}{9\sqrt{3}}R^3$.

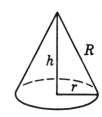

30. Let x be how far P is upstream from where the man starts (see figure), then the total time to reach T is

$t = $ (time from M to P) $+$ (time from P to T)

$\;\; = \dfrac{\sqrt{x^2 + 1}}{r_R} + \dfrac{1 - x}{r_W}$ for $0 \le x \le 1$,

where r_R and r_W are the rates at which he can row and walk, respectively.

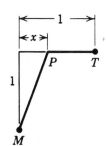

(a) $t = \dfrac{\sqrt{x^2+1}}{3} + \dfrac{1-x}{5}$, $\dfrac{dt}{dx} = \dfrac{x}{3\sqrt{x^2+1}} - \dfrac{1}{5}$ so $\dfrac{dt}{dx} = 0$ when $5x = 3\sqrt{x^2+1}$,

$25x^2 = 9(x^2+1)$, $x^2 = 9/16$, $x = 3/4$. If $x = 0, 3/4, 1$ then $t = 8/15, 7/15, \sqrt{2}/3$ so the time is a minimum when $x = 3/4$ mile.

(b) $t = \dfrac{\sqrt{x^2+1}}{4} + \dfrac{1-x}{5}$, $\dfrac{dt}{dx} = \dfrac{x}{4\sqrt{x^2+1}} - \dfrac{1}{5}$ so $\dfrac{dt}{dx} = 0$ when $x = 4/3$ which is not in the interval $[0,1]$. Check the endpoints to find that the time is a minimum when $x = 1$ (he should row directly to the town).

31. (a) $C'(x) = 4 + 0.2x$, $C'(100) = 24$ (b) $C'(100) = 24$

    (c) $C(101) - C(100) = 24.1$

    (d) $R(x) = 10x$, $R'(x) = 10$;

        $P(x) = R(x) - C(x)$, $P'(x) = R'(x) - C'(x) = 10 - (4 + 0.2x) = 6 - 0.2x$

32. (a) $R(x) = px$ but $p = 1000 - x$ so $R(x) = (1000 - x)x$

    (b) $P(x) = R(x) - C(x) = (1000 - x)x - (3000 + 20x) = -3000 + 980x - x^2$

    (c) $P'(x) = 980 - 2x$, $P'(x) = 0$ for $0 < x < 500$ when $x = 490$; test the points $0, 490, 500$ to find that the profit is a maximum when $x = 490$.

    (d) $P(490) = 237{,}100$ (e) $p = 1000 - x = 1000 - 490 = 510$.

33. Let $P(x,y)$ be a point on the curve $x^2 + y^2 = 1$. The distance between $P(x,y)$ and $P_0(2,0)$ is $D = \sqrt{(x-2)^2 + y^2}$, but $y^2 = 1 - x^2$ so $D = \sqrt{(x-2)^2 + 1 - x^2} = \sqrt{5 - 4x}$ for $-1 \le x \le 1$, $\dfrac{dD}{dx} = -\dfrac{2}{\sqrt{5-4x}}$ which has no critical points for $-1 < x < 1$. If $x = -1, 1$ then $D = 3, 1$ so the closest point occurs when $x = 1$ and $y = 0$.

34. Let $P(x,y)$ be a point on $y = \sqrt{x}$, then the distance D between P and $(2,0)$ is

$D = \sqrt{(x-2)^2 + y^2} = \sqrt{(x-2)^2 + x} = \sqrt{x^2 - 3x + 4}$, for $0 \le x \le 3$. For convenience we find the extrema for D^2 instead, so $D^2 = x^2 - 3x + 4$, $dD^2/dx = 2x - 3 = 0$ when $x = 3/2$. If $x = 0, 3/2, 3$ then $D^2 = 4, 7/4, 4$ so $D = 2, \sqrt{7}/2, 2$. The points $(0,0)$ and $(3, \sqrt{3})$ are at the greatest distance, and $(3/2, \sqrt{3/2})$ the shortest distance from $(2,0)$.

35. The area of the window is $A = 2rh + \pi r^2/2$,

the perimeter is $p = 2r + 2h + \pi r$ thus

$h = \dfrac{1}{2}[p - (2 + \pi)r]$ so

$A = r[p - (2 + \pi)r] + \pi r^2/2$

$\quad = pr - (2 + \pi/2)r^2$ for $0 \le r \le p/(2 + \pi)$,

$dA/dr = p - (4 + \pi)r$, $dA/dr = 0$ when

$r = p/(4 + \pi)$. $d^2A/dr^2 < 0$, so A is

maximum when $r = p/(4 + \pi)$.

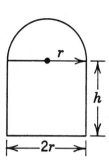

36. The vertical line of length D divides the triangle into two smaller triangles each with a base of length D. The altitudes of these triangles are $x - a$ and $b - x$ so the area A of the large triangle is $A = (x - a)D/2 + (b - x)D/2 = (b - a)D/2$. The area is maximum when D is maximum. The slope of the line is $(kb^2 - ka^2)/(b - a) = k(a + b)$ so its equation is $y - ka^2 = k(a + b)(x - a)$, or $y = k(a + b)x - kab$. Thus $D = k(a + b)x - kab - kx^2$ for $a \le x \le b$; $dD/dx = k(a + b) - 2kx$ which is 0 when $x = (a + b)/2$. If $x = a, (a + b)/2, b$ then $D = 0, k(b - a)^2/4, 0$ so the area of the triangle is greatest when $D = k(b - a)^2/4$, and its area is $A = k(b - a)^3/8$.

37. **(a)** Let $x = $ diameter of the sphere, $y = $ length of an edge of the cube. The combined volume is $V = \dfrac{1}{6}\pi x^3 + y^3$ and the surface area is $S = \pi x^2 + 6y^2 = $ constant. Thus

$y = \dfrac{(S - \pi x^2)^{1/2}}{6^{1/2}}$ and $V = \dfrac{\pi}{6}x^3 + \dfrac{(S - \pi x^2)^{3/2}}{6^{3/2}}$ for $0 \le x \le \sqrt{\dfrac{S}{\pi}}$;

$\dfrac{dV}{dx} = \dfrac{\pi}{2}x^2 - \dfrac{3\pi}{6^{3/2}}x(S - \pi x^2)^{1/2} = \dfrac{\pi}{2\sqrt{6}}x(\sqrt{6}x - \sqrt{S - \pi x^2})$. $\dfrac{dV}{dx} = 0$ when $x = 0$, or

when $\sqrt{6}x = \sqrt{S - \pi x^2}$, $6x^2 = S - \pi x^2$, $x^2 = \dfrac{S}{6 + \pi}$, $x = \sqrt{\dfrac{S}{6 + \pi}}$. If $x = 0$, $\sqrt{\dfrac{S}{6 + \pi}}$,

$\sqrt{\dfrac{S}{\pi}}$, then $V = \dfrac{S^{3/2}}{6^{3/2}}, \dfrac{S^{3/2}}{6\sqrt{6 + \pi}}, \dfrac{S^{3/2}}{6\sqrt{\pi}}$ so that V is smallest when $x = \sqrt{\dfrac{S}{6 + \pi}}$, and hence

when $y = \sqrt{\dfrac{S}{6 + \pi}}$, thus $x = y$.

(b) From part (a), the sum of the volumes is greatest when there is no cube.

38. Let x and y be as shown in the figure,

then the area enclosed is $A = (x + 100)y$.

But $x + (100 + x) + 2y = 200$ because there

are 200 ft of additional fence; solve this

equation for y to get $y = 50 - x$ so

$A = (x + 100)(50 - x)$

$\quad = 5000 - 50x - x^2$ for $0 \le x \le 50$,

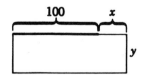

$dA/dx = -50 - 2x$ which has no critical points for $0 < x < 50$. If $x = 0, 50$ then $A = 5000, 0$ so the largest area is enclosed when $x = 0$ and $y = 50$. Use 50 ft along each side perpendicular to the original fence and the remaining (100 ft) along the side parallel to the original fence.

39. **(a)** Let $y = x^2 - 3x + 2$ for $1 \leq x \leq 5/2$, then $dy/dx = 2x - 3$, $dy/dx = 0$ when $x = 3/2$. If $x = 1, 3/2, 5/2$ then $y = 0, -1/4, 3/4$ so $-1/4 \leq x^2 - 3x + 2 \leq 3/4$ for $1 \leq x \leq 5/2$. Thus $|x^2 - 3x + 2| \leq 3/4$ so $M = 3/4$.

    (b) There are no critical values for $3/2 < x < 7/4$. If $x = 3/2, 7/4$ then $y = -1/4, -3/16$ so $-1/4 \leq x^2 - 3x + 2 \leq -3/16$. Thus $|x^2 - 3x + 2| \geq 3/16$ so $m = 3/16$.

40. Let $y = x/2 - \sin x$ for $0 \leq x \leq \pi$, then $dy/dx = 1/2 - \cos x$, $dy/dx = 0$ when $\cos x = 1/2$ or $x = \pi/3$. If $x = 0, \pi/3, \pi$ then $y = 0, \pi/6 - \sqrt{3}/2, \pi/2$ thus $\pi/6 - \sqrt{3}/2 \leq x/2 - \sin x \leq \pi/2$ and $|x/2 - \sin x| \leq \pi/2$ so the graphs are farthest apart when $x = \pi$.

41. Let $v = $ speed of light in the medium. The total time required for the light to travel from A to P to B is

$$t = \text{(total distance from } A \text{ to } P \text{ to } B)/v = \frac{1}{v}(\sqrt{(c-x)^2 + a^2} + \sqrt{x^2 + b^2}),$$

$$\frac{dt}{dx} = \frac{1}{v}\left[-\frac{c-x}{\sqrt{(c-x)^2 + a^2}} + \frac{x}{\sqrt{x^2 + b^2}}\right]$$

and $\dfrac{dt}{dx} = 0$ when $\dfrac{x}{\sqrt{x^2 + b^2}} = \dfrac{c-x}{\sqrt{(c-x)^2 + a^2}}$. But $x/\sqrt{x^2 + b^2} = \sin\theta_2$ and

$(c-x)/\sqrt{(c-x)^2 + a^2} = \sin\theta_1$ thus $dt/dx = 0$ when $\sin\theta_2 = \sin\theta_1$ so $\theta_2 = \theta_1$.

42. The total time required for the light to travel from A to P to B is

$$t = \text{(time from } A \text{ to } P) + \text{(time from } P \text{ to } B) = \frac{\sqrt{x^2 + a^2}}{v_1} + \frac{\sqrt{(c-x)^2 + b^2}}{v_2},$$

$$\frac{dt}{dx} = \frac{x}{v_1\sqrt{x^2 + a^2}} - \frac{c-x}{v_2\sqrt{(c-x)^2 + b^2}} \text{ but } x/\sqrt{x^2 + a^2} = \sin\theta_1 \text{ and}$$

$(c-x)/\sqrt{(c-x)^2 + b^2} = \sin\theta_2$ thus $\dfrac{dt}{dx} = \dfrac{\sin\theta_1}{v_1} - \dfrac{\sin\theta_2}{v_2}$ so $\dfrac{dt}{dx} = 0$ when $\dfrac{\sin\theta_1}{v_1} = \dfrac{\sin\theta_2}{v_2}$.

43. **(a)** The rate at which the farmer walks is analogous to the speed of light in Fermat's principle.

    (b) the best path occurs when $\theta_1 = \theta_2$ (see figure).

    (c) by similar triangles,

$$x/(1/4) = (1-x)/(3/4)$$
$$3x = 1 - x$$
$$4x = 1$$
$$x = 1/4.$$

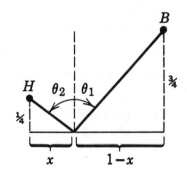

EXERCISE SET 4.8

1. Let x and y be two numbers, then their product is $P = xy$. But $x + y = 20$ thus $y = 20 - x$ so
$$P = x(20 - x) = 20x - x^2 \text{ for } -\infty < x < +\infty,$$
$$dP/dx = 20 - 2x, \ dP/dx = 0 \text{ when } x = 10, \ d^2P/dx^2 = -2 \text{ so}$$
    (a) P is a maximum when $x = 10$ and $y = 10$ and
    (b) P has no minimum.

2. Let x and y be the dimensions of a rectangle; the perimeter is $p = 2x + 2y$. But $A = xy$ thus $y = A/x$ so $p = 2x + 2A/x$ for $x > 0$, $dp/dx = 2 - 2A/x^2 = 2(x^2 - A)/x^2$, $dp/dx = 0$ when $x = \sqrt{A}$, $d^2p/dx^2 = 4A/x^3 > 0$ if $x > 0$ so
    (a) p is a minimum when $x = \sqrt{A}$ and $y = \sqrt{A}$ and
    (b) p has no maximum.

3. Let $x =$ length of each side that uses the \$1 per foot fencing,
    $y =$ length of each side that uses the \$2 per foot fencing.
    The cost is $C = (1)(2x) + (2)(2y) = 2x + 4y$, but $A = xy = 3200$ thus $y = 3200/x$ so
$$C = 2x + 12800/x \text{ for } x > 0,$$
$$dC/dx = 2 - 12800/x^2, \ dC/dx = 0 \text{ when } x = 80, \ d^2C/dx^2 > 0 \text{ so}$$
    C is least when $x = 80$, $y = 40$.

4. Let $x =$ length of each edge of base, $y =$ height. The cost is
    $C = $ (cost of top and bottom) $+$ (cost of sides) $= (2)(2x^2) + (3)(4xy) = 4x^2 + 12xy$,
    but $V = x^2y = 2250$ thus $y = 2250/x^2$ so $C = 4x^2 + 27000/x$ for $x > 0$, $dC/dx = 8x - 27000/x^2$, $dC/dx = 0$ when $x = \sqrt[3]{3375} = 15$, $d^2C/dx^2 > 0$ so C is least when $x = 15$, $y = 10$.

5. Let $x =$ length of each edge of base, $y =$ height, $k = $ \$/cm^2 for the sides. The cost is
    $C = (2k)(2x^2) + (k)(4xy) = 4k(x^2 + xy)$, but $V = x^2y = 2000$ thus $y = 2000/x^2$ so
    $C = 4k(x^2 + 2000/x)$ for $x > 0$ $dC/dx = 4k(2x - 2000/x^2)$, $dC/dx = 0$ when
    $x = \sqrt[3]{1000} = 10$, $d^2C/dx^2 > 0$ so C is least when $x = 10$, $y = 20$.

6. Let x and y be the dimensions shown in the figure and V the volume, then $V = x^2y$. The amount of material is to be 1000 ft^2, thus
    (area of base) + (area of sides) = 1000,

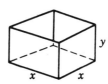

$x^2 + 4xy = 1000$, $y = \dfrac{1000 - x^2}{4x}$ so $V = x^2\dfrac{1000 - x^2}{4x} = \dfrac{1}{4}(1000x - x^3)$ for $0 < x \le 10\sqrt{10}$.

$\dfrac{dV}{dx} = \dfrac{1}{4}(1000 - 3x^2)$, $\dfrac{dV}{dx} = 0$ when $x = \sqrt{1000/3} = 10\sqrt{10/3}$. If $x = 0, 10\sqrt{10/3}, 10\sqrt{10}$

then $V = 0, \dfrac{5000}{3}\sqrt{10/3}, 0$; the volume is greatest for $x = 10\sqrt{10/3}$ ft and $y = 5\sqrt{10/3}$ ft.

7. Let $x =$ height and width, $y =$ length. The surface area is $S = 2x^2 + 3xy$ where $x^2y = V$, so $y = V/x^2$ and $S = 2x^2 + 3V/x$ for $x > 0$; $dS/dx = 4x - 3V/x^2$, $dS/dx = 0$ when $x = \sqrt[3]{3V/4}$,

$d^2S/dx^2 > 0$ so S is minimum when $x = \sqrt[3]{\dfrac{3V}{4}}$, $y = \dfrac{4}{3}\sqrt[3]{\dfrac{3V}{4}}$.

8. $V = \pi r^2 h$ where $S = 2\pi r^2 + 2\pi rh$ so $h = \dfrac{S - 2\pi r^2}{2\pi r}$, $V = \dfrac{1}{2}(Sr - 2\pi r^3)$ for $r > 0$.

$\dfrac{dV}{dr} = \dfrac{1}{2}(S - 6\pi r^2) = 0$ if $r = \sqrt{S/(6\pi)}$, $\dfrac{d^2V}{dr^2} = -6\pi r < 0$ so V is maximum when

$r = \sqrt{S/(6\pi)}$ and $h = \dfrac{S - 2\pi r^2}{2\pi r} = \dfrac{S - 2\pi r^2}{2\pi r^2}r = \dfrac{S - S/3}{S/3}r = 2r$, thus the height is equal to the diameter of the base.

9. The surface area is $S = \pi r^2 + 2\pi rh$
where $V = \pi r^2 h = 500$ so $h = 500/(\pi r^2)$
and $S = \pi r^2 + 1000/r$ for $r > 0$;
$dS/dr = 2\pi r - 1000/r^2 = (2\pi r^3 - 1000)/r^2$,
$dS/dr = 0$ when $r = \sqrt[3]{500/\pi}$, $d^2S/dr^2 > 0$
for $r > 0$ so S is minimum when
$r = \sqrt[3]{500/\pi}$ and
$h = \dfrac{500}{\pi r^2} = \dfrac{500}{\pi r^3}r = \dfrac{500}{\pi(500/\pi)}\sqrt[3]{500/\pi}$
$\quad = \sqrt[3]{500/\pi}$.

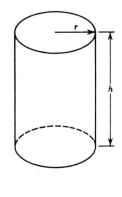

10. The area of the sheet of paper is
$A = xy$ where $(x - 2)(y - 4) = 72$,
$y = 4(x + 16)/(x - 2)$ so
$A = 4(x^2 + 16x)/(x - 2)$ for $x > 2$,
$dA/dx = 4(x^2 - 4x - 32)/(x - 2)^2$
$\quad = 4(x - 8)(x + 4)/(x - 2)^2$,
$dA/dx = 0$ for $x > 2$ when $x = 8$, by
the first derivative test A is
least when $x = 8$, $y = 16$.

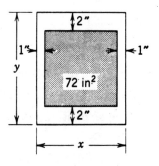

11. The area of the paper is

$A = \pi r L = \pi r \sqrt{r^2 + h^2}$, but

$V = \dfrac{1}{3}\pi r^2 h = 10$ thus $h = 30/(\pi r^2)$

so $A = \pi r \sqrt{r^2 + 900/(\pi^2 r^4)}$.

To simplify the computations let $S = A^2$,

$S = \pi^2 r^2 \left(r^2 + \dfrac{900}{\pi^2 r^4} \right) = \pi^2 r^4 + \dfrac{900}{r^2}$ for $r > 0$,

$\dfrac{dS}{dr} = 4\pi^2 r^3 - \dfrac{1800}{r^3} = \dfrac{4(\pi^2 r^6 - 450)}{r^3}$, $dS/dr = 0$ when $r = \sqrt[6]{450/\pi^2}$,

$d^2 S/dr^2 > 0$, so S and hence A is least when $r = \sqrt[6]{450/\pi^2}$, $h = \dfrac{30}{\pi}\sqrt[3]{\pi^2/450}$.

12. If $P(x_0, y_0)$ is on the curve $y = 1 - x^2$, then $y_0 = 1 - x_0^2$. At P the slope of the tangent line is $-2x_0$ so its equation is $y - (1 - x_0^2) = -2x_0(x - x_0)$, or $y = -2x_0 x + x_0^2 + 1$. The y-intercept is $x_0^2 + 1$ and the x-intercept is $\dfrac{1}{2}(x_0 + 1/x_0)$ so the area A of the triangle is

$A = \dfrac{1}{4}(x_0^2 + 1)(x_0 + 1/x_0) = \dfrac{1}{4}(x_0^3 + 2x_0 + 1/x_0)$ for $0 \le x_0 \le 1$.

$dA/dx_0 = \dfrac{1}{4}(3x_0^2 + 2 - 1/x_0^2) = \dfrac{1}{4}(3x_0^4 + 2x_0^2 - 1)/x_0^2$ which is 0 when $x_0^2 = -1$ (reject), or

when $x_0^2 = 1/3$ so $x_0 = 1/\sqrt{3}$. $d^2 A/dx_0^2 = \dfrac{1}{4}(6x_0 + 2/x_0^3) > 0$ at $x_0 = 1/\sqrt{3}$ so a relative minimum and hence the absolute minimum occurs there.

13. Let (x, y) be a point on the curve, then the square of the distance between (x, y) and $(0, 2)$ is $S = x^2 + (y - 2)^2$ where $x^2 - y^2 = 1$, $x^2 = y^2 + 1$ so

$S = (y^2 + 1) + (y - 2)^2 = 2y^2 - 4y + 5$ for any y, $dS/dy = 4y - 4$, $dS/dy = 0$ when $y = 1$,

$d^2 S/dy^2 > 0$ so S is least when $y = 1$ and $x = \pm\sqrt{2}$.

14. The square of the distance between a point (x, y) on the curve and the point $(0, 9)$ is

$S = x^2 + (y - 9)^2$ where $x = 2y^2$ so $S = 4y^4 + (y - 9)^2$ for any y,

$dS/dy = 16y^3 + 2(y - 9) = 2(8y^3 + y - 9)$, $dS/dy = 0$ when $y = 1$ (which is the only real solution), $d^2 S/dy^2 > 0$ so S is least when $y = 1$, $x = 2$.

15. The area of the triangle is $A = \dfrac{1}{2}ab$. Equate slopes to get $\dfrac{b - 3}{0 - 1} = \dfrac{0 - 3}{a - 1}$, $b = \dfrac{3a}{a - 1}$ so

$A = \dfrac{3}{2}\dfrac{a^2}{a - 1}$ for $a > 1$, $\dfrac{dA}{da} = \dfrac{3a(a - 2)}{(a - 1)^2}$, $\dfrac{dA}{da} = 0$ for $a > 1$ when $a = 2$.

(a) there is no maximum for A because $\lim\limits_{a \to 1+} A = +\infty$.

(b) by the first derivative test A is minimum when $a = 2$ so the slope is $m = \dfrac{0-3}{2-1} = -3$.

16. The profit is

$$P = (\text{profit on nondefective}) - (\text{loss on defective}) = 100(x-y) - 20y = 100x - 120y$$

but $y = 0.01x + 0.00003x^2$ so $P = 100x - 120(0.01x + 0.00003x^2) = 98.8x - 0.0036x^2$ for $x > 0$, $dP/dx = 98.8 - 0.0072x$, $dP/dx = 0$ when $x = 98.8/0.0072 \approx 13,722$, $d^2P/dx^2 < 0$ so the profit is maximum at a production level of about 13,722 pounds.

17. The distance between the particles is $D = \sqrt{(1-t-t)^2 + (t-2t)^2} = \sqrt{5t^2 - 4t + 1}$ for $t \geq 0$. For convenience, we minimize D^2 instead, so $D^2 = 5t^2 - 4t + 1$, $dD^2/dt = 10t - 4$, which is 0 when $t = 2/5$. $d^2D^2/dt^2 > 0$ so D^2 and hence D is minimum when $t = 2/5$. The minimum distance is $D = 1/\sqrt{5}$.

18. The distance between the particles is $D = \sqrt{(2t-t)^2 + (2-t^2)^2} = \sqrt{t^4 - 3t^2 + 4}$ for $t \geq 0$. For convenience we minimize D^2 instead so $D^2 = t^4 - 3t^2 + 4$, $dD^2/dt = 4t^3 - 6t = 4t(t^2 - 3/2)$, which is 0 for $t > 0$ when $t = \sqrt{3/2}$. $d^2D^2/dt^2 = 12t^2 - 6 > 0$ when $t = \sqrt{3/2}$ so D^2 and hence D is minimum there. The minimum distance is $D = \sqrt{7}/2$.

19. If $P(x_0, y_0)$ is on the curve $y = 1/x^2$, then $y_0 = 1/x_0^2$. At P the slope of the tangent line is $-2/x_0^3$ so its equation is $y - \dfrac{1}{x_0^2} = -\dfrac{2}{x_0^3}(x - x_0)$, or $y = -\dfrac{2}{x_0^3}x + \dfrac{3}{x_0^2}$. The tangent line crosses the y-axis at $\dfrac{3}{x_0^2}$, and the x-axis at $\dfrac{3}{2}x_0$. The length of the segment then is

$$L = \sqrt{\dfrac{9}{x_0^4} + \dfrac{9}{4}x_0^2} \text{ for } x_0 > 0. \text{ For convenience, we minimize } L^2 \text{ instead, so } L^2 = \dfrac{9}{x_0^4} + \dfrac{9}{4}x_0^2,$$

$\dfrac{dL^2}{dx_0} = -\dfrac{36}{x_0^5} + \dfrac{9}{2}x_0 = \dfrac{9(x_0^6 - 8)}{2x_0^5}$, which is 0 when $x_0^6 = 8$, $x_0 = \sqrt{2}$. $\dfrac{d^2L^2}{dx_0^2} > 0$ so L^2 and hence L is minimum when $x_0 = \sqrt{2}$, $y_0 = 1/2$.

20. $I = k\dfrac{\cos\phi}{\ell^2}$, k the constant of proportionality. If h is the height of the lamp above the table then $\cos\phi = h/\ell$ and $\ell = \sqrt{h^2 + r^2}$ so $I = k\dfrac{h}{\ell^3} = k\dfrac{h}{(h^2 + r^2)^{3/2}}$ for $h > 0$, $\dfrac{dI}{dh} = k\dfrac{r^2 - 2h^2}{(h^2 + r^2)^{5/2}}$, $\dfrac{dI}{dh} = 0$ when $h = r/\sqrt{2}$, by the first derivative test I is maximum when $h = r/\sqrt{2}$.

21. At each point (x, y) on the curve the slope of the tangent line is $m = \dfrac{dy}{dx} = -\dfrac{2x}{(1+x^2)^2}$ for any x, $\dfrac{dm}{dx} = \dfrac{2(3x^2 - 1)}{(1+x^2)^3}$, $\dfrac{dm}{dx} = 0$ when $x = \pm 1/\sqrt{3}$, by the first derivative test the only relative

maximum occurs at $x = -1/\sqrt{3}$, which is the absolute maximum because $\lim\limits_{x \to \pm\infty} m = 0$. The tangent line has greatest slope at the point $(-1/\sqrt{3}, 3/4)$.

22. The area of the triangle is $A = \dfrac{1}{2}hb$.

    By similar triangles (see figure)

    $$\frac{b/2}{h} = \frac{R}{\sqrt{h^2 - 2Rh}},$$

    $$b = \frac{2Rh}{\sqrt{h^2 - 2Rh}} \text{ so}$$

    $$A = \frac{Rh^2}{\sqrt{h^2 - 2Rh}} \text{ for } h > 2R,$$

    $$\frac{dA}{dh} = \frac{Rh^2(h - 3R)}{(h^2 - 2Rh)^{3/2}}, \frac{dA}{dh} = 0 \text{ for } h > 2R$$

    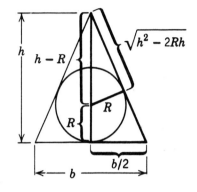

    when $h = 3R$, by the first derivative test A is minimum when $h = 3R$. If $h = 3R$ then $b = 2\sqrt{3}R$ (the triangle is equilateral).

23. The volume of the cone is $V = \dfrac{1}{3}\pi r^2 h$.

    By similar triangles (see figure)

    $$\frac{r}{h} = \frac{R}{\sqrt{h^2 - 2Rh}}, r = \frac{Rh}{\sqrt{h^2 - 2Rh}} \text{ so}$$

    $$V = \frac{1}{3}\pi R^2 \frac{h^3}{h^2 - 2Rh} = \frac{1}{3}\pi R^2 \frac{h^2}{h - 2R}$$

    $$\text{for } h > 2R, \frac{dV}{dh} = \frac{1}{3}\pi R^2 \frac{h(h - 4R)}{(h - 2R)^2},$$

    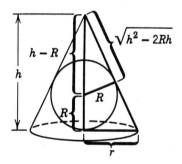

    $$\frac{dV}{dh} = 0 \text{ for } h > 2R \text{ when } h = 4R,$$

    by the first derivative test V is minimum when $h = 4R$. If $h = 4R$ then $r = \sqrt{2}R$.

24. $$s = (x_1 - \bar{x})^2 + (x_2 - \bar{x})^2 + \cdots + (x_n - \bar{x})^2,$$
    $$ds/d\bar{x} = -2(x_1 - \bar{x}) - 2(x_2 - \bar{x}) - \cdots - 2(x_n - \bar{x}),$$
    $$ds/d\bar{x} = 0 \text{ when}$$

    $$(x_1 - \bar{x}) + (x_2 - \bar{x}) + \cdots + (x_n - \bar{x}) = 0$$
    $$(x_1 + x_2 + \cdots x_n) - (\bar{x} + \bar{x} + \cdots + \bar{x}) = 0$$
    $$(x_1 + x_2 + \cdots + x_n) - n\bar{x} = 0$$

    $$\bar{x} = \frac{1}{n}(x_1 + x_2 + \cdots + x_n),$$

    $d^2 s/d\bar{x}^2 = 2 + 2 + \cdots + 2 = 2n > 0$, so s is minimum when $\bar{x} = \dfrac{1}{n}(x_1 + x_2 + \cdots + x_n)$.

25. With x and y as shown in the figure, the maximum length of pipe will be the smallest value of $L = x + y$. By similar triangles

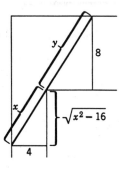

$$\frac{y}{8} = \frac{x}{\sqrt{x^2 - 16}}, \ y = \frac{8x}{\sqrt{x^2 - 16}} \text{ so}$$

$$L = x + \frac{8x}{\sqrt{x^2 - 16}} \text{ for } x > 4,$$

$$\frac{dL}{dx} = 1 - \frac{128}{(x^2 - 16)^{3/2}}, \ \frac{dL}{dx} = 0 \text{ when}$$

$$(x^2 - 16)^{3/2} = 128$$
$$x^2 - 16 = 128^{2/3} = 16(2^{2/3})$$
$$x^2 = 16(1 + 2^{2/3})$$
$$x = 4(1 + 2^{2/3})^{1/2},$$

$d^2L/dx^2 = 384x/(x^2 - 16)^{5/2} > 0$ if $x > 4$ so L is smallest when $x = 4(1 + 2^{2/3})^{1/2}$. For this value of x, $L = 4(1 + 2^{2/3})^{3/2}$.

26. Let L, L_1, and L_2 be as shown in the figure, then $L = L_1 + L_2 = 8 \csc \theta + \sec \theta$,

$$\frac{dL}{d\theta} = -8 \csc \theta \cot \theta + \sec \theta \tan \theta, \ 0 < \theta < \pi/2$$

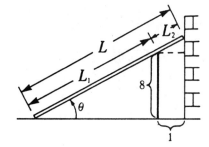

$$= -\frac{8 \cos \theta}{\sin^2 \theta} + \frac{\sin \theta}{\cos^2 \theta} = \frac{-8 \cos^3 \theta + \sin^3 \theta}{\sin^2 \theta \cos^2 \theta};$$

$$\frac{dL}{d\theta} = 0 \text{ if } \sin^3 \theta = 8 \cos^3 \theta, \ \tan^3 \theta = 8,$$

$\tan \theta = 2$ which gives the absolute minimum

for L because $\lim\limits_{\theta \to 0^+} L = \lim\limits_{\theta \to \pi/2^-} L = +\infty$. If $\tan \theta = 2$, then $\csc \theta = \sqrt{5}/2$ and $\sec \theta = \sqrt{5}$ so $L = 8(\sqrt{5}/2) + \sqrt{5} = 5\sqrt{5}$ ft.

27. Let x = distance from the weaker light source, I = the intensity at that point, and k the constant of proportionality. Then

$$I = \frac{kS}{x^2} + \frac{8kS}{(90 - x)^2} \text{ for } 0 < x < 90; \ \frac{dI}{dx} = -\frac{2kS}{x^3} + \frac{16kS}{(90 - x)^3} = \frac{2kS[8x^3 - (90 - x)^3]}{x^3(90 - x)^3},$$

which is 0 when $8x^3 = (90 - x)^3$, $2x = 90 - x$, $x = 30$. $\frac{dI}{dx} < 0$ if $x < 30$, and $\frac{dI}{dx} > 0$ if $x > 30$, so the intensity is minimum at a distance of 30 cm from the weaker source.

28. If $f(x_0)$ is a maximum then $f(x) \leq f(x_0)$ for all x in some open interval containing x_0 thus $\sqrt{f(x)} \leq \sqrt{f(x_0)}$ because $\sqrt{x}$ is an increasing function, so $\sqrt{f(x_0)}$ is a maximum of $\sqrt{f(x)}$ at x_0. The proof is similar for a minimum value, simply replace $\leq$ by $\geq$.

29. Minimize $S = L^2 = (x - x_1)^2 + (y - y_1)^2$ where $ax + by + c = 0$. If $b \neq 0$ then $y = -\dfrac{a}{b}x - \dfrac{c}{b}$ so

$$S = (x - x_1)^2 + \left(-\frac{a}{b}x - \frac{c}{b} - y_1\right)^2, \quad dS/dx = 2(x - x_1)^2 + 2\left(-\frac{a}{b}x - \frac{c}{b} - y_1\right)^2\left(-\frac{a}{b}\right),$$

$dS/dx = 0$ when $x = \dfrac{b^2 x_1 - aby_1 - ac}{a^2 + b^2}$, $d^2 S/dx^2 = 2(1 + a^2/b^2) > 0$ so S and hence L is minimum. Substitution of this value into the formula for S and simplification eventually gives $S = \dfrac{(ax_1 + by_1 + c)^2}{a^2 + b^2}$ so $L = \dfrac{|ax_1 + by_1 + c|}{\sqrt{a^2 + b^2}}$. The special case for $b = 0$ is treated in a similar way.

EXERCISE SET 4.9

1. $f(x) = x^2 - 2$, $f'(x) = 2x$, $x_{n+1} = x_n - \dfrac{x_n^2 - 2}{2x_n}$

   $x_1 = 1$, $x_2 = 1.5$, $x_3 = 1.416666667, \cdots, x_5 = x_6 = 1.414213562$

2. $f(x) = x^2 - 7$, $f'(x) = 2x$, $x_{n+1} = x_n - \dfrac{x_n^2 - 7}{2x_n}$

   $x_1 = 3$, $x_2 = 2.666666667$, $x_3 = 2.645833333, \cdots, x_5 = x_6 = 2.645751311$

3. $f(x) = x^3 - 6$, $f'(x) = 3x^2$, $x_{n+1} = x_n - \dfrac{x_n^3 - 6}{3x_n^2}$

   $x_1 = 2$, $x_2 = 1.833333333$, $x_3 = 1.817263545, \cdots, x_5 = x_6 = 1.817120593$

4. $f(x) = x^3 + x - 1$, $f'(x) = 3x^2 + 1$, $x_{n+1} = x_n - \dfrac{x_n^3 + x_n - 1}{3x_n^2 + 1}$

   $x_1 = 1$, $x_2 = 0.75$, $x_3 = 0.686046512, \cdots, x_5 = x_6 = 0.682327804$

5. $f(x) = x^3 - x + 3$, $f'(x) = 3x^2 - 1$, $x_{n+1} = x_n - \dfrac{x_n^3 - x_n + 3}{3x_n^2 - 1}$

   $x_1 = -2$, $x_2 = -1.727272727$, $x_3 = -1.673691174, \cdots, x_5 = x_6 = -1.671699882$

6. $f(x) = x^5 - x + 1$, $f'(x) = 5x^4 - 1$, $x_{n+1} = x_n - \dfrac{x_n^5 - x_n + 1}{5x_n^4 - 1}$

   $x_1 = -1$, $x_2 = -1.25$, $x_3 = -1.178459394, \cdots, x_6 = x_7 = -1.167303978$

7. $f(x) = x^5 + x^4 - 5$, $f'(x) = 5x^4 + 4x^3$, $x_{n+1} = x_n - \dfrac{x_n^5 + x_n^4 - 5}{5x_n^4 + 4x_n^3}$

   $x_1 = 1$, $x_2 = 1.333333333$, $x_3 = 1.239420573$, $\cdots$, $x_6 = x_7 = 1.224439550$

8. $f(x) = 2x^2 + 4x - 3$, $f'(x) = 4x + 4$, $x_{n+1} = x_n - \dfrac{2x_n^2 + 4x_n - 3}{4x_n + 4}$

   $x_1 = -3$, $x_2 = -2.625$, $x_3 = -2.581730769$, $\cdots$, $x_5 = x_6 = -2.581138830$

9. $f(x) = 2x^2 + 4x - 3$, $f'(x) = 4x + 4$, $x_{n+1} = x_n - \dfrac{2x_n^2 + 4x_n - 3}{4x_n + 4}$

   $x_1 = 1$, $x_2 = 0.625$, $x_3 = 0.581730769$, $\cdots$, $x_5 = x_6 = 0.581138830$

10. $f(x) = x^4 + x - 3$, $f'(x) = 4x^3 + 1$, $x_{n+1} = x_n - \dfrac{x_n^4 + x_n - 3}{4x_n^3 + 1}$

    $x_1 = 1$, $x_2 = 1.2$, $x_3 = 1.165419616$, $\cdots$, $x_5 = x_6 = 1.164035140$

11. $f(x) = x^4 + x - 3$, $f'(x) = 4x^3 + 1$, $x_{n+1} = x_n - \dfrac{x_n^4 + x_n - 3}{4x_n^3 + 1}$

    $x_1 = -2$, $x_2 = -1.645161290$, $x_3 = -1.485723955$, $\cdots$, $x_6 = x_7 = -1.452626879$

12. $f(x) = x^5 - 5x^3 - 2$, $f'(x) = 5x^4 - 15x^2$, $x_{n+1} = x_n - \dfrac{x_n^5 - 5x_n^3 - 2}{5x_n^4 - 15x_n^2}$

    $x_1 = 2$, $x_2 = 2.5$, $x_3 = 2.327384615$, $\cdots$, $x_7 = x_8 = 2.273791732$

13. $f(x) = 2\sin x - x$, $f'(x) = 2\cos x - 1$, $x_{n+1} = x_n - \dfrac{2\sin x_n - x_n}{2\cos x_n - 1}$

    $x_1 = 2$, $x_2 = 1.900995594$, $x_3 = 1.895511645$, $x_4 = x_5 = 1.895494267$

14. $f(x) = \sin x - x^2$, $f'(x) = \cos x - 2x$, $x_{n+1} = x_n - \dfrac{\sin x_n - x_n^2}{\cos x_n - 2x_n}$

    $x_1 = 1$, $x_2 = 0.891395995$, $x_3 = 0.876984845$, $\cdots$, $x_5 = x_6 = 0.876726215$

15. $f(x) = x - \tan x$, $f'(x) = 1 - \sec^2 x = -\tan^2 x$, $x_{n+1} = x_n + \dfrac{x_n - \tan x_n}{\tan^2 x_n}$

    $x_1 = 4.5$, $x_2 = 4.493613903$, $x_3 = 4.493409655$, $x_4 = x_5 = 4.493409458$

16. (a) $f(x) = \dfrac{1}{x} - a$, $f'(x) = -\dfrac{1}{x^2}$, $x_{n+1} = x_n(2 - ax_n)$

    (b) $a = 17$; $x_1 = 0.05$, $x_2 = 0.0575$, $x_3 = 0.058793750$, $x_4 = x_5 = 0.058823529$

17. (a) $f(x) = x^2 - a$, $f'(x) = 2x$, $x_{n+1} = \dfrac{1}{2}\left(x_n + \dfrac{a}{x_n}\right)$

    (b) $a = 10$; $x_1 = 3$, $x_2 = 3.166666667$, $x_3 = 3.162280702$, $x_4 = x_5 = 3.162277660$

18. At the point of intersection, $x^2 + 1 = x^3$, $x^3 - x^2 - 1 = 0$. Let $f(x) = x^3 - x^2 - 1$. By graphing $y = x^2 + 1$ and $y = x^3$ it is evident that there is only one point of intersection and it occurs in the interval $[1, 2]$; note that $f(1) < 0$ and $f(2) > 0$. $f'(x) = 3x^2 - 2x$ so

$$x_{n+1} = x_n - \frac{x_n^3 - x_n^2 - 1}{3x_n^2 - 2x_n}; \ x_1 = 2, \ x_2 = 1.625, \ x_3 = 1.485785953, \cdots, \ x_6 = x_7 = 1.465571232$$

19. At the point of intersection, $x^3 = 0.5x - 1$, $x^3 - 0.5x + 1 = 0$. Let $f(x) = x^3 - 0.5x + 1$. By graphing $y = x^3$ and $y = 0.5x - 1$ it is evident that there is only one point of intersection and it occurs in the interval $[-2, -1]$; note that $f(-2) < 0$ and $f(-1) > 0$. $f'(x) = 3x^2 - 0.5$ so

$$x_{n+1} = x_n - \frac{x_n^3 - 0.5x + 1}{3x_n^2 - 0.5}; \ x_1 = -1, \ x_2 = -1.2, \ x_3 = -1.166492147, \cdots,$$

$$x_5 = x_6 = -1.165373043$$

20. Graph $y = x^2/4$ and $y = 2x/(x^2 + 1)$ to see that they intersect at $x = 0$ and at a point near $x = 2$; $x^2/4 = 2x/(x^2 + 1)$, $x^4 + x^2 - 8x = 0$, $x(x^3 + x - 8) = 0$ so $x = 0$ or $x^3 + x - 8 = 0$. Let $f(x) = x^3 + x - 8$, then $f'(x) = 3x^2 + 1$ so $x_{n+1} = x_n - \dfrac{x_n^3 + x_n - 8}{3x_n^2 + 1}$.

$x_1 = 2, \ x_2 = 1.846153846, \ x_3 = 1.833826690, \cdots, x_5 = x_6 = 1.833750958.$

21. The graphs of $y = x^2$ and $y = \sqrt{2x + 1}$ intersect at points near $x = -0.5$ and $x = 1$; $x^2 = \sqrt{2x + 1}$, $x^4 - 2x - 1 = 0$. Let $f(x) = x^4 - 2x - 1$, then $f'(x) = 4x^3 - 2$ so

$$x_{n+1} = x_n - \frac{x_n^4 - 2x_n - 1}{4x_n^3 - 2}.$$

If $x_1 = -0.5$, then $x_2 = -0.475$, $x_3 = -0.474626695$, $x_4 = x_5 = -0.474626618$;

if $x_1 = 1$, then $x_2 = 2$, $x_3 = 1.633333333, \cdots, x_8 = x_9 = 1.395336994.$

22. The graphs of $y = x^3/8 + 1$ and $y = \cos 2x$ intersect at $x = 0$ and at a point near $x = -2$; $x^3/8 + 1 = \cos 2x$, $x^3 - 8\cos 2x + 8 = 0$. Let $f(x) = x^3 - 8\cos 2x + 8$, then $f'(x) = 3x^2 + 16\sin 2x$ so $x_{n+1} = x_n - \dfrac{x_n^3 - 8\cos 2x_n + 8}{3x_n^2 + 16\sin 2x_n}$.

$x_1 = -2, \ x_2 = -2.216897577, \ x_3 = -2.193821581, \cdots, x_5 = x_6 = -2.193618950.$

23. If $x = 1$, then $y^4 + y = 1$, $y^4 + y - 1 = 0$. Graph $z = y^4$ and $z = 1 - y$ to see that they intersect near $y = -1$ and $y = 1$. Let $f(y) = y^4 + y - 1$, then $f'(y) = 4y^3 + 1$ so $y_{n+1} = y_n - \dfrac{y_n^4 + y_n - 1}{4y_n^3 + 1}$.

If $y_1 = -1$, then $y_2 = -1.333333333$, $y_3 = -1.235807860, \cdots, y_6 = y_7 = -1.220744085$;

if $y_1 = 1$, then $y_2 = 0.8$, $y_3 = 0.731233596, \cdots, y_6 = y_7 = 0.724491959.$

24. If $x = 1$, then $2y - \cos y = 0$. Graph $z = 2y$ and $z = \cos y$ to see that they intersect near $y = 0.5$. Let $f(y) = 2y - \cos y$, then $f'(y) = 2 + \sin y$ so $y_{n+1} = y_n - \dfrac{2y_n - \cos y_n}{2 + \sin y_n}$.

    $y_1 = 0.5$, $y_2 = 0.450626693$, $y_3 = 0.450183648$, $y_4 = y_5 = 0.450183611$.

25. $f'(x) = x^3 + 2x + 5$; solve $f'(x) = 0$ to find the critical points. Graph $y = x^3$ and $y = -2x - 5$ to see that they intersect at a point near $x = -1$; $f''(x) = 3x^2 + 2$ so $x_{n+1} = x_n - \dfrac{x_n^3 + 2x_n + 5}{3x_n^2 + 2}$.

    $x_1 = -1$, $x_2 = -1.4$, $x_3 = -1.330964467, \cdots, x_5 = x_6 = -1.328268856$ so the minimum value of $f(x)$ occurs at $x \approx -1.328268856$ because $f''(x) > 0$; its value is approximately -4.098859132.

26. From a rough sketch of $y = x \sin x$ we see that the maximum occurs at a point near $x = 2$, which will be a point where $f'(x) = x \cos x + \sin x = 0$. $f''(x) = 2 \cos x - x \sin x$ so

    $$x_{n+1} = x_n - \frac{x_n \cos x_n + \sin x_n}{2 \cos x_n - x_n \sin x_n} = x_n - \frac{x_n + \tan x_n}{2 - x_n \tan x_n}.$$

    $x_1 = 2$, $x_2 = 2.029048281$, $x_3 = 2.028757866$, $x_4 = x_5 = 2.028757838$; the maximum value is approximately 1.819705741.

27. Let $f(x)$ be the square of the distance between $(1,0)$ and any point (x, x^2) on the parabola, then $f(x) = (x-1)^2 + (x^2 - 0)^2 = x^4 + x^2 - 2x + 1$ and $f'(x) = 4x^3 + 2x - 2$. Solve $f'(x) = 0$ to find the critical points; $f''(x) = 12x^2 + 2$ so $x_{n+1} = x_n - \dfrac{4x_n^3 + 2x_n - 2}{12x_n^2 + 2} = x_n - \dfrac{2x_n^3 + x_n - 1}{6x_n^2 + 1}$.

    $x_1 = 1$, $x_2 = 0.714285714$, $x_3 = 0.605168701, \cdots, x_6 = x_7 = 0.589754512$; the coordinates are approximately $(0.589754512, 0.347810385)$.

28. The area is $A = xy = x \cos x$ so $dA/dx = \cos x - x \sin x$. Find x so that $dA/dx = 0$; $d^2A/dx^2 = -2 \sin x - x \cos x$ so $x_{n+1} = x_n + \dfrac{\cos x_n - x_n \sin x_n}{2 \sin x_n + x_n \cos x_n} = x_n + \dfrac{1 - x_n \tan x_n}{2 \tan x_n + x_n}$.

    $x_1 = 1$, $x_2 = 0.864536397$, $x_3 = 0.860339078$, $x_4 = x_5 = 0.860333589$; $y \approx 0.652184624$.

29. Let s be the arc length, and L the length of the chord, then $s = 1.5L$. But $s = r\theta$ and $L = 2r \sin(\theta/2)$ so $r\theta = 3r \sin(\theta/2)$, $\theta - 3 \sin(\theta/2) = 0$. Let $f(\theta) = \theta - 3 \sin(\theta/2)$, then $f'(\theta) = 1 - 1.5 \cos(\theta/2)$ so $\theta_{n+1} = \theta_n - \dfrac{\theta_n - 3 \sin(\theta_n/2)}{1 - 1.5 \cos(\theta_n/2)}$.

    $\theta_1 = 3$, $\theta_2 = 2.991592920$, $\theta_3 = 2.991563137$, $\theta_4 = \theta_5 = 2.991563136$ rad so $\theta \approx 171°$.

30. $r^2(\theta - \sin \theta)/2 = \pi r^2/4$ so $\theta - \sin \theta - \pi/2 = 0$. Let $f(\theta) = \theta - \sin \theta - \pi/2$, then $f'(\theta) = 1 - \cos \theta$ so $\theta_{n+1} = \dfrac{\theta_n - \sin \theta_n - \pi/2}{1 - \cos \theta_n}$.

    $\theta_1 = 2$, $\theta_2 = 2.339014106$, $\theta_3 = 2.310063197, \cdots, \theta_5 = \theta_6 = 2.309881460$ rad; $\theta \approx 132°$.

EXERCISE SET 4.10

1. $f(2) = f(4) = 0$, $f'(x) = 2x - 6$, $2c - 6 = 0$, $c = 3$

2. $f(0) = f(2) = 0$, $f'(x) = 3x^2 - 6x + 2$, $3c^2 - 6c + 2 = 0$; $c = \dfrac{6 \pm \sqrt{36 - 24}}{6} = 1 \pm \sqrt{3}/3$

3. $f(\pi/2) = f(3\pi/2) = 0$, $f'(x) = -\sin x$, $-\sin c = 0$, $c = \pi$

4. $f(-1) = f(1) = 0$, $f'(x) = \dfrac{x^2 - 4x + 1}{(x - 2)^2}$, $\dfrac{c^2 - 4c + 1}{(c - 2)^2} = 0$, $c^2 - 4c + 1 = 0$

    $c = \dfrac{4 \pm \sqrt{16 - 4}}{2} = 2 \pm \sqrt{3}$, of which only $c = 2 - \sqrt{3}$ is in $(-1, 1)$

5. $f(0) = f(4) = 0$, $f'(x) = \dfrac{1}{2} - \dfrac{1}{2\sqrt{x}}$, $\dfrac{1}{2} - \dfrac{1}{2\sqrt{c}} = 0$, $c = 1$

6. $f(1) = f(3) = 0$, $f'(x) = -\dfrac{2}{x^3} + \dfrac{4}{3x^2}$, $-\dfrac{2}{c^3} + \dfrac{4}{3c^2} = 0$, $-6 + 4c = 0$, $c = 3/2$

7. $f(-4) = 12$, $f(6) = 42$, $f'(x) = 2x + 1$, $2c + 1 = \dfrac{42 - 12}{6 - (-4)} = 3$, $c = 1$

8. $f(-1) = -6$, $f(2) = 6$, $f'(x) = 3x^2 + 1$, $3c^2 + 1 = \dfrac{6 - (-6)}{2 - (-1)} = 4$, $c^2 = 1$, $c = \pm 1$ of which only

    $c = 1$ is in $(-1, 2)$

9. $f(0) = 1$, $f(3) = 2$, $f'(x) = \dfrac{1}{2\sqrt{x + 1}}$, $\dfrac{1}{2\sqrt{c + 1}} = \dfrac{2 - 1}{3 - 0} = \dfrac{1}{3}$

    $\sqrt{c + 1} = 3/2$, $c + 1 = 9/4$, $c = 5/4$

10. $f(3) = 10/3$, $f(4) = 17/4$, $f'(x) = 1 - 1/x^2$, $1 - 1/c^2 = \dfrac{17/4 - 10/3}{4 - 3} = 11/12$, $c^2 = 12$,

    $c = \pm 2\sqrt{3}$ of which only $c = 2\sqrt{3}$ is in $(3, 4)$

11. $f(-5) = 0$, $f(3) = 4$, $f'(x) = -\dfrac{x}{\sqrt{25 - x^2}}$, $-\dfrac{c}{\sqrt{25 - c^2}} = \dfrac{4 - 0}{3 - (-5)} = \dfrac{1}{2}$, $-2c = \sqrt{25 - c^2}$,

    $4c^2 = 25 - c^2$, $c^2 = 5$, $c = -\sqrt{5}$

    (we reject $c = \sqrt{5}$ because it does not satisfy the equation $-2c = \sqrt{25 - c^2}$)

12. $f(2) = 1$, $f(5) = 1/4$, $f'(x) = -1/(x - 1)^2$, $-\dfrac{1}{(c - 1)^2} = \dfrac{1/4 - 1}{5 - 2} = -\dfrac{1}{4}$, $(c - 1)^2 = 4$,

    $c - 1 = \pm 2$, $c = -1$ (reject), or $c = 3$

13. **(a)** $f'(x) = \sec^2 x$, $\sec^2 c = 0$ has no solution   **(b)** $\tan x$ is not continuous on $[0, \pi]$

14. **(a)** $f(-1) = 1$, $f(8) = 4$, $f'(x) = \dfrac{2}{3}x^{-1/3}$

$\dfrac{2}{3}c^{-1/3} = \dfrac{4-1}{8-(-1)} = \dfrac{1}{3}$, $c^{1/3} = 2$, $c = 8$ which is not in $(-1, 8)$.

(b) $x^{2/3}$ is not differentiable at $x = 0$, which is in $(-1, 8)$.

15. Let $f(x) = \sin x$ and $x \neq y$. By the Mean-Value Theorem there is a number c between x and y such that

$\dfrac{\sin x - \sin y}{x - y} = \cos c$, $\dfrac{|\sin x - \sin y|}{|x - y|} = |\cos c| \leq 1$

so $|\sin x - \sin y| \leq |x - y|$, which also holds when $x = y$.

16. Let $f(x) = \tan x$ and $x \neq y$. By the Mean-Value Theorem there is a number c between x and y such that $\dfrac{\tan x - \tan y}{x - y} = \sec^2 c$ so $\dfrac{|\tan x - \tan y|}{|x - y|} = \sec^2 c \geq 1$, $|\tan x - \tan y| \geq |x - y|$, which also holds when $x = y$. Replace y by $-y$ to get $|\tan x + \tan y| \geq |x + y|$.

17. Let $f(x) = \sqrt{x}$. By the Mean-Value Theorem there is a number c between x and y such that

$\dfrac{\sqrt{y} - \sqrt{x}}{y - x} = \dfrac{1}{2\sqrt{c}} < \dfrac{1}{2\sqrt{x}}$ for c in (x, y), thus $\sqrt{y} - \sqrt{x} < \dfrac{y - x}{2\sqrt{x}}$;

multiply through and rearrange to get $\sqrt{xy} < \dfrac{1}{2}(x + y)$.

18. If $x > 1$, then there is a number c in $(1, x)$ such that $\dfrac{f(x) - f(1)}{x - 1} = f'(c)$ so $\dfrac{f(x)}{x - 1} = \dfrac{1}{c} < 1$, $f(x) < x - 1$. If $0 < x < 1$, then there is a number c in $(x, 1)$ such that $\dfrac{f(1) - f(x)}{1 - x} = f'(c)$ so $\dfrac{-f(x)}{1 - x} = \dfrac{1}{c} > 1$, $-f(x) > 1 - x$, $f(x) < x - 1$. If $x = 1$, then $f(x) = 0$ and $x - 1 = 0$ so $f(x) = x - 1$. Thus $f(x) \leq x - 1$ for all x in $(0, +\infty)$.

19. $f'(x) = 2a_2 x + a_1$,

$2a_2 c + a_1 = \dfrac{(a_2 b^2 + a_1 b + a_0) - (a_2 a^2 + a_1 a + a_0)}{b - a}$

$= \dfrac{a_2(b^2 - a^2) + a_1(b - a)}{b - a} = a_2(b + a) + a_1$, so $c = \dfrac{1}{2}(b + a)$.

20. Let $f(x) = x^6 - 2x^2 + x$; $f(0) = f(1) = 0$ and $f'(x) = 6x^5 - 4x + 1$, so there is at least one number c in $(0, 1)$ where $f'(c) = 0$.

21. $f(0) = f(1) = 0$, $f'(x) = 3ax^2 + 2bx - (a+b)$, so there is at least one number c in $(0,1)$ where $f'(c) = 0$.

22. Suppose that $f(x)$ has at least two distinct real solutions r_1 and r_2 in I. Then $f(r_1) = f(r_2) = 0$ so by Rolle's Theorem there is at least one number between r_1 and r_2 where $f'(x) = 0$, but this contradicts the assumption that $f'(x) \neq 0$, so $f(x) = 0$ must have fewer than two distinct solutions in I.

23. Let $f(x) = x^3 + 4x - 1$. Assume that $f(x) = 0$ has at least two distinct real solutions r_1 and r_2. Then $f(r_1) = f(r_2) = 0$ and so by Rolle's Theorem there is at least one number c between r_1 and r_2 where $f'(c) = 0$. But $f'(x) = 3x^2 + 4$ is never zero, so $f(x) = 0$ must have fewer than two distinct real solutions.

24. Let $f(x) = ax^3 + bx^2 + cx + d$. If $f(x) = 0$ has at least two distinct real solutions r_1 and r_2, then $f(r_1) = f(r_2) = 0$ and by Rolle's Theorem there is at least one number between r_1 and r_2 where $f'(x) = 0$. But $f'(x) = 3ax^2 + 2bx + c = 0$ for
$$x = (-2b \pm \sqrt{4b^2 - 12ac})/(6a) = (-b \pm \sqrt{b^2 - 3ac})/(3a),$$ which are not real if $b^2 - 3ac < 0$
so $f(x) = 0$ must have fewer than two distinct real solutions.

25. Assume that $f(x) = 0$ has at least four distinct real solutions $r_1 < r_2 < r_3 < r_4$, then by Rolle's Theorem there is at least one number in each of the intervals (r_1, r_2), (r_2, r_3) and (r_3, r_4) so that $f'(x) = 0$ at least three times. Apply Rolle's Theorem to $f'(x)$ to show that $f''(x) = 0$ at least twice; again to $f''(x)$ to show that $f'''(x) = 0$ at least once. But $f'''(x) = 60x^2 + 24ax + 6b$, and $f'''(x) = 0$ if $10x^2 + 4ax + b = 0$. Use the quadratic formula to get $x = \dfrac{-4a \pm \sqrt{16a^2 - 40b}}{20}$, which has no real solutions if $16a^2 - 40b < 0$, $16a^2 < 40b$, $2a^2 < 5b$.

26. $f(0) = 2$, $f(1) = -4$, and $f(2) = 11$ so by Theorem 2.7.10 there is at least one number r_1 in $(0,1)$ and at least one number r_2 in $(1,2)$ where $f(r_1) = f(r_2) = 0$ so $f(x) = 0$ has at least two distinct real solutions. If there are more than two distinct real solutions, then $f'(x) = 0$ at least twice. But $f'(x) = 4x^3 - 7 = 0$ has only one real solution so $f(x) = 0$ has exactly two distinct real solutions.

27. $\dfrac{d}{dx}[f^2(x) + g^2(x)] = 2f(x)f'(x) + 2g(x)g'(x) = 2f(x)g(x) + 2g(x)[-f(x)] = 0$,
so $f^2(x) + g^2(x)$ is constant.

28. $\dfrac{d}{dx}[f^2(x) - g^2(x)] = 2f(x)f'(x) - 2g(x)g'(x) = 2f(x)g(x) - 2g(x)f(x) = 0$ so $f^2(x) - g^2(x)$ is constant.

29. $f'(x) = 3(x-1)^2$, $g'(x) = (x^2+3)+2x(x-3) = 3x^2-6x+3 = 3(x^2-2x+1) = 3(x-1)^2$,
so $f'(x) = g'(x)$ and hence $f(x) - g(x) = k$. Expand $f(x)$ and $g(x)$ to get
$f(x) - g(x) = (x^3 - 3x^2 + 3x - 1) - (x^3 - 3x^2 + 3x - 9) = 8$.

30. $f'(x) = \dfrac{5}{(3-x)^2} = \dfrac{5}{(x-3)^2} = g'(x)$ so $f(x) - g(x) = k$; $f(x) - g(x) = \dfrac{x+2}{3-x} + \dfrac{5}{x-3} = -1$.

31. If $f'(x) = g'(x)$, then $f(x) = g(x) + k$. Let $x = 1$,
$f(1) = g(1) + k = (1)^3 - 4(1) + 6 + k = 3 + k = 2$, so $k = -1$. $f(x) = x^3 - 4x + 5$.

32. If $f'(x) = g'(x)$, then $f(x) = g(x) + k$. Let $x = -3$,
$f(-3) = g(-3) + k = \sqrt{9+7} + k = 4 + k = 1$, so $k = -3$, $f(x) = \sqrt{x^2+7} - 3$.

33. Let $h = f - g$, then h is continuous on $[a, b]$, differentiable on (a, b), and $h(a) = f(a) - g(a) = 0$, $h(b) = f(b) - g(b) = 0$. By Rolle's Theorem there is some c in (a, b) where $h'(c) = 0$. But $h'(c) = f'(c) - g'(c)$ so $f'(c) - g'(c) = 0$, $f'(c) = g'(c)$.

34. Similar to the proof of part (a) with $f'(c) < 0$.

35. Similar to the proof of part (a) with $f'(c) = 0$.

36. (a) Suppose $f'(x) = 0$ more than once in (a, b), say at c_1 and c_2. Then $f'(c_1) = f'(c_2) = 0$ and by using Rolle's Theorem on f', there is some c between c_1 and c_2 where $f''(c) = 0$, which contradicts the fact that $f''(x) > 0$ so $f'(x) = 0$ at most once in (a, b).

(b) If $f''(x) > 0$ for all x in (a, b), then f is concave up on (a, b) and has at most one relative extremum, which would be a relative minimum, on (a, b).

37. From the Mean-Value Theorem there is a point c in (a, b) where
$$f'(c) = \frac{f(b) - f(a)}{b - a} = \frac{0}{b - a} = 0.$$

38. From the Mean-Value Theorem there is some t_0 in (a, b) where $f'(t_0) = \dfrac{f(b) - f(a)}{b - a}$, but
$f'(t_0)$ is the instantaneous velocity at t_0 and $\dfrac{f(b) - f(a)}{b - a}$ is the average velocity over $[a, b]$.

39. Similar to proof given in text; assume that $f(x) < 0$ and replace the word "maximum" by "minimum".

40. $f'(x) = \dfrac{1}{2\sqrt{x}}$, $\dfrac{1}{2\sqrt{c}} = \dfrac{\sqrt{4}-\sqrt{3}}{4-3} = 2 - \sqrt{3}$. But $\dfrac{1}{4} < \dfrac{1}{2\sqrt{c}} < \dfrac{1}{2\sqrt{3}}$ for c in $(3, 4)$ so
$\dfrac{1}{4} < 2 - \sqrt{3} < \dfrac{1}{2\sqrt{3}}$, $0.25 < 2 - \sqrt{3} < 0.29$, $-1.75 < -\sqrt{3} < -1.71$, $1.71 < \sqrt{3} < 1.75$.

41. Let $s(t)$ be the position function of the automobile for $0 \le t \le 5$, then by the Mean-Value Theorem there is at least one point c in $(0,5)$ where

$s'(c) = v(c) = [s(5) - s(0)]/(5 - 0) = 4/5 = 0.8$ mi/min $= 48$ mi/hr.

42. Let $T(t)$ be the temperature at time t, where $t = 0$ at 11 A.M. and $t = 12$ at 11 P.M.

    (a) By the Mean-Value Theorem there is at least one point c in $(0, 12)$ where
        $T'(c) = [T(12) - T(0)]/(12 - 0) = (52 - 76)/12 = -2°\text{F/hr}.$

    (b) Assume that $T(t_1) = 88°\text{F}$ where $0 < t_1 < 12$, then there is at least one point c in $(t_1, 12)$ where $T'(c) = [T(12) - T(t_1)]/(12 - t_1) = (52 - 88)/(12 - t_1) = -36/(12 - t_1)$. But $12 - t_1 < 12$ so $T'(c) < -36/12 = -3°\text{F/hr}.$

EXERCISE SET 4.11

1. **(a)** positive, negative, slowing down   **(b)** positive, positive, speeding up
    (c) negative, positive, slowing down

2. **(a)** positive, slowing down   **(b)** negative, slowing down
    (c) positive, speeding up

3. **(a)** left because $v = ds/dt < 0$ at t_0.
    (b) negative because $a = d^2s/dt^2$ and the curve is concave down at $t_0 (d^2s/dt^2 < 0)$.
    (c) speeding up because v and a have the same sign.
    (d) $v < 0$ and $a > 0$ at t_1 so the particle is slowing down because v and a have opposite signs.

4. **(a)** C **(b)** A **(c)** B

5. **(a)** At 60 mi/hr the slope of the estimated tangent line is about 4.6 mi/hr per sec. Use 1 mi $= 5,280$ ft and 1 hr $= 3600$ sec to get $a = dv/dt \approx 4.6(5,280)/(3600) \approx 6.7$ ft/sec^2.
    (b) The slope of the tangent to the curve is maximum at $t = 0$.

6. **(a)** $v \approx (50 - 10)/(15 - 5) = 40/10 = 4$ m/sec.
    (b)

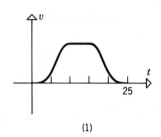
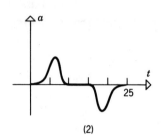

(1)   (2)

7. $v = 3t^2 - 12t$, $a = 6t - 12$

t	s	v	$|v|$	a	direction; motion
1	-5	-9	9	-6	left; speeding up
2	-16	-12	12	0	left; neither
3	-27	-9	9	6	left; slowing down
4	-32	0	0	12	stopped
5	-25	15	15	18	right; speeding up

8. $v = -\dfrac{200t}{(t^2 + 12)^2}$, speed $= |v| = \dfrac{200t}{(t^2 + 12)^2}$ for $t \geq 0$. $\dfrac{d|v|}{dt} = \dfrac{600(4 - t^2)}{(t^2 + 12)^3} = 0$ when $t = 2$,
    which is the only critical point in $(0, +\infty)$. By the first derivative test there is a relative
    maximum, and hence an absolute maximum, at $t = 2$. The maximum speed is $25/16$ ft/sec to
    the left.

9. **(a)** $v = 10t - 22$, speed $= |v| = |10t - 22|$. $d|v|/dt$ does not exist at $t = 2.2$ which is the only
    critical point. If $t = 1, 2.2, 3$ then $|v| = 12, 0, 8$. The maximum speed is 12.
    (b) the distance from the origin is $|s| = |5t^2 - 22t| = |t(5t - 22)|$, but $t(5t - 22) < 0$ for
    $1 \leq t \leq 3$ so $|s| = -(5t^2 - 22t) = 22t - 5t^2$, $d|s|/dt = 22 - 10t$, thus the only critical
    point is $t = 2.2$. $d^2|s|/dt^2 < 0$ so the particle is farthest from the origin when $t = 2.2$. Its
    position is $s = 5(2.2)^2 - 22(2.2) = -24.2$.

10. $s = -3t + 2$

    $v = -3$

    $a = 0$

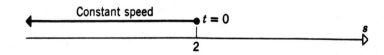

11. $s = 1 + 6t - t^2$
    $v = 2(3 - t)$
    $a = -2$

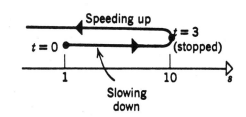

12. $s = t^3 - 6t^2 + 9t + 1$
    $v = 3(t - 1)(t - 3)$
    $a = 6(t - 2)$

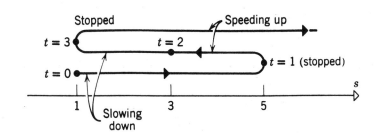

13. $s = t^3 - 9t^2 + 24t$
    $v = 3(t - 2)(t - 4)$
    $a = 6(t - 3)$

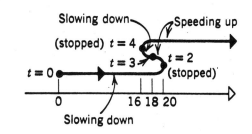

14. $s = t + \dfrac{9}{t + 1}$
    $v = \dfrac{(t + 4)(t - 2)}{(t + 1)^2}$
    $a = \dfrac{18}{(t + 1)^3}$

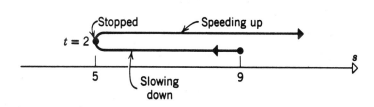

15. $\quad s = \begin{cases} \cos t, & 0 \le t \le 2\pi \\ 1, & t > 2\pi \end{cases}$

$\qquad v = \begin{cases} -\sin t, & 0 \le t \le 2\pi \\ 0, & t > 2\pi \end{cases}$

$\qquad a = \begin{cases} -\cos t, & 0 \le t < 2\pi \\ 0, & t > 2\pi \end{cases}$

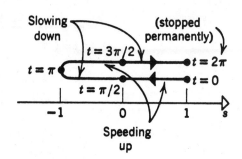

16. $\quad s = t^3 - 6t^2 + 1, \ v = 3t^2 - 12t, \ a = 6t - 12.$

    (a) $a = 0$ when $t = 2$; $s = -15$, $v = -12$.

    (b) $v = 0$ when $3t^2 - 12t = 3t(t - 4) = 0$, $t = 0$ or $t = 4$. If $t = 0$, then $s = 1$ and $a = -12$; if $t = 4$, then $s = -31$ and $a = 12$.

17. $\quad s = 4t^{3/2} - 3t^2, \ v = 6t^{1/2} - 6t, \ a = 3t^{-1/2} - 6.$

    (a) $a = 0$ when $3t^{-1/2} = 6$, $t = 1/4$; $s = 5/16$, $v = 3/2$.

    (b) $v = 0$ when $6t^{1/2}(1 - t^{1/2}) = 0$ for $t > 0$, $t = 1$; $s = 1$, $a = -3$.

18. $\quad v = \dfrac{2t}{\sqrt{2t^2 + 1}}, \ \lim\limits_{t \to +\infty} v = \dfrac{2}{\sqrt{2}} = \sqrt{2}.$

19.   **(a)** $\quad a = \dfrac{dv}{dt} = \dfrac{dv}{ds}\dfrac{ds}{dt} = v\dfrac{dv}{ds}$ because $v = \dfrac{ds}{dt}$.

    (b) $\quad v = \dfrac{3}{2\sqrt{3t + 7}} = \dfrac{3}{2s}; \dfrac{dv}{ds} = -\dfrac{3}{2s^2}; a = -\dfrac{9}{4s^3} = -9/500.$

20. $\quad v = \dfrac{5 - t^2}{(t^2 + 5)^2}; v > 0$ for $0 \le t < \sqrt{5}$, and $v < 0$ for $t > \sqrt{5}$ so the particle will start to reverse its direction of motion when $t = \sqrt{5}$ seconds and $s = \sqrt{5}/10$ ft.

21.   **(a)** $\quad s_1 = s_2$ if they collide, so $\dfrac{1}{2}t^2 - t + 3 = -\dfrac{1}{4}t^2 + t + 1$, $\dfrac{3}{4}t^2 - 2t + 2 = 0$ which has no real solution.

    (b) Find the minimum value of $D = |s_1 - s_2| = \left|\dfrac{3}{4}t^2 - 2t + 2\right|$. From part (a), $\dfrac{3}{4}t^2 - 2t + 2$

    is never zero, and for $t = 0$ it is positive, hence it is always positive, so $D = \dfrac{3}{4}t^2 - 2t + 2$.

    $\dfrac{dD}{dt} = \dfrac{3}{2}t - 2 = 0$ when $t = \dfrac{4}{3}$. $\dfrac{d^2D}{dt^2} > 0$ so D is minimum when $t = \dfrac{4}{3}$, $D = \dfrac{2}{3}$.

(c) $v_1 = t - 1$, $v_2 = -\dfrac{1}{2}t + 1$. $v_1 < 0$ if $0 \le t < 1$, $v_1 > 0$ if $t > 1$; $v_2 < 0$ if $t > 2$, $v_2 > 0$ if $0 \le t < 2$. They are moving in opposite directions during the intervals $0 \le t < 1$ and $t > 2$.

22. (a) $s_A - s_B = 20 - 0 = 20$ ft
    (b) $s_A = s_B$, $15t^2 + 10t + 20 = 5t^2 + 40t$, $10t^2 - 30t + 20 = 0$, $(t-2)(t-1) = 0$, $t = 1$ or $t = 2$ seconds.
    (c) $v_A = v_B$, $30t + 10 = 10t + 40$, $20t = 30$, $t = 3/2$ seconds. When $t = 3/2$, $s_A = 275/4$ and $s_B = 285/4$ so car B is ahead of car A.

23. (a) From the estimated tangent to the graph at the point where $v = 2000$, $dv/ds \approx -1.25$ ft/sec per ft.
    (b) $a = v\, dv/ds \approx (2000)(-1.25) = -2500$ ft/sec^2.

24. (a) v_{ave} is the slope of the line through the points $(t_0, s(t_0))$, $(t_1, s(t_1))$.
    (b) a_{ave} is the slope of the line through the points $(t_0, v(t_0))$, $(t_1, v(t_1))$.
    (c) $v_{ave} = \dfrac{s(4) - s(2)}{4 - 2} = \dfrac{16 - (-4)}{2} = 10$; $v(t) = ds/dt = 3t^2 - 6t$ so

    $a_{ave} = \dfrac{v(4) - v(2)}{4 - 2} = \dfrac{24 - 0}{2} = 12$.

25. (a) $\lim\limits_{t_1 \to t_0} v_{ave} = \lim\limits_{t_1 \to t_0} \dfrac{s(t_1) - s(t_0)}{t_1 - t_0} = s'(t_0) = v(t_0)$
    (b) similar to part (a) with a in place of v.

26. $r'(t) = 2v(t)v'(t)/[2\sqrt{v^2(t)}] = v(t)a(t)/|v(t)|$ so $r'(t) > 0$ (speed is increasing) if v and a have the same sign, and $r'(t) < 0$ (speed is decreasing) if v and a have opposite signs.

SUPPLEMENTARY EXERCISES CHAPTER 4

1. $V = \pi R^2 h - \pi r^2 h = \pi(R^2 - r^2)h$, $dV/dt = \pi[(R^2 - r^2)dh/dt + h(2R\, dR/dt - 2r\, dr/dt)]$.
   But $dR/dt = dr/dt = 2$, $dh/dt = -3$ so for $R = 7$, $r = 4$, and $h = 5$
   $dV/dt = \pi[(49 - 16)(-3) + 5(14(2) - 8(2))] = -39\pi$. The volume is decreasing at the rate of 39π m^3/sec.

2. At any instant of time the volume of
    fluid is $V = \frac{1}{2}xy(20) = 10xy$. By
    similar triangles $y/x = 8/10$,
    $y = 8x/10$ so $V = 8x^2$ and
    $dV/dt = 16x\ dx/dt$. But $dV/dt = 4$
    so when $x = 1$ we get $4 = 16\ dx/dt$,
    $dx/dt = 1/4$ ft/min.

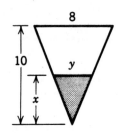

3. By similar triangles
    $x/48 = 10/y$, $x = 480/y$ so
    $dx/dt = -(480/y^2)dy/dt$. But
    $dy/dt = 32$ when $y = 16$ thus
    $dx/dt = -(480/16^2)(32) = -60$.
    The shadow is moving toward the pole
    at the rate of 60 ft/sec.

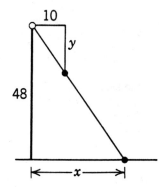

4. $f'(x) = -1/x^2$, no critical points in $(-2, -1)$; $f(-2) = -1/2$, $f(-1) = -1$ so $m = -1$ at $x = -1$ and $M = -1/2$ at $x = -2$.

5. $f'(x) = x^2(3 - 4x)$, critical points $x = 0, 3/4$; $f(-1) = -2$, $f(0) = 0$, $f(3/4) = 27/256$, $f(3/2) = -27/16$. $m = -2$ at $x = -1$, $M = 27/256$ at $x = 3/4$.

6. $f'(x) = \dfrac{x(7x - 12)}{3(x - 2)^{2/3}}$, critical points $x = 2, 12/7$; $f(2) = 0$, $f(12/7) = -\dfrac{144^3}{49}\sqrt{2/7} \approx -1.9$, $f(3) = 9$, $\lim\limits_{x \to 0+} f(x) = 0$. $m \approx -1.9$ at $x = 12/7$, $M = 9$ at $x = 3$.

7. $f'(x) = 2(3 - x^2)/(x^2 + 3)^2$, critical point $x = \sqrt{3}$; $f(\sqrt{3}) = \sqrt{3}/3$, $f(2) = 4/7$, $\lim\limits_{x \to 0+} f(x) = 0$. No minimum on $(0, 2]$, $M = \sqrt{3}/3$ at $x = \sqrt{3}$.

8. $f'(x) = 10x^3(x - 2)$, critical points $x = 0, 2$; $f(0) = 7$, $f(2) = -9$, $\lim\limits_{x \to -1+} f(x) = 0$, $\lim\limits_{x \to 3-} f(x) = 88$. $m = -9$ at $x = 2$, no maximum.

9. $x^2 - 2x \geq 0$ when $x \leq 0$ or $x \geq 2$, $x^2 - 2x < 0$ when $0 < x < 2$

$$f'(x) = \begin{cases} -2x + 2, & x < 0 \text{ or } x > 2 \\ 2x - 2, & 0 < x < 2 \end{cases}$$

and $f'(x)$ does not exist when $x = 0, 2$. The only critical point in $(1, 3)$ is $x = 2$; $f(1) = -1$, $f(2) = 0$, $f(3) = -3$, $m = -3$ at $x = 3$, $M = 0$ at $x = 2$.

10. $f(x) = \sin x + \cos x$, $f'(x) = \cos x - \sin x$, $x_{n+1} = x_n - \dfrac{\sin x_n + \cos x_n}{\cos x_n - \sin x_n} = x_n - \dfrac{\tan x_n + 1}{1 - \tan x_n}$

$x_1 = 2$, $x_2 = 2.372064374$, $x_3 = 2.356193158$, $x_4 = x_5 = 2.356194490$.

11. $f(x) = x^3 - 4x + 1$, $f'(x) = 3x^2 - 4$, $x_{n+1} = x_n - \dfrac{x_n^3 - 4x_n + 1}{3x_n^2 - 4}$

$x_1 = -2$, $x_2 = -2.125$, $x_3 = -2.114975450, \cdots, x_5 = x_6 = -2.114907541$

$x_1 = 0$, $x_2 = 0.25$, $x_3 = 0.254098361$, $x_4 = x_5 = 0.254101688$

$x_1 = 2$, $x_2 = 1.875$, $x_3 = 1.860978520, \cdots, x_5 = x_6 = 1.860805853$.

12. $f'(x) = 4x(x^2 - 3)$

$f''(x) = 12(x^2 - 1)$

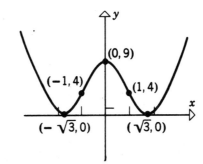

13. $f'(x) = -\dfrac{2x}{(1 + x^2)^2}$

$f''(x) = \dfrac{2(3x^2 - 1)}{(1 + x^2)^3}$

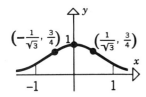

14. $f'(x) = 2/(1+x)^2$

  $f''(x) = -4/(1+x)^3$

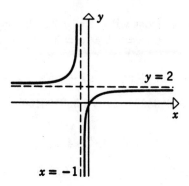

15. $f'(x) = \dfrac{2(x^3+1)}{x^2}$

  $f''(x) = \dfrac{2(x^3-2)}{x^3}$

  $f(x) = x^2 - \dfrac{2}{x}$ so $f(x)$ is

  asymptotic to $y = x^2$ for $|x|$ large.

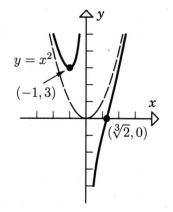

16. $f'(x) = \dfrac{5-3x}{3(1+x)^{1/3}(3-x)^{2/3}}$

  $f''(x) = -\dfrac{32}{9(1+x)^{4/3}(3-x)^{5/3}}$

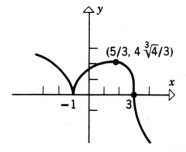

17. $f'(x) = -4\cos x \sin x$

     $= -2\sin 2x$

  $f''(x) = -4\cos 2x$

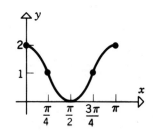

18. $f'(x) = 1 - \sec^2 x$

   $f''(x) = -2\sec^2 x \tan x$

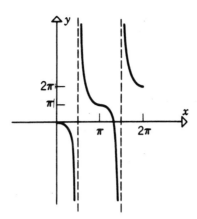

19. $f'(x) = \dfrac{3(8 - x)}{(x + 8)^3}$

   $f''(x) = \dfrac{6(x - 16)}{(x + 8)^4}$

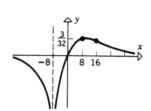

20. $\dfrac{dy}{dx} = \dfrac{\cos x}{2 + \sin y}$, $\dfrac{dy}{dx} = 0$ when $\cos x = 0$. Using the first derivative test, if x_0 is a critical point then $\cos x$ changes sign from $+$ to $-$ or from $-$ to $+$ as x increases through x_0 while $2 + \sin y$ remains $+$ so there is a relative extremum at each critical point.

   $\dfrac{d^2 y}{dx^2} = -\dfrac{(2 + \sin y)\sin x + \cos x \cos y(dy/dx)}{(2 + \sin y)^2}$. Using the second derivative test, when

   $dy/dx = 0$ the critical points satisfy $\cos x = 0$ but $\sin x = \pm 1$ whenever $\cos x = 0$ so

   $\dfrac{d^2 y}{dx^2} = -\dfrac{(2 + \sin y)(\pm 1) + 0}{(2 + \sin y)^2} = \pm 1/(2 + \sin y)$ which is either $+$ or $-$ at a critical point so there is a relative extremum at each critical point.

21. $f'(x) = 4x^3 - 18x^2 + 24x - 8$

   $f''(x) = 12x^2 - 36x + 24 = 12(x - 1)(x - 2)$

   $f''(x) = 0$ when $x = 1, 2$; $f(1) = 2$, $f(2) = 3$. The inflection points are $(1, 2)$ and $(2, 3)$ because the concavity changes at these points.

   $f'(1) = 2$ so the tangent line at $(1, 2)$ is $y - 2 = 2(x - 1)$, $y = 2x$.

   $f'(2) = 0$ so the tangent line at $(2, 3)$ is $y = 3$.

22. $f'(x) = \dfrac{7(x-7)(x-1)}{x^{2/3}}$; critical points $x = 0, 1, 7$ relative max at $x = 1$, relative min at $x = 7$, vertical tangent at $x = 0$.

23. $f'(x) = 2\cos x + 2\sin 2x = 2\cos x + 4\sin x\cos x = 2\cos x(1 + 2\sin x)$;
    $f'(x) = 0$ when $\cos x = 0$ or $\sin x = -1/2$; critical points $x = \pi/2, 3\pi/2, 7\pi/6, 11\pi/6$
    relative max at $x = \pi/2, 3\pi/2$, relative min at $x = 7\pi/6, 11\pi/6$

24. $f'(x) = \dfrac{3}{2}(2 - \sqrt{x-1})$; $f'(x) = 0$ when $\sqrt{x-1} = 2$; critical point $x = 5$, relative max at $x = 5$

25. $f'(x) = \dfrac{x-9}{18x^{3/2}}$; critical point $x = 9$ (0 is not a critical point, it is not in the domain of f)
    $f''(x) = \dfrac{27-x}{36x^{5/2}}$; $f''(9) > 0$, relative min at $x = 9$

26. $f'(x) = 2(x^3 - 4)/x^2$; critical point $x = \sqrt[3]{4}$
    $f''(x) = 2 + 16/x^3$; $f''(\sqrt[3]{4}) > 0$, relative min at $x = \sqrt[3]{4}$

27. $f'(x) = \sin x(2\cos x + 1)$; $f'(x) = 0$ when $\sin x = 0$ or $\cos x = -1/2$, in $(0, 2\pi)$ the critical points are $x = \pi, 2\pi/3, 4\pi/3$
    $f''(x) = 2\cos 2x + \cos x$; $f''(\pi) > 0$, $f''(2\pi/3) < 0$, $f''(4\pi/3) < 0$
    relative max at $x = 2\pi/3, 4\pi/3$, relative min at $x = \pi$

28. Let x and y be the numbers, then $x + y = 20$ thus $y = 20 - x$ for $0 \le x \le 20$.
    (a) $S = x^2 + y^2 = x^2 + (20-x)^2 = 2x^2 - 40x + 400$, $dS/dx = 4x - 40$, critical point at $x = 10$. If $x = 0, 10, 20$ then $S = 400, 200, 400$. S is a maximum for the numbers 0 and 20.
    (b) $P = x^2 y^3 = x^2(20 - x)^3$, $dP/dx = 5x(8 - x)(20 - x)^2$, critical point at $x = 8$. P is maximum for $0 \le x \le 20$ when $x = 8$, $y = 12$.

29. Let (x, y) be a point in the first quadrant that is on the ellipse, then $A = (2x)(2y) = 4xy$. But, from the equation of the ellipse, $y^2 = \dfrac{9}{16}(16 - x^2)$ so with
    $S = A^2 = 16x^2 y^2$,
    $S = 9x^2(16 - x^2) = 9(16x^2 - x^4)$ for $0 < x < 4$,
    $dS/dx = 36x(8 - x^2)$, critical point at $x = \sqrt{8} = 2\sqrt{2}$.
    $d^2S/dx^2 > 0$ at $x = 2\sqrt{2}$ thus S and hence A is
    maximum there. If $x = 2\sqrt{2}$ then $y = 3\sqrt{2}/2$.
    The dimensions of the rectangle are $4\sqrt{2}$ by $3\sqrt{2}$.

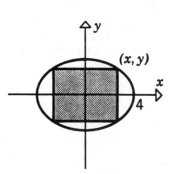

30. If (x, y) is a point on the curve, then its distance L from the origin is $L = \sqrt{x^2 + y^2}$ where $y^2 = \frac{5}{2}(x+1)$ so with $S = L^2 = x^2 + \frac{5}{2}(x+1)$ for $x \geq -1$, $dS/dx = 2x + 5/2$, $dS/dx = 0$ when $x = -5/4$ so there are no critical points for $x > -1$. If $x = -1$ then $S = 1$. $\lim\limits_{x \to +\infty} S = +\infty$. The point nearest the origin occurs when $x = -1$, $y = 0$.

31. Let k be the amount of light admitted per unit area of clear glass. The total amount of light admitted by the entire window is
$$T = k \cdot (\text{area of clear glass}) + \frac{1}{2}k \cdot (\text{area of blue glass}) = 2krh + \frac{1}{4}\pi kr^2.$$
But $P = 2h + 2r + \pi r$ which gives $h = \frac{1}{2}(P - 2r - \pi r)$ so
$$T = kr(P - 2r - \pi r) + \frac{1}{4}\pi kr^2 = k\left[Pr - \left(2 + \pi - \frac{\pi}{4}\right)r^2\right]$$
$$= k\left[Pr - \frac{8 + 3\pi}{4}r^2\right] \text{ for } 0 < r < \frac{P}{2 + \pi},$$
$$\frac{dT}{dr} = k\left(P - \frac{8 + 3\pi}{2}r\right), \frac{dT}{dr} = 0 \text{ when } r = \frac{2P}{8 + 3\pi}.$$

This is the only critical point and $d^2T/dr^2 < 0$ there so the most light is admitted when $r = 2P/(8 + 3\pi)$ ft.

32. The total cost C is
$$C = c \cdot (\text{hours to travel 3000 mi at a speed of } v \text{ mph})$$
$$= c \cdot \frac{3000}{v} = (a + bv^n)\frac{3000}{v} = 3000(av^{-1} + bv^{n-1}) \text{ for } v > 0,$$
$$dC/dv = 3000[-av^{-2} + b(n-1)v^{n-2}] = 3000[-a + b(n-1)v^n]/v^2,$$
$$dC/dv = 0 \text{ when } v = \left[\frac{a}{b(n-1)}\right]^{1/n}. \text{ This is the only critical point and } dC/dv \text{ changes sign}$$
from $-$ to $+$ at this point so the total cost is least when $v = \left[\dfrac{a}{b(n-1)}\right]^{1/n}$ mph.

33. The total area of material used is
$$A = A_{\text{top}} + A_{\text{bottom}} + A_{\text{side}} = (2r)^2 + (2r)^2 + 2\pi rh = 8r^2 + 2\pi rh.$$
The volume is $V = \pi r^2 h$ thus $h = V/(\pi r^2)$ so $A = 8r^2 + 2V/r$ for $r > 0$,
$dA/dr = 16r - 2V/r^2 = 2(8r^3 - V)/r^2$, $dA/dr = 0$ when $r = \sqrt[3]{V}/2$. This is the only critical point, $d^2A/dr^2 > 0$ there so the least material is used when $r = \sqrt[3]{V}/2$, $\dfrac{r}{h} = \dfrac{r}{V/(\pi r^2)} = \dfrac{\pi}{V}r^3$
and, for $r = \sqrt[3]{V}/2$, $\dfrac{r}{h} = \dfrac{\pi}{V}\dfrac{V}{8} = \dfrac{\pi}{8}$.

34. $P =$ (total daily sales) $-$ (total daily cost)

$= x(50 - 0.5x) - (0.25x^2 + 35x + 25) = -0.75x^2 + 15x - 25$ for

$0 < x < 100$, $dP/dx = -1.5x + 15$, critical point $x = 10$. $d^2P/dx^2 < 0$ so the profit is maximum when $x = 10$.

35. f is continuous on $[-2, 2]$, $f'(x) = -x/\sqrt{4 - x^2}$ so f is differentiable on $(-2, 2)$, $f(-2) = f(2) = 0$; hypotheses are satisfied. $f'(c) = 0$ for $c = 0$.

36. f is continuous on $[-1, 1]$, $f'(x) = \dfrac{2}{3}x^{-1/3}$ and $f'(0)$ does not exist, $f(-1) = f(1) = 0$; all hypotheses are not satisfied.

37. f is continuous on $[0, \sqrt{\pi}]$, $f'(x) = 2x\cos(x^2)$ so f is differentiable on $(0, \sqrt{\pi})$, $f(0) = f(\sqrt{\pi}) = 0$; hypotheses are satisfied. $f'(c) = 0$ when $2c\cos(c^2) = 0$ which yields $c = 0, \pm\sqrt{\pi/2}$ of which only $c = \sqrt{\pi/2}$ is in $(0, \sqrt{\pi})$.

38. f is continuous on $[-2, 2]$ but f does not have a derivative at $x = 1$ so all hypotheses are not satisfied.

39. f is continuous on $[0, 4]$ and differentiable on $(0, 4)$. $f'(c) = \dfrac{f(4) - f(0)}{4 - 0}$, $\dfrac{1}{2\sqrt{c}} = \dfrac{1}{2}$, $c = 1$

40. f is continuous on $[2, 3]$, $f'(x) = -2/(x - 1)^2$ so f is differentiable on $(2, 3)$.

$f'(c) = \dfrac{f(3) - f(2)}{3 - 2}$, $-\dfrac{2}{(c - 1)^2} = -1$, $(c - 1)^2 = 2$, $c = 1 \pm \sqrt{2}$ of which only

$c = 1 + \sqrt{2}$ is in $(2, 3)$.

41. By inspection, f is continuous on $[0, 2]$ and differentiable on $(0, 2)$ except perhaps at $x = 1$. For $x = 1$, $\lim\limits_{x \to 1^-} f(x) = \lim\limits_{x \to 1^+} f(x) = f(1)$ so f is continuous at $x = 1$.

$\lim\limits_{x \to 1^-} f'(x) = \lim\limits_{x \to 1^-}(-2x) = -2$, $\lim\limits_{x \to 1^+} f'(x) = \lim\limits_{x \to 1^+}(-2/x^2) = -2$ so f is differentiable at $x = 1$ (see theorem preceding Exercise 71, Section 3.3). $f'(c) = \dfrac{f(2) - f(0)}{2 - 0} = \dfrac{1 - 3}{2} = -1$ so $c \neq 1$. If $x < 1$ then $f'(x) = -2x$ thus $f'(c) = -1$ for $c = 1/2$. If $x > 1$ then $f'(x) = -2/x^2$ thus $f'(c) = -1$ for $c = \sqrt{2}$. The values of c are $1/2$, $\sqrt{2}$.

CHAPTER 5
Integration

EXERCISE SET 5.2

1. $x^9/9 + C$

2. $\int x^{-6}dx = -\frac{1}{5}x^{-5} + C = -\frac{1}{5x^5} + C$

3. $\frac{7}{12}x^{12/7} + C$

4. $\int x^{2/3}dx = \frac{3}{5}x^{5/3} + C$

5. $4\int t^{-1/2}dt = 8\sqrt{t} + C$

6. $\frac{1}{2}\int x^{-3}dx = -\frac{1}{4}x^{-2} + C$

7. $\int x^{7/2}dx = \frac{2}{9}x^{9/2} + C$

8. $u^4/4 - u^2 + 7u + C$

9. $\int (x^{-3} + x^{1/2} - 3x^{1/4} + x^2)dx = -\frac{1}{2}x^{-2} + \frac{2}{3}x^{3/2} - \frac{12}{5}x^{5/4} + \frac{1}{3}x^3 + C$

10. $\frac{3}{5}x^{5/3} - 5x^{4/5} + 4x + C$

11. $\int (7y^{-3/4} - y^{1/3} + 4y^{1/2})dy = 28y^{1/4} - \frac{3}{4}y^{4/3} + \frac{8}{3}y^{3/2} + C$

12. $\int (4 + 4y^2 + y^4)dy = 4y + \frac{4}{3}y^3 + \frac{1}{5}y^5 + C$

13. $\int (x + x^4)dx = x^2/2 + x^5/5 + C$

14. $\int (2 - x + 2x^2 - x^3)dx = 2x - \frac{1}{2}x^2 + \frac{2}{3}x^3 - \frac{1}{4}x^4 + C$

15. $\int x^{1/3}(4 - 4x + x^2)dx = \int (4x^{1/3} - 4x^{4/3} + x^{7/3})dx = 3x^{4/3} - \frac{12}{7}x^{7/3} + \frac{3}{10}x^{10/3} + C$

16. $\int (t^{-3} - 2)dt = -\frac{1}{2}t^{-2} - 2t + C$

17. $\int (x + 2x^{-2} - x^{-4})dx = x^2/2 - 2/x + 1/(3x^3) + C$

18. $\int (t^{-2} - \cos t)dt = -1/t - \sin t + C$

19. $-4\cos x + 2\sin x + C$ **20.** $4\tan x - \csc x + C$

21. $\int (\sec^2 x + \sec x \tan x)dx = \tan x + \sec x + C$

22. $\frac{2}{3}\theta^{3/2} + \cot\theta + C$ **23.** $\int (\sec x \tan x + 1)dx = \sec x + x + C$

24. $\int \sin y \, dy = -\cos y + C$ **25.** $\int \sec x \tan x \, dx = \sec x + C$

26. $\int \frac{2\sin x \cos x}{\cos x}dx = 2\int \sin x \, dx = -2\cos x + C$

27. $\int (1 + \sin\theta)d\theta = \theta - \cos\theta + C$ **28.** $\int (\phi + 2\csc^2\phi)d\phi = \phi^2/2 - 2\cot\phi + C$

29. $\int (\cos\theta - 5\sec^2\theta)d\theta = \sin\theta - 5\tan\theta + C$

30. $\int \sin x \, dx = -\cos x + C$

31. $F(x) = \int x^{1/3}dx = \frac{3}{4}x^{4/3} + C, \ F(1) = \frac{3}{4} + C = 2, \ C = 5/4; \ F(x) = \frac{3}{4}x^{4/3} + \frac{5}{4}$

32. $f'(x) = -\sin x, \ f(x) = -\int \sin x \, dx = \cos x + C, \ f(0) = 1 + C = 2, \ C = 1, \ f(x) = \cos x + 1$

33. $f'(x) = \frac{2}{3}x^{3/2} + C_1; \ f(x) = \frac{4}{15}x^{5/2} + C_1 x + C_2$

34. $f'(x) = x^2/2 + \sin x + C_1$, use $f'(0) = 2$ to get $C_1 = 2$ so $f'(x) = x^2/2 + \sin x + 2$,
   $f(x) = x^3/6 - \cos x + 2x + C_2$, use $f(0) = 1$ to get $C_2 = 2$ so $f(x) = x^3/6 - \cos x + 2x + 2$

35. $dy/dx = 2x + 1, y = \int (2x + 1)dx = x^2 + x + C; y = 0$ when $x = -3$
   so $(-3)^2 + (-3) + C = 0, C = -6$ thus $y = x^2 + x - 6$.

36. $dy/dx = x^2, y = \int x^2 dx = x^3/3 + C; y = 2$ when $x = -1$ so $(-1)^3/3 + C = 2, C = 7/3$

thus $y = x^3/3 + 7/3$.

37. $dy/dx = \int 6x dx = 3x^2 + C_1$. The slope of the tangent line is -3 so $dy/dx = -3$ when $x = 1$.

Thus $3(1)^2 + C_1 = -3$, $C_1 = -6$ so $dy/dx = 3x^2 - 6$, $y = \int (3x^2 - 6)dx = x^3 - 6x + C_2$; If

$x = 1$, then $y = 5 - 3(1) = 2$ so $(1)^2 - 6(1) + C_2 = 2, C_2 = 7$ thus $y = x^3 - 6x + 7$.

38. $dT/dx = C_1$, $T = C_1 x + C_2$; $T = 25$ when $x = 0$ so $C_2 = 25$, $T = C_1 x + 25$. $T = 85$ when $x = 50$ so $50C_1 + 25 = 85$, $C_1 = 1.2$, $T = 1.2x + 25$.

39. $\dfrac{d}{dx}\left[\sqrt{x^3 + 5}\right] = \dfrac{3x^2}{2\sqrt{x^3 + 5}}$ so $\displaystyle\int \dfrac{3x^2}{2\sqrt{x^3 + 5}}dx = \sqrt{x^3 + 5} + C$.

40. $\dfrac{d}{dx}\left[\dfrac{x}{x^2 + 3}\right] = \dfrac{3 - x^2}{(x^2 + 3)^2}$ so $\displaystyle\int \dfrac{3 - x^2}{(x^2 + 3)^2}dx = \dfrac{x}{x^2 + 3} + C$.

41. $\dfrac{d}{dx}\left[\sin\left(2\sqrt{x}\right)\right] = \dfrac{\cos\left(2\sqrt{x}\right)}{\sqrt{x}}$ so $\displaystyle\int \dfrac{\cos\left(2\sqrt{x}\right)}{\sqrt{x}}dx = \sin\left(2\sqrt{x}\right) + C$

42. $\dfrac{d}{dx}[\sin x - x\cos x] = x\sin x$ so $\displaystyle\int x\sin x\, dx = \sin x - x\cos x + C$.

43. (a) $F'(x) = G'(x) = 3x + 4$.
(b) $F(x) = (9x^2 + 24x + 16)/6 = 3x^2/2 + 4x + 8/3 = G(x) + 8/3$

44. (a) $F'(x) = G'(x) = 10x/(x^2 + 5)^2$
(b) $F(x) = \dfrac{x^2}{x^2 + 5} = \dfrac{(x^2 + 5) - 5}{x^2 + 5} = 1 - \dfrac{5}{x^2 + 5} = G(x) + 1$.

45. $f(x) = \dfrac{d}{dx}(5x^3 - 3x + C) = 15x^2 - 3$.   **46.** $g(t) = \dfrac{d}{dt}\left(\dfrac{1}{\sqrt{4 - t^2}} + C\right) = -\dfrac{t}{\sqrt{4 - t^2}}$

47. $\displaystyle\int (\sec^2 x - 1)dx = \tan x - x + C$ **48.** $\displaystyle\int (\csc^2 x - 1)dx = -\cot x - x + C$

49. $\dfrac{d}{dx}\left[\displaystyle\int f(x)dx - \int g(x)dx\right] = \dfrac{d}{dx}\left[\displaystyle\int f(x)dx\right] - \dfrac{d}{dx}\left[\displaystyle\int g(x)dx\right] = f(x) - g(x)$

50. **(a)** $F'(x) = F_1'(x) = f(x)$, $F_1(x) - F(x) = \begin{cases} 2, & x > 0 \\ 3, & x < 0 \end{cases}$ so $F_1(x) \neq F(x)$ plus a constant.

(b) no, because $(-\infty, 0) \cup (0, +\infty)$ is not an interval.

EXERCISE SET 5.3

1. **(a)** $\displaystyle\int u^{23} du = u^{24}/24 + C = (x^2 + 1)^{24}/24 + C$

(b) $\displaystyle -\int u^3 du = -u^4/4 + C = -(\cos^4 x)/4 + C$

(c) $\displaystyle 2\int \sin u\, du = -2\cos u + C = -2\cos\sqrt{x} + C$

(d) $\displaystyle\frac{3}{8}\int u^{-1/2} du = \frac{3}{4}u^{1/2} + C = \frac{3}{4}\sqrt{4x^2 + 5} + C$

2. **(a)** $\displaystyle\frac{1}{4}\int \sec^2 u\, du = \frac{1}{4}\tan u + C = \frac{1}{4}\tan(4x + 1) + C$

(b) $\displaystyle\frac{1}{4}\int u^{1/2} du = \frac{1}{6}u^{3/2} + C = \frac{1}{6}(1 + 2y^2)^{3/2} + C$

(c) $\displaystyle\frac{1}{\pi}\int u^{1/2} du = \frac{2}{3\pi}u^{3/2} + C = \frac{2}{3\pi}\sin^{3/2}\pi\theta + C$

(d) $\displaystyle\int u^{4/5} du = \frac{5}{9}u^{9/5} + C = \frac{5}{9}(x^2 + 7x + 3)^{9/5} + C$

3. **(a)** $\displaystyle -\int u\, du = -\frac{1}{2}u^2 + C = -\frac{1}{2}\cot^2 x + C$

(b) $\displaystyle\int u^9 du = \frac{1}{10}u^{10} + C = \frac{1}{10}(1 + \sin t)^{10} + C$

(c) $\displaystyle\int (u - 1)^2 u^{1/2} du = \int (u^{5/2} - 2u^{3/2} + u^{1/2})du = \frac{2}{7}u^{7/2} - \frac{4}{5}u^{5/2} + \frac{2}{3}u^{3/2} + C$

$\displaystyle = \frac{2}{7}(1 + x)^{7/2} - \frac{4}{5}(1 + x)^{5/2} + \frac{2}{3}(1 + x)^{3/2} + C$

(d) $\displaystyle\int \csc^2 u\, du = -\cot u + C = -\cot(\sin x) + C$

4. $u = 3x - 1$, $du = 3dx$; $\displaystyle\frac{1}{3}\int u^5 du = \frac{1}{18}u^6 + C = \frac{1}{18}(3x - 1)^6 + C$

5. $u = 2 - x^2$, $du = -2x\, dx$; $\displaystyle -\frac{1}{2}\int u^3 du = -u^4/8 + C = -(2 - x^2)^4/8 + C$

6. $u = 3x$, $du = 3dx$; $\dfrac{1}{3}\displaystyle\int \sin u\, du = -\dfrac{1}{3}\cos u + C = -\dfrac{1}{3}\cos 3x + C$

7. $u = 8x$, $du = 8dx$; $\dfrac{1}{8}\displaystyle\int \cos u\, du = \dfrac{1}{8}\sin u + C = \dfrac{1}{8}\sin 8x + C$

8. $u = 5x$, $du = 5dx$; $\dfrac{1}{5}\displaystyle\int \sec^2 u\, du = \dfrac{1}{5}\tan u + C = \dfrac{1}{5}\tan 5x + C$

9. $u = 4x$, $du = 4dx$; $\dfrac{1}{4}\displaystyle\int \sec u \tan u\, du = \dfrac{1}{4}\sec u + C = \dfrac{1}{4}\sec 4x + C$

10. $u = 3t + 1$, $du = 3dt$; $\dfrac{1}{3}\displaystyle\int u^{1/2} du = \dfrac{2}{9}u^{3/2} + C = \dfrac{2}{9}(3t + 1)^{3/2} + C$

11. $u = 7t^2 + 12$, $du = 14t\, dt$; $\dfrac{1}{14}\displaystyle\int u^{1/2} du = \dfrac{1}{21}u^{3/2} + C = \dfrac{1}{21}(7t^2 + 12)^{3/2} + C$

12. $u = 4 - 5x^2$, $du = -10x\, dx$; $-\dfrac{1}{10}\displaystyle\int u^{-1/2} du = -\dfrac{1}{5}u^{1/2} + C = -\dfrac{1}{5}\sqrt{4 - 5x^2} + C$

13. $u = x^3 + 1$, $du = 3x^2 dx$; $\dfrac{1}{3}\displaystyle\int u^{-1/2} du = \dfrac{2}{3}u^{1/2} + C = \dfrac{2}{3}\sqrt{x^3 + 1} + C$

14. $u = 1 - 3x$, $du = -3dx$; $-\dfrac{1}{3}\displaystyle\int u^{-2} du = \dfrac{1}{3}u^{-1} + C = \dfrac{1}{3}(1 - 3x)^{-1} + C$

15. $u = 4x^2 + 1$, $du = 8x\, dx$; $\dfrac{1}{8}\displaystyle\int u^{-3} du = -\dfrac{1}{16}u^{-2} + C = -\dfrac{1}{16}(4x^2 + 1)^{-2} + C$

16. $u = 3x^2$, $du = 6x\, dx$; $\dfrac{1}{6}\displaystyle\int \cos u\, du = \dfrac{1}{6}\sin u + C = \dfrac{1}{6}\sin(3x^2) + C$

17. $u = 5/x$, $du = -(5/x^2)dx$; $-\dfrac{1}{5}\displaystyle\int \sin u\, du = \dfrac{1}{5}\cos u + C = \dfrac{1}{5}\cos(5/x) + C$

18. $u = \sqrt{x}$, $du = \dfrac{1}{2\sqrt{x}}dx$; $2\displaystyle\int \sec^2 u\, du = 2\tan u + C = 2\tan\sqrt{x} + C$

19. $u = x^3$, $du = 3x^2 dx$; $\dfrac{1}{3}\displaystyle\int \sec^2 u\, du = \dfrac{1}{3}\tan u + C = \dfrac{1}{3}\tan(x^3) + C$

20. $u = \cos 2t$, $du = -2\sin 2t\, dt$; $-\dfrac{1}{2}\displaystyle\int u^3 du = -\dfrac{1}{8}u^4 + C = -\dfrac{1}{8}\cos^4 2t + C$

21. $u = \sin 3t$, $du = 3 \cos 3t \, dt$; $\dfrac{1}{3} \displaystyle\int u^5 du = \dfrac{1}{18} u^6 + C = \dfrac{1}{18} \sin^6 3t + C$

22. $u = 5 + \cos 2\theta$, $du = -2 \sin 2\theta \, d\theta$; $-\dfrac{1}{2} \displaystyle\int u^{-3} du = \dfrac{1}{4} u^{-2} + C = \dfrac{1}{4}(5 + \cos 2\theta)^{-2} + C$

23. $u = 2 - \sin 4\theta$, $du = -4 \cos 4\theta \, d\theta$; $-\dfrac{1}{4} \displaystyle\int u^{1/2} du = -\dfrac{1}{6} u^{3/2} + C = -\dfrac{1}{6}(2 - \sin 4\theta)^{3/2} + C$

24. $u = \tan 5x$, $du = 5 \sec^2 5x \, dx$; $\dfrac{1}{5} \displaystyle\int u^3 du = \dfrac{1}{20} u^4 + C = \dfrac{1}{20} \tan^4 5x + C$

25. $u = \sec 2x$, $du = 2 \sec 2x \tan 2x \, dx$; $\dfrac{1}{2} \displaystyle\int u^2 du = \dfrac{1}{6} u^3 + C = \dfrac{1}{6} \sec^3 2x + C$

26. $u = \sin \theta$, $du = \cos \theta \, d\theta$; $\displaystyle\int \sin u \, du = -\cos u + C = -\cos(\sin \theta) + C$

27. $u = \cos 3\theta$, $du = -3 \sin 3\theta \, d\theta$; $-\dfrac{1}{3} \displaystyle\int \sec^2 u \, du = -\dfrac{1}{3} \tan u + C = -\dfrac{1}{3} \tan(\cos 3\theta) + C$

28. $u = a + bx$, $du = b \, dx$, $dx = \dfrac{1}{b} du$

    $\dfrac{1}{b} \displaystyle\int u^{1/n} du = \dfrac{n}{b(n+1)} u^{(n+1)/n} + C = \dfrac{n}{b(n+1)}(a + bx)^{(n+1)/n} + C$

29. $u = \sin(a + bx)$, $du = b \cos(a + bx) dx$

    $\dfrac{1}{b} \displaystyle\int u^n du = \dfrac{1}{b(n+1)} u^{n+1} + C = \dfrac{1}{b(n+1)} \sin^{n+1}(a + bx) + C$

30. $\displaystyle\int [(2x - 3)^2]^{2/3} dx = \int (2x - 3)^{4/3} dx$; $u = 2x - 3$, $du = 2dx$

    $\dfrac{1}{2} \displaystyle\int u^{4/3} du = \dfrac{3}{14} u^{7/3} + C = \dfrac{3}{14}(2x - 3)^{7/3} + C$

31. $u = x - 3$, $x = u + 3$, $dx = du$

    $\displaystyle\int (u + 3) u^{1/2} du = \int (u^{3/2} + 3u^{1/2}) du = \dfrac{2}{5} u^{5/2} + 2u^{3/2} + C = \dfrac{2}{5}(x - 3)^{5/2} + 2(x - 3)^{3/2} + C$

32. $u = 2 - x$, $x = 2 - u$, $dx = -du$

$$-\int (2-u)^2 u^{1/2} du = -\int (4 - 4u + u^2) u^{1/2} du = -\int (4u^{1/2} - 4u^{3/2} + u^{5/2}) du$$

$$= -\frac{8}{3} u^{3/2} + \frac{8}{5} u^{5/2} - \frac{2}{7} u^{7/2} + C$$

$$= -\frac{8}{3}(2-x)^{3/2} + \frac{8}{5}(2-x)^{5/2} - \frac{2}{7}(2-x)^{7/2} + C$$

33. $u = y + 1$, $y = u - 1$, $dy = du$

$$\int \frac{u-1}{u^{1/2}} du = \int (u^{1/2} - u^{-1/2}) du = \frac{2}{3} u^{3/2} - 2u^{1/2} + C = \frac{2}{3}(y+1)^{3/2} - 2(y+1)^{1/2} + C$$

34. $\displaystyle \int \sin^2 2\theta \sin 2\theta \, d\theta = \int (1 - \cos^2 2\theta) \sin 2\theta \, d\theta$; $u = \cos 2\theta$, $du = -2 \sin 2\theta \, d\theta$,

$$-\frac{1}{2} \int (1 - u^2) du = -\frac{1}{2} u + \frac{1}{6} u^3 + C = -\frac{1}{2} \cos 2\theta + \frac{1}{6} \cos^3 2\theta + C$$

35. $u = 3\theta$, $du = 3 \, d\theta$

$$\frac{1}{3} \int \tan^2 u \, du = \frac{1}{3} \int (\sec^2 u - 1) du = \frac{1}{3}(\tan u - u) + C = \frac{1}{3}(\tan 3\theta - 3\theta) + C$$

36. $\displaystyle \int \sqrt{1 + x^{-2/3}} \, dx = \int x^{-1/3} \sqrt{x^{2/3} + 1} \, dx$; $u = x^{2/3} + 1$, $du = \frac{2}{3} x^{-1/3} dx$

$$\frac{3}{2} \int u^{1/2} du = u^{3/2} + C = (x^{2/3} + 1)^{3/2} + C$$

37. $u = \sqrt{x - 1}$, $u^2 = x - 1$, $x = u^2 + 1$, $dx = 2u \, du$

$$\int (u^2 + 1)^2 u (2u) du = 2 \int (u^4 + 2u^2 + 1) u^2 du = 2 \int (u^6 + 2u^4 + u^2) du$$

$$= \frac{2}{7} u^7 + \frac{4}{5} u^5 + \frac{2}{3} u^3 + C$$

$$= \frac{2}{7}(x - 1)^{7/2} + \frac{4}{5}(x-1)^{5/2} + \frac{2}{3}(x-1)^{3/2} + C$$

38. **(a)** with $u = \sin x$, $du = \cos x \, dx$; $\displaystyle \int u \, du = \frac{1}{2} u^2 + C = \frac{1}{2} \sin^2 x + C$;

with $u = \cos x$, $du = -\sin x \, dx$; $\displaystyle -\int u \, du = -\frac{1}{2} u^2 + C = -\frac{1}{2} \cos^2 x + C$

(b) because they differ by a constant:

$$\left(\frac{1}{2} \sin^2 x + C \right) - \left(-\frac{1}{2} \cos^2 x + C \right) = \frac{1}{2}(\sin^2 x + \cos^2 x) = 1/2.$$

39. **(a)** First method: $\int (25x^2 - 10x + 1)dx = \dfrac{25}{3}x^3 - 5x^2 + x + C;$

second method: $\dfrac{1}{5}\int u^2 du = \dfrac{1}{15}u^3 + C = \dfrac{1}{15}(5x - 1)^3 + C$

(b) $\dfrac{1}{15}(5x - 1)^3 + C = \dfrac{1}{15}(125x^3 - 75x^2 + 15x - 1) + C = \dfrac{25}{3}x^3 - 5x^2 + x - \dfrac{1}{15} + C;$
the answers differ by a constant.

40. $f(x) = \int \sqrt{3x + 1}dx = \dfrac{2}{9}(3x + 1)^{3/2} + C,$

$f(1) = \dfrac{16}{9} + C = 5, \ C = \dfrac{29}{9}$ so $f(x) = \dfrac{2}{9}(3x + 1)^{3/2} + \dfrac{29}{9}$

41. $f(x) = \int (6 - 5\ \sin 2x)dx = 6x + \dfrac{5}{2}\cos 2x + C,$

$f(0) = \dfrac{5}{2} + C = 3, \ C = \dfrac{1}{2}$ so $f(x) = 6x + \dfrac{5}{2}\cos 2x + \dfrac{1}{2}$

42. $u = 5x, \ du = 5\ dx; \ \dfrac{1}{5}\int f'(u)du = \dfrac{1}{5}f(u) + C = \dfrac{1}{5}f(5x) + C$

43. $u = 3x + 2, \ du = 3\ dx; \ \dfrac{1}{3}\int f'(u)du = \dfrac{1}{3}f(u) + C = \dfrac{1}{3}f(3x + 2) + C$

44. $u = 3x^2, \ du = 6x\ dx; \ \dfrac{1}{6}\int f'(u)du = \dfrac{1}{6}f(u) + C = \dfrac{1}{6}f(3x^2) + C$

45. $u = 2/x, \ du = -(2/x^2)dx; \ -\dfrac{1}{2}\int f'(u)du = -\dfrac{1}{2}f(u) + C = -\dfrac{1}{2}f(2/x) + C$

EXERCISE SET 5.4

1. **(a)** $1 + 8 + 27 = 36$ **(b)** $5 + 8 + 11 + 14 + 17 = 55$
   (c) $20 + 12 + 6 + 2 + 0 + 0 = 40$ **(d)** $1 + 1 + 1 + 1 + 1 + 1 = 6$

2. **(a)** $1 + 0 - 3 + 0 = -2$ **(b)** $1 - 1 + 1 - 1 + 1 - 1 = 0$
   (c) $\pi + \pi + \cdots + \pi = 14\pi$ **(d)** $2^4 + 2^5 + 2^6 = 112$
       (14 terms)

3. $\displaystyle\sum_{k=1}^{10} k$

4. $\displaystyle\sum_{k=1}^{20} 3k$

5. $\displaystyle\sum_{k=1}^{49} k(k+1)$

6. $\displaystyle\sum_{k=0}^{4} 2^k$

7. $\displaystyle\sum_{k=1}^{10} 2k$

8. $\displaystyle\sum_{k=1}^{8}(2k-1)$

9. $\displaystyle\sum_{k=1}^{6}(-1)^{k+1}(2k-1)$

10. $\displaystyle\sum_{k=1}^{5}(-1)^{k+1}\frac{1}{k}$

11. $\displaystyle\sum_{k=1}^{5}(-1)^k\frac{1}{k}$

12. $\displaystyle\sum_{k=0}^{3}\cos\frac{k\pi}{7}$

13. $\displaystyle\sum_{k=1}^{4}\sin\frac{(2k-1)\pi}{8}$

14. $\displaystyle\sum_{k=1}^{5} 2^k$

15. $\displaystyle\sum_{k=1}^{5}\frac{k}{k+1}$

16. $\displaystyle\sum_{k=4}^{n}(k^2-1)$

17. (a) $\displaystyle\sum_{k=1}^{5}(-1)^{k+1}a_k$ (b) $\displaystyle\sum_{k=0}^{5}(-1)^{k+1}b_k$ (c) $\displaystyle\sum_{k=0}^{n}a_k x^k$ (d) $\displaystyle\sum_{k=0}^{5}a^{5-k}b^k$

18. $\dfrac{1}{2}(100)(100+1)=5050$

19. $\displaystyle\sum_{k=1}^{100}k-\sum_{k=1}^{2}k=\frac{1}{2}(100)(100+1)-(1+2)=5050-3=5047$

20. $\displaystyle 7\sum_{k=1}^{100}k+\sum_{k=1}^{100}1=\frac{7}{2}(100)(101)+100=35,450$

21. $\dfrac{1}{6}(20)(21)(41)=2,870$ 22. $\displaystyle\sum_{k=1}^{20}k^2-\sum_{k=1}^{3}k^2=2,870-14=2,856$

23. $\displaystyle 4\sum_{k=1}^{6}k^3-2\sum_{k=1}^{6}k+\sum_{k=1}^{6}1=4\left[\frac{1}{4}(6)^2(7)^2\right]-2\left[\frac{1}{2}(6)(7)\right]+6=1728$

24. $\displaystyle\sum_{k=1}^{6}k-\sum_{k=1}^{6}k^3=\frac{1}{2}(6)(7)-\frac{1}{4}(6)^2(7)^2=-420$

25. $\displaystyle\sum_{k=1}^{30} k(k^2 - 4) = \sum_{k=1}^{30}(k^3 - 4k) = \sum_{k=1}^{30}k^3 - 4\sum_{k=1}^{30}k = \frac{1}{4}(30)^2(31)^2 - 4 \times \frac{1}{2}(30)(31) = 214,365$

26. **(a)** $\displaystyle\sum_{k=1}^{n}(4k - 3) = 4\sum_{k=1}^{n}k - \sum_{k=1}^{n}3 = 4 \times \frac{1}{2}n(n + 1) - 3n = 2n^2 - n.$

     (b) $\displaystyle\sum_{k=1}^{n-1}k^2 = \frac{1}{6}(n - 1)[(n - 1) + 1][2(n - 1) + 1] = \frac{1}{6}n(n - 1)(2n - 1)$

27. $\displaystyle\sum_{k=1}^{n}\frac{3k}{n} = \frac{3}{n}\sum_{k=1}^{n}k = \frac{3}{n} \times \frac{1}{2}n(n + 1) = \frac{3}{2}(n + 1)$

28. $\displaystyle\sum_{k=1}^{n-1}\frac{k^2}{n} = \frac{1}{n}\sum_{k=1}^{n-1}k^2 = \frac{1}{n} \times \frac{1}{6}(n - 1)(n)(2n - 1) = \frac{1}{6}(n - 1)(2n - 1)$

29. $\displaystyle\sum_{k=1}^{n-1}\frac{k^3}{n^2} = \frac{1}{n^2}\sum_{k=1}^{n-1}k^3 = \frac{1}{n^2} \times \frac{1}{4}(n - 1)^2 n^2 = \frac{1}{4}(n - 1)^2$

30. $\displaystyle\sum_{k=1}^{n}\left(\frac{5}{n} - \frac{2k}{n}\right) = \frac{5}{n}\sum_{k=1}^{n}1 - \frac{2}{n}\sum_{k=1}^{n}k = \frac{5}{n}(n) - \frac{2}{n} \times \frac{1}{2}n(n + 1) = 4 - n.$

31. $\displaystyle\frac{1 + 2 + 3 + \cdots + n}{n^2} = \sum_{k=1}^{n}\frac{k}{n^2} = \frac{1}{n^2}\sum_{k=1}^{n}k = \frac{1}{n^2} \times \frac{1}{2}n(n + 1) = \frac{n + 1}{2n}; \lim_{n \to +\infty}\frac{n + 1}{2n} = \frac{1}{2}.$

32. $\displaystyle\frac{1^2 + 2^2 + 3^2 + \cdots + n^2}{n^3} = \sum_{k=1}^{n}\frac{k^2}{n^3} = \frac{1}{n^3}\sum_{k=1}^{n}k^2 = \frac{1}{n^3} \times \frac{1}{6}n(n + 1)(2n + 1) = \frac{(n + 1)(2n + 1)}{6n^2};$

     $\displaystyle\lim_{n \to +\infty}\frac{(n + 1)(2n + 1)}{6n^2} = \lim_{n \to +\infty}\frac{1}{6}(1 + 1/n)(2 + 1/n) = \frac{1}{3}.$

33. $\displaystyle\sum_{k=1}^{n}\frac{5k}{n^2} = \frac{5}{n^2}\sum_{k=1}^{n}k = \frac{5}{n^2} \times \frac{1}{2}n(n + 1) = \frac{5(n + 1)}{2n}; \lim_{n \to +\infty}\frac{5(n + 1)}{2n} = \frac{5}{2}.$

34. $\displaystyle\sum_{k=1}^{n-1}\frac{2k^2}{n^3} = \frac{2}{n^3}\sum_{k=1}^{n-1}k^2 = \frac{2}{n^3} \times \frac{1}{6}(n - 1)(n)(2n - 1) = \frac{(n - 1)(2n - 1)}{3n^2};$

     $\displaystyle\lim_{n \to +\infty}\frac{(n - 1)(2n - 1)}{3n^2} = \lim_{n \to +\infty}\frac{1}{3}(1 - 1/n)(2 - 1/n) = \frac{2}{3}.$

35. $\displaystyle\sum_{k=1}^{n-1}\left(\frac{9}{n}-\frac{k}{n^2}\right)=\frac{9}{n}\sum_{k=1}^{n-1}1-\frac{1}{n^2}\sum_{k=1}^{n-1}k=\frac{9}{n}(n-1)-\frac{1}{n^2}\times\frac{1}{2}(n-1)(n)=\frac{17}{2}\left(\frac{n-1}{n}\right);$

$\displaystyle\lim_{n\to+\infty}\frac{17}{2}\left(\frac{n-1}{n}\right)=\frac{17}{2}.$

36. $1\cdot2+2\cdot3+\cdots+n(n+1)=\displaystyle\sum_{k=1}^{n}k(k+1)$

$\displaystyle=\sum_{k=1}^{n}k^2+\sum_{k=1}^{n}k$

$\displaystyle=\frac{1}{6}n(n+1)(2n+1)+\frac{1}{2}n(n+1)=\frac{1}{3}n(n+1)(n+2).$

37. $1+3+5+\cdots+(2n-1)=\displaystyle\sum_{k=1}^{n}(2k-1)=2\sum_{k=1}^{n}k-\sum_{k=1}^{n}1=2\times\frac{1}{2}n(n+1)-n=n^2.$

38. $\left(1-\dfrac{1}{2}\right)+\left(\dfrac{1}{2}-\dfrac{1}{3}\right)+\cdots+\left(\dfrac{1}{50}-\dfrac{1}{51}\right)=\dfrac{50}{51}$

39. $(3^5-3^4)+(3^6-3^5)+\cdots+(3^{17}-3^{16})=3^{17}-3^4$

40. $(2^2-2)+(2^3-2^2)+\cdots+(2^{101}-2^{100})=2^{101}-2$

41. $\left(\dfrac{1}{2^2}-\dfrac{1}{1^2}\right)+\left(\dfrac{1}{3^2}-\dfrac{1}{2^2}\right)+\cdots+\left(\dfrac{1}{20^2}-\dfrac{1}{19^2}\right)=\dfrac{1}{20^2}-1=-\dfrac{399}{400}$

42. $(a_1-a_2)+(a_2-a_3)+\cdots+(a_n-a_{n+1})=a_1-a_{n+1}$

43. $(a_1-a_0)+(a_2-a_1)+\cdots+(a_n-a_{n-1})=a_n-a_0$

44. **(a)** $\displaystyle\sum_{k=1}^{n}\frac{1}{k(k+1)}=\sum_{k=1}^{n}\left(\frac{1}{k}-\frac{1}{k+1}\right)$

$\displaystyle=\left(1-\frac{1}{2}\right)+\left(\frac{1}{2}-\frac{1}{3}\right)+\left(\frac{1}{3}-\frac{1}{4}\right)+\cdots+\left(\frac{1}{n}-\frac{1}{n+1}\right)$

$\displaystyle=1-\frac{1}{n+1}=\frac{n}{n+1}.$

(b) $\displaystyle\lim_{n\to+\infty}\frac{n}{n+1}=1$

45. **(a)** $\displaystyle\sum_{k=1}^{n}\frac{1}{(2k-1)(2k+1)}=\frac{1}{2}\sum_{k=1}^{n}\left(\frac{1}{2k-1}-\frac{1}{2k+1}\right)$

$$=\frac{1}{2}\left[\left(1-\frac{1}{3}\right)+\left(\frac{1}{3}-\frac{1}{5}\right)+\left(\frac{1}{5}-\frac{1}{7}\right)+\cdots+\left(\frac{1}{2n-1}-\frac{1}{2n+1}\right)\right]$$

$$=\frac{1}{2}\left[1-\frac{1}{2n+1}\right]=\frac{n}{2n+1}$$

(b) $\displaystyle\lim_{n\to+\infty}\frac{n}{2n+1}=\frac{1}{2}$

46. **(a)** $m+m+\cdots+m=m(m+1)$
    ($m+1$ terms)

(b) 5

(c) $x+x+\cdots+x=nx$
    (n terms)

(d) $\displaystyle c\sum_{i=1}^{n}i^2=\frac{1}{6}n(n+1)(2n+1)c$

47. **(a)** $n+n+\cdots+n=n^2$
    (n terms)

(b) -3

(c) $\displaystyle x\sum_{k=1}^{n}k=\frac{1}{2}n(n+1)x$

(d) $c+c+\cdots+c=(n-m+1)c$
    ($n-m+1$ terms)

48. **(a)** $\displaystyle\sum_{j=0}^{5}2^{j}$

(b) $\displaystyle\sum_{j=1}^{6}2^{j-1}$

(c) $\displaystyle\sum_{j=2}^{7}2^{j-2}$

49. **(a)** $\displaystyle\sum_{k=0}^{14}(k+4)(k+1)$

(b) $\displaystyle\sum_{k=5}^{19}(k-1)(k-4)$

50. **(a)** $\displaystyle\sum_{k=1}^{5}(k+4)2^{k+8}$

(b) $\displaystyle\sum_{k=9}^{13}(k-4)2^{k}$

51. $\displaystyle\sum_{k=1}^{18}k\sin\frac{\pi}{k}$

52. none are valid

53. both are valid

54.
$$S - rS = \sum_{k=0}^{n} ar^k - \sum_{k=0}^{n} ar^{k+1}$$
$$= (a + ar + ar^2 + \cdots + ar^n) - (ar + ar^2 + ar^3 + \cdots + ar^{n+1})$$
$$= a - ar^{n+1} = a(1 - r^{n+1})$$

so $(1 - r)S = a(1 - r^{n+1})$, hence $S = a(1 - r^{n+1})/(1 - r)$.

55. **(a)** $\displaystyle \sum_{k=0}^{19} 3^{k+1} = \sum_{k=0}^{19} 3(3^k) = \frac{3(1 - 3^{20})}{1 - 3} = \frac{3}{2}(3^{20} - 1)$

(b) $\displaystyle \sum_{k=0}^{25} 2^{k+5} = \sum_{k=0}^{25} 2^5 2^k = \frac{2^5(1 - 2^{26})}{1 - 2} = 2^{31} - 2^5$

(c) $\displaystyle \sum_{k=0}^{100} (-1)\left(\frac{-1}{2}\right)^k = \frac{(-1)(1 - (-1/2)^{101})}{1 - (-1/2)} = -\frac{2}{3}(1 + 1/2^{101})$

56. $\displaystyle \sum_{k=1}^{n} \sin^k \theta = \sum_{k=0}^{n-1} \sin^{k+1} \theta = \sum_{k=0}^{n-1} (\sin \theta) \sin^k \theta = \frac{\sin \theta(1 - \sin^n \theta)}{1 - \sin \theta}$ if $\sin \theta \neq 1$.

If $\sin \theta = 1$, then $\displaystyle \sum_{k=1}^{n} (1)^k = \sum_{k=1}^{n} 1 = n$.

57. $\displaystyle \sum_{i=1}^{4}\left[\sum_{j=1}^{5} i + \sum_{j=1}^{5} j\right] \sum_{i=1}^{4}\left[5i + \frac{1}{2}(5)(6)\right] = 5\sum_{i=1}^{4} i + \sum_{i=1}^{4} 15 = 5 \cdot \frac{1}{2}(4)(5) + (4)(15) = 110$

58. $\displaystyle \sum_{i=1}^{n} (x_1 - \bar{x}) = \sum_{i=1}^{n} x_i - \sum_{i=1}^{n} \bar{x} = \sum_{i=1}^{n} x_i - n\bar{x}$ but $\bar{x} = \frac{1}{n}\sum_{i=1}^{n} x_i$ thus

$\displaystyle \sum_{i=1}^{n} x_i = n\bar{x}$ so $\displaystyle \sum_{i=1}^{n} (x_i - \bar{x}) = n\bar{x} - n\bar{x} = 0$.

59. $\displaystyle \sum_{k=1}^{n} (a_k - b_k) = (a_1 - b_1) + (a_2 - b_2) + \cdots + (a_n - b_n)$

$$= (a_1 + a_2 + \cdots + a_n) - (b_1 + b_2 + \cdots + b_n) = \sum_{k=1}^{n} a_k - \sum_{k=1}^{n} b_k$$

60. $\sum_{k=1}^{n} \left[(k+1)^4 - k^4\right] = (n+1)^4 - 1$ (telescoping sum), expand the

quantity in brackets to get $\sum_{k=1}^{n}(4k^3 + 6k^2 + 4k + 1) = (n+1)^4 - 1$,

$4\sum_{k=1}^{n} k^3 + 6\sum_{k=1}^{n} k^2 + 4\sum_{k=1}^{n} k + \sum_{k=1}^{n} 1 = (n+1)^4 - 1$

$\sum_{k=1}^{n} k^3 = \frac{1}{4}\left[(n+1)^4 - 1 - 6\sum_{k=1}^{n} k^2 - 4\sum_{k=1}^{n} k - \sum_{k=1}^{n} 1\right]$

$= \frac{1}{4}[(n+1)^4 - 1 - n(n+1)(2n+1) - 2n(n+1) - n]$

$= \frac{1}{4}(n+1)[(n+1)^3 - n(2n+1) - 2n - 1]$

$= \frac{1}{4}(n+1)(n^3 + n^2) = \frac{1}{4}n^2(n+1)^2$

EXERCISE SET 5.5

1. $\Delta x = \dfrac{6-2}{4} = 1, \; f(x) = 3x + 1$

    (a) $c_k = 2, 3, 4, 5; \; \sum_{k=1}^{4} f(c_k)\Delta x = (7 + 10 + 13 + 16)(1) = 46$

    (b) $d_k = 3, 4, 5, 6; \; \sum_{k=1}^{4} f(d_k)\Delta x = (10 + 13 + 16 + 19)(1) = 58$

2. $\Delta x = \dfrac{9-1}{4} = 2, \; f(x) = 1/x$

    (a) $c_k = 3, 5, 7, 9; \; \sum_{k=1}^{4} f(c_k)\Delta x = \left(\frac{1}{3} + \frac{1}{5} + \frac{1}{7} + \frac{1}{9}\right)(2) = \dfrac{496}{315} \approx 1.575$

    (b) $d_k = 1, 3, 5, 7; \; \sum_{k=1}^{4} f(d_k)\Delta x = \left(1 + \frac{1}{3} + \frac{1}{5} + \frac{1}{7}\right)(2) = \dfrac{352}{105} \approx 3.352$

3. $\Delta x = \pi/4$, $f(x) = \cos x$

   (a) $c_k = -\pi/2, -\pi/4, \pi/4, \pi/2$

   $$\sum_{k=1}^{4} f(c_k)\Delta x = (0 + \sqrt{2}/2 + \sqrt{2}/2 + 0)(\pi/4) = \sqrt{2}\,\pi/4 \approx 1.111$$

   (b) $d_k = -\pi/4, 0, 0, \pi/4$

   $$\sum_{k=1}^{4} f(d_k)\Delta x = (\sqrt{2}/2 + 1 + 1 + \sqrt{2}/2)(\pi/4) = (2 + \sqrt{2})\pi/4 \approx 2.682$$

4. $\Delta x = 1/4$, $f(x) = 2x - x^2$

   (a) $c_k = 5/4, 3/2, 7/4, 2$

   $$\sum_{k=1}^{4} f(c_k)\Delta x = (15/16 + 3/4 + 7/16 + 0)(1/4) = 17/32 \approx 0.531$$

   (b) $d_k = 1, 5/4, 3/2, 7/4$

   $$\sum_{k=1}^{4} f(d_k)\Delta x = (1 + 15/16 + 3/4 + 7/16)(1/4) = 25/32 \approx 0.781$$

5. $\Delta x = \dfrac{3}{n}$, $c_k = 1 + (k-1)\dfrac{3}{n}$

$$f(c_k)\Delta x = \frac{1}{2}c_k\Delta x = \frac{1}{2}\left[1 + (k-1)\frac{3}{n}\right]\frac{3}{n} = \frac{1}{2}\left[\frac{3}{n} + (k-1)\frac{9}{n^2}\right]$$

$$\sum_{k=1}^{n} f(c_k)\Delta x = \frac{1}{2}\left[\sum_{k=1}^{n}\frac{3}{n} + \frac{9}{n^2}\sum_{k=1}^{n}(k-1)\right] = \frac{1}{2}\left[3 + \frac{9}{n^2}\cdot\frac{1}{2}(n-1)n\right] = \frac{3}{2} + \frac{9}{4}\frac{n-1}{n}$$

$$A = \lim_{n\to+\infty}\left[\frac{3}{2} + \frac{9}{4}\left(1 - \frac{1}{n}\right)\right] = \frac{3}{2} + \frac{9}{4} = \frac{15}{4}$$

6. $\Delta x = \dfrac{5}{n}$, $c_k = 0 + k\dfrac{5}{n}$; $f(c_k)\Delta x = (-c_k + 5)\Delta x = \left(-k\dfrac{5}{n} + 5\right)\dfrac{5}{n} = -\dfrac{25}{n^2}k + \dfrac{25}{n}$

$$\sum_{k=1}^{n} f(c_k)\Delta x = -\frac{25}{n^2}\sum_{k=1}^{n}k + \sum_{k=1}^{n}\frac{25}{n} = -\frac{25}{n^2}\cdot\frac{1}{2}n(n+1) + 25 = 25 - \frac{25}{2}\left(\frac{n+1}{n}\right)$$

$$A = \lim_{n\to+\infty}\left[25 - \frac{25}{2}\left(1 + \frac{1}{n}\right)\right] = 25 - \frac{25}{2} = \frac{25}{2}$$

7. $\Delta x = \dfrac{1}{n}$, $c_k = (k-1)\dfrac{1}{n}$; $f(c_k)\Delta x = c_k^2 \Delta x = (k-1)^2 \dfrac{1}{n^2} \cdot \dfrac{1}{n} = \dfrac{1}{n^3}(k-1)^2$

$$\sum_{k=1}^{n} f(c_k)\Delta x = \frac{1}{n^3}\sum_{k=1}^{n}(k-1)^2 = \frac{1}{n^3}\sum_{k=1}^{n-1} k^2 = \frac{1}{n^3} \cdot \frac{1}{6}(n-1)(n)(2n-1) = \frac{1}{6}\frac{(n-1)(2n-1)}{n^2}$$

$$A = \lim_{n \to +\infty} \frac{1}{6}\left(1 - \frac{1}{n}\right)\left(2 - \frac{1}{n}\right) = \frac{1}{6}(1)(2) = \frac{1}{3}$$

8. $\Delta x = \dfrac{3}{n}$, $c_k = k\dfrac{3}{n}$

$$f(c_k)\Delta x = \left(4 - \frac{1}{4}c_k^2\right)\Delta x = \left(4 - \frac{1}{4}\frac{9k^2}{n^2}\right)\frac{3}{n} = \frac{12}{n} - \frac{27k^2}{4n^3}$$

$$\sum_{k=1}^{n} f(c_k)\Delta x = \sum_{k=1}^{n}\frac{12}{n} - \frac{27}{4n^3}\sum_{k=1}^{n} k^2$$

$$= 12 - \frac{27}{4n^3} \cdot \frac{1}{6}n(n+1)(2n+1) = 12 - \frac{9}{8}\frac{(n+1)(2n+1)}{n^2}$$

$$A = \lim_{n \to +\infty}\left[12 - \frac{9}{8}\left(1 + \frac{1}{n}\right)\left(2 + \frac{1}{n}\right)\right] = 12 - \frac{9}{8}(1)(2) = 39/4$$

9. $\Delta x = \dfrac{4}{n}$, $c_k = 2 + (k-1)\dfrac{4}{n}$

$$f(c_k)\Delta x = c_k^3 \Delta x = \left[2 + \frac{4}{n}(k-1)\right]^3 \frac{4}{n} = \frac{32}{n}\left[1 + \frac{2}{n}(k-1)\right]^3$$

$$= \frac{32}{n}\left[1 + \frac{6}{n}(k-1) + \frac{12}{n^2}(k-1)^2 + \frac{8}{n^3}(k-1)^3\right]$$

$$\sum_{k=1}^{n} f(c_k)\Delta x = \frac{32}{n}\left[\sum_{k=1}^{n}1 + \frac{6}{n}\sum_{k=1}^{n}(k-1) + \frac{12}{n^2}\sum_{k=1}^{n}(k-1)^2 + \frac{8}{n^3}\sum_{k=1}^{n}(k-1)^3\right]$$

$$= \frac{32}{n}\left[n + \frac{6}{n}\sum_{k=1}^{n-1}k + \frac{12}{n^2}\sum_{k=1}^{n-1}k^2 + \frac{8}{n^3}\sum_{k=1}^{n-1}k^3\right]$$

$$= \frac{32}{n}\left[n + \frac{6}{n}\cdot\frac{1}{2}(n-1)(n) + \frac{12}{n^2}\cdot\frac{1}{6}(n-1)(n)(2n-1) + \frac{8}{n^3}\cdot\frac{1}{4}(n-1)^2 n^2\right]$$

$$= 32\left[1 + 3\frac{n-1}{n} + 2\frac{(n-1)(2n-1)}{n^2} + 2\frac{(n-1)^2}{n^2}\right]$$

$$A = \lim_{n \to +\infty} 32\left[1 + 3\left(1 - \frac{1}{n}\right) + 2\left(1 - \frac{1}{n}\right)\left(2 - \frac{1}{n}\right) + 2\left(1 - \frac{1}{n}\right)^2\right]$$

$$= 32[1 + 3(1) + 2(1)(2) + 2(1)^2] = 320$$

10. $\Delta x = \dfrac{2}{n}$, $c_k = -3 + k\dfrac{2}{n}$; $f(c_k)\Delta x = (1 - c_k^3)\Delta x = \left[1 - \left(-3 + \dfrac{2}{n}k\right)^3\right]\dfrac{2}{n}$

$$= \dfrac{2}{n}\left[28 - \dfrac{54}{n}k + \dfrac{36}{n^2}k^2 - \dfrac{8}{n^3}k^3\right]$$

$$\sum_{k=1}^{n} f(c_k)\Delta x = \dfrac{2}{n}\left[28n - 27(n+1) + 6\dfrac{(n+1)(2n+1)}{n} - 2\dfrac{(n+1)^2}{n}\right]$$

$$A = \lim_{n\to+\infty} 2\left[28 - 27\left(1 + \dfrac{1}{n}\right) + 6\left(1 + \dfrac{1}{n}\right)\left(2 + \dfrac{1}{n}\right) - 2\left(1 + \dfrac{1}{n}\right)^2\right]$$

$$= 2(28 - 27 + 12 - 2) = 22$$

11. $\Delta x = \dfrac{3}{n}$, $d_k = 1 + \dfrac{3}{n}k$; $f(d_k)\Delta x = \dfrac{1}{2}d_k\Delta x = \dfrac{1}{2}\left(1 + \dfrac{3}{n}k\right)\dfrac{3}{n} = \dfrac{3}{2}\left[\dfrac{1}{n} + \dfrac{3}{n^2}k\right]$

$$\sum_{k=1}^{n} f(d_k)\Delta x = \dfrac{3}{2}\left[\sum_{k=1}^{n}\dfrac{1}{n} + \sum_{k=1}^{n}\dfrac{3}{n^2}k\right] = \dfrac{3}{2}\left[1 + \dfrac{3}{n^2}\cdot\dfrac{1}{2}n(n+1)\right] = \dfrac{3}{2}\left[1 + \dfrac{3}{2}\dfrac{n+1}{n}\right]$$

$$A = \lim_{n\to+\infty}\dfrac{3}{2}\left[1 + \dfrac{3}{2}\left(1 + \dfrac{1}{n}\right)\right] = \dfrac{3}{2}\left(1 + \dfrac{3}{2}\right) = \dfrac{15}{4}$$

12. $\Delta x = \dfrac{5}{n}$, $d_k = \dfrac{5}{n}(k-1)$

$$f(d_k)\Delta x = [-d_k + 5]\Delta x = \left[-\dfrac{5}{n}(k-1) + 5\right]\dfrac{5}{n} = -\dfrac{25}{n^2}(k-1) + \dfrac{25}{n}$$

$$\sum_{k=1}^{n} f(d_k)\Delta x = -\dfrac{25}{n^2}\sum_{k=1}^{n}(k-1) + \dfrac{25}{n}\sum_{k=1}^{n}1$$

$$= -\dfrac{25}{n^2}\dfrac{1}{2}(n-1)n + \dfrac{25}{n}\cdot n = -\dfrac{25}{2}\dfrac{n-1}{n} + 25$$

$$A = \lim_{n\to+\infty}\left[-\dfrac{25}{2}\left(1 - \dfrac{1}{n}\right) + 25\right] = -\dfrac{25}{2} + 25 = \dfrac{25}{2}$$

13. $\Delta x = \dfrac{1}{n}$, $d_k = \dfrac{k}{n}$; $f(d_k)\Delta x = d_k^2\Delta x = \dfrac{k^2}{n^2}\dfrac{1}{n} = \dfrac{k^2}{n^3}$

$$\sum_{k=1}^{n} f(d_k)\Delta x = \sum_{k=1}^{n}\dfrac{k^2}{n^3} = \dfrac{1}{n^3}\dfrac{1}{6}n(n+1)(2n+1) = \dfrac{1}{6}\dfrac{(n+1)(2n+1)}{n^2}$$

$$A = \lim_{n\to+\infty}\dfrac{1}{6}\left(1 + \dfrac{1}{n}\right)\left(2 + \dfrac{1}{n}\right) = \dfrac{1}{3}$$

14. $\Delta x = \dfrac{b-a}{n}$, $c_k = a + \dfrac{b-a}{n}(k-1)$

$$f(c_k)\Delta x = mc_k\Delta x = m\left[a + \frac{b-a}{n}(k-1)\right]\frac{b-a}{n} = m(b-a)\left[\frac{a}{n} + \frac{b-a}{n^2}(k-1)\right]$$

$$\sum_{k=1}^{n} f(c_k)\Delta x = m(b-a)\left[a + \frac{b-a}{2}\cdot\frac{n-1}{n}\right]$$

$$A = \lim_{n\to+\infty} m(b-a)\left[a + \frac{b-a}{2}\left(1 - \frac{1}{n}\right)\right] = m(b-a)\frac{b+a}{2} = \frac{1}{2}m(b^2 - a^2)$$

15. **(a)** Using inscribed rectangles, $\Delta x = \dfrac{b}{n}$, $c_k = \dfrac{b}{n}(k-1)$

$$f(c_k)\Delta x = c_k^3\Delta x = \frac{b^4}{n^4}(k-1)^3$$

$$\sum_{k=1}^{n} f(c_k)\Delta x = \frac{b^4}{n^4}\sum_{k=1}^{n}(k-1)^3 = \frac{b^4}{n^4}\sum_{k=1}^{n-1}k^3 = \frac{b^4}{4}\frac{(n-1)^2}{n^2}$$

$$A = \lim_{n\to+\infty}\frac{b^4}{4}\left(1 - \frac{1}{n}\right)^2 = b^4/4$$

(b) $\Delta x = \dfrac{b-a}{n}$, $c_k = a + \dfrac{b-a}{n}(k-1)$

$$f(c_k)\Delta x = c_k^3\Delta x = \left[a + \frac{b-a}{n}(k-1)\right]^3\frac{b-a}{n}$$

$$= \frac{b-a}{n}\left[a^3 + \frac{3a^2(b-a)}{n}(k-1) + \frac{3a(b-a)^2}{n^2}(k-1)^2 + \frac{(b-a)^3}{n^3}(k-1)^3\right]$$

$$\sum_{k=1}^{n} f(c_k)\Delta x = (b-a)\left[a^3 + \frac{3}{2}a^2(b-a)\frac{n-1}{n} + \frac{1}{2}a(b-a)^2\frac{(n-1)(2n-1)}{n^2}\right.$$

$$\left. + \frac{1}{4}(b-a)^3\frac{(n-1)^2}{n^2}\right]$$

$$A = \lim_{n\to+\infty}\sum_{k=1}^{n} f(c_k)\Delta x$$

$$= (b-a)\left[a^3 + \frac{3}{2}a^2(b-a) + a(b-a)^2 + \frac{1}{4}(b-a)^3\right] = \frac{1}{4}(b^4 - a^4).$$

16. Divide the interval $[0,1]$ along the y-axis into n subintervals and let $f(y) = x = y^2$ then $A = \lim\limits_{n\to+\infty}\sum\limits_{k=1}^{n} f(c_k)\Delta y$ where c_k is the value of y in the k-th subinterval so that $f(c_k)$ is minimum;

$$\Delta y = \frac{1}{n}, \ c_k = \frac{1}{n}(k-1), \ f(c_k)\Delta y = c_k^2 \Delta y = \frac{1}{n^3}(k-1)^2,$$

$$\sum_{k=1}^{n} f(c_k)\Delta y = \frac{1}{6}\frac{(n-1)(2n-1)}{n^2}, \ A = \lim_{n \to +\infty} \frac{1}{6}\left(1-\frac{1}{n}\right)\left(2-\frac{1}{n}\right) = \frac{1}{3}$$

17. **(a)** $\Delta x = \dfrac{b-a}{n}, \ c_k = a + \dfrac{b-a}{n}(k-1); \ f(c_k)\Delta x = \dfrac{b-a}{n}\left[a + \dfrac{b-a}{n}(k-1)\right]$

$$\sum_{k=1}^{n} f(c_k)\Delta x = (b-a)\left[a + \frac{b-a}{2}\cdot\frac{n-1}{n}\right]$$

$$A = \lim_{n \to +\infty}(b-a)\left[a + \frac{b-a}{2}\left(1-\frac{1}{n}\right)\right] = \frac{1}{2}(b^2 - a^2)$$

(b) $\Delta x = \dfrac{b-a}{n}, \ d_k = a + \dfrac{b-a}{n}k; \ f(d_k)\Delta x = \dfrac{b-a}{n}\left[a + \dfrac{b-a}{n}k\right]$

$$\sum_{k=1}^{n} f(d_k)\Delta x = (b-a)\left[a + \frac{b-a}{2}\cdot\frac{n+1}{n}\right]$$

$$A = \lim_{n \to +\infty}(b-a)\left[a + \frac{b-a}{2}\left(1+\frac{1}{n}\right)\right] = \frac{1}{2}(b^2 - a^2)$$

(c) The region is enclosed by a trapezoid so its area is

$$A = \frac{1}{2}(b-a)(b+a)$$

$$= \frac{1}{2}(b^2 - a^2).$$

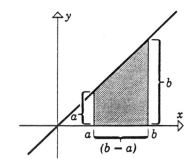

18. **(a)** 0.668771403, 0.680803382, 0.688172179
    (b) 0.718771403, 0.705803382, 0.698172179

19. **(a)** 0.584145862, 0.623823864, 0.649145594
    (b) 0.761923639, 0.712712753, 0.684701150

20. **(a)** 4.884074734, 5.115572731, 5.248762738
    (b) 5.684074734, 5.515572731, 5.408762738

21. (a) 0.919403170, 0.960215997, 0.984209789
(b) 1.076482803, 1.038755813, 1.015625715

EXERCISE SET 5.6

1. (a) $(4/3)(1) + (5/2)(1) + (4)(2) = 71/6$
(b) 2

2. (a) $(\sqrt{2}/2)(\pi/2) + (-1)(3\pi/4) + (0)(\pi/2) + (\sqrt{2}/2)(\pi/4) = 3(\sqrt{2} - 2)\pi/8$
(b) $3\pi/4$

3. (a) $(-9/4)(1) + (3)(2) + (63/16)(1) + (-5)(3) = -117/16$
(b) 3

4. (a) $(-8)(2) + (0)(1) + (0)(1) + (8)(2) = 0$
(b) 2

5. $\sum_{k=1}^{4} f(c_k)\Delta x = (1/3 + 1/5 + 1/7 + 1/9)(2) = 496/315$

$\sum_{k=1}^{4} f(x_k^*)\Delta x = (1/2 + 1/4 + 1/6 + 1/8)(2) = 25/12$

$\sum_{k=1}^{4} f(d_k)\Delta x = (1 + 1/3 + 1/5 + 1/7)(2) = 352/105$

$496/315 = 1984/1260$, $25/12 = 2625/1260$, $352/105 = 4224/1260$,
$1984/1260 \le 2625/1260 \le 4224/1260$

6. $\displaystyle\int_{1}^{2} x^3\,dx$ **7.** $\displaystyle\int_{-3}^{3} 4x(1 - 3x)\,dx$ **8.** $\displaystyle\int_{0}^{\pi/2} \sin^2 x\,dx$

9. $\displaystyle\lim_{\max \Delta x_k \to 0} \sum_{k=1}^{n} 2x_k^*\Delta x_k;\ a = 1,\ b = 2$

10. $\displaystyle\lim_{\max \Delta x_k \to 0} \sum_{k=1}^{n} (1 + \cos x_k^*)\,\Delta x_k,\ a = -\pi/2,\ b = \pi/2$

11. $\displaystyle\lim_{\max \Delta x_k \to 0} \sum_{k=1}^{n} \frac{x_k^*}{x_k^* + 1}\Delta x_k;\ a = 0,\ b = 1$

12. (a)

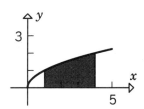

(b)

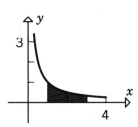

(c)

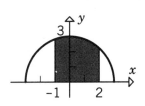

(d)

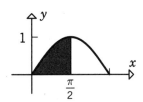

13. (a) 0.8   **(b)** −2.6   **(c)** −1.8   **(d)** −0.3

14. (a) $A = \dfrac{1}{2}(3)(3) = 9/2$ **(b)** $-A = -\dfrac{1}{2}(1)(1+2) = -3/2$

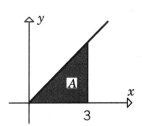

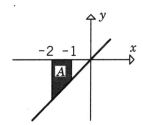

(c) $-A_1 + A_2 = -\dfrac{1}{2} + 8 = 15/2$

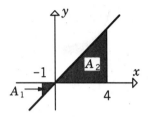

(d) $-A_1 + A_2 = 0$

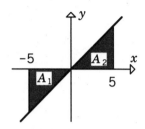

15.   **(a)** $A = \dfrac{1}{2}(1)(2) = 1$

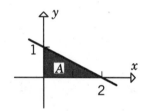

(b) $A = \dfrac{1}{2}(2)(3/2 + 1/2) = 2$

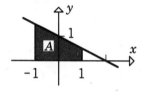

(c) $-A = -\dfrac{1}{2}(1/2)(1) = -1/4$

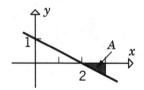

(d) $A_1 - A_2 = 1 - 1/4 = 3/4$

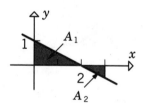

16. $A = (6)(5) = 30$

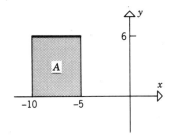

17. $A_1 - A_2 = \frac{1}{2}(2)(1/2) - \frac{1}{2}(6)(3/2)$

$$= -4$$

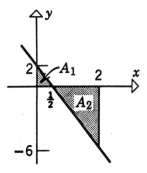

18. $A_1 + A_2 = \frac{1}{2}(2)(2) + \frac{1}{2}(1)(1) = 5/2$

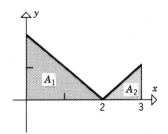

19. $A_1 + A_2 = \frac{1}{2}(5)(5/2) + \frac{1}{2}(1)(1/2)$

$$= 13/2$$

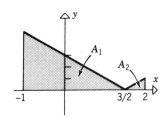

20. $\frac{1}{4}\pi(2)^2 = \pi$

21. $\frac{1}{2}[\pi(1)^2] = \pi/2$

22. $A_1 + A_2 = (2)(3) + \pi(3)^2/4$
$$= 6 + 9\pi/4$$

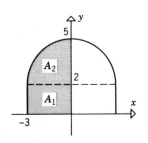

23. $\sqrt{10x - x^2} = \sqrt{25 - (x - 5)^2};\ \int_0^{10} \sqrt{10x - x^2}\,dx = \frac{1}{2}[\pi(5)^2] = 25\pi/2$

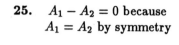

24. $-A_1 + A_2 = 0$ because $A_1 = A_2$ by symmetry

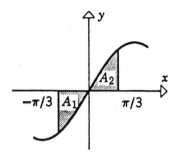

25. $A_1 - A_2 = 0$ because $A_1 = A_2$ by symmetry

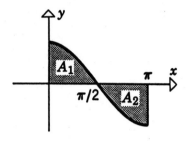

26. $A_1 + A_2 = \dfrac{1}{2}(2)(1) + (2)(2) = 5$

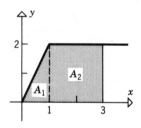

27. $A_1 + A_2 = (3)(2) + \dfrac{1}{2}(2)(5 + 3) = 14$

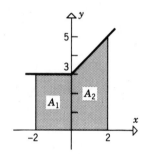

28. **(a)** $\displaystyle\sum_{k=1}^{n} f(x_k^*)\Delta x_k = \sum_{k=1}^{n} f(x_k^*)\Delta x$

$$= \Delta x \sum_{k=1}^{n} f(x_k^*) = \Delta x\,[f(x_1^*) + f(x_2^*) + \cdots + f(x_n^*)]$$

(b) $x_k^* = a + \dfrac{1}{2}\Delta x + (k - 1)\Delta x = a - \dfrac{1}{2}\Delta x + k\Delta x.$

29. 0.692835360, 0.693069098, 0.693134682

30. 1.539761515, 1.536350316, 1.534939069

31. 3.142425985, 3.141800987, 3.141625987

32. Each subinterval of a partition of $[a, b]$ contains both rational and irrational numbers. If x_k^* is rational then

$$\sum_{k=1}^{n} f(x_k^*)\Delta x_k = \sum_{k=1}^{n}(1)\Delta x_k = \sum_{k=1}^{n}\Delta x_k = b - a \text{ so } \lim_{\max \Delta x_k \to 0}\sum_{k=1}^{n} f(x_k^*)\Delta x_k = b - a.$$

If x_k^* is irrational then $\displaystyle\lim_{\max \Delta x_k \to 0}\sum_{k=1}^{n} f(x_k^*)\Delta x_k = 0$. f is not integrable on $[a, b]$ because the preceding limits are not equal.

33. f is not bounded on $[0,1]$ because $\displaystyle\lim_{x \to 0^+} f(x) = +\infty$, so f is not integrable on $[0,1]$.

34. $f(x)$ is discontinuous at the point $x = 0$ because $\displaystyle\lim_{x \to 0}\sin\frac{1}{x}$ does not exist. f is continuous elsewhere. $-1 \le f(x) \le 1$ for x in $[-1, 1]$ so f is bounded there. By part (b), Theorem 5.6.6, f is integrable on $[-1, 1]$.

35. Let $S_n = \displaystyle\sum_{k=1}^{n} f(x_k^*)\Delta x_k$. From definition 5.6.7, for any $\epsilon > 0$ there are numbers $\delta_1 > 0$ and $\delta_2 > 0$ such that $|S_n - L_1| < \epsilon$ for $\max \Delta x_k < \delta_1$ and $|S_n - L_2| < \epsilon$ for $\max \Delta x_k < \delta_2$. If $\delta = \min(\delta_1, \delta_2)$ then $|S_n - L_1| < \epsilon$ and $|S_n - L_2| < \epsilon$ for $\max \Delta x_k < \delta$ thus

$$|L_1 - L_2| = |L_1 - S_n + S_n - L_2| = |(L_1 - S_n) + (S_n - L_2)| \le |S_n - L_1| + |S_n - L_2| < \epsilon + \epsilon = 2\epsilon$$

so $|L_1 - L_2| < 2\epsilon$ for $\max \Delta x_k < \delta$. Suppose $L_1 \ne L_2$ and let $\epsilon = \frac{1}{2}|L_1 - L_2|$ then $|L_1 - L_2| < 2\epsilon$ yields $|L_1 - L_2| < |L_1 - L_2|$ which is false so $L_1 \ne L_2$ is impossible.

36. Let $S_n = \displaystyle\sum_{k=1}^{n} f(x_k^*)\Delta x_k$ and $S = \displaystyle\int_a^b f(x)dx$ then $\displaystyle\sum_{k=1}^{n} cf(x_k^*)\Delta x_k = cS_n$ and we want to prove that $\displaystyle\lim_{\max \Delta x_k \to 0} cS_n = cS$. If $c = 0$ the result follows immediately, so suppose that $c \ne 0$ then for any $\epsilon > 0$, $|cS_n - cS| = |c||S_n - S| < \epsilon$ if $|S_n - S| < \epsilon/|c|$. But because f is integrable on $[a, b]$, there is a number $\delta > 0$ such that $|S_n - S| < \epsilon/|c|$ whenever $\max \Delta x_k < \delta$ so $|cS_n - cS| < \epsilon$ and hence $\displaystyle\lim_{\max \Delta x_k \to 0} cS_n = cS$.

37. Let $R_n = \displaystyle\sum_{k=1}^{n} f(x_k^*)\Delta x_k$, $S_n = \displaystyle\sum_{k=1}^{n} g(x_k^*)\Delta x_k$, $T_n = \displaystyle\sum_{k=1}^{n}[f(x_k^*) + g(x_k^*)]\Delta x_k$, $R = \displaystyle\int_a^b f(x)dx$,

and $S = \displaystyle\int_a^b g(x)dx$ then $T_n = R_n + S_n$ and we want to prove that $\displaystyle\lim_{\max \Delta x_k \to 0} T_n = R + S$.

$$|T_n - (R + S)| = |(R_n - R) + (S_n - S)| \le |R_n - R| + |S_n - S|$$

so for any $\epsilon > 0$ $|T_n - (R + S)| < \epsilon$ if $|R_n - R| + |S_n - S| < \epsilon$.

Because f and g are integrable on $[a, b]$, there are numbers δ_1 and δ_2 such that

$|R_n - R| < \epsilon/2$ for max $\Delta x_k < \delta_1$ and $|S_n - S| < \epsilon/2$ for max $\Delta x_k < \delta_2$.

If $\delta = \min(\delta_1, \delta_2)$ then $|R_n - R| < \epsilon/2$ and $|S_n - S| < \epsilon/2$ for max $\Delta x_k < \delta$ thus $|R_n - R| + |S_n - S| < \epsilon$ and so $|T_n - (R + S)| < \epsilon$ for max $\Delta x_k < \delta$ which shows that

$$\lim_{\max \Delta x_k \to 0} T_n = R + S.$$

EXERCISE SET 5.7

1. $\left. \frac{1}{4}x^4 \right]_2^3 = 65/4$

2. $\left. \frac{1}{5}x^5 \right]_{-1}^1 = 2/5$

3. $\left. \frac{1}{2}x^2 + \frac{1}{5}x^5 \right]_{-1}^2 = 81/10$

4. $\left. \frac{1}{3}x^3 - 2x^2 + 7x \right]_{-3}^0 = 48$

5. $\left. \frac{1}{3}t^3 - t^2 + 8t \right]_1^2 = 22/3$

6. $\left. \frac{1}{6}x^6 - \frac{1}{4}x^4 + x^2 \right]_0^1 = 11/12$

7. $\int_1^3 x^{-2}dx = \left. -\frac{1}{x} \right]_1^3 = 2/3$

8. $\int_1^2 x^{-6}dx = \left. -\frac{1}{5x^5} \right]_1^2 = 31/160$

9. $\left. -\frac{1}{2x^2} + \frac{2}{x} - \frac{1}{3x^3} \right]_1^2 = -1/3$

10. $\left. -\frac{1}{3u^3} - \frac{3}{u} + \frac{1}{4u^4} \right]_{-2}^{-1} = 389/192$

11. $\left. \frac{2}{3}x^{3/2} \right]_1^9 = 52/3$

12. $\left. \frac{5}{2}x^{2/5} \right]_1^4 = \frac{5}{2}(4^{2/5} - 1)$

13. $\left. \frac{4}{5}y^{5/2} \right]_4^9 = 844/5$

14. $\left. 3x^{5/3} + \frac{4}{x} \right]_1^8 = 179/2$

15. $\left. 6\sqrt{x} - \frac{10}{3}x^{3/2} + \frac{2}{\sqrt{x}} \right]_1^4 = -55/3$

16. $\left. 8\sqrt{y} + \frac{4}{3}y^{3/2} - \frac{2}{3y^{3/2}} \right]_4^9 = 10819/324$

17. $\left. -\cos\theta \right]_{-\pi/2}^{\pi/2} = 0$

18. $\left. \tan\theta \right]_0^{\pi/4} = 1$

19. $\displaystyle\int_{-\pi/4}^{\pi/4} \cos x\, dx = \sin x \Big]_{-\pi/4}^{\pi/4} = \sqrt{2}$

20. $\displaystyle \frac{1}{2}x^2 - \sec x \Big]_0^1 = 3/2 - \sec(1)$

21. $\displaystyle \frac{1}{2}x^2 - 2\cot x \Big]_{\pi/6}^{\pi/2} = \pi^2/9 + 2\sqrt{3}$

22. $\displaystyle a^{1/2}x - \frac{2}{3}x^{3/2} \Big]_a^{4a} = -\frac{5}{3}a^{3/2}$

23. $\displaystyle\int_0^{3/2} (3 - 2x)dx + \int_{3/2}^2 (2x - 3)dx = (3x - x^2)\Big]_0^{3/2} + (x^2 - 3x)\Big]_{3/2}^2 = 9/4 + 1/4 = 5/2$

24. $\displaystyle\int_1^2 (-x + 2)dx + \int_2^5 (x - 2)dx = -\frac{1}{2}x^2 + 2x\Big]_1^2 + \frac{1}{2}x^2 - 2x\Big]_2^5 = 5$

25. $\displaystyle\int_0^{\pi/2} \cos x\, dx + \int_{\pi/2}^{3\pi/4} (-\cos x)dx = \sin x\Big]_0^{\pi/2} - \sin x\Big]_{\pi/2}^{3\pi/4} = 2 - \sqrt{2}/2$

26. $\displaystyle\int_{-1}^0 \sqrt{2 - x}\, dx + \int_0^2 \sqrt{2 + x}\, dx = -\frac{2}{3}(2 - x)^{3/2}\Big]_{-1}^0 + \frac{2}{3}(2 + x)^{3/2}\Big]_0^2$

$$= -\frac{2}{3}(2\sqrt{2} - 3\sqrt{3}) + \frac{2}{3}(8 - 2\sqrt{2}) = \frac{2}{3}(8 - 4\sqrt{2} + 3\sqrt{3})$$

27. $\displaystyle\int_{-2}^0 x^2 dx + \int_0^3 (-x)dx = \frac{1}{3}x^3\Big]_{-2}^0 - \frac{1}{2}x^2\Big]_0^3 = -11/6$

28. $\displaystyle\int_0^1 \sqrt{x}\, dx + \int_1^4 \frac{1}{x^2}\, dx = \frac{2}{3}x^{3/2}\Big]_0^1 - \frac{1}{x}\Big]_1^4 = 17/12$

29. $\displaystyle\int_{-1}^2 x\, dx + 2\int_{-1}^2 f(x)dx = \frac{1}{2}x^2\Big]_{-1}^2 + 2(3) = 15/2$

30. $\displaystyle 3\int_1^4 f(x)dx - \int_1^4 g(x)dx = 3(2) - 10 = -4$

31. $\displaystyle\int_1^5 f(x)dx = \int_0^5 f(x)dx - \int_0^1 f(x)dx = 1 - (-2) = 3.$

32. $\displaystyle\int_3^{-2} f(x)dx = -\int_{-2}^3 f(x)dx = -\left[\int_{-2}^1 f(x)dx + \int_1^3 f(x)dx\right] = -(2 - 6) = 4$

33. negative, because $\sqrt{x}/(1-x) < 0$ for $2 \le x \le 3$.

34. positive, because $x^4/\sqrt{3-x} > 0$ for $-3 \le x \le -1$.

35. positive, because $x^2/(3 - \cos x) > 0$ for $0 < x \le 4$.

36. negative, because $(x^3 - 9)/(|x| + 1) < 0$ for $-2 \le x \le 2$.

37. negative, because $\displaystyle\int_2^0 x^2 \sin \sqrt{x}\, dx = -\int_0^2 x^2 \sin \sqrt{x}\, dx$ and $x^2 \sin \sqrt{x} > 0$ for $0 < x \le 2$.

38. positive, because $\displaystyle\int_0^{-1} \sqrt[3]{x^2 - 2}\, dx = -\int_{-1}^0 \sqrt[3]{x^2 - 2}\, dx$ and $\sqrt[3]{x^2 - 2} < 0$ for $-1 \le x \le 0$.

39. $\displaystyle\int_1^2 \frac{x}{x^4 + 1}\, dx < \int_1^2 \frac{1}{x^3}\, dx = -\frac{1}{2x^2}\bigg]_1^2 = 3/8.$

40. $\displaystyle\int_4^9 \frac{1}{\sqrt{x^3 + 1}}\, dx < \int_4^9 \frac{1}{x^{3/2}}\, dx = -\frac{2}{\sqrt{x}}\bigg]_4^9 = 1/3$

41. $\displaystyle m = \int_1^3 \frac{1}{x^{1.01}}\, dx = -\frac{100}{x^{0.01}}\bigg]_1^3 = 1.092599583;$

$\displaystyle M = \int_1^3 \frac{1}{x^{0.99}}\, dx = 100 x^{0.01}\bigg]_1^3 = 1.104669194$

42. $\displaystyle m = \int_1^3 \frac{1}{x^{1.001}}\, dx = -\frac{1000}{x^{0.001}}\bigg]_1^3 = 1.098009035;$

$\displaystyle M = \int_1^3 \frac{1}{x^{0.999}}\, dx = 1000 x^{0.001}\bigg]_1^3 = 1.099215984.$

43. $0.665867079;\ \displaystyle\int_1^3 \frac{1}{x^2}\, dx = -\frac{1}{x}\bigg]_1^3 = 2/3$

44. $1.000257067;\ \displaystyle\int_0^{\pi/2} \sin x\, dx = -\cos x\bigg]_0^{\pi/2} = 1$

45. $\dfrac{\sqrt{1}+\sqrt{2}+\sqrt{3}+\cdots+\sqrt{n}}{n^{3/2}} = \displaystyle\sum_{k=1}^{n}\dfrac{\sqrt{k}}{n^{3/2}} = \sum_{k=1}^{n}\sqrt{\dfrac{k}{n}}\dfrac{1}{n} = \sum_{k=1}^{n}f(x_k^*)\Delta x,$ where

$f(x) = \sqrt{x}, x_k^* = k/n$, and $\Delta x = 1/n$, so $\displaystyle\lim_{n\to+\infty}\sum_{k=1}^{n}f(x_k^*)\Delta x = \int_0^1 \sqrt{x}\,dx = 2/3.$

46. $\dfrac{1^4+2^4+3^4+\cdots+n^4}{n^5} = \displaystyle\sum_{k=1}^{n}\dfrac{k^4}{n^5} = \sum_{k=1}^{n}\left(\dfrac{k}{n}\right)^4\dfrac{1}{n} = \sum_{k=1}^{n}f(x_k^*)\Delta x,$ where $f(x) = x^4, x_k^* = k/n,$

and $\Delta x = 1/n$, so $\displaystyle\lim_{n\to+\infty}\sum_{k=1}^{n}f(x_k^*)\Delta x = \int_0^1 x^4 dx = 1/5.$

47. $A = \displaystyle\int_0^3 (x^2+1)dx = \dfrac{1}{3}x^3 + x\,\Big]_0^3 = 12$

48. $A = \displaystyle\int_1^2 (-x^2+3x-2)dx = -\dfrac{1}{3}x^3 + \dfrac{3}{2}x^2 - 2x\,\Big]_1^2 = 1/6$

49. $A = \displaystyle\int_0^{2\pi/3} 3\sin x\,dx = -3\cos x\,\Big]_0^{2\pi/3} = 9/2$

50. $A = -\displaystyle\int_{-2}^{-1} x^3 dx = -\dfrac{1}{4}x^4\,\Big]_{-2}^{-1} = 15/4$

51. $A_1 = \displaystyle\int_{-3}^{-2} (x^2-3x-10)dx$

$= \dfrac{1}{3}x^3 - \dfrac{3}{2}x^2 - 10x\,\Big]_{-3}^{-2} = 23/6,$

$A_2 = -\displaystyle\int_{-2}^{5} (x^2-3x-10)dx = 343/6,$

$A_3 = \displaystyle\int_{5}^{8} (x^2-3x-10)dx = 243/6,$

$A = A_1 + A_2 + A_3 = 203/2$

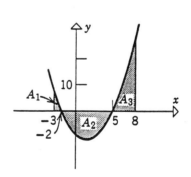

52. (a) $\big[F(x)+G(x)\big]_a^b = [F(b)+G(b)] - [F(a)+G(a)]$

$= [F(b)-F(a)] + [G(b)-G(a)] = F(x)\big]_a^b + G(x)\big]_a^b$

(b) $\big[F(x)-G(x)\big]_a^b = [F(b)-G(b)] - [F(a)-G(a)]$

$= [F(b)-F(a)] - [G(b)-G(a)] = F(x)\big]_a^b - G(x)\big]_a^b$

(c) $\left[cF(x)\right]_a^b = cF(b) - cF(a) = c[F(b) - F(a)] = c\left[F(x)\right]_a^b$

53. (b), (c) are always valid. Use $f(x) = g(x) = 1$ to show that (a), (d), and (e) are false.

54. $\int_a^b \left[\sum_{k=1}^n f_k(x)\right] dx = \sum_{k=1}^n \int_a^b f_k(x) dx$

EXERCISE SET 5.8

1. **(a)** $\int_1^3 u^7 du$ **(b)** $-\frac{1}{2}\int_7^4 u^{1/2} du$ **(c)** $\frac{1}{\pi}\int_{-\pi}^\pi \sin u\, du$

    (d) $\int_0^1 u^2 du$ **(e)** $\frac{1}{2}\int_3^4 (u-3)u^{1/2} du$ **(f)** $\int_{-3}^0 (u+5)u^{20} du$

2. $u = 4x - 2,\ \frac{1}{4}\int_2^6 u^3 du = \frac{1}{16}u^4\Big]_2^6 = 80,\ \text{or}\ \frac{1}{16}(4x-2)^4\Big]_1^2 = 80$

3. $u = 2x + 1,\ \frac{1}{2}\int_1^3 u^4 du = \frac{1}{10}u^5\Big]_1^3 = 121/5,\ \text{or}\ \frac{1}{10}(2x+1)^5\Big]_0^1 = 121/5$

4. $u = 4 - 3x,\ -\frac{1}{3}\int_1^{-2} u^8 du = -\frac{1}{27}u^9\Big]_1^{-2} = 19,\ \text{or}\ -\frac{1}{27}(4-3x)^9\Big]_1^2 = 19$

5. $u = 1 - 2x,\ -\frac{1}{2}\int_3^1 u^3 du = -\frac{1}{8}u^4\Big]_3^1 = 10,\ \text{or}\ -\frac{1}{8}(1-2x)^4\Big]_{-1}^0 = 10$

6. $u = 4 - x,\ \int_9^4 (u-4)u^{1/2} du = \int_9^4 (u^{3/2} - 4u^{1/2})du = \frac{2}{5}u^{5/2} - \frac{8}{3}u^{3/2}\Big]_9^4 = -506/15$

    or $\frac{2}{5}(4-x)^{5/2} - \frac{8}{3}(4-x)^{3/2}\Big]_{-5}^0 = -506/15$

7. $u = 1 + x,\ \int_1^9 (u-1)u^{1/2} du = \int_1^9 (u^{3/2} - u^{1/2})du = \frac{2}{5}u^{5/2} - \frac{2}{3}u^{3/2}\Big]_1^9 = 1192/15,$

    or $\frac{2}{5}(1+x)^{5/2} - \frac{2}{3}(1+x)^{3/2}\Big]_0^8 = 1192/15$

8. $u = 3x$, $\dfrac{2}{3} \displaystyle\int_0^{\pi/2} \cos u \, du = \dfrac{2}{3} \sin u \Big]_0^{\pi/2} = 2/3$, or $\dfrac{2}{3} \sin 3x \Big]_0^{\pi/6} = 2/3$

9. $u = x/2$, $8 \displaystyle\int_0^{\pi/4} \sin u \, du = -8 \cos u \Big]_0^{\pi/4} = 8 - 4\sqrt{2}$, or $-8 \cos(x/2) \Big]_0^{\pi/2} = 8 - 4\sqrt{2}$

10. $u = \dfrac{1}{4}x - \dfrac{1}{4}$, $4 \displaystyle\int_{-\pi/4}^{\pi/4} \sec^2 u \, du = 4 \tan u \Big]_{-\pi/4}^{\pi/4} = 8$, or $4 \tan \left(\dfrac{1}{4}x - \dfrac{1}{4} \right) \Big]_{1-\pi}^{1+\pi} = 8$

11. $u = x^2 + 2$, $\dfrac{1}{2} \displaystyle\int_6^3 u^{-3} du = -\dfrac{1}{4u^2} \Big]_6^3 = -1/48$, or $-\dfrac{1}{4} \dfrac{1}{(x^2+2)^2} \Big]_{-2}^{-1} = -1/48$

12. $\dfrac{3}{4b}(a + bx)^{4/3} \Big]_0^1 = \dfrac{3}{4b}[(a + b)^{4/3} - a^{4/3}]$

13. $\dfrac{2}{3}(3u + 1)^{1/2} \Big]_0^1 = 2/3$ 14. $\dfrac{2}{15}(5x - 1)^{3/2} \Big]_1^2 = \dfrac{38}{15}$

15. $\dfrac{2}{3}(x^3 + 9)^{1/2} \Big]_{-1}^1 = \dfrac{2}{3}(\sqrt{10} - 2\sqrt{2})$ 16. $\dfrac{1}{10}(t^3 + 1)^{20} \Big]_{-1}^0 = 1/10$

17. $u = x^2 + 4x + 7$, $\dfrac{1}{2} \displaystyle\int_{12}^{28} u^{-1/2} du = u^{1/2} \Big]_{12}^{28} = \sqrt{28} - \sqrt{12} = 2(\sqrt{7} - \sqrt{3})$

18. $\displaystyle\int_1^2 \dfrac{1}{(x - 3)^2} dx = -\dfrac{1}{x - 3} \Big]_1^2 = 1/2$

19. $\dfrac{1}{2} \sin^2 x \Big]_{-3\pi/4}^{-\pi/4} = 0$ 20. $\dfrac{2}{3}(\tan x)^{3/2} \Big]_0^{\pi/4} = 2/3$

21. $\dfrac{5}{2} \sin(x^2) \Big]_0^{\sqrt{\pi}} = 0$ 22. $-t \cos tx \Big]_0^{2\pi/t} = 0$

23. $u = \sqrt{x}$, $2 \displaystyle\int_\pi^{2\pi} \sin u \, du = -2 \cos u \Big]_\pi^{2\pi} = -4$

24. $\dfrac{1}{2}\sin^2\theta\Big]_{-\pi/4}^{\pi} = -1/4$

25. $u = \sin 3x,\ \dfrac{1}{3}\displaystyle\int_0^{-1} u^2\,du = \dfrac{1}{9}u^3\Big]_0^{-1} = -1/9$

26. $u = 7 - 3\sin 2x,\ -\dfrac{1}{6}\displaystyle\int_7^4 u^{-1/2}\,du = -\dfrac{1}{3}u^{1/2}\Big]_7^4 = \dfrac{1}{3}(\sqrt{7} - 2)$

27. $u = 3\theta,\ \dfrac{1}{3}\displaystyle\int_{\pi/4}^{\pi/3}\sec^2 u\,du = \dfrac{1}{3}\tan u\Big]_{\pi/4}^{\pi/3} = (\sqrt{3} - 1)/3$

28. $u = 5 + x,\ \displaystyle\int_4^9 \dfrac{u - 5}{\sqrt{u}}\,du = \int_4^9 (u^{1/2} - 5u^{-1/2})\,du = \dfrac{2}{3}u^{3/2} - 10u^{1/2}\Big]_4^9 = 8/3$

29. $u = 4 - 3y,\ y = \dfrac{1}{3}(4 - u),\ dy = -\dfrac{1}{3}du$

$$-\dfrac{1}{27}\int_4^1 \dfrac{16 - 8u + u^2}{u^{1/2}}\,du = \dfrac{1}{27}\int_1^4 (16u^{-1/2} - 8u^{1/2} + u^{3/2})\,du$$

$$= \dfrac{1}{27}\left[32u^{1/2} - \dfrac{16}{3}u^{3/2} + \dfrac{2}{5}u^{5/2}\right]_1^4 = 106/405$$

30. $A = \displaystyle\int_0^1 \dfrac{dx}{(3x + 1)^2} = -\dfrac{1}{3(3x + 1)}\Big]_0^1 = \dfrac{1}{4}$

31. $A = \displaystyle\int_0^{\pi/8} 3\,\cos 2x\,dx = \dfrac{3}{2}\sin 2x\Big]_0^{\pi/8} = 3\sqrt{2}/4$

32. $\dfrac{1}{3}\displaystyle\int_0^5 \sqrt{25 - u^2}\,du = \dfrac{1}{3}\left[\dfrac{1}{4}\pi(5)^2\right] = \dfrac{25}{12}\pi$

33. $\displaystyle\int_{-2}^2 \sqrt{4 - u^2}\,du = \dfrac{1}{2}[\pi(2)^2] = 2\pi$

34. $\dfrac{1}{2}\displaystyle\int_0^4 \sqrt{16 - u^2}\,du = \dfrac{1}{2}\left[\dfrac{1}{4}\pi(4)^2\right] = 2\pi$

35. $-\dfrac{1}{2}\displaystyle\int_1^0 \sqrt{1 - u^2}\,du = \dfrac{1}{2}\int_0^1 \sqrt{1 - u^2}\,du = \dfrac{1}{2}\cdot\dfrac{1}{4}[\pi(1)^2] = \pi/8$

36. $u = 3x$, $\dfrac{1}{3} \displaystyle\int_0^9 f(u)\,du = \dfrac{5}{3}$

37. $u = 1/x$, $-\displaystyle\int_2^1 f(u)\,du = \int_1^2 f(u)\,du = 3$

38. $u = x^2$, $\dfrac{1}{2} \displaystyle\int_4^0 f(u)\,du = -\dfrac{1}{2}\int_0^4 f(u)\,du = -\dfrac{1}{2}$.

39. $u = 3x + 1$, $\dfrac{1}{3} \displaystyle\int_1^4 f(u)\,du = \dfrac{5}{3}$

40. $u = 1 - x$, $\displaystyle\int_0^1 x^m(1-x)^n\,dx = -\int_1^0 (1-u)^m u^n\,du = \int_0^1 u^n(1-u)^m\,du = \int_0^1 x^n(1-x)^m\,dx$

41. $\sin x = \cos(\pi/2 - x)$,

$$\int_0^{\pi/2} \sin^n x\,dx = \int_0^{\pi/2} \cos^n(\pi/2 - x)\,dx = -\int_{\pi/2}^0 \cos^n u\,du \ (u = \pi/2 - x)$$

$$= \int_0^{\pi/2} \cos^n u\,du = \int_0^{\pi/2} \cos^n x\,dx \ \text{(by replacing } u \text{ by } x)$$

42. **(a)** Let $u = -x$ then

$$\int_{-a}^a f(x)\,dx = -\int_a^{-a} f(-u)\,du = \int_{-a}^a f(-u)\,du = -\int_{-a}^a f(u)\,du$$

so, replacing u by x in the latter integral,

$$\int_{-a}^a f(x)\,dx = -\int_{-a}^a f(x)\,dx, \ 2\int_{-a}^a f(x)\,dx = 0, \ \int_{-a}^a f(x)\,dx = 0$$

The graph of f is symmetric about the origin so $\displaystyle\int_{-a}^0 f(x)\,dx$ is the negative of $\displaystyle\int_0^a f(x)\,dx$

thus $\displaystyle\int_{-a}^a f(x)\,dx = \int_{-a}^0 f(x) + \int_0^a f(x)\,dx = 0$

(b) $\displaystyle\int_{-a}^a f(x)\,dx = \int_{-a}^0 f(x)\,dx + \int_0^a f(x)\,dx$, let $u = -x$ in $\displaystyle\int_{-a}^0 f(x)\,dx$ to get

$$\int_{-a}^0 f(x)\,dx = -\int_a^0 f(-u)\,du = \int_0^a f(-u)\,du = \int_0^a f(u)\,du = \int_0^a f(x)\,dx$$

so $\displaystyle\int_{-a}^a f(x)\,dx = \int_0^a f(x)\,dx + \int_0^a f(x)\,dx = 2\int_0^a f(x)\,dx$

The graph of $f(x)$ is symmetric about the y-axis so there is as much signed area to the left of the y-axis as there is to the right.

43. $2k$, because $f(-x) = f(x)$ on $[-2, 2]$.   **44.** 0, because $f(-x) = -f(x)$ on $[-3, 3]$.

45. 0, because $f(-x) = -f(x)$ on $[-1, 1]$.   **46.** $k/2$, because $f(-x) = f(x)$ on $[-1, 1]$.

47. $\displaystyle\sum_{k=1}^{n} \sin[\pi(k/n)](1/n) = \sum_{k=1}^{n} f(x_k^*)\Delta x$, where $f(x) = \sin(\pi x)$, $x_k^* = k/n$, and $\Delta x = 1/n$ so

$$\lim_{n \to +\infty} \sum_{k=1}^{n} f(x_k^*)\Delta x = \int_0^1 \sin(\pi x)dx = -\frac{1}{\pi}\cos(\pi x)\Big]_0^1 = 2/\pi.$$

48. Let $u = t - x$, then $du = -dx$ and

$$\int_0^t f(t-x)g(x)dx = -\int_t^0 f(u)g(t-u)du = \int_0^t f(u)g(t-u)du;$$

the result follows by replacing u by x in the last integral.

49. **(a)** $\displaystyle I = -\int_a^0 \frac{f(a-u)}{f(a-u)+f(u)}du = \int_0^a \frac{f(a-u)+f(u)-f(u)}{f(a-u)+f(u)}du$

$$= \int_0^a du - \int_0^a \frac{f(u)}{f(a-u)+f(u)}du, I = a - I \text{ so } 2I = a, I = a/2$$

(b) $3/2$ **(c)** $\pi/4$

50. $x = \dfrac{1}{u}$, $dx = -\dfrac{1}{u^2}du$, $I = \displaystyle\int_{-1}^1 \frac{1}{1+1/u^2}(-1/u^2)du = -\int_{-1}^1 \frac{1}{u^2+1}du = -I$ so $I = 0$ which is

impossible because $\dfrac{1}{1+x^2}$ is positive on $[-1, 1]$. The substitution $u = 1/x$ is not valid because u is not continuous for all x in $[-1, 1]$.

EXERCISE SET 5.9

1. $\displaystyle f_{ave} = \frac{1}{3-1}\int_1^3 3x\,dx = \frac{3}{4}x^2\Big]_1^3 = 6.$

2. $\displaystyle f_{ave} = \frac{1}{2-(-1)}\int_{-1}^2 x^2\,dx = \frac{1}{9}x^3\Big]_{-1}^2 = 1.$

3. $\displaystyle f_{ave} = \frac{1}{\pi-0}\int_0^\pi \sin x\,dx = -\frac{1}{\pi}\cos x\Big]_0^\pi = 2/\pi.$

4. $f_{\text{ave}} = \dfrac{1}{\pi - 0} \displaystyle\int_0^\pi \cos 2x\, dx = \dfrac{1}{2\pi} \sin 2x \Big]_0^\pi = 0$

5. $f_{\text{ave}} = \dfrac{1}{5 - 0} \displaystyle\int_0^5 \sqrt{3x + 1}\, dx = \dfrac{2}{45}(3x + 1)^{3/2} \Big]_0^5 = 14/5.$

6. $f_{\text{ave}} = \dfrac{1}{4 - 1} \displaystyle\int_1^4 \dfrac{1}{\sqrt{x}}\, dx = \dfrac{2}{3}\sqrt{x} \Big]_1^4 = 2/3$

7. $f_{\text{ave}} = \dfrac{1}{2 - (-2)} \displaystyle\int_{-2}^2 \sqrt{4 - x^2}\, dx = \dfrac{1}{4} \times \dfrac{1}{2}\pi(2)^2 = \pi/2.$

8. **(a)** $f_{\text{ave}} = \dfrac{1}{4 - 0} \displaystyle\int_0^4 2x\, dx = 4$

(b) $2x^* = 4,$
$\quad x^* = 2$

(c)

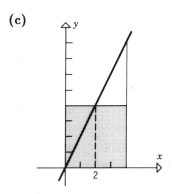

9. **(a)** $f_{\text{ave}} = \dfrac{1}{2 - 0} \displaystyle\int_0^2 x^2\, dx = 4/3$

(b) $(x^*)^2 = 4/3,\, x^* = \pm 2/\sqrt{3},$
but only $2/\sqrt{3}$ is in $[0, 2]$.

(c)

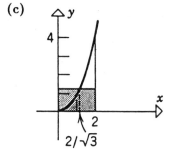

10. $f_{\text{ave}} = \dfrac{1}{2} \displaystyle\int_1^3 \dfrac{1}{x^2}\, dx = \dfrac{1}{3};\ \dfrac{1}{(x^*)^2} = \dfrac{1}{3},\ x^* = \sqrt{3}$

11. $f_{\text{ave}} = \dfrac{1}{9} \displaystyle\int_0^9 x^{1/2}\, dx = 2;\ \sqrt{x^*} = 2,\ x^* = 4$

12. $f_{\text{ave}} = \dfrac{1}{2\pi} \displaystyle\int_{-\pi}^\pi \sin x\, dx = 0;\ \sin x^* = 0,\ x^* = -\pi, 0, \pi$

13. $f_{\text{ave}} = \dfrac{1}{x_1 - x_0} \displaystyle\int_{x_0}^{x_1} (\alpha x + \beta)\, dx = \dfrac{1}{2}\alpha(x_0 + x_1) + \beta;$

$\alpha x^* + \beta = \dfrac{1}{2}\alpha(x_0 + x_1) + \beta,\ x^* = (x_0 + x_1)/2.$

14. $V_{\text{rms}}^2 = \dfrac{1}{1/f - 0} \displaystyle\int_0^{1/f} V_p^2 \sin^2(2\pi ft)\,dt$

$\quad = \dfrac{1}{2} f V_p^2 \displaystyle\int_0^{1/f} [1 - \cos(4\pi ft)]\,dt$

$\quad = \dfrac{1}{2} f V_p^2 \left[t - \dfrac{1}{4\pi f}\sin(4\pi ft)\right]_0^{1/f} = \dfrac{1}{2} V_p^2,$ so $V_{\text{rms}} = V_p/\sqrt{2}.$

15. $V_p/\sqrt{2} = 120,\ V_p = 120\sqrt{2} \approx 169.7$ volts

16. **(a)** $\dfrac{s(t_1) - s(t_0)}{t_1 - t_0} = \dfrac{1}{t_1 - t_0} s(t)\Big]_{t_0}^{t_1} = \dfrac{1}{t_1 - t_0}\displaystyle\int_{t_0}^{t_1} v(t)\,dt$

$\quad$ **(b)** $v_{\text{ave}} = \dfrac{1}{5}\displaystyle\int_0^5 32t\,dt = 80$

17. $a_{\text{ave}} = \dfrac{v(t_1) - v(t_0)}{t_1 - t_0} = \dfrac{1}{t_1 - t_0} v(t)\Big]_{t_0}^{t_1} = \dfrac{1}{t_1 - t_0}\displaystyle\int_{t_0}^{t_1} a(t)\,dt$

18. **(a)** $v_{\text{ave}} = \dfrac{1}{3}\displaystyle\int_1^4 (3t^3 + 2)\,dt = 263/4$ $\qquad$ **(b)** $a_{\text{ave}} = \dfrac{1}{7}\displaystyle\int_2^9 t^{1/2}\,dt = \dfrac{2}{21}(27 - 2\sqrt{2})$

$\quad$ **(c)** $v_{\text{ave}} = \dfrac{1}{t_1 - t_0}\displaystyle\int_{t_0}^{t_1} (32t + v_0)\,dt = 16(t_0 + t_1) + v_0$

19. time to fill tank = (volume of tank)/(rate of filling) = $[\pi(3)^2 5]/(1) = 45\pi$, force on bottom at time t = weight of water in tank at time t = (62.4) (rate of filling)(time) = $62.4t$,

$\quad$ force$_{\text{ave}} = \dfrac{1}{45\pi}\displaystyle\int_0^{45\pi} 62.4t\,dt = 1404\pi$ lb.

20. $f_{\text{ave}} = \dfrac{1}{b - a}\displaystyle\int_a^b k\,dt = k$

21. **(a)** $\displaystyle\int_a^b [f(x) - f_{\text{ave}}]\,dx = \displaystyle\int_a^b f(x)\,dx - \displaystyle\int_a^b f_{\text{ave}}\,dx = \displaystyle\int_a^b f(x)\,dx - f_{\text{ave}}(b - a) = 0$

$\quad$ because $f_{\text{ave}}(b - a) = \displaystyle\int_a^b f(x)\,dx.$

$\quad$ **(b)** No, because if $\displaystyle\int_a^b [f(x) - c]\,dx = 0$ then $\displaystyle\int_a^b f(x)\,dx - c(b - a) = 0$ so

$\quad c = \dfrac{1}{b - a}\displaystyle\int_a^b f(x)\,dx = f_{\text{ave}}$ is the only value.

22. **(a)** $\cos 2x$ **(b)** $F(x) = \dfrac{1}{2}\sin 2t \Big]_{\pi/4}^{x} = \dfrac{1}{2}\sin 2x - \dfrac{1}{2}$, $F'(x) = \cos 2x$

23. **(a)** $x^3 + 1$ **(b)** $F(x) = \dfrac{1}{4}t^4 + t \Big]_{1}^{x} = \dfrac{1}{4}x^4 + x - \dfrac{5}{4}$; $F'(x) = x^3 + 1$

24. $\dfrac{1}{1 + \sqrt{x}}$ **25.** $\sin\sqrt{x}$ **26.** $\dfrac{x}{\cos x}$

27. $|x|$ **28.** $\displaystyle\int_{1}^{x} \dfrac{1}{1 + t^2}\,dt$ **29.** $\displaystyle\int_{2}^{x} \dfrac{1}{t - 1}\,dt$

30. $\displaystyle\int_{-3}^{x} \dfrac{1}{t - 1}\,dt$ **31.** $\displaystyle\int_{0}^{x} \dfrac{1}{t - 1}\,dt$

32. **(a)** $(-3, 3)$ because f is continuous there and 1 is in $(-3, 3)$
     (b) at $x = 1$ because $F(1) = 0$

33. **(a)** $(0, +\infty)$ because f is continuous there and 1 is in $(0, +\infty)$.
     (b) at $x = 1$ because $F(1) = 0$

34. $F'(x) = \sqrt{3x^2 + 1}$, $F''(x) = \dfrac{3x}{\sqrt{3x^2 + 1}}$
     (a) 0 **(b)** $\sqrt{13}$ **(c)** $6/\sqrt{13}$

35. $F'(x) = \dfrac{\cos x}{x^2 + 3}$, $F''(x) = \dfrac{-(x^2 + 3)\sin x - 2x\cos x}{(x^2 + 3)^2}$
     (a) 0 **(b)** $1/3$ **(c)** 0

36. **(a)** $F'(x) = \dfrac{x - 3}{x^2 + 7} = 0$ when $x = 3$, which is a relative minimum, and hence the absolute minimum, by the first derivative test.
     (b) increasing on $(3, +\infty)$, decreasing on $(-\infty, 3)$.
     (c) $F''(x) = \dfrac{7 + 6x - x^2}{(x^2 + 7)^2} = \dfrac{(7 - x)(1 + x)}{(x^2 + 7)^2}$; concave up on $(-1, 7)$, concave down on $(-\infty, -1)$ and $(7, +\infty)$.

37. The domain is $(-\infty, +\infty)$; $F(x)$ is 0 if $x = 1$, positive if $x > 1$, and negative if $x < 1$.

38. The domain is $(-\infty, +\infty)$; $F(x)$ is 0 if $x = 2$, and negative if $x \neq 2$.

39. The domain is $[-2, 2]$; $F(x)$ is 0 if $x = -1$, positive if $-1 < x \le 2$, and negative if $-2 \le x < -1$.

40. The domain is $(-\infty, 2]$; $F(x)$ is 0 if $x = -3$, positive if $-3 < x \le 2$, and negative if $x < -3$.

41. $x < 0 : F(x) = \displaystyle\int_{-1}^{x} (-t)dt = -\frac{1}{2}t^2 \Big]_{-1}^{x} = \frac{1}{2}(1 - x^2)$,

$x \ge 0 : F(x) = \displaystyle\int_{-1}^{0} (-t)dt + \int_{0}^{x} t\, dt = \frac{1}{2} + \frac{1}{2}x^2$; $F(x) = \begin{cases} (1 - x^2)/2, & x < 0 \\ (1 + x^2)/2, & x \ge 0 \end{cases}$

42. $0 \le x \le 2 : F(x) = \displaystyle\int_{0}^{x} t\, dt = \frac{1}{2}x^2$,

$x > 2 : F(x) = \displaystyle\int_{0}^{2} t\, dt + \int_{2}^{x} 2\, dt = 2 + 2(x - 2) = 2x - 2$; $F(x) = \begin{cases} x^2/2, & 0 \le x \le 2 \\ 2x - 2, & x > 2 \end{cases}$

43. $x \le 0 : F(x) = \displaystyle\int_{-1}^{x} t^2 dt = \frac{1}{3}t^3 \Big]_{-1}^{x} = \frac{1}{3}(x^3 + 1)$,

$x > 0 : F(x) = \displaystyle\int_{-1}^{0} t^2 dt + \int_{0}^{x} 2t\, dt = \frac{1}{3} + x^2$; $F(x) = \begin{cases} (x^3 + 1)/3, & x \le 0 \\ x^2 + 1/3, & x > 0 \end{cases}$

44. Let $u = g(x)$ then

$$\frac{d}{dx} \int_{a}^{g(x)} f(t)dt = \frac{d}{dx} \int_{a}^{u} f(t)dt = \frac{d}{du} \left[\int_{a}^{u} f(t)dt \right] \frac{du}{dx} = f(u)g'(x) = f(g(x))g'(x)$$

45. $\dfrac{1}{x^3}(3x^2) = \dfrac{3}{x}$

46. $\dfrac{\cos x}{1 + \sin^2 x}$

47. $F'(x) = \dfrac{1}{1 + x^2} + \dfrac{1}{1 + (1/x)^2}(-1/x^2) = 0$ so F is constant on $(0, +\infty)$.

48. If f is continuous on an open interval I and $g(x)$, $h(x)$, and a are in I then

$$\int_{h(x)}^{g(x)} f(t)dt = \int_{h(x)}^{a} f(t)dt + \int_{a}^{g(x)} f(t)dt = -\int_{a}^{h(x)} f(t)dt + \int_{a}^{g(x)} f(t)dt$$

so $\dfrac{d}{dx} \displaystyle\int_{h(x)}^{g(x)} f(t)dt = -f(h(x))h'(x) + f(g(x))g'(x)$

49. **(a)** $\sin^2(x^3)(3x^2) - \sin^2(x^2)(2x) = 3x^2 \sin^2(x^3) - 2x \sin^2(x^2)$

(b) $\dfrac{1}{1 + x}(1) - \dfrac{1}{1 - x}(-1) = \dfrac{2}{1 - x^2}$

50. $F'(x) = \dfrac{1}{3x}(3) - \dfrac{1}{x}(1) = 0$ so $F(x)$ is constant on $(0, +\infty)$.

51. $\displaystyle\int_x^b f(t)dt = -\int_b^x f(t)dt$ so $\dfrac{d}{dx}\int_x^b f(t)dt = -\dfrac{d}{dx}\int_b^x f(t)dt = -f(x)$

52. $F'(x) = f(x)$, thus $F'(x)$ has a value at each x in I because f is continuous on I so F is continuous on I because a function that is differentiable at a point is also continuous at that point.

SUPPLEMENTARY EXERCISES CHAPTER 5

1. $-x^{-2}/2 + 2\sqrt{x} + 5\cos x + C$

2. $\displaystyle\int (2t - 1/t^2 + 2/t^3)dt = t^2 + 1/t - 1/t^2 + C$

3. $u = \sqrt{x} + 2,\ 2\displaystyle\int u^8 du = \dfrac{2}{9}u^9 + C = \dfrac{2}{9}(\sqrt{x} + 2)^9 + C$

4. $u = 2x^4 - 1,\ \dfrac{1}{8}\displaystyle\int \cos u\, du = \dfrac{1}{8}\sin(2x^4 - 1) + C$

5. $u = \sqrt{2x^2 - 5},\ du = 2x/\sqrt{2x^2 - 5}dx,\ \dfrac{1}{2}\displaystyle\int \sin u\, du = -\dfrac{1}{2}\cos\sqrt{2x^2 - 5} + C$

6. $\displaystyle\int \sqrt{\cos\theta}(2\sin\theta\cos\theta)d\theta = 2\int \cos^{3/2}\theta \sin\theta\, d\theta = -\dfrac{4}{5}\cos^{5/2}\theta + C$

7. $\displaystyle\int (3x^{1/2} + x^{11/6})dx = 2x^{3/2} + \dfrac{6}{17}x^{17/6} + C$

8. $\displaystyle\int (x^{4/3} + 1)^{-2}x^{1/3}dx,\ u = x^{4/3} + 1,\ \dfrac{3}{4}\int u^{-2}du = (-3/4)/(x^{4/3} + 1) + C$

9. $u = \sin 5t,\ \dfrac{1}{5}\displaystyle\int \sec^2 u\, du = \dfrac{1}{5}\tan(\sin 5t) + C$

10. $\displaystyle\int \cot^2 x\csc^2 x\, dx,\ u = \cot x,\ -\int u^2 du = -\dfrac{1}{3}\cot^3 x + C$

11.   **(a)** $\displaystyle\int (y^5 + 4y^3 + 4y)dy = \dfrac{1}{6}y^6 + y^4 + 2y^2 + C$

(b) $\frac{1}{6}(y^2+2)^3 + C$

[answer to (b)] − [answer to (a)]

$$= \frac{1}{6}(y^6 + 6y^4 + 12y^2 + 8) + C - \left(\frac{1}{6}y^6 + y^4 + 2y^2 + C\right) = 4/3$$

12. $-\frac{1}{2}\int_{-1}^{1} u^{1/5}\,du = -\frac{5}{12}u^{6/5}\Big]_{-1}^{1} = 0$

13. $\int_{0}^{1} u^4\,du = 1/5$ **14.** $\frac{1}{2}\int_{16}^{25} u^{-1/2}\,du = u^{1/2}\Big]_{16}^{25} = 1$

15. $u = x - 1,\ x = u + 1,\ \int_{1}^{4}\frac{u-1}{\sqrt{u}}\,du = \int_{1}^{4}(u^{1/2} - u^{-1/2})\,du = \frac{2}{3}u^{3/2} - 2u^{1/2}\Big]_{1}^{4} = 8/3$

16. $\frac{1}{3}\int_{1/4}^{1} u^{-1/2}\,du = \frac{2}{3}u^{1/2}\Big]_{1/4}^{1} = 1/3$ **17.** $\frac{4}{\pi}\int_{\pi/2}^{\pi}\cos u\,du = \frac{4}{\pi}\sin u\Big]_{\pi/2}^{\pi} = -4/\pi$

18. $\int_{-2}^{0}(-x)\,dx + \int_{0}^{2} x^3\,dx = -\frac{1}{2}x^2\Big]_{-2}^{0} + \frac{1}{4}x^4\Big]_{0}^{2} = 6$

19. $\int_{-2}^{1/2} -(2x-1)\,dx + \int_{1/2}^{2}(2x-1)\,dx = (-x^2+x)\Big]_{-2}^{1/2} + (x^2-x)\Big]_{1/2}^{2} = 17/2$

20. $\int_{1}^{x}\frac{1}{\sqrt{t}}\,dt = 2\sqrt{t}\Big]_{1}^{x} = 2(\sqrt{x}-1) = 3,\ \sqrt{x} = 5/2,\ x = 25/4.$

21. $\int_{0}^{x}\frac{1}{(3t+1)^2}\,dt = -\frac{1}{3(3t+1)}\Big]_{0}^{x} = -\frac{1}{3(3x+1)} + \frac{1}{3} = \frac{1}{6},\ 3x+1 = 2,\ x = 1/3$

22. $\int_{2}^{x}(4t-1)\,dt = (2t^2-t)\Big]_{2}^{x} = 2x^2 - x - 6 = 9,\ 2x^2 - x - 15 = 0,$

$(2x+5)(x-3) = 0,\ x = -5/2$ and $x = 3.$

23. **(a)** $5+5+5+5 = 20$ **(b)** $2+2+2+2 = 8$

(c) $n+n+n+n = 4n$ **(d)** $0 + 1/5 + 2/6 = 8/15$

(e) $6/4 + 6/9 + 6/16 = 61/24$ **(f)** 9

(g) $\sin(0) + \sin(\pi/4) + \sin(\pi/2) + \sin(3\pi/4) + \sin(\pi) = 0 + \sqrt{2}/2 + 1 + \sqrt{2}/2 + 0 = 1 + \sqrt{2}$

(h) $\sqrt{2}/2 + (\sqrt{2}/2)^2 + (\sqrt{2}/2)^3 + (\sqrt{2}/2)^4 = 3\sqrt{2}/4 + 3/4$

24. **(a)** $\displaystyle\sum_{k=1}^{100}(k+2)k = \sum_{k=1}^{100}k^2 + 2\sum_{k=1}^{100}k = \frac{1}{6}(100)(101)(201) + 2\cdot\frac{1}{2}(100)(101) = 348,450$

(b) $\displaystyle\sum_{k=1}^{100}(202-2k) = \sum_{k=1}^{100}202 - 2\sum_{k=1}^{100}k = (100)(202) - 2\cdot\frac{1}{2}(100)(101) = 10,100$

25. **(a)** $\displaystyle\sum_{k=1}^{9}(-1)^{k+1}\left(\frac{k}{k+1}\right)^2 = \sum_{k=2}^{10}(-1)^k\left(\frac{k-1}{k}\right)^2$

(b) $\displaystyle\sum_{k=1}^{11}(-1)^{k+1}\frac{\pi^{k+1}}{k} = \sum_{k=2}^{12}(-1)^k\frac{\pi^k}{k-1}$

26. **(a)** $\Delta x = 2/n,\ c_k = 1 + 2k/n$

$$\sum_{k=1}^{n}f(c_k)\Delta x = \sum_{k=1}^{n}[6 - 2(1+2k/n)](2/n) = \frac{8}{n}\sum_{k=1}^{n}1 - \frac{8}{n^2}\sum_{k=1}^{n}k = 8 - 4\frac{n+1}{n}$$

(b) $d_k = 1 + 2(k-1)/n$

$$\sum_{k=1}^{n}f(d_k)\Delta x = \sum_{k=1}^{n}[6 - 2(1+2(k-1)/n)]\,(2/n)$$

$$= \frac{8}{n}\sum_{k=1}^{n}1 - \frac{8}{n^2}\sum_{k=1}^{n}(k-1) = 8 - 4\frac{n-1}{n}$$

(c) $\text{area} = \displaystyle\lim_{n\to+\infty}[8 - 4(1+1/n)] = 8 - 4 = 4;\ \int_{1}^{3}(6-2x)dx = 4$

27. **(a)** $\Delta x = 4/n,\ c_k = 4k/n$

$$\sum_{k=1}^{n}f(c_k)\Delta x = \sum_{k=1}^{n}(16 - 16k^2/n^2)(4/n)$$

$$= \frac{64}{n}\sum_{k=1}^{n}1 - \frac{64}{n^3}\sum_{k=1}^{n}k^2 = 64 - \frac{32}{3}\frac{(n+1)(2n+1)}{n^2}$$

(b) $d_k = 4(k-1)/n$

$$\sum_{k=1}^{n}f(d_k)\Delta x = \sum_{k=1}^{n}(16 - 16(k-1)^2/n^2)(4/n) = \frac{64}{n}\sum_{k=1}^{n}1 - \frac{64}{n^3}\sum_{k=1}^{n}(k-1)^2$$

$$= 64 - \frac{32}{3}\frac{(n-1)(2n-1)}{n^2}$$

(c)   area $= \lim\limits_{n \to +\infty} \left[64 - \dfrac{32}{3}\left(1 + \dfrac{1}{n}\right)\left(2 + \dfrac{1}{n}\right)\right] = 128/3; \displaystyle\int_0^4 (16 - x^2)dx = 128/3$

28.   **(a)** $\Delta x = 3/n,\ c_k = 1 + 3(k-1)/n$

$$\sum_{k=1}^{n} f(c_k)\Delta x = \sum_{k=1}^{n}[3 + 6(k-1)/n + 9(k-1)^2/n^2](3/n)$$

$$= \frac{9}{n}\sum_{k=1}^{n}1 + \frac{18}{n^2}\sum_{k=1}^{n}(k-1) + \frac{27}{n^3}\sum_{k=1}^{n}(k-1)^2$$

$$= 9 + 9\frac{n-1}{n} + \frac{9}{2}\frac{(n-1)(2n-1)}{n^2}$$

(b) $d_k = 1 + 3k/n$

$$\sum_{k=1}^{n} f(d_k)\Delta x = \sum_{k=1}^{n}(3 + 6k/n + 9k^2/n^2)(3/n) = \frac{9}{n}\sum_{k=1}^{n}1 + \frac{18}{n^2}\sum_{k=1}^{n}k + \frac{27}{n^3}\sum_{k=1}^{n}k^2$$

$$= 9 + 9\frac{n+1}{n} + \frac{9}{2}\frac{(n+1)(2n+1)}{n^2}$$

(c) $\lim\limits_{n\to+\infty}[9 + 9(1 - 1/n) + (9/2)(1 - 1/n)(2 - 1/n)] = 27; \displaystyle\int_1^4 (x^2 + 2)dx = 27$

29.   **(a)** $\Delta x = 2/n$, because f is constant c_k can be chosen anywhere in the k-th subinterval so

$f(c_k) = 6$ and $\displaystyle\sum_{k=1}^{n} f(c_k)\Delta x = \sum_{k=1}^{n}(6)(2/n) = 12$

(b)   same as for (a)

(c)   area $= \lim\limits_{n\to+\infty} 12 = 12; \displaystyle\int_{-1}^{1} 6\,dx = 12$

30. $\Delta x_k = \dfrac{4k^2}{n^2} - \dfrac{4(k-1)^2}{n^2} = \dfrac{4}{n^2}(2k - 1),\ x_k^* = \dfrac{4k^2}{n^2},$

$f(x_k^*) = \dfrac{2k}{n},\ f(x_k^*)\Delta x_k = \dfrac{8k}{n^3}(2k - 1) = \dfrac{8}{n^3}(2k^2 - k),$

$\displaystyle\sum_{k=1}^{n} f(x_k^*)\Delta x_k = \frac{8}{n^3}\sum_{k=1}^{n}(2k^2 - k) = \frac{8}{n^3}\left[\frac{1}{3}n(n+1)(2n+1) - \frac{1}{2}n(n+1)\right] = \frac{4}{3}\frac{(n+1)(4n-1)}{n^2},$

$\displaystyle\lim_{n\to+\infty}\sum_{k=1}^{n} f(x_k^*)\Delta x_k = \lim_{n\to+\infty}\frac{4}{3}\left(1 + \frac{1}{n}\right)\left(4 - \frac{1}{n}\right) = \frac{16}{3}.$

31.   **(a)** $2\displaystyle\int_3^5 P(x)dx + \int_3^5 Q(x)dx = 2(3) + (4) = 10$

(b) $-\int_1^5 P(x)dx = -(-1) = 1$

(c) $-\int_3^5 Q(u)du = -\int_3^5 Q(x)dx = -4$

(d) $\int_3^5 P(x)dx + \int_5^1 P(x)dx = \int_3^5 P(x)dx - \int_1^5 P(x)dx = (3) - (-1) = 4$

32. If $x^2 \le f(x) \le 6$ then $\int_{-1}^2 x^2 dx \le \int_{-1}^2 f(x)dx \le \int_{-1}^2 6\,dx$, $3 \le \int_{-1}^2 f(x)dx \le 18$

33. $f_{\text{ave}} = \int_{-2}^{-1} 3x^2 dx = 7$; $3(x^*)^2 = 7$, $x^* = \pm\sqrt{7/3}$ but only $-\sqrt{7/3}$ is in $[-2, -1]$

34. $f_{\text{ave}} = \dfrac{1}{4}\int_0^4 x(x^2+9)^{-1/2}dx = \dfrac{1}{4}(x^2+9)^{1/2}\Big]_0^4 = 1/2$;

$\dfrac{x^*}{\sqrt{(x^*)^2+9}} = \dfrac{1}{2}$, $2x^* = \sqrt{(x^*)^2+9}$, $4(x^*)^2 = (x^*)^2+9$, $x^* = \pm\sqrt{3}$ but only $\sqrt{3}$ is in $[0,4]$.

35. $f_{\text{ave}} = \dfrac{1}{4}\int_{-3}^1 (2+|x|)dx = \dfrac{1}{4}\left[\int_{-3}^0 (2-x)dx + \int_0^1 (2+x)dx\right] = \dfrac{1}{4}[21/2 + 5/2] = 13/4$;

$2+|x^*| = 13/4$, $|x^*| = 5/4$, $x^* = \pm 5/4$ but only $-5/4$ is in $[-3, 1]$

36. $f_{\text{ave}} = \dfrac{1}{\pi}\int_0^\pi \sin^2 x\,dx = \dfrac{1}{\pi}\int_0^\pi \dfrac{1}{2}(1 - \cos\ 2x)dx = \dfrac{1}{2\pi}\left(x - \dfrac{1}{2}\sin 2x\right)\Big]_0^\pi = 1/2$;

$\sin^2 x^* = 1/2$, $\sin x^* = \pm 1/\sqrt{2}$, $x^* = \pi/4$, $3\pi/4$ for x^* in $[0, \pi]$

CHAPTER 6
Applications of the Definite Integral

EXERCISE SET 6.1

1. $A = \int_{-1}^{2} (x^2 + 1 - x)dx = (x^3/3 + x - x^2/2)\Big]_{-1}^{2} = 9/2$

2. $A = \int_{0}^{4} (\sqrt{x} + x/4)dx = (2x^{3/2}/3 + x^2/8)\Big]_{0}^{4} = 22/3$

3. $A = \int_{1}^{2} (y - 1/y^2)dy = (y^2/2 + 1/y)\Big]_{1}^{2} = 1$

4. $A = \int_{0}^{2} (2 - y^2 + y)dy = (2y - y^3/3 + y^2/2)\Big]_{0}^{2} = 10/3$

5. (a) $A = \int_{0}^{4} (4x - x^2)dx = 32/3$

   (b) $A = \int_{0}^{16} (\sqrt{y} - y/4)dy = 32/3$

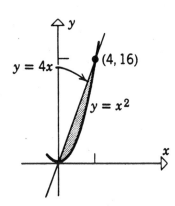

6. Eliminate x to get $y^2 = 4(y+4)/2$, $y^2 - 2y - 8 = 0$, $(y-4)(y+2) = 0$; $y = -2, 4$ with corresponding values of $x = 1, 4$.

(a) $A = \int_0^1 [2\sqrt{x} - (-2\sqrt{x})]dx$

$+ \int_1^4 [2\sqrt{x} - (2x-4)]dx$

$= \int_0^1 4\sqrt{x}\,dx + \int_1^4 (2\sqrt{x} - 2x + 4)dx$

$= 8/3 + 19/3 = 9$

(b) $A = \int_{-2}^4 [(y/2+2) - y^2/4]dy = 9$

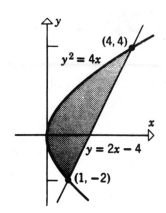

7. Eliminate x to get $y^2 = y + 2$,

$y^2 - y - 2 = 0, (y+1)(y-2) = 0,$

$y = -1$ and 2 with corresponding values

of $x = 1/2$ and 2.

(a) $A = \int_0^{1/2} [\sqrt{2x} - (-\sqrt{2x})]dx$

$+ \int_{1/2}^2 [\sqrt{2x} - (2x-2)]dx$

$= \int_0^{1/2} 2\sqrt{2}x^{1/2}dx + \int_{1/2}^2 (\sqrt{2}x^{1/2} - 2x + 2)dx$

$= 2/3 + 19/12 = 9/4$

(b) $A = \int_{-1}^2 [(y/2+1) - y^2/2]dy = 9/4$

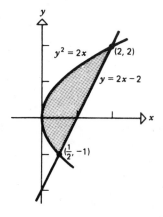

8. $A = \int_0^{1/2} (x - x^3)dx = 7/64$

9. $A = \int_{1/4}^1 (\sqrt{x} - x^2)dx = 49/192$

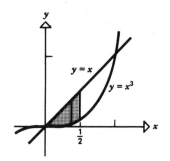

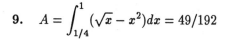

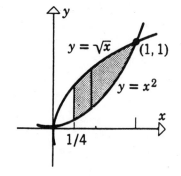

10. $A = \int_0^2 [0 - (x^3 - 4x)]dx$

$= \int_0^2 (4x - x^3)dx = 4$

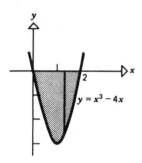

11. $A = \int_{\pi/4}^{\pi/2} (0 - \cos 2x)dx$

$= -\int_{\pi/4}^{\pi/2} \cos 2x\, dx = 1/2$

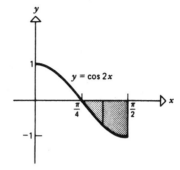

12. $A = \int_0^1 (x^3 - 4x^2 + 3x)dx$

$+ \int_1^3 [-(x^3 - 4x^2 + 3x)]dx$

$= 5/12 + 32/12 = 37/12$

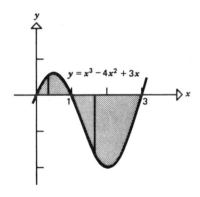

13. $A = \int_0^4 [0 - (y^2 - 4y)]dy$

$= \int_0^4 (4y - y^2)dy = 32/3$

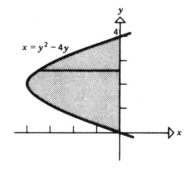

14. $A = \int_{\pi/4}^{3\pi/4} \sin y \, dy = \sqrt{2}$

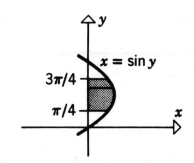

15. Equate $\sec^2 x$ and 2 to get $\sec^2 x = 2$,
$\sec x = \pm\sqrt{2}$, $x = \pm\pi/4$

$A = \int_{-\pi/4}^{\pi/4} (2 - \sec^2 x) dx = \pi - 2$

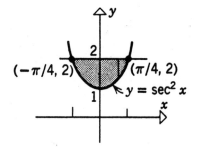

16. $A = \int_{-1}^{2} [(x + 2) - x^2] dx = 9/2$

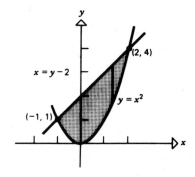

17. Eliminate y to get $6 - x = x^2 + 4$,

$x^2 + x - 2 = 0$, $(x + 2)(x - 1) = 0$,

$x = -2, 1$ with corresponding values of $y = 8, 5$.

$$A = \int_{-2}^{1} [(6 - x) - (x^2 + 4)]dx$$

$$= \int_{-2}^{1} (2 - x - x^2)dx = 9/2$$

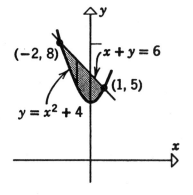

18. $$A = \int_{0}^{8} [y^{1/3} - (-y)]dy$$

$$= \int_{0}^{8} [y^{1/3} + y]dy = 44$$

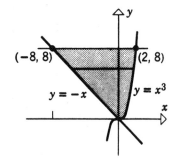

19. $$A = \int_{-1}^{4} [(y + 6) - (-y^2)]dy$$

$$= \int_{-1}^{4} (y + 6 + y^2)dy$$

$$= 355/6$$

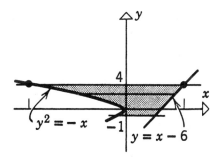

20. $A = \int_0^{2/5} (4x - x)dx + \int_{2/5}^1 (-x + 2 - x)dx$

$= \int_0^{2/5} 3x\, dx + \int_{2/5}^1 (2 - 2x)dx$

$= 3/5$

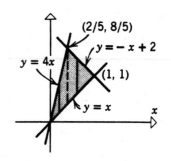

21. $y = 2 + |x - 1| = \begin{cases} 3 - x, & x \le 1 \\ 1 + x, & x \ge 1 \end{cases}$,

$A = \int_{-5}^1 \left[\left(-\frac{1}{5}x + 7 \right) - (3 - x) \right] dx$

$\quad + \int_1^5 \left[\left(-\frac{1}{5}x + 7 \right) - (1 + x) \right] dx$

$= \int_{-5}^1 \left(\frac{4}{5}x + 4 \right) dx + \int_1^5 \left(6 - \frac{6}{5}x \right) dx$

$= 72/5 + 48/5 = 24$

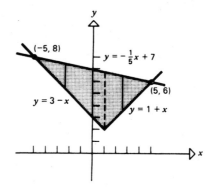

22. The region is symmetric about the origin so

$$A = 2 \int_{-2}^0 (x^3 - 4x)dx = 8$$

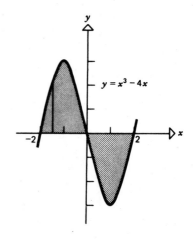

23. $A = \int_{-1}^{0} (y^3 - y)dy + \int_{0}^{1} -(y^3 - y)dy$

$\qquad = 1/2$

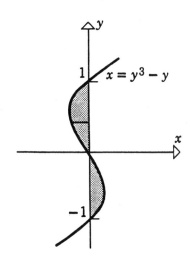

24.   Equate $y = x^3 - 2x^2$ and $y = 2x^2 - 3x$

to get $x^3 - 4x^2 + 3x = 0$,

$x(x - 1)(x - 3) = 0;\ x = 0, 1, 3$

with corresponding values of $y = 0, -1, 9$.

$A = \int_{0}^{1} [(x^3 - 2x^2) - (2x^2 - 3x)]dx$

$\qquad + \int_{1}^{3} [(2x^2 - 3x) - (x^3 - 2x^2)]dx$

$\qquad = \int_{0}^{1} (x^3 - 4x^2 + 3x)dx + \int_{1}^{3} (-x^3 + 4x^2 - 3x)dx = 37/12$

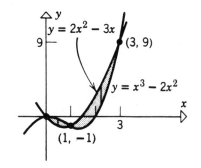

25.   From the symmetry of the region

$A = 2 \int_{\pi/4}^{5\pi/4} (\sin x - \cos x)dx = 4\sqrt{2}$

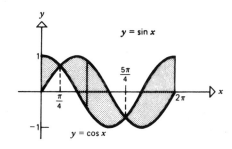

26. $A = \displaystyle\int_0^2 [y - (y^2 - 2)]\,dy = \dfrac{10}{3}$

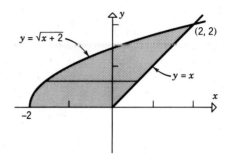

27. $A = \displaystyle\int_1^4 \left(y - \dfrac{1}{\sqrt{y}}\right) dy = 11/2$

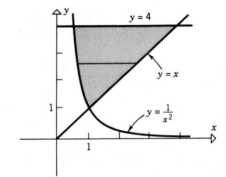

28. The line through $(0,0)$ and

$(5\pi/6, 1/2)$ is $y = \dfrac{3}{5\pi}x$;

$A = \displaystyle\int_0^{5\pi/6} \left(\sin x - \dfrac{3}{5\pi}x\right) dx$

$\quad = \dfrac{\sqrt{3}}{2} - \dfrac{5}{24}\pi + 1$

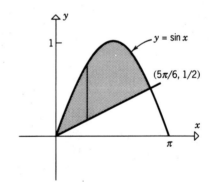

29. The tangent line at $(4, 2)$ is

$$y = \frac{1}{4}x + 1;$$

$$A = \int_0^4 \left[\left(\frac{1}{4}x + 1\right) - \sqrt{x} \right] dx = 2/3$$

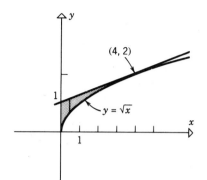

30. (a) $A = \int_1^b \frac{1}{x^2} dx = 1 - \frac{1}{b}$ (b) $\lim\limits_{b \to +\infty} A = \lim\limits_{b \to +\infty} \left(1 - \frac{1}{b}\right) = 1$

31. (a) $A = \int_1^b x^{-1/2} dx = 2(\sqrt{b} - 1)$ (b) $\lim\limits_{b \to +\infty} A = +\infty$

32. $\int_0^k x^2 dx = \int_k^2 x^2 dx$

$$\frac{1}{3}k^3 = \frac{1}{3}(8 - k^3)$$

$$k^3 = 4$$

$$k = \sqrt[3]{4}$$

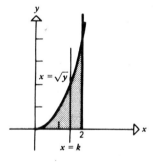

33. $\int_0^k 2\sqrt{y}\,dy = \int_k^9 2\sqrt{y}\,dy$

$$\int_0^k y^{1/2}\,dy = \int_k^9 y^{1/2}\,dy$$

$$\frac{2}{3}k^{3/2} = \frac{2}{3}(27 - k^{3/2})$$

$$k^{3/2} = 27/2$$

$$k = (27/2)^{2/3} = 9/\sqrt[3]{4}$$

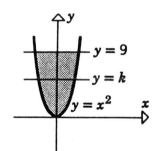

34. **(a)** $A = \int_0^2 (2x - x^2)dx = 4/3$

(b) $y = mx$ intersects $y = 2x - x^2$ where $mx = 2x - x^2$, $x^2 + (m-2)x = 0$, $x(x+m-2) = 0$ so $x = 0$ or $x = 2 - m$. The area below the curve and above the line is

$$\int_0^{2-m} (2x - x^2 - mx)dx = \int_0^{2-m} [(2-m)x - x^2]dx$$

$$= \frac{1}{2}(2-m)x^2 - \frac{1}{3}x^3\Big]_0^{2-m} = \frac{1}{6}(2-m)^3$$

so $(2-m)^3/6 = (1/2)(4/3) = 2/3$, $(2 - m^3) = 4$, $m = 2 - \sqrt[3]{4}$.

35. Solve for y to get $y = (b/a)\sqrt{a^2 - x^2}$ for the upper half of the ellipse; make use of symmetry to get $A = 4\int_0^a \frac{b}{a}\sqrt{a^2 - x^2}dx = \frac{4b}{a}\int_0^a \sqrt{a^2 - x^2}dx = \frac{4b}{a} \times \frac{1}{4}\pi a^2 = \pi ab$.

36. Solve $x^{1/2} + y^{1/2} = a^{1/2}$ for y to get

$y = (a^{1/2} - x^{1/2})^2 = a - 2a^{1/2}x^{1/2} + x$

$A = \int_0^a (a - 2a^{1/2}x^{1/2} + x)dx = a^2/6$

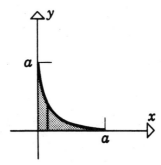

37. **(a)** It gives the area of the region that is between f and g when $f(x) > g(x)$ <u>minus</u> the area of the region between f and g when $f(x) < g(x)$, for $a \le x \le b$.

(b) It gives the area of the region that is between f and g for $a \le x \le b$.

38. Let A be the area between the curve and the x-axis and A_R the area of the rectangle, then

$A = \int_0^b kx^m dx = \frac{k}{m+1}x^{m+1}\Big]_0^b = \frac{kb^{m+1}}{m+1}$, $A_R = b(kb^m) = kb^{m+1}$, so
$A/A_R = 1/(m+1)$.

39. The curves intersect at $x = 0$ and, by Newton's Method, at $x \approx 2.595739080 = b$, so

$A \approx \int_0^b (\sin x - 0.2x)dx = -\cos x - 0.1x^2\Big]_0^b \approx 1.180898334$

40. By Newton's Method, the points of intersection are at $x \approx \pm 0.824132312$, so with
$b = 0.824132312$ we have $A \approx 2\int_0^b (\cos x - x^2)dx = 2(\sin x - x^3/3)\Big]_0^b \approx 1.094753609$

EXERCISE SET 6.2

1. $V = \pi \int_{-1}^{3} (3-x)dx = 8\pi$

2. $V = \pi \int_{0}^{1} [(2-x^2)^2 - x^2]dx = \pi \int_{0}^{1} (4 - 5x^2 + x^4)dx = 38\pi/15$

3. $V = \pi \int_{0}^{2} \frac{1}{4}(3-y)^2 dy = 13\pi/6$

4. $V = \pi \int_{1/2}^{2} (4 - 1/y^2)dy = 9\pi/2$

5. $V = \pi \int_{0}^{2} x^4 dx = 32\pi/5$

6. $V = \pi \int_{\pi/4}^{\pi/3} \sec^2 x \, dx = \pi(\sqrt{3} - 1)$

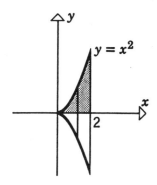

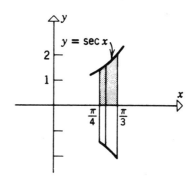

7. $V = \pi \int_{1}^{2} (1+x^3)^2 dx$

$= \pi \int_{1}^{2} (1 + 2x^3 + x^6)dx$

$= 373\pi/14$

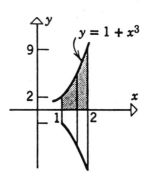

8. $V = \pi \int_1^4 \frac{1}{x^2} dx$

   $= \pi \int_1^4 x^{-2} dx$

   $= 3\pi/4$

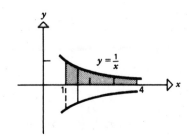

9. $V = \pi \int_{-3}^3 (9 - x^2)^2 dx$

   $= \pi \int_{-3}^3 (81 - 18x^2 + x^4) dx$

   $= 1296\pi/5$

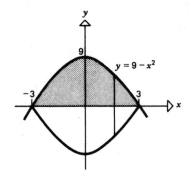

10. $V = \pi \int_{\pi/4}^{\pi/2} \cos x \, dx = (1 - \sqrt{2}/2)\pi$

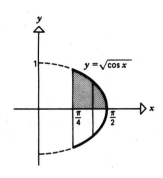

11. $V = \pi \int_0^4 [(4x)^2 - (x^2)^2] dx$

   $= \pi \int_0^4 (16x^2 - x^4) dx = 2048\pi/15$

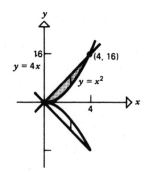

12. $V = \pi \displaystyle\int_{-3}^{3} (81 - x^4)\,dx$

$= 1944\pi/5$

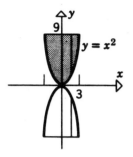

13. $V = \pi \displaystyle\int_{0}^{\pi/4} (\cos^2 x - \sin^2 x)\,dx$

$= \pi \displaystyle\int_{0}^{\pi/4} \cos 2x\,dx = \pi/2$

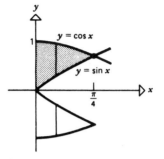

14. $V = \pi \displaystyle\int_{-1}^{2} [(x+3)^2 + (x^2+1)^2]\,dx$

$= \displaystyle\int_{-1}^{2} (8 + 6x - x^2 - x^4)\,dx = 117\pi/5$

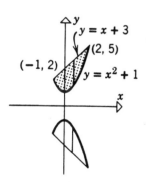

15. $V = \pi \int_0^1 [(\sqrt{x})^2 - x^2] dx$

$= \pi \int_0^1 (x - x^2) dx = \pi/6$

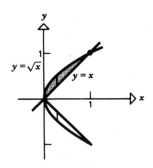

16. $V = \pi \int_0^1 [(x^2)^2 - (x^3)^2] dx$

$= \pi \int_0^1 (x^4 - x^6) dx = 2\pi/35$

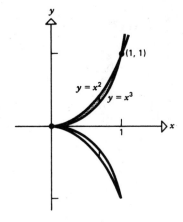

17. $V = \pi \int_0^1 y^{2/3} dy = 3\pi/5$

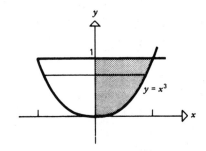

18. $V = \pi \int_{-1}^1 (1 - y^2)^2 dy$

$= \pi \int_{-1}^1 (1 - 2y^2 + y^4) dy = 16\pi/15$

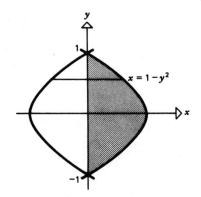

19. $V = \pi \int_{-1}^{3} (1+y)dy = 8\pi$

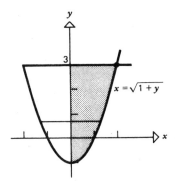

20. $V = \pi \int_{0}^{\pi/2} \cos y \, dy = \pi$

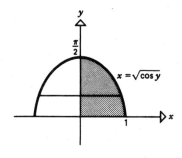

21. $V = \pi \int_{\pi/4}^{3\pi/4} \csc^2 y \, dy = 2\pi$

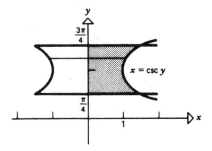

22. $V = \pi \int_{1}^{3} \frac{4}{y^2} dy = 8\pi/3$

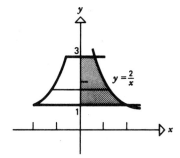

23. $V = \pi \int_{1}^{3} (9 - y^2)dy = 28\pi/3$

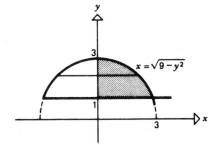

24. $V = \pi \int_{0}^{3} [2^2 - (y+1)]dy$

$\quad = \pi \int_{0}^{3} (3 - y)dy = 9\pi/2$

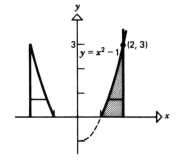

25. $V = \pi \displaystyle\int_{2}^{9} [(y-1)^{2/3} - 1]dy$

$\quad = 58\pi/5$

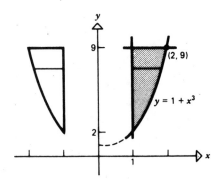

26. $V = \pi \displaystyle\int_{0}^{1} (y - y^4)dy$

$\quad = 3\pi/10$

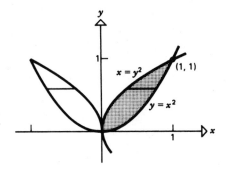

27. $V = \pi \displaystyle\int_{-1}^{2} [(y+2)^2 - y^4]dy$

$\quad = 72\pi/5$

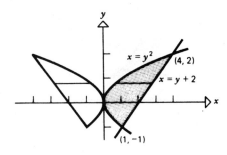

28. $V = \pi \displaystyle\int_{-1}^{1} [(2+y^2)^2 - (1-y^2)^2]dy$

$\quad = \pi \displaystyle\int_{-1}^{1} (3 + 6y^2)dy = 10\pi$

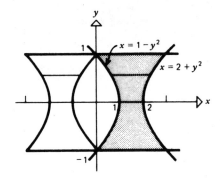

29. $V = \pi \displaystyle\int_{-4}^{4} [(25 - x^2) - 9]dx$

$\quad = 2\pi \displaystyle\int_{0}^{4} (16 - x^2)dx$

$\quad = 256\pi/3$

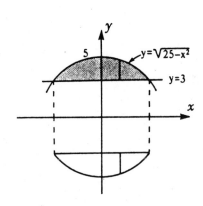

30. $x = h \pm \sqrt{r^2 - y^2}$,

$$V = \pi \int_{-r}^{r} \left[(h + \sqrt{r^2 - y^2})^2 - (h - \sqrt{r^2 - y^2})^2 \right] dy$$

$$= 4\pi h \int_{-r}^{r} \sqrt{r^2 - y^2} \, dy$$

$$= 4\pi h \left(\frac{1}{2} \pi r^2 \right) = 2\pi^2 r^2 h$$

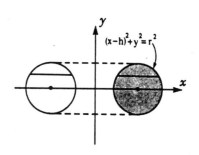

31. **(a)** $V(b) = \pi \int_{1}^{b} \frac{1}{x^2} dx = \pi(1 - 1/b)$ **(b)** $\lim\limits_{b \to +\infty} \pi(1 - 1/b) = \pi$

32. **(a)** $V = \pi \int_{0}^{h} k^2 dx = \pi k^2 h, B = \pi k^2$, so $V = hB$

(b) $V = \pi \int_{0}^{h} k^2 x \, dx = \frac{1}{2} \pi k^2 h^2, B = \pi k^2 h$, so $V = \frac{1}{2} hB$

(c) $V = \pi \int_{0}^{h} k^2 x^2 dx = \frac{1}{3} \pi k^2 h^3, B = \pi k^2 h^2$, so $V = \frac{1}{3} hB$

(d) $V = \pi \int_{0}^{h} k^2 x^{2m} dx = \frac{1}{2m+1} \pi k^2 h^{2m+1}, B = \pi k^2 x^{2m}$, so $V = \frac{1}{2m+1} hB, 2m+1 = n$,
$m = (n-1)/2$

33. $V = \pi \int_{0}^{b} x \, dx = \pi b^2/2; \pi b^2/2 = 2, b^2 = 4/\pi, b = 2/\sqrt{\pi}$

34. $V = \pi \int_{b}^{2} \frac{1}{x^2} dx = \pi(1/b - 1/2); \pi(1/b - 1/2) = 3, b = 2\pi/(\pi + 6)$

35. $V = \pi \int_{0}^{3} (9 - y^2)^2 dy$

$$= \pi \int_{0}^{3} (81 - 18y^2 + y^4) dy$$

$$= 648\pi/5$$

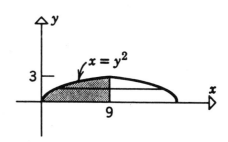

36. $V = \pi \int_0^9 [3^2 - (3 - \sqrt{x})^2] dx$

$\qquad = \pi \int_0^9 (6\sqrt{x} - x) dx$

$\qquad = 135\pi/2$

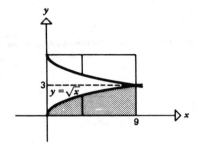

37. $V = \pi \int_0^1 [(\sqrt{x} + 1)^2 - (x + 1)^2] dx$

$\qquad = \pi \int_0^1 (2\sqrt{x} - x - x^2) dx = \pi/2$

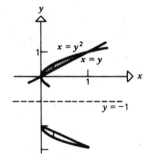

38. $V = \pi \int_0^1 [(y + 1)^2 - (y^2 + 1)^2] dy$

$\qquad = \pi \int_0^1 (2y - y^2 - y^4) dy = 7\pi/15$

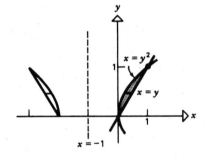

39. $V = \pi \displaystyle\int_{-a}^{a} \frac{b^2}{a^2}(a^2 - x^2)dx$

$\quad = 4\pi ab^2/3$

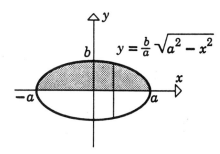

40. $V = \pi \displaystyle\int_{0}^{4} x\,dx + \pi \displaystyle\int_{0}^{6}(6 - x)^2 dx$

$\quad = 8\pi + 8\pi/3 = 32\pi/3$

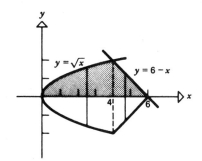

41. $V = \pi \displaystyle\int_{-1}^{0}(x + 1)dx$

$\qquad + \pi \displaystyle\int_{0}^{1}[(x + 1) - 2x]dx$

$\qquad = \pi/2 + \pi/2 = \pi$

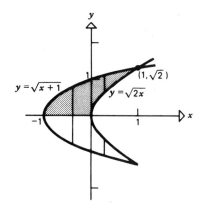

42. **(a)** $\displaystyle\int_{a}^{b} \pi[f(x)]^2 dx$ **(b)** $\displaystyle\int_{a}^{b} \pi([f(x)]^2 - [g(x)]^2)dx$

(c) $\displaystyle\int_{c}^{d} \pi[g(y)]^2 dy$ **(d)** $\displaystyle\int_{c}^{d} \pi([f(y)]^2 - [g(y)]^2)dy$

43. By similar triangles, $R/r = y/h$ so
$R = ry/h$ and $A(y) = \pi r^2 y^2/h^2$.

$V = (\pi r^2/h^2) \displaystyle\int_{0}^{h} y^2 dy = \pi r^2 h/3$

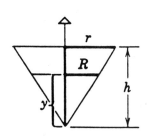

44. If $x = r/2$ then from $y^2 = r^2 - x^2$

we get $y = \pm\sqrt{3}r/2$,

$A(y) = \pi[(r^2 - y^2) - r^2/4] = \pi(3r^2/4 - y^2)$,

$$V = \pi \int_{-\sqrt{3}r/2}^{\sqrt{3}r/2} (3r^2/4 - y^2)dy$$

$$= 2\pi \int_0^{\sqrt{3}r/2} (3r^2/4 - y^2)dy = \sqrt{3}\pi r^3/2$$

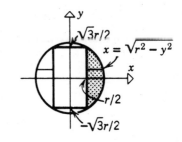

45. $V = 2\pi \int_0^{L/2} [(r^2 - y^2) - (r^2 - L^2/4)]dy$

$$= 2\pi \int_0^{L/2} (L^2/4 - y^2)dy$$

$$= \pi L^3/6$$

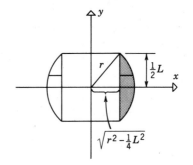

46. (a) Find the volume generated by revolving the shaded region about the y-axis.

$$V = \pi \int_{-r}^{-r+h} (r^2 - y^2)dy$$

$$= \frac{\pi}{3}h^2(3r - h).$$

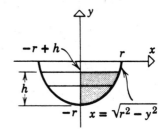

(b) Find dh/dt when $h = 5$ given that $dV/dt = 1/2$ and $r = 10$. From part (a),

$V = \frac{\pi}{3}(30h^2 - h^3)$, $\frac{dV}{dt} = \frac{\pi}{3}(60h - 3h^2)\frac{dh}{dt}$, $\frac{1}{2} = \frac{\pi}{3}(300 - 75)\frac{dh}{dt}$, $\frac{dh}{dt} = 1/(150\pi)$ ft/min

47. (a)   **(b)**

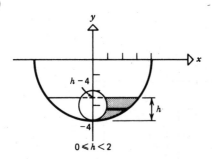

$0 \leqslant h < 2$

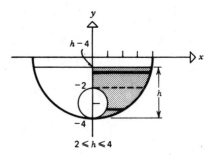

$2 \leqslant h \leqslant 4$

If the cherry is partially submerged then $0 \le h < 2$ as shown in Figure (a); if it is totally submerged then $2 \le h \le 4$ as shown in Figure (b). The radius of the glass is 4 cm and that of the cherry is 1 cm so points on the sections shown in the figures satisfy the equations $x^2 + y^2 = 16$ and $x^2 + (y+3)^2 = 1$. We will find the volumes of the solids that are generated when the shaded regions are revolved about the y-axis.

For $0 \le h < 2$,

$$V = \pi \int_{-4}^{h-4} [(16 - y^2) - (1 - (y+3)^2)]dy = 6\pi \int_{-4}^{h-4} (y+4)dy = 3\pi h^2;$$

for $2 \le h \le 4$,

$$V = \pi \int_{-4}^{-2} [(16 - y^2) - (1 - (y+3)^2)]dy + \pi \int_{-2}^{h-4} (16 - y^2)dy$$

$$= 6\pi \int_{-4}^{-2} (y+4)dy + \pi \int_{-2}^{h-4} (16 - y^2)dy = 12\pi + \frac{1}{3}\pi(12h^2 - h^3 - 40)$$

$$= \frac{1}{3}\pi(12h^2 - h^3 - 4)$$

so

$$V = \begin{cases} 3\pi h^2 & \text{if } 0 \le h < 2 \\ \frac{1}{3}\pi(12h^2 - h^3 - 4) & \text{if } 2 \le h \le 4 \end{cases}.$$

48. $V = \int_0^h A\, dy = Ah$

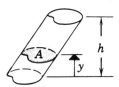

49. $A(x) = \pi(x^2/4)^2 = \pi x^4/16,\ V = \int_0^{20} (\pi x^4/16)dx = 40,000\pi\ \text{ft}^3$

50. $V = \pi \int_0^1 (x - x^4)dx = 3\pi/10$

51. With $y = \sqrt{9 - x^2}$, which is the upper
half of the circle, $A(x)$ is the area
of an equilateral triangle whose
sides are each of length $2y$ so

$$A(x) = \frac{\sqrt{3}}{4}(2y)^2 = \sqrt{3}y^2 = \sqrt{3}(9 - x^2),$$

$$V = \int_{-3}^{3} \sqrt{3}(9 - x^2)dx$$

$$= 2\sqrt{3}\int_{0}^{3}(9 - x^2)dx = 36\sqrt{3}.$$

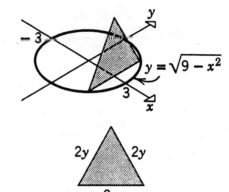

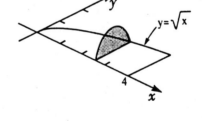

52. $A(x) = \frac{1}{2}\pi\left(\frac{1}{2}\sqrt{x}\right)^2 = \frac{1}{8}\pi x,$

$$V = \int_{0}^{4} \frac{1}{8}\pi x\, dx = \pi$$

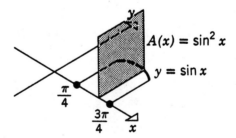

53. $V = \int_{\pi/4}^{3\pi/4} \sin^2 x\, dx$

$$= \frac{1}{2}\int_{\pi/4}^{3\pi/4}(1 - \cos 2x)dx$$

$$= (\pi + 2)/4$$

54. $A(x) = \dfrac{1}{2}\left(\dfrac{1}{2}\dfrac{1}{x}\right)\left(\dfrac{1}{x}\right) = \dfrac{1}{4x^2}$,

$V = \displaystyle\int_1^3 \dfrac{1}{4x^2}dx = \dfrac{1}{6}$

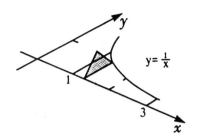

55. $\tan\theta = h/x$ so $h = x\tan\theta$,

$A(y) = \dfrac{1}{2}hx = \dfrac{1}{2}x^2\tan\theta = \dfrac{1}{2}(r^2 - y^2)\tan\theta$

because $x^2 = r^2 - y^2$,

$V = \dfrac{1}{2}\tan\theta \displaystyle\int_{-r}^r (r^2 - y^2)dy$

$= \tan\theta \displaystyle\int_0^r (r^2 - y^2)dy = \dfrac{2}{3}r^3\tan\theta$

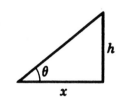

56. $A(x) = (x\tan\theta)(2\sqrt{r^2 - x^2})$

$= 2\tan\theta\, x\sqrt{r^2 - x^2}$,

$V = 2\tan\theta \displaystyle\int_0^r x\sqrt{r^2 - x^2}dx$

$= \dfrac{2}{3}r^3\tan\theta$

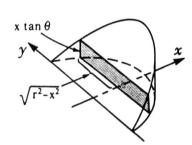

57. Each cross section perpendicular to the y-axis is a square so

$A(y) = x^2 = r^2 - y^2$,

$\dfrac{1}{8}V = \displaystyle\int_0^r (r^2 - y^2)dy$

$V = 8(2r^3/3) = 16r^3/3$

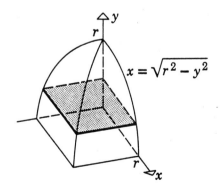

58. Suppose the height of both solids extends along an x-axis from $x = a$ to $x = b$. Let $A_1(x)$ and $A_2(x)$ be the cross-sectional areas of the two solids for each x in $[a, b]$. If $A_1(x)$ and $A_2(x)$ are integrable then $V_1 = \int_a^b A_1(x)dx$ and $V_2 = \int_a^b A_2(x)dx$, but $A_1(x) = A_2(x)$ so $V_1 = V_2$.

59. **(a)** If $V = \int_0^h A(x)dx$, then $\dfrac{dV}{dt} = \dfrac{dV}{dh}\dfrac{dh}{dt} = A(h)\dfrac{dh}{dt}$ so $A(h)\dfrac{dh}{dt} = -kA(h)$, $\dfrac{dh}{dt} = -k$.

(b) If $dh/dt = -k$, then $h = -kt + C$. But $h = h_0$ when $t = 0$ so $C = h_0$, thus $h = h_0 - kt$; $h = 0$ when $t = h_0/k$.

EXERCISE SET 6.3

1. $V = \int_1^2 2\pi x(x^2)dx = 2\pi \int_1^2 x^3 dx = 15\pi/2$

2. $V = \int_0^{\sqrt{2}} 2\pi x(\sqrt{4 - x^2} - x)dx = 2\pi \int_0^{\sqrt{2}} (x\sqrt{4 - x^2} - x^2)dx = \dfrac{8\pi}{3}(2 - \sqrt{2})$

3. $V = \int_0^1 2\pi y(2y - 2y^2)dy = 4\pi \int_0^1 (y^2 - y^3)dy = \pi/3$

4. $V = \int_0^2 2\pi y[y - (y^2 - 2)]dy = 2\pi \int_0^2 (y^2 - y^3 + 2y)dy = 16\pi/3$

5. $V = \int_0^1 2\pi(x)(x^3)dx$

$= 2\pi \int_0^1 x^4 dx = 2\pi/5$

6. $V = \int_4^9 2\pi x(\sqrt{x})dx$

$= 2\pi \int_4^9 x^{3/2} dx = 844\pi/5$

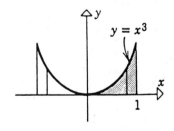

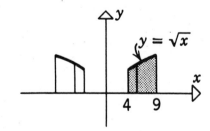

7. $V = \displaystyle\int_1^3 2\pi x(1/x)\,dx$

$= 2\pi \displaystyle\int_1^3 dx = 4\pi$

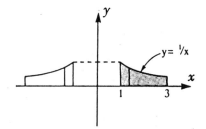

8. $V = \displaystyle\int_0^{\sqrt{\pi}/2} 2\pi x \cos(x^2)\,dx = \pi/\sqrt{2}$

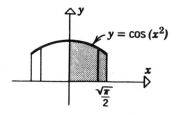

9. $V = \displaystyle\int_1^2 2\pi x[(2x-1)-(-2x+3)]\,dx$

$= 8\pi \displaystyle\int_1^2 (x^2 - x)\,dx = 20\pi/3$

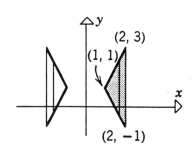

10. $V = \displaystyle\int_0^1 2\pi x(\sqrt{x} - x^2)\,dx$

$= 2\pi \displaystyle\int_0^1 (x^{3/2} - x^3)\,dx = 3\pi/10$

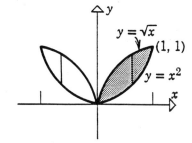

11. $V = \displaystyle\int_0^2 2\pi x(4 - x^2)^{1/3}dx$

$\qquad + \displaystyle\int_2^4 2\pi x[-(4 - x^2)^{1/3}]dx$

$\qquad = 3\pi\sqrt[3]{4}(1 + 3\sqrt[3]{3})$

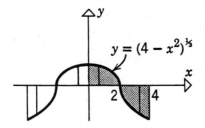

12. $V = \displaystyle\int_0^2 2\pi x(2x - x^2)dx$

$\qquad = 2\pi \displaystyle\int_0^2 (2x^2 - x^3)dx = \dfrac{8}{3}\pi$

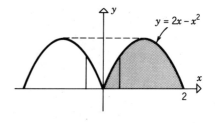

13. $V = \displaystyle\int_0^1 2\pi y^3\,dy = \pi/2$

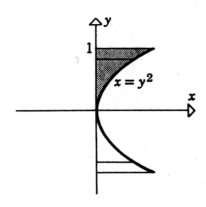

14. $V = \displaystyle\int_2^3 2\pi y(2y)dy$

$\qquad = 4\pi \displaystyle\int_2^3 y^2\,dy = 76\pi/3$

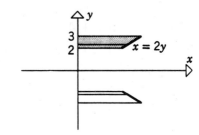

15. $V = \int_0^1 2\pi y(1 - \sqrt{y})dy$

$= 2\pi \int_0^1 (y - y^{3/2})dy = \pi/5$

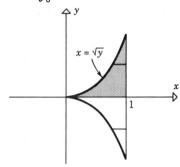

16. $V = \int_1^4 2\pi y(5 - y - 4/y)dy$

$= 2\pi \int_1^4 (5y - y^2 - 4)dy = 9\pi$

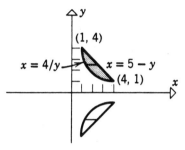

17. **(b)** $V = 2\pi \int_0^\pi x \sin x\, dx = 2\pi(\sin x - x \cos x)\Big]_0^\pi = 2\pi^2$

18. **(b)** $V = 2\pi \int_0^{\pi/2} x \cos x\, dx = 2\pi(\cos x + x \sin x)\Big]_0^{\pi/2} = \pi^2 - 2\pi$

19. **(a)** $V = \int_0^1 2\pi x(x^3 - 3x^2 + 2x)dx = 7\pi/30$

  (b) much easier; the method of
       slicing would require that x
       be expressed in terms of y.

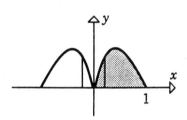

20. $V = \int_1^2 2\pi(x + 1)(1/x^3)dx$

$= 2\pi \int_1^2 (x^{-2} + x^{-3})dx = 7\pi/4$

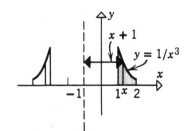

21. $V = \displaystyle\int_0^1 2\pi(1-y)y^{1/3}dy$

$\quad = 2\pi\displaystyle\int_0^1 (y^{1/3} - y^{4/3})dy = 9\pi/14$

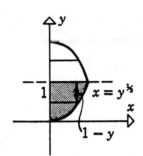

22. **(a)** $\displaystyle\int_a^b 2\pi x[f(x) - g(x)]dx$

(b) $\displaystyle\int_c^d 2\pi y[f(y) - g(y)]dy$

23. $x = \dfrac{h}{r}(r - y)$ is an equation of

line through $(0, r)$ and $(h, 0)$ so

$V = \displaystyle\int_0^r 2\pi y \left[\dfrac{h}{r}(r - y)\right] dy$

$\quad = \dfrac{2\pi h}{r}\displaystyle\int_0^r (ry - y^2)dy = \pi r^2 h/3$

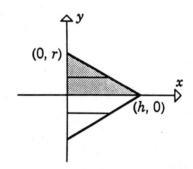

24. $V = \displaystyle\int_0^{k/4} 2\pi(k/2 - x)2\sqrt{kx}dx$

$\quad = 2\pi\sqrt{k}\displaystyle\int_0^{k/4} (kx^{1/2} - 2x^{3/2})dx$

$\quad = 7\pi k^3/60$

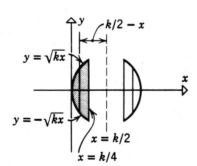

25. $V = \int_0^a 2\pi x (2\sqrt{r^2 - x^2})dx$

$\qquad = 4\pi \int_0^a x(r^2 - x^2)^{1/2} dx$

$\qquad = -\dfrac{4\pi}{3}(r^2 - x^2)^{3/2}\Big]_0^a$

$\qquad = \dfrac{4\pi}{3}\left[r^3 - (r^2 - a^2)^{3/2}\right]$

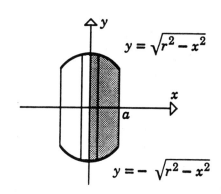

26. $V = \int_{-a}^a 2\pi(b - x)(2\sqrt{a^2 - x^2})dx$

$\qquad = 4\pi b \int_{-a}^a \sqrt{a^2 - x^2}\,dx - 4\pi \int_{-a}^a x\sqrt{a^2 - x^2}\,dx$

$\qquad = 4\pi b \cdot \text{(area of a semicircle of radius } a) - 4\pi(0)$

$\qquad = 2\pi^2 a^2 b$

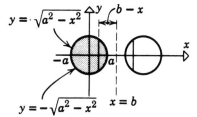

27. $V_x = \pi \int_{1/2}^b \dfrac{1}{x^2}dx = \pi(2 - 1/b),\ V_y = 2\pi \int_{1/2}^b dx = \pi(2b - 1);$

$V_x = V_y$ if $2 - 1/b = 2b - 1$, $2b^2 - 3b + 1 = 0$, solve to get $b = 1/2$ (reject) or $b = 1$.

EXERCISE SET 6.4

1. **(a)** $L = \int_1^2 \sqrt{1 + 2^2}\,dx = \sqrt{5}\int_1^2 dx = \sqrt{5}$

$\qquad$ **(b)** $L = \int_2^4 \sqrt{1 + (1/2)^2}\,dy = \dfrac{1}{2}\sqrt{5}\int_2^4 dy = \sqrt{5}$

$\qquad$ **(c)** $L = \sqrt{(2 - 1)^2 + (4 - 2)^2} = \sqrt{5}$ ($y = 2x$ is a line).

2. **(a)** $L = \int_{k_1}^{k_2} \sqrt{1 + m^2}\,dx = (k_2 - k_1)\sqrt{1 + m^2}$

(b) If $m > 0$, $L = \int_{mk_1+b}^{mk_2+b} \sqrt{1 + 1/m^2}\,dy = m(k_2 - k_1)\sqrt{\dfrac{m^2+1}{m^2}} = (k_2 - k_1)\sqrt{m^2+1}$;

if $m < 0$, $L = \int_{mk_2+b}^{mk_1+b} \sqrt{1 + 1/m^2}\,dy = m(k_1 - k_2)\sqrt{\dfrac{m^2+1}{m^2}} = (k_2 - k_1)\sqrt{m^2+1}$;

(c) $L = \sqrt{(k_2 - k_1)^2 + [(mk_2 + b) - (mk_1 + b)]^2}$

$\qquad = \sqrt{(k_2 - k_1)^2 + m^2(k_2 - k_1)^2} = (k_2 - k_1)\sqrt{1 + m^2}$

3. $f'(x) = \dfrac{9}{2}x^{1/2}$, $1 + [f'(x)]^2 = 1 + \dfrac{81}{4}x$,

$L = \int_0^1 \sqrt{1 + 81x/4}\,dx = \dfrac{8}{243}\left(1 + \dfrac{81}{4}x\right)^{3/2}\Bigg]_0^1 = (85\sqrt{85} - 8)/243$

4. $g'(y) = y(y^2 + 2)^{1/2}$, $1 + [g'(y)]^2 = 1 + y^2(y^2 + 2) = y^4 + 2y^2 + 1 = (y^2 + 1)^2$,

$L = \int_0^1 \sqrt{(y^2 + 1)^2}\,dy = \int_0^1 (y^2 + 1)\,dy = 4/3$

5. $\dfrac{dy}{dx} = \dfrac{2}{3}x^{-1/3}$, $1 + \left(\dfrac{dy}{dx}\right)^2 = 1 + \dfrac{4}{9}x^{-2/3} = \dfrac{9x^{2/3} + 4}{9x^{2/3}}$,

$L = \int_1^8 \dfrac{\sqrt{9x^{2/3} + 4}}{3x^{1/3}}\,dx = \dfrac{1}{18}\int_{13}^{40} u^{1/2}\,du$, $u = 9x^{2/3} + 4$

$\qquad\qquad = \dfrac{1}{27}u^{3/2}\Bigg]_{13}^{40} = \dfrac{1}{27}(40\sqrt{40} - 13\sqrt{13}) = \dfrac{1}{27}(80\sqrt{10} - 13\sqrt{13})$

or (alternate solution)

$x = y^{3/2}$, $\dfrac{dx}{dy} = \dfrac{3}{2}y^{1/2}$, $1 + \left(\dfrac{dx}{dy}\right)^2 = 1 + \dfrac{9}{4}y = \dfrac{4 + 9y}{4}$,

$L = \dfrac{1}{2}\int_1^4 \sqrt{4 + 9y}\,dy = \dfrac{1}{18}\int_{13}^{40} u^{1/2}\,du = \dfrac{1}{27}(80\sqrt{10} - 13\sqrt{13})$.

6. $f'(x) = \dfrac{1}{4}x^3 - x^{-3}$,

$1 + [f'(x)]^2 = 1 + \left(\dfrac{1}{16}x^6 - \dfrac{1}{2} + x^{-6}\right) = \dfrac{1}{16}x^6 + \dfrac{1}{2} + x^{-6} = \left(\dfrac{1}{4}x^3 + x^{-3}\right)^2$,

$L = \int_2^3 \sqrt{\left(\dfrac{1}{4}x^3 + x^{-3}\right)^2}\,dx = \int_2^3 \left(\dfrac{1}{4}x^3 + x^{-3}\right)dx = 595/144$

7. $x = g(y) = \dfrac{1}{24}y^3 + 2y^{-1}$, $g'(y) = \dfrac{1}{8}y^2 - 2y^{-2}$,

$1 + [g'(y)]^2 = 1 + \left(\dfrac{1}{64}y^4 - \dfrac{1}{2} + 4y^{-4}\right) = \dfrac{1}{64}y^4 + \dfrac{1}{2} + 4y^{-4} = \left(\dfrac{1}{8}y^2 + 2y^{-2}\right)^2$,

$L = \displaystyle\int_2^4 \left(\dfrac{1}{8}y^2 + 2y^{-2}\right)dy = 17/6$

8. $g'(y) = \dfrac{1}{2}y^3 - \dfrac{1}{2}y^{-3}$, $1 + [g'(y)]^2 = 1 + \left(\dfrac{1}{4}y^6 - \dfrac{1}{2} + \dfrac{1}{4}y^{-6}\right) = \left(\dfrac{1}{2}y^3 + \dfrac{1}{2}y^{-3}\right)^2$,

$L = \displaystyle\int_1^4 \left(\dfrac{1}{2}y^3 + \dfrac{1}{2}y^{-3}\right)dy = 2055/64$

9. **(a)**

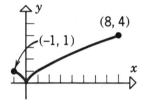

(b) dy/dx does not exist at $x = 0$

(c) $x = g(y) = y^{3/2}$, $g'(y) = \dfrac{3}{2}y^{1/2}$,

$L = \displaystyle\int_0^1 \sqrt{1 + 9y/4}\,dy$　(portion for $-1 \le x \le 0$)

$\quad + \displaystyle\int_0^4 \sqrt{1 + 9y/4}\,dy$　(portion for $0 \le x \le 8$)

$= \dfrac{8}{27}\left(\dfrac{13}{8}\sqrt{13} - 1\right) + \dfrac{8}{27}(10\sqrt{10} - 1) = (13\sqrt{13} + 80\sqrt{10} - 16)/27$

10. By implicit differentiation $\dfrac{dy}{dx} = -\left(\dfrac{y}{x}\right)^{1/3}$ so

$1 + \left(\dfrac{dy}{dx}\right)^2 = 1 + \left(\dfrac{y}{x}\right)^{2/3} = \dfrac{x^{2/3} + y^{2/3}}{x^{2/3}} = \dfrac{a^{2/3}}{x^{2/3}}$,

$L = \displaystyle\int_{-a}^{-a/8} \dfrac{a^{1/3}}{(-x^{1/3})}dx = -a^{1/3}\int_{-a}^{-a/8} x^{-1/3}dx = 9a/8$

11.   **(a)** f' is continuous on $[a, b]$ because f is smooth so by Theorem 4.6.4 f' has a maximum value M and a minimum value m on $[a, b]$.

     (b) From part (a)

$$m \le f'(x) \le M$$
$$m^2 \le [f'(x)]^2 \le M^2$$
$$1 + m^2 \le 1 + [f'(x)]^2 \le 1 + M^2$$
$$\sqrt{1 + m^2} \le \sqrt{1 + [f'(x)]^2} \le \sqrt{1 + M^2}$$
$$\int_a^b \sqrt{1 + m^2}\, dx \le \int_a^b \sqrt{1 + [f'(x)]^2}\, dx \le \int_a^b \sqrt{1 + M^2}\, dx$$
$$(b - a)\sqrt{1 + m^2} \le L \le (b - a)\sqrt{1 + M^2}$$

12. $f'(x) = \cos x \ge 0$ for $0 \le x \le \pi/4$, $\sqrt{2}/2 \le \cos x \le 1$ for $0 \le x \le \pi/4$ so

$$(\pi/4)\sqrt{1 + 1/2} \le L \le (\pi/4)\sqrt{1 + 1}, \quad \frac{\pi}{4}\sqrt{\frac{3}{2}} \le L \le \frac{\pi}{4}\sqrt{2}$$

13. 4.645975301   **14.**   3.820197789

EXERCISE SET 6.5

1. $S = \displaystyle\int_0^1 2\pi(7x)\sqrt{1 + 49}\, dx = 70\pi\sqrt{2} \int_0^1 x\, dx = 35\pi\sqrt{2}$

2. $f'(x) = \dfrac{1}{2\sqrt{x}}$, $1 + [f'(x)]^2 = 1 + \dfrac{1}{4x}$

    $S = \displaystyle\int_1^4 2\pi\sqrt{x}\sqrt{1 + \dfrac{1}{4x}}\, dx = 2\pi \int_1^4 \sqrt{x + 1/4}\, dx = \pi(17\sqrt{17} - 5\sqrt{5})/6$

3. $f'(x) = -x/\sqrt{4 - x^2}$, $1 + [f'(x)]^2 = 1 + \dfrac{x^2}{4 - x^2} = \dfrac{4}{4 - x^2}$,

    $S = \displaystyle\int_{-1}^1 2\pi\sqrt{4 - x^2}(2/\sqrt{4 - x^2})\, dx = 4\pi \int_{-1}^1 dx = 8\pi$

4. $y = f(x) = x^3$ for $1 \le x \le 2$, $f'(x) = 3x^2$,

    $S = \displaystyle\int_1^2 2\pi x^3 \sqrt{1 + 9x^4}\, dx = \dfrac{\pi}{27}(1 + 9x^4)^{3/2}\Big]_1^2 = 5\pi(29\sqrt{145} - 2\sqrt{10})/27$

5. $f'(x) = \frac{1}{2}x^{-1/2} - \frac{1}{2}x^{1/2}$, $1 + [f'(x)]^2 = 1 + \frac{1}{4}x^{-1} - \frac{1}{2} + \frac{1}{4}x = \left(\frac{1}{2}x^{-1} + \frac{1}{2}x\right)^2$,

$$S = \int_1^3 2\pi\left(x^{1/2} - \frac{1}{3}x^{3/2}\right)\left(\frac{1}{2}x^{-1} + \frac{1}{2}x\right)dx = \frac{\pi}{3}\int_1^3 (3 + 2x - x^2)dx = 16\pi/9$$

6. $f'(x) = x^2 - \frac{1}{4}x^{-2}$, $1 + [f'(x)]^2 = 1 + \left(x^4 - \frac{1}{2} + \frac{1}{16}x^{-4}\right) = \left(x^2 + \frac{1}{4}x^{-2}\right)^2$,

$$S = \int_1^2 2\pi\left(\frac{1}{3}x^3 + \frac{1}{4}x^{-1}\right)\left(x^2 + \frac{1}{4}x^{-2}\right)dx = 2\pi\int_1^2\left(\frac{1}{3}x^5 + \frac{1}{3}x + \frac{1}{16}x^{-3}\right)dx = 515\pi/64$$

7. $S = \int_0^2 2\pi(9y + 1)\sqrt{82}\,dy = 2\pi\sqrt{82}\int_0^2 (9y + 1)dy = 40\pi\sqrt{82}$

8. $g'(y) = 3y^2$, $S = \int_0^1 2\pi y^3\sqrt{1 + 9y^4}\,dy = \pi(10\sqrt{10} - 1)/27$

9. $g'(y) = -y/\sqrt{9 - y^2}$, $1 + [g'(y)]^2 = \dfrac{9}{9 - y^2}$,

$$S = \int_{-2}^2 2\pi\sqrt{9 - y^2} \cdot \frac{3}{\sqrt{9 - y^2}}dy = 6\pi\int_{-2}^2 dy = 24\pi$$

10. $g'(y) = -(1 - y)^{-1/2}$, $1 + [g'(y)]^2 = \dfrac{2 - y}{1 - y}$,

$$S = \int_{-1}^0 2\pi(2\sqrt{1 - y})\frac{\sqrt{2 - y}}{\sqrt{1 - y}}dy = 4\pi\int_{-1}^0 \sqrt{2 - y}\,dy = 8\pi(3\sqrt{3} - 2\sqrt{2})/3$$

11. $x = g(y) = \frac{1}{4}y^4 + \frac{1}{8}y^{-2}$, $g'(y) = y^3 - \frac{1}{4}y^{-3}$,

$$1 + [g'(y)]^2 = 1 + \left(y^6 - \frac{1}{2} + \frac{1}{16}y^{-6}\right) = \left(y^3 + \frac{1}{4}y^{-3}\right)^2$$

$$S = \int_1^2 2\pi\left(\frac{1}{4}y^4 + \frac{1}{8}y^{-2}\right)\left(y^3 + \frac{1}{4}y^{-3}\right)dy = \frac{\pi}{16}\int_1^2 (8y^7 + 6y + y^{-5})dy = 16,911\pi/1024$$

12. $x = 11 - y$ for $0 \le y \le 2$, $S = \int_0^2 2\pi(11 - y)\sqrt{1 + 1}\,dy = 2\pi\sqrt{2}\int_0^2 (11 - y)dy = 40\pi\sqrt{2}$

13. Revolve the line segment joining the points $(0, 0)$ and (h, r) about the x-axis. An equation of the line segment is $y = (r/h)x$ for $0 \le x \le h$ so

$$S = \int_0^h 2\pi(r/h)x\sqrt{1 + r^2/h^2}\,dx = \frac{2\pi r}{h^2}\sqrt{r^2 + h^2}\int_0^h x\,dx = \pi r\sqrt{r^2 + h^2}$$

14. $f(x) = \sqrt{r^2 - x^2}$, $f'(x) = -x/\sqrt{r^2 - x^2}$, $1 + [f'(x)]^2 = r^2/(r^2 - x^2)$,

$$S = \int_{-r}^{r} 2\pi\sqrt{r^2 - x^2}(r/\sqrt{r^2 - x^2})dx = 2\pi r \int_{-r}^{r} dx = 4\pi r^2$$

15. $f(x) = \sqrt{r^2 - x^2}$, $f'(x) = -x/\sqrt{r^2 - x^2}$, $1 + [f'(x)]^2 = r^2/(r^2 - x^2)$,

$$S = \int_{a}^{a+h} 2\pi\sqrt{r^2 - x^2}(r/\sqrt{r^2 - x^2})dx = 2\pi r \int_{a}^{a+h} dx = 2\pi rh$$

16. $S = \int_{a}^{b} 2\pi[f(x) + k]\sqrt{1 + [f'(x)]^2}dx$

17. **(a)** length of arc of sector = circumference of base of cone, $\ell\theta = 2\pi r, \theta = 2\pi r/\ell;$

$$S = \text{ area of sector } = \frac{1}{2}\ell^2(2\pi r/\ell) = \pi r\ell$$

    (b) $S = \pi r_2\ell_2 - \pi r_1\ell_1$
$$= \pi r_2(\ell_1 + \ell) - \pi r_1\ell_1$$
$$= \pi[(r_2 - r_1)\ell_1 + r_2\ell]$$

Using similar triangles

$$\ell_2/r_2 = \ell_1/r_1$$
$$r_1\ell_2 = r_2\ell_1$$
$$r_1(\ell_1 + \ell) = r_2\ell_1$$
$$(r_2 - r_1)\ell_1 = r_1\ell$$

so $S = \pi(r_1\ell + r_2\ell) = \pi(r_1 + r_2)\ell$

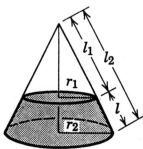

18. $2\pi k\sqrt{1 + [f'(x)]^2} \le 2\pi f(x)\sqrt{1 + [f'(x)]^2} \le 2\pi K\sqrt{1 + [f'(x)]^2}$, so

$$\int_{a}^{b} 2\pi k\sqrt{1 + [f'(x)]^2}dx \le \int_{a}^{b} 2\pi f(x)\sqrt{1 + [f'(x)]^2}dx \le \int_{a}^{b} 2\pi K\sqrt{1 + [f'(x)]^2}dx,$$

$$2\pi k\int_{a}^{b} \sqrt{1 + [f'(x)]^2}dx \le S \le 2\pi K\int_{a}^{b} \sqrt{1 + [f'(x)]^2}dx, \quad 2\pi kL \le S \le 2\pi KL$$

19. **(a)** $1 \le \sqrt{1 + [f'(x)]^2}$ so $2\pi f(x) \le 2\pi f(x)\sqrt{1 + [f'(x)]^2}$. By part (b) of Theorem 5.7.4

$$\int_{a}^{b} 2\pi f(x)dx \le \int_{a}^{b} 2\pi f(x)\sqrt{1 + [f'(x)]^2}dx$$

$$2\pi \int_{a}^{b} f(x)dx \le S, \quad 2\pi A \le S$$

    (b) $2\pi A = S$ if $f'(x) = 0$ for all x in $[a, b]$ so $f(x)$ is constant on $[a, b]$.

EXERCISE SET 6.6

1. $s(t) = \int (2t - 3)dt = t^2 - 3t + C$, $s(1) = (1)^2 - 3(1) + C = 5$, $C = 7$, $s(t) = t^2 - 3t + 7$.

2. $s(t) = \int 3t^2 dt = t^3 + C$, $s(0) = 0^3 + C = 0$, $C = 0$, $s(t) = t^3$.

3. $s(t) = \int (t^3 - 2t^2 + 1)dt = \frac{1}{4}t^4 - \frac{2}{3}t^3 + t + C$,

    $s(0) = \frac{1}{4}(0)^4 - \frac{2}{3}(0)^3 + 0 + C = 1$, $C = 1$, $s(t) = \frac{1}{4}t^4 - \frac{2}{3}t^3 + t + 1$.

4. $s(t) = \int (1 + \sin t)dt = t - \cos t + C$, $s(0) = 0 - \cos 0 + C = -3$, $C = -2$, $s(t) = t - \cos t - 2$.

5. $v(t) = \int 4\,dt = 4t + C_1$, $v(0) = 4(0) + C_1 = 1$, $C_1 = 1$, $v(t) = 4t + 1$,

    $s(t) = \int (4t + 1)dt = 2t^2 + t + C_2$, $s(0) = 2(0)^2 + 0 + C_2 = 0$, $C_2 = 0$, $s(t) = 2t^2 + t$.

6. $v(t) = \int (t^2 - 3t + 1)dt = \frac{1}{3}t^3 - \frac{3}{2}t^2 + t + C_1$,

    $v(0) = \frac{1}{3}(0)^3 - \frac{3}{2}(0)^2 + 0 + C_1 = 0$, $C_1 = 0$, $v(t) = \frac{1}{3}t^3 - \frac{3}{2}t^2 + t$,

    $s(t) = \int \left(\frac{1}{3}t^3 - \frac{3}{2}t^2 + t \right) dt = \frac{1}{12}t^4 - \frac{1}{2}t^3 + \frac{1}{2}t^2 + C_2$,

    $s(0) = \frac{1}{12}(0)^4 - \frac{1}{2}(0)^3 + \frac{1}{2}(0)^2 + C_2 = 0$, $C_2 = 0$, $s(t) = \frac{1}{12}t^4 - \frac{1}{2}t^3 + \frac{1}{2}t^2$.

7. $v(t) = \int 4\cos 2t\,dt = 2\sin 2t + C_1$, $v(0) = 2\sin 0 + C_1 = -1$, $C_1 = -1$,

    $v(t) = 2\sin 2t - 1$, $s(t) = \int (2\sin 2t - 1)dt = -\cos 2t - t + C_2$,

    $s(0) = -\cos 0 - 0 + C_2 = -3$, $C_2 = -2$, $s(t) = -\cos 2t - t - 2$.

8. $v(t) = \int \frac{1}{\sqrt{2t + 3}}dt = \sqrt{2t + 3} + C_1$, $v(3) = 3 + C_1 = 1$, $C_1 = -2$,

    $v(t) = \sqrt{2t + 3} - 2$, $s(t) = \int (\sqrt{2t + 3} - 2)dt = \frac{1}{3}(2t + 3)^{3/2} - 2t + C_2$,

    $s(3) = 3 + C_2 = 0$, $C_2 = -3$, $s(t) = \frac{1}{3}(2t + 3)^{3/2} - 2t - 3$.

9. (a) $s = \int \sin \frac{1}{2}\pi t \, dt = -\frac{2}{\pi}\cos\frac{1}{2}\pi t + C$

$s = 0$ when $t = 0$ which gives $C = \frac{2}{\pi}$ so $s = -\frac{2}{\pi}\cos\frac{1}{2}\pi t + \frac{2}{\pi}$.

$a = \dfrac{dv}{dt} = \dfrac{\pi}{2}\cos\frac{1}{2}\pi t$. When $t = 1 : s = 2/\pi$, $v = 1$, $|v| = 1$, $a = 0$.

(b) $v = -3\int t \, dt = -\frac{3}{2}t^2 + C_1$, $v = 0$ when $t = 0$ which gives $C_1 = 0$ so $v = -\frac{3}{2}t^2$.

$s = -\frac{3}{2}\int t^2 \, dt = -\frac{1}{2}t^3 + C_2$, $s = 1$ when $t = 0$ which gives $C_2 = 1$ so $s = -\frac{1}{2}t^3 + 1$.

When $t = 1 : s = 1/2$, $v = -3/2$, $|v| = 3/2$, $a = -3$.

10. Take $t = 0$ when deceleration begins, then $a = -10$ so $v = -10t + C_1$, but $v = 88$ when $t = 0$ which gives $C_1 = 88$ thus $v = -10t + 88$, $t \geq 0$

(a) $v = 45$ mph $= 66$ ft/sec, $66 = -10t + 88$, $t = 2.2$ sec.

(b) $v = 0$ (the car is stopped) when $t = 8.8$ sec.

$s = \int v \, dt = \int (-10t + 88)dt = -5t^2 + 88t + C_2$, and taking $s = 0$ when $t = 0$, $C_2 = 0$ so $s = -5t^2 + 88t$. At $t = 8.8$, $s = 387.2$. The car travels 387.2 ft before coming to a stop.

11. If $a(t) = k$ then $v(t) = \int k \, dt = kt + C_1$, but $v(0) = 60$ mph $= 88$ ft/sec so $k(0) + C_1 = 88$, $C_1 = 88$, $v(t) = kt + 88$; $s(t) = \int (kt + 88)dt = \frac{1}{2}kt^2 + 88t + C_2$, $s(0) = 0$ so $C_2 = 0$, $s(t) = \frac{1}{2}kt^2 + 88t$. $v(t) = 0$ at the instant when the car comes to a stop so $kt + 88 = 0$, $t = -88/k$; $s(t) = 180$ at this instant so $\frac{1}{2}k(-88/k)^2 + 88(-88/k) = 180$, $-3872/k = 180$, $k \approx -21.5$ ft/sec^2.

12. $dv/dt = 3$, $v = 3t + C_1$, but $v = v_0$ when $t = 0$ so $C_1 = v_0$, $v = 3t + v_0$. From $ds/dt = v = 3t + v_0$ we get $s = 3t^2/2 + v_0 t + C_2$ and, with $s = 0$ when $t = 0$, $C_2 = 0$ so $s = 3t^2/2 + v_0 t$. $s = 40$ when $t = 4$ thus $40 = 3(4)^2/2 + v_0(4)$, $v_0 = 4$ m/sec.

13. $s = 0$ and $v = 112$ when $t = 0$ so $v(t) = -32t + 112$, $s(t) = -16t^2 + 112t$.

(a) $v(3) = 16$ ft/sec, $v(5) = -48$ ft/sec.

(b) $v = 0$ when the projectile is at its maximum height so $-32t + 112 = 0$, $t = 7/2$ sec, $s(7/2) = -16(7/2)^2 + 112(7/2) = 196$ ft.

(c) $s = 0$ when it reaches the ground so $-16t^2 + 112t = 0$, $-16t(t - 7) = 0$, $t = 0, 7$ of which $t = 7$ is when it is at ground level on its way down. $v(7) = -112$, $|v| = 112$ ft/sec.

14. $s = 112$ when $t = 0$ so $s(t) = -16t^2 + v_0 t + 112$. But $s = 0$ when $t = 2$ thus $-16(2)^2 + v_0(2) + 112 = 0$, $v_0 = -24$ ft/sec.

15.   **(a)** $s(t) = 0$ when it hits the ground, $s(t) = -16t^2 + 16t = -16t(t-1) = 0$ when $t = 1$ sec.
      (b) The projectile moves upward until it gets to its highest point where $v(t) = 0$, $v(t) = -32t + 16 = 0$ when $t = 1/2$ sec.

16.   **(a)** $s(t) = 0$ when the rock hits the ground, $s(t) = -16t^2 + 555 = 0$ when $t = \sqrt{555}/4$ sec.
      (b) $v(t) = -32t$, $v(\sqrt{555}/4) = -8\sqrt{555}$, the speed at impact is $8\sqrt{555}$ ft/sec.

17.   **(a)** $s(t) = 0$ when the package hits the ground,
           $s(t) = -16t^2 + 20t + 200 = 0$ when (use the quadratic formula) $t = (5 + 5\sqrt{33})/8$ sec.
      (b) $v(t) = -32t + 20$, $v[(5 + 5\sqrt{33})/8] = -20\sqrt{33}$, the speed at impact is $20\sqrt{33}$ ft/sec.

18.   **(a)** $s(t) = 0$ when the stone hits the ground,
           $s(t) = -16t^2 - 96t + 112 = -16(t^2 + 6t - 7) = -16(t+7)(t-1) = 0$ when $t = 1$ sec.
      (b) $v(t) = -32t - 96$, $v(1) = -128$, the speed at impact is 128 ft/sec.

19. $s(t) = -4.9t^2 + 49t + 150$ and $v(t) = -9.8t + 49$.
      (a) The projectile reaches its maximum height when $v(t) = 0$, $-9.8t + 49 = 0$, $t = 5$ sec.
      (b) $s(5) = -4.9(5)^2 + 49(5) + 150 = 272.5$ m.
      (c) The projectile reaches its starting point when $s(t) = 150$, $-4.9t^2 + 49t + 150 = 150$, $-4.9t(t - 10) = 0$, $t = 10$ sec.
      (d) $v(10) = -9.8(10) + 49 = -49$ m/sec.
      (e) $s(t) = 0$ when the projectile hits the ground, $-4.9t^2 + 49t + 150 = 0$ when (use the quadratic formula) $t \approx 12.46$ sec.
      (f) $v(12.46) = -9.8(12.46) + 49 \approx -73.1$, the speed at impact is about 73.1 m/sec.

20.   Take $s = 0$ at the water level and let h be the height of the bridge, then $s = h$ and $v = 0$ when $t = 0$ so $s(t) = -16t^2 + h$
      (a) $s = 0$ when $t = 4$ thus $-16(4)^2 + h = 0$, $h = 256$ ft.
      (b) First, find how long it takes for the stone to hit the water (find t for $s = 0$) : $-16t^2 + h = 0$, $t = \sqrt{h}/4$. Next, find how long it takes the sound to travel to the bridge: this time is $h/1080$ because the speed is constant at 1080 ft/sec. Finally, use the fact that the total of these two times must be 4 sec: $\dfrac{h}{1080} + \dfrac{\sqrt{h}}{4} = 4$, $h + 270\sqrt{h} = 4320$, $h + 270\sqrt{h} - 4320 = 0$, and by the quadratic formula $\sqrt{h} = \dfrac{-270 \pm \sqrt{(270)^2 + 4(4320)}}{2}$, reject the negative value to get $\sqrt{h} \approx 15.15$, $h \approx 229.5$ ft.

21. $s(t) = -16t^2 + v_0 t$, $v(t) = -32t + v_0$; $v = 0$ when it reaches maximum height so $-32t + v_0 = 0$, $t = v_0/32$ is the time it takes to get there, thus $s(v_0/32) = -16(v_0/32)^2 + v_0(v_0/32) = 1,000$, $v_0^2 = 64,000$, $v_0 = 80\sqrt{10}$ ft/sec (positive because fired upward).

22. $s = -16t^2 + 40$ and $v = -32t$. Solve $s = -16t^2 + 40$ for t to get $t = \sqrt{40 - s}/4$ so $v = -8\sqrt{40 - s}$.

23. $s = -16t^2 + v_0 t + s_0$, but $s_0 = 0$ so $s = -16t^2 + v_0 t$. $s = 0$ when $t = 8$ so $0 = -16(8)^2 + v_0(8)$, $v_0 = 128$ ft/sec. $v = 0$ at its highest point so $-32t + 128 = 0$, $t = 4$, $s = -16(4)^2 + 128(4) = 256$ ft.

24. Solve for t in (4) to get $t = (v_0 - v)/g$, so from (6)
$$s = -(v_0 - v)^2/(2g) + v_0(v_0 - v)/g + s_0,$$
$$2g(s - s_0) = 2v_0(v_0 - v) - (v_0 - v)^2 = (v_0 - v)(v_0 + v) = v_0^2 - v^2, \quad v^2 = v_0^2 - 2g(s - s_0).$$

25. **(a)** negative, because v is decreasing
   (b) increasing, because the graph of $v(t)$ is concave up
   (c) negative, because the area between the graph of $v(t)$ and the t-axis appears to be greater where $v < 0$ compared to where $v > 0$.

26. displacement $= \displaystyle\int_0^4 (2t - 4)dt = t^2 - 4t \Big]_0^4 = 0$

   distance $= \displaystyle\int_0^4 |2t - 4|dt = \int_0^2 (-2t + 4)dt + \int_2^4 (2t - 4)dt = 4 + 4 = 8$

27. displacement $= \displaystyle\int_0^2 (t^2 + t - 2)dt = 2/3$

   distance $= \displaystyle\int_0^2 |t^2 + t - 2|dt = \int_0^1 -(t^2 + t - 2)dt + \int_1^2 (t^2 + t - 2)dt = 7/6 + 11/6 = 3$

28. displacement $= \displaystyle\int_0^5 |t - 3|dt = \int_0^3 -(t - 3)dt + \int_3^5 (t - 3)dt = 13/2$

   distance $= \displaystyle\int_0^5 |t - 3|dt = 13/2$

29. displacement $= \displaystyle\int_0^\pi \cos t \, dt = 0$

   distance $= \displaystyle\int_0^\pi |\cos t|dt = \int_0^{\pi/2} \cos t \, dt + \int_{\pi/2}^\pi - \cos t \, dt = 1 + 1 = 2$

30. displacement $= \displaystyle\int_{\pi/4}^{\pi} 3 \sin t \, dt = 3 + 3\sqrt{2}/2$

distance $= \displaystyle\int_{\pi/4}^{\pi} 3|\sin t|dt = \int_{\pi/4}^{\pi} 3 \sin t \, dt = 3 + 3\sqrt{2}/2$

31. $v(t) = t^3 - 3t^2 + 2t = t(t-1)(t-2)$

displacement $= \displaystyle\int_{0}^{3} (t^3 - 3t^2 + 2t)dt = 9/4$

distance $= \displaystyle\int_{0}^{3} |v(t)|dt = \int_{0}^{1} v(t)dt + \int_{1}^{2} -v(t)dt + \int_{2}^{3} v(t)dt = 11/4$

32. $v(t) = -2t + 3$

displacement $= \displaystyle\int_{1}^{4} (-2t + 3)dt = -6$

distance $= \displaystyle\int_{1}^{4} |-2t + 3|dt = \int_{1}^{3/2} (-2t + 3)dt + \int_{3/2}^{4} (2t - 3)dt = 13/2$

33. $v(t) = \dfrac{1}{2}t^2 - 2t$

displacement $= \displaystyle\int_{1}^{5} (\tfrac{1}{2}t^2 - 2t)dt = -10/3$

distance $= \displaystyle\int_{1}^{5} |\tfrac{1}{2}t^2 - 2t|dt = \int_{1}^{4} -(\tfrac{1}{2}t^2 - 2t)dt + \int_{4}^{5} (\tfrac{1}{2}t^2 - 2t)dt = 17/3$

34. $v(t) = -\cos t + 2$

displacement $= \displaystyle\int_{\pi/4}^{\pi/2} (-\cos t + 2)dt = (\pi + \sqrt{2} - 2)/2$

distance $= \displaystyle\int_{\pi/4}^{\pi/2} |-\cos t + 2|dt = \int_{\pi/4}^{\pi/2} (-\cos t + 2)dt = (\pi + \sqrt{2} - 2)/2$

35. $v(t) = \dfrac{2}{5}\sqrt{5t + 1} + \dfrac{8}{5}$

displacement $= \displaystyle\int_{0}^{3} \left(\frac{2}{5}\sqrt{5t + 1} + \frac{8}{5}\right) dt = \frac{4}{75}(5t + 1)^{3/2} + \frac{8}{5}t \Big]_{0}^{3} = 204/25$

distance $= \displaystyle\int_{0}^{3} |v(t)|dt = \int_{0}^{3} v(t)dt = 204/25$

36. Acceleration is the slope of the tangent to the graph of the velocity $v(t)$. If the acceleration did not increase, then it could have been constant or have decreased so the graph of $v(t)$ would be a straight line or a curve that is concave down (see Figure). The distance traveled is the area under the graph of $v(t)$, so the minimum distance traveled is the area of the trapezoid which is $(1/2)(5 + 50)(20) = 550$ ft.

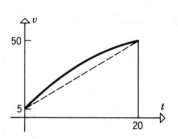

EXERCISE SET 6.7

1. (a) $W = 30[5 - (-2)] = 210$ ft·lb

(b) $W = \int_1^6 x^{-2} dx = 5/6$ ft·lb

2. (a) $F(x) = kx, F(0.05) = 0.05k = 45, k = 900$ N/m

(b) $W = \int_0^{0.03} 900x\ dx = 0.405$ J

(c) $W = \int_{0.05}^{0.10} 900x\ dx = 3.375$ J

3. $F(x) = kx, F(0.2) = 0.2k = 100, k = 500$ N/m, $W = \int_0^{0.8} 500x dx = 160$ J

4. $F(x) = kx, F(1/2) = k/2 = 6, k = 12$ N/m, $W = \int_0^2 12x\ dx = 24$ J

5. $W = \int_0^1 kx\ dx = k/2 = 10, k = 20$ lb/ft

6. $W = \int_0^6 (9-x)62.4(25\pi)dx$

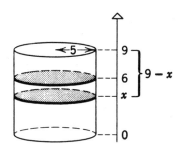

$= 1560\pi \int_0^6 (9-x)dx$

$= 56,160\pi \text{ ft·lb}$

7. $W = \int_0^6 (9-x)\rho(25\pi)dx = 900\pi\rho \text{ ft·lb}$

8. $r/10 = x/15, r = 2x/3$

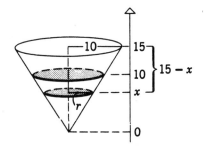

$W = \int_0^{10} (15-x)62.4(4\pi x^2/9)dx$

$= \frac{83.2}{3}\pi \int_0^{10} (15x^2 - x^3)dx$

$= 208,000\pi/3 \text{ ft·lb}$

9. $w/4 = x/3, w = 4x/3$

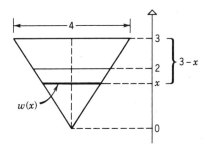

$W = \int_0^2 (3-x)(9810)(4x/3)(6)dx$

$= 78480 \int_0^2 (3x - x^2)dx$

$= 261,600 \text{ J}$

10. $W = 2\sqrt{4-x^2}$

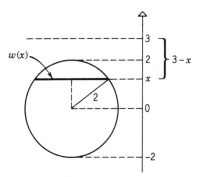

$W = \int_{-2}^2 (3-x)(50)(2\sqrt{4-x^2})(10)dx$

$= 3000 \int_{-2}^2 \sqrt{4-x^2}dx - 1000 \int_{-2}^2 x\sqrt{4-x^2}dx$

$= 3000[\pi(2)^2/2] - 0 = 6000\pi \text{ ft·lb}$

11. **(a)** $W = \displaystyle\int_0^9 (10 - x)62.4(300)dx$

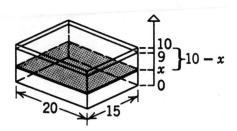

$= 18,720 \displaystyle\int_0^9 (10 - x)dx$

$= 926,640$ ft·lb

(b) to empty the pool in one hour
would require $926,640/3600 = 257.4$
ft·lb of work per second so
hp of motor $= 257.4/550 = 0.468$

12. All of the water must be lifted 200 ft, assuming that the level of water in the lake changes by only a negligible amount. The work done is equal to the total weight of water needed to fill the tank times 200.

$$\text{volume of tank} = \frac{1}{2}\left(\frac{4}{3}\pi r^3\right) = \frac{2}{3}\pi(1000) = 2000\pi/3\,\text{ft}^3$$
$$\text{weight of water} = 62.4(2000\pi/3) = 41,600\pi\,\text{lb}$$
$$W = (41,600\pi)(200) = 8,320,000\pi\ \text{ft·lb}$$

13. $W = \displaystyle\int_0^{100} 15(100 - x)dx$

$= 75,000$ ft·lb

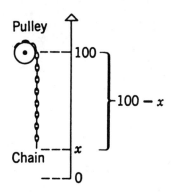

14. When the rocket is x ft above the
ground

$$\text{total weight} = \text{weight of rocket} \\ + \text{weight of fuel} \\ = 3 + [40 - 2(x/1000)] \\ = 43 - x/500 \text{ tons},$$

$$W = \int_0^{3000} (43 - x/500)dx = 120,000 \text{ ft·tons}$$

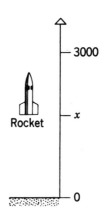

15. (a) $F(4000) = k/(4000)^2 = 6000$, $k = 9.6 \times 10^{10}$

(b) $W = \int_{4000}^{5000} 9.6 \times 10^{10} x^{-2} dx = 4,800,000 \text{ mi·lb}$

16. Let $F(x)$ be the force needed to hold
charge A at position x, then

$$F(x) = \frac{c}{(a-x)^2}, \quad F(-a) = \frac{c}{4a^2} = k,$$

so $c = 4a^2 k$. $W = \int_{-a}^{0} 4a^2 k(a-x)^{-2} dx = 2ak \text{ J}$

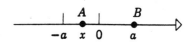

EXERCISE SET 6.8

1. (a) $F = \rho hA = (62.4)(5)(9) = 2,808 \text{ lb}$ (b) $F = (40)(10)(9) = 3,600 \text{ lb}$

2. $F = \int_0^2 62.4x(4)dx$

$= 249.6 \int_0^2 x \, dx$

$= 499.2 \text{ lb}$

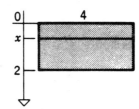

3. $F = \displaystyle\int_1^3 9810x(4)\,dx$

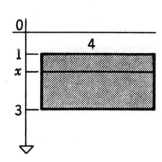

    $= 39240 \displaystyle\int_1^3 x\,dx$

    $= 156{,}960\,\text{N}$

4.   By similar triangles

$$\frac{w(x)}{4} = \frac{2\sqrt{3} - x}{2\sqrt{3}}, \; w(x) = \frac{2}{\sqrt{3}}(2\sqrt{3} - x),$$

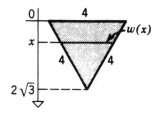

$$F = \int_0^{2\sqrt{3}} 62.4x\left[\frac{2}{\sqrt{3}}(2\sqrt{3} - x)\right]dx$$

$$= \frac{124.8}{\sqrt{3}} \int_0^{2\sqrt{3}} (2\sqrt{3}x - x^2)\,dx = 499.2\,\text{lb}$$

5.   by similar triangles

$$\frac{w(x)}{6} = \frac{10 - x}{8}$$

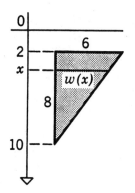

$$w(x) = \frac{3}{4}(10 - x),$$

$$F = \int_2^{10} 62.4x\left[\frac{3}{4}(10 - x)\right]dx$$

$$= 46.8 \int_2^{10} (10x - x^2)\,dx = 6988.8\,\text{lb}$$

6. $w(x) = 16 + 2u(x)$, but

$$\frac{u(x)}{4} = \frac{12 - x}{8} \text{ so } u(x) = \frac{1}{2}(12 - x),$$

$$w(x) = 16 + (12 - x) = 28 - x,$$

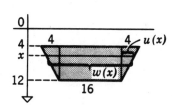

$$F = \int_4^{12} 62.4x(28 - x)\,dx$$

$$= 62.4 \int_4^{12} (28x - x^2)\,dx = 77{,}209.6\,\text{lb}$$

7. $F = \displaystyle\int_0^5 9810x(2\sqrt{25 - x^2})dx$

$= 19,620 \displaystyle\int_0^5 x(25 - x^2)^{1/2}dx$

$= 8.175 \times 10^5$ N

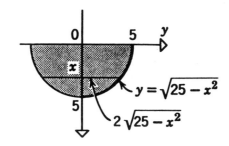

$$y = \sqrt{25 - x^2}$$

$$2\sqrt{25 - x^2}$$

8. $F = \displaystyle\int_0^2 50x(2\sqrt{4 - x^2})dx$

$= 100 \displaystyle\int_0^2 x(4 - x^2)^{1/2}dx$

$= 800/3$ lb

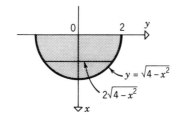

$$y = \sqrt{4 - x^2}$$

$$2\sqrt{4 - x^2}$$

9. Find the forces on the upper and
lower halves and add them:

$\dfrac{w_1(x)}{\sqrt{2}a} = \dfrac{x}{\sqrt{2}a/2}$, $w_1(x) = 2x$

$F_1 = \displaystyle\int_0^{\sqrt{2}a/2} \rho x(2x)dx$

$= 2\rho \displaystyle\int_0^{\sqrt{2}a/2} x^2 dx = \sqrt{2}\rho a^3/6,$

$\dfrac{w_2(x)}{\sqrt{2}a} = \dfrac{\sqrt{2}a - x}{\sqrt{2}a/2}$, $w_2(x) = 2(\sqrt{2}a - x)$

$F_2 = \displaystyle\int_{\sqrt{2}a/2}^{\sqrt{2}a} \rho x[2(\sqrt{2}a - x)]dx = 2\rho \displaystyle\int_{\sqrt{2}a/2}^{\sqrt{2}a} (\sqrt{2}ax - x^2)dx = \sqrt{2}\rho a^3/3,$

$F = F_1 + F_2 = \sqrt{2}\rho a^3/6 + \sqrt{2}\rho a^3/3 = \rho a^3/\sqrt{2}$

10. $h(x) = x \sin 60° = \sqrt{3}x/2$,

$$F - \int_0^{100} 02.4(\sqrt{3}x/2)(200)dx$$

$$= 6240\sqrt{3} \int_0^{100} x\,dx$$

$$= 31,200,000\sqrt{3}\,\text{lb}$$

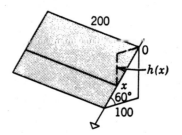

11. $\sqrt{16^2 + 4^2} = \sqrt{272} = 4\sqrt{17}$ is the

other dimension of the bottom.

$(h(x) - 4)/4 = x/(4\sqrt{17})$

$h(x) = x/\sqrt{17} + 4$,

$$F = \int_0^{4\sqrt{17}} 62.4(x/\sqrt{17} + 4)10dx$$

$$= 624 \int_0^{4\sqrt{17}} (x/\sqrt{17} + 4)dx$$

$$= 14,976\sqrt{17}\,\text{lb}$$

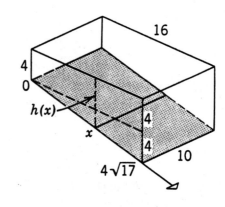

12. $F = \int_h^{h+2} \rho_0 x(2)dx$

$$= 2\rho_0 \int_h^{h+2} x\,dx$$

$$= 4\rho_0(h + 1)$$

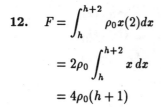

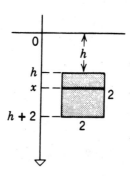

13. **(a)** From Exercise 12, $F = 4\rho_0(h+1)$ so (assuming that ρ_0 is constant) $dF/dt = 4\rho_0(dh/dt)$ which is a positive constant if dh/dt is a positive constant.

(b) If $dh/dt = 20$ then $dF/dt = 80\rho_0$ lb/min from part (a).

SUPPLEMENTARY EXERCISES CHAPTER 6

1. **(a)** $\displaystyle\int_0^2 (x + 2 - x^2)\,dx$

   (b) $\displaystyle\int_0^2 \sqrt{y}\,dy + \int_2^4 (\sqrt{y} - y + 2)\,dy$

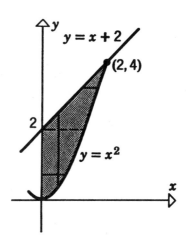

2. **(a)** solve $x = 4y - y^2$ for y:

   $y^2 - 4y + x = 0$,

   $y = \dfrac{4 \pm \sqrt{16 - 4x}}{2} = 2 \pm \sqrt{4 - x}$

   so the lower boundary of the
   region is $y = 2 - \sqrt{4 - x}$ because
   $y \le 2$, and the area is

   $$\int_0^4 (x/2 - 2 + \sqrt{4 - x})\,dx$$

   (b) $\displaystyle\int_0^2 [(4y - y^2) - 2y]\,dy = \int_0^2 (2y - y^2)\,dy$

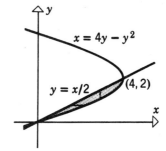

3. (a) $\displaystyle\int_0^9 [\sqrt{x} - (-\sqrt{x})]dx = \int_0^9 2\sqrt{x}\,dx$

(b) $\displaystyle\int_{-3}^3 (9 - y^2)dy$

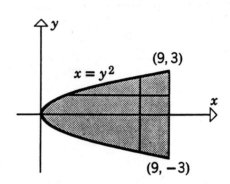

y

$x = y^2$

$(9, 3)$

x

$(9, -3)$

4. (a) $\displaystyle\int_0^2 \pi[(x + 2)^2 - x^4]dx$

(b) $\displaystyle\int_0^2 2\pi y(\sqrt{y})dy + \int_2^4 2\pi y[\sqrt{y} - (y - 2)]dy = \int_0^2 2\pi y^{3/2}dy + \int_2^4 2\pi y(\sqrt{y} - y + 2)dy$

5. (a) $\displaystyle\int_0^2 2\pi x(x + 2 - x^2)dx$ (b) $\displaystyle\int_0^2 \pi y\,dy + \int_2^4 \pi[y - (y - 2)^2]dy$

6. (a) $\displaystyle\int_0^4 \pi[x^2/4 - (2 - \sqrt{4 - x})^2]dx$

(b) $\displaystyle\int_0^2 2\pi y[(4y - y^2) - 2y]dy = \int_0^2 2\pi y(2y - y^2)dy$

7. (a) $\displaystyle\int_0^4 2\pi x[x/2 - (2 - \sqrt{4 - x})]dx$ (b) $\displaystyle\int_0^2 \pi[(4y - y^2)^2 - 4y^2]dy$

8. (a) $\displaystyle\int_0^9 \pi x\,dx$ (b) $\displaystyle\int_0^3 2\pi y(9 - y^2)dy$

9. (a) $\displaystyle\int_0^9 2\pi x(2\sqrt{x})dx = \int_0^9 4\pi x^{3/2}dx$ (b) $\displaystyle\int_{-3}^3 \pi(81 - y^4)dy$

10. **(a)** $A = \displaystyle\int_0^{\pi/4} (\cos x - \sin x)\,dx$

$= \sqrt{2} - 1$

(b) $V = \displaystyle\int_0^{\pi/4} \pi(\cos^2 x - \sin^2 x)\,dx$

$= \pi \displaystyle\int_0^{\pi/4} \cos 2x\,dx = \pi/2$

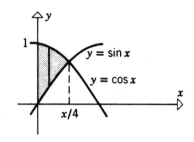

11. **(a)** $A = \displaystyle\int_0^4 \sqrt{4-y}\,dy = 16/3$

(b) $V = \displaystyle\int_0^4 \pi(4-y)\,dy = 8\pi$

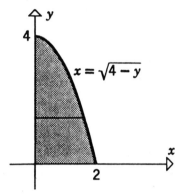

12. $\displaystyle\int_a^b [f(x) - g(x)]\,dx + \int_b^c [g(x) - f(x)]\,dx + \int_c^d [f(x) - g(x)]\,dx$

13. $A = \displaystyle\int_{-1}^0 (x^3 - x)\,dx + \int_0^1 (x - x^3)\,dx$

$+ \displaystyle\int_1^2 (x^3 - x)\,dx$

$= 1/4 + 1/4 + 9/4 = 11/4$

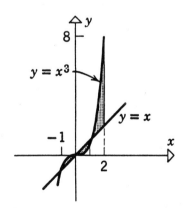

14. $V = \int_0^1 (x - x^2)^2 dx$

$= \int_0^1 (x^2 - 2x^3 + x^4) dx$

$= 1/30$

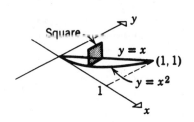

15. Let r be the radius of the semicircle shown in the figure, then by similar triangles

$2r/a = (b - y)/b$, $r = \dfrac{a}{2b}(b - y)$ so

$A(y) = \dfrac{1}{2}\pi r^2 = \dfrac{1}{2}\pi \dfrac{a^2}{4b^2}(b - y)^2 = \dfrac{\pi a^2}{8b^2}(b - y)^2$,

$V = \int_0^b A(y) dy = \int_0^b \dfrac{\pi a^2}{8b^2}(b - y)^2 dy = \pi a^2 b/24$

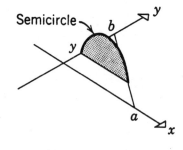

16. $V = \int_0^{\sqrt{\pi/2}} 2\pi x \cos(x^2) dx = \pi$

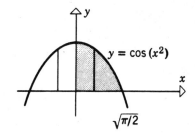

17. **(a)** $V = \int_0^4 2\pi(4 - x)\sqrt{x}\,dx$

$= 2\pi \int_0^4 (4x^{1/2} - x^{3/2}) dx$

$= 256\pi/15$

(b) $V = \int_0^4 \pi[4 - (2 - \sqrt{x})^2] dx$

$= \pi \int_0^4 (4x^{1/2} - x) dx = 40\pi/3$

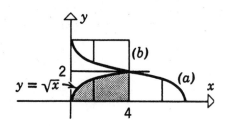

18. $V = \displaystyle\int_{-L/2}^{L/2} \pi[4R(x^2 - L^2/4)/L^2]^2 dx$

$\quad = \dfrac{2\pi R^2}{L^4} \displaystyle\int_0^{L/2} (16x^4 - 8L^2x^2 + L^4)dx$

$\quad = 8\pi R^2 L/15$

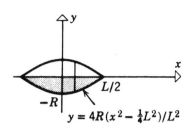

$y = 4R(x^2 - \tfrac{1}{4}L^2)/L^2$

19. $y = \dfrac{x^{3/2}}{\sqrt{8}},\ 0 \le x \le 2;\ y' = \dfrac{3x^{1/2}}{2\sqrt{8}},\ L = \displaystyle\int_0^2 \sqrt{1 + \dfrac{9}{32}x}\,dx = 61/27$

20. $y' = x(x^2 + 2)^{1/2},\ 1 + (y')^2 = 1 + x^2(x^2 + 2) = (x^2 + 1)^2,\ L = \displaystyle\int_0^3 (x^2 + 1)dx = 12$

21. $y' = \dfrac{1}{2}x^4 - \dfrac{1}{2}x^{-4},\ 1 + (y')^2 = 1 + \left(\dfrac{1}{4}x^{16} - \dfrac{1}{2} + \dfrac{1}{4}x^{-16}\right) = \left(\dfrac{1}{2}x^4 + \dfrac{1}{2}x^{-4}\right)^2,$

$\quad L = \displaystyle\int_1^2 \left(\dfrac{1}{2}x^4 + \dfrac{1}{2}x^{-4}\right) dx = 779/240$

22. $y' = x^2 - \dfrac{1}{4}x^{-2},\ 1 + (y')^2 = 1 + \left(x^4 - \dfrac{1}{2} + \dfrac{1}{16}x^{-4}\right) = \left(x^2 + \dfrac{1}{4}x^{-2}\right)^2,$

$\quad L = \displaystyle\int_1^2 \left(x^2 + \dfrac{1}{4}x^{-2}\right) dx = 59/24$

23. $y' = 3x^2,\ 1 + (y')^2 = 1 + 9x^4,\ S = \displaystyle\int_1^2 2\pi x^3 \sqrt{1 + 9x^4}\,dx = \pi(145^{3/2} - 10^{3/2})/27$

24. $x = y^2/12,\ dx/dy = y/6,\ 1 + (dx/dy)^2 = (36 + y^2)/36,$

$\quad S = \displaystyle\int_0^6 2\pi y \dfrac{\sqrt{36 + y^2}}{6}\,dy = \dfrac{\pi}{3} \displaystyle\int_0^6 y(36 + y^2)^{1/2}dy = 24\pi(2\sqrt{2} - 1)$

25. $y' = x^{1/2} - \dfrac{1}{4}x^{-1/2},\ 1 + (y')^2 = 1 + \left(x - \dfrac{1}{2} + \dfrac{1}{16}x^{-1}\right) = \left(x^{1/2} + \dfrac{1}{4}x^{-1/2}\right)^2,$

$\quad S = \displaystyle\int_0^9 2\pi x \left(x^{1/2} + \dfrac{1}{4}x^{-1/2}\right) dx = 2\pi \displaystyle\int_0^9 \left(x^{3/2} + \dfrac{1}{4}x^{1/2}\right) dx = 1017\pi/5$

26. $S = \int_0^9 2\pi(9-x)\left(x^{1/2} + \frac{1}{4}x^{-1/2}\right) dx$

$= 18\pi \int_0^9 \left(x^{1/2} + \frac{1}{4}x^{-1/2}\right) dx$ — (answer to Exercise 25) $= 351\pi - 1017\pi/5 = 738\pi/5$

27. $y' = \frac{1}{2}x^{-1/2} - \frac{1}{2}x^{1/2}, \ 1 + (y')^2 = \left(\frac{1}{2}x^{-1/2} + \frac{1}{2}x^{1/2}\right)^2,$

$S = \int_0^3 2\pi x\left(\frac{1}{2}x^{-1/2} + \frac{1}{2}x^{1/2}\right) dx = \pi \int_0^3 (x^{1/2} + x^{3/2})dx = 28\pi\sqrt{3}/5$

28. $y' = (1-x)/\sqrt{2x - x^2}, \ 1 + (y')^2 = 1 + \frac{(1-x)^2}{2x - x^2} = \frac{1}{2x - x^2},$

$S = \int_{1/2}^1 2\pi\sqrt{2x - x^2}\ \frac{1}{\sqrt{2x - x^2}}\ dx = 2\pi \int_{1/2}^1 dx = \pi$

29. $F(x) = kx, \ F(4) = 4k = 2, \ k = 1/2, \ W = \int_2^4 \frac{1}{2}x\ dx = 3 \text{ in·lb}$

30. $W = \int_0^3 kx\ dx = 9k/2 = 180, \ k = 40 \text{ lb/in}$

31. $F(x) = 250 + \frac{3}{4}(40 - x) = 280 - \frac{3}{4}x,$

$W = \int_0^{40}\left(280 - \frac{3}{4}x\right) dx = 10,600 \text{ ft·lb}$

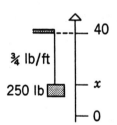

32. $r/3 = x/5, \ r = 3x/5$

$W = \int_0^5 64x\pi(3x/5)^2 dx$

$= \frac{576}{25}\pi \int_0^5 x^3 dx$

$= 3600\pi \text{ ft·lb}$

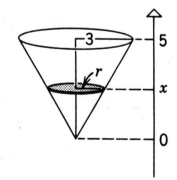

33. $A(y) = \pi x^2 = \pi(y/2 + 4)$,

$$W = \int_{-8}^{0} 62.4(4 - y)[\pi(y/2 + 4)]dy$$

$$= 31.2\pi \int_{-8}^{0} (32 - 4y - y^2)dy$$

$$= 6656\pi \ \text{ft·lb}$$

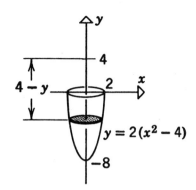

34. $x = D - y$, $F(y) = \dfrac{k}{(D-y)^2}$

$$W = \int_{0}^{2D/3} \frac{k}{(D-y)^2}dy$$

$$= k\int_{0}^{2D/3} (D-y)^{-2}dy$$

$$= 2k/D \ \text{J}$$

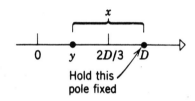

Hold this pole fixed

35. By similar triangles

$$w(x)/4 = (x-1)/2$$

$$w(x) = 2(x-1)$$

$$F = \int_{1}^{3} \rho x[2(x-1)]dx$$

$$= 2\rho \int_{1}^{3} (x^2 - x)dx = 28\rho/3 \ \text{lb}$$

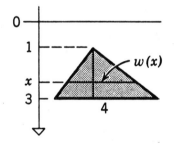

36. $[w(x)/2]^2 = r^2 - x^2$

$$w(x) = 2\sqrt{r^2 - x^2}$$

$$F = \int_{0}^{r} \rho x[2\sqrt{r^2 - x^2}]dx$$

$$= 2\rho \int_{0}^{r} x(r^2 - x^2)^{1/2}dx = 2\rho r^3/3 \ \text{lb}$$

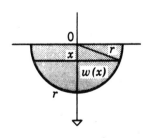

CHAPTER 7
Logarithm and Exponential Functions

EXERCISE SET 7.1

1. (a) $f(g(x)) = 4(x/4) = x$, $g(f(x)) = (4x)/4 = x$, f and g are inverse functions
   (b) $f(g(x)) = 3(3x - 1) + 1 = 9x - 2 \neq x$ so f and g are not inverse functions
   (c) $f(g(x)) = \sqrt[3]{(x^3 + 2) - 2} = x$, $g(f(x)) = (x - 2) + 2 = x$, f and g are inverse functions
   (d) $f(g(x)) = (x^{1/4})^4 = x$, $g(f(x)) = (x^4)^{1/4} = |x| \neq x$, f and g are not inverse functions

2. $f'(x) = -1$; f is decreasing on $(-\infty, +\infty)$ so f has an inverse.

3. $f'(x) = 3$; f is increasing on $(-\infty, +\infty)$ so f has an inverse.

4. $f(x) = (x - 1)^2$; f does not have an inverse because f is not one-to-one, for example $f(0) = f(2) = 1$.

5. $f(x) = (2 + x)(1 - x)$; f does not have an inverse because f is not one-to-one, for example $f(-2) = f(1) = 0$.

6. f does not have an inverse because f is not one-to-one, for example $f(-1) = f(2) = 4$.

7. f does not have an inverse because f is not one-to-one, for example $f(0) = f(1) = -1$.

8. $f(x) = (x - 1)^3$; f has an inverse because two different numbers cannot have the same cube so f is one-to-one.

9. $f(x) = (x - 1)^3$; f has an inverse because two different numbers cannot have the same cube so f is one-to-one.

10. $f'(x) = 5x^4 + 24x^2 + 2 \geq 2$ for $-\infty < x < +\infty$; f is increasing on $(-\infty, +\infty)$ so f has an inverse.

11. $f'(x) = 10x^4 + 3x^2 + 3 \geq 3$ for $-\infty < x < +\infty$; f is increasing on $(-\infty, +\infty)$ so f has an inverse.

12. f does not have an inverse because f is not one-to-one, for example $f(1/2) = f(2) = 5/2$.

13. $f'(x) = \cos x > 0$ for $-\pi/2 < x < \pi/2$; f is increasing on $(-\pi/2, \pi/2)$ so f has an inverse.

14. $f'(x) = \sec^2 x \geq 1$ for $-\pi/2 < x < \pi/2$; f is increasing on $(-\pi/2, \pi/2)$ so f has an inverse.

15. $y = f^{-1}(x)$, $x = f(y) = y^5$, $y = x^{1/5} = f^{-1}(x)$

16. $y = f^{-1}(x)$, $x = f(y) = 6y$, $y = \dfrac{1}{6}x = f^{-1}(x)$

17. $y = f^{-1}(x)$, $x = f(y) = 7y - 6$, $y = \dfrac{1}{7}(x + 6) = f^{-1}(x)$

18. $y = f^{-1}(x)$, $x = f(y) = \dfrac{y+1}{y-1}$, $xy - x = y + 1$, $(x - 1)y = x + 1$, $y = \dfrac{x+1}{x-1} = f^{-1}(x)$

19. $y = f^{-1}(x)$, $x = f(y) = 3y^3 - 5$, $y = \sqrt[3]{(x + 5)/3} = f^{-1}(x)$

20. $y = f^{-1}(x)$, $x = f(y) = \sqrt[5]{4y + 2}$, $y = \dfrac{1}{4}(x^5 - 2) = f^{-1}(x)$

21. $y = f^{-1}(x)$, $x = f(y) = \sqrt[3]{2y - 1}$, $y = (x^3 + 1)/2 = f^{-1}(x)$

22. $y = f^{-1}(x)$, $x = f(y) = \dfrac{5}{y^2 + 1}$, $y = \sqrt{\dfrac{5-x}{x}} = f^{-1}(x)$

23. $y = f^{-1}(x)$, $x = f(y) = 3/y^2$, $y = -\sqrt{3/x} = f^{-1}(x)$

24. $y = f^{-1}(x)$, $x = f(y) = \begin{cases} 2y, & y \le 0 \\ y^2, & y > 0 \end{cases}$, $y = f^{-1}(x) = \begin{cases} x/2, & x \le 0 \\ \sqrt{x}, & x > 0 \end{cases}$

25. $y = f^{-1}(x)$, $x = f(y) = \begin{cases} 5/2 - y, & y < 2 \\ 1/y, & y \ge 2 \end{cases}$, $y = f^{-1}(x) = \begin{cases} 5/2 - x, & x > 1/2 \\ 1/x, & x \le 1/2 \end{cases}$

26. $y = f^{-1}(x)$, $x = f(y) = 2y^3 + 5y + 3$, $\dfrac{dx}{dy} = 6y^2 + 5$, $\dfrac{dy}{dx} = \dfrac{1}{6y^2 + 5}$;

    check: $1 = 6y^2 \dfrac{dy}{dx} + 5 \dfrac{dy}{dx}$, $\dfrac{dy}{dx} = \dfrac{1}{6y^2 + 5}$.

27. $y = f^{-1}(x)$, $x = f(y) = 5y^3 + y - 7$, $\dfrac{dx}{dy} = 15y^2 + 1$, $\dfrac{dy}{dx} = \dfrac{1}{15y^2 + 1}$;

    check: $1 = 15y^2 \dfrac{dy}{dx} + \dfrac{dy}{dx}$, $\dfrac{dy}{dx} = \dfrac{1}{15y^2 + 1}$.

28. $y = f^{-1}(x)$, $x = f(y) = 1/y^2$, $\dfrac{dx}{dy} = -2y^{-3}$, $\dfrac{dy}{dx} = -y^3/2$;

    check: $1 = -2y^{-3} \dfrac{dy}{dx}$, $\dfrac{dy}{dx} = -y^3/2$.

29. $y = f^{-1}(x)$, $x = f(y) = \tan 2y$, $\dfrac{dx}{dy} = 2\sec^2 2y$, $\dfrac{dy}{dx} = \dfrac{1}{2\sec^2 2y}$;

check: $1 = (2\sec^2 2y)\dfrac{dy}{dx}$, $\dfrac{dy}{dx} = \dfrac{1}{2\sec^2 2y}$.

30. $y = f^{-1}(x)$, $x = f(y) = 5y - \sin 2y$, $\dfrac{dx}{dy} = 5 - 2\cos 2y$, $\dfrac{dy}{dx} = \dfrac{1}{5 - 2\cos 2y}$;

check: $1 = (5 - 2\cos 2y)\dfrac{dy}{dx}$, $\dfrac{dy}{dx} = \dfrac{1}{5 - 2\cos 2y}$.

31. $y = f^{-1}(x)$, $x = f(y) = 2y^5 + y^3 + 1$, $\dfrac{dx}{dy} = 10y^4 + 3y^2$, $\dfrac{dy}{dx} = \dfrac{1}{10y^4 + 3y^2}$;

check: $1 = 10y^4\dfrac{dy}{dx} + 3y^2\dfrac{dy}{dx}$, $\dfrac{dy}{dx} = \dfrac{1}{10y^4 + 3y^2}$.

32. $y = f^{-1}(x)$, $x = f(y) = y^7 + 2y^5 + y^3$, $\dfrac{dx}{dy} = 7y^6 + 10y^4 + 3y^2$, $\dfrac{dy}{dx} = \dfrac{1}{7y^6 + 10y^4 + 3y^2}$;

check: $1 = 7y^6\dfrac{dy}{dx} + 10y^4\dfrac{dy}{dx} + 3y^2\dfrac{dy}{dx}$, $\dfrac{dy}{dx} = \dfrac{1}{7y^6 + 10y^4 + 3y^2}$.

33. **(a)** $f(g(x)) = f(\sqrt{x})$
$= (\sqrt{x})^2 = x, x > 1$;
$g(f(x)) = g(x^2)$
$= \sqrt{x^2} = x, x > 1.$

(b)

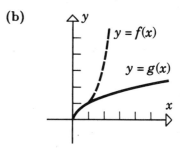

(c) No, because $f(g(x)) = x$ for every x in the domain of g is not satisfied (the domain of g is $x > 0$).

34. $y = f^{-1}(x)$, $x = f(y) = ay^2 + by + c$, $ay^2 + by + c - x = 0$, use the quadratic formula to get
$$y = \dfrac{-b \pm \sqrt{b^2 - 4a(c - x)}}{2a};$$

(a) $f^{-1}(x) = \dfrac{-b + \sqrt{b^2 - 4a(c - x)}}{2a}$ **(b)** $f^{-1}(x) = \dfrac{-b - \sqrt{b^2 - 4a(c - x)}}{2a}$

35. $y = f^{-1}(x)$, $x = f(y) = (y + 2)^4$ for $y \geq 0$, $y = f^{-1}(x) = x^{1/4} - 2$ for $x \geq 16$.

36. $y = f^{-1}(x)$, $x = f(y) = \sqrt{y+3}$ for $y \geq -3$, $y = f^{-1}(x) = x^2 - 3$ for $x \geq 0$.

37. $y = f^{-1}(x)$, $x = f(y) = -\sqrt{3 - 2y}$ for $y \leq 3/2$, $y = f^{-1}(x) = (3 - x^2)/2$ for $x \leq 0$.

38. $y = f^{-1}(x)$, $x = f(y) = 3y^2 + 5y - 2$ for $y \geq 0$, $3y^2 + 5y - 2 - x = 0$ for $y \geq 0$,
     $y = f^{-1}(x) = (-5 + \sqrt{12x + 49})/6$ for $x \geq -2$.

39. $y = f^{-1}(x)$, $x = f(y) = y - 5y^2$ for $y \geq 1$, $5y^2 - y + x = 0$ for $y \geq 1$,
     $y = f^{-1}(x) = (1 + \sqrt{1 - 20x})/10$ for $x \leq -4$.

40. $f(f(x)) = x$ thus $f = f^{-1}$ so the graph is symmetric about $y = x$.

41. (a) $f(f(x)) = \dfrac{3 - \dfrac{3 - x}{1 - x}}{1 - \dfrac{3 - x}{1 - x}} = \dfrac{3 - 3x - 3 + x}{1 - x - 3 + x} = x$ so $f = f^{-1}$

     (b) symmetric about the line $y = x$

42. $y = m(x - x_0)$ is an equation of the line. The graph of the inverse of $f(x) = m(x - x_0)$ will be
     the reflection of this line about $y = x$. Solve $y = m(x - x_0)$ for x to get $x = y/m + x_0 = f^{-1}(y)$
     so $y = f^{-1}(x) = x/m + x_0$.

43. (a) $f(x) = x^3 - 3x^2 + 2x = x(x - 1)(x - 2)$ so $f(0) = f(1) = f(2) = 0$ thus f is not one-to-one.

     (b) $f'(x) = 3x^2 - 6x + 2$, $f'(x) = 0$ when $x = \dfrac{6 \pm \sqrt{36 - 24}}{6} = 1 \pm \sqrt{3}/3$. $f'(x) > 0$ (f is
          increasing) if $x < 1 - \sqrt{3}/3$, $f'(x) < 0$ (f is decreasing) if $1 - \sqrt{3}/3 < x < 1 + \sqrt{3}/3$, so
          $f(x)$ takes on values less than $f(1 - \sqrt{3}/3)$ on both sides of $1 - \sqrt{3}/3$ thus $1 - \sqrt{3}/3$ is
          the largest value of k.

44. (a) $f(x) = x^3(x - 2)$ so $f(0) = f(2) = 0$ thus f is not one to one.
     (b) $f'(x) = 4x^3 - 6x^2 = 4x^2(x - 3/2)$, $f'(x) = 0$ when $x = 0$ or $3/2$; f is decreasing on
          $(-\infty, 3/2]$ and increasing on $[3/2, +\infty)$ so $3/2$ is the smallest value of k.

45. If $f^{-1}(x) = 1$, then $x = f(1) = 2(1)^3 + 5(1) + 3 = 10$.

46. If $f^{-1}(x) = 2$, then $x = f(2) = (2)^3/[(2)^2 + 1] = 8/5$.

47. $f'(x) = 3x^2 + 1$, $f'(2) = 13$ so $(f^{-1})'(10) = 1/13$.

48. $f'(x) = 5x^4 + 6x^2 + 1$, $f'(-1) = 12$ so $(f^{-1})'(0) = 1/12$.

49. $f'(x) = 2 \cos 2x$, $f'(\pi/12) = \sqrt{3}$ so $(f^{-1})'(1/2) = 1/\sqrt{3}$.

50. $f'(x) = 3x^2 + 2/x^2, f'(1) = 5$ so $(f^{-1})'(-1) = 1/5$.

51. (a) $f'(x) = \sqrt[3]{1+x^2} > 0$ on $(-\infty, +\infty)$ so f is one-to-one there because f is increasing.

   (b) $f(1) = 0, f'(1) = \sqrt[3]{2}$ so $(f^{-1})'(0) = 1/\sqrt[3]{2}$.

52. (a) Suppose $x_1 \neq x_2$ where x_1 and x_2 are in the domain of g and $g(x_1), g(x_2)$ are in the domain of f then $g(x_1) \neq g(x_2)$ because g is one-to-one so $f(g(x_1)) \neq f(g(x_2))$ because f is one-to-one thus $f \circ g$ is one-to-one because $(f \circ g)(x_1) \neq (f \circ g)(x_2)$ if $x_1 \neq x_2$.

   (b) f, g, and $f \circ g$ all have inverses because they are all one-to-one. Let $h = (f \circ g)^{-1}$ then $(f \circ g)(h(x)) = f[g(h(x))] = x$, apply f^{-1} to both sides to get $g(h(x)) = f^{-1}(x)$, then apply g^{-1} to get $h(x) = g^{-1}(f^{-1}(x)) = (g^{-1} \circ f^{-1})(x)$, so $h = g^{-1} \circ f^{-1}$

53.

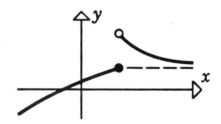

54. Suppose that g and h are both inverses of f then $f(g(x)) = x$, $h[f(g(x))] = h(x)$, but $h[f(g(x))] = g(x)$ because h is an inverse of f so $g(x) = h(x)$.

55. $F'(x) = 2f'(2g(x))g'(x)$ so $F'(3) = 2f'(2g(3))g'(3)$. By inspection $f(1) = 3$, so $g(3) = f^{-1}(3) = 1$ and $g'(3) = (f^{-1})'(3) = 1/f'(f^{-1}(3)) = 1/f'(1) = 1/7$ because $f'(x) = 4x^3 + 3x^2$. Thus $F'(3) = 2f'(2)(1/7) = 2(44)(1/7) = 88/7$.

EXERCISE SET 7.2

1. (a) -4 (b) 4 (c) $1/4$

2. (a) $1/16$ (b) 8 (c) $1/3$

3. (a) 2.9690 (b) 0.0341

4. (a) 1.8882 (b) 0.9381

5. (a) $\log_2 16 = \log_2(2^4) = 4$

   (b) $\log_2 \left(\dfrac{1}{32} \right) = \log_2(2^{-5}) = -5$

   (c) $\log_4 4 = 1$

   (d) $\log_9 3 = \log_9(9^{1/2}) = 1/2$

6. **(a)** $\log_{10}(0.001) = \log_{10}(10^{-3}) = -3$ **(b)** $\log_{10}(10^4) = 4$

     (c) $\ln(e^3) = 3$ **(d)** $\ln(\sqrt{e}) = \ln(e^{1/2}) = 1/2$

7. **(a)** 1.3655   **(b)** -0.3011 8.   **(a)** -0.5229 **(b)** 1.1447

9. **(a)** $2\ln a + \dfrac{1}{2}\ln b + \dfrac{1}{2}\ln c = 2r + s/2 + t/2.$ **(b)** $\ln b - 3\ln a - \ln c = s - 3r - t.$

10. **(a)** $\dfrac{1}{3}\ln c - \ln a - \ln b = t/3 - r - s.$ **(b)** $\dfrac{1}{2}(\ln a + 3\ln b - 2\ln c) = r/2 + 3s/2 - t.$

11. **(a)** $1 + \log x + \dfrac{1}{2}\log(x - 3)$ **(b)** $2\ln|x| + 3\ln\sin x - \dfrac{1}{2}\ln(x^2 + 1)$

12. **(a)** $\dfrac{1}{3}\log(x + 2) - \log\cos 5x$ **(b)** $\dfrac{1}{2}\ln(x^2 + 1) - \dfrac{1}{2}\ln(x^3 + 5)$

13. $\log\dfrac{2^4(16)}{3} = \log(256/3)$

14. $\log\sqrt{x} - \log(\sin^3 2x) + \log 100 = \log\dfrac{100\sqrt{x}}{\sin^3 2x}$

15. $\ln\dfrac{\sqrt[3]{x}(x + 1)^2}{\cos x}$

16. $1 + x = 10^3 = 1000,\ x = 999$ 17. $\sqrt{x} = 10^{-1} = 0.1,\ x = 0.01$

18. $x^2 = e^4,\ x = \pm e^2$ 19. $1/x = e^{-2},\ x = e^2$

20. $x = 7$ 21. $2x = 8,\ x = 4$

22. $\log_{10} x^3 = 30,\ x^3 = 10^{30},\ x = 10^{10}$ 23. $\log_{10} x = 5,\ x = 10^5$

24. $\ln 4x - \ln x^6 = \ln 2,\ \ln\dfrac{4}{x^5} = \ln 2,\ \dfrac{4}{x^5} = 2,\ x^5 = 2,\ x = \sqrt[5]{2}.$

25. $\ln 2x^2 = \ln 3,\ 2x^2 = 3,\ x^2 = 3/2,\ x = \sqrt{3/2}$ (we discard $-\sqrt{3/2}$ because it does not satisfy the original equation).

26. $\ln 3^x = \ln 2,\ x\ln 3 = \ln 2,\ x = \dfrac{\ln 2}{\ln 3}$ 27. $\ln 5^{-2x} = \ln 3,\ -2x\ln 5 = \ln 3,\ x = -\dfrac{\ln 3}{2\ln 5}$

28. $e^{-2x} = 5/3$, $-2x = \ln(5/3)$, $x = -\dfrac{1}{2}\ln(5/3)$

29. $e^{3x} = 7/2$, $3x = \ln(7/2)$, $x = \dfrac{1}{3}\ln(7/2)$

30. $e^x(1 - 2x) = 0$ so $e^x = 0$ (impossible) or $1 - 2x = 0$, $x = 1/2$

31. $e^{-x}(x + 2) = 0$ so $e^{-x} = 0$ (impossible) or $x + 2 = 0$, $x = -2$

32. $e^{2x} - e^x - 6 = 0$, $(e^x + 2)(e^x - 3) = 0$ so $e^x = -2$ (impossible) or $e^x = 3$, $x = \ln 3$

33. $e^{-2x} - 3e^{-x} + 2 = 0$, $(e^{-x} - 1)(e^{-x} - 2) = 0$; if $e^{-x} - 1 = 0$, then $x = 0$, if $e^{-x} - 2 = 0$, then $x = -\ln 2$.

34. $e^x = 2 - 2e^x$, $3e^x = 2$, $x = \ln(2/3)$

35. $4 - 12e^{2x} = 1$, $12e^{2x} = 3$, $e^{2x} = 1/4$, $x = \frac{1}{2}\ln(1/4) = -\ln 2$

36. **(a), (b)**   **(c), (d)**

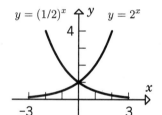   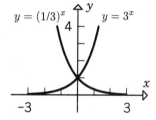

37. $\log(1/2) < 0$ so $3\log(1/2) < 2\log(1/2)$

38. **(a)** Since $b^1 = b$, it follows that $\log_b b = 1$.

(b) Let $x = \log_b a$ and $y = \log_b c$, then $a = b^x$ and $c = b^y$ so $a/c = b^x/b^y = b^{x-y}$ or equivalently, $\log_b(a/c) = x - y = \log_b a - \log_b c$.

(c) Let $x = \log_b a$, then $a = b^x$ so $a^r = (b^x)^r = b^{rx}$ or equivalently, $\log_b a^r = rx = r\log_b a$.

(d) Let $x = \log_b c$, then $c = b^x$ so $1/c = 1/b^x = b^{-x}$ or equivalently,
$\log_b(1/c) = -x = -\log_b c$.

39. **(a)** Let $x = \log_a c$, then $a^x = c$ so $\log_b a^x = \log_b c$, $x\log_b a = \log_b c$, $x = (\log_b c)/(\log_b a)$.

(b) $\log_2 7.35 = (\log 7.35)/(\log 2) = (\ln 7.35)/(\ln 2) \approx 2.8777$;
$\log_5 0.6 = (\log 0.6)/(\log 5) = (\ln 0.6)/(\ln 5) \approx -0.3174$

40. **(a)** Let $c = b$ to get $\log_a b = (\log_b b)/(\log_b a) = 1/(\log_b a)$ so $(\log_a b)(\log_b a) = 1$.

(b) $(\log_9 81)(\log_3 32) - (\log_2[3^4])(\log_3[2^5]) = (4\log_2 3)(5\log_3 2) = 20(\log_2 3)(\log_3 2) = 20$

41. $75e^{-t/125} = 15, t = -125\ln(1/5) = 125\ln 5 \approx 201$ days.

42. **(a)** If $t = 0$, then $Q = 12$ grams.

(b) $Q = 12e^{-0.055(4)} = 12e^{-0.22} \approx 9.63$ grams.

(c) $12e^{-0.055t} = 6, e^{-0.055t} = 0.5, t = -(\ln 0.5)/(0.055) \approx 12.6$ hours.

43. **(a)** 7.4; basic **(b)** 4.2; acidic **(c)** 6.4; acidic **(d)** 5.9; basic

44. **(a)** $\log[H^+] = -2.44, [H^+] = 10^{-2.44} \approx 3.6 \times 10^{-3}$ mol/L

(b) $\log[H^+] = -8.06, [H^+] = 10^{-8.06} \approx 8.7 \times 10^{-9}$ mol/L

45. **(a)** 140 dB; damage **(b)** 120 dB; damage

(c) 80 dB; no damage **(d)** 75 dB; no damage

46. Suppose that $I_1 = 3I_2$ and $L_1 = 10\log_{10} I_1/I_0$, $L_2 = 10\log_{10} I_2/I_0$. Then

$I_1/I_0 = 3I_2/I_0$, $\log_{10} I_1/I_0 = \log_{10} 3I_2/I_0 = \log_{10} 3 + \log_{10} I_2/I_0$, $L_1 = 10\log_{10} 3 + L_2$,

$L_1 - L_2 = 10\log_{10} 3 \approx 4.8$ decibels.

47. Let I_A and I_B be the intensities of the automobile and blender, respectively. Then

$\log_{10} I_A/I_0 = 7$ and $\log_{10} I_B/I_0 = 9.3$, $I_A = 10^7 I_0$ and $I_B = 10^{9.3} I_0$, so $I_B/I_A = 10^{2.3} \approx 200$.

48. The decibel level of the nth echo is $120(2/3)^n$;

$120(2/3)^n < 10$ if $(2/3)^n < 1/12, n > \dfrac{\log(1/12)}{\log(2/3)} = \dfrac{\log 12}{\log 1.5} \approx 6.13$ so 6 echoes can be heard.

49. **(a)** $\log E = 4.4 + 1.5(8.2) = 16.7, E = 10^{16.7} \approx 5 \times 10^{16}$ J

(b) Let M_1 and M_2 be the magnitudes of earthquakes with energies of E and $10E$, respectively. Then $1.5(M_2 - M_1) = \log(10E) - \log E = \log 10 = 1$,

$M_2 - M_1 = 1/1.5 = 2/3 \approx 0.67$.

50. Let E_1 and E_2 be the energies of earthquakes with magnitudes M and $M + 1$, respectively. Then $\log E_2 - \log E_1 = \log(E_2/E_1) = 1.5, E_2/E_1 = 10^{1.5} \approx 31.6$.

51. If $t = -2x$, then $x = -t/2$ and $\lim\limits_{x \to 0}(1 - 2x)^{1/x} = \lim\limits_{t \to 0}(1 + t)^{-2/t} = \lim\limits_{t \to 0}[(1 + t)^{1/t}]^{-2} = e^{-2}$.

52. If $t = 3/x$, then $x = 3/t$ and $\lim\limits_{x \to +\infty}(1 + 3/x)^x = \lim\limits_{t \to 0^+}(1 + t)^{3/t} = \lim\limits_{t \to 0^+}[(1 + t)^{1/t}]^3 = e^3$.

EXERCISE SET 7.3

1. $3x + 2 > 0, x > -2/3$

2. $1 - 2x > 0, x < 1/2$

3. $4 - x^2 > 0, x^2 < 4, -2 < x < 2$

4. $|5 - 3x| > 0$; all $x \neq 5/3$

5. $1 + \ln x \geq 0, \ln x \geq -1, x \geq e^{-1}$

6. $\ln x > 0, x > 1$

7. (a) $x^2 > 0$; all $x \neq 0$

(b) $x > 0$

8. $4/x$

9. $\dfrac{1}{2x}(2) = 1/x$

10. $\dfrac{1}{x^3}(3x^2) = 3/x$

11. $2(\ln x)\left(\dfrac{1}{x}\right) = \dfrac{2\ln x}{x}$

12. $\dfrac{1}{\sin x}(\cos x) = \cot x$

13. $\dfrac{1}{\tan x}(\sec^2 x) = \dfrac{\sec^2 x}{\tan x}$

14. $\dfrac{1}{2 + \sqrt{x}}\left(\dfrac{1}{2\sqrt{x}}\right) = \dfrac{1}{2\sqrt{x}(2 + \sqrt{x})}$

15. $\dfrac{1}{x/(1 + x^2)}\left[\dfrac{(1 + x^2)(1) - x(2x)}{(1 + x^2)^2}\right] = \dfrac{1 - x^2}{x(1 + x^2)}$

16. $\dfrac{1}{\ln x}\left(\dfrac{1}{x}\right) = \dfrac{1}{x \ln x}$

17. $\dfrac{3x^2 - 14x}{x^3 - 7x^2 - 3}$

18. $x^3\left(\dfrac{1}{x}\right) + (3x^2)\ln x = x^2(1 + 3\ln x)$

19. $\dfrac{1}{2}(\ln x)^{-1/2}\left(\dfrac{1}{x}\right) = \dfrac{1}{2x\sqrt{\ln x}}$

20. $-\dfrac{1}{x}\sin(\ln x)$

21. $\cos(5/\ln x)\dfrac{d}{dx}[5(\ln x)^{-1}] = \cos(5/\ln x)[-5(\ln x)^{-2}(1/x)] = -\dfrac{5\cos(5/\ln x)}{x(\ln x)^2}$

22. $\dfrac{1}{2\sqrt{1 + \ln^2 x}}\dfrac{d}{dx}(1 + \ln^2 x) = \dfrac{\ln x}{x\sqrt{1 + \ln^2 x}}$

23. $-\dfrac{2x^3}{3 - 2x} + 3x^2\ln(3 - 2x)$

24. $3x[\ln(x^2 - 2x)]^2 \left(\dfrac{2x - 2}{x^2 - 2x}\right) + [\ln(x^2 - 2x)]^3 = \dfrac{6(x - 1)}{x - 2}[\ln(x^2 - 2x)]^2 + [\ln(x^2 - 2x)]^3$

25. $2(x^2 + 1)[\ln(x^2 + 1)]\dfrac{2x}{x^2 + 1} + 2x[\ln(x^2 + 1)]^2 = 4x\ln(x^2 + 1) + 2x[\ln(x^2 + 1)]^2$

26. $\dfrac{(1 + \ln x)(1/x) - (\ln x)(1/x)}{(1 + \ln x)^2} = \dfrac{1}{x(1 + \ln x)^2}$

27. $\dfrac{(1 + \ln x)(2x) - x^2(0 + 1/x)}{(1 + \ln x)^2} = \dfrac{x(1 + 2\ln x)}{(1 + \ln x)^2}$

28. $\dfrac{1}{\dfrac{1 - \cos \pi x}{1 + \cos \pi x}} \dfrac{(1 + \cos \pi x)(\pi \sin \pi x) - (1 - \cos \pi x)(-\pi \sin \pi x)}{(1 + \cos \pi x)^2}$

$= \dfrac{2\pi \sin \pi x}{(1 - \cos \pi x)(1 + \cos \pi x)} = \dfrac{2\pi \sin \pi x}{1 - \cos^2 \pi x} = \dfrac{2\pi \sin \pi x}{\sin^2 \pi x} = 2\pi \csc \pi x$

29. $\dfrac{dy}{dx} + \dfrac{1}{xy}\left(x\dfrac{dy}{dx} + y\right) = 0, \ \dfrac{dy}{dx} = -\dfrac{y}{x(y + 1)}$

30. $\dfrac{dy}{dx} = \dfrac{1}{x \tan y}\left(x \sec^2 y\dfrac{dy}{dx} + \tan y\right), \ \dfrac{dy}{dx} = \dfrac{\tan y}{x(\tan y - \sec^2 y)}$

31. $\dfrac{1}{2}\ln|x| + C$

32. $u = x^5 + 1, \ du = 5x^4 dx, \ \displaystyle\int \dfrac{1}{u}du = \ln|u| + C = \ln|x^5 + 1| + C$

33. $u = x^3 - 4, \ du = 3x^2 dx, \ \dfrac{1}{3}\displaystyle\int \dfrac{1}{u}du = \dfrac{1}{3}\ln|x^3 - 4| + C$

34. $\displaystyle\int \left(1 + \dfrac{1}{t}\right) dt = t + \ln|t| + C$

35. $u = \tan x, \ du = \sec^2 x\, dx, \ \displaystyle\int \dfrac{1}{u}du = \ln|\tan x| + C$

36. $\displaystyle\int \dfrac{\cos x}{\sin x}dx = \ln|\sin x| + C$

37. $u = 1 + \cos 3\theta, \ du = -3\sin 3\theta d\theta$

$-\dfrac{1}{3}\displaystyle\int \dfrac{1}{u}du = -\dfrac{1}{3}\ln|1 + \cos 3\theta| + C = -\dfrac{1}{3}\ln(1 + \cos 3\theta) + C \ \text{because } 1 + \cos 3\theta \geq 0$

38. $u = \ln x, \; du = \dfrac{1}{x} dx, \; \displaystyle\int \frac{1}{u} du = \ln|\ln x| + C$

39. divide $x^2 + 1$ into x^3 to get

$$\int \frac{x^3}{x^2+1} dx = \int \left[x - \frac{x}{x^2+1}\right] dx = \int x \, dx - \int \frac{x}{x^2+1} dx = \frac{1}{2}x^2 - \frac{1}{2}\ln(x^2+1) + C$$

40. $u = \ln x, \; du = \dfrac{1}{x} dx, \; \displaystyle\int \cos u \, du = \sin(\ln x) + C$

41. $u = \ln y, \; du = \dfrac{1}{y} dy, \; \displaystyle\int u^3 du = \frac{1}{4}(\ln y)^4 + C$

42. $u = 1 - 2\sqrt{x}, \; du = -\dfrac{1}{\sqrt{x}} dx, \; -\displaystyle\int \frac{1}{u} du = -\ln|1 - 2\sqrt{x}| + C$

43. $u = 3x + 2, \; \dfrac{1}{3}\displaystyle\int_2^5 \frac{1}{u} du = \frac{1}{3}\ln|u|\Big]_2^5 = \frac{1}{3}(\ln 5 - \ln 2) = \frac{1}{3}\ln\frac{5}{2}$

44. $u = 1 - 2x, \; -\dfrac{3}{2}\displaystyle\int_{-1}^{-7} \frac{1}{u} du = -\frac{3}{2}\ln|u|\Big]_{-1}^{-7} = -\frac{3}{2}(\ln 7 - \ln 1) = -\frac{3}{2}\ln 7$

45. $u = x^2 + 5, \; \dfrac{1}{2}\displaystyle\int_6^5 \frac{1}{u} du = \frac{1}{2}\ln|u|\Big]_6^5 = \frac{1}{2}(\ln 5 - \ln 6) = \frac{1}{2}\ln\frac{5}{6}$

46. $u = 1 + \sqrt{x}, \; 2\displaystyle\int_2^3 \frac{1}{u} du = 2\ln|u|\Big]_2^3 = 2(\ln 3 - \ln 2) = 2\ln\frac{3}{2}$

47. $\dfrac{d}{dx}\left[\ln\cos x - \dfrac{1}{2}\ln(4 - 3x^2)\right] = -\tan x + \dfrac{3x}{4 - 3x^2}$

48. $\dfrac{d}{dx}\left(\dfrac{1}{2}[\ln(x-1) - \ln(x+1)]\right) = \dfrac{1}{2}\left(\dfrac{1}{x-1} - \dfrac{1}{x+1}\right)$

49. $\dfrac{d}{dx}\left[\dfrac{1}{2}\ln x + \dfrac{1}{3}\ln(x+3) + \dfrac{1}{5}\ln(3x-2)\right] = \dfrac{1}{2x} + \dfrac{1}{3(x+3)} + \dfrac{3}{5(3x-2)}$

50. $\dfrac{d}{dx}\left[\dfrac{1}{2}\ln x + \dfrac{1}{3}\ln(x+1) - \ln\sin x - \ln\sec x\right] = \dfrac{1}{2x} + \dfrac{1}{3(x+1)} - \cot x - \tan x$

51. $\ln|y| = \ln|x| + \dfrac{1}{3}\ln|1 + x^2|, \; \dfrac{dy}{dx} = x^3\sqrt{1 + x^2}\left[\dfrac{1}{x} + \dfrac{2x}{3(1 + x^2)}\right]$

52. $\ln|y| = \dfrac{1}{5}[\ln|x-1| - \ln|x+1|]$, $\dfrac{dy}{dx} = \dfrac{1}{5}\sqrt[5]{\dfrac{x-1}{x+1}}\left[\dfrac{1}{x-1} - \dfrac{1}{x+1}\right]$

53. $\ln|y| = \dfrac{1}{3}\ln|x^2 - 8| + \dfrac{1}{2}\ln|x^3 + 1| - \ln|x^6 - 7x + 5|$

$\dfrac{dy}{dx} = \dfrac{(x^2-8)^{1/3}\sqrt{x^3+1}}{x^6 - 7x + 5}\left[\dfrac{2x}{3(x^2-8)} + \dfrac{3x^2}{2(x^3+1)} - \dfrac{6x^5 - 7}{x^6 - 7x + 5}\right]$

54. $\ln|y| = \ln|\sin x| + \ln|\cos x| + 3\ln|\tan x| - \dfrac{1}{2}\ln|x|$

$\dfrac{dy}{dx} = \dfrac{\sin x \cos x \tan^3 x}{\sqrt{x}}\left[\cot x - \tan x + \dfrac{3\sec^2 x}{\tan x} - \dfrac{1}{2x}\right]$

55. **(a)** $u = \dfrac{ab}{t}$, $t = \dfrac{ab}{u}$, $dt = -\dfrac{ab}{u^2}du$, $\displaystyle\int_a^{ab}\dfrac{1}{t}dt = \int_b^1\dfrac{u}{ab}\left(-\dfrac{ab}{u^2}\right)du = \int_1^b\dfrac{1}{u}du = \int_1^b\dfrac{1}{t}dt$

(b) $\ln(ab) = \displaystyle\int_1^{ab}\dfrac{1}{t}dt = \int_1^a\dfrac{1}{t}dt + \int_a^{ab}\dfrac{1}{t}dt = \int_1^a\dfrac{1}{t}dt + \int_1^b\dfrac{1}{t}dt = \ln a + \ln b$

56. $\Delta x = 0.1$, $c_k = 1 + 0.1k$, $d_k = 1 + 0.1(k-1)$

$A_1 = \displaystyle\sum_{k=1}^{10}\dfrac{1}{c_k}\Delta x > 0.6687$, $A_2 = \sum_{k=1}^{10}\dfrac{1}{d_k}\Delta x < 0.7188$; $\ln 2 \approx 0.6931$

57. $\log_b x = \dfrac{\ln x}{\ln b}$, $\dfrac{d}{dx}[\log_b x] = \dfrac{1}{\ln b}\cdot\dfrac{1}{x}$

58. $\log_x e = \dfrac{\ln e}{\ln x} = \dfrac{1}{\ln x}$, $\dfrac{d}{dx}[\log_x e] = -\dfrac{1}{x(\ln x)^2}$

59. $\log_x 2 = \dfrac{\ln 2}{\ln x}$, $\dfrac{d}{dx}[\log_x 2] = -\dfrac{\ln 2}{x(\ln x)^2}$

60. $\dfrac{1}{n+k} = \dfrac{1}{1+k/n}\dfrac{1}{n}$ so $\displaystyle\sum_{k=1}^{n}\dfrac{1}{n+k} = \sum_{k=1}^{n}f(x_k^*)\Delta x$ where $f(x) = \dfrac{1}{1+x}$, $x_k^* = \dfrac{k}{n}$, and $\Delta x = \dfrac{1}{n}$

for $0 \le x \le 1$. Thus $\displaystyle\lim_{n\to+\infty}\sum_{k=1}^{n}\dfrac{1}{n+k} = \lim_{n\to+\infty}\sum_{k=1}^{n}f(x_k^*)\Delta x = \int_0^1\dfrac{1}{1+x}dx = \ln 2$.

61. $\dfrac{k}{n^2+k^2} = \dfrac{k/n}{1+k^2/n^2}\dfrac{1}{n}$ so $\displaystyle\sum_{k=1}^{n}\dfrac{k}{n^2+k^2} = \sum_{k=1}^{n}f(x_k^*)\Delta x$ where $f(x) = \dfrac{x}{1+x^2}$, $x_k^* = \dfrac{k}{n}$, and

$\Delta x = \dfrac{1}{n}$, $0 \le x \le 1$; $\displaystyle\lim_{n\to+\infty}\sum_{k=1}^{n}\dfrac{k}{n^2+k^2} = \lim_{n\to+\infty}\sum_{k=1}^{n}f(x_k^*)\Delta x = \int_0^1\dfrac{x}{1+x^2}dx = \dfrac{1}{2}\ln 2$.

62. $f'(1) = \lim\limits_{h \to 0} \dfrac{\ln(1+h) - \ln 1}{h} = \lim\limits_{h \to 0} \dfrac{\ln(1+h)}{h} = \dfrac{1}{x}\Big|_{x=1} = 1.$

63. Let $f(x) = x^2 - \ln x$, then $f'(x) = 2x - 1/x = (2x^2 - 1)/x$; $f'(x) = 0$ if $x = 1/\sqrt{2}$ at which there is a relative minimum and hence the absolute minimum on $(0, +\infty)$. The minimum value is $1/2 - \ln(1/\sqrt{2}) = (1 + \ln 2)/2.$

64. Let $f(x) = \sqrt{x}\ln x$, then $f'(x) = 1/\sqrt{x} + (\ln x)/(2\sqrt{x}) = (2 + \ln x)/(2\sqrt{x})$; $f'(x) = 0$ if $2 + \ln x = 0, \ln x = -2, x = e^{-2}$ at which the absolute minimum occurs. The minimum value is $-2/e.$

65. Let $f(x) = (\ln^2 x)/x$, then $f'(x) = (2\ln x - \ln^2 x)/x^2 = (2 - \ln x)(\ln x)/x^2$; $f'(x) = 0$ if $x = 1$ or $x = e^2$, at which there is a relative minimum and a relative maximum, respectively. The relative minimum value is $f(1) = 0$; the relative maximum value is $f(e^2) = 4/e^2.$

66. $f(x) = \sqrt{x} - \ln x$, $f'(x) = \dfrac{1}{2\sqrt{x}} - \dfrac{1}{x} = \dfrac{\sqrt{x} - 2}{2\sqrt{x}}$, $f'(x) = 0$ when $x = 4$; $f(x)$ has a relative minimum, and hence the absolute minimum, at $x = 4$ so $f(x) \geq f(4) = 2 - \ln 2 > 0$, $\sqrt{x} - \ln x > 0, \ln x < \sqrt{x}.$

67. Let $f(x) = x - 1 - \ln x$, then $f'(x) = 1 - 1/x = (x - 1)/x$, $f'(x) = 0$ when $x = 1$ where the minimum value occurs, so $f(x) \geq f(1) = 0, x - 1 - \ln x \geq 0, \ln x \leq x - 1.$

68. Let $f(x) = 1 - 1/x - \ln x$, then $f'(x) = 1/x^2 - 1/x = (1 - x)/x^2$, $f'(x) = 0$ when $x = 1$ where the maximum value occurs, so $f(x) \leq f(1) = 0, 1 - 1/x - \ln x \leq 0, \ln x \geq 1 - 1/x.$

69. $p = c/v$ so the average pressure with respect to volume is

$$p_{ave} = \frac{1}{v_1 - v_0} \int_{v_0}^{v_1} \frac{c}{v}\,dv = \frac{c}{v_1 - v_0}(\ln v_1 - \ln v_0) = \frac{c}{v_1 - v_0}\ln(v_1/v_0)$$

70. **(a)** $A = \displaystyle\int_1^b \frac{1}{x}\,dx = \ln x\Big]_1^b = \ln b$; $\lim\limits_{b \to +\infty} A = +\infty$

  (b) $V = \pi\displaystyle\int_1^b \frac{1}{x^2}\,dx = -\frac{\pi}{x}\Big]_1^b = \pi(1 - 1/b)$; $\lim\limits_{b \to +\infty} V = \pi$

71. $A = \displaystyle\int_0^{\pi/3} \tan x\,dx = \int_0^{\pi/3} \frac{\sin x}{\cos x}\,dx = -\ln|\cos x|\,\Big]_0^{\pi/3} = \ln 2$

72. Washers: $V = \int_{1/9}^{4} \pi \left(9 - \frac{1}{y}\right) dy = \pi(9y - \ln y)\Big]_{1/9}^{4} = \pi(35 - \ln 36);$

   shells: $V = \int_{1/2}^{3} 2\pi \, x(4 - 1/x^2) dx = 2\pi(2x^2 - \ln x)\Big]_{1/2}^{3} = \pi(35 - \ln 36).$

73. $V = \pi \int_{1}^{4} \frac{1}{x} dx = \pi \ln |x|\Big]_{1}^{4} = \pi \ln 4$

74. $f(x) = \sin x - \ln x, x_{n+1} = x_n - \dfrac{\sin x_n - \ln x_n}{\cos x_n - 1/x_n};$

   $x_1 = 2.2, x_2 = 2.219212031, x_3 = 2.219107152, x_4 = x_5 = 2.219107149.$

75. $f(x) = \ln x - x + 2, x_{n+1} = x_n - \dfrac{\ln x_n - x_n + 2}{1/x_n - 1};$

   $x_1 = 0.2, x_2 = 0.152359478, x_3 = 0.158447821, \cdots, x_5 = x_6 = 0.158594340;$

   $x_1 = 3, x_2 = 3.147918433, x_3 = 3.146193441, x_4 = x_5 = 3.146193221.$

EXERCISE SET 7.4

1. (a) $x^{-1}, x > 0$ (b) $x^2, x \neq 0$

   (c) $-x^2, -\infty < x < +\infty$ (d) $-x, -\infty < x < +\infty$

   (e) $x^3, x > 0$ (f) $\ln x + x, x > 0$

   (g) $x - \sqrt[3]{x}, -\infty < x < +\infty$ (h) $\dfrac{e^x}{x}, x > 0$

2. $f(\ln 3) = e^{-2\ln 3} = e^{\ln(1/9)} = 1/9$

3. $f(\ln 2) = e^{\ln 2} + 3e^{-\ln 2} = 2 + 3e^{\ln(1/2)} = 2 + 3/2 = 7/2$

4. (a) $3^\pi = e^{\pi \ln 3}$ (b) $2^{\sqrt{2}} = e^{\sqrt{2}\ln 2}$

5. (a) $\pi^{-x} = e^{-x \ln \pi}$ (b) $x^{2x} = e^{2x \ln x}$

6. $7e^{7x}$ 7. $-10xe^{-5x^2}$ 8. $-\dfrac{1}{x^2} e^{1/x}$

9. $x^3 e^x + 3x^2 e^x = x^2 e^x(x + 3)$ 10. $e^x \cos(e^x)$

11. $\dfrac{dy}{dx} = \dfrac{(e^x + e^{-x})(e^x + e^{-x}) - (e^x - e^{-x})(e^x - e^{-x})}{(e^x + e^{-x})^2}$

$\qquad = \dfrac{(e^{2x} + 2 + e^{-2x}) - (e^{2x} - 2 + e^{-2x})}{(e^x + e^{-x})^2} = 4/(e^x + e^{-x})^2$

12. $\dfrac{dy}{dx} = \dfrac{(\ln x)e^x - e^x(1/x)}{(\ln x)^2} = \dfrac{e^x(x \ln x - 1)}{x(\ln x)^2}$

13. $(x \sec^2 x + \tan x)e^{x \tan x}$

14. $\dfrac{15}{2}x^2(1 + 5x^3)^{-1/2} \exp(\sqrt{1 + 5x^3})$

15. $(1 - 3e^{3x})e^{(x - e^{3x})}$

16. $\dfrac{1}{\cos(e^x)}[-\sin(e^x)]e^x = -e^x \tan(e^x)$

17. $\dfrac{(x - 1)e^{-x}}{1 - xe^{-x}} = \dfrac{x - 1}{e^x - x}$

18. $\dfrac{e^x}{2\sqrt{1 + e^x}}$

19. $e^{ax}(a \cos bx - b \sin bx)$

20. $\dfrac{abe^{-x}}{(1 + be^{-x})^2}$

21. $y = e^{\ln(x^3 + 1)} = x^3 + 1, \ dy/dx = 3x^2$

22. $f'(x) = 2^x \ln 2; \ y = 2^x, \ \ln y = x \ln 2, \ \dfrac{1}{y}y' = \ln 2, \ y' = y \ln 2 = 2^x \ln 2$

23. $f'(x) = -3^{-x} \ln 3; \ y = 3^{-x}, \ \ln y = -x \ln 3, \ \dfrac{1}{y}y' = -\ln 3, \ y' = -y \ln 3 = -3^{-x} \ln 3$

24. $f'(x) = \pi^{\sin x}(\ln \pi) \cos x;$

$\qquad y = \pi^{\sin x}, \ \ln y = (\sin x) \ln \pi, \ \dfrac{1}{y}y' = (\ln \pi) \cos x, \ y' = \pi^{\sin x}(\ln \pi) \cos x$

25. $f'(x) = \pi^{x \tan x}(\ln \pi)(x \sec^2 x + \tan x);$

$\qquad y = \pi^{x \tan x}, \ \ln y = (x \tan x) \ln \pi, \ \dfrac{1}{y}y' = (\ln \pi)(x \sec^2 x + \tan x)$

$\qquad y' = \pi^{x \tan x}(\ln \pi)(x \sec^2 x + \tan x)$

26. $f'(x) = (\sqrt{2})^{x \ln x}(\ln \sqrt{2})(1 + \ln x);$

$\qquad y = (\sqrt{2})^{x \ln x}, \ \ln y = (x \ln x) \ln \sqrt{2}, \ \dfrac{1}{y}y' = (\ln \sqrt{2})(1 + \ln x),$

$\qquad y' = (\sqrt{2})^{x \ln x}(\ln \sqrt{2})(1 + \ln x)$

27. **(a)** Because x^x is not of the form a^x where a is constant.

(b) $y = x^x$, $\ln y = x \ln x$, $\dfrac{1}{y} y' = 1 + \ln x$, $y' = x^x(1 + \ln x)$

28. $\ln y = (\sin x) \ln x$, $\dfrac{1}{y} \dfrac{dy}{dx} = \dfrac{\sin x}{x} + (\cos x) \ln x$, $\dfrac{dy}{dx} = x^{\sin x} \left[\dfrac{\sin x}{x} + (\cos x) \ln x \right]$

29. $\ln y = (\ln x) \ln(x^3 - 2x)$, $\dfrac{1}{y} \dfrac{dy}{dx} = \dfrac{3x^2 - 2}{x^3 - 2x} \ln x + \dfrac{1}{x} \ln(x^3 - 2x)$,

$\dfrac{dy}{dx} = (x^3 - 2x)^{\ln x} \left[\dfrac{3x^2 - 2}{x^3 - 2x} \ln x + \dfrac{1}{x} \ln(x^3 - 2x) \right]$

30. $\ln y = (\ln x) \ln(x^2 + 3)$, $\dfrac{1}{y} \dfrac{dy}{dx} = \dfrac{2x}{x^2 + 3} \ln x + \dfrac{1}{x} \ln(x^2 + 3)$,

$\dfrac{dy}{dx} = (x^2 + 3)^{\ln x} \left[\dfrac{2x}{x^2 + 3} \ln x + \dfrac{1}{x} \ln(x^2 + 3) \right]$

31. $\ln y = (\tan x) \ln(\ln x)$, $\dfrac{1}{y} \dfrac{dy}{dx} = \dfrac{1}{x \ln x} \tan x + (\sec^2 x) \ln(\ln x)$,

$\dfrac{dy}{dx} = (\ln x)^{\tan x} \left[\dfrac{\tan x}{x \ln x} + (\sec^2 x) \ln(\ln x) \right]$

32. $\ln y = \dfrac{1}{x} \ln(1 + x)$, $\dfrac{1}{y} \dfrac{dy}{dx} = \dfrac{1}{x(1 + x)} - \dfrac{1}{x^2} \ln(1 + x)$,

$\dfrac{dy}{dx} = (1 + x)^{1/x} \left[\dfrac{1}{x(1 + x)} - \dfrac{1}{x^2} \ln(1 + x) \right]$

33. $\ln y = e^x \ln x$, $\dfrac{1}{y} \dfrac{dy}{dx} = \dfrac{e^x}{x} + e^x \ln x$, $\dfrac{dy}{dx} = x^{(e^x)} \left[\dfrac{e^x}{x} + e^x \ln x \right]$

34. $y = e^{3x}$, $y' = 3e^{3x}$, $y'' = 9e^{3x}$ so $y'' - 9y = 9e^{3x} - 9(e^{3x}) = 0$;

$y = e^{-3x}$, $y' = -3e^{-3x}$, $y'' = 9e^{-3x}$ so $y'' - 9y = 9e^{-3x} - 9(e^{-3x}) = 0$.

35. $y = Ae^{2x} + Be^{-4x}$, $y' = 2Ae^{2x} - 4Be^{-4x}$, $y'' = 4Ae^{2x} + 16Be^{-4x}$ so

$y'' + 2y' - 8y = (4Ae^{2x} + 16Be^{-4x}) + 2(2Ae^{2x} - 4Be^{-4x}) - 8(Ae^{2x} + Be^{-4x}) = 0$.

36. $y = Ae^{kt}$, $dy/dt = kAe^{kt} = k(Ae^{kt}) = ky$.

37. **(a)** $f'(x) = ke^{kx}$, $f''(x) = k^2 e^{kx}$, $f'''(x) = k^3 e^{kx}, \ldots, f^{(n)}(x) = k^n e^{kx}$

(b) $f'(x) = -ke^{-kx}$, $f''(x) = k^2 e^{-kx}$, $f'''(x) = -k^3 e^{-kx}, \ldots, f^{(n)}(x) = (-1)^n k^n e^{-kx}$

38. $\dfrac{dy}{dt} = e^{-\lambda t}(\omega A \cos \omega t - \omega B \sin \omega t) + (-\lambda)e^{-\lambda t}(A \sin \omega t + B \cos \omega t)$

   $= e^{-\lambda t}[(\omega A - \lambda B)\cos \omega t - (\omega B + \lambda A)\sin \omega t]$

39. $f'(x) = \dfrac{1}{\sqrt{2\pi}\sigma} \exp\left[-\dfrac{1}{2}\left(\dfrac{x-\mu}{\sigma}\right)^2\right] \dfrac{d}{dx}\left[-\dfrac{1}{2}\left(\dfrac{x-\mu}{\sigma}\right)^2\right]$

   $= \dfrac{1}{\sqrt{2\pi}\sigma} \exp\left[-\dfrac{1}{2}\left(\dfrac{x-\mu}{\sigma}\right)^2\right]\left[-\left(\dfrac{x-\mu}{\sigma}\right)\left(\dfrac{1}{\sigma}\right)\right]$

   $= -\dfrac{1}{\sqrt{2\pi}\sigma^3}(x-\mu)\exp\left[-\dfrac{1}{2}\left(\dfrac{x-\mu}{\sigma}\right)^2\right]$

40. $\displaystyle\int e^{-x}\,dx = -e^{-x} + C$ **41.** $-\dfrac{1}{5}e^{-5x} + C$

42. $e^{\tan x} + C$ **43.** $e^{\sin x} + C$

44. $\dfrac{1}{4}\displaystyle\int e^{x^4}(4x^3)\,dx = \dfrac{1}{4}e^{x^4} + C$ **45.** $-\dfrac{1}{6}\displaystyle\int e^{-2x^3}(-6x^2)\,dx = -\dfrac{1}{6}e^{-2x^3} + C$

46. $u = e^x - e^{-x}$, $du = (e^x + e^{-x})dx$, $\displaystyle\int \dfrac{1}{u}du = \ln\left|e^x - e^{-x}\right| + C$

47. $u = 1 + e^x$, $du = e^x dx$, $\displaystyle\int \dfrac{1}{u}du = \ln(1 + e^x) + C$

48. $\displaystyle\int e^{x/2}\,dx = 2e^{x/2} + C = 2\sqrt{e^x} + C$

49. $u = 1 + e^{2t}$, $du = 2e^{2t}dt$, $\dfrac{1}{2}\displaystyle\int u^{1/2}du = \dfrac{1}{3}(1 + e^{2t})^{3/2} + C$

50. $u = x^2 + 6x$, $du = 2(x + 3)dx$, $\dfrac{1}{2}\displaystyle\int \exp(u)du = \dfrac{1}{2}\exp(x^2 + 6x) + C$

51. $\displaystyle\int e^{\sin x}\cos x\,dx = e^{\sin x} + C = \exp(\sin x) + C$

52. $u = 1 + e^x$, $du = e^x dx$, $\displaystyle\int \sin u\,du = -\cos(1 + e^x) + C$

53. $u = 2 - e^{-x}$, $du = e^{-x}dx$, $\displaystyle\int \sec^2 u\,du = \tan(2 - e^{-x}) + C$

54. $\dfrac{2^{5x}}{5\ln 2} + C$

55. $\dfrac{\pi^{\sin x}}{\ln \pi} + C$

56. $\dfrac{e}{3}x^3 - \left(\dfrac{1}{2}\ln 2\right)\cos x + C$

57. $\dfrac{1}{2}x^2 \ln 3 - 4\pi e^2 \sin x + C$

58. $e^{2\ln x} = e^{\ln x^2} = x^2,\ x > 0,$ so $\displaystyle\int e^{2\ln x}\,dx = \int x^2\,dx = \dfrac{1}{3}x^3 + C$

59. $\ln(e^x) + \ln(e^{-x}) = \ln(e^x e^{-x}) = \ln 1 = 0$ so $\displaystyle\int [\ln(e^x) + \ln(e^{-x})]\,dx = C$

60. $u = \sqrt{y},\ du = \dfrac{1}{2\sqrt{y}}dy,\ 2\displaystyle\int \dfrac{1}{e^u}du = 2\int e^{-u}\,du = -2e^{-\sqrt{y}} + C$

61. $u = \sqrt{y},\ du = \dfrac{1}{2\sqrt{y}}dy,\ 2\displaystyle\int e^u\,du = 2e^{\sqrt{y}} + C$

62. $-\dfrac{1}{3}e^{-3x}\Big]_0^{\ln 2} = -\dfrac{1}{3}(e^{-3\ln 2} - e^0) = -\dfrac{1}{3}\left(\dfrac{1}{8} - 1\right) = 7/24$

63. $u = 3 - 4e^x,\ du = -4e^x dx,\ u = -1$ when $x = 0,\ u = -17$ when $x = \ln 5$

$-\dfrac{1}{4}\displaystyle\int_{-1}^{-17} u\,du = -\dfrac{1}{8}u^2\Big]_{-1}^{-17} = -36$

64. $u = -x^2,\ du = -2x\,dx,\ u = -1$ when $x = 1,\ u = -2$ when $x = \sqrt{2}$

$-\dfrac{1}{2}\displaystyle\int_{-1}^{-2} 4^u\,du = -\dfrac{1}{2}\dfrac{4^u}{\ln 4}\Big]_{-1}^{-2} = -\dfrac{1}{2\ln 4}(4^{-2} - 4^{-1}) = \dfrac{3}{64\ln 2}$

65. $3x - e^x\big]_1^2 = 3 + e - e^2$

66. $\ln(x + e)\big]_0^e = \ln(2e) - \ln e = \ln 2$

67. $u = e^x + 4,\ du = e^x dx,\ u = e^{-\ln 3} + 4 = \dfrac{1}{3} + 4 = \dfrac{13}{3}$ when $x = -\ln 3,$

$u = e^{\ln 3} + 4 = 3 + 4 = 7$ when $x = \ln 3,\ \displaystyle\int_{13/3}^{7} \dfrac{1}{u}du = \ln u\Big]_{13/3}^{7} = \ln(7) - \ln(13/3) = \ln(21/13)$

68. Multiply both sides of the equation by $e^{1/x}$ to get $e^{2/x} - 1 = 0,\ e^{2/x} = 1,\ 2/x = \ln 1 = 0,$ which has no solution.

69. $g(x) = e^{-x}f(x),\ g'(x) = e^{-x}f'(x) - e^{-x}f(x) = e^{-x}[f'(x) - f(x)] = 0$ if $f'(x) = f(x)$ thus $g(x) = k$ because $g'(x) = 0$ so $e^{-x}f(x) = k,\ f(x) = ke^x.$

70. $x = ae^{kt} + be^{-kt}$, $dx/dt = ake^{kt} - bke^{-kt}$,
$d^2x/dt^2 = ak^2e^{kt} + bk^2e^{-kt} = k^2(ae^{kt} + be^{-kt}) = k^2x$

71. $2^x = 3^{x+1}$, $\ln(2^x) = \ln(3^{x+1})$, $x\ln 2 = (x+1)\ln 3$, $x\ln 2 = x\ln 3 + \ln 3$,
$x(\ln 2 - \ln 3) = \ln 3$, $x = \dfrac{\ln 3}{\ln 2 - \ln 3} = \dfrac{\ln 3}{\ln(2/3)}$

72. Let $P(x_0, y_0)$ be a point on $y = e^{3x}$ then $y_0 = e^{3x_0}$. $dy/dx = 3e^{3x}$ so $m_{\tan} = 3e^{3x_0}$ at P and an equation of the tangent line at P is $y - y_0 = 3e^{3x_0}(x - x_0)$, $y - e^{3x_0} = 3e^{3x_0}(x - x_0)$. If the line passes through the origin then $(0,0)$ must satisfy the equation so $-e^{3x_0} = -3x_0 e^{3x_0}$ which gives $x_0 = 1/3$ and thus $y_0 = e$. The point is $(1/3, e)$.

73. $f'(x) = exe^{-1}$

74. (a) $y' = -xe^{-x} + e^{-x} = e^{-x}(1 - x)$, $xy' = xe^{-x}(1 - x) = y(1 - x)$
(b) $y' = -x^2 e^{-x^2/2} + e^{-x^2/2} = e^{-x^2/2}(1 - x^2)$, $xy' = xe^{-x^2/2}(1 - x^2) = y(1 - x^2)$

75. $\dfrac{dk}{dT} = k_0 \exp\left[-\dfrac{q}{2}\dfrac{T - T_0}{T_0 T}\right]\left(-\dfrac{q}{2T^2}\right) = -\dfrac{qk_0}{2T^2}\exp\left[-\dfrac{q}{2}\dfrac{T - T_0}{T_0 T}\right]$

76. Multiply both sides of the equation by e^y and rearrange to get $e^{2y} - xe^y - 1 = 0$ which is quadratic in e^y so, by the quadratic formula, $e^y = \dfrac{1}{2}(x \pm \sqrt{x^2 + 4})$. Because e^y must be positive we take $e^y = \dfrac{1}{2}(x + \sqrt{x^2 + 4})$ so $y = \ln\left[\dfrac{1}{2}(x + \sqrt{x^2 + 4})\right]$.

77. Divide $e^x + 3$ into e^{2x} to get $\dfrac{e^{2x}}{e^x + 3} = e^x - \dfrac{3e^x}{e^x + 3}$ so
$$\int \dfrac{e^{2x}}{e^x + 3}dx = \int e^x dx - 3\int \dfrac{e^x}{e^x + 3}dx = e^x - 3\ln(e^x + 3) + C$$

78. $y = f^{-1}(x)$, $x = f(y) = e^{2y+1}$, $2y + 1 = \ln x$, $y = \dfrac{1}{2}(\ln x - 1) = f^{-1}(x)$

79. $y = f^{-1}(x)$, $x = f(y) = e^{1/y}$, $1/y = \ln x$, $y = \dfrac{1}{\ln x} = f^{-1}(x)$

80. $y = f^{-1}(x)$, $x = f(y) = 4\ln(y + 1)$, $y + 1 = e^{x/4}$, $y = e^{x/4} - 1 = f^{-1}(x)$

81. $y = f^{-1}(x)$, $x = f(y) = 1 - \ln(3y)$, $\ln(3y) = 1 - x$, $y = \dfrac{1}{3}e^{1-x} = f^{-1}(x)$

82. $\displaystyle\sum_{k=1}^{n}\frac{e^{k/n}}{n} = \sum_{k=1}^{n}f(x_k^*)\Delta x$ where $f(x) = e^x, x_k^* = k/n$, and $\Delta x = 1/n$ for $0 \le x \le 1$. Thus

$$\lim_{n\to+\infty}\sum_{k=1}^{n}\frac{e^{k/n}}{n} = \lim_{n\to+\infty}\sum_{k=1}^{n}f(x_k^*)\Delta x = \int_0^1 e^x\,dx = e - 1.$$

83. Let $f(x) = x^3 e^{-2x}$, then $f'(x) = -2x^3 e^{-2x} + 3x^2 e^{-2x} = x^2 e^{-2x}(3 - 2x); f'(x) = 0$ if $x = 0$ or $x = 3/2$. The maximum value occurs at $x = 3/2$ so the maximum value is $f(3/2) = (27/8)e^{-3}$.

84. Let $f(x) = 1 + x - e^x$, then $f'(x) = 1 - e^x, f'(x) = 0$ when $x = 0$ where the maximum value occurs, so $f(x) \le f(0) = 0, 1 + x - e^x \le 0, e^x \ge 1 + x$.

85. $A = \displaystyle\int_0^{\ln 3}(3 - e^x)\,dx$

$\qquad = (3x - e^x)]_0^{\ln 3} = 3\ln 3 - 2$

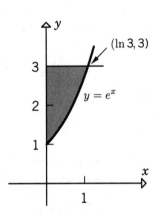

86. $\displaystyle\int_0^k e^{2x}\,dx = 3, \frac{1}{2}e^{2x}\Big]_0^k = 3, \frac{1}{2}(e^{2k} - 1) = 3, e^{2k} = 7, k = \frac{1}{2}\ln 7.$

87. $V = \pi\displaystyle\int_0^{\ln 3} e^{2x}\,dx = \frac{\pi}{2}e^{2x}\Big]_0^{\ln 3} = 4\pi.$

88. **(b)** $V = 2\pi\displaystyle\int_0^2 xe^x\,dx = 2\pi(xe^x - e^x)\Big]_0^2 = 2\pi(e^2 + 1).$

89. The area of the region shown in the diagram is $A = \displaystyle\int_1^5 \ln x\,dx$.

If $y = \ln x$, then $x = e^y$ so

$A = \displaystyle\int_0^{\ln 5}(5 - e^y)\,dy = (5y - e^y)\Big]_0^{\ln 5}$

$\qquad = 5\ln 5 - 4.$

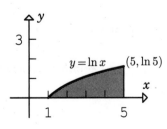

90. The volume of the solid obtained
by revolving the region shown in
the diagram about the y-axis is

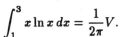

$$V = 2\pi \int_1^3 x \ln x \, dx \text{ so}$$

$$\int_1^3 x \ln x \, dx = \frac{1}{2\pi} V.$$

By the method of washers,

$$V = \pi \int_0^{\ln 3} (9 - e^{2y}) dy = \pi \left(9y - \frac{1}{2} e^{2y} \right) \Big]_0^{\ln 3} = \pi (9 \ln 3 - 4) \text{ so}$$

$$\int_1^3 x \ln x \, dx = (9 \ln 3 - 4)/2$$

91. $f(x) = e^x + x^2 - 2, x_{n+1} = x_n - \dfrac{e^{x_n} + x_n^2 - 2}{e^{x_n} + 2x_n}$

$x_1 = -1.5, \cdots, x_5 = x_6 = -1.315973778;$

$x_1 = 0.5, \cdots, x_4 = x_5 = 0.537274449$ so

$-1.315973778 < x < 0.537274449.$

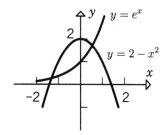

92. $f(x) = x^2 - 2^x, x_{n+1} = x_n - \dfrac{x_n^2 - 2^{x_n}}{2x_n - (\ln 2)2^{x_n}}$

$x_1 = -0.5, \cdots, x_5 = x_6 = -0.766664696;$

by inspection, $x = 2$ and $x = 4$ are
also solutions.

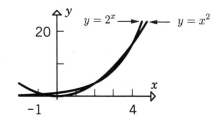

93. (a) $\dfrac{dS}{df} = \dfrac{(e^{bf}-1)(3af^2)-af^3(be^{bf})}{(e^{bf}-1)^2} = \dfrac{af^2(3e^{bf}-3-bfe^{bf})}{(e^{bf}-1)^2}$, $dS/df = 0$ if $f = 0$ (where
     the minimum value occurs), and if $3e^{bf} - 3 - bfe^{bf} = 0$, or $3e^{-bf} + bf - 3 = 0$ (where
     the maximum value occurs).

(b) $f(x) = 3e^{-x} + x - 3$, $x_{n+1} = x_n - \dfrac{3e^{-x_n} + x_n - 3}{1 - 3e^{-x_n}}$, $x_1 = 3, \cdots, x_4 = x_5 = 2.821439372$.

(c) $f \approx 2.821439372/b = (2.821439372)T/(4.8043 \times 10^{-11}) \approx 5.87 \times 10^{10}T$.

94. For any $N > 0$, $e^x > N$ if $\ln e^x > \ln N$, $x > \ln N$; choose $x_0 = \ln N$.

95. For any $\epsilon > 0$, $0 < e^x < \epsilon$ if $\ln e^x < \ln \epsilon$, $x < \ln \epsilon$; choose $x_0 = \ln \epsilon$.

96. $\ln y = \ln x^{1/\ln x} = \dfrac{\ln x}{\ln x} = 1$

so $y = e$ for $x > 0$, $x \neq 1$.

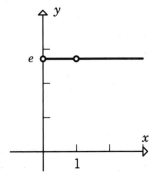

97. $y = x^x$, $\ln y = x \ln x$, $y'/y = 1 + \ln x$, $y' = x^x(1 + \ln x)$; $y' = 0$ when $\ln x = -1$, $x = e^{-1}$ at
     which there is a relative minimum and hence the absolute minimum for $x > 0$. The minimum
     value is $e^{-1/e}$.

98. $y = x^{1/x}$, $\ln y = \dfrac{\ln x}{x}$, $\dfrac{1}{y}\dfrac{dy}{dx} = \dfrac{1 - \ln x}{x^2}$, $\dfrac{dy}{dx} = x^{1/x}\dfrac{1 - \ln x}{x^2}$, $\dfrac{dy}{dx} = 0$ when $x = e$ which locates
     a relative maximum, and hence the absolute maximum. The maximum value is $e^{1/e}$.

99. (a) The area under $1/t$ for $x \leq t \leq x + 1$ is less than the area of the rectangle with altitude
          $1/x$ and base 1, but greater than the area of the rectangle with altitude $1/(x + 1)$ and
          base 1.

(b) $\displaystyle\int_x^{x+1} \dfrac{1}{t}dt = \ln t \Big]_x^{x+1} = \ln(x + 1) - \ln x = \ln(1 + 1/x)$, so
     $1/(x + 1) < \ln(1 + 1/x) < 1/x$ for $x > 0$.

(c) From part (b), $e^{1/(x+1)} < e^{\ln(1+1/x)} < e^{1/x}$, $e^{1/(x+1)} < 1 + 1/x < e^{1/x}$,
     $e^{x/(x+1)} < (1 + 1/x)^x < e$; by the Squeezing Theorem, $\displaystyle\lim_{x \to +\infty} (1 + 1/x)^x = e$.

(d) Use the inequality $e^{x/(x+1)} < (1 + 1/x)^x$ to get $e < (1 + 1/x)^{x+1}$ so
     $(1 + 1/x)^x < e < (1 + 1/x)^{x+1}$.

EXERCISE SET 7.5

1.   **(a)** $+\infty$ **(b)** 0   2.   **(a)** 0   **(b)** $+\infty$

3.   **(a)** $+\infty$ **(b)** $+\infty$ 4.   **(a)** $+\infty$ **(b)** $-\infty$

5.   **(a)** 1   **(b)** 1   6.   **(a)** 1   **(b)** 1

7.   **(a)** $+\infty$ **(b)** 0   8.   **(a)** 0   **(b)** 0

9.

10.

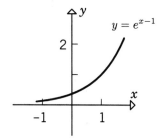

11.

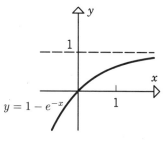

12.

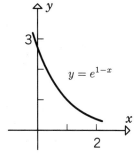

13.   **(a)** yes, because $\lim\limits_{x \to 0} f(x) = f(0)$

      (b) no, because $\lim\limits_{x \to 0^+} f'(x) = \lim\limits_{x \to 0^+} e^x = 1$

           and $\lim\limits_{x \to 0^-} f'(x) = \lim\limits_{x \to 0^-} (-e^{-x}) = -1$ so

           $\lim\limits_{x \to 0^+} f'(x) \neq \lim\limits_{x \to 0^-} f'(x)$

      (c) $f(x) = \begin{cases} e^x, & x \geq 0 \\ e^{-x}, & x < 0 \end{cases}$

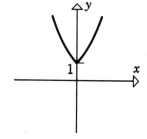

14. **(a)** The oscillations of $e^x \cos x$ about zero increase as $x \to +\infty$ so the limit does not exist.

  (b) 0

15. $e^x \cos x = e^x$ when $\cos x = 1$

    $x = 0, \pm 2\pi, \pm 4\pi, \ldots$

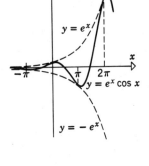

  $e^x \cos x = -e^x$ when $\cos x = -1$

    $x = \pm\pi, \pm 3\pi, \pm 5\pi, \ldots$

  $e^x \cos x = 0$ when $\cos x = 0$

    $x = \pm\pi/2, \pm 3\pi/2, \pm 5\pi/2, \ldots$

  $-1 \le \cos x \le 1$ thus

  $-e^x \le e^x \cos x \le e^x$ and so

  $\lim\limits_{x \to -\infty} e^x \cos x = 0$ by the Squeezing Theorem.

  $f(x) = e^x \cos x,\ f'(x) = e^x(\cos x - \sin x),$

  $f'(x) = 0$ when $\sin x = \cos x,$

  $\tan x = 1,\ x = \pi/4 + n\pi,\ n = 0, \pm 1, \pm 2, \ldots$

  $f''(x) = -2e^x \sin x,\ f''(x) = 0$ when $x = 0, \pm\pi, \pm 2\pi, \ldots$

16. $\lim\limits_{x \to +\infty} \dfrac{e^x + e^{-x}}{e^x - e^{-x}} = \lim\limits_{x \to +\infty} \dfrac{1 + e^{-2x}}{1 - e^{-2x}} = 1$ **17.** $\lim\limits_{x \to -\infty} \dfrac{e^x + e^{-x}}{e^x - e^{-x}} = \lim\limits_{x \to -\infty} \dfrac{e^{2x} + 1}{e^{2x} - 1} = -1$

18. $\lim\limits_{x \to +\infty} \dfrac{2 + e^x}{1 + 3e^x} = \lim\limits_{x \to +\infty} \dfrac{2e^{-x} + 1}{e^{-x} + 3} = 1/3$ **19.** 0

20. **(a)** $f(x) = \dfrac{1}{\sqrt{2\pi}\sigma} \exp\left[-\dfrac{1}{2}\left(\dfrac{x-\mu}{\sigma}\right)^2\right], f'(x) = -\dfrac{1}{\sqrt{2\pi}\sigma^3}(x-\mu)\exp\left[-\dfrac{1}{2}\left(\dfrac{x-\mu}{\sigma}\right)^2\right],$

    $f''(x) = \dfrac{1}{\sqrt{2\pi}\sigma^5}[(x-\mu)^2 - \sigma^2]\exp\left[-\dfrac{1}{2}\left(\dfrac{x-\mu}{\sigma}\right)^2\right],$

    $f'(x) = 0$ when $x = \mu$; relative maximum at $\left(\mu, \dfrac{1}{\sqrt{2\pi}\sigma}\right)$

    $f''(x) = 0$ when $(x-\mu)^2 = \sigma^2, x = \mu \pm \sigma$; inflection points at $\left(\mu \pm \sigma, \dfrac{1}{\sqrt{2\pi}\sigma}e^{-1/2}\right)$

  (b) $\lim\limits_{x \to \pm\infty} f(x) = 0$ **(c)**

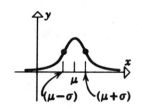

21. $\dfrac{d}{dx}[e^x]\Big|_{x=0} = \lim\limits_{h\to 0}\dfrac{e^{(0+h)} - e^0}{h} = \lim\limits_{h\to 0}\dfrac{e^h - 1}{h} = 1$

22. $\lim\limits_{x\to 0}\dfrac{e^{2x} - e^x}{x} = \lim\limits_{x\to 0}\dfrac{(e^{2x} - e^x) - (e^0 - e^0)}{x - 0} = \dfrac{d}{dx}[e^{2x} - e^x]\Big|_{x=0} = (2e^{2x} - e^x)\Big|_{x=0} = 1$

23. $\lim\limits_{x\to 0}\dfrac{1 - e^{-x}}{x} = \lim\limits_{x\to 0} -\dfrac{e^{-x} - e^0}{x - 0} = -\dfrac{d}{dx}[e^{-x}]\Big|_{x=0} = e^{-x}\Big|_{x=0} = 1$

24. $\lim\limits_{x\to a}\dfrac{e^x - e^a}{x - a} = \dfrac{d}{dx}[e^x]\Big|_{x=a} = e^x\Big|_{x=a} = e^a$

25. let $h = 1/x$ then $x = 1/h$ and $\lim\limits_{x\to +\infty} x(e^{1/x} - 1) = \lim\limits_{h\to 0+}\dfrac{e^h - 1}{h} = \dfrac{d}{dx}[e^x]\Big|_{x=0} = 1$

26. **(a)** $\lim\limits_{x\to +\infty} xe^{-2x} = 0,\ \lim\limits_{x\to -\infty} xe^{-2x} = -\infty.$

   (b) $y = xe^{-2x}$

   $y' = -2\left(x - \dfrac{1}{2}\right)e^{-2x}$

   $y'' = 4(x - 1)e^{-2x}$

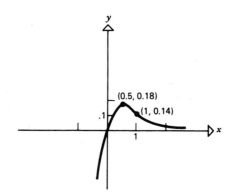

$(0.5, 0.18)$
$(1, 0.14)$

27. **(a)** $\lim\limits_{x\to +\infty} xe^x = +\infty,\ \lim\limits_{x\to -\infty} xe^x = 0.$

   (b) $y = xe^x$
   $y' = (x + 1)e^x$
   $y'' = (x + 2)e^x$

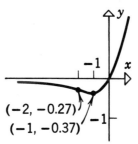

$(-2, -0.27)$
$(-1, -0.37)$

28. (a) $\lim\limits_{x \to +\infty} x^2 e^{2x} = +\infty, \quad \lim\limits_{x \to -\infty} x^2 e^{2x} = 0.$

(b) $y = x^2 e^{2x}$

$y' = 2x(x+1)e^{2x}$

$y'' = 2(2x^2 + 4x + 1)e^{2x}$

$y'' = 0$ if $2x^2 + 4x + 1 = 0,$

$x = \dfrac{-4 \pm \sqrt{16-8}}{2}$

$= -1 \pm \sqrt{2}/2$

$\approx -0.29, -1.71$

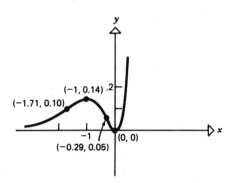

29. (a) $\lim\limits_{x \to +\infty} \dfrac{x^2}{e^{2x}} = 0, \quad \lim\limits_{x \to -\infty} \dfrac{x^2}{e^{2x}} = +\infty.$

(b) $y = x^2/e^{2x} = x^2 e^{-2x}$

$y' = 2x(1-x)e^{-2x}$

$y'' = 2(2x^2 - 4x + 1)e^{-2x}$

$y'' = 0$ if $2x^2 - 4x + 1 = 0$

$x = \dfrac{4 \pm \sqrt{16-8}}{2},$

$= 1 \pm \sqrt{2}/2 \approx 0.29, 1.71$

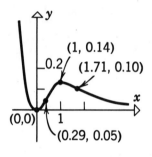

30. (a) $\lim\limits_{x \to +\infty} \dfrac{e^x}{x} = +\infty, \quad \lim\limits_{x \to -\infty} \dfrac{e^x}{x} = 0, \quad \lim\limits_{x \to 0^+} \dfrac{e^x}{x} = +\infty, \quad \lim\limits_{x \to 0^-} \dfrac{e^x}{x} = -\infty.$

(b) $y = \dfrac{e^x}{x}$

$y' = \dfrac{x-1}{x^2} e^x$

$y'' = \dfrac{x^2 - 2x + 2}{x^3} e^x$

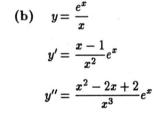

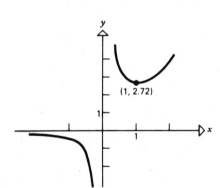

31. (a) 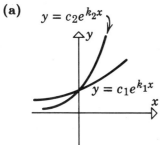   (b) 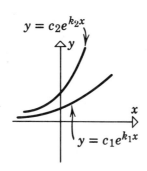   (c)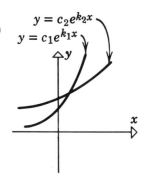

32. Reflect the graphs in Exercise 31 about the y-axis.

33. $m_{\text{line}} = \dfrac{1/e - 1}{1 - 0} = \dfrac{1 - e}{e}$, an equation

   of the line is $y = \dfrac{1 - e}{e}x + 1$ so

   $$A = \int_0^1 \left(\frac{1 - e}{e}x + 1 - e^{-x} \right) dx$$

   $$= \frac{1 - e}{2e}x^2 + x + e^{-x} \bigg]_0^1 = \frac{3 - e}{2e}$$

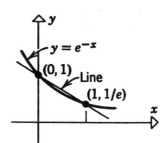

34. $A = xy = xe^{-x}, dA/dx = e^{-x}(1 - x), dA/dx = 0$ when $x = 1$. The maximum area is
     $A = (1)e^{-1} = e^{-1}$.

35. (a) If $\ln x < \sqrt{x}$, then $x < e^{\sqrt{x}}, 1/x > 1/e^{\sqrt{x}} = e^{-\sqrt{x}}$.

     (b) $\displaystyle\lim_{x \to +\infty} e^{x - n\sqrt{x}} = \lim_{x \to +\infty} e^{\sqrt{x}(\sqrt{x} - n)} = +\infty$ so $\displaystyle\lim_{x \to +\infty} \frac{e^x}{x^n} = +\infty$ because $\dfrac{e^x}{x^n} > e^{x - n\sqrt{x}}$.

36. $\displaystyle\lim_{x \to +\infty} \frac{x^n}{e^x} = \lim_{x \to +\infty} \frac{1}{(e^x/x^n)} = 0.$

37. If $x > 1$, then $0 < \ln x < \sqrt{x}, 0 < \dfrac{\ln x}{x^n} < \dfrac{\sqrt{x}}{x^n} = \dfrac{1}{x^{(n-1/2)}}$, but $\displaystyle\lim_{x \to +\infty} \frac{1}{x^{(n-1/2)}} = 0$ so

   $\displaystyle\lim_{x \to +\infty} \frac{\ln x}{x^n} = 0.$

38. $\displaystyle\lim_{x \to +\infty} \frac{x^n}{\ln x} = \lim_{x \to +\infty} \frac{1}{(\ln x)/x^n} = +\infty.$

39. $\displaystyle\lim_{x \to 0^+} x^n \ln x = \lim_{t \to +\infty} \frac{\ln(1/t)}{t^n} = \lim_{t \to +\infty} \frac{-\ln t}{t^n} = 0.$

40. $y = \ln x, x > 0$
$y = \ln(-x), x < 0$

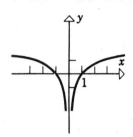

41. $y = -\ln x$

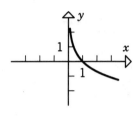

42. $y = \dfrac{1}{2}\ln x$

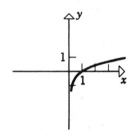

43. $y = \ln(x - 1)$

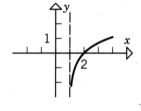

44. $y = x \ln x$
$y' = 1 + \ln x$
$y'' = 1/x$
$y' = 0$ when $x = e^{-1}$
$\displaystyle\lim_{x \to 0+} y = 0$

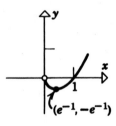

45. $y = \dfrac{\ln x}{x^2}$

$y' = \dfrac{1 - 2\ln x}{x^3}$

$y'' = \dfrac{6\ln x - 5}{x^4}$

$y' = 0$ if $x = e^{1/2}$

$y'' = 0$ if $x = e^{5/6}$

$\displaystyle\lim_{x \to +\infty} y = 0, \ \lim_{x \to 0+} y = -\infty$

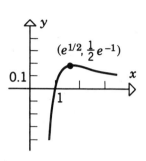

46. $y = x^2 \ln x$

$y' = x(1 + 2\ln x)$

$y'' = 3 + 2\ln x$

$y' = 0$ if $x = e^{-1/2}$

$y'' = 0$ if $x = e^{-3/2}$

$\displaystyle\lim_{x \to 0+} y = 0, \ \lim_{x \to +\infty} y = +\infty, \ \lim_{x \to 0+} y' = 0$

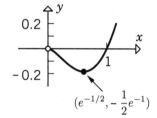

47. $(\ln x)/x \leq 1/e$ so $e\ln x \leq x, \ln(x^e) \leq x, x^e \leq e^x$ with equality only for $x = e$ because the maximum value of $(\ln x)/x$ occurs only at $x = e$.

EXERCISE SET 7.6

1.

	(a)	(b)	(c)	(d)	(e)	(f)
$\sinh x_0$	-2	$-3/4$	$-4/3$	$1/\sqrt{3}$	$8/15$	-1
$\cosh x_0$	$\sqrt{5}$	$5/4$	$5/3$	$2/\sqrt{3}$	$17/15$	$\sqrt{2}$
$\tanh x_0$	$-2/\sqrt{5}$	$-3/5$	$-4/5$	$1/2$	$8/17$	$-1/\sqrt{2}$
$\coth x_0$	$-\sqrt{5}/2$	$-5/3$	$-5/4$	2	$17/8$	$-\sqrt{2}$
$\operatorname{sech} x_0$	$1/\sqrt{5}$	$4/5$	$3/5$	$\sqrt{3}/2$	$15/17$	$1/\sqrt{2}$
$\operatorname{csch} x_0$	$-1/2$	$-4/3$	$-3/4$	$\sqrt{3}$	$15/8$	-1

(a) $\cosh^2 x_0 = 1 + \sinh^2 x_0 = 1 + (-2)^2 = 5$, $\cosh x_0 = \sqrt{5}$

(b) $\sinh^2 x_0 = \cosh^2 x_0 - 1 = \dfrac{25}{16} - 1 = \dfrac{9}{16}$, $\sinh x_0 = -\dfrac{3}{4}$ (because $x_0 < 0$)

(c) $\sec h^2 x_0 = 1 - \tanh^2 x_0 = 1 - \left(-\dfrac{4}{5}\right)^2 = 1 - \dfrac{16}{25} = \dfrac{9}{25}$, $\sec h\, x_0 = \dfrac{3}{5}$, $\cosh x_0 = \dfrac{1}{\sec h\, x_0} = \dfrac{5}{3}$,

from $\dfrac{\sinh x_0}{\cosh x_0} = \tanh x_0$ we get $\sinh x_0 = \left(\dfrac{5}{3}\right)\left(-\dfrac{4}{5}\right) = -\dfrac{4}{3}$

(d) $\csc h^2 x_0 = \coth^2 x_0 - 1 = 4 - 1 = 3$, $\csc h\, x_0 = \sqrt{3}$, $\sinh x_0 = \dfrac{1}{\csc h\, x_0} = \dfrac{1}{\sqrt{3}}$, from

$\dfrac{\cosh x_0}{\sinh x_0} = \coth x_0$ we get $\cosh x_0 = \left(\dfrac{1}{\sqrt{3}}\right)(2) = \dfrac{2}{\sqrt{3}}$

(e) $\cosh x_0 = \dfrac{1}{\sec h\, x_0} = \dfrac{17}{15}$, $\sinh^2 x_0 = \cosh^2 x_0 - 1 = \dfrac{289}{225} - 1 = \dfrac{64}{255}$, $\sinh x_0 = \dfrac{8}{15}$ (because

$x_0 > 0$)

(f) $\sinh x_0 = \dfrac{1}{\csc h\, x_0} = -1$, $\cosh^2 x_0 = 1 + \sinh^2 x_0 = 2$, $\cosh x_0 = \sqrt{2}$

2. $\cosh(x + y) = \dfrac{1}{2}[e^{(x+y)} + e^{-(x+y)}] = \dfrac{1}{2}[e^x e^y + e^{-x} e^{-y}]$

$= \dfrac{1}{2}[(\cosh x + \sinh x)(\cosh y + \sinh y) + (\cosh x - \sinh x)(\cosh y - \sinh y)]$

$= \cosh x \cosh y + \sinh x \sinh y$

3. from (6b) and (1), $\cosh 2x = \cosh^2 x + \sinh^2 x$ and $\cosh^2 x = 1 + \sinh^2 x$ so $\cosh 2x = 2\sinh^2 x + 1$

4. from (6b) and (1), $\cosh 2x = \cosh^2 x + \sinh^2 x$ and $\sinh^2 x = \cosh^2 x - 1$ so
$\cosh 2x = 2\cosh^2 x - 1$

5. $\cosh(-x) = \dfrac{1}{2}[e^{(-x)} + e^{-(-x)}] = \dfrac{1}{2}(e^{-x} + e^x) = \cosh x$

6. $\sinh(-x) = \dfrac{1}{2}[e^{(-x)} - e^{-(-x)}] = \dfrac{1}{2}(e^{-x} - e^x) = -\dfrac{1}{2}(e^x - e^{-x}) = -\sinh x$

7. $\tanh(x + y) = \dfrac{\sinh(x + y)}{\cosh(x + y)} = \dfrac{\sinh x \cosh y + \cosh x \sinh y}{\cosh x \cosh y + \sinh x \sinh y}$

$= \dfrac{\dfrac{\sinh x \cosh y}{\cosh x \cosh y} + \dfrac{\cosh x \sinh y}{\cosh x \cosh y}}{\dfrac{\cosh x \cosh y}{\cosh x \cosh y} + \dfrac{\sinh x \sinh y}{\cosh x \cosh y}} = \dfrac{\tanh x + \tanh y}{1 + \tanh x \tanh y}$

8. $\tanh(x - y) = \dfrac{\sinh(x - y)}{\cosh(x - y)} = \dfrac{\sinh x \cosh y - \cosh x \sinh y}{\cosh x \cosh y - \sinh x \sinh y}$,

the result follows by dividing numerator and denominator by $\cosh x \cosh y$ as in Exercise 7.

9. $\tanh 2x = \dfrac{\sinh 2x}{\cosh 2x} = \dfrac{2\sinh x \cosh x}{\cosh^2 x + \sinh^2 x}$ (from (6a) and (6b))

$\qquad = \dfrac{2\tanh x}{1 + \tanh^2 x}$ (after dividing numerator and denominator by $\cosh^2 x$)

10. from (7b) with x replaced by $\dfrac{x}{2}$: $\cosh x = 2\cosh^2 \dfrac{x}{2} - 1$,

$2\cosh^2 \dfrac{x}{2} = \cosh x + 1$, $\cosh^2 \dfrac{x}{2} = \dfrac{1}{2}(\cosh x + 1)$,

$\cosh \dfrac{x}{2} = \sqrt{\dfrac{1}{2}(\cosh x + 1)}$ (because $\cosh \dfrac{x}{2} > 0$)

11. from (7a) with x replaced by $\dfrac{x}{2}$: $\cosh x = 2\sinh^2 \dfrac{x}{2} + 1$,

$2\sinh^2 \dfrac{x}{2} = \cosh x - 1$, $\sinh^2 \dfrac{x}{2} = \dfrac{1}{2}(\cosh x - 1)$, $\sinh \dfrac{x}{2} = \pm\sqrt{\dfrac{1}{2}(\cosh x - 1)}$

12. adding (4a) to (9a):

$\sinh(x+y) + \sinh(x-y) = 2\sinh x \cosh y$, then with $a = x+y$ and $b = x-y$ we get $x = \dfrac{a+b}{2}$ and $y = \dfrac{a-b}{2}$ so $\sinh a + \sinh b = 2\sinh \dfrac{a+b}{2} \cosh \dfrac{a-b}{2}$, the result follows by replacing a by x and b by y.

13. add (4b) to (9b) then let $x = \dfrac{a+b}{2}$ and $y = \dfrac{a-b}{2}$.

14. $\cosh 3x = \cosh(2x + x) = \cosh 2x \cosh x + \sinh 2x \sinh x$

$\qquad = (2\cosh^2 x - 1)\cosh x + (2\sinh x \cosh x)\sinh x = 2\cosh^3 x - \cosh x + 2\sinh^2 x \cosh x$

$\qquad = 2\cosh^3 x - \cosh x + 2(\cosh^2 x - 1)\cosh x = 4\cosh^3 x - 3\cosh x$

15. (a) $\dfrac{d}{dx}(\sinh x) = \dfrac{d}{dx}\left[\dfrac{1}{2}(e^x - e^{-x})\right] = \dfrac{1}{2}(e^x + e^{-x}) = \cosh x$

(b) $\dfrac{d}{dx}(\coth x) = \dfrac{d}{dx}\left[\dfrac{e^x + e^{-x}}{e^x - e^{-x}}\right] = \dfrac{(e^x - e^{-x})(e^x - e^{-x}) - (e^x + e^{-x})(e^x + e^{-x})}{(e^x - e^{-x})^2}$

$\qquad = \dfrac{(e^{2x} - 2 + e^{-2x}) - (e^{2x} + 2 + e^{-2x})}{(e^x - e^{-x})^2} = -\dfrac{4}{(e^x - e^{-x})^2} = -\operatorname{csch}^2 x$

(c) $\dfrac{d}{dx}(\text{sech } x) = \dfrac{d}{dx}\left[\dfrac{2}{e^x + e^{-x}}\right]$

$\qquad\qquad = \dfrac{d}{dx}[2(e^x + e^{-x})^{-1}] = -2(e^x + e^{-x})^{-2}(e^x - e^{-x})$

$\qquad\qquad = -\dfrac{2}{(e^x + e^{-x})}\dfrac{e^x - e^{-x}}{e^x + e^{-x}} = -\text{ sech } x \tanh x$

(d) proceed as in (c) using $\dfrac{2}{e^x - e^{-x}}$

16. $4x^3 \sinh(x^4)$

17. $4\cosh(4x - 8)$

18. $\dfrac{2\,\text{sech}^2 2x}{\tanh 2x}$

19. $-\dfrac{1}{x}\,\text{csch}^2(\ln x)$

20. $-2e^{2x}\,\text{sech}(e^{2x})\tanh(e^{2x})$

21. $\dfrac{1}{x^2}\,\text{csch}(1/x)\coth(1/x)$

22. $6\sinh^2(2x)\cosh(2x)$

23. $\dfrac{2 + 5\cosh(5x)\sinh(5x)}{\sqrt{4x + \cosh^2(5x)}}$

24. $-3\cosh(\cos 3x)\sin 3x$

25. $x^{5/2}\tanh(\sqrt{x})\text{sech}^2(\sqrt{x}) + 3x^2\tanh^2(\sqrt{x})$

26. $\dfrac{1}{2}\sinh(2x - 3) + C$

27. $\dfrac{1}{7}\sinh^7 x + C$

28. $-\dfrac{1}{3}\coth(3x) + C$

29. $\dfrac{2}{3}(\tanh x)^{3/2} + C$

30. $-\dfrac{1}{3}\coth^3 x + C$

31. $\ln(\cosh x) + C$

32. $\ln(\cosh x) + C$

33. $-\dfrac{1}{3}\,\text{sech}^3 x + C$

34. $\dfrac{1}{10}\ln(3 + 5\cosh 2x) + C$

35. $2\sinh(\sqrt{x}) + C$

36. (a) $\sinh(\ln 3) = \dfrac{1}{2}(e^{\ln 3} - e^{-\ln 3}) = \dfrac{1}{2}\left(3 - \dfrac{1}{3}\right) = \dfrac{4}{3}$

$\qquad$ (b) $\cosh(-\ln 2) = \dfrac{1}{2}(e^{-\ln 2} + e^{\ln 2}) = \dfrac{1}{2}\left(\dfrac{1}{2} + 2\right) = \dfrac{5}{4}$

(c) $\tanh(2\ln 5) = \dfrac{e^{2\ln 5} - e^{-2\ln 5}}{e^{2\ln 5} + e^{-2\ln 5}} = \dfrac{25 - 1/25}{25 + 1/25} = \dfrac{312}{313}$

(d) $\sinh(-3\ln 2) = \dfrac{1}{2}(e^{-3\ln 2} - e^{3\ln 2}) = \dfrac{1}{2}\left(\dfrac{1}{8} - 8\right) = -\dfrac{63}{16}$

37. **(a)** $\dfrac{1}{2}(e^{\ln x} + e^{-\ln x}) = \dfrac{1}{2}\left(x + \dfrac{1}{x}\right) = \dfrac{x^2 + 1}{2x}$, $x > 0$

(b) $\dfrac{1}{2}(e^{\ln x} - e^{-\ln x}) = \dfrac{1}{2}\left(x - \dfrac{1}{x}\right) = \dfrac{x^2 - 1}{2x}$, $x > 0$

(c) $\dfrac{e^{2\ln x} - e^{-2\ln x}}{e^{2\ln x} + e^{-2\ln x}} = \dfrac{x^2 - 1/x^2}{x^2 + 1/x^2} = \dfrac{x^4 - 1}{x^4 + 1}$, $x > 0$

(d) $\dfrac{1}{2}(e^{-\ln x} + e^{\ln x}) = \dfrac{1}{2}\left(\dfrac{1}{x} + x\right) = \dfrac{1 + x^2}{2x}$, $x > 0$

38. **(a)** $|\tanh x| = \dfrac{|\sinh x|}{\cosh x} = \dfrac{|\sinh x|}{\sqrt{1 + \sinh^2 x}} < \dfrac{|\sinh x|}{\sqrt{\sinh^2 x}} = \dfrac{|\sinh x|}{|\sinh x|} = 1$, $x \neq 0$

so $-1 < \tanh x < 1$ is true for all x (including 0 because $\tanh 0 = 0$)

(b) $\displaystyle\lim_{x \to +\infty} \dfrac{e^x - e^{-x}}{e^x + e^{-x}} = \lim_{x \to +\infty} \dfrac{1 - e^{-2x}}{1 + e^{-2x}} = 1$

(c) $\displaystyle\lim_{x \to -\infty} \dfrac{e^x - e^{-x}}{e^x + e^{-x}} = \lim_{x \to -\infty} \dfrac{e^{2x} - 1}{e^{2x} + 1} = -1$

39. positive on $(0, +\infty)$, negative on $(-\infty, 0)$, increasing on $(-\infty, +\infty)(dy/dx = \operatorname{sech}^2 x > 0)$
concave up on $(-\infty, 0)$, concave down on $(0, +\infty)(d^2y/dx^2 = -2\operatorname{sech}^2 x \tanh x)$

41. **(a)** $\cosh x = \sqrt{1 + \sinh^2 x} \geq \sqrt{1} = 1$

(b) $\cosh x \geq 1$ (part (a)) so $0 < \dfrac{1}{\cosh x} \leq 1$, $0 < \operatorname{sech} x \leq 1$

42. **(a)** $\displaystyle\lim_{x \to +\infty} \operatorname{csch} x = \lim_{x \to +\infty} \dfrac{2}{e^x - e^{-x}} = 0$, $\displaystyle\lim_{x \to -\infty} \operatorname{csch} x = \lim_{x \to -\infty} \dfrac{2}{e^x - e^{-x}} = 0$

(b) $\displaystyle\lim_{x \to 0^+} \dfrac{2}{e^x - e^{-x}} = \lim_{x \to 0^+} \dfrac{2e^x}{e^{2x} - 1} = +\infty$ because $e^{2x} \to 1^+$ as $x \to 0^+$ so $e^{2x} - 1 \to 0^+$;

$\displaystyle\lim_{x \to 0^-} \dfrac{2}{e^x - e^{-x}} = \lim_{x \to 0^-} \dfrac{2e^x}{e^{2x} - 1} = -\infty$ because $e^{2x} \to 1^-$ as $x \to 0^-$ so $e^{2x} - 1 \to 0^-$

43. using $\sinh x + \cosh x = e^x$ (5a), $(\sinh x + \cosh x)^n = (e^x)^n = e^{nx} = \sinh nx + \cosh nx$

44. **(a)** $\sinh x = \dfrac{1}{2}e^x - \dfrac{1}{2}e^{-x}$ and

$\cosh x = \dfrac{1}{2}e^x + \dfrac{1}{2}e^{-x}$, both

contain $\dfrac{1}{2}e^{-x}$ which is close to

zero for x large and positive.

(b)

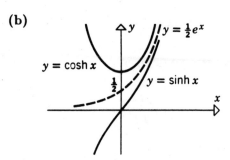

45. **(a)** $\displaystyle\lim_{x\to+\infty}\dfrac{\cosh x}{e^x} = \lim_{x\to+\infty}\dfrac{e^x+e^{-x}}{2e^x} = \lim_{x\to+\infty}\dfrac{1}{2}(1+e^{-2x}) = 1/2$

(b) $\displaystyle\lim_{x\to+\infty}\dfrac{\sinh ax}{e^x} = \lim_{x\to+\infty}\dfrac{e^{ax}-e^{-ax}}{2e^x} = \lim_{x\to+\infty}\dfrac{1}{2}[e^{(a-1)x}-e^{-(a+1)x}]$

$$= \begin{cases} +\infty\,, a > 1 \\ 1/2\,, a = 1 \\ 0\ \ ,0 < a < 1 \end{cases}$$

46. $\displaystyle\int_{-a}^{a} e^{tx}\,dx = \dfrac{1}{t}e^{tx}\Big]_{-a}^{a} = \dfrac{1}{t}(e^{ax}-e^{-ax}) = \dfrac{2\sinh at}{t}$

47. $A = \displaystyle\int_{0}^{\ln 3}\sinh 2x\,dx = \dfrac{1}{2}\cosh 2x\Big]_{0}^{\ln 3} = \dfrac{1}{2}[\cosh(2\ln 3) - 1]$,

but $\cosh(2\ln 3) = \cosh(\ln 9) = \dfrac{1}{2}(e^{\ln 9}+e^{-\ln 9}) = \dfrac{1}{2}(9+1/9) = 41/9$ so $A = \dfrac{1}{2}[41/9-1] = 16/9$.

48. $\displaystyle\int_{0}^{1}\cosh ax\,dx = 2, \dfrac{1}{a}\sinh ax\Big]_{0}^{1} = 2, \dfrac{1}{a}\sinh a = 2, \sinh a = 2a;$

let $f(a) = \sinh a - 2a$, then $a_{n+1} = a_n - \dfrac{\sinh a_n - 2a_n}{\cosh a_n - 2}, a_1 = 2.2, \cdots, a_4 = a_5 = 2.177318985.$

49. $V = \pi\displaystyle\int_{0}^{5}(\cosh^2 2x - \sinh^2 2x)dx = \pi\int_{0}^{5}dx = 5\pi$

50. $V = \pi\displaystyle\int_{0}^{\ln 2}\operatorname{sech}^2 x\,dx = \pi\tanh x\Big]_{0}^{\ln 2} = \pi\tanh(\ln 2) = 3\pi/5.$

51. $y' = \sinh x, 1 + (y')^2 = 1 + \sinh^2 x = \cosh^2 x$

$L = \displaystyle\int_{0}^{\ln 2}\cosh x\,dx = \sinh x\Big]_{0}^{\ln 2} = \sinh(\ln 2) = \dfrac{1}{2}(e^{\ln 2}-e^{-\ln 2}) = \dfrac{1}{2}\left(2-\dfrac{1}{2}\right) = \dfrac{3}{4}$

52. $y' = \sinh(x/a)$, $1 + (y')^2 = 1 + \sinh^2(x/a) = \cosh^2(x/a)$

$$L = \int_0^{x_1} \cosh(x/a)dx = a\sinh(x/a)\Big]_0^{x_1} = a\sinh(x_1/a)$$

53. **(a)** $y' = \sinh(x/a)$, $1 + (y')^2 = 1 + \sinh^2(x/a) = \cosh^2(x/a)$

$$L = 2\int_0^b \cosh(x/a)\,dx = 2a\sinh(x/a)\Big]_0^b = 2a\sinh(b/a)$$

(b) The highest point is at $x = b$, the lowest at $x = 0$,
   so $S = a\cosh(b/a) - a\cosh(0) = a\cosh(b/a) - a$.

54. From part (a) of Exercise 53, $L = 2a\sinh(b/a)$ so $120 = 2a\sinh(50/a)$, $a\sinh(50/a) = 60$. Let
   $u = 50/a$, then $a = 50/u$ so $(50/u)\sinh u = 60$, $\sinh u = 1.2u$. If $f(u) = \sinh u - 1.2u$, then
   $$u_{n+1} = u_n - \frac{\sinh u_n - 1.2u_n}{\cosh u_n - 1.2}; u_1 = 1, \cdots, u_5 = u_6 = 1.064868548 \approx 50/a \text{ so } a \approx 46.95415231.$$
   From part (b), $S = a\cosh(b/a) - a \approx 46.95415231[\cosh(1.064868548) - 1] \approx 29.2\,\text{ft}$.

55. From part (b) of Exercise 53, $S = a\cosh(b/a) - a$ so $30 = a\cosh(200/a) - a$. Let $u = 200/a$,
   then $a = 200/u$ so $30 = (200/u)[\cosh u - 1]$, $\cosh u - 1 = 0.15u$. If $f(u) = \cosh u - 0.15u - 1$,
   then $u_{n+1} = u_n - \dfrac{\cosh u_n - 0.15u_n - 1}{\sinh u_n - 0.15}; u_1 = 0.3, \cdots, u_4 = u_5 = 0.297792782 \approx 200/a$ so
   $a \approx 671.6079505$. From part (a),
   $L = 2a\sinh(b/a) \approx 2(671.6079505)\sinh(0.297792782) \approx 405.9\,\text{ft}$.

EXERCISE SET 7.7

1. $\dfrac{1}{y}dy = \dfrac{1}{x}dx$, $\ln|y| = \ln|x| + C_1$, $\ln\left|\dfrac{y}{x}\right| = C_1$, $\dfrac{y}{x} = \pm e^{C_1} = C$, $y = Cx$

2. $y\,dy = \dfrac{x^3}{1+x^4}dx$, $\dfrac{1}{2}y^2 = \dfrac{1}{4}\ln(1+x^4) + C_1$, $y^2 = \ln\sqrt{1+x^4} + C$

3. $\dfrac{1}{1+y}dy = -\dfrac{x}{\sqrt{1+x^2}}dx$, $\ln|1+y| = -\sqrt{1+x^2} + C_1$,
   $1 + y = \pm e^{-\sqrt{1+x^2}+C_1} = \pm e^{C_1}e^{-\sqrt{1+x^2}} = Ce^{-\sqrt{1+x^2}}$, $y = Ce^{-\sqrt{1+x^2}} - 1$

4. $\dfrac{1}{\tan y}dy = \dfrac{3}{\sec x}dx$, $\dfrac{\cos y}{\sin y}dy = 3\cos x\,dx$, $\ln|\sin y| = 3\sin x + C_1$,
   $\sin y = \pm e^{3\sin x + C_1} = \pm e^{C_1}e^{3\sin x} = Ce^{3\sin x}$

5. $e^y \, dy = \dfrac{\sin x}{\cos^2 x} dx = \sec x \tan x \, dx$, $e^y = \sec x + C$, $y = \ln(\sec x + C)$

6. $\dfrac{dy}{dx} = (1-y) + (1-y)x^2 = (1-y)(1+x^2)$, $\dfrac{1}{1-y} dy = (1+x^2)dx$,

   $-\ln|1-y| = x + \dfrac{1}{3}x^3 + C_1$, $1 - y = \pm e^{-x-\frac{1}{3}x^3 - C_1} = \pm e^{-C_1}e^{-x-\frac{1}{3}x^3} = Ce^{-x-\frac{1}{3}x^3}$,

   $y = 1 - Ce^{-x-\frac{1}{3}x^3}$

7. $\rho = e^{\int 3dx} = e^{3x}$, $e^{3x}y = \displaystyle\int e^x \, dx = e^x + C$, $y = e^{-2x} + Ce^{-3x}$

8. $\rho = e^{\int -\frac{5}{x}dx} = e^{-5\ln x} = x^{-5}$, $x^{-5}y = \displaystyle\int x^{-4}dx = -\dfrac{1}{3}x^{-3} + C$, $y = -\dfrac{1}{3}x^2 + Cx^5$

9. $\rho = e^{\int dx} = e^x$, $e^x y = \displaystyle\int e^x \cos(e^x)dx = \sin(e^x) + C$, $y = e^{-x}\sin(e^x) + Ce^{-x}$

10. $\dfrac{dy}{dx} + 2y = \dfrac{1}{2}$, $\rho = e^{\int 2dx} = e^{2x}$, $e^{2x}y = \displaystyle\int \dfrac{1}{2}e^{2x}dx = \dfrac{1}{4}e^{2x} + C$, $y = \dfrac{1}{4} + Ce^{-2x}$

11. $y' + \dfrac{3}{x}y = -2x^3$, $\rho = e^{\int \frac{3}{x}dx} = e^{3\ln x} = x^3$,

    $x^3 y = \displaystyle\int -2x^6 dx = -\dfrac{2}{7}x^7 + C$, $y = -\dfrac{2}{7}x^4 + Cx^{-3}$

12. $\dfrac{dy}{dx} + y = \dfrac{1}{1+e^x}$, $\rho = e^{\int dx} = e^x$,

    $e^x y = \displaystyle\int \dfrac{e^x}{1+e^x}dx = \ln(1+e^x) + C$, $y = e^{-x}\ln(1+e^x) + Ce^{-x}$

13. $\rho = e^{\int -x \, dx} = e^{-x^2/2}$, $e^{-x^2/2}y = \displaystyle\int xe^{-x^2/2}dx = -e^{-x^2/2} + C$,

    $y = -1 + Ce^{x^2/2}$, $3 = -1 + C$, $C = 4$, $y = -1 + 4e^{x^2/2}$

14. $2y \, dy = 3x^2(x^3+1)^{-1/2}dx$, $y^2 = 2(x^3+1)^{1/2} + C$, $1 = 6 + C$, $C = -5$, $y^2 = 2\sqrt{x^3+1} - 5$

15. $\rho = e^{\int dt} = e^t$, $e^t y = \displaystyle\int 2e^t \, dt = 2e^t + C$, $y = 2 + Ce^{-t}$, $1 = 2 + C$, $C = -1$, $y = 2 - e^{-t}$

16. $\dfrac{dy}{dx} = (x+2)e^y$, $e^{-y}dy = (x+2)dx$, $-e^{-y} = \dfrac{1}{2}x^2 + 2x + C$, $-1 = C$,

    $-e^{-y} = \dfrac{1}{2}x^2 + 2x - 1$, $e^{-y} = -\dfrac{1}{2}x^2 - 2x + 1$, $y = -\ln\left(1 - 2x - \dfrac{1}{2}x^2\right)$

17. $y^2 t \dfrac{dy}{dt} = t - 1$, $y^2 dy = \left(1 - \dfrac{1}{t}\right) dt$, $\dfrac{1}{3} y^3 = t - \ln t + C$,

$9 = 1 + C$, $C = 8$, $\dfrac{1}{3} y^3 = t - \ln t + 8$, $y = \sqrt[3]{3t - 3\ln t + 24}$

18. $y' + \dfrac{\sinh x}{\cosh x} y = \cosh x$, $\rho = e^{\int \frac{\sinh x}{\cosh x} dx} = e^{\ln \cosh x} = \cosh x$,

$(\cosh x) y = \displaystyle\int \cosh^2 x \, dx = \int \dfrac{1}{2}(\cosh 2x + 1) dx$

$$= \dfrac{1}{4} \sinh 2x + \dfrac{1}{2} x + C = \dfrac{1}{2} \sinh x \cosh x + \dfrac{1}{2} x + C$$

$y = \dfrac{1}{2} \sinh x + \dfrac{1}{2} x \operatorname{sech} x + C \operatorname{sech} x$, $\dfrac{1}{4} = C$, $y = \dfrac{1}{2} \sinh x + \dfrac{1}{2} x \operatorname{sech} x + \dfrac{1}{4} \operatorname{sech} x$

19. $\dfrac{dy}{dx} = \dfrac{y^2}{3\sqrt{x}}$, $\dfrac{1}{y^2} dy = \dfrac{1}{3\sqrt{x}} dx$, $-\dfrac{1}{y} = \dfrac{2}{3}\sqrt{x} + C$; $y = -1$ when $x = 1$ so $1 = \dfrac{2}{3} + C$,

$C = \dfrac{1}{3}$, $-\dfrac{1}{y} = \dfrac{2}{3}\sqrt{x} + \dfrac{1}{3}$, $y = -\dfrac{3}{2\sqrt{x} + 1}$

20. $\dfrac{dy}{dx} = \dfrac{3x^2}{2y}$, $2y \, dy = 3x^2 dx$, $y^2 = x^3 + C$; $y = 1$ when $x = 1$ so $1 = 1 + C$, $C = 0$, $y^2 = x^3$

21. $\dfrac{dy}{dx} = x e^y$, $e^{-y} dy = x \, dx$, $-e^{-y} = \dfrac{1}{2} x^2 + C$; $y = 0$ when $x = 2$ so $-1 = 2 + C$, $C = -3$,

$-e^{-y} = \dfrac{1}{2} x^2 - 3$, $y = -\ln\left(3 - \dfrac{1}{2} x^2\right)$

22. $\dfrac{dy}{dx} = 2y + 3$, $\dfrac{1}{2y + 3} dy = dx$, $\dfrac{1}{2} \ln(2y + 3) = x + C$; $y = -1$ when $x = 1$ so $0 = 1 + C$,

$C = -1$, $\dfrac{1}{2} \ln(2y + 3) = x - 1$, $2y + 3 = e^{2(x-1)}$, $y = \dfrac{1}{2} e^{2(x-1)} - \dfrac{3}{2}$

23. **(a)** $A(h) = \pi(1)^2 = \pi$, $\pi \dfrac{dh}{dt} = -0.025\sqrt{h}$, $\dfrac{\pi}{\sqrt{h}} dh = -0.025 dt$, $2\pi\sqrt{h} = -0.025t + C$; $h = 4$

when $t = 0$ so $4\pi = C$, $2\pi\sqrt{h} = -0.025t + 4\pi$, $\sqrt{h} = 2 - \dfrac{0.025}{2\pi} t$, $h \approx (2 - 0.003979t)^2$.

(b) $h = 0$ when $t \approx 2/0.003979 \approx 502.6 \, \text{sec} \approx 8.4 \, \text{min}$

24. (a) $A(h) = 6\left[2\sqrt{4 - (h-2)^2}\right]$

$\qquad = 12\sqrt{4h - h^2}$,

$\qquad 12\sqrt{4h - h^2}\,\dfrac{dh}{dt} = -0.025\sqrt{h}$,

$\qquad 12\sqrt{4 - h}\,dh = -0.025dt$,

$\qquad -8(4 - h)^{3/2} = -0.025t + C$;

$\qquad h = 4$ when $t = 0$ so $C = 0$,

$\qquad (4 - h)^{3/2} = (0.025/8)t$,

$\qquad 4 - h = (0.025/8)^{2/3}t^{2/3}$,

$\qquad h \approx 4 - 0.021375t^{2/3}$

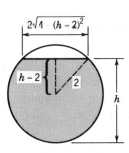

(b) $h = 0$ when $t \approx (4/0.021375)^{3/2} \approx 2560$ sec ≈ 42.7 min

25. $\dfrac{dv}{dt} = -0.04v^2$, $\dfrac{1}{v^2}dv = -0.04dt$, $-\dfrac{1}{v} = -0.04t + C$; $v = 50$ when $t = 0$ so $-\dfrac{1}{50} = C$,

$-\dfrac{1}{v} = -0.04t - \dfrac{1}{50}$, $v = \dfrac{50}{2t + 1}$. But $v = \dfrac{dx}{dt}$ so $\dfrac{dx}{dt} = \dfrac{50}{2t + 1}$, $x = 25\ln(2t + 1) + C_1$; $x = 0$

when $t = 0$ so $C_1 = 0$, $x = 25\ln(2t + 1)$.

26. $\dfrac{dv}{dt} = -0.02\sqrt{v}$, $\dfrac{1}{\sqrt{v}}dv = -0.02dt$, $2\sqrt{v} = -0.02t + C$; $v = 9$ when $t = 0$ so $6 = C$,

$2\sqrt{v} = -0.02t + 6$, $v = (3 - 0.01t)^2$. But $v = \dfrac{dx}{dt}$ so $\dfrac{dx}{dt} = (3 - 0.01t)^2$, $x = -\dfrac{100}{3}(3 - 0.01t)^3 + C_1$;

$x = 0$ when $t = 0$ so $C_1 = 900$, $x = 900 - \dfrac{100}{3}(3 - 0.01t)^3$.

27. (a) $\dfrac{dv}{dt} = \dfrac{ck}{m_0 - kt} - g$, $v = -c\ln(m_0 - kt) - gt + C$; $v = 0$ when $t = 0$ so $0 = -c\ln m_0 + C$,

$\qquad C = c\ln m_0$, $v = c\ln m_0 - c\ln(m_0 - kt) - gt = c\ln\dfrac{m_0}{m_0 - kt} - gt$.

(b) $m_0 - kt = 0.2m_0$ when $t = 100$ so

$\qquad v = 2500\ln\dfrac{m_0}{0.2m_0} - 9.8(100) = 2500\ln 5 - 980 \approx 3044\,\text{m/sec}$.

28. (a) $\dfrac{m}{mg - kv}dv = dt$, $-\dfrac{m}{k}\ln(mg - kv) = t + C$; $v = 0$ when $t = 0$ so $C = -\dfrac{m}{k}\ln(mg)$,

$\qquad -\dfrac{m}{k}\ln(mg - kv) = t - \dfrac{m}{k}\ln(mg)$, $\ln(mg - kv) - \ln(mg) = -\dfrac{k}{m}t$, $\ln\dfrac{mg - kv}{mg} = -\dfrac{k}{m}t$,

$\qquad mg - kv = mge^{-\frac{k}{m}t}$, $v = \dfrac{mg}{k}\left(1 - e^{-\frac{k}{m}t}\right)$.

(b) $\lim\limits_{t \to +\infty} v(t) = mg/k$

(c) $v = \dfrac{dx}{dt} = \dfrac{mg}{k}\left(1 - e^{-\frac{k}{m}t}\right)$, $x = \dfrac{mg}{k}t + \dfrac{m^2g}{k^2}e^{-\frac{k}{m}t} + C_1$;

$x = 0$ when $t = 0$ so $C_1 = -\dfrac{m^2g}{k^2}$, $x = \dfrac{mg}{k}t + \dfrac{m^2g}{k^2}\left(e^{-\frac{k}{m}t} - 1\right)$.

29. (a) $v\,dv = -\dfrac{gR^2}{x^2}dx$, $\dfrac{1}{2}v^2 = \dfrac{gR^2}{x} + C$; $v = v_0$ when $x = R$ so $\dfrac{1}{2}v_0^2 = gR + C$,

$C = \dfrac{1}{2}v_0^2 - gR$, $\dfrac{1}{2}v^2 = \dfrac{gR^2}{x} + \dfrac{1}{2}v_0^2 - gR$, $v^2 = \dfrac{2gR^2}{x} + v_0^2 - 2gR$.

(b) From the result in part (a), $v^2 > 0$ for all $x \geq R$ if $v_0^2 - 2gR \geq 0$, $v_0 \geq \sqrt{2gR}$.

(c) 1 mi = 5280 ft so 32 ft/sec^2 = 32/5280 mi/sec^2,

$v_0 = \sqrt{2gR} = \sqrt{2(32/5280)(3960)} \approx 6.9$ mi/sec.

30. (a) By the chain rule, $\dfrac{dv}{dt} = \dfrac{dv}{dx}\dfrac{dx}{dt} = \dfrac{dv}{dx}v$ so $m\dfrac{dv}{dt} = mv\dfrac{dv}{dx}$.

(b) $\dfrac{mv}{kv^2 + mg}dv = -dx$, $\dfrac{m}{2k}\ln(kv^2 + mg) = -x + C$; $v = v_0$ when $x = 0$ so

$C = \dfrac{m}{2k}\ln(kv_0^2 + mg)$, $\dfrac{m}{2k}\ln(kv^2 + mg) = -x + \dfrac{m}{2k}\ln(kv_0^2 + mg)$, $x = \dfrac{m}{2k}\ln\dfrac{kv_0^2 + mg}{kv^2 + mg}$.

(c) $x = x_{\max}$ when $v = 0$ so

$x_{\max} = \dfrac{m}{2k}\ln\dfrac{kv_0^2 + mg}{mg} = \dfrac{3.56 \times 10^{-3}}{2(7.3 \times 10^{-6})}\ln\dfrac{(7.3 \times 10^{-6})(988)^2 + (3.56 \times 10^{-3})(9.8)}{(3.56 \times 10^{-3})(9.8)}$

≈ 1298 m

31. $\dfrac{dy}{dt}$ = rate in $-$ rate out, where y is the amount of salt at time t,

$\dfrac{dy}{dt} = (4)(2) - \left(\dfrac{y}{50}\right)(2) = 8 - \dfrac{1}{25}y$ so $\dfrac{dy}{dt} + \dfrac{1}{25}y = 8$ and $y(0) = 25$.

$\rho = e^{\int \frac{1}{25}dt} = e^{t/25}$, $e^{t/25}y = \displaystyle\int 8e^{t/25}dt = 200e^{t/25} + C$,

$y = 200 + Ce^{-t/25}$, $25 = 200 + C$, $C = -175$,

(a) $y = 200 - 175e^{-t/25}$

(b) when $t = 25$, $y = 200 - 175e^{-1} \approx 136$ lb

32. $\dfrac{dy}{dt} = (5)(10) - \dfrac{y}{200}(10) = 50 - \dfrac{1}{20}y$ so $\dfrac{dy}{dt} + \dfrac{1}{20}y = 50$ and $y(0) = 0$.

$\rho = e^{\int \frac{1}{20}dt} = e^{t/20}$, $e^{t/20}y = \displaystyle\int 50e^{t/20}dt = 1000e^{t/20} + C$,

$y = 1000 + Ce^{-t/20}$, $0 = 1000 + C$, $C = -1000$;

(a) $y = 1000 - 1000e^{-t/20}$

(b) when $t = 30$, $y = 1000 - 1000e^{-1.5} \approx 777$ lb

33. At time t there are $500 + (20 - 10)t = 500 + 10t$ gallons of brine in the tank so

$$\frac{dy}{dt} = 0 - \frac{y}{500 + 10t}(10) = -\frac{y}{50 + t}, \quad \frac{dy}{dt} + \frac{1}{50 + t}y = 0 \text{ and } y(0) = 50,$$

$$\rho = e^{\int 1/(50+t)dt} = e^{\ln(50+t)} = 50 + t, \; (50 + t)y = C, \; y = \frac{C}{50 + t},$$

$$50 = C/50, \; C = 2500, \; y = \frac{2500}{50 + t}$$

The tank reaches the point of overflowing when $500 + 10t = 1000$, $t = 50$ min so $y = 2500/(50 + 50) = 25$ lb.

34. **(a)** $y = 10,000e^{0.01t}$ where y is the number of bacteria present after t hours.

(b) $y = 10,000e^{0.05} \approx 10,513$

(c) $10,000e^{0.01t} = 45,000$, $e^{0.01t} = 4.5$, $0.01t = \ln 4.5$, $t = (\ln 4.5)/0.01 \approx 150$ hours

35. **(a)** From (28), $k = -\frac{1}{T}\ln 2 = -\frac{1}{140}\ln 2 \approx -0.005$ so $y = 10e^{-0.005t}$ (approximately).

(b) 10 weeks $= 70$ days so $y = 10e^{-0.35} \approx 7$ mg

36. **(a)** $y = 15,000e^{kt}$, but $y = 5000$ when $t = 10$ so $5000 = 15,000e^{10k}$, $e^{10k} = 1/3$,

$$k = \frac{1}{10}\ln(1/3) = -\frac{1}{10}\ln 3 \approx -0.11, \; y = 15,000e^{-0.11t}$$

(b) From (28), $T = 10\frac{\ln 2}{\ln 3} \approx 6.3$ hours

37. $100e^{0.02t} = 5000$, $e^{0.02t} = 50$, $t = \frac{1}{0.02}\ln 50 \approx 196$ days

38. From Example 10, $y = y_0e^{-0.00012t}$ so when $y = 0.3y_0$, $0.3y_0 = y_0e^{-0.00012t}$, $e^{-0.00012t} = 0.3$,

$$t = -\frac{\ln 0.3}{0.00012} \approx 10,000 \text{ years}$$

39. $y = y_0e^{kt}$, but $y = 0.6y_0$ when $t = 5$ so $0.6y_0 = y_0e^{5k}$, $e^{5k} = 0.6$

$$k = \frac{1}{5}\ln 0.6 \text{ so } T = -5\frac{\ln 2}{\ln 0.6} \approx 6.8 \text{ years}$$

40. **(a)** $p = p_0e^{kh}$

(b) $p = 15e^{kh}$, but $p = 12$ when $h = 5000$ thus $e^{5000k} = 12/15 = 0.8$,

$$k = \frac{\ln 0.8}{5000} \text{ so when } h = 10,000, \; p = 15e^{10,000k} = 15e^{2\ln 0.8} = 15(0.64) = 9.6 \text{ lb/in}^2$$

41. **(a)** $y = 10,000e^{kt}$, but $y = 12,000$ when $t = 10$ so $10,000e^{10k} = 12,000$, $k = \dfrac{1}{10}\ln 1.2$.

When $t = 20$, $y = 10,000e^{20k} = 10,000e^{2\ln 1.2} = 10,000(1.44) = 14,400$.

(b) From (27), $T = 10\dfrac{\ln 2}{\ln 1.2} \approx 38$ years

42. $A = A_0e^{kt}$, $A = A_1$ when $t = t_1$ and $A = A_2$ when $t = t_2$, so $A_0e^{kt_1} = A_1(i)$ and $A_0e^{kt_2} = A_2$

(ii). Divide (i) by (ii) to get $e^{k(t_1-t_2)} = A_1/A_2$, $k = \dfrac{1}{t_1 - t_2}\ln(A_1/A_2)$

43. $\dfrac{dT}{dt} = k(T - C)$, $k < 0$

$\dfrac{dT}{dt} - kT = -kC$, $\rho = e^{\int -kdt} = e^{-kt}$, $e^{-kt}T = \displaystyle\int -kCe^{-kt}dt = Ce^{-kt} + K$,

$T = C + Ke^{kt}$. But $T = T_0$ when $t = 0$ so $T_0 = C + K$, $K = T_0 - C$, $T = C + (T_0 - C)e^{kt}$

44. $T = (200 - 80)e^{kt} + 80 = 120e^{kt} + 80$, but $T = 120$ when $t = 1/2$ hour so $120e^{k/2} + 80 = 120$, $e^{k/2} = 1/3$, $k = 2\ln(1/3) = -2\ln 3$ thus when $t = 1$,

$T = 120e^k + 80 = 120e^{-2\ln 3} + 80 = 120(1/9) + 80 \approx 93.3°$

45. **(a)** In t years the interest will be compounded nt times at an interest rate of r/n each time. The value at the end of 1 interval is $P + (r/n)P = P(1 + r/n)$, at the end of 2 intervals it is $P(1 + r/n) + (r/n)P(1 + r/n) = P(1 + r/n)^2$, and continuing in this fashion the value at the end of nt intervals is $P(1 + r/n)^{nt}$.

(b) Let $x = r/n$, then $n = r/x$ and

$\displaystyle\lim_{n \to +\infty} P(1 + r/n)^{nt} = \lim_{x \to 0^+} P(1 + x)^{rt/x} = \lim_{x \to 0^+} P[(1 + x)^{1/x}]^{rt} = Pe^{rt}$.

(c) The rate of increase is $dA/dt = rPe^{rt} = rA$.

46. **(a)** $A = 1000e^{(0.08)(5)} = 1000e^{0.4} \approx \$1,491.82$

(b) $Pe^{(0.08)(10)} = 10,000$, $Pe^{0.8} = 10,000$, $P = 10,000e^{-0.8} \approx \$4,493.29$

(c) From (27) with $k = r = 0.08$, $T = (\ln 2)/0.08 \approx 8.7$ years.

47. Let $y = y_0e^{kt}$ with $y = y_1$ when $t = t_1$ and $y = y_1/2$ when $t = t_1 + T$ then $y_0e^{kt_1} = y_1$ (i) and

$y_0e^{k(t_1+T)} = y_1/2$ (ii). Divide (i) by (ii) to get $e^{-kT} = 2$, $T = -\dfrac{1}{k}\ln 2$.

48. Let $y = y_0e^{kt}$ with $y = y_1$ when $t = t_1$ and $y = 3y_1$ when $t = t_1 + T$ then $y_0e^{kt_1} = y_1$ (i) and

$y_0e^{k(t_1+T)} = 3y_1$ (ii). Divide (ii) by (i) to get $e^{kT} = 3$, $T = \dfrac{1}{k}\ln 3$.

SUPPLEMENTARY EXERCISES CHAPTER 7

1. **(a)** $f(g(x)) = m\left(\dfrac{1}{mx}\right) = 1/x \neq x$; f and g are not inverses.

   (b) $f(g(x)) = \dfrac{3}{(3-x)/x+1} = x$, $g(f(x)) = \dfrac{3-3/(x+1)}{3/(x+1)} = x$; f and g are inverses.

   (c) $f(g(x)) = (x^{1/3}+2)^3 - 8 = x + 6x^{2/3} + 12x^{1/3} \neq x$; f and g are not inverses.

   (d) $f(g(x)) = x+1-1 = x$, $g(f(x)) = \sqrt[3]{x^3 - 1 + 1} = x$; f and g are inverses.

   (e) $f(g(x)) = \sqrt{e^{2\ln x}} = \sqrt{x^2} = x$ where $x > 0$, $g(f(x)) = 2\ln\sqrt{e^x} = \ln e^x = x$; f and g are inverses.

2. $y = f^{-1}(x)$, $x = f(y) = 8y^3 - 1$, $y = \dfrac{1}{2}(x+1)^{1/3} = f^{-1}(x)$.

3. $f(0) = f(2)$; f is not one-to-one so $f^{-1}(x)$ does not exist.

4. $y = f^{-1}(x)$, $x = f(y) = y^2 - 2y + 1 = (y-1)^2$, $y - 1 = \sqrt{x}$, $y = 1 + \sqrt{x} = f^{-1}(x)$.

5. $y = f^{-1}(x)$, $x = f(y) = e^{2y} + 1$, $e^{2y} = x - 1$, $y = \dfrac{1}{2}\ln(x-1) = f^{-1}(x)$.

6. $f(-1) = f(1) = \exp(1) + 1$ so $f^{-1}(x)$ does not exist.

7. f^{-1} will exist if and only if f is one-to-one. Let x_1, x_2 be any two distinct points in the domain of $y = f(x) = (ax + b)/(cx + d)$.
   $y_1 = f(x_1) = (ax_1 + b)/(cx_1 + d)$, $y_2 = f(x_2) = (ax_2 + b)/(cx_2 + d)$,
   $$y_2 - y_1 = \dfrac{(ax_2 + b)(cx_1 + d) - (ax_1 + b)(cx_2 + d)}{(cx_2 + d)(cx_1 + d)}$$
   $$= \dfrac{ad(x_2 - x_1) - bc(x_2 - x_1)}{(cx_2 + d)(cx_1 + d)} = \dfrac{(ad - bc)(x_2 - x_1)}{(cx_2 + d)(cx_2 + d)}$$
   f will be one-to-one if $y_1 \neq y_2$ (or equivalently $y_2 - y_1 \neq 0$) whenever $x_1 \neq x_2$, which occurs when $ad - bc \neq 0$. To find $f^{-1}(x)$ in this case, solve $y = (ax + b)/(cx + d)$ for x to get $x = (-dy + b)/(cy - a) = f^{-1}(y)$ so $f^{-1}(x) = (-dx + b)/(cx - a)$.

8. $f(f(x)) = \dfrac{\dfrac{x+2}{x-1} + 2}{\dfrac{x+2}{x-1} - 1} = x$

9. (a) $f(x) = \begin{cases} 2x - 5, & x \geq 5/2 \\ -2x + 5, & x < 5/2 \end{cases}$, $f'(x) = \begin{cases} 2, & x > 5/2 \\ -2, & x < 5/2 \end{cases}$

   and $f'(x)$ does not exist at $x = 5/2$. $f(x)$ is minimum when $x = 5/2$ and f is decreasing for $x < 5/2$ because $f'(x) < 0$, so f is one-to-one for x in the interval $(-\infty, 5/2)$

   (b) $f'(x) = 2(x+2)$, so f is decreasing for $x < -2$ and increasing for $x > -2$. f is one-to-one for x in $(-2, +\infty)$

   (c) $f'(x) = -\sin(x - 2\pi/3)$, $f'(x) = 0$ when $x - 2\pi/3 = n\pi$, $x = 2\pi/3 + n\pi$ where n is an integer. $f'(-\pi/3) = f'(2\pi/3) = 0$ and $f'(x) > 0$ if $-\pi/3 < x < 2\pi/3$ so f is one-to-one for x in $(-\pi/3, 2\pi/3)$.

10. $y = f^{-1}(x)$, $x = f(y) = y^3 - 8$, $y = (x + 8)^{1/3} = f^{-1}(x)$; $f'(x) = 3x^2$,

    $f'(f^{-1}(x)) = 3[(x + 8)^{1/3}]^2 = 3(x + 8)^{2/3}$, $(f^{-1})'(x) = \dfrac{1}{3(x + 8)^{2/3}}$.

11. $y = f^{-1}(x)$, $x = f(y) = \dfrac{3}{y + 1}$, $y = \dfrac{3}{x} - 1 = f^{-1}(x)$; $f'(x) = -\dfrac{3}{(x + 1)^2}$,

    $f'(f^{-1}(x)) = -\dfrac{3}{(3/x)^2} = -\dfrac{x^2}{3}$, $(f^{-1})'(x) = -\dfrac{3}{x^2}$.

12. $y = f^{-1}(x)$, $x = f(y) = my + b$, $y = \dfrac{1}{m}(x - b) = f^{-1}(x)$; $f'(x) = m$, $f'(f^{-1}(x)) = m$,

    $(f^{-1})'(x) = \dfrac{1}{m}$.

13. $y = f^{-1}(x)$, $x = f(y) = e^{y/2}$, $y = 2\ln x = f^{-1}(x)$; $f'(x) = \dfrac{1}{2}e^{x/2}$, $f'(f^{-1}(x)) = \dfrac{1}{2}e^{\ln x} = \dfrac{x}{2}$,

    $(f^{-1})'(x) = \dfrac{2}{x}$.

14. The midpoint of the line segment joining (a, b) and (b, a) is $\left(\dfrac{a + b}{2}, \dfrac{a + b}{2}\right)$ which lies on $y = x$. The slope of the line segment is $(a - b)/(b - a) = -1$ which is the negative reciprocal of the slope of $y = x$ so the lines are perpendicular.

15. (a) $\ln(1/12) = -\ln 12 = -\ln(2^2 \cdot 3) = -(2\ln 2 + \ln 3) = -(2r + s)$

    (b) $\ln(9/\sqrt{8}) = \ln(3^2 \cdot 2^{-3/2}) = 2\ln 3 - \dfrac{3}{2}\ln 2 = 2s - 3r/2$

    (c) $\ln(\sqrt[4]{8/3}) = \dfrac{1}{4}\ln(2^3/3) = \dfrac{1}{4}(3\ln 2 - \ln 3) = (3r - s)/4$

16. (a) $e^{2-\ln x} = e^2/e^{\ln x} = e^2/x$

    (b) $\exp(\ln x^2 - 2\ln y) = \exp(\ln x^2)/\exp(\ln y^2) = x^2/y^2$

    (c) $\ln[x^3 \exp(-x^2)] = \ln x^3 + \ln[\exp(-x^2)] = 3\ln x - x^2$

17. (a) $25^x = 3^{1-x}$, $(5^2)^x = 3^{1-x}$, $5^{2x} = 3^{1-x}$, $\ln 5^{2x} = \ln 3^{1-x}$,

$2x \ln 5 = (1-x) \ln 3$, $x = (\ln 3)/(2\ln 5 + \ln 3)$

(b) $\sinh x = \dfrac{1}{4} \cosh x$, $\dfrac{1}{2}(e^x - e^{-x}) = \dfrac{1}{8}(e^x + e^{-x})$, $3e^x = 5e^{-x}$, $e^{2x} = 5/3$, $x = (\ln 5 - \ln 3)/2$

18. $3\ln(e^{2x}(e^x)^3) + 2\exp(\ln 1) = 3\ln e^{5x} + 2 = 15x + 2$

19. (a) $\cosh x = (1 + \sinh^2 x)^{1/2} = (1 + 9/25)^{1/2} = \sqrt{34}/5$

(b) $\tanh x = \sinh x / \cosh x = -3/\sqrt{34}$

(c) $\sinh 2x = 2\sinh x \cosh x = -6\sqrt{34}/25$

20. (a) $2^e = e^{e\ln 2}$ (b) $(\sqrt{2})^\pi = 2^{\pi/2} = e^{(\pi/2)\ln 2}$

21. $y = e^{-x/2}$, $dy/dx = -\dfrac{1}{2}e^{-x/2} = -1/(2\sqrt{e^x})$

22. $y = e^{-\sqrt{x}}$, $dy/dx = -e^{-\sqrt{x}}/(2\sqrt{x}) = -1/(2\sqrt{x}\,e^{\sqrt{x}})$

23. $dy/dx = (\ln x - 1)/(\ln x)^2$ **24.** $y = -e^x \ln x$, $dy/dx = -e^x(\ln x + 1/x)$

25. $y = x/x = 1$, $dy/dx = 0$

26. $y = \dfrac{1}{2}\ln(x^2 + 2x)$, $dy/dx = (x+1)/(x^2 + 2x)$

27. $y = x\ln 10 - \ln\sin x$, $dy/dx = \ln 10 - \cot x$

28. $dy/dx = 2e^{-2x}\sin(e^{-2x})$

29. $y = x^4 e^{\tan x}$, $dy/dx = x^3 e^{\tan x}(x\sec^2 x + 4)$

30. $y = \ln|a+x| - \ln|a-x|$, $dy/dx = 1/(a+x) + 1/(a-x) = 2a/(a^2 - x^2)$

31. $dy/dx = \dfrac{1 + x/\sqrt{x^2 + a^2}}{x + \sqrt{x^2 + a^2}} = 1/\sqrt{x^2 + a^2}$

32. $dy/dx = \dfrac{3\sec^2 3x + 3\sec 3x \tan 3x}{\tan 3x + \sec 3x} = 3\sec 3x$

33. $y = \exp(3x^2)$, $dy/dx = 6x\exp(3x^2)$

34. $y = 3\ln x - \dfrac{1}{2}\ln(5 + \sin x)$, $dy/dx = \dfrac{3}{x} - \dfrac{\cos x}{2(5 + \sin x)}$

35. $y = (\ln \sqrt{x})^{1/2}$, $dy/dx = \dfrac{1}{2}(\ln \sqrt{x})^{-1/2} \left(\dfrac{1}{2x}\right) = 1/(4x\sqrt{\ln \sqrt{x}})$

36. $dy/dx = 5e^{5x} + 5e(5x)^{e-1}$

37. $dy/dx = \pi^x(\pi x^{\pi-1}) + x^\pi(\pi^x \ln \pi) = \pi^x x^{\pi-1}(\pi + x \ln \pi)$

38. $y = 4e^{3x}/e^{5x/2} = 4e^{x/2}$, $dy/dx = 2e^{x/2}$

39. $dy/dx = 5 \cosh[\tanh(5x)] \operatorname{sech}^2(5x)$

40. $4x^3 + e^{xy}(xy' + y) - 2yy' = 0$, $y' = (4x^3 + ye^{xy})/(2y - xe^{xy})$

41. $y = e^{3x}(1 + 2e^{-x} + e^{-2x}) = e^{3x} + 2e^{2x} + e^x$, $dy/dx = 3e^{3x} + 4e^{2x} + e^x$.

42. $\ln y = x^3 \ln \cosh x$, $y'/y = x^3 \tanh x + 3x^2 \ln \cosh x$, $y' = x^2(\cosh x)^{x^3}(x \tanh x + 3 \ln \cosh x)$

43. $y = e^{ax} \sin bx$, $y' = e^{ax}[b \cos bx + a \sin bx]$,
$y'' = e^{ax}[2ab \cos bx + (a^2 - b^2) \sin bx]$ so $y'' - 2ay' + (a^2 + b^2)y = 0$

44. Let $y = u^v$ then $\ln y = v \ln u$, $\dfrac{1}{y}\dfrac{dy}{dx} = v\left(\dfrac{1}{u}\dfrac{du}{dx}\right) + (\ln u)\dfrac{dv}{dx}$,

$\dfrac{dy}{dx} = u^v\left[\dfrac{v}{u}\dfrac{du}{dx} + \ln u\dfrac{dv}{dx}\right] = vu^{v-1}\dfrac{du}{dx} + u^v \ln u\dfrac{dv}{dx}$

when u is constant, $d(u^v)/dx = u^v \ln u\, dv/dx$; when v is constant, $d(u^v)/dx = vu^{v-1}du/dx$

45. **(a)** $dy = -e^{-x}dx$ **(b)** $dy = \dfrac{1}{1+x}dx$ **(c)** $dy = 2x(\ln 2)2^{x^2}dx$

46. $y = 3^{2x}5^{7x} = e^{2x \ln 3}e^{7x \ln 5} = e^{(2\ln 3 + 7\ln 5)x}$ so $y = e^{kx}$ where $k = 2\ln 3 + 7\ln 5$ thus
$dy/dx = ke^{kx} = ky$

47. **(a)** $\dfrac{1}{\sqrt{4 + e^{\ln x}}}\left(\dfrac{1}{x}\right) = \dfrac{1}{x\sqrt{4 + x}}$ **(b)** $\sqrt{\ln e^{5x} + e^{5x}}(5e^{5x}) = 5e^{5x}\sqrt{5x + e^{5x}}$

48. $y = F(x) = \displaystyle\int_{-\pi}^{x}(3\sin^2 2t + 2\cos^2 3t)^{1/2}dt$

49. $Y = \ln y = \ln(Ce^{kt}) = \ln C + kt$ which is linear in t and Y so the graph is a straight line.

50. **(a)** $u = 4 + e^{2x}$, $du = 2e^{2x}dx$, $\dfrac{1}{2}\displaystyle\int u\, du = \dfrac{1}{4}(4 + e^{2x})^2 + C$

(b) $\int (4e^{2x} + e^{4x})dx = 2e^{2x} + \frac{1}{4}e^{4x} + C$

The results in (a) and (b) differ by a constant:

$$\left[\frac{1}{4}(4 + e^{2x})^2 + C\right] - \left[2e^{2x} + \frac{1}{4}e^{4x} + C\right] = \left(4 + 2e^{2x} + \frac{1}{4}e^{4x} + C\right) - \left[2e^{2x} + \frac{1}{4}e^{4x} + C\right] = 4$$

51. $u = 1 + e^x$, $\int \frac{1}{u}du = \ln(1 + e^x) + C$

52. $\int (e^{-x} + 1)dx = -e^{-x} + x + C$ **53.** $\dfrac{x^{e+1}}{e+1} + C$

54. $u = 5 - 2x^3$, $-\frac{1}{6}\int \frac{1}{u}du = -\frac{1}{6}\ln|5 - 2x^3| + C$

55. $\int \left(\frac{4}{x} - \frac{3}{x^2}\right) dx = 4\ln|x| + 3/x + C$

56. $u = \ln x^2 = 2\ln|x|$, $\frac{1}{2}\int u^2 du = \frac{1}{6}(\ln x^2)^3 + C$

57. $u = 2\sec x - 1$, $\frac{1}{2}\int \frac{1}{u}du = \frac{1}{2}\ln|2\sec x - 1| + C$

58. $\frac{1}{5}\ln(3 + e^{5x}) + C$

59. $u = \sin 2x$, $\frac{1}{2}\int \exp(u)du = \frac{1}{2}\exp(\sin 2x) + C$

60. $\int \dfrac{\sinh(3x+1)}{\cosh(3x+1)}dx = \frac{1}{3}\ln[\cosh(3x+1)] + C$

61. $u = \tanh x$, $\int u\, du = \frac{1}{2}\tanh^2 x + C$

62. $\int (4e^{2x} + e^{-x})dx = 2e^{2x} - e^{-x} + C$ **63.** $u = \ln x$, $\int_1^2 \frac{1}{u}du = \ln 2$

64. $\int_0^1 e^{-x/2}dx = 2(1 - e^{-1/2})$ **65.** $u = \tan x$, $\int_0^1 2^u du = \left.\dfrac{2^u}{\ln 2}\right]_0^1 = \dfrac{1}{\ln 2}$

66. $u = \sqrt{x}$, $2\int_1^2 e^{-u}\,du = 2(e^{-1} - e^{-2})$

67. $\dfrac{d}{dx}\left[\dfrac{e^{kx}}{k} + C\right] = e^{kx}$

68. **(a)** $\dfrac{d}{dx}(10^x)\Big|_{x=0} = 10^x \ln 10\Big|_{x=0} = \ln 10$

   (b) $\dfrac{d}{dx}(e^{x^2})\Big|_{x=3} = 2xe^{x^2}\Big|_{x=3} = 6e^9$

   (c) $\dfrac{d}{dx}(\ln x)\Big|_{x=e^2} = \dfrac{1}{x}\Big|_{x=e^2} = e^{-2}$

   (d) $\dfrac{d}{dx}(2^x)\Big|_{x=1} = 2^x \ln 2\Big|_{x=1} = 2\ln 2$

69. $y = x^3 e^{-x}$
    $y' = x^2(3 - x)e^{-x}$
    $y' = 0$ when $x = 0, 3$
    $y'' = x(x^2 - 6x + 6)e^{-x}$
    $y'' = 0$ when $x = 0, 3 \pm \sqrt{3}$

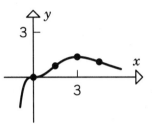

70. $f'(x) = x(2 - x)e^{-x}$; critical points $x = 0, 2$; $f''(x) = (x^2 - 4x + 2)e^{-x}$
   $f''(0) > 0$, relative min at $x = 0$; $f''(2) < 0$, relative max at $x = 2$.

71. $y'' = e^y y' + 2y' + 1$. If x_0 is a critical point of y then when $x = x_0$, $y' = 0$ and
   $y'' = e^{y_0}(0) + 2(0) + 1 = 1 > 0$ so a relative minimum occurs at x_0.

72. $-1 \le \sin 2x \le 1$ so $-e^{-x/2} \le e^{-x/2}\sin 2x \le e^{-x/2}$; $e^{-x/2}\sin 2x = e^{-x/2}$ when $\sin 2x = 1$,
   $2x = \pi/2 + 2\pi n$ where n is an integer, $x = \pi/4 + \pi n$, so $x = \pi/4$, $5\pi/4$ for x in $[-\pi/2, 3\pi/2]$.
   Similarly $e^{-x/2}\sin 2x = -e^{-x/2}$ when $x = -\pi/4$, $3\pi/4$. The x-intercepts occur when
   $e^{-x/2}\sin 2x = 0$, $\sin 2x = 0$, $2x = n\pi$, $x = n\pi/2$, so $x = -\pi/2, 0, \pi/2, \pi, 3\pi/2$.

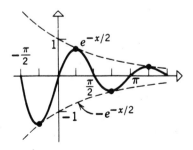

73. $A = \displaystyle\int_0^b e^{-2x}\,dx = -\frac{1}{2}(e^{-2b}-1) = \frac{1}{2}-\frac{1}{2}e^{-2b}$. If $A = 1/4$ then $1/2 - e^{-2b}/2 = 1/4$, $e^{-2b} = 1/2$,

$b = (1/2)\ln 2$. $\displaystyle\lim_{b\to+\infty} A = 1/2$

74. $V = \pi\displaystyle\int_1^3 16(2x-1)^{-1}\,dx = 8\pi\ln(2x-1)\Big]_1^3 = 8\pi\ln 5$

75. $y' = \sinh x$, $1 + (y')^2 = 1 + \sinh^2 x = \cosh^2 x$,

$S = \displaystyle\int_0^1 2\pi\cosh x(\cosh x)\,dx = 2\pi\int_0^1 \cosh^2 x\,dx = \pi\int_0^1 (1+\cosh 2x)\,dx$

$= \pi\left(x + \frac{1}{2}\sinh 2x\right)\Big]_0^1 = \pi(2+\sinh 2)/2$

76. Let $y =$ amount undissolved after t min, then $dy/dt = ky$ so $y = y_0 e^{kt} = 9e^{kt}$. But $y = 6$ when $t = 1$ so $9e^k = 6$, $k = \ln(2/3)$. After 3 min $y = 9e^{3k} = 9e^{3\ln(2/3)} = 9(2/3)^3 = 8/3$ g.

77. Let $y =$ population (in millions) t years after 1970, then $y = 205e^{0.018t}$.

   (a) $t = 2000 - 1970 = 30$ for the year 2000 so $y = 205e^{(0.018)(30)} = 205e^{0.54} \approx 352$ million.

   (b) 1 billion = 1000 million, $205e^{0.018t} = 1000$ when $t = (1/0.018)\ln(1000/205) \approx 88$. The population will reach one billion in the year $1970 + 88 = 2058$.

CHAPTER 8

Inverse Trigonometric and Hyperbolic Functions

EXERCISE SET 8.1

1. (a) $-\pi/2$ (b) π (c) $-\pi/4$ (d) $\pi/4$ (e) 0 (f) $\pi/2$

2. (a) $\pi/3$ (b) $\pi/3$ (c) $\pi/4$ (d) $3\pi/4$ (e) $4\pi/3$ (f) $-5\pi/6$

3. $\theta = -\pi/3$; $\cos\theta = 1/2$, $\tan\theta = -\sqrt{3}$, $\cot\theta = -1/\sqrt{3}$, $\sec\theta = 2$, $\csc\theta = -2/\sqrt{3}$

4. $\theta = \pi/3$; $\sin\theta = \sqrt{3}/2$, $\tan\theta = \sqrt{3}$, $\cot\theta = 1/\sqrt{3}$, $\sec\theta = 2$, $\csc\theta = 2/\sqrt{3}$

5. $\tan\theta = 4/3$, $0 < \theta < \pi/2$; use the triangle shown to get $\sin\theta = 4/5$, $\cos\theta = 3/5$, $\cot\theta = 3/4$, $\sec\theta = 5/3$, $\csc\theta = 5/4$.

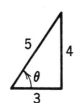

6.

	domain	range
$\sin^{-1}$	$[-1,1]$	$[-\pi/2, \pi/2]$
$\cos^{-1}$	$[-1,1]$	$[0, \pi]$
$\tan^{-1}$	$(-\infty, +\infty)$	$(-\pi/2, \pi/2)$
$\cot^{-1}$	$(-\infty, +\infty)$	$(0, \pi)$
$\sec^{-1}$	$(-\infty, -1] \cup [1, +\infty)$	$[0, \pi/2) \cup [\pi, 3\pi/2)$
$\csc^{-1}$	$(-\infty, -1] \cup [1, +\infty)$	$(0, \pi/2] \cup (-\pi, -\pi/2]$

7. (a) $\pi/7$ (b) $\sin^{-1}(\sin\pi) = \sin^{-1}(\sin 0) = 0$
    (c) $\sin^{-1}(\sin(5\pi/7)) = \sin^{-1}(\sin(2\pi/7)) = 2\pi/7$
    (d) Note that $\pi/2 < 630 - 200\pi < \pi$ so
    $$\sin(630) = \sin(630 - 200\pi) = \sin(\pi - (630 - 200\pi)) = \sin(201\pi - 630)$$
    where $0 < 201\pi - 630 < \pi/2$; $\sin^{-1}(\sin 630) = \sin^{-1}(\sin(201\pi - 630)) = 201\pi - 630$.

8. (a) $\pi/7$ (b) π

    (c) $\cos^{-1}(\cos(12\pi/7)) = \cos^{-1}(\cos(2\pi/7)) = 2\pi/7$

    (d) Note that $-\pi/2 < 200 - 64\pi < 0$ so $\cos(200) = \cos(200 - 64\pi) = \cos(64\pi - 200)$ where
        $0 < 64\pi - 200 < \pi/2$; $\cos^{-1}(\cos 200) = \cos^{-1}(\cos(64\pi - 200)) = 64\pi - 200$.

9. (a) $0 \le x \le \pi$ (b) $-1 \le x \le 1$

    (c) $-\pi/2 < x < \pi/2$ (d) $-\infty < x < +\infty$

    (e) $0 < x \le \pi/2$ or $-\pi < x \le -\pi/2$ (f) $|x| \ge 1$

10. Let $\theta = \sin^{-1}(-3/4)$ then
    $\sin\theta = -3/4$, $-\pi/2 < \theta < 0$
    and (see figure) $\sec\theta = 4/\sqrt{7}$

    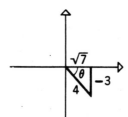

11. Let $\theta = \cos^{-1}(3/5)$,
    $\sin 2\theta = 2\sin\theta\cos\theta$
    $\qquad\quad = 2(4/5)(3/5) = 24/25$

12. $\tan^{-1}(-1) = -\pi/4$ 13. $\sin^{-1}(1) = \pi/2$

14. Let $\alpha = \sin^{-1}(2/3)$,
    $\beta = \cos^{-1}(1/3)$,
    $\sin(\alpha + \beta) = \sin\alpha\cos\beta + \cos\alpha\sin\beta$
    $\qquad\qquad = (2/3)(1/3) + (\sqrt{5}/3)(2\sqrt{2}/3)$
    $\qquad\qquad = 2(1 + \sqrt{10})/9$

15. Let $\theta = \sec^{-1}(3/2)$,

$$\tan 2\theta = \frac{2\tan\theta}{1 - \tan^2\theta}$$

$$= \frac{2(\sqrt{5}/2)}{1 - 5/4} = -4\sqrt{5}$$

16. $\tan(\alpha + \beta) = \dfrac{\tan\alpha + \tan\beta}{1 - \tan\alpha\tan\beta}$,

$$\tan(\tan^{-1}x + \tan^{-1}y) = \frac{\tan(\tan^{-1}x) + \tan(\tan^{-1}y)}{1 - \tan(\tan^{-1}x)\tan(\tan^{-1}y)} = \frac{x+y}{1-xy}$$

so $\quad \tan^{-1}x + \tan^{-1}y = \tan^{-1}\dfrac{x+y}{1-xy}$.

17. (a) $\tan^{-1}\dfrac{1}{2} + \tan^{-1}\dfrac{1}{3} = \tan^{-1}\dfrac{1/2 + 1/3}{1 - (1/2)(1/3)} = \tan^{-1}1 = \pi/4$

(b) $2\tan^{-1}\dfrac{1}{3} = \tan^{-1}\dfrac{1}{3} + \tan^{-1}\dfrac{1}{3} = \tan^{-1}\dfrac{1/3 + 1/3}{1 - (1/3)(1/3)} = \tan^{-1}\dfrac{3}{4}$,

$2\tan^{-1}\dfrac{1}{3} + \tan^{-1}\dfrac{1}{7} = \tan^{-1}\dfrac{3}{4} + \tan^{-1}\dfrac{1}{7} = \tan^{-1}\dfrac{3/4 + 1/7}{1 - (3/4)(1/7)} = \tan^{-1}1 = \pi/4$

18. (a) $\sin(\cos^{-1}x) = \sqrt{1 - x^2}$ **(b)** $\tan(\cos^{-1}x) = \dfrac{\sqrt{1 - x^2}}{x}$

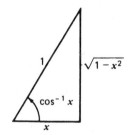

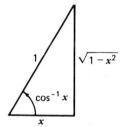

(c) $\csc(\tan^{-1}x) = \dfrac{\sqrt{1+x^2}}{x}$ **(d)** $\sin(\tan^{-1}x) = \dfrac{x}{\sqrt{1+x^2}}$

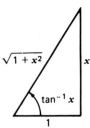   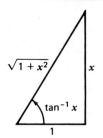

19. **(a)** $\cos(\tan^{-1}x) = \dfrac{1}{\sqrt{1+x^2}}$ **(b)** $\tan(\cot^{-1}x) = \dfrac{1}{x}$

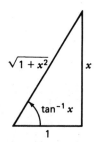   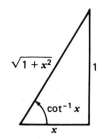

(c) $\sin(\sec^{-1}x) = \dfrac{\sqrt{x^2-1}}{x}$ **(d)** $\cot(\csc^{-1}x) = \sqrt{x^2-1}$

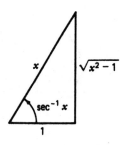   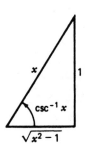

20. **(a)** $A = \tan^{-1}1, B = \tan^{-1}2, C = \tan^{-1}3$, and $A + B + C = \pi$.

(b) $\alpha = \tan^{-1}1, \beta = \tan^{-1}\frac{1}{2}, \gamma = \tan^{-1}\frac{1}{3}$, and $\alpha + \beta + \gamma = \pi/2$.

21.   **(a)**

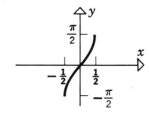

                                              (b)

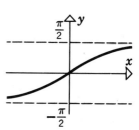

22.   **(a)**

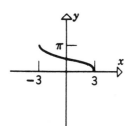

                                              (b)

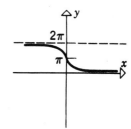

23.   **(a)** let $\theta = \sin^{-1}(-x)$ then $\sin\theta = -x$, $-\pi/2 \le \theta \le \pi/2$. But $\sin(-\theta) = -\sin\theta$ and $-\pi/2 \le -\theta \le \pi/2$ so $\sin(-\theta) = -(-x) = x$, $-\theta = \sin^{-1}x$, $\theta = -\sin^{-1}x$.

    (b) proof is similar to that in part (a).

24.   **(a)** Let $\theta = \cos^{-1}(-x)$ then $\cos\theta = -x$, $0 \le \theta \le \pi$. But $\cos(\pi - \theta) = -\cos\theta$ and $0 \le \pi - \theta \le \pi$ so $\cos(\pi - \theta) = x$, $\pi - \theta = \cos^{-1}x$, $\theta = \pi - \cos^{-1}x$

    (b) Let $\theta = \sec^{-1}(-x)$ for $x \ge 1$ then $\sec\theta = -x$ for $\pi \le \theta < 3\pi/2$. But $\sec(\theta - \pi) = -\sec\theta$ and $0 \le \theta - \pi < \pi/2$ so $\sec(\theta - \pi) = x$, $\theta - \pi = \sec^{-1}x$, $\theta = \pi + \sec^{-1}x$.

25.   If $-1 \le x < 0$ then $0 < -x \le 1$ so $\sin^{-1}(-x) + \cos^{-1}(-x) = \pi/2$, but $\sin^{-1}(-x) = -\sin^{-1}x$ and $\cos^{-1}(-x) = \pi - \cos^{-1}x$ thus $-\sin^{-1}x + (\pi - \cos^{-1}x) = \pi/2$, $\sin^{-1}x + \cos^{-1}x = \pi/2$.

26.   **(a)** $y = \cot^{-1}x$, $x = \cot y$, $\tan y = 1/x$, $y = \tan^{-1}(1/x)$.
    (b) $y = \sec^{-1}x$, $x = \sec y$, $\cos y = 1/x$, $y = \cos^{-1}(1/x)$.
    (c) $y = \csc^{-1}x$, $x = \csc y$, $\sin y = 1/x$, $y = \sin^{-1}(1/x)$.

27.   **(a)** $55.0°$ **(b)** $33.6°$ **(c)** $25.8°$

28. $x = 2\pi - \cos^{-1}k$ **29.** $x = \pi + \tan^{-1}k$

30. $2x = \sin^{-1}k$ or $2x = \pi - \sin^{-1}k$ so $x = \frac{1}{2}\sin^{-1}k$ or $x = \pi/2 - \frac{1}{2}\sin^{-1}k$.

31. $x = \pi - \sin^{-1}(0.37) \approx 2.7626$ **32.** $x = \pi + \cos^{-1}(0.85) \approx 3.6964$

33. $x = \tan^{-1}(3.16) - \pi \approx -1.8773$

34. $\theta = 180° + \sin^{-1}(0.61) \approx 217.6°$

35. $\theta = -\cos^{-1}(0.23) \approx -76.7°$

36. $\theta = 180° - \tan^{-1}(0.45) \approx 155.8°$

37. **(b)** $\theta = \sin^{-1}\frac{R}{R+h} = \sin^{-1}\frac{6378}{16,378} \approx 23°$

38. **(a)** If $\gamma = 90°$, then $\sin \gamma = 1$, $\sqrt{1 - \sin^2 \iota \sin^2 \gamma} = \sqrt{1 - \sin^2 \iota} = \cos \iota$,
$D = \tan \iota \tan \lambda = (\tan 23.55°)(\tan 65°) \approx 0.934684245$ so $h \approx 21.2$ hours.

(b) If $\gamma = 270°$, then $\sin \gamma = -1$, $D = -\tan \iota \tan \lambda \approx -0.934684245$ so $h \approx 2.8$ hours.

39. $\sin 2\theta = gR/v^2 = (9.8)(18)/(14)^2 = 0.9$, $2\theta = \sin^{-1}(0.9)$ or $2\theta = 180° - \sin^{-1}(0.9)$ so
$\theta = \frac{1}{2}\sin^{-1}(0.9) \approx 32°$ or $\theta = 90° - \frac{1}{2}\sin^{-1}(0.9) \approx 58°$. The ball will have a lower
parabolic trajectory for $\theta = 32°$ and hence will result in the shorter time of flight.

40. $4^2 = 2^2 + 3^2 - 2(2)(3)\cos\theta$, $\cos\theta = -1/4$, $\theta = \cos^{-1}(-1/4) \approx 104°$

41. $y = 0$ when $x^2 = 6000v^2/g$, $x = 10v\sqrt{60/g} = 1000\sqrt{30}$ for $v = 400$ and $g = 32$;
$\tan \theta = 3000/x = 3/\sqrt{30}$, $\theta = \tan^{-1}(3/\sqrt{30}) \approx 29°$.

42. $\theta = \alpha - \beta$,

$\cot \alpha = \dfrac{x}{a+b}$ and $\cot \beta = \dfrac{x}{b}$

so $\theta = \cot^{-1}\dfrac{x}{a+b} - \cot^{-1}\dfrac{x}{b}$

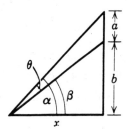

43. **(a)** $\sin^{-1} X = \tan^{-1}\dfrac{X}{\sqrt{1 - X^2}}$

$= ATN\dfrac{X}{\sqrt{1 - X^2}}$

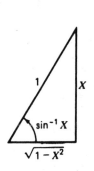

(b) $\sin^{-1} X + \cos^{-1} X = \pi/2$

$\cos^{-1} X = \pi/2 - \sin^{-1} X$

$= \pi/2 - \tan^{-1}\dfrac{X}{\sqrt{1 - X^2}}$

$\approx 1.5708 - \tan^{-1}\dfrac{X}{\sqrt{1 - X^2}}$

$= 1.5708 - ATN\dfrac{X}{\sqrt{1 - X^2}}$

EXERCISE SET 8.2

1. (a) $\dfrac{1}{\sqrt{1-x^2/9}}(1/3) = 1/\sqrt{9-x^2}$

    (b) $-2/\sqrt{1-(2x+1)^2}$

2. (a) $2x/(1+x^4)$

    (b) $-\dfrac{1}{1+x}\left(\dfrac{1}{2}x^{-1/2}\right) = -\dfrac{1}{2(1+x)\sqrt{x}}$

3. (a) $\dfrac{1}{x^7\sqrt{x^{14}-1}}(7x^6) = \dfrac{7}{x\sqrt{x^{14}-1}}$

    (b) $-1/\sqrt{e^{2x}-1}$

4. (a) $y = 1/\tan x = \cot x,\ dy/dx = -\csc^2 x$

    (b) $y = (\tan^{-1} x)^{-1},\ dy/dx = -(\tan^{-1} x)^{-2}\left(\dfrac{1}{1+x^2}\right)$

5. (a) $\dfrac{1}{\sqrt{1-1/x^2}}(-1/x^2) = -\dfrac{1}{|x|\sqrt{x^2-1}}$

    (b) $\dfrac{\sin x}{\sqrt{1-\cos^2 x}} = \dfrac{\sin x}{|\sin x|} = \left\{ \begin{array}{ll} 1, & \sin x > 0 \\ -1, & \sin x < 0 \end{array} \right.$

6. (a) $-\dfrac{1}{(\cos^{-1} x)\sqrt{1-x^2}}$

    (b) $-\dfrac{1}{2\sqrt{\cot^{-1} x}(1+x^2)}$

7. (a) $\dfrac{e^x}{x\sqrt{x^2-1}} + e^x \sec^{-1} x$

    (b) $\dfrac{3x^2(\sin^{-1} x)^2}{\sqrt{1-x^2}} + 2x(\sin^{-1} x)^3$

8. (a) 0

    (b) 0

9. (a) $\dfrac{1}{1+(1-x)^2/(1+x)^2}\left[\dfrac{(1+x)(-1)-(1-x)(1)}{(1+x)^2}\right] = -\dfrac{2}{(1+x)^2+(1-x)^2} = -1/(x^2+1)$

    (b) $10(1+x\csc^{-1} x)^9(-1/\sqrt{x^2-1}+\csc^{-1} x)$

10. (a) $\dfrac{-3e^{-3x}}{\sqrt{1-e^{-6x}}}$

    (b) $\dfrac{2xe^{2x}+e^{2x}}{1+x^2e^{4x}}$

11. (a) $\dfrac{1}{1+(1-x)/(1+x)} \cdot \dfrac{1}{2}\left(\dfrac{1-x}{1+x}\right)^{-1/2} \dfrac{(1+x)(-1)-(1-x)(1)}{(1+x)^2} = -\dfrac{1}{2\sqrt{1-x^2}}$

(b) $\dfrac{x+2x\ln x}{\sqrt{1-x^4\ln^2 x}}$

12. $x^3 + x\tan^{-1} y = e^y$, $3x^2 + \dfrac{x}{1+y^2}y' + \tan^{-1} y = e^y y'$, $y' = \dfrac{(3x^2+\tan^{-1} y)(1+y^2)}{(1+y^2)e^y - x}$

13. $\sin^{-1}(xy) = \cos^{-1}(x-y)$, $\dfrac{1}{\sqrt{1-x^2y^2}}(xy'+y) = -\dfrac{1}{\sqrt{1-(x-y)^2}}(1-y')$,

$y' = \dfrac{y\sqrt{1-(x-y)^2}+\sqrt{1-x^2y^2}}{\sqrt{1-x^2y^2}-x\sqrt{1-(x-y)^2}}$

14. $\sin^{-1} x\Big]_0^{1/\sqrt{2}} = \sin^{-1}(1/\sqrt{2}) - \sin^{-1} 0 = \pi/4$

15. $\tan^{-1} x\Big]_{-1}^{1} = \tan^{-1} 1 - \tan^{-1}(-1) = \pi/4 - (-\pi/4) = \pi/2$

16. $\sec^{-1} x\Big]_{\sqrt{2}}^{2} = \sec^{-1} 2 - \sec^{-1}\sqrt{2} = \pi/3 - \pi/4 = \pi/12$

17. $\sec^{-1} x\Big]_{-\sqrt{2}}^{-2/\sqrt{3}} = \sec^{-1}(-2/\sqrt{3}) - \sec^{-1}(-\sqrt{2}) = 7\pi/6 - 5\pi/4 = -\pi/12$

18. $u = 2x$, $\dfrac{1}{2}\displaystyle\int \dfrac{1}{\sqrt{1-u^2}}\,du = \dfrac{1}{2}\sin^{-1} 2x + C$

19. $u = 4x$, $\dfrac{1}{4}\displaystyle\int \dfrac{1}{1+u^2}\,du = \dfrac{1}{4}\tan^{-1} 4x + C$

20. $u = 3x$, $\displaystyle\int \dfrac{1}{u\sqrt{u^2-1}}\,du = \sec^{-1} 3x + C$

21. $u = e^x$, $\displaystyle\int \dfrac{1}{1+u^2}\,du = \tan^{-1}(e^x) + C$

22. $u = e^{-x}$, $-\displaystyle\int_{1/2}^{\sqrt{3}/2} \dfrac{1}{\sqrt{1-u^2}}\,du = -\sin^{-1} u\Big]_{1/2}^{\sqrt{3}/2} = -\sin^{-1}\dfrac{\sqrt{3}}{2} + \sin^{-1}\dfrac{1}{2} = -\dfrac{\pi}{3} + \dfrac{\pi}{6} = -\dfrac{\pi}{6}$

23. $u = \sqrt{x}$, $2\displaystyle\int_{1}^{\sqrt{3}} \dfrac{1}{u^2+1}\,du = 2\tan^{-1} u\Big]_{1}^{\sqrt{3}} = 2(\tan^{-1}\sqrt{3} - \tan^{-1} 1) = 2(\pi/3 - \pi/4) = \pi/6$

24. $u = t^2$, $\dfrac{1}{2}\displaystyle\int \dfrac{1}{u^2 + 1}\,du = \dfrac{1}{2}\tan^{-1}(t^2) + C$

25. $u = \tan x$, $\displaystyle\int \dfrac{1}{\sqrt{1 - u^2}}\,du = \sin^{-1}(\tan x) + C$

26. $u = \cos\theta$, $-\displaystyle\int \dfrac{1}{u^2 + 1}\,du = -\tan^{-1}(\cos\theta) + C$

27. $u = \ln x$, $\displaystyle\int \dfrac{1}{\sqrt{1 - u^2}}\,du = \sin^{-1}(\ln x) + C$

28. For (17), let $x = au$ then $dx = a\,du$,

$$\int \frac{1}{\sqrt{a^2 - x^2}}\,dx = \int \frac{a}{\sqrt{a^2 - a^2 u^2}}\,du = \int \frac{1}{\sqrt{1 - u^2}}\,du = \sin^{-1}(x/a) + C$$

For (19), with $x = au$,

$$\int \frac{1}{x\sqrt{x^2 - a^2}}\,dx = \int \frac{a}{au\sqrt{a^2 u^2 - a^2}}\,du = \frac{1}{a}\int \frac{1}{u\sqrt{u^2 - 1}}\,du = \frac{1}{a}\sec^{-1}(x/a) + C$$

29. **(a)** $\sin^{-1}(x/3) + C$ **(b)** $(1/\sqrt{5})\tan^{-1}(x/\sqrt{5}) + C$
     (c) $(1/\sqrt{\pi})\sec^{-1}(x/\sqrt{\pi}) + C$

30. **(a)** $u = e^x$, $\displaystyle\int \dfrac{1}{4 + u^2}\,du = \dfrac{1}{2}\tan^{-1}(e^x/2) + C$

     (b) $u = 2x$, $\dfrac{1}{2}\displaystyle\int \dfrac{1}{\sqrt{9 - u^2}}\,du = \dfrac{1}{2}\sin^{-1}(2x/3) + C$,

     (c) $u = \sqrt{5}y$, $\displaystyle\int \dfrac{1}{u\sqrt{u^2 - 3}}\,du = \dfrac{1}{\sqrt{3}}\sec^{-1}(\sqrt{5}y/\sqrt{3}) + C$

31. $u = \sqrt{3}x^2$, $\dfrac{1}{2\sqrt{3}}\displaystyle\int_0^{\sqrt{3}} \dfrac{1}{\sqrt{4 - u^2}}\,du = \dfrac{1}{2\sqrt{3}}\sin^{-1}\dfrac{u}{2}\Bigg]_0^{\sqrt{3}} = \dfrac{1}{2\sqrt{3}}\left(\dfrac{\pi}{3}\right) = \dfrac{\pi}{6\sqrt{3}}$

32. $u = \sqrt{x}$, $2\displaystyle\int_1^{\sqrt{2}} \dfrac{1}{\sqrt{4 - u^2}}\,du = 2\sin^{-1}\dfrac{u}{2}\Bigg]_1^{\sqrt{2}} = 2(\pi/4 - \pi/6) = \pi/6$

33. $u = 3x$, $\dfrac{1}{3}\displaystyle\int_0^{2\sqrt{3}} \dfrac{1}{4 + u^2}\,du = \dfrac{1}{6}\tan^{-1}\dfrac{u}{2}\Bigg]_0^{2\sqrt{3}} = \dfrac{1}{6}(\pi/3) = \pi/18$

34. $u = x^2$, $\dfrac{1}{2}\displaystyle\int_1^3 \dfrac{1}{3+u^2}du = \dfrac{1}{2\sqrt{3}}\tan^{-1}\dfrac{u}{\sqrt{3}}\Big]_1^3 = \dfrac{1}{2\sqrt{3}}(\pi/3 - \pi/6) = \dfrac{\pi}{12\sqrt{3}}$

35. $A = \displaystyle\int_0^{1/6} \dfrac{1}{\sqrt{1-9x^2}}dx = \dfrac{1}{3}\int_0^{1/2}\dfrac{1}{\sqrt{1-u^2}}du = \dfrac{1}{3}\sin^{-1}u\Big]_0^{1/2} = \pi/18$

36. $x = \sin y$, $A = \displaystyle\int_0^{\pi/2}\sin y\, dy = -\cos y\Big]_0^{\pi/2} = 1$

37. $V = \displaystyle\int_{-2}^2 \pi\dfrac{1}{4+x^2}dx = \dfrac{\pi}{2}\tan^{-1}(x/2)\Big]_{-2}^2 = \pi^2/4$

38. **(a)** $V = 2\pi\displaystyle\int_1^b \dfrac{x}{1+x^4}dx = \pi\tan^{-1}(x^2)\Big]_1^b = \pi\left[\tan^{-1}(b^2) - \dfrac{\pi}{4}\right]$

(b) $\displaystyle\lim_{b\to+\infty} V = \pi\left(\dfrac{\pi}{2} - \dfrac{\pi}{4}\right) = \dfrac{1}{4}\pi^2$

39. $A = \displaystyle\int_0^{\pi/2}(1-\sin y)dy$

$= (y + \cos y)]_0^{\pi/2} = \pi/2 - 1$

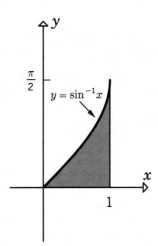

40. $\theta = \cot^{-1}\dfrac{x}{a+b} - \cot^{-1}\dfrac{x}{b}$,

$\dfrac{d\theta}{dx} = -\dfrac{1}{1 + x^2/(a+b)^2}\left(\dfrac{1}{a+b}\right) + \dfrac{1}{1+x^2/b^2}\left(\dfrac{1}{b}\right) = \dfrac{a[b(a+b) - x^2]}{[(a+b)^2 + x^2](b^2 + x^2)}$,

$d\theta/dx = 0$ when $x = \sqrt{b(a+b)}$. By the first derivative test θ is a maximum there.

41. $\theta = \pi - (\alpha + \beta)$

$= \pi - \cot^{-1}(x-2) - \cot^{-1}\dfrac{5-x}{4}$,

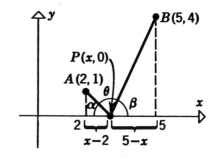

$\dfrac{d\theta}{dx} = \dfrac{1}{1+(x-2)^2} + \dfrac{-1/4}{1+(5-x)^2/16}$

$= -\dfrac{3(x^2 - 2x - 7)}{[1+(x-2)^2][16+(5-x)^2]}$

$d\theta/dx = 0$ when $x = \dfrac{2 \pm \sqrt{4+28}}{2} = 1 \pm 2\sqrt{2}$,

only $1 + 2\sqrt{2}$ is in $[2,5]$; $d\theta/dx > 0$ for x in $[2, 1+2\sqrt{2})$,

$d\theta/dx < 0$ for x in $(1+2\sqrt{2}, 5]$, θ is maximum when $x = 1 + 2\sqrt{2}$.

42. $\theta = \cot^{-1}(x/4)$

$\dfrac{d\theta}{dt} = -\dfrac{1}{1+x^2/16}\dfrac{1}{4}\dfrac{dx}{dt}$

$= -\dfrac{4}{16+x^2}\dfrac{dx}{dt}$

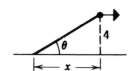

$\dfrac{d\theta}{dt}\bigg|_{x=10} = -\dfrac{4}{16+100}(800) = -800/29$ radians/hr.

43. $\theta = \tan^{-1}(x/3)$

$\dfrac{d\theta}{dt} = \dfrac{3}{9+x^2}\dfrac{dx}{dt}, \quad \dfrac{dx}{dt} = \dfrac{9+x^2}{3}\dfrac{d\theta}{dt}$

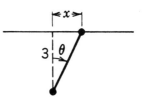

$\dfrac{dx}{dt}\bigg|_{x=2} = \dfrac{9+4}{3}(4\pi) = 52\pi/3$ mi/min

44. $\theta = \sin^{-1}(x/25)$

$\dfrac{d\theta}{dt} = \dfrac{1}{\sqrt{625-x^2}}\dfrac{dx}{dt} = \dfrac{1}{y}\dfrac{dx}{dt}$

$\dfrac{d\theta}{dt}\bigg|_{y=20} = \dfrac{1}{20}(4) = 1/5$ radian/sec

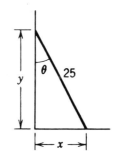

45. $\theta = \alpha - \beta$

$\quad = \cot^{-1}(x/12) - \cot^{-1}(x/2)$

$\dfrac{d\theta}{dx} = -\dfrac{12}{144 + x^2} + \dfrac{2}{4 + x^2}$

$\quad = \dfrac{10(24 - x^2)}{(144 + x^2)(4 + x^2)}$

$d\theta/dx = 0$ when $x = \sqrt{24} = 2\sqrt{6}$, by

the first derivative test θ is

maximum there.

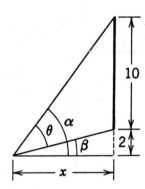

46. **(a)** $\dfrac{d}{dx}(2\sin^{-1}\sqrt{x}) = \dfrac{1}{\sqrt{x}\sqrt{1-x}} = \dfrac{1}{\sqrt{x - x^2}}$ and

$\dfrac{d}{dx}\sin^{-1}(2x - 1) = \dfrac{2}{\sqrt{1 - (2x - 1)^2}} = \dfrac{1}{\sqrt{x - x^2}}$ so

$2\sin^{-1}\sqrt{x} = \sin^{-1}(2x - 1) + k$; let $x = 1/4$ to get $2(\pi/6) = (-\pi/6) + k$, $k = \pi/2$.

(b) $\dfrac{d}{dx}\sin^{-1}(\tanh x) = \dfrac{\text{sech}^2 x}{\sqrt{1 - \tanh^2 x}} = \dfrac{\text{sech}^2 x}{\text{sech}\, x} = \text{sech}\, x$ and

$\dfrac{d}{dx}\tan^{-1}(\sinh x) = \dfrac{\cosh x}{1 + \sinh^2 x} = \dfrac{\cosh x}{\cosh^2 x} = \text{sech}\, x$ so

$\sin^{-1}(\tanh x) = \tan^{-1}(\sinh x) + k$; let $x = 0$ to get $0 = 0 + k$, $k = 0$.

47. By the Mean-Value Theorem on the interval $[0, x]$,

$\dfrac{\tan^{-1} x - \tan^{-1} 0}{x - 0} = \dfrac{\tan^{-1} x}{x} = \dfrac{1}{1 + c^2}$ for c in $(0, x)$, but

$\dfrac{1}{1 + x^2} < \dfrac{1}{1 + c^2} < 1$ for c in $(0, x)$ so $\dfrac{1}{1 + x^2} < \dfrac{\tan^{-1} x}{x} < 1$, $\dfrac{x}{1 + x^2} < \tan^{-1} x < x$.

48. $\dfrac{n}{n^2 + k^2} = \dfrac{1}{1 + k^2/n^2}\dfrac{1}{n}$ so $\displaystyle\sum_{k=1}^{n} \dfrac{n}{n^2 + k^2} = \sum_{k=1}^{n} f(x_k^*)\Delta x$ where $f(x) = \dfrac{1}{1 + x^2}$, $x_k^* = \dfrac{k}{n}$, and

$\Delta x = \dfrac{1}{n}$ for $0 \le x \le 1$. Thus $\displaystyle\lim_{n \to +\infty} \sum_{k=1}^{n} \dfrac{n}{n^2 + k^2} = \lim_{n \to +\infty} \sum_{k=1}^{n} f(x_k^*)\Delta x = \int_0^1 \dfrac{1}{1 + x^2}dx = \dfrac{\pi}{4}$.

49. **(a)** $A = \displaystyle\int_0^{0.8} \dfrac{1}{\sqrt{1 - x^2}}dx = \sin^{-1} x \Big]_0^{0.8} = \sin^{-1}(0.8)$

(b) The calculator was in degree mode instead of radian mode; the correct answer is 0.93.

50. **(a)** $\dfrac{m/k}{v^2 + mg/k}dv = -dt, \ \dfrac{m}{k}\sqrt{\dfrac{k}{mg}}\tan^{-1}\left(\sqrt{\dfrac{k}{mg}}v\right) = -t + C;$

$v = v_0$ when $t = 0$ so $C = \sqrt{\dfrac{m}{kg}}\tan^{-1}\left(\sqrt{\dfrac{k}{mg}}v_0\right),$

$\sqrt{\dfrac{m}{kg}}\tan^{-1}\left(\sqrt{\dfrac{k}{mg}}v\right) = \sqrt{\dfrac{m}{kg}}\tan^{-1}\left(\sqrt{\dfrac{k}{mg}}v_0\right) - t,$

$\tan^{-1}\left(\sqrt{\dfrac{k}{mg}}v\right) = \tan^{-1}\left(\sqrt{\dfrac{k}{mg}}v_0\right) - \sqrt{\dfrac{kg}{m}}t,$

$v = \sqrt{\dfrac{mg}{k}}\tan\left[\tan^{-1}\left(\sqrt{\dfrac{k}{mg}}v_0\right) - \sqrt{\dfrac{kg}{m}}t\right].$

(b) $v = 0$ at the highest point so $t = \sqrt{\dfrac{m}{kg}}\tan^{-1}\left(\sqrt{\dfrac{k}{mg}}v_0\right) \approx 10.6$ seconds for $v_0 = 988$, $g = 9.8$, $m = 3.56 \times 10^{-3}$, and $k = 7.3 \times 10^{-6}$.

EXERCISE SET 8.3

1. **(a)** let $y = \cosh^{-1}x$, then $x = \cosh y = \dfrac{1}{2}(e^y + e^{-y})$, $e^y - 2x + e^{-y} = 0$, $e^{2y} - 2xe^y + 1 = 0$,

$e^y = \dfrac{2x \pm \sqrt{4x^2 - 4}}{2} = x \pm \sqrt{x^2 - 1}$. To determine which sign to take, note that $y \geq 0$ so $e^{-y} \leq e^y$, $x = (e^y + e^{-y})/2 \leq (e^y + e^y)/2 = e^y$, hence $e^y \geq x$ thus $e^y = x + \sqrt{x^2 - 1}$, $y = \cosh^{-1}x = \ln(x + \sqrt{x^2 - 1})$.

(b) $\dfrac{d}{dx}(\cosh^{-1}x) = \dfrac{1 + x/\sqrt{x^2 - 1}}{x + \sqrt{x^2 - 1}} = 1/\sqrt{x^2 - 1}$

2. **(a)** let $y = \tanh^{-1}x$ then $x = \tanh y = \dfrac{e^y - e^{-y}}{e^y + e^{-y}} = \dfrac{e^{2y} - 1}{e^{2y} + 1}$, $xe^{2y} + x = e^{2y} - 1$,

$e^{2y}(x - 1) = -x - 1$, $e^{2y} = (1 + x)/(1 - x)$, $2y = \ln\dfrac{1 + x}{1 - x}$, $y = \dfrac{1}{2}\ln\dfrac{1 + x}{1 - x}.$

(b) $\dfrac{d}{dx}(\tanh^{-1}x) = \dfrac{d}{dx}\left[\dfrac{1}{2}(\ln(1 + x) - \ln(1 - x))\right] = \dfrac{1}{2}\left(\dfrac{1}{1 + x} + \dfrac{1}{1 - x}\right) = 1/(1 - x^2).$

3. **(a)** let $y = \text{sech}^{-1}x$ then $x = \text{sech} \ y = 1/\cosh y$, $\cosh y = 1/x$, $y = \cosh^{-1}(1/x)$; the proofs for the remaining two are similar.

(b) $\dfrac{d}{dx}(\text{sech}^{-1}x) = \dfrac{d}{dx}(\cosh^{-1}(1/x)) = \dfrac{(-1/x^2)}{\sqrt{1/x^2-1}} = -\dfrac{1}{x\sqrt{1-x^2}}$; the remaining two are done similarly.

(c) $\text{sech}^{-1}x = \cosh^{-1}(1/x) = \ln\left[\dfrac{1}{x}+\sqrt{\dfrac{1}{x^2}-1}\right] = \ln\left[\dfrac{1+\sqrt{1-x^2}}{x}\right]$; the remaining two are done similarly.

5. **(a)** $\ln(3+\sqrt{8})$ | **(b)** $\ln(\sqrt{5}-2)$

6. **(a)** $\dfrac{1}{2}\ln 7$ | **(b)** $-\dfrac{1}{2}\ln 9$

7. **(a)** $\dfrac{1}{\sqrt{1+x^2/9}}\left(\dfrac{1}{3}\right) = 1/\sqrt{9+x^2}$ | **(b)** $2/\sqrt{(2x+1)^2-1}$

8. **(a)** $2x/(1-x^4)$ | **(b)** $1/[2(1-x)\sqrt{x}]$

9. **(a)** $-\dfrac{7x^6}{x^7\sqrt{1-x^{14}}} = -\dfrac{7}{x\sqrt{1-x^{14}}}$ | **(b)** $-1/\sqrt{1+e^{2x}}$

10. **(a)** $2(\tanh^{-1}x)/(1-x^2)$ | **(b)** $-(\tanh^{-1}x)^{-2}/(1-x^2)$

11. **(a)** $\dfrac{1}{\sqrt{1+1/x^2}}(-1/x^2) = -\dfrac{1}{|x|\sqrt{x^2+1}}$

(b) $\dfrac{\sinh x}{\sqrt{\cosh^2 x-1}} = \dfrac{\sinh x}{|\sinh x|} = \begin{cases} 1, & x>0 \\ -1, & x<0 \end{cases}$

12. **(a)** $1/[(\cosh^{-1}x)\sqrt{x^2-1}]$ | **(b)** $1/[2(1-x^2)\sqrt{\coth^{-1}x}]$

13. **(a)** $-\dfrac{e^x}{x\sqrt{1-x^2}}+e^x\,\text{sech}^{-1}x$

(b) $3x^2(\sinh^{-1}x)^2/\sqrt{1+x^2}+2x(\sinh^{-1}x)^3$

14. **(a)** $(\text{sech}^2 x)/\sqrt{1+\tanh^2 x}$ | **(b)** $1/[\sqrt{(\sinh^{-1}x)^2-1}\sqrt{1+x^2}]$

15. **(a)** $\dfrac{1}{1-(1-x)^2/(1+x)^2}\left[-\dfrac{2}{(1+x)^2}\right] = -1/(2x)$

(b) $10(1+x\,\text{csch}^{-1}x)^9\left(-\dfrac{x}{|x|\sqrt{1+x^2}}+\text{csch}^{-1}x\right)$

16. $u = 3x$, $\dfrac{1}{3}\displaystyle\int \dfrac{1}{\sqrt{1+u^2}}\,du = \dfrac{1}{3}\sinh^{-1}3x + C$

17. $x = \sqrt{2}u$, $\displaystyle\int \dfrac{\sqrt{2}}{\sqrt{2u^2 - 2}}\,du = \int \dfrac{1}{\sqrt{u^2 - 1}}\,du = \cosh^{-1}(x/\sqrt{2}) + C$

18. $x = 5u/3$, $\displaystyle\int \dfrac{5/3}{\sqrt{25u^2 - 25}}\,du = \dfrac{1}{3}\int \dfrac{1}{\sqrt{u^2 - 1}}\,du = \dfrac{1}{3}\cosh^{-1}(3x/5) + C$

19. $u = e^x$, $\displaystyle\int \dfrac{1}{u\sqrt{1-u^2}}\,du = -\operatorname{sech}^{-1}(e^x) + C$

20. $u = \cos\theta$, $-\displaystyle\int \dfrac{1}{\sqrt{1+u^2}}\,du = -\sinh^{-1}(\cos\theta) + C$

21. $u = x^3$, $\dfrac{1}{3}\displaystyle\int \dfrac{1}{u\sqrt{1+u^2}}\,du = -\dfrac{1}{3}\operatorname{csch}^{-1}|x^3| + C$

22. $\tanh^{-1}x\big]_0^{1/2} = \tanh^{-1}(1/2) - \tanh^{-1}(0) = \dfrac{1}{2}\ln\dfrac{1+1/2}{1-1/2} = \dfrac{1}{2}\ln 3 \approx \dfrac{1}{2}(1.0986) = 0.5493$

23. $\coth^{-1}x\big]_2^3 = \coth^{-1}3 - \coth^{-1}2$

$\qquad = \dfrac{1}{2}\ln\dfrac{3+1}{3-1} - \dfrac{1}{2}\ln\dfrac{2+1}{2-1} = \dfrac{1}{2}\ln 2 - \dfrac{1}{2}\ln 3 \approx \dfrac{1}{2}(0.6931 - 1.0986) \approx -0.2028$

24. $\sinh^{-1}t\big]_0^{\sqrt{3}} = \sinh^{-1}\sqrt{3} - \sinh^{-1}0$

$\qquad = \ln(\sqrt{3} + \sqrt{3+1}) = \ln(\sqrt{3} + 2) \approx \ln(1.7 + 2) = \ln 3.7 \approx 1.3$

25. **(a)**   **(b)**

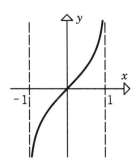

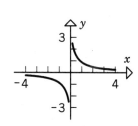

26. **(a)** 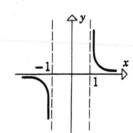 **(b)**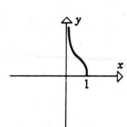

27. $\dfrac{d}{dx}(\operatorname{sech}^{-1}|x|) = \dfrac{d}{dx}(\operatorname{sech}^{-1}\sqrt{x^2}) = -\dfrac{1}{\sqrt{x^2}\sqrt{1-x^2}}\dfrac{x}{\sqrt{x^2}} = -\dfrac{1}{x\sqrt{1-x^2}}$

28. Similar to solution of Exercise 27

29. If $-1 < x < 1$ then $\dfrac{1+x}{1-x} > 0$, $\tanh^{-1}x = \dfrac{1}{2}\ln\dfrac{1+x}{1-x} = \dfrac{1}{2}\ln\left|\dfrac{1+x}{1-x}\right|$; if $|x| > 1$ then

$\dfrac{x+1}{x-1} > 0$, but $\dfrac{x+1}{x-1} = \left|\dfrac{1+x}{1-x}\right|$ so $\coth^{-1}x = \dfrac{1}{2}\ln\dfrac{x+1}{x-1} = \dfrac{1}{2}\ln\left|\dfrac{1+x}{1-x}\right|$,

$\displaystyle\int\dfrac{1}{1-x^2}\,dx = \dfrac{1}{2}\ln\left|\dfrac{1+x}{1-x}\right| + C$

30. Let $u = ax$ then $du = a\,dx$,

(a) $\displaystyle\int\dfrac{1}{\sqrt{a^2+u^2}}\,du = \int\dfrac{a}{\sqrt{a^2+a^2x^2}}\,dx = \int\dfrac{1}{\sqrt{1+x^2}}\,dx = \sinh^{-1}(u/a) + C$

(b) $\displaystyle\int\dfrac{1}{\sqrt{u^2-a^2}}\,du = \int\dfrac{1}{\sqrt{x^2-1}}\,dx = \cosh^{-1}(u/a) + C,\ \ u > a$

(c) $\displaystyle\int\dfrac{1}{a^2-u^2}\,du = \dfrac{1}{a}\int\dfrac{1}{1-x^2}\,dx = \begin{cases}\dfrac{1}{a}\tanh^{-1}(u/a) + C, |u| < a \\[2mm] \dfrac{1}{a}\coth^{-1}(u/a) + C, |u| > a\end{cases} = \dfrac{1}{2a}\ln\left|\dfrac{a+u}{a-u}\right| + C$

31. Let $y = \sinh^{-1}x$ then $x = \sinh y$, $\dfrac{dy}{dx} = \dfrac{1}{dx/dy} = \dfrac{1}{\cosh y} = \dfrac{1}{\sqrt{1+\sinh^2 y}} = \dfrac{1}{\sqrt{1+x^2}}$.

32. (a) $\displaystyle\lim_{x\to+\infty}\sinh^{-1}x = \lim_{x\to+\infty}\ln(x + \sqrt{x^2+1}) = +\infty$

(b) $\displaystyle\lim_{x\to+\infty}\coth^{-1}x = \lim_{x\to+\infty}\dfrac{1}{2}\ln\dfrac{x+1}{x-1} = \lim_{x\to+\infty}\dfrac{1}{2}\ln\dfrac{1+1/x}{1-1/x} = \dfrac{1}{2}\ln 1 = 0$

(c) $\displaystyle\lim_{x\to 0^+}\operatorname{csch}^{-1}x = \lim_{x\to 0^+}\ln\left(\dfrac{1}{x} + \dfrac{\sqrt{1+x^2}}{|x|}\right) = +\infty$

(d) $\displaystyle\lim_{x\to+\infty}(\cosh^{-1}x - \ln x) = \lim_{x\to+\infty}[\ln(x + \sqrt{x^2-1}) - \ln x]$

$$= \lim_{x\to+\infty}\ln\frac{x + \sqrt{x^2-1}}{x} = \lim_{x\to+\infty}\ln(1 + \sqrt{1 - 1/x^2}) = \ln 2$$

33. Let $u = -x$, $\displaystyle\int\frac{1}{\sqrt{x^2-1}}dx = -\int\frac{1}{\sqrt{u^2-1}}du = -\cosh^{-1}u + C = -\cosh^{-1}(-x) + C.$

34. $-\cosh^{-1}(-x) = -\ln(-x + \sqrt{x^2-1}) = \ln\dfrac{1}{-x + \sqrt{x^2-1}}$

$$= \ln(-x - \sqrt{x^2-1}) = \ln|x + \sqrt{x^2-1}|$$

35. **(a)** $vdv = 16x\,dx$, $v^2/2 = 8x^2 + C$; $v = 0$ when $x = 1/4$ so $C = -1/2$, $v^2/2 = 8x^2 - 1/2$, $v^2 = 16x^2 - 1$, $v = \sqrt{16x^2 - 1}$.

(b) $\dfrac{dx}{dt} = \sqrt{16x^2 - 1}$, $\dfrac{1}{\sqrt{16x^2-1}}dx = dt$, $\dfrac{1}{4}\cosh^{-1}(4x) = t + C$; $x = 1/4$ when $t = 0$ so

$C = \dfrac{1}{4}\cosh^{-1}(1) = 0$, $\dfrac{1}{4}\cosh^{-1}(4x) = t$, $x = \dfrac{1}{4}\cosh(4t)$. If $x = 2$, then

$t = \dfrac{1}{4}\cosh^{-1}(8) \approx 0.7$ sec.

36. **(a)** $\dfrac{1/g}{1 - kv^2/(mg)}dv = dt$, $\sqrt{\dfrac{m}{kg}}\tanh^{-1}\left(\sqrt{\dfrac{k}{mg}}v\right) = t + C$; $v = 0$ when $t = 0$ so $C = 0$,

$\tanh^{-1}\left(\sqrt{\dfrac{k}{mg}}v\right) = \sqrt{\dfrac{kg}{m}}t$, $v = \sqrt{\dfrac{mg}{k}}\tanh\left(\sqrt{\dfrac{kg}{m}}t\right)$

(b) $\displaystyle\lim_{t\to+\infty}v = \sqrt{mg/k}$

(c) $v = \dfrac{dx}{dt} = \sqrt{\dfrac{mg}{k}}\tanh\left(\sqrt{\dfrac{kg}{m}}t\right) = \sqrt{\dfrac{mg}{k}}\dfrac{\sinh(\sqrt{kg/mt})}{\cosh(\sqrt{kg/mt})}$,

$x = \dfrac{m}{k}\ln\left[\cosh\left(\sqrt{\dfrac{kg}{m}}t\right)\right] + C$; $x = 0$ when $t = 0$ so $C = 0$, $x = \dfrac{m}{k}\ln\left[\cosh(\sqrt{\dfrac{kg}{m}}t)\right]$.

SUPPLEMENTARY EXERCISES CHAPTER 8

1. **(a)** $2\pi/3$ **(b)** $3/4$

(c) $\cos[\sin^{-1}(4/5)] = 3/5$

(d) $\cos[\sin^{-1}(-4/5)] = \cos[-\sin^{-1}(4/5)] = \cos[\sin^{-1}(4/5)] = 3/5$

2. **(a)** $-\pi/4$ **(b)** $-2\pi/3$
    (c) $\cos^{-1}[\cos(-\pi/3)] = \cos^{-1}[\cos(\pi/3)] = \pi/3$
    (d) $\sin[-\sec^{-1}(2/\sqrt{3})] = \sin(-\pi/6) = -1/2$

3. **(a)** $\pi/4$
    (b) $\sin^{-1}[\sin(5\pi/4)] = \sin^{-1}[\sin(-\pi/4)] = -\pi/4$
    (c) $\tan(\sec^{-1} 5) = 2\sqrt{6}$
    (d) $\tan^{-1}[\cot(\pi/6)] = \tan^{-1}(\sqrt{3}) = \pi/3$

4. **(a)** let $\theta = \csc^{-1} x$, $\sin 2\theta = 2\sin\theta\cos\theta = 2(1/x)(\sqrt{x^2-1}/x) = 2\sqrt{x^2-1}/x^2$
    (b) let $\theta = \sin^{-1} x$, $\cos 2\theta = 1 - 2\sin^2\theta = 1 - 2x^2$
    (c) let $\theta = \tan^{-1} x$, $\sin 2\theta = 2\sin\theta\cos\theta = 2(x/\sqrt{1+x^2})(1/\sqrt{1+x^2}) = 2x/(1+x^2)$

5. **(a)** let $\alpha = \cos^{-1}(4/5)$, $\beta = \sin^{-1}(5/13)$
        $\cos(\alpha + \beta) = \cos\alpha\cos\beta - \sin\alpha\sin\beta = (4/5)(12/13) - (3/5)(5/13) = 33/65$
    (b) let $\alpha = \sin^{-1}(4/5)$, $\beta = \cos^{-1}(5/13)$
        $\sin(\alpha + \beta) = \sin\alpha\cos\beta + \cos\alpha\sin\beta = (4/5)(5/13) + (3/5)(12/13) = 56/65$
    (c) let $\alpha = \tan^{-1}(1/3)$, $\beta = \tan^{-1}(2)$; $\tan(\alpha + \beta) = \dfrac{\tan\alpha + \tan\beta}{1 - \tan\alpha\tan\beta} = \dfrac{1/3 + 2}{1 - (1/3)(2)} = 7$

6. $\operatorname{csch} u = -5/12, \sinh u = 1/\operatorname{csch} u = -12/5, \cosh^2 u = 1 + \sinh^2 u = 169/25, \cosh u = 13/5,$
    $\coth u = \cosh u/\sinh u = -13/12, \sinh 2u = 2\sinh u\cosh u = -312/25.$

7. $\tanh u = -3/5, \operatorname{sech}^2 u = 1 - \tanh^2 u = 16/25, \operatorname{sech} u = 4/5, \cosh u = 5/4,$
    $\sinh u = (\tanh u)(\cosh u) = -3/4, \cosh 2u = \cosh^2 u + \sinh^2 u = 34/16.$

8. **(a)**   **(b)**

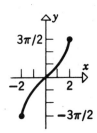

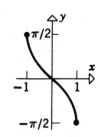

9. (a)

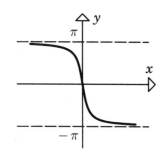

(b)

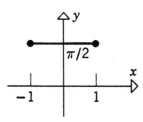

$$f(x) = \cos^{-1} x + \sin^{-1} x = \pi/2$$

10. $e^x/\sqrt{1 - e^{2x}} + 6/(1 + 9x^2)$

11. $-[\sec^{-1}(x^2)]^{-2} \dfrac{1}{x^2\sqrt{x^4 - 1}}(2x) = -\dfrac{2[\sec^{-1}(x^2)]^{-2}}{x\sqrt{x^4 - 1}}$

12. $x/\sqrt{1 - x^2} + \sin^{-1} x - x/\sqrt{1 - x^2} = \sin^{-1} x$

13. $(\sec x \tan x)/\sqrt{\sec^2 x - 1} = (\sec x \tan x)/|\tan x|$

14. $y'/(1 + y^2) = 1/\sqrt{1 - x^2}$, $y' = (1 + y^2)/\sqrt{1 - x^2}$

15. $1/[1 - (\ln x)^2] + \tanh^{-1}(\ln x)$

16. $\dfrac{1}{1 + 4x^2/(1 - x^2)^2} \dfrac{2(1 + x^2)}{(1 - x^2)^2} = \dfrac{2(1 + x^2)}{(1 - x^2)^2 + 4x^2} = \dfrac{2(1 + x^2)}{(1 + x^2)^2} = \dfrac{2}{1 + x^2}$

17. $3/[2\sqrt{\sin^{-1} 3x}\sqrt{1 - 9x^2}]$ **18.** $-2(\sin^{-1} 2x)^{-2}/\sqrt{1 - 4x^2}$

19. $\exp(\sec^{-1} x)/(x\sqrt{x^2 - 1})$

20. $\dfrac{(\ln x)/(1 + x^2) - (\tan^{-1} x)/x}{(\ln x)^2} = \dfrac{x \ln x - (1 + x^2)\tan^{-1} x}{x(1 + x^2)(\ln x)^2}$

21. $\pi^{\sin^{-1} x}(\ln \pi)/\sqrt{1 - x^2}$ **22.** $\pi(\sinh^{-1} x)^{\pi - 1}/\sqrt{1 + x^2}$

23. $y = \tanh^{-1}(1/\coth x) = \tanh^{-1}(\tanh x)$ if $x \neq 0$, so $y = x$, $dy/dx = 1$ if $x \neq 0$.

24. (a) $f'(x) = \dfrac{1}{1 + x^2} + \dfrac{(-1/x^2)}{1 + 1/x^2} = 0$ for x in the intervals $(-\infty, 0)$ and $(0, +\infty)$ so $f(x) = C_1$
  on $(-\infty, 0)$ and $f(x) = C_2$ on $(0, +\infty)$

   (b) Let $x = -1$ then $C_1 = f(-1) = (-\pi/4) + (-\pi/4) = -\pi/2$;
   let $x = 1$ then $C_2 = f(1) = (\pi/4) + (\pi/4) = \pi/2$.

25. $y = \tan^{-1} x,\ y' = 1/(1+x^2),\ y'' = -2x/(1+x^2)^2;\ \sin y = x/\sqrt{1+x^2},\ \cos y = 1/\sqrt{1+x^2},$

$-2\sin y \cos^3 y = -2\dfrac{x}{(1+x^2)^{1/2}}\dfrac{1}{(1+x^2)^{3/2}} = -2x/(1+x^2)^2 = y''$

26. $u = 2x,\ \dfrac{1}{2}\displaystyle\int \dfrac{1}{\sqrt{9-u^2}}du = \dfrac{1}{2}\sin^{-1}(2x/3) + C$

27. $u = e^x,\ \displaystyle\int \dfrac{1}{1-u^2}du = \dfrac{1}{2}\ln\left|\dfrac{1+e^x}{1-e^x}\right| + C$

28. $u = \sin x,\ \displaystyle\int \dfrac{\cos x}{\sin x\sqrt{1-\sin^2 x}}dx = \int \dfrac{1}{u\sqrt{1-u^2}}du = -\operatorname{sech}^{-1}|\sin x| + C$

29. $u = \ln x,\ \displaystyle\int \dfrac{1}{\sqrt{u^2-1}}du = \cosh^{-1}(\ln x) + C,\ x > e$

30. $u = e^{-x},\ -\displaystyle\int \dfrac{1}{\sqrt{1-u^2}}du = -\sin^{-1}(e^{-x}) + C$

31. $u = 3x,\ \dfrac{1}{3}\displaystyle\int_{2/\sqrt{3}}^{2} \dfrac{1}{u\sqrt{u^2-1}}du = \dfrac{1}{3}\sec^{-1} u\Big]_{2/\sqrt{3}}^{2} = \dfrac{1}{3}(\pi/3 - \pi/6) = \pi/18$

32. $u = x^2,\ \dfrac{1}{2}\displaystyle\int_{0}^{2} \dfrac{1}{4+u^2}du = \dfrac{1}{4}\tan^{-1}(u/2)\Big]_{0}^{2} = \pi/16$

33. $\displaystyle\int \dfrac{1}{x^{1/2}+x^{3/2}}dx = \int \dfrac{1}{x^{1/2}(1+x)}dx,\ u = x^{1/2},\ 2\int \dfrac{1}{1+u^2}du = 2\tan^{-1}\sqrt{x} + C$

34. $u = x^3,\ \dfrac{1}{3}\displaystyle\int \dfrac{1}{\sqrt{1+u^2}}du = \dfrac{1}{3}\sinh^{-1}(x^3) + C$

35. $u = \sqrt{x},\ 2\displaystyle\int_{1/2}^{1/\sqrt{2}} \dfrac{1}{\sqrt{1-u^2}}du = 2\sin^{-1} u\Big]_{1/2}^{1/\sqrt{2}} = 2\left(\dfrac{\pi}{4} - \dfrac{\pi}{6}\right) = \pi/6$

36. $dy/dt = a,\ dx/dt = -b,\ \theta = \sin^{-1}(x/y),$

$\dfrac{d\theta}{dt} = \dfrac{1}{\sqrt{1-x^2/y^2}}\left[\dfrac{y(dx/dt) - x(dy/dt)}{y^2}\right]$

$= \dfrac{y(dx/dt) - x(dy/dt)}{y\sqrt{y^2-x^2}}$

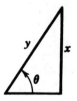

When both legs are 1, $y = \sqrt{2}$ so

$$\left.\frac{d\theta}{dt}\right|_{x=1, y=\sqrt{2}} = \frac{\sqrt{2}(-b) - (1)(a)}{\sqrt{2}\sqrt{2-1}} = -(a + \sqrt{2}b)/\sqrt{2},$$

θ is decreasing at the rate of $(a + \sqrt{2}b)/\sqrt{2}$ radians/sec.

37. $f'(x) = \dfrac{2}{1 + 4x^2} - \dfrac{1}{1 + x^2} = \dfrac{1 - 2x^2}{(1 + 4x^2)(1 + x^2)}$, the critical point is $x = 1/\sqrt{2}$ for $x > 0$,

$f'(x) > 0$ for $0 < x < 1/\sqrt{2}$ and $f'(x) < 0$ for $x > 1/\sqrt{2}$ so $f(x)$ assumes its maximum value
at $x = 1/\sqrt{2}$

38. $A = \displaystyle\int_{-\sqrt{3}}^{\sqrt{3}} \frac{1}{9 + x^2}\,dx = \left.\frac{1}{3}\tan^{-1}(x/3)\right]_{-\sqrt{3}}^{\sqrt{3}} = \frac{1}{3}[(\pi/6) - (-\pi/6)] = \pi/9$

CHAPTER 9
Techniques of Integration

EXERCISE SET 9.1

1. $3\int \dfrac{x}{4x-1}dx = \dfrac{3}{16}(4x + \ln|4x - 1|) + C$ (#6; $a = -1$, $b = 4$)

2. $\dfrac{1}{9}[2/(2 - 3x) + \ln|2 - 3x|] + C$ (#8; $a = 2$, $b = -3$)

3. $\dfrac{1}{5}\ln\left|\dfrac{x}{2x+5}\right| + C$ (#11; $a = 5$, $b = 2$)

4. $-\dfrac{1}{x} - 5\ln\left|\dfrac{1 - 5x}{x}\right| + C$ (#12; $a = 1$, $b = -5$)

5. $\dfrac{1}{30}(6x + 6)(2x - 3)^{3/2} + C = \dfrac{1}{5}(x + 1)(2x - 3)^{3/2} + C$ (#14; $a = -3$, $b = 2$)

6. $\dfrac{2}{3}(-x - 4)\sqrt{2 - x} + C = -\dfrac{2}{3}(x + 4)\sqrt{2 - x} + C$ (#17; $a = 2$, $b = -1$)

7. $\dfrac{1}{2}\ln\left|\dfrac{\sqrt{4 - 3x} - 2}{\sqrt{4 - 3x} + 2}\right| + C$ (#20; $a = 4$, $b = -3$)

8. $\tan^{-1}\dfrac{\sqrt{3x - 4}}{2} + C$ (#20; $a = -4$, $b = 3$)

9. $\dfrac{1}{2\sqrt{5}}\ln\left|\dfrac{x + \sqrt{5}}{x - \sqrt{5}}\right| + C$ (#25; $a = \sqrt{5}$)   10. $\dfrac{1}{6}\ln\left|\dfrac{x - 3}{x + 3}\right| + C$ (#26; $a = 3$)

11. $\dfrac{x}{2}\sqrt{x^2 - 3} - \dfrac{3}{2}\ln\left|x + \sqrt{x^2 - 3}\right| + C$ (#28; $a^2 = 3$)

12. $-\dfrac{\sqrt{x^2 + 5}}{x} + \ln\left|x + \sqrt{x^2 + 5}\right| + C$ (#33; $a^2 = 5$)

13. $\dfrac{x}{2}\sqrt{x^2 + 4} - 2\ln\left|x + \sqrt{x^2 + 4}\right| + C$ (#34; $a^2 = 4$)

14. $\dfrac{\sqrt{x^2 - 2}}{2x} + C$ (#37; $a^2 = 2$)   15. $\dfrac{x}{2}\sqrt{9 - x^2} + \dfrac{9}{2}\sin^{-1}\dfrac{x}{3} + C$ (#41; $a = 3$)

16. $-\dfrac{\sqrt{4-x^2}}{x} - \sin^{-1}\dfrac{x}{2} + C$ (#44; $a = 2$)

17. $\sqrt{3-x^2} - \sqrt{3}\ln\left|\dfrac{\sqrt{3}+\sqrt{3-x^2}}{x}\right| + C$ (#43; $a = \sqrt{3}$)

18. $-\dfrac{\sqrt{6x-x^2}}{3x} + C$ (#57; $a = 3$)   19. $-\dfrac{\sin 5x}{10} + \dfrac{\sin x}{2} + C$ (#80; $m = 3$, $n = 2$)

20. $-\dfrac{\cos 7x}{14} - \dfrac{\cos(-3x)}{(-6)} + C = -\dfrac{\cos 7x}{14} + \dfrac{\cos 3x}{6} + C$ (#82; $m = 2$, $n = 5$)

21. $\dfrac{x^4}{16}[4\ln x - 1] + C$ (#104; $n = 3$)

22. $\displaystyle\int x^{-1/2}\ln x\,dx = 4\sqrt{x}[(1/2)\ln x - 1] + C$ (#104; $n = -1/2$)

23. $\dfrac{e^{-2x}}{13}(-2\sin 3x - 3\cos 3x) + C$ (#106; $a = -2$, $b = 3$)

24. $\dfrac{e^x}{5}(\cos 2x + \sin 2x) + C$ (#107; $a = 1$, $b = 2$)

25. $\dfrac{1}{2}\displaystyle\int \dfrac{u}{(4-3u)^2}du = \dfrac{1}{18}\left[\dfrac{4}{4-3u} + \ln|4-3u|\right] + C$ (#8; $a = 4, b = -3$)

$$= \dfrac{1}{18}\left[\dfrac{4}{4-3e^{2x}} + \ln|4-3e^{2x}|\right] + C$$

26. $\dfrac{1}{2}\displaystyle\int \dfrac{1}{u(3-u)}du = \dfrac{1}{6}\ln\left|\dfrac{u}{3-u}\right| + C$ (#11; $a = 3, b = -1$) $= \dfrac{1}{6}\ln\left|\dfrac{\sin 2x}{3-\sin 2x}\right| + C$

27. $\dfrac{2}{3}\displaystyle\int \dfrac{1}{u^2+4}du = \dfrac{1}{3}\tan^{-1}\dfrac{u}{2} + C$ (#24; $a = 2$) $= \dfrac{1}{3}\tan^{-1}\dfrac{3\sqrt{x}}{2} + C$

28. $\dfrac{1}{4}\displaystyle\int \dfrac{1}{9+u^2}du = \dfrac{1}{12}\tan^{-1}\dfrac{u}{3} + C$ (# 24; $a = 3$) $= \dfrac{1}{12}\tan^{-1}\dfrac{\sin 4x}{3} + C$

29. $\dfrac{1}{3}\displaystyle\int \dfrac{1}{\sqrt{u^2-4}}du = \dfrac{1}{3}\ln\left|u+\sqrt{u^2-4}\right| + C$ (#27; $a^2 = 4$) $= \dfrac{1}{3}\ln\left|3x+\sqrt{9x^2-4}\right| + C$

30. $\dfrac{1}{2\sqrt{2}}\displaystyle\int \sqrt{u^2+3}\,du = \dfrac{1}{2\sqrt{2}}\left[\dfrac{u}{2}\sqrt{u^2+3}+\dfrac{3}{2}\ln\left|u+\sqrt{u^2+3}\right|\right]+C \quad (\#28;\ a^2=3)$

$$= \dfrac{1}{4\sqrt{2}}\left[\sqrt{2}\,x^2\sqrt{2x^4+3}+3\ln\left(\sqrt{2}\,x^2+\sqrt{2x^4+3}\right)\right]+C$$

31. $\dfrac{1}{54}\displaystyle\int \dfrac{u^2}{\sqrt{5-u^2}}\,du = \dfrac{1}{54}\left[-\dfrac{u}{2}\sqrt{5-u^2}+\dfrac{5}{2}\sin^{-1}\dfrac{u}{\sqrt{5}}\right]+C \quad (\#45;\ a=\sqrt{5})$

$$= \dfrac{1}{108}\left[-3x^2\sqrt{5-9x^4}+5\sin^{-1}\dfrac{3x^2}{\sqrt{5}}\right]+C$$

32. $2\displaystyle\int \dfrac{1}{u^2\sqrt{3-u^2}}\,du = -\dfrac{2\sqrt{3-u^2}}{3u}+C \quad (\#47;\ a^2=3) = -\dfrac{\sqrt{3-4x^2}}{3x}+C$

33. $\displaystyle\int \sin^2 u\,du = \dfrac{1}{2}u-\dfrac{1}{4}\sin 2u+C \quad (\#70) = \dfrac{1}{2}\ln x-\dfrac{1}{4}\sin(2\ln x)+C$

34. $-\dfrac{1}{2}\displaystyle\int \cos^2 u\,du = -\dfrac{1}{2}\left[\dfrac{1}{2}u+\dfrac{1}{4}\sin 2u\right]+C \quad (\#71) = -\dfrac{1}{4}e^{-2x}-\dfrac{1}{8}\sin\left(2e^{-2x}\right)+C$

35. $\dfrac{1}{4}\displaystyle\int ue^u\,du = \dfrac{1}{4}e^u(u-1)+C \quad (\#98) = \dfrac{1}{4}e^{-2x}(-2x-1)+C = -\dfrac{1}{4}e^{-2x}(2x+1)+C$

36. $\dfrac{1}{5}\displaystyle\int \ln u\,du = \dfrac{1}{5}[u\ln u-u]+C \quad (\#103) = \dfrac{1}{5}[(5x-1)\ln(5x-1)-(5x-1)]+C$

37. $u=\cos 3x,\quad -\dfrac{1}{3}\displaystyle\int \dfrac{1}{u(u+1)^2}\,du = -\dfrac{1}{3}\left[\dfrac{1}{u+1}+\ln\left|\dfrac{u}{u+1}\right|\right]+C \quad (\#13;\ a=1, b=1)$

$$= -\dfrac{1}{3}\left[\dfrac{1}{\cos 3x+1}+\ln\left|\dfrac{\cos 3x}{\cos 3x+1}\right|\right]+C$$

38. $u=\ln x,\quad \displaystyle\int \dfrac{u}{\sqrt{4u-1}}\,du = \dfrac{1}{24}(4u+2)(\sqrt{4u-1})+C \quad (\#17;\ a=-1, b=4)$

$$= \dfrac{1}{12}(2\ln x+1)\sqrt{4\ln x-1}+C$$

39. $u=4x^2,\quad \dfrac{1}{8}\displaystyle\int \dfrac{1}{u^2-1}\,du = \dfrac{1}{16}\ln\left|\dfrac{u-1}{u+1}\right|+C \quad (\#26;\ a=1) = \dfrac{1}{16}\ln\left|\dfrac{4x^2-1}{4x^2+1}\right|+C$

40. $u=2e^x,\quad \dfrac{1}{2}\displaystyle\int \dfrac{1}{3-u^2}\,du = \dfrac{1}{4\sqrt{3}}\ln\left|\dfrac{u+\sqrt{3}}{u-\sqrt{3}}\right|+C \quad (\#25;\ a=\sqrt{3}) = \dfrac{1}{4\sqrt{3}}\ln\left|\dfrac{2e^x+\sqrt{3}}{2e^x-\sqrt{3}}\right|+C$

41. $u = 2e^x$, $\quad \dfrac{1}{2}\displaystyle\int\sqrt{3-u^2}\,du = \dfrac{1}{2}\left[\dfrac{u}{2}\sqrt{3-u^2} + \dfrac{3}{2}\sin^{-1}\dfrac{u}{\sqrt{3}}\right] + C \quad$ (#41; $a = \sqrt{3}$)

$$= \dfrac{1}{2}e^x\sqrt{3-4e^{2x}} + \dfrac{3}{4}\sin^{-1}\dfrac{2e^x}{\sqrt{3}} + C$$

42. $u = 3x$, $\quad 3\displaystyle\int\dfrac{\sqrt{4-u^2}}{u^2}\,du = 3\left[-\dfrac{\sqrt{4-u^2}}{u} - \sin^{-1}\dfrac{u}{2}\right] + C \quad$ (#44; $a = 2$)

$$= -\dfrac{\sqrt{4-9x^2}}{x} - 3\sin^{-1}\dfrac{3x}{2} + C$$

43. $u = 3x$,

$$\dfrac{1}{3}\int\sqrt{(5/3)u - u^2}\,du = \dfrac{1}{3}\left[\dfrac{u-5/6}{2}\sqrt{(5/3)u - u^2} + \dfrac{25}{72}\sin^{-1}\left(\dfrac{u-5/6}{5/6}\right)\right] + C \text{ (#50; } a = 5/6)$$

$$= \dfrac{18x-5}{36}\sqrt{5x - 9x^2} + \dfrac{25}{216}\sin^{-1}\dfrac{18x-5}{5} + C$$

44. $u = \sqrt{5}\,x$, $\quad \displaystyle\int\dfrac{1}{u\sqrt{u/\sqrt{5} - u^2}}\,du = -\dfrac{\sqrt{u/\sqrt{5} - u^2}}{u/(2\sqrt{5})} + C \quad$ (#57; $a = 1/(2\sqrt{5})$)

$$= -2\dfrac{\sqrt{x-5x^2}}{x} + C$$

45. $u = 3x$, $\quad \dfrac{1}{9}\displaystyle\int u\sin u\,du = \dfrac{1}{9}[\sin u - u\cos u] + C \quad$ (#83) $= \dfrac{1}{9}[\sin 3x - 3x\cos 3x] + C$

46. $u = \sqrt{x}$, $x = u^2$, $dx = 2u\,du$,

$$2\int u\cos u\,du = 2[\cos u + u\sin u] + C \quad \text{(#84)} = 2[\cos\sqrt{x} + \sqrt{x}\sin\sqrt{x}] + C$$

47. $u = -\sqrt{x}$, $x = u^2$, $dx = 2u\,du$,

$$2\int ue^u\,du = 2e^u(u-1) + C \quad \text{(#98)} = 2e^{-\sqrt{x}}(-\sqrt{x}-1) + C = -2e^{-\sqrt{x}}(\sqrt{x}+1) + C$$

48. $u = 2 - 3x^2$, $\quad -\dfrac{1}{6}\displaystyle\int\ln u\,du = -\dfrac{1}{6}[u\ln u - u] + C \quad$ (#103)

$$= -\dfrac{1}{6}\left[(2-3x^2)\ln(2-3x^2) - (2-3x^2)\right] + C$$

49. $\displaystyle\int\dfrac{1}{(x+2)^2 - 9}\,dx$; $u = x + 2$,

$$\int\dfrac{1}{u^2 - 9}\,du = \dfrac{1}{6}\ln\left|\dfrac{u-3}{u+3}\right| + C \quad \text{(#26; } a = 3) = \dfrac{1}{6}\ln\left|\dfrac{x-1}{x+5}\right| + C$$

50. $\int \sqrt{4-(x+1)^2}\,dx; \; u = x+1,$

$$\int \sqrt{4-u^2}\,du = \frac{u}{2}\sqrt{4-u^2} + 2\sin^{-1}\frac{u}{2} + C \quad (\#41; a = 2)$$

$$= \frac{x+1}{2}\sqrt{3-2x-x^2} + 2\sin^{-1}\frac{x+1}{2} + C$$

51. $\int \frac{x}{\sqrt{9-(x-2)^2}}\,dx; \; u = x-2, \; x = u+2,$

$$\int \frac{u+2}{\sqrt{9-u^2}}\,du = \int \frac{u}{\sqrt{9-u^2}}\,du + 2\int \frac{1}{\sqrt{9-u^2}}\,du$$

$$= -\sqrt{9-u^2} + 2\sin^{-1}\frac{u}{3} + C \quad (\#4 \text{ and } \#40)$$

$$= -\sqrt{5+4x-x^2} + 2\sin^{-1}\frac{x-2}{3} + C$$

52. $\int \frac{x}{(x+3)^2+4}\,dx; \; u = x+3, \; x = u-3,$

$$\int \frac{u-3}{u^2+4}\,du = \int \frac{u}{u^2+4}\,du - 3\int \frac{1}{u^2+4}\,du$$

$$= \frac{1}{2}\ln(u^2+4) - \frac{3}{2}\tan^{-1}\frac{u}{2} + C \quad (\#5 \text{ and } \#24)$$

$$= \frac{1}{2}\ln(x^2+6x+13) - \frac{3}{2}\tan^{-1}\frac{x+3}{2} + C$$

53. $\int_2^x \frac{1}{t(4-t)}\,dt = \frac{1}{4}\ln\frac{t}{4-t}\Big]_2^x \quad (\#11; a = 4, b = -1)$

$$= \frac{1}{4}\left[\ln\frac{x}{4-x} - \ln 1\right] = \frac{1}{4}\ln\frac{x}{4-x}, \frac{1}{4}\ln\frac{x}{4-x} = 0.5, \ln\frac{x}{4-x} = 2,$$

$$\frac{x}{4-x} = e^2, \; x = 4e^2 - e^2 x, \; x(1+e^2) = 4e^2, \; x = 4e^2/(1+e^2) \approx 3.523188312.$$

54. $\int_1^x \frac{1}{t\sqrt{2t-1}}\,dt = 2\tan^{-1}\sqrt{2t-1}\Big]_1^x \quad (\#20; a = -1, b = 2)$

$$= 2\left(\tan^{-1}\sqrt{2x-1} - \tan^{-1}1\right) = 2\left(\tan^{-1}\sqrt{2x-1} - \pi/4\right),$$

$2(\tan^{-1}\sqrt{2x-1} - \pi/4) = 1, \; \tan^{-1}\sqrt{2x-1} = 1/2 + \pi/4, \; \sqrt{2x-1} = \tan(1/2 + \pi/4),$
$x = [1 + \tan^2(1/2 + \pi/4)]/2 \approx 6.307993516.$

55. $A = \int_0^4 \sqrt{25 - x^2}\, dx = \left(\frac{1}{2}x\sqrt{25 - x^2} + \frac{25}{2}\sin^{-1}\frac{x}{5}\right)\Big]_0^4$ (#41; $a = 5$)

$$= 6 + \frac{25}{2}\sin^{-1}\frac{4}{5} \approx 17.59119022$$

56. $A = \int_{2/3}^2 \sqrt{9x^2 - 4}\, dx$; $u = 3x$,

$A = \frac{1}{3}\int_2^6 \sqrt{u^2 - 4}\, du = \frac{1}{3}\left(\frac{1}{2}u\sqrt{u^2 - 4} - 2\ln\left|u + \sqrt{u^2 - 4}\right|\right)\Big]_2^6$ (#28; $a^2 = 4$)

$$= \frac{1}{3}\left(3\sqrt{32} - 2\ln(6 + \sqrt{32}) + 2\ln 2\right)$$

$$= 4\sqrt{2} - \frac{2}{3}\ln(3 + 2\sqrt{2}) \approx 4.481689467$$

57. $A = \int_0^1 \frac{1}{25 - 16x^2}\, dx$; $u = 4x$,

$A = \frac{1}{4}\int_0^4 \frac{1}{25 - u^2}\, du = \frac{1}{40}\ln\left|\frac{u + 5}{u - 5}\right|\Big]_0^4$ (#25; $a = 5$) $= \frac{1}{40}\ln 9 \approx 0.054930614$

58. $A = \int_1^4 \sqrt{x}\ln x\, dx = \frac{4}{9}x^{3/2}\left(\frac{3}{2}\ln x - 1\right)\Big]_1^4$ (#104; $n = 1/2$)

$$= \frac{4}{9}(12\ln 4 - 7) \approx 4.282458815$$

59. $V = 2\pi\int_0^{\pi/2} x\cos x\, dx = 2\pi(\cos x + x\sin x)\Big]_0^{\pi/2}$ (#84) $= \pi(\pi - 2) \approx 3.586419094$

60. $V = 2\pi\int_4^8 x\sqrt{x - 4}\, dx = \frac{4\pi}{15}(3x + 8)(x - 4)^{3/2}\Big]_4^8$ (#14; $a = -4, b = 1$)

$$= \frac{1024}{15}\pi \approx 214.4660584$$

61. $V = 2\pi\int_0^3 xe^{-x}\, dx$; $u = -x$,

$V = 2\pi\int_0^{-3} ue^u\, du = 2\pi e^u(u - 1)\Big]_0^{-3}$ (#98) $= 2\pi(1 - 4e^{-3}) \approx 5.031899801$

62. $V = 2\pi\int_1^5 x\ln x\, dx = \frac{\pi}{2}x^2(2\ln x - 1)\Big]_1^5$ (#104; $n = 1$) $= \pi(25\ln 5 - 12) \approx 88.70584620$

63. $L = \int_0^2 \sqrt{1 + 16x^2}\, dx;\ u = 4x,$

$$L = \frac{1}{4}\int_0^8 \sqrt{1 + u^2}\, du = \frac{1}{4}\left(\frac{u}{2}\sqrt{1 + u^2} + \frac{1}{2}\ln\left|u + \sqrt{1 + u^2}\right|\right)\Big]_0^8 \quad (\#28;\ a^2 = 1)$$

$$= \sqrt{65} + \frac{1}{8}\ln(8 + \sqrt{65}) \approx 8.409316783$$

64. $L = \int_1^3 \sqrt{1 + 9/x^2}\, dx = \int_1^3 \frac{\sqrt{x^2 + 9}}{x}\, dx$

$$= \left(\sqrt{x^2 + 9} - 3\ln\left|\frac{3 + \sqrt{x^2 + 9}}{x}\right|\right)\Big]_1^3 \quad (\#31;\ a = 3)$$

$$= 3\sqrt{2} - \sqrt{10} + 3\ln\frac{3 + \sqrt{10}}{1 + \sqrt{2}} \approx 3.891581644$$

65. $S = 2\pi\int_0^\pi (\sin x)\sqrt{1 + \cos^2 x}\, dx;\ u = \cos x,$

$$S = -2\pi\int_1^{-1} \sqrt{1 + u^2}\, du = 4\pi\int_0^1 \sqrt{1 + u^2}\, du$$

$$= 4\pi\left(\frac{u}{2}\sqrt{1 + u^2} + \frac{1}{2}\ln\left|u + \sqrt{1 + u^2}\right|\right)\Big]_0^1 \quad (\#28;\ a^2 = 1)$$

$$= 2\pi[\sqrt{2} + \ln(1 + \sqrt{2})] \approx 14.42359944$$

66. $S = 2\pi\int_1^4 \frac{1}{x}\sqrt{1 + 1/x^4}\, dx = 2\pi\int_1^4 \frac{\sqrt{x^4 + 1}}{x^3}\, dx;\ u = x^2,$

$$S = \pi\int_1^{16} \frac{\sqrt{u^2 + 1}}{u^2}\, du = \pi\left(-\frac{\sqrt{u^2 + 1}}{u} + \ln\left|u + \sqrt{u^2 + 1}\right|\right)\Big]_1^{16} \quad (\#33;\ a^2 = 1)$$

$$= \pi\left(\sqrt{2} - \frac{\sqrt{257}}{16} + \ln\frac{16 + \sqrt{257}}{1 + \sqrt{2}}\right) \approx 9.417237485$$

EXERCISE SET 9.2

1. $u = x,\ dv = e^{-x}dx,\ du = dx,\ v = -e^{-x}$

$$\int xe^{-x}\, dx = -xe^{-x} + \int e^{-x}dx = -xe^{-x} - e^{-x} + C$$

2. $u = x$, $dv = e^{3x} dx$, $du = dx$, $v = \dfrac{1}{3}e^{3x}$

$$\int xe^{3x} dx = \frac{1}{3}xe^{3x} - \frac{1}{3}\int e^{3x} dx = \frac{1}{3}xe^{0x} - \frac{1}{9}e^{3r} + C$$

3. $u = x^2$, $dv = e^x dx$, $du = 2x\,dx$, $v = e^x$; $\displaystyle\int x^2 e^x dx = x^2 e^x - 2\int xe^x dx.$

For $\displaystyle\int xe^x dx$ use $u = x$, $dv = e^x dx$, $du = dx$, $v = e^x$ to get

$$\int xe^x dx = xe^x - e^x + C_1 \text{ so } \int x^2 e^x dx = x^2 e^x - 2xe^x + 2e^x + C$$

4. $u = x^2$, $dv = e^{-2x} dx$, $du = 2x\,dx$, $v = -\dfrac{1}{2}e^{-2x}$; $\displaystyle\int x^2 e^{-2x} dx = -\frac{1}{2}x^2 e^{-2x} + \int xe^{-2x} dx.$

For $\displaystyle\int xe^{-2x} dx$ use $u = x$, $dv = e^{-2x} dx$ to get

$$\int xe^{-2x} dx = -\frac{1}{2}xe^{-2x} + \frac{1}{2}\int e^{-2x} dx = -\frac{1}{2}xe^{-2x} - \frac{1}{4}e^{-2x} + C$$

so $\displaystyle\int x^2 e^{-2x} dx = -\frac{1}{2}x^2 e^{-2x} - \frac{1}{2}xe^{-2x} - \frac{1}{4}e^{-2x} + C$

5. $u = x$, $dv = \sin 2x\,dx$, $du = dx$, $v = -\dfrac{1}{2}\cos 2x$

$$\int x \sin 2x\,dx = -\frac{1}{2}x \cos 2x + \frac{1}{2}\int \cos 2x\,dx = -\frac{1}{2}x \cos 2x + \frac{1}{4}\sin 2x + C$$

6. $u = x$, $dv = \cos 3x\,dx$, $du = dx$, $v = \dfrac{1}{3}\sin 3x$

$$\int x \cos 3x\,dx = \frac{1}{3}x \sin 3x - \frac{1}{3}\int \sin 3x\,dx = \frac{1}{3}x \sin 3x + \frac{1}{9}\cos 3x + C$$

7. $u = x^2$, $dv = \cos x\,dx$, $du = 2x\,dx$, $v = \sin x$; $\displaystyle\int x^2 \cos x\,dx = x^2 \sin x - 2\int x \sin x\,dx$

For $\displaystyle\int x \sin x\,dx$ use $u = x$, $dv = \sin x\,dx$ to get

$$\int x \sin x\,dx = -x \cos x + \sin x + C_1 \text{ so } \int x^2 \cos x\,dx = x^2 \sin x + 2x \cos x - 2\sin x + C$$

8. $u = x^2$, $dv = \sin x\,dx$, $du = 2x\,dx$, $v = -\cos x$

$$\int x^2 \sin x\,dx = -x^2 \cos x + 2\int x \cos x\,dx; \text{ for } \int x \cos x\,dx \text{ use } u = x,\ dv = \cos x\,dx \text{ to get}$$

$$\int x \cos x\,dx = x \sin x + \cos x + C_1 \text{ so } \int x^2 \sin x\,dx = -x^2 \cos x + 2x \sin x + 2\cos x + C$$

9. $u = \ln x$, $dv = \sqrt{x}\,dx$, $du = \dfrac{1}{x}dx$, $v = \dfrac{2}{3}x^{3/2}$

$$\int \sqrt{x}\ln x\,dx = \frac{2}{3}x^{3/2}\ln x - \frac{2}{3}\int x^{1/2}dx = \frac{2}{3}x^{3/2}\ln x - \frac{4}{9}x^{3/2} + C$$

10. $u = \ln x$, $dv = x\,dx$, $du = \dfrac{1}{x}dx$, $v = \dfrac{1}{2}x^2$

$$\int x\ln x\,dx = \frac{1}{2}x^2\ln x - \frac{1}{2}\int x\,dx = \frac{1}{2}x^2\ln x - \frac{1}{4}x^2 + C$$

11. $u = (\ln x)^2$, $dv = dx$, $du = 2\dfrac{\ln x}{x}dx$, $v = x$; $\displaystyle\int (\ln x)^2 dx = x(\ln x)^2 - 2\int \ln x\,dx$.

Use $u = \ln x$, $dv = dx$ to get

$$\int \ln x\,dx = x\ln x - \int dx = x\ln x - x + C_1 \text{ so } \int (\ln x)^2 dx = x(\ln x)^2 - 2x\ln x + 2x + C$$

12. $u = \ln x$, $dv = \dfrac{1}{\sqrt{x}}dx$, $du = \dfrac{1}{x}dx$, $v = 2\sqrt{x}$

$$\int \frac{\ln x}{\sqrt{x}}dx = 2\sqrt{x}\ln x - 2\int \frac{1}{\sqrt{x}}dx = 2\sqrt{x}\ln x - 4\sqrt{x} + C$$

13. $u = \ln(2x + 3)$, $dv = dx$, $du = \dfrac{2}{2x + 3}dx$, $v = x$

$$\int \ln(2x + 3)dx = x\ln(2x + 3) - \int \frac{2x}{2x + 3}dx$$

but $\displaystyle\int \frac{2x}{2x + 3}dx = \int \left(1 - \frac{3}{2x + 3}\right)dx = x - \frac{3}{2}\ln(2x + 3) + C_1$ so

$$\int \ln(2x + 3)dx = x\ln(2x + 3) - x + \frac{3}{2}\ln(2x + 3) + C$$

14. $u = \ln(x^2 + 4)$, $dv = dx$, $du = \dfrac{2x}{x^2 + 4}dx$, $v = x$

$$\int \ln(x^2 + 4)dx = x\ln(x^2 + 4) - 2\int \frac{x^2}{x^2 + 4}dx$$

but $\displaystyle\int \frac{x^2}{x^2 + 4}dx = \int \left(1 - \frac{4}{x^2 + 4}\right)dx = x - 2\tan^{-1}\frac{x}{2} + C_1$ so

$$\int \ln(x^2 + 4)dx = x\ln(x^2 + 4) - 2x + 4\tan^{-1}\frac{x}{2} + C$$

15. $u = \sin^{-1} x$, $dv = dx$, $du = 1/\sqrt{1 - x^2}dx$, $v = x$

$$\int \sin^{-1} x\,dx = x\sin^{-1} x - \int x/\sqrt{1 - x^2}dx = x\sin^{-1} x + \sqrt{1 - x^2} + C$$

16. $u = \cos^{-1}(2x)$, $dv = dx$, $du = -\dfrac{2}{\sqrt{1-4x^2}}dx$, $v = x$

$$\int \cos^{-1}(2x)dx = x\cos^{-1}(2x) + \int \frac{2x}{\sqrt{1-4x^2}}dx = x\cos^{-1}(2x) - \frac{1}{2}\sqrt{1-4x^2} + C$$

17. $u = \tan^{-1}(2x)$, $dv = dx$, $du = \dfrac{2}{1+4x^2}dx$, $v = x$

$$\int \tan^{-1}(2x)dx = x\tan^{-1}(2x) - \int \frac{2x}{1+4x^2}dx = x\tan^{-1}(2x) - \frac{1}{4}\ln(1+4x^2) + C$$

18. $u = \tan^{-1}x$, $dv = x\,dx$, $du = \dfrac{1}{1+x^2}dx$, $v = \dfrac{1}{2}x^2$

$$\int x\tan^{-1}x\,dx = \frac{1}{2}x^2\tan^{-1}x - \frac{1}{2}\int \frac{x^2}{1+x^2}dx$$

but $\displaystyle\int \frac{x^2}{1+x^2}dx = \int \left(1 - \frac{1}{1+x^2}\right)dx = x - \tan^{-1}x + C_1$ so

$$\int x\tan^{-1}x\,dx = \frac{1}{2}x^2\tan^{-1}x - \frac{1}{2}x + \frac{1}{2}\tan^{-1}x + C$$

19. $u = e^x$, $dv = \sin x\,dx$, $du = e^x dx$, $v = -\cos x$; $\displaystyle\int e^x \sin x\,dx = -e^x\cos x + \int e^x\cos x\,dx$.

For $\displaystyle\int e^x\cos x\,dx$ use $u = e^x$, $dv = \cos x\,dx$ to get $\displaystyle\int e^x\cos x = e^x\sin x - \int e^x\sin x\,dx$ so

$$\int e^x \sin x\,dx = -e^x\cos x + e^x\sin x - \int e^x\sin x\,dx,$$

$$2\int e^x\sin x\,dx = e^x(\sin x - \cos x) + C_1, \quad \int e^x\sin x\,dx = \frac{1}{2}e^x(\sin x - \cos x) + C$$

20. $u = e^{-3\theta}$, $dv = \sin 3\theta\,d\theta$, $du = -3e^{-3\theta}d\theta$, $v = -\dfrac{1}{3}\cos 3\theta$

$$\int e^{-3\theta}\sin 3\theta\,d\theta = -\frac{1}{3}e^{-3\theta}\cos 3\theta - \int e^{-3\theta}\cos 3\theta\,d\theta. \text{ For } \int e^{-3\theta}\cos 3\theta\,d\theta \text{ use}$$

$u = e^{-3\theta}$, $dv = \cos 3\theta\,d\theta$ to get $\displaystyle\int e^{-3\theta}\cos 3\theta\,d\theta = \frac{1}{3}e^{-3\theta}\sin 3\theta + \int e^{-3\theta}\sin 3\theta\,d\theta$ so

$$\int e^{-3\theta}\sin 3\theta\,d\theta = -\frac{1}{3}e^{-3\theta}\cos 3\theta - \frac{1}{3}e^{-3\theta}\sin 3\theta - \int e^{-3\theta}\sin 3\theta\,d\theta,$$

$$\int e^{-3\theta}\sin 3\theta\,d\theta = -\frac{1}{6}e^{-3\theta}(\cos 3\theta + \sin 3\theta) + C$$

21. $u = e^{ax}$, $dv = \sin bx\, dx$, $du = ae^{ax} dx$, $v = -\dfrac{1}{b}\cos bx$

$$\int e^{ax} \sin bx\, dx = -\frac{1}{b} e^{ax} \cos bx + \frac{a}{b} \int e^{ax} \cos bx\, dx. \text{ Use } u = e^{ax},\ dv = \cos bx\, dx \text{ to get}$$

$$\int e^{ax} \cos bx\, dx = \frac{1}{b} e^{ax} \sin bx - \frac{a}{b} \int e^{ax} \sin bx\, dx \text{ so}$$

$$\int e^{ax} \sin bx\, dx = -\frac{1}{b} e^{ax} \cos bx + \frac{a}{b^2} e^{ax} \sin bx - \frac{a^2}{b^2} \int e^{ax} \sin bx\, dx,$$

$$\int e^{ax} \sin bx\, dx = \frac{e^{ax}}{a^2 + b^2} (a \sin bx - b \cos bx) + C$$

22. $u = e^{2x}$, $dv = \cos 3x\, dx$, $du = 2e^{2x} dx$, $v = \dfrac{1}{3}\sin 3x$

$$\int e^{2x} \cos 3x\, dx = \frac{1}{3} e^{2x} \sin 3x - \frac{2}{3} \int e^{2x} \sin 3x\, dx. \text{ Use } u = e^{2x},\ dv = \sin 3x\, dx \text{ to get}$$

$$\int e^{2x} \sin 3x\, dx = -\frac{1}{3} e^{2x} \cos 3x + \frac{2}{3} \int e^{2x} \cos 3x\, dx \text{ so}$$

$$\int e^{2x} \cos 3x\, dx = \frac{1}{3} e^{2x} \sin 3x + \frac{2}{9} e^{2x} \cos 3x - \frac{4}{9} \int e^{2x} \cos 3x\, dx,$$

$$\frac{13}{9} \int e^{2x} \cos 3x\, dx = \frac{1}{9} e^{2x} (3 \sin 3x + 2 \cos 3x) + C_1,$$

$$\int e^{2x} \cos 3x\, dx = \frac{1}{13} e^{2x} (3 \sin 3x + 2 \cos 3x) + C$$

23. $u = \sin(\ln x)$, $dv = dx$, $du = \dfrac{\cos(\ln x)}{x} dx$, $v = x$

$$\int \sin(\ln x)dx = x \sin(\ln x) - \int \cos(\ln x)dx. \text{ Use } u = \cos(\ln x),\ dv = dx \text{ to get}$$

$$\int \cos(\ln x)dx = x \cos(\ln x) + \int \sin(\ln x)dx \text{ so}$$

$$\int \sin(\ln x)dx = x \sin(\ln x) - x \cos(\ln x) - \int \sin(\ln x)dx,$$

$$\int \sin(\ln x)dx = (x/2)[\sin(\ln x) - \cos(\ln x)] + C$$

24. $u = \cos(\ln x)$, $dv = dx$, $du = -\dfrac{1}{x} \sin(\ln x)dx$, $v = x$

$$\int \cos(\ln x)dx = x \cos(\ln x) + \int \sin(\ln x)dx. \text{ Use } u = \sin(\ln x),\ dv = dx \text{ to get}$$

$$\int \sin(\ln x)dx = x \sin(\ln x) - \int \cos(\ln x)dx \text{ so}$$

$$\int \cos(\ln x)dx = x\cos(\ln x) + x\sin(\ln x) - \int \cos(\ln x)dx,$$

$$\int \cos(\ln x)dx = \frac{1}{2}x[\cos(\ln x) + \sin(\ln x)] + C$$

25. $u = x,\ dv = \sec^2 x\,dx,\ du = dx,\ v = \tan x$

$$\int x\sec^2 x\,dx = x\tan x - \int \tan x\,dx = x\tan x - \int \frac{\sin x}{\cos x}dx = x\tan x + \ln|\cos x| + C$$

26. $u = x,\ dv = \tan^2 x\,dx = (\sec^2 x - 1)dx,\ du = dx,\ v = \tan x - x$

$$\int x\tan^2 x\,dx = x\tan x - x^2 - \int(\tan x - x)dx$$

$$= x\tan x - x^2 + \ln|\cos x| + \frac{1}{2}x^2 + C = x\tan x - \frac{1}{2}x^2 + \ln|\cos x| + C$$

27. $u = x^2,\ dv = xe^{x^2}dx,\ du = 2x\,dx,\ v = \frac{1}{2}e^{x^2}$

$$\int x^3 e^{x^2}dx = \frac{1}{2}x^2 e^{x^2} - \int xe^{x^2}dx = \frac{1}{2}x^2 e^{x^2} - \frac{1}{2}e^{x^2} + C$$

28. $u = xe^x,\ dv = \dfrac{1}{(x+1)^2}dx,\ du = (x+1)e^x\,dx,\ v = -\dfrac{1}{x+1}$

$$\int \frac{xe^x}{(x+1)^2}dx = -\frac{xe^x}{x+1} + \int e^x\,dx = -\frac{xe^x}{x+1} + e^x + C = \frac{e^x}{x+1} + C$$

29. $u = x,\ dv = e^{-5x}dx,\ du = dx,\ v = -\dfrac{1}{5}e^{-5x}$

$$\int_0^1 xe^{-5x}dx = -\frac{1}{5}xe^{-5x}\Big]_0^1 + \frac{1}{5}\int_0^1 e^{-5x}dx$$

$$= -\frac{1}{5}e^{-5} - \frac{1}{25}e^{-5x}\Big]_0^1 = -\frac{1}{5}e^{-5} - \frac{1}{25}(e^{-5} - 1) = (1 - 6e^{-5})/25$$

30. $u = x,\ dv = e^{2x}dx,\ du = dx,\ v = \dfrac{1}{2}e^{2x}$

$$\int_0^2 xe^{2x}dx = \frac{1}{2}xe^{2x}\Big]_0^2 - \frac{1}{2}\int_0^2 e^{2x}dx = e^4 - \frac{1}{4}e^{2x}\Big]_0^2 = e^4 - \frac{1}{4}(e^4 - 1) = (3e^4 + 1)/4$$

31. $u = \ln x,\ dv = x^2dx,\ du = \dfrac{1}{x}dx,\ v = \dfrac{1}{3}x^3$

$$\int_1^e x^2\ln x\,dx = \frac{1}{3}x^3\ln x\Big]_1^e - \frac{1}{3}\int_1^e x^2dx = \frac{1}{3}e^3 - \frac{1}{9}x^3\Big]_1^e = \frac{1}{3}e^3 - \frac{1}{9}(e^3 - 1) = (2e^3 + 1)/9$$

32. $u = \ln x$, $dv = \dfrac{1}{x^2}dx$, $du = \dfrac{1}{x}dx$, $v = -\dfrac{1}{x}$

$$\int_{\sqrt{e}}^{e} \frac{\ln x}{x^2}dx = -\frac{1}{x}\ln x\Big]_{\sqrt{e}}^{e} + \int_{\sqrt{e}}^{e} \frac{1}{x^2}dx$$

$$= -\frac{1}{e} + \frac{1}{\sqrt{e}}\ln\sqrt{e} - \frac{1}{x}\Big]_{\sqrt{e}}^{e} = -\frac{1}{e} + \frac{1}{2\sqrt{e}} - \frac{1}{e} + \frac{1}{\sqrt{e}} = \frac{3\sqrt{e}-4}{2e}$$

33. $u = \ln(x+3)$, $dv = dx$, $du = \dfrac{1}{x+3}dx$, $v = x$

$$\int_{-2}^{2} \ln(x+3)dx = x\ln(x+3)\big]_{-2}^{2} - \int_{-2}^{2}\frac{x}{x+3}dx = 2\ln 5 + 2\ln 1 - \int_{-2}^{2}\left[1 - \frac{3}{x+3}\right]dx$$

$$= 2\ln 5 - [x - 3\ln(x+3)]_{-2}^{2} = 2\ln 5 - (2 - 3\ln 5) + (-2 - 3\ln 1) = 5\ln 5 - 4$$

34. $u = \sin^{-1} x$, $dv = dx$, $du = \dfrac{1}{\sqrt{1-x^2}}dx$, $v = x$

$$\int_{0}^{1/2} \sin^{-1} x\, dx = x\sin^{-1} x\big]_{0}^{1/2} - \int_{0}^{1/2}\frac{x}{\sqrt{1-x^2}}dx = \frac{1}{2}\sin^{-1}\frac{1}{2} + \sqrt{1-x^2}\Big]_{0}^{1/2}$$

$$= \frac{1}{2}\left(\frac{\pi}{6}\right) + \sqrt{\frac{3}{4}} - 1 = \frac{\pi}{12} + \frac{\sqrt{3}}{2} - 1$$

35. $u = \sec^{-1}\sqrt{\theta}$, $dv = d\theta$, $du = \dfrac{1}{2\theta\sqrt{\theta-1}}d\theta$, $v = \theta$

$$\int_{2}^{4} \sec^{-1}\sqrt{\theta}\,d\theta = \theta\sec^{-1}\sqrt{\theta}\Big]_{2}^{4} - \frac{1}{2}\int_{2}^{4}\frac{1}{\sqrt{\theta-1}}d\theta = 4\sec^{-1}2 - 2\sec^{-1}\sqrt{2} - \sqrt{\theta-1}\Big]_{2}^{4}$$

$$= 4\left(\frac{\pi}{3}\right) - 2\left(\frac{\pi}{4}\right) - \sqrt{3} + 1 = \frac{5\pi}{6} - \sqrt{3} + 1$$

36. $u = \sec^{-1} x$, $dv = x\,dx$, $du = \dfrac{1}{x\sqrt{x^2-1}}dx$, $v = \dfrac{1}{2}x^2$

$$\int_{1}^{2} x\sec^{-1} x\, dx = \frac{1}{2}x^2\sec^{-1} x\Big]_{1}^{2} - \frac{1}{2}\int_{1}^{2}\frac{x}{\sqrt{x^2-1}}dx$$

$$= \frac{1}{4}[(4)(\pi/3) - (1)(0)] - \frac{1}{2}\sqrt{x^2-1}\Big]_{1}^{2} = 2\pi/3 - \sqrt{3}/2$$

37. $u = x$, $dv = \sin 4x\,dx$, $du = dx$, $v = -\dfrac{1}{4}\cos 4x$

$$\int_{0}^{\pi/2} x\sin 4x\, dx = -\frac{1}{4}x\cos 4x\Big]_{0}^{\pi/2} + \frac{1}{4}\int_{0}^{\pi/2}\cos 4x\, dx = -\pi/8 + \frac{1}{16}\sin 4x\Big]_{0}^{\pi/2} = -\pi/8$$

38. $\int_0^\pi (x + x\cos x)dx = \frac{1}{2}x^2\Big]_0^\pi + \int_0^\pi x\cos x\,dx = \frac{\pi^2}{2} + \int_0^\pi x\cos x\,dx;$

$u = x,\ dv = \cos x\,dx,\ du = dx,\ v = \sin x$

$\int_0^\pi x\cos x\,dx = x\sin x\Big]_0^\pi - \int_0^\pi \sin x\,dx = \cos x\Big]_0^\pi = -2$ so $\int_0^\pi (x + x\cos x)dx = \pi^2/2 - 2$

39. $u = \tan^{-1}\sqrt{x},\ dv = \sqrt{x}dx,\ du = \dfrac{1}{2\sqrt{x}(1+x)}dx,\ v = \dfrac{2}{3}x^{3/2}$

$\int_1^3 \sqrt{x}\tan^{-1}\sqrt{x}dx = \frac{2}{3}x^{3/2}\tan^{-1}\sqrt{x}\Big]_1^3 - \frac{1}{3}\int_1^3 \frac{x}{1+x}dx$

$\qquad = \frac{2}{3}x^{3/2}\tan^{-1}\sqrt{x}\Big]_1^3 - \frac{1}{3}\int_1^3 \left[1 - \frac{1}{1+x}\right]dx$

$\qquad = \left[\frac{2}{3}x^{3/2}\tan^{-1}\sqrt{x} - \frac{1}{3}x + \frac{1}{3}\ln|1+x|\right]_1^3 = (2\sqrt{3}\pi - \pi/2 - 2 + \ln 2)/3$

40. $u = \ln(x^2 + 1),\ dv = dx,\ du = \dfrac{2x}{x^2+1}dx,\ v = x$

$\int_0^2 \ln(x^2 + 1)dx = x\ln(x^2 + 1)\Big]_0^2 - \int_0^2 \frac{2x^2}{x^2+1}dx = 2\ln 5 - 2\int_0^2 \left(1 - \frac{1}{x^2+1}\right)dx$

$\qquad = 2\ln 5 - 2(x - \tan^{-1}x)\Big]_0^2 = 2\ln 5 - 4 + 2\tan^{-1}2$

41. $u = x^2,\ dv = \dfrac{x}{\sqrt{x^2+1}}dx,\ du = 2x\,dx,\ v = \sqrt{x^2+1}$

$\int_0^1 \frac{x^3}{\sqrt{x^2+1}}dx = x^2\sqrt{x^2+1}\Big]_0^1 - 2\int_0^1 x(x^2+1)^{1/2}dx$

$\qquad = \sqrt{2} - \frac{2}{3}(x^2+1)^{3/2}\Big]_0^1 = \sqrt{2} - \frac{2}{3}[2\sqrt{2} - 1] = (2 - \sqrt{2})/3$

42. $u^2 = x^2 + 1,\ x^2 = u^2 - 1,\ 2x\,dx = 2u\,du,\ x\,dx = u\,du$

$\int_0^1 \frac{x^3}{\sqrt{x^2+1}}dx = \int_0^1 \frac{x^2}{\sqrt{x^2+1}}x\,dx = \int_1^{\sqrt{2}} \frac{u^2-1}{u}u\,du$

$\qquad = \int_1^{\sqrt{2}} (u^2 - 1)du = \left(\frac{1}{3}u^3 - u\right)\Big]_1^{\sqrt{2}} = (2 - \sqrt{2})/3$

43. **(a)** $A = \int_1^e \ln x\,dx = (x\ln x - x)\Big]_1^e = 1$

(b) $V = \pi \int_1^e (\ln x)^2 dx = \pi(x(\ln x)^2 - 2x \ln x + 2x) \Big]_1^e = \pi(e-2)$

44. $A = \int_0^{\pi/2} (x - x \sin x) dx = \frac{1}{2}x^2 \Big]_0^{\pi/2} - \int_0^{\pi/2} x \sin x \, dx$

$$= \frac{\pi^2}{8} - (-x \cos x + \sin x) \Big]_0^{\pi/2} = \pi^2/8 - 1$$

45. $V = 2\pi \int_0^\pi x \sin x \, dx = 2\pi(-x \cos x + \sin x) \Big]_0^\pi = 2\pi^2$

46. $V = 2\pi \int_0^{\pi/2} x \cos x \, dx = 2\pi(\cos x + x \sin x)]_0^{\pi/2} = \pi(\pi - 2)$

47. (a) $\int \sin^3 x \, dx = -\frac{1}{3} \sin^2 x \cos x + \frac{2}{3} \int \sin x \, dx = -\frac{1}{3} \sin^2 x \cos x - \frac{2}{3} \cos x + C$

(b) $\int \sin^4 x \, dx = -\frac{1}{4} \sin^3 x \cos x + \frac{3}{4} \int \sin^2 x \, dx,$

$\int \sin^2 x \, dx = -\frac{1}{2} \sin x \cos x + \frac{1}{2}x + C_1$ so

$\int_0^{\pi/4} \sin^4 x \, dx = -\frac{1}{4} \sin^3 x \cos x - \frac{3}{8} \sin x \cos x + \frac{3}{8}x \Big]_0^{\pi/4}$

$$= -\frac{1}{4}(1/\sqrt{2})^3(1/\sqrt{2}) - \frac{3}{8}(1/\sqrt{2})(1/\sqrt{2}) + 3\pi/32 = 3\pi/32 - 1/4$$

48. (a) $\int \cos^5 x \, dx = \frac{1}{5} \cos^4 x \sin x + \frac{4}{5} \int \cos^3 x \, dx$

$$= \frac{1}{5} \cos^4 x \sin x + \frac{4}{5} \left[\frac{1}{3} \cos x \sin x + \frac{2}{3} \sin x \right] + C$$

$$= \frac{1}{5} \cos^4 x \sin x + \frac{4}{15} \cos x \sin x + \frac{8}{15} \sin x + C$$

(b) $\int \cos^6 x \, dx = \frac{1}{6} \cos^5 x \sin x + \frac{5}{6} \int \cos^4 x \, dx$

$$= \frac{1}{6} \cos^5 x \sin x + \frac{5}{6} \left[\frac{1}{4} \cos^3 x \sin x + \frac{3}{4} \int \cos^2 x \, dx \right]$$

$$= \frac{1}{6} \cos^5 x \sin x + \frac{5}{24} \cos^3 x \sin x + \frac{5}{8} \left[\frac{1}{2} \cos x \sin x + \frac{1}{2}x \right] + C,$$

$\frac{1}{6} \cos^5 x \sin x + \frac{5}{24} \cos^3 x \sin x + \frac{5}{16} \cos x \sin x + \frac{5}{16}x \Big]_0^{\pi/2} = 5\pi/32$

49. (a) $u = 5x$,

$$\int \cos^3 5x \, dx = \frac{1}{5} \int \cos^3 u \, du = \frac{1}{5} \left[\frac{1}{3} \cos^2 u \sin u + \frac{2}{3} \int \cos u \, du \right]$$

$$= \frac{1}{15} \cos^2 u \sin u + \frac{2}{15} \sin u + C = \frac{1}{15} \cos^2 5x \sin 5x + \frac{2}{15} \sin 5x + C$$

(b) $u = x^2$,

$$\int x \cos^4(x^2) dx = \frac{1}{2} \int \cos^4 u \, du = \frac{1}{2} \left[\frac{1}{4} \cos^3 u \sin u + \frac{3}{4} \int \cos^2 u \, du \right]$$

$$= \frac{1}{8} \cos^3 u \sin u + \frac{3}{8} \left[\frac{1}{2} \cos u \sin u + \frac{1}{2} \int du \right]$$

$$= \frac{1}{8} \cos^3 u \sin u + \frac{3}{16} \cos u \sin u + \frac{3}{16} u + C$$

$$= \frac{1}{8} \cos^3(x^2) \sin(x^2) + \frac{3}{16} \cos(x^2) \sin(x^2) + \frac{3}{16} x^2 + C$$

50. (a) $u = 2x$,

$$\int \sin^4 2x \, dx = \frac{1}{2} \int \sin^4 u \, du = \frac{1}{2} \left[-\frac{1}{4} \sin^3 u \cos u + \frac{3}{4} \int \sin^2 u \, du \right]$$

$$= -\frac{1}{8} \sin^3 u \cos u + \frac{3}{8} \left[-\frac{1}{2} \sin u \cos u + \frac{1}{2} \int du \right]$$

$$= -\frac{1}{8} \sin^3 u \cos u - \frac{3}{16} \sin u \cos u + \frac{3}{16} u + C$$

$$= -\frac{1}{8} \sin^3 2x \cos 2x - \frac{3}{16} \sin 2x \cos 2x + \frac{3}{8} x + C$$

(b) $u = \sqrt{x}$,

$$\int \frac{\sin^3 \sqrt{x}}{\sqrt{x}} dx = 2 \int \sin^3 u \, du = 2 \left[-\frac{1}{3} \sin^2 u \cos u + \frac{2}{3} \int \sin u \, du \right]$$

$$= -\frac{2}{3} \sin^2 u \cos u - \frac{4}{3} \cos u + C = -\frac{2}{3} \sin^2 \sqrt{x} \cos \sqrt{x} - \frac{4}{3} \cos \sqrt{x} + C$$

51. $u = \sin^{n-1} x$, $dv = \sin x \, dx$, $du = (n-1) \sin^{n-2} x \cos x \, dx$, $v = -\cos x$

$$\int \sin^n x \, dx = -\sin^{n-1} x \cos x + (n-1) \int \sin^{n-2} x \cos^2 x \, dx$$

$$= -\sin^{n-1} x \cos x + (n-1) \int \sin^{n-2} x (1 - \sin^2 x) dx$$

$$= -\sin^{n-1} x \cos x + (n-1) \int \sin^{n-2} x \, dx - (n-1) \int \sin^n x \, dx,$$

$$n \int \sin^n x \, dx = -\sin^{n-1} x \cos x + (n-1) \int \sin^{n-2} x \, dx,$$

$$\int \sin^n x \, dx = -\frac{1}{n} \sin^{n-1} x \cos x + \frac{n-1}{n} \int \sin^{n-2} x \, dx$$

52. **(a)** $u = \sec^{n-2} x, \; dv = \sec^2 x \, dx, \; du = (n-2)\sec^{n-2} x \tan x \, dx, \; v = \tan x$

$$\int \sec^n x \, dx = \sec^{n-2} x \tan x - (n-2) \int \sec^{n-2} x \tan^2 x \, dx$$

$$= \sec^{n-2} x \tan x - (n-2) \int \sec^{n-2} x (\sec^2 x - 1) dx$$

$$= \sec^{n-2} x \tan x - (n-2) \int \sec^n x \, dx + (n-2) \int \sec^{n-2} x \, dx,$$

$$(n-1) \int \sec^n x \, dx = \sec^{n-2} x \tan x + (n-2) \int \sec^{n-2} x \, dx,$$

$$\int \sec^n x \, dx = \frac{1}{n-1} \sec^{n-2} x \tan x + \frac{n-2}{n-1} \int \sec^{n-2} x \, dx$$

(b) $\displaystyle \int \sec^4 x \, dx = \frac{1}{3} \sec^2 x \tan x + \frac{2}{3} \int \sec^2 x \, dx = \frac{1}{3} \sec^2 x \tan x + \frac{2}{3} [\tan x + 0] + C$

$$= \frac{1}{3} \sec^2 x \tan x + \frac{2}{3} \tan x + C$$

53. **(a)** $u = x^n, \; dv = e^x dx, \; du = nx^{n-1}dx, \; v = e^x; \; \displaystyle \int x^n e^x dx = x^n e^x - n \int x^{n-1} e^x dx$

(b) $\displaystyle \int x^3 e^x dx = x^3 e^x - 3 \int x^2 e^x dx = x^3 e^x - 3 \left[x^2 e^x - 2 \int x e^x dx \right]$

$$= x^3 e^x - 3x^2 e^x + 6 \left[x e^x - \int e^x dx \right] = x^3 e^x - 3x^2 e^x + 6x e^x - 6e^x + C$$

54. **(a)** $u = 3x,$

$$\int x^2 e^{3x} dx = \frac{1}{27} \int u^2 e^u du = \frac{1}{27} \left[u^2 e^u - 2 \int u e^u du \right] = \frac{1}{27} u^2 e^u - \frac{2}{27} \left[u e^u - \int e^u du \right]$$

$$= \frac{1}{27} u^2 e^u - \frac{2}{27} u e^u + \frac{2}{27} e^u + C = \frac{1}{3} x^2 e^{3x} - \frac{2}{9} x e^{3x} + \frac{2}{27} e^{3x} + C$$

(b) $u = -\sqrt{x},$

$$\int_0^1 x e^{-\sqrt{x}} dx = 2 \int_0^{-1} u^3 e^u du,$$

$$\int u^3 e^u\,du = u^3 e^u - 3\int u^2 e^u\,du = u^3 e^u - 3\left[u^2 e^u - 2\int u e^u\,du\right]$$

$$= u^3 e^u - 3u^2 e^u + 6\left[u e^u - \int e^u\,du\right] = u^3 e^u - 3u^2 e^u + 6u e^u - 6e^u + C,$$

$$2\int_0^{-1} u^3 e^u\,du = 2(u^3 - 3u^2 + 6u - 6)e^u\Big]_0^{-1} = 12 - 32e^{-1}$$

55. $u = x,\ dv = f''(x)dx,\ du = dx,\ v = f'(x)$

$$\int_{-1}^{1} x\,f''(x)dx = xf'(x)]_{-1}^{1} - \int_{-1}^{1} f'(x)dx$$

$$= f'(1) - f'(-1) - f(x)]_{-1}^{1} = f'(1) - f'(-1) + f(-1) - f(1)$$

56. **(a)** $\displaystyle\int xe^x\,dx = x(e^x + C_1) - \int (e^x + C_1)dx = xe^x + C_1 x - e^x - C_1 x + C = xe^x - e^x + C$

(b) $u(v + C_1) - \displaystyle\int (v + C_1)du = uv + C_1 u - \int v\,du - C_1 u = uv - \int v\,du$

57. $du = -(1/x^2)dx,\ v = x;\ \displaystyle\int \frac{1}{x}dx = 1 + \int \frac{1}{x}dx$ so $0 = 1$???

The "obvious" cancellation of the indefinite integrals causes the problem. Instead, proceed as follows:

$$\int \frac{1}{x}dx - \int \frac{1}{x}dx = 1,\ \int (0)dx = 1,\ \text{but}\ \int (0)dx = C\ \text{so}\ C = 1.$$

EXERCISE SET 9.3

1. $u = \cos x,\ -\displaystyle\int u^5\,du = -\frac{1}{6}\cos^6 x + C$ **2.** $u = \sin 3x,\ \frac{1}{3}\displaystyle\int u^4\,du = \frac{1}{15}\sin^5 3x + C$

3. $u = \sin ax,\ \dfrac{1}{a}\displaystyle\int u\,du = \frac{1}{2a}\sin^2 ax + C$

4. $\displaystyle\int \cos^2 3x\,dx = \frac{1}{2}\int (1 + \cos 6x)dx = \frac{1}{2}x + \frac{1}{12}\sin 6x + C$

5. $\displaystyle\int \sin^2 5\theta\,d\theta = \frac{1}{2}\int (1 - \cos 10\theta)d\theta = \frac{1}{2}\theta - \frac{1}{20}\sin 10\theta + C$

6. $\displaystyle\int \cos^3 at\, dt = \int (1 - \sin^2 at) \cos at\, dt$

$$= \int \cos at\, dt - \int \sin^2 at \cos at\, dt = \frac{1}{a}\sin at - \frac{1}{3a}\sin^3 at + C$$

7. $\displaystyle\int \cos^4(x/4)dx = \frac{1}{4}\int [1 + \cos(x/2)]^2 dx = \frac{1}{4}\int [1 + 2\cos(x/2) + \cos^2(x/2)]dx$

$$= \frac{1}{4}\int \left[1 + 2\cos(x/2) + \frac{1}{2}(1 + \cos x) \right] dx = \frac{1}{4}\int \left[\frac{3}{2} + 2\cos(x/2) + \frac{1}{2}\cos x \right] dx$$

$$= \frac{3}{8}x + \sin(x/2) + \frac{1}{8}\sin x + C$$

8. $\displaystyle\int \sin^5 x\, dx = \int (1 - \cos^2 x)^2 \sin x\, dx$

$$= \int (1 - 2\cos^2 x + \cos^4 x)\sin x\, dx = -\cos x + \frac{2}{3}\cos^3 x - \frac{1}{5}\cos^5 x + C$$

9. $\displaystyle\int \cos^5 \theta\, d\theta = \int (1 - \sin^2 \theta)^2 \cos \theta\, d\theta = \int (1 - 2\sin^2 \theta + \sin^4 \theta)\cos \theta\, d\theta$

$$= \sin \theta - \frac{2}{3}\sin^3 \theta + \frac{1}{5}\sin^5 \theta + C$$

10. $\displaystyle\int \sin^3 x \cos^3 x\, dx = \int \sin^3 x(1 - \sin^2 x)\cos x\, dx$

$$= \int (\sin^3 x - \sin^5 x)\cos x\, dx = \frac{1}{4}\sin^4 x - \frac{1}{6}\sin^6 x + C$$

11. $\displaystyle\int \sin^2 2t \cos^3 2t\, dt = \int \sin^2 2t(1 - \sin^2 2t)\cos 2t\, dt = \int (\sin^2 2t - \sin^4 2t)\cos 2t\, dt$

$$= \frac{1}{6}\sin^3 2t - \frac{1}{10}\sin^5 2t + C$$

12. $\displaystyle\int \sin^4 x \cos^5 x\, dx = \int \sin^4 x(1 - \sin^2 x)^2 \cos x\, dx$

$$= \int (\sin^4 x - 2\sin^6 x + \sin^8 x)\cos x\, dx = \frac{1}{5}\sin^5 x - \frac{2}{7}\sin^7 x + \frac{1}{9}\sin^9 x + C$$

13. $\displaystyle\int \cos^4 x \sin^3 x\, dx = \int \cos^4 x(1 - \cos^2 x)\sin x\, dx$

$$= \int (\cos^4 x - \cos^6 x)\sin x\, dx = -\frac{1}{5}\cos^5 x + \frac{1}{7}\cos^7 x + C$$

14. $\displaystyle\int \sin^3 2x \cos^2 2x\, dx = \int (1 - \cos^2 2x) \cos^2 2x \sin 2x\, dx$

$$= \int (\cos^2 2x - \cos^4 2x) \sin 2x\, dx = -\frac{1}{6} \cos^3 2x + \frac{1}{10} \cos^5 2x + C$$

15. $\displaystyle\int \sin^5 \theta \cos^4 \theta\, d\theta = \int (1 - \cos^2 \theta)^2 \cos^4 \theta \sin \theta\, d\theta$

$$= \int (\cos^4 \theta - 2\cos^6 \theta + \cos^8 \theta) \sin \theta\, d\theta = -\frac{1}{5} \cos^5 \theta + \frac{2}{7} \cos^7 \theta - \frac{1}{9} \cos^9 \theta + C$$

16. $\displaystyle u = \cos x, \; -\int u^{1/5} du = -\frac{5}{6} \cos^{6/5} x + C$

17. $\displaystyle\int \sin^2 x \cos^2 x\, dx = \frac{1}{4} \int (1 - \cos 2x)(1 + \cos 2x)dx = \frac{1}{4} \int (1 - \cos^2 2x)dx = \frac{1}{4} \int \sin^2 2x\, dx$

$$= \frac{1}{8} \int (1 - \cos 4x)dx = \frac{1}{8}x - \frac{1}{32} \sin 4x + C$$

18. $\displaystyle\int \sin^2 x \cos^4 x\, dx = \frac{1}{8} \int (1 - \cos 2x)(1 + \cos 2x)^2 dx = \frac{1}{8} \int (1 - \cos^2 2x)(1 + \cos 2x)dx$

$$= \frac{1}{8} \int \sin^2 2x\, dx + \frac{1}{8} \int \sin^2 2x \cos 2x\, dx = \frac{1}{16} \int (1 - \cos 4x)dx + \frac{1}{48} \sin^3 2x$$

$$= \frac{1}{16}x - \frac{1}{64} \sin 4x + \frac{1}{48} \sin^3 2x + C$$

19. $\displaystyle\int \sin x \cos 2x\, dx = \frac{1}{2} \int (\sin 3x - \sin x)dx = -\frac{1}{6} \cos 3x + \frac{1}{2} \cos x + C$

20. $\displaystyle\int \sin 3\theta \cos 2\theta\, d\theta = \frac{1}{2} \int (\sin 5\theta + \sin \theta)d\theta = -\frac{1}{10} \cos 5\theta - \frac{1}{2} \cos \theta + C$

21. $\displaystyle\int \sin x \cos(x/2)dx = \frac{1}{2} \int [\sin(3x/2) + \sin(x/2)]dx = -\frac{1}{3} \cos(3x/2) - \cos(x/2) + C$

22. $\displaystyle\int \sin ax \cos bx\, dx = \frac{1}{2} \int [\sin(a+b)x + \sin(a-b)x]dx = -\frac{\cos(a+b)x}{2(a+b)} - \frac{\cos(a-b)x}{2(a-b)} + C$

23. $\displaystyle u = \cos x, \; -\int u^{-8} du = 1/(7 \cos^7 x) + C$ **24.** $\displaystyle u = \cos \theta, \; -\int u^{1/2} du = -\frac{2}{3} \cos^{3/2} \theta + C$

25. $\displaystyle\int_0^{\pi/4} \cos^3 x \, dx = \int_0^{\pi/4} (1 - \sin^2 x) \cos x \, dx$

$$= \sin x - \frac{1}{3}\sin^3 x \Big]_0^{\pi/4} = (\sqrt{2}/2) - \frac{1}{3}(\sqrt{2}/2)^3 = 5\sqrt{2}/12$$

26. $\displaystyle\int_{-\pi}^{\pi} \cos^2 5\theta \, d\theta = \frac{1}{2}\int_{-\pi}^{\pi} (1 + \cos 10\theta) d\theta = \frac{1}{2}\left(\theta + \frac{1}{10}\sin 10\theta\right)\Big]_{-\pi}^{\pi} = \pi$

27. $\displaystyle\int_0^{\pi/3} \sin^4 3x \cos^3 3x \, dx = \int_0^{\pi/3} \sin^4 3x(1 - \sin^2 3x) \cos 3x \, dx = \frac{1}{15}\sin^5 3x - \frac{1}{21}\sin^7 3x \Big]_0^{\pi/3} = 0$

28. $\displaystyle\int_0^{\pi/2} \sin^2(x/2) \cos^2(x/2) dx = \frac{1}{4}\int_0^{\pi/2} \sin^2 x \, dx = \frac{1}{8}\int_0^{\pi/2} (1 - \cos 2x) dx$

$$= \frac{1}{8}\left(x - \frac{1}{2}\sin 2x\right)\Big]_0^{\pi/2} = \pi/16$$

29. $\displaystyle\int_0^{\pi/6} \sin 2x \cos 4x \, dx = \frac{1}{2}\int_0^{\pi/6} (\sin 6x - \sin 2x) dx = -\frac{1}{12}\cos 6x + \frac{1}{4}\cos 2x \Big]_0^{\pi/6}$

$$= [(-1/12)(-1) + (1/4)(1/2)] - [-1/12 + 1/4] = 1/24$$

30. $\displaystyle\int_0^{2\pi} \sin^2 kx \, dx = \frac{1}{2}\int_0^{2\pi} (1 - \cos 2kx) dx = \frac{1}{2}\left(x - \frac{1}{2k}\sin 2kx\right)\Big]_0^{2\pi} = \pi - \frac{1}{4k}\sin 4\pi k$

31. **(a)** $\displaystyle\int_0^{2\pi} \sin mx \cos nx \, dx = \frac{1}{2}\int_0^{2\pi} [\sin(m+n)x + \sin(m-n)x] dx$

$$= -\frac{\cos(m+n)x}{2(m+n)} - \frac{\cos(m-n)x}{2(m-n)}\Big]_0^{2\pi},$$

$m + n$ and $m - n$ are integers so $\cos[(m+n)2\pi] = \cos[(m-n)2\pi] = 1$ thus

$$\int_0^{2\pi} \sin mx \cos nx \, dx = \left[\left(-\frac{1}{2(m+n)} - \frac{1}{2(m-n)}\right) + \left(\frac{1}{2(m+n)} + \frac{1}{2(m-n)}\right)\right] = 0$$

(b) $\displaystyle\int_0^{2\pi} \cos mx \cos nx \, dx = \frac{1}{2}\int_0^{2\pi} [\cos(m+n)x + \cos(m-n)x] dx$

$$= \frac{\sin(m+n)x}{2(m+n)} + \frac{\sin(m-n)x}{2(m-n)}\Big]_0^{2\pi} = 0$$

(c) $\displaystyle\int_0^{2\pi} \sin mx \sin nx\, dx = \frac{1}{2}\int_0^{2\pi} [\cos(m-n)x - \cos(m+n)x]dx$

$$= \frac{\sin(m-n)x}{2(m-n)} + \frac{\sin(m+n)x}{2(m+n)}\Bigg]_0^{2\pi} = 0$$

32. $\displaystyle V = \pi\int_0^\pi \sin^2 x\, dx = \frac{\pi}{2}\int_0^\pi (1-\cos 2x)dx = \frac{\pi}{2}\left(x - \frac{1}{2}\sin 2x\right)\Bigg]_0^\pi = \pi^2/2$

33. $\displaystyle V = \pi\int_0^{\pi/4} (\cos^2 x - \sin^2 x)dx = \pi\int_0^{\pi/4} \cos 2x\, dx = \frac{1}{2}\pi\sin 2x\Bigg]_0^{\pi/4} = \pi/2$

34. (a) $\displaystyle\int_0^{\pi/2} \sin^n x\, dx = -\frac{1}{n}\sin^{n-1} x \cos x\Bigg]_0^{\pi/2} + \frac{n-1}{n}\int_0^{\pi/2} \sin^{n-2} x\, dx$

$$= \frac{n-1}{n}\int_0^{\pi/2} \sin^{n-2} x\, dx$$

(b) By repeated application of the formula in part (a)

$$\int_0^{\pi/2} \sin^n x\, dx = \left(\frac{n-1}{n}\right)\left(\frac{n-3}{n-2}\right)\int_0^{\pi/2} \sin^{n-4} x\, dx$$

$$= \begin{cases} \left(\dfrac{n-1}{n}\right)\left(\dfrac{n-3}{n-2}\right)\left(\dfrac{n-5}{n-4}\right)\cdots\left(\dfrac{1}{2}\right)\displaystyle\int_0^{\pi/2} dx, n \text{ even} \\[3mm] \left(\dfrac{n-1}{n}\right)\left(\dfrac{n-3}{n-2}\right)\left(\dfrac{n-5}{n-4}\right)\cdots\left(\dfrac{2}{3}\right)\displaystyle\int_0^{\pi/2} \sin x\, dx, n \text{ odd} \end{cases}$$

$$= \begin{cases} \dfrac{1\cdot 3\cdot 5\cdots(n-1)}{2\cdot 4\cdot 6\cdots n}\cdot\dfrac{\pi}{2}, n \text{ even} \\[3mm] \dfrac{2\cdot 4\cdot 6\cdots(n-1)}{3\cdot 5\cdot 7\cdots n}, n \text{ odd} \end{cases}$$

35. (a) $\displaystyle\int_0^{\pi/2} \sin^3 x\, dx = \frac{2}{3}$

(b) $\displaystyle\int_0^{\pi/2} \sin^4 x\, dx = \frac{1\cdot 3}{2\cdot 4}\cdot\frac{\pi}{2} = 3\pi/16$

(c) $\displaystyle\int_0^{\pi/2} \sin^5 x\, dx = \frac{2\cdot 4}{3\cdot 5} = 8/15$

(d) $\displaystyle\int_0^{\pi/2} \sin^6 x\, dx = \frac{1\cdot 3\cdot 5}{2\cdot 4\cdot 6}\cdot\frac{\pi}{2} = 5\pi/32$

36. Similar to proof in Exercise 34.

37. For (6), $\displaystyle\int \sin^3 x \, dx = -\frac{1}{3}\sin^2 x \cos x + \frac{2}{3}\int \sin x \, dx = -\frac{1}{3}\sin^2 x \cos x - \frac{2}{3}\cos x + C$,

but $\sin^2 x = 1 - \cos^2 x$ so

$$\int \sin^3 x \, dx = -\frac{1}{3}(1 - \cos^2 x)\cos x - \frac{2}{3}\cos x + C = -\cos x + \frac{1}{3}\cos^3 x + C$$

The derivation of (7) is similar.

EXERCISE SET 9.4

1. $\displaystyle\frac{1}{3}\tan(3x + 1) + C$

2. $\displaystyle-\frac{1}{5}\ln|\cos 5x| + C$

3. $\displaystyle\frac{1}{2}\ln|\cos(e^{-2x})| + C$

4. $\displaystyle\frac{1}{3}\ln|\sin 3x| + C$

5. $\displaystyle\frac{1}{2}\ln|\sec 2x + \tan 2x| + C$

6. $2\ln|\sec\sqrt{x} + \tan\sqrt{x}| + C$

7. $u = \tan x, \displaystyle\int u^2 \, du = \frac{1}{3}\tan^3 x + C$

8. $\displaystyle\int \tan^5 x(1 + \tan^2 x)\sec^2 x \, dx = \int (\tan^5 x + \tan^7 x)\sec^2 x \, dx = \frac{1}{6}\tan^6 x + \frac{1}{8}\tan^8 x + C$

9. $\displaystyle\int \tan^3 4x(1 + \tan^2 4x)\sec^2 4x \, dx = \int (\tan^3 4x + \tan^5 4x)\sec^2 4x \, dx$

$$= \frac{1}{16}\tan^4 4x + \frac{1}{24}\tan^6 4x + C$$

10. $\displaystyle\int \tan^4 \theta(1 + \tan^2 \theta)\sec^2 \theta \, d\theta = \frac{1}{5}\tan^5 \theta + \frac{1}{7}\tan^7 \theta + C$

11. $\displaystyle\int \sec^4 x(\sec^2 x - 1)\sec x \tan x \, dx = \int (\sec^6 x - \sec^4 x)\sec x \tan x \, dx = \frac{1}{7}\sec^7 x - \frac{1}{5}\sec^5 x + C$

12. $\displaystyle\int (\sec^2 \theta - 1)^2 \sec \theta \tan \theta \, d\theta = \int (\sec^4 \theta - 2\sec^2 \theta + 1)\sec \theta \tan \theta \, d\theta$

$$= \frac{1}{5}\sec^5 \theta - \frac{2}{3}\sec^3 \theta + \sec \theta + C$$

13. $\int (\sec^2 x - 1)^2 \sec x \, dx = \int (\sec^5 x - 2\sec^3 x + \sec x) dx$

$$= \int \sec^5 x \, dx - 2\int \sec^3 x \, dx + \int \sec x \, dx$$

$$= \frac{1}{4}\sec^3 x \tan x + \frac{3}{4}\int \sec^3 x \, dx - 2\int \sec^3 x \, dx + \ln|\sec x + \tan x|$$

$$= \frac{1}{4}\sec^3 x \tan x - \frac{5}{4}\left[\frac{1}{2}\sec x \tan x + \frac{1}{2}\ln|\sec x + \tan x|\right] + \ln|\sec x + \tan x| + C$$

$$= \frac{1}{4}\sec^3 x \tan x - \frac{5}{8}\sec x \tan x + \frac{3}{8}\ln|\sec x + \tan x| + C$$

14. $\int [\sec^2(x/2) - 1]\sec^3(x/2)dx = \int [\sec^5(x/2) - \sec^3(x/2)]dx$

$$= 2\left[\int \sec^5 u \, du - \int \sec^3 u \, du\right] (u = x/2)$$

$$= 2\left[\left(\frac{1}{4}\sec^3 u \tan u + \frac{3}{4}\int \sec^3 u \, du\right) - \int \sec^3 u \, du\right] \quad \text{(formula (3))}$$

$$= \frac{1}{2}\sec^3 u \tan u - \frac{1}{2}\int \sec^3 u \, du$$

$$= \frac{1}{2}\sec^3 u \tan u - \frac{1}{4}\sec u \tan u - \frac{1}{4}|\sec u + \tan u| + C \quad \text{(Example 1)}$$

$$= \frac{1}{2}\sec^3 \frac{x}{2} \tan \frac{x}{2} - \frac{1}{4}\sec \frac{x}{2} \tan \frac{x}{2} - \frac{1}{4}\ln\left|\sec \frac{x}{2} + \tan \frac{x}{2}\right| + C$$

15. $\int \sec^2 2t(\sec 2t \tan 2t)dt = \frac{1}{6}\sec^3 2t + C$

16. $\int \sec^4 x(\sec x \tan x)dx = \frac{1}{5}\sec^5 x + C$

17. $\int \sec^4 x \, dx = \int (1 + \tan^2 x)\sec^2 x \, dx = \int (\sec^2 x + \tan^2 x \sec^2 x)dx = \tan x + \frac{1}{3}\tan^3 x + C$

18. Using reduction formula (3),

$$\int \sec^5 x \, dx = \frac{1}{4}\sec^3 x \tan x + \frac{3}{4}\int \sec^3 x \, dx$$

$$= \frac{1}{4}\sec^3 x \tan x + \frac{3}{8}\sec x \tan x + \frac{3}{8}\ln|\sec x + \tan x| + C$$

19. $u = \pi x$, use reduction formula (3) to get

$$\frac{1}{\pi}\int \sec^6 u\, du = \frac{1}{\pi}\left[\frac{1}{5}\sec^4 u \tan u + \frac{4}{5}\int \sec^4 u\, du\right]$$

$$= \frac{1}{5\pi}\sec^4 u \tan u + \frac{4}{5\pi}\left[\frac{1}{3}\sec^2 u \tan u + \frac{2}{3}\tan u\right] + C$$

$$= \frac{1}{5\pi}\sec^4 \pi x \tan \pi x + \frac{4}{15\pi}\sec^2 \pi x \tan \pi x + \frac{8}{15\pi}\tan \pi x + C$$

20. $u = 4x$, use reduction formula (4) to get

$$\frac{1}{4}\int \tan^3 u\, du = \frac{1}{4}\left[\frac{1}{2}\tan^2 u + \ln|\cos u|\right] + C = \frac{1}{8}\tan^2 4x + \frac{1}{4}\ln|\cos 4x| + C$$

21. Use reduction formula (4) to get $\displaystyle\int \tan^4 x\, dx = \frac{1}{3}\tan^3 x - \tan x + x + C$

22. Use reduction formula (4) to get

$$\int \tan^7 \theta\, d\theta = \frac{1}{6}\tan^6 \theta - \frac{1}{4}\tan^4 \theta + \frac{1}{2}\tan^2 \theta + \ln|\cos \theta| + C$$

23. $u = \tan(x^2)$, $\displaystyle\frac{1}{2}\int u^2\, du = \frac{1}{6}\tan^3(x^2) + C$

24. $u = 1 - 2x$,

$$-\frac{1}{2}\int \tan^2 u \sec u\, du = -\frac{1}{2}\int (\sec^3 u - \sec u)du$$

$$= -\frac{1}{4}\sec(1 - 2x)\tan(1 - 2x) + \frac{1}{4}\ln|\sec(1 - 2x) + \tan(1 - 2x)| + C$$

25. $\displaystyle\int (\csc^2 x - 1)\csc^2 x(\csc x \cot x)dx = \int (\csc^4 x - \csc^2 x)(\csc x \cot x)dx$

$$= -\frac{1}{5}\csc^5 x + \frac{1}{3}\csc^3 x + C$$

26. $\displaystyle\int \frac{\cos^2 3t}{\sin^2 3t}\cdot\frac{1}{\cos 3t}dt = \int \csc 3t \cot 3t\, dt = -\frac{1}{3}\csc 3t + C$

27. $\displaystyle\int (\csc^2 x - 1)\cot x\, dx = \int \csc x(\csc x \cot x)dt - \int \frac{\cos x}{\sin x}dx = -\frac{1}{2}\csc^2 x - \ln|\sin x| + C$

28. $\displaystyle\int (\cot^2 x + 1)\csc^2 x\, dx = -\frac{1}{3}\cot^3 x - \cot x + C$

29. $\displaystyle\int \tan^{1/2} x(1+\tan^2 x)\sec^2 x\,dx = \frac{2}{3}\tan^{3/2}x + \frac{2}{7}\tan^{7/2}x + C$

30. $\displaystyle\int \sec^{1/2} x(\sec x \tan x)dx = \frac{2}{3}\sec^{3/2}x + C$

31. $\displaystyle\int_0^{\pi/6}(\sec^2 2x - 1)dx = \frac{1}{2}\tan 2x - x\Big]_0^{\pi/6} = \sqrt{3}/2 - \pi/6$

32. $\displaystyle\int_0^{\pi/6}\sec^2\theta(\sec\theta\tan\theta)d\theta = \frac{1}{3}\sec^3\theta\Big]_0^{\pi/6} = (1/3)(2/\sqrt{3})^3 - 1/3 = 8\sqrt{3}/27 - 1/3$

33. $u = x/2$,

$$2\int_0^{\pi/4}\tan^5 u\,du = \frac{1}{2}\tan^4 u - \tan^2 u - 2\ln|\cos u|\Big]_0^{\pi/4} = 1/2 - 1 - 2\ln(1/\sqrt{2}) = -1/2 + \ln 2$$

34. $\displaystyle\int_{\pi/4}^{\pi/2}\csc^2 x(\csc x \cot x)dx = -\frac{1}{3}\csc^3 x\Big]_{\pi/4}^{\pi/2} = -\frac{1}{3}(1 - 2\sqrt{2}) = (2\sqrt{2}-1)/3$

35. $y' = \tan x,\ 1 + (y')^2 = 1 + \tan^2 x = \sec^2 x$,

$$L = \int_0^{\pi/4}\sqrt{\sec^2 x}\,dx = \int_0^{\pi/4}\sec x\,dx = \ln|\sec x + \tan x|\Big]_0^{\pi/4} = \ln(\sqrt{2}+1)$$

36. $\displaystyle V = \pi\int_0^{\pi/4}(1 - \tan^2 x)dx = \pi\int_0^{\pi/4}(2 - \sec^2 x)dx = \pi(2x - \tan x)\Big]_0^{\pi/4} = \frac{1}{2}\pi(\pi - 2)$

37. **(a)** $\displaystyle\int \csc x\,dx = \int \sec(\pi/2 - x)dx = -\ln|\sec(\pi/2 - x) + \tan(\pi/2 - x)| + C$
$$= -\ln|\csc x + \cot x| + C$$

(b) $\displaystyle -\ln|\csc x + \cot x| = \ln\frac{1}{|\csc x + \cot x|} = \ln\frac{|\csc x - \cot x|}{|\csc^2 x - \cot^2 x|} = \ln|\csc x - \cot x|.$

$$-\ln|\csc x + \cot x| = -\ln\left|\frac{1}{\sin x} + \frac{\cos x}{\sin x}\right| = \ln\left|\frac{\sin x}{1 + \cos x}\right|$$

$$= \ln\left|\frac{2\sin(x/2)\cos(x/2)}{2\cos^2(x/2)}\right| = \ln|\tan(x/2)|$$

38. $\sin x + \cos x = \sqrt{2}[(1/\sqrt{2})\sin x + (1/\sqrt{2})\cos x]$

$$= \sqrt{2}[\sin x \cos(\pi/4) + \cos x \sin(\pi/4)] = \sqrt{2}\sin(x + \pi/4)$$

$$\int \frac{dx}{\sin x + \cos x} = \frac{1}{\sqrt{2}}\int \csc(x + \pi/4)dx = -\frac{1}{\sqrt{2}}\ln|\csc(x + \pi/4) + \cot(x + \pi/4)| + C$$

39. $a\sin x + b\cos x = \sqrt{a^2 + b^2}\left[\dfrac{a}{\sqrt{a^2 + b^2}}\sin x + \dfrac{b}{\sqrt{a^2 + b^2}}\cos x\right]$

$$= \sqrt{a^2 + b^2}(\sin x \cos\theta + \cos x \sin\theta)$$

where $\cos\theta = a/\sqrt{a^2 + b^2}$ and $\sin\theta = b/\sqrt{a^2 + b^2}$ so $a\sin x + b\cos x = \sqrt{a^2 + b^2}\sin(x + \theta)$

and $\displaystyle\int \frac{dx}{a\sin x + b\cos x} = \frac{1}{\sqrt{a^2 + b^2}}\int \csc(x + \theta)dx$

$$= -\frac{1}{\sqrt{a^2 + b^2}}\ln|\csc(x + \theta) + \cot(x + \theta)| + C$$

40. $u = \sec x,\ dv = \sec^2 x\,dx,\ du = \sec x \tan x\,dx,\ v = \tan x$

$$\int \sec^3 x\,dx = \sec x \tan x - \int \sec x \tan^2 x\,dx = \sec x \tan x - \int \sec x(\sec^2 x - 1)dx$$

$$= \sec x \tan x - \int \sec^3 x\,dx + \int \sec x\,dx,$$

$$\int \sec^3 x\,dx = \frac{1}{2}\sec x \tan x + \frac{1}{2}\ln|\sec x + \tan x| + C$$

EXERCISE SET 9.5

1. $x = 2\sin\theta,\ dx = 2\cos\theta\,d\theta,$

$$4\int \cos^2\theta\,d\theta = 2\int(1 + \cos 2\theta)d\theta = 2\theta + \sin 2\theta + C$$

$$= 2\theta + 2\sin\theta\cos\theta + C = 2\sin^{-1}(x/2) + \frac{1}{2}x\sqrt{4 - x^2} + C$$

2. $x = \dfrac{1}{2}\sin\theta,\ dx = \dfrac{1}{2}\cos\theta\,d\theta,$

$$\frac{1}{2}\int \cos^2\theta\,d\theta = \frac{1}{4}\int(1 + \cos 2\theta)d\theta = \frac{1}{4}\theta + \frac{1}{8}\sin 2\theta + C$$

$$= \frac{1}{4}\theta + \frac{1}{4}\sin\theta\cos\theta + C = \frac{1}{4}\sin^{-1}2x + \frac{1}{2}x\sqrt{1 - 4x^2} + C$$

3. $x = 3\sin\theta$, $dx = 3\cos\theta\,d\theta$,

$$9\int \sin^2\theta\,d\theta = \frac{9}{2}\int(1-\cos 2\theta)d\theta = \frac{9}{2}\theta - \frac{9}{4}\sin 2\theta + C - \frac{9}{2}\theta - \frac{9}{2}\sin\theta\cos\theta + C$$

$$= \frac{9}{2}\sin^{-1}(x/3) - \frac{1}{2}x\sqrt{9-x^2} + C$$

4. $x = 4\sin\theta$, $dx = 4\cos\theta\,d\theta$,

$$\frac{1}{16}\int\frac{1}{\sin^2\theta}d\theta = \frac{1}{16}\int\csc^2\theta\,d\theta = -\frac{1}{16}\cot\theta + C = -\frac{\sqrt{16-x^2}}{16x} + C$$

5. $x = 2\tan\theta$, $dx = 2\sec^2\theta\,d\theta$,

$$\frac{1}{8}\int\frac{1}{\sec^2\theta}d\theta = \frac{1}{8}\int\cos^2\theta\,d\theta = \frac{1}{16}\int(1+\cos 2\theta)d\theta = \frac{1}{16}\theta + \frac{1}{32}\sin 2\theta + C$$

$$= \frac{1}{16}\theta + \frac{1}{16}\sin\theta\cos\theta + C = \frac{1}{16}\tan^{-1}\frac{x}{2} + \frac{x}{8(4+x^2)} + C$$

6. $x = \tan\theta$, $dx = \sec^2\theta\,d\theta$,

$$\int\frac{1}{\sec\theta}d\theta = \int\cos\theta\,d\theta = \sin\theta + C = \frac{x}{\sqrt{x^2+1}} + C$$

7. $x = 3\sec\theta$, $dx = 3\sec\theta\tan\theta\,d\theta$,

$$3\int\tan^2\theta\,d\theta = 3\int(\sec^2\theta - 1)d\theta = 3\tan\theta - 3\theta + C = \sqrt{x^2-9} - 3\sec^{-1}\frac{x}{3} + C$$

8. $x = 4\sec\theta$, $dx = 4\sec\theta\tan\theta\,d\theta$,

$$\frac{1}{16}\int\frac{1}{\sec\theta}d\theta = \frac{1}{16}\int\cos\theta\,d\theta = \frac{1}{16}\sin\theta + C = \frac{\sqrt{x^2-16}}{16x} + C$$

9. $x = \sqrt{2}\sin\theta$, $dx = \sqrt{2}\cos\theta\,d\theta$,

$$2\sqrt{2}\int\sin^3\theta\,d\theta = 2\sqrt{2}\left(-\cos\theta + \frac{1}{3}\cos^3\theta\right) + C = -2\sqrt{2-x^2} + \frac{1}{3}(2-x^2)^{3/2} + C$$

10. $x = \sqrt{5}\sin\theta$, $dx = \sqrt{5}\cos\theta\,d\theta$,

$$25\sqrt{5}\int\sin^3\theta\cos^2\theta\,d\theta = 25\sqrt{5}\left(-\frac{1}{3}\cos^3\theta + \frac{1}{5}\cos^5\theta\right) + C$$

$$= -\frac{5}{3}(5-x^2)^{3/2} + \frac{1}{5}(5-x^2)^{5/2} + C$$

11. $x = \sqrt{3}\tan\theta$, $dx = \sqrt{3}\sec^2\theta\,d\theta$,

$$\frac{1}{3}\int\frac{1}{\sec\theta}d\theta = \frac{1}{3}\int\cos\theta\,d\theta = \frac{1}{3}\sin\theta + C = \frac{x}{3\sqrt{3+x^2}} + C$$

12. $x = \sqrt{5}\tan\theta$, $dx = \sqrt{5}\sec^2\theta\,d\theta$,

$$5\int \tan^2\theta\sec\theta\,d\theta = 5\int(\sec^3\theta - \sec\theta)d\theta = 5\left(\frac{1}{2}\sec\theta\tan\theta - \frac{1}{2}\ln|\sec\theta + \tan\theta|\right) + C_1$$

$$= \frac{1}{2}x\sqrt{5 + x^2} - \frac{5}{2}\ln\frac{\sqrt{5 + x^2} + x}{\sqrt{5}} + C_1 = \frac{1}{2}x\sqrt{5 + x^2} - \frac{5}{2}\ln(\sqrt{5 + x^2} + x) + C$$

13. $x = \frac{3}{2}\sec\theta$, $dx = \frac{3}{2}\sec\theta\tan\theta\,d\theta$,

$$\frac{2}{9}\int \frac{1}{\sec\theta}d\theta = \frac{2}{9}\int \cos\theta\,d\theta = \frac{2}{9}\sin\theta + C = \frac{\sqrt{4x^2 - 9}}{9x} + C$$

14. $t = \tan\theta$, $dt = \sec^2\theta\,d\theta$,

$$\int \frac{\sec^3\theta}{\tan\theta}d\theta = \int \frac{\tan^2\theta + 1}{\tan\theta}\sec\theta\,d\theta = \int(\sec\theta\tan\theta + \csc\theta)d\theta$$

$$= \sec\theta - \ln|\csc\theta + \cot\theta| + C = \sqrt{1 + t^2} - \ln\frac{\sqrt{1 + t^2} + 1}{|t|} + C$$

15. $x = \sin\theta$, $dx = \cos\theta\,d\theta$, $\int \frac{1}{\cos^2\theta}d\theta = \int \sec^2\theta\,d\theta = \tan\theta + C = x/\sqrt{1 - x^2} + C$

16. $x = 5\tan\theta$, $dx = 5\sec^2\theta\,d\theta$,

$$\frac{1}{25}\int \frac{\sec\theta}{\tan^2\theta}d\theta = \frac{1}{25}\int \csc\theta\cot\theta\,d\theta = -\frac{1}{25}\csc\theta + C = -\frac{\sqrt{x^2 + 25}}{25x} + C$$

17. $x = \sec\theta$, $dx = \sec\theta\tan\theta\,d\theta$

$$\int \sec\theta\,d\theta = \ln|\sec\theta + \tan\theta| + C = \ln\left|x + \sqrt{x^2 - 1}\right| + C$$

18. $1 + 2x^2 + x^4 = (1 + x^2)^2$, $x = \tan\theta$, $dx = \sec^2\theta\,d\theta$,

$$\int \frac{1}{\sec^2\theta}d\theta = \int \cos^2\theta\,d\theta = \frac{1}{2}\int(1 + \cos 2\theta)d\theta = \frac{1}{2}\theta + \frac{1}{4}\sin 2\theta + C$$

$$= \frac{1}{2}\theta + \frac{1}{2}\sin\theta\cos\theta + C = \frac{1}{2}\tan^{-1}x + \frac{x}{2(1 + x^2)} + C$$

19. $x = \frac{3}{2}\sin\theta$, $dx = \frac{3}{2}\cos\theta\,d\theta$,

$$\frac{2}{9}\int \frac{1}{\sin^2\theta}d\theta = \frac{2}{9}\csc^2\theta\,d\theta = -\frac{2}{9}\cot\theta + C = -\frac{\sqrt{9 - 4x^2}}{9x} + C$$

20. $x = 5\sec\theta$, $dx = 5\sec\theta\tan\theta\,d\theta$,

$$25\int\sec^3\theta\,d\theta = \frac{25}{2}\sec\theta\tan\theta + \frac{25}{2}\ln|\sec\theta + \tan\theta| + C_1$$

$$= \frac{1}{2}x\sqrt{x^2 - 25} + \frac{25}{2}\ln|x + \sqrt{x^2 - 25}| + C$$

21. $x = \frac{1}{3}\sec\theta$, $dx = \frac{1}{3}\sec\theta\tan\theta\,d\theta$,

$$\frac{1}{3}\int\frac{\sec\theta}{\tan^2\theta}d\theta = \frac{1}{3}\int\csc\theta\cot\theta\,d\theta = -\frac{1}{3}\csc\theta + C = -x/\sqrt{9x^2 - 1} + C$$

22. $u = \sin\theta$, $-\int\frac{1}{\sqrt{2 - u^2}}du = -\sin^{-1}\left(\frac{\sin\theta}{\sqrt{2}}\right) + C$

23. $e^x = \sin\theta$, $e^x\,dx = \cos\theta\,d\theta$,

$$\int\cos^2\theta\,d\theta = \frac{1}{2}\int(1 + \cos 2\theta)d\theta = \frac{1}{2}\theta + \frac{1}{4}\sin 2\theta + C = \frac{1}{2}\sin^{-1}(e^x) + \frac{1}{2}e^x\sqrt{1 - e^{2x}} + C$$

24. $x = \frac{2}{3}\sin\theta$, $dx = \frac{2}{3}\cos\theta\,d\theta$,

$$\frac{1}{24}\int_0^{\pi/6}\frac{1}{\cos^3\theta}d\theta = \frac{1}{24}\int_0^{\pi/6}\sec^3\theta\,d\theta = \frac{1}{48}\sec\theta\tan\theta + \frac{1}{48}\ln|\sec\theta + \tan\theta|\Bigg]_0^{\pi/6}$$

$$= \frac{1}{48}[(2/\sqrt{3})(1/\sqrt{3}) + \ln|2/\sqrt{3} + 1/\sqrt{3}|] = \frac{1}{48}\left(\frac{2}{3} + \frac{1}{2}\ln 3\right)$$

25. $x = 4\sin\theta$, $dx = 4\cos\theta\,d\theta$,

$$1024\int_0^{\pi/2}\sin^3\theta\cos^2\theta\,d\theta = 1024\left[-\frac{1}{3}\cos^3\theta + \frac{1}{5}\cos^5\theta\right]_0^{\pi/2} = 1024(1/3 - 1/5) = 2048/15$$

26. $x = \sqrt{2}\sec\theta$, $dx = \sqrt{2}\sec\theta\tan\theta\,d\theta$, $2\int_0^{\pi/4}\tan^2\theta\,d\theta = 2\tan\theta - 2\theta\Bigg]_0^{\pi/4} = 2 - \pi/2$

27. $x = \sec\theta$, $dx = \sec\theta\tan\theta\,d\theta$, $\int_{\pi/4}^{\pi/3}\frac{1}{\sec\theta}d\theta = \int_{\pi/4}^{\pi/3}\cos\theta\,d\theta = \sin\theta\Bigg]_{\pi/4}^{\pi/3} = (\sqrt{3} - \sqrt{2})/2$

28. $x = (1/\sqrt{2})\sin\theta$, $dx = (1/\sqrt{2})\cos\theta\,d\theta$,

$$\frac{1}{\sqrt{2}}\int_{-\pi/2}^{\pi/2}\cos^4\theta\,d\theta = \frac{1}{\sqrt{2}}\left(\frac{3}{8}\theta + \frac{1}{4}\sin 2\theta + \frac{1}{32}\sin 4\theta\right)\Bigg]_{-\pi/2}^{\pi/2} = \frac{3\pi}{8\sqrt{2}}$$

29. $x = \sqrt{3}\tan\theta$, $dx = \sqrt{3}\sec^2\theta\,d\theta$,

$$\frac{1}{9}\int_{\pi/6}^{\pi/3}\frac{\sec\theta}{\tan^4\theta}d\theta = \frac{1}{9}\int_{\pi/6}^{\pi/3}\frac{\cos^3\theta}{\sin^4\theta}d\theta = \frac{1}{9}\int_{\pi/6}^{\pi/3}\frac{1-\sin^2\theta}{\sin^4\theta}\cos\theta\,d\theta$$

$$= \frac{1}{9}\int_{1/2}^{\sqrt{3}/2}\frac{1-u^2}{u^4}du \quad (u = \sin\theta)$$

$$= \frac{1}{9}\int_{1/2}^{\sqrt{3}/2}(u^{-4}-u^{-2})du = \frac{1}{9}\left[-\frac{1}{3u^3}+\frac{1}{u}\right]_{1/2}^{\sqrt{3}/2} = \frac{10\sqrt{3}+18}{243}$$

30. $x = \sqrt{3}\tan\theta$, $dx = \sqrt{3}\sec^2\theta\,d\theta$,

$$\frac{\sqrt{3}}{3}\int_0^{\pi/3}\frac{\tan^3\theta}{\sec^3\theta}d\theta = \frac{\sqrt{3}}{3}\int_0^{\pi/3}\sin^3\theta\,d\theta = \frac{\sqrt{3}}{3}\left(-\cos\theta+\frac{1}{3}\cos^3\theta\right)\Big]_0^{\pi/3}$$

$$= \frac{\sqrt{3}}{3}\left[\left(-\frac{1}{2}+\frac{1}{24}\right)-\left(-1+\frac{1}{3}\right)\right] = 5\sqrt{3}/72$$

31. $u = x^2 + 4$, $du = 2x\,dx$, $\dfrac{1}{2}\displaystyle\int\dfrac{1}{u}du = \dfrac{1}{2}\ln|u| + C = \dfrac{1}{2}\ln(x^2+4) + C.$

$x = 2\tan\theta$, $dx = 2\sec^2\theta\,d\theta$,

$$\int\tan\theta\,d\theta = \ln|\sec\theta| + C_1 = \ln\frac{\sqrt{x^2+4}}{2} + C_1 = \ln(x^2+4)^{1/2} - \ln 2 + C_1$$

$$= \frac{1}{2}\ln(x^2+4) + C \text{ with } C = C_1 - \ln 2$$

32. $A = 4\displaystyle\int_0^r\sqrt{r^2-x^2}dx$; $x = r\sin\theta$, $dx = r\cos\theta\,d\theta$,

$$A = 4r^2\int_0^{\pi/2}\cos^2\theta\,d\theta = 2r^2\left(\theta+\frac{1}{2}\sin 2\theta\right)\Big]_0^{\pi/2} = \pi r^2$$

33. $y' = \dfrac{1}{x}$, $1 + (y')^2 = 1 + \dfrac{1}{x^2} = \dfrac{x^2+1}{x^2}$,

$$L = \int_1^2\sqrt{\frac{x^2+1}{x^2}}dx = \int_1^2\frac{\sqrt{x^2+1}}{x}dx; \; x = \tan\theta, \; dx = \sec^2\theta\,d\theta,$$

$$L = \int_{\pi/1}^{\tan^{-1}2} \frac{\sec^3\theta}{\tan\theta}\,d\theta = \int_{\pi/4}^{\tan^{-1}2} \frac{\tan^2\theta+1}{\tan\theta}\sec\theta\,d\theta = \int_{\pi/4}^{\tan^{-1}2}\left[\sec\theta\tan\theta + \frac{\sec\theta}{\tan\theta}\right]d\theta$$

$$= \int_{\pi/4}^{\tan^{-1}2}(\sec\theta\tan\theta + \csc\theta)d\theta = \sec\theta - \ln|\csc\theta + \cot\theta|\Big]_{\pi/4}^{\tan^{-1}2}$$

$$= \left[\sqrt{5} - \ln\left|\frac{\sqrt{5}}{2} + \frac{1}{2}\right|\right] - \left[\sqrt{2} - \ln|\sqrt{2}+1|\right] = \sqrt{5} - \sqrt{2} + \ln\frac{2+2\sqrt{2}}{1+\sqrt{5}}$$

34. $y' = 2x$, $1 + (y')^2 = 1 + 4x^2$,

$$L = \int_0^1 \sqrt{1+4x^2}\,dx; \quad x = \frac{1}{2}\tan\theta, \quad dx = \frac{1}{2}\sec^2\theta\,d\theta,$$

$$L = \frac{1}{2}\int_0^{\tan^{-1}2}\sec^3\theta\,d\theta = \frac{1}{2}\left(\frac{1}{2}\sec\theta\tan\theta + \frac{1}{2}\ln|\sec\theta + \tan\theta|\right)\Big]_0^{\tan^{-1}2}$$

$$= \frac{1}{4}(\sqrt{5})(2) + \frac{1}{4}\ln|\sqrt{5}+2| = \frac{1}{2}\sqrt{5} + \frac{1}{4}\ln(2+\sqrt{5})$$

35. $y' = 2x$, $1 + (y')^2 = 1 + 4x^2$,

$$S = 2\pi\int_0^1 x^2\sqrt{1+4x^2}\,dx; \quad x = \frac{1}{2}\tan\theta, \quad dx = \frac{1}{2}\sec^2\theta\,d\theta,$$

$$S = \frac{\pi}{4}\int_0^{\tan^{-1}2}\tan^2\theta\sec^3\theta\,d\theta = \frac{\pi}{4}\int_0^{\tan^{-1}2}(\sec^2\theta - 1)\sec^3\theta\,d\theta$$

$$= \frac{\pi}{4}\int_0^{\tan^{-1}2}(\sec^5\theta - \sec^3\theta)d\theta$$

$$= \frac{\pi}{4}\left[\frac{1}{4}\sec^3\theta\tan\theta - \frac{1}{8}\sec\theta\tan\theta - \frac{1}{8}\ln|\sec\theta + \tan\theta|\right]_0^{\tan^{-1}2} = \frac{\pi}{32}[18\sqrt{5} - \ln(2+\sqrt{5})]$$

36. $V = \pi\int_0^1 y^2\sqrt{1-y^2}\,dy; \quad y = \sin\theta, \quad dy = \cos\theta\,d\theta,$

$$V = \pi\int_0^{\pi/2}\sin^2\theta\cos^2\theta\,d\theta = \frac{\pi}{4}\int_0^{\pi/2}\sin^2 2\theta\,d\theta = \frac{\pi}{8}\int_0^{\pi/2}(1-\cos 4\theta)d\theta$$

$$= \frac{\pi}{8}\left(\theta - \frac{1}{4}\sin 4\theta\right)\Big]_0^{\pi/2} = \frac{\pi^2}{16}$$

37. **(a)** $x = 3\sinh u$, $dx = 3\cosh u\,du$, $\displaystyle\int du = u + C = \sinh^{-1}(x/3) + C$

(b) $x = 3\tan\theta$, $dx = 3\sec^2\theta\,d\theta$,

$$\int \sec\theta\,d\theta = \ln|\sec\theta + \tan\theta| + C = \ln(\sqrt{x^2+9}/3 + x/3) + C$$

but $\sinh^{-1}(x/3) = \ln(x/3 + \sqrt{x^2/9+1}) = \ln(x/3 + \sqrt{x^2+9}/3)$ so the results agree.

38. (a) $x = \cosh u$, $dx = \sinh u\,du$,

$$\int \sinh^2 u\,du = \frac{1}{2}\int(\cosh 2u - 1)du = \frac{1}{4}\sinh 2u - \frac{1}{2}u + C$$

$$= \frac{1}{2}\sinh u\cosh u - \frac{1}{2}u + C = \frac{1}{2}x\sqrt{x^2-1} - \frac{1}{2}\cosh^{-1}x + C$$

because $\cosh u = x$, and $\sinh u = \sqrt{\cosh^2 u - 1} = \sqrt{x^2-1}$.

(b) $x = \sec\theta$, $dx = \sec\theta\tan\theta\,d\theta$,

$$\int \tan^2\theta\sec\theta\,d\theta = \int(\sec^3\theta - \sec\theta)d\theta = \frac{1}{2}\sec\theta\tan\theta - \frac{1}{2}\ln|\sec\theta + \tan\theta| + C$$

$$= \frac{1}{2}x\sqrt{x^2-1} - \frac{1}{2}\ln(x + \sqrt{x^2-1}) + C,$$

but $\cosh^{-1}x = \ln(x + \sqrt{x^2-1})$ so the results in (a) and (b) agree.

39. $\displaystyle\int \frac{1}{(x-2)^2+9}dx = \frac{1}{3}\tan^{-1}\left(\frac{x-2}{3}\right) + C$

40. $\displaystyle\int \frac{1}{\sqrt{1-(x-1)^2}}dx = \sin^{-1}(x-1) + C$

41. $\displaystyle\int \frac{1}{\sqrt{9-(x-1)^2}}dx = \sin^{-1}\left(\frac{x-1}{3}\right) + C$

42. $\displaystyle\int \frac{1}{16(x+1/2)^2+1}dx = \frac{1}{16}\int \frac{1}{(x+1/2)^2+1/16}dx = \frac{1}{4}\tan^{-1}(4x+2) + C$

43. $\displaystyle\int \frac{1}{\sqrt{(x-3)^2+1}}dx = \sinh^{-1}(x-3) + C.$

<u>Alternate solution:</u> let $x - 3 = \tan\theta$,

$$\int \sec\theta\,d\theta = \ln|\sec\theta + \tan\theta| + C = \ln(\sqrt{x^2-6x+10} + x - 3) + C.$$

44. $\int \dfrac{x}{(x+3)^2+1}\,dx$, let $u=x+3$,

$$\int \frac{u-3}{u^2+1}\,du = \int \left(\frac{u}{u^2+1}-\frac{3}{u^2+1}\right)du = \frac{1}{2}\ln(u^2+1)-3\tan^{-1}u+C$$

$$= \frac{1}{2}\ln(x^2+6x+10)-3\tan^{-1}(x+3)+C$$

45. $\int \sqrt{4-(x+1)^2}\,dx$, let $x+1=2\sin\theta$,

$$4\int \cos^2\theta\,d\theta = 2\theta+\sin 2\theta+C = 2\theta+2\sin\theta\cos\theta+C$$

$$= 2\sin^{-1}\left(\frac{x+1}{2}\right)+\frac{1}{2}(x+1)\sqrt{3-2x-x^2}+C$$

46. $\int \dfrac{e^x}{\sqrt{(e^x+1/2)^2+3/4}}\,dx$, let $u=e^x+1/2$,

$$\int \frac{1}{\sqrt{u^2+3/4}}\,du = \sinh^{-1}(2u/\sqrt3)+C = \sinh^{-1}(\frac{2e^x+1}{\sqrt3})+C$$

<u>Alternate solution:</u> let $e^x+1/2 = \dfrac{\sqrt3}{2}\tan\theta$,

$$\int \sec\theta\,d\theta = \ln|\sec\theta+\tan\theta|+C = \ln\left(\frac{2\sqrt{e^{2x}+e^x+1}}{\sqrt3}+\frac{2e^x+1}{\sqrt3}\right)+C_1$$

$$= \ln(2\sqrt{e^{2x}+e^x+1}+2e^x+1)+C.$$

47. $\int \dfrac{1}{2(x+1)^2+5}\,dx = \dfrac{1}{2}\int \dfrac{1}{(x+1)^2+5/2}\,dx = \dfrac{1}{\sqrt{10}}\tan^{-1}\sqrt{2/5}(x+1)+C$

48. $\int \dfrac{\cos\theta}{(\sin\theta-3)^2+3}\,d\theta$, let $u=\sin\theta-3$, $\int \dfrac{1}{u^2+3}\,du = \dfrac{1}{\sqrt3}\tan^{-1}[(\sin\theta-3)/\sqrt3]+C$

49. $\int \dfrac{2x+5}{(x+1)^2+4}\,dx$, let $u=x+1$,

$$\int \frac{2u+3}{u^2+4}\,du = \int \left[\frac{2u}{u^2+4}+\frac{3}{u^2+4}\right]du = \ln(u^2+4)+\frac{3}{2}\tan^{-1}(u/2)+C$$

$$= \ln(x^2+2x+5)+\frac{3}{2}\tan^{-1}\left(\frac{x+1}{2}\right)+C$$

50. $\int \dfrac{2x+3}{4(x+1/2)^2+4}\,dx$, let $u = x + 1/2$,

$$\int \frac{2u+2}{4u^2+4}\,du = \frac{1}{2}\int \left(\frac{u}{u^2+1} + \frac{1}{u^2+1}\right)\,du = \frac{1}{4}\ln(u^2+1) + \frac{1}{2}\tan^{-1}u + C$$

$$= \frac{1}{4}\ln(x^2+x+5/4) + \frac{1}{2}\tan^{-1}(x+1/2) + C$$

51. $\int \dfrac{x+3}{\sqrt{(x+1)^2+1}}\,dx$, let $u = x + 1$,

$$\int \frac{u+2}{\sqrt{u^2+1}}\,du = \int\left[u(u^2+1)^{-1/2} + \frac{2}{\sqrt{u^2+1}}\right]du = \sqrt{u^2+1} + 2\sinh^{-1}u + C$$

$$= \sqrt{x^2+2x+2} + 2\sinh^{-1}(x+1) + C$$

Alternate solution: let $x + 1 = \tan\theta$,

$$\int (\tan\theta+2)\sec\theta\,d\theta = \int \sec\theta\tan\theta\,d\theta + 2\int \sec\theta\,d\theta = \sec\theta + 2\ln|\sec\theta+\tan\theta| + C$$

$$= \sqrt{x^2+2x+2} + 2\ln(\sqrt{x^2+2x+2}+x+1) + C.$$

52. $\displaystyle\int_1^2 \frac{1}{\sqrt{4x-x^2}}\,dx = \int_1^2 \frac{1}{\sqrt{4-(x-2)^2}}\,dx = \sin^{-1}\frac{x-2}{2}\bigg]_1^2 = \pi/6$

53. $\displaystyle\int_0^1 \sqrt{4x-x^2}\,dx = \int_0^1 \sqrt{4-(x-2)^2}\,dx$, let $x - 2 = 2\sin\theta$,

$$4\int_{-\pi/2}^{-\pi/6} \cos^2\theta\,d\theta = 2\theta + \sin 2\theta\bigg]_{-\pi/2}^{-\pi/6} = \frac{2\pi}{3} - \frac{\sqrt{3}}{2}$$

EXERCISE SET 9.6

1. $\dfrac{A}{(x-2)} + \dfrac{B}{(x+5)}$

2. $\dfrac{5}{x(x-3)(x+3)} = \dfrac{A}{x} + \dfrac{B}{x-3} + \dfrac{C}{x+3}$

3. $\dfrac{2x-3}{x^2(x-1)} = \dfrac{A}{x} + \dfrac{B}{x^2} + \dfrac{C}{x-1}$

4. $\dfrac{A}{x+2} + \dfrac{B}{(x+2)^2} + \dfrac{C}{(x+2)^3}$

5. $\dfrac{A}{x} + \dfrac{B}{x^2} + \dfrac{C}{x^3} + \dfrac{Dx+E}{x^2+1}$

6. $\dfrac{A}{x-1} + \dfrac{Bx+C}{x^2+5}$

7. $\dfrac{Ax+B}{x^2+5} + \dfrac{Cx+D}{(x^2+5)^2}$

8. $\dfrac{A}{x-2} + \dfrac{Bx+C}{x^2+1} + \dfrac{Dx+E}{(x^2+1)^2}$

9. $\dfrac{1}{(x+4)(x-1)} = \dfrac{A}{x+4} + \dfrac{B}{x-1}$; $A = -\dfrac{1}{5}$, $B = \dfrac{1}{5}$

$-\dfrac{1}{5}\displaystyle\int \dfrac{1}{x+4}\,dx + \dfrac{1}{5}\int \dfrac{1}{x-1}\,dx = -\dfrac{1}{5}\ln|x+4| + \dfrac{1}{5}\ln|x-1| + C = \dfrac{1}{5}\ln\left|\dfrac{x-1}{x+4}\right| + C$

10. $\dfrac{1}{(x+1)(x+7)} = \dfrac{A}{x+1} + \dfrac{B}{x+7}$; $A = \dfrac{1}{6}$, $B = -\dfrac{1}{6}$

$\dfrac{1}{6}\displaystyle\int \dfrac{1}{x+1}\,dx - \dfrac{1}{6}\int \dfrac{1}{x+7}\,dx = \dfrac{1}{6}\ln|x+1| - \dfrac{1}{6}\ln|x+7| + C = \dfrac{1}{6}\ln\left|\dfrac{x+1}{x+7}\right| + C$

11. $\dfrac{x}{(x-2)(x-3)} = \dfrac{A}{x-2} + \dfrac{B}{x-3}$; $A = -2$, $B = 3$

$-2\displaystyle\int \dfrac{1}{x-2}\,dx + 3\int \dfrac{1}{x-3}\,dx = -2\ln|x-2| + 3\ln|x-3| + C$

12. $\dfrac{5x-4}{x(x-4)} = \dfrac{A}{x} + \dfrac{B}{x-4}$; $A = 1$, $B = 4$; $\displaystyle\int \dfrac{1}{x}\,dx + 4\int \dfrac{1}{x-4}\,dx = \ln|x| + 4\ln|x-4| + C$

13. $\dfrac{11x+17}{(2x-1)(x+4)} = \dfrac{A}{2x-1} + \dfrac{B}{x+4}$; $A = 5$, $B = 3$

$5\displaystyle\int \dfrac{1}{2x-1}\,dx + 3\int \dfrac{1}{x+4}\,dx = \dfrac{5}{2}\ln|2x-1| + 3\ln|x+4| + C$

14. $\dfrac{5x-5}{(x-3)(3x+1)} = \dfrac{A}{x-3} + \dfrac{B}{3x+1}$; $A = 1$, $B = 2$

$\displaystyle\int \dfrac{1}{x-3}\,dx + 2\int \dfrac{1}{3x+1}\,dx = \ln|x-3| + \dfrac{2}{3}\ln|3x+1| + C$

15. $\dfrac{1}{(x-1)(x+2)(x-3)} = \dfrac{A}{x-1} + \dfrac{B}{x+2} + \dfrac{C}{x-3}$; $A = -\dfrac{1}{6}$, $B = \dfrac{1}{15}$, $C = \dfrac{1}{10}$

$-\dfrac{1}{6}\displaystyle\int \dfrac{1}{x-1}\,dx + \dfrac{1}{15}\int \dfrac{1}{x+2}\,dx + \dfrac{1}{10}\int \dfrac{1}{x-3}\,dx$

$= -\dfrac{1}{6}\ln|x-1| + \dfrac{1}{15}\ln|x+2| + \dfrac{1}{10}\ln|x-3| + C$

16. $\dfrac{1}{x(x+1)(x-1)} = \dfrac{A}{x} + \dfrac{B}{x+1} + \dfrac{C}{x-1}$; $A = -1$, $B = \dfrac{1}{2}$, $C = \dfrac{1}{2}$

$$-\int \frac{1}{x}dx + \frac{1}{2}\int \frac{1}{x+1}dx + \frac{1}{2}\int \frac{1}{x-1}dx = -\ln|x| + \frac{1}{2}\ln|x+1| + \frac{1}{2}\ln|x-1| + C$$

$$= \frac{1}{2}\ln\left|\frac{(x+1)(x-1)}{x^2}\right| + C = \frac{1}{2}\ln\frac{|x^2-1|}{x^2} + C$$

17. $\dfrac{2x^2 - 9x - 9}{x(x+3)(x-3)} = \dfrac{A}{x} + \dfrac{B}{x+3} + \dfrac{C}{x-3}$; $A = 1$, $B = 2$, $C = -1$

$$\int \frac{1}{x}dx + 2\int \frac{1}{x+3}dx - \int \frac{1}{x-3}dx = \ln|x| + 2\ln|x+3| - \ln|x-3| + C = \ln\left|\frac{x(x+3)^2}{x-3}\right| + C$$

18. $\dfrac{2x^2 + 4x - 8}{x(x+2)(x-2)} = \dfrac{A}{x} + \dfrac{B}{x+2} + \dfrac{C}{x-2}$; $A = 2$, $B = -1$, $C = 1$

$$2\int \frac{1}{x}dx - \int \frac{1}{x+2}dx + \int \frac{1}{x-2}dx = 2\ln|x| - \ln|x+2| + \ln|x-2| + C = \ln\left|\frac{x^2(x-2)}{x+2}\right| + C$$

19. $\dfrac{x^2 + 2}{x+2} = x - 2 + \dfrac{6}{x+2}$, $\int\left(x - 2 + \dfrac{6}{x+2}\right)dx = \dfrac{1}{2}x^2 - 2x + 6\ \ln|x+2| + C$

20. $\dfrac{x^2 - 4}{x-1} = x + 1 - \dfrac{3}{x-1}$, $\int\left(x + 1 - \dfrac{3}{x-1}\right)dx = \dfrac{1}{2}x^2 + x - 3\ \ln|x-1| + C$

21. $\dfrac{3x^2 - 10}{x^2 - 4x + 4} = 3 + \dfrac{12x - 22}{x^2 - 4x + 4}$, $\dfrac{12x - 22}{(x-2)^2} = \dfrac{A}{x-2} + \dfrac{B}{(x-2)^2}$; $A = 12$, $B = 2$

$$\int 3dx + 12\int \frac{1}{x-2}dx + 2\int \frac{1}{(x-2)^2}dx = 3x + 12\ln|x-2| - 2/(x-2) + C$$

22. $\dfrac{x^2}{x^2 - 3x + 2} = 1 + \dfrac{3x - 2}{x^2 - 3x + 2}$, $\dfrac{3x - 2}{(x-1)(x-2)} = \dfrac{A}{x-1} + \dfrac{B}{x-2}$; $A = -1$, $B = 4$

$$\int dx - \int \frac{1}{x-1}dx + 4\int \frac{1}{x-2}dx = x - \ln|x-1| + 4\ln|x-2| + C$$

23. $\dfrac{x^3}{x^2 - 3x + 2} = x + 3 + \dfrac{7x - 6}{x^2 - 3x + 2}$, $\dfrac{7x - 6}{(x-1)(x-2)} = \dfrac{A}{x-1} + \dfrac{B}{x-2}$; $A = -1$, $B = 8$

$$\int(x+3)dx - \int \frac{1}{x-1}dx + 8\int \frac{1}{x-2}dx = \frac{1}{2}x^2 + 3x - \ln|x-1| + 8\ln|x-2| + C$$

24. $\dfrac{x^3}{x^2-x-6}=x+1+\dfrac{7x+6}{x^2-x-6}$, $\dfrac{7x+6}{(x-3)(x+2)}=\dfrac{A}{x-3}+\dfrac{B}{x+2}$; $A=\dfrac{27}{5}$, $B=\dfrac{8}{5}$

$$\int(x+1)dx+\frac{27}{5}\int\frac{1}{x-3}dx+\frac{8}{5}\int\frac{1}{x+2}dx=\frac{1}{2}x^2+x+\frac{27}{5}\ln|x-3|+\frac{8}{5}\ln|x+2|+C$$

25. $\dfrac{x^5+2x^2+1}{x^3-x}=x^2+1+\dfrac{2x^2+x+1}{x^3-x}$,

$$\frac{2x^2+x+1}{x(x+1)(x-1)}=\frac{A}{x}+\frac{B}{x+1}+\frac{C}{x-1}; \ A=-1, B=1, C=2$$

$$\int(x^2+1)dx-\int\frac{1}{x}dx+\int\frac{1}{x+1}dx+2\int\frac{1}{x-1}dx$$

$$=\frac{1}{3}x^3+x-\ln|x|+\ln|x+1|+2\ln|x-1|+C=\frac{1}{3}x^3+x+\ln\left|\frac{(x+1)(x-1)^2}{x}\right|+C$$

26. $\dfrac{2x^5-x^3-1}{x^3-4x}=2x^2+7+\dfrac{28x-1}{x^3-4x}$,

$$\frac{28x-1}{x(x+2)(x-2)}=\frac{A}{x}+\frac{B}{x+2}+\frac{C}{x-2}; \ A=\frac{1}{4}, B=-\frac{57}{8}, C=\frac{55}{8}$$

$$\int(2x^2+7)dx+\frac{1}{4}\int\frac{1}{x}dx-\frac{57}{8}\int\frac{1}{x+2}dx+\frac{55}{8}\int\frac{1}{x-2}dx$$

$$=\frac{2}{3}x^3+7x+\frac{1}{4}\ln|x|-\frac{57}{8}\ln|x+2|+\frac{55}{8}\ln|x-2|+C$$

27. $\dfrac{2x^2+3}{x(x-1)^2}=\dfrac{A}{x}+\dfrac{B}{x-1}+\dfrac{C}{(x-1)^2}$; $A=3, B=-1, C=5$

$$3\int\frac{1}{x}dx-\int\frac{1}{x-1}dx+5\int\frac{1}{(x-1)^2}dx=3\ln|x|-\ln|x-1|-5/(x-1)+C$$

28. $\dfrac{3x^2-x+1}{x^2(x-1)}=\dfrac{A}{x}+\dfrac{B}{x^2}+\dfrac{C}{x-1}$; $A=0, B=-1, C=3$

$$-\int\frac{1}{x^2}dx+3\int\frac{1}{x-1}dx=1/x+3\ln|x-1|+C$$

29. $\dfrac{x^2+x-16}{(x+1)(x-3)^2}=\dfrac{A}{x+1}+\dfrac{B}{x-3}+\dfrac{C}{(x-3)^2}$; $A=-1, B=2, C=-1$

$$-\int\frac{1}{x+1}dx+2\int\frac{1}{x-3}dx-\int\frac{1}{(x-3)^2}dx$$

$$=-\ln|x+1|+2\ln|x-3|+\frac{1}{x-3}+C=\ln\frac{(x-3)^2}{|x+1|}+\frac{1}{x-3}+C$$

30. $\dfrac{2x^2 - 2x - 1}{x^2(x-1)} = \dfrac{A}{x} + \dfrac{B}{x^2} + \dfrac{C}{x-1};\; A = 3,\, B = 1,\, C = -1$

$3\displaystyle\int \dfrac{1}{x}\,dx + \int \dfrac{1}{x^2}\,dx - \int \dfrac{1}{x-1}\,dx = 3\ln|x| - \dfrac{1}{x} - \ln|x-1| + C$

31. $\dfrac{x^2}{(x+2)^3} = \dfrac{A}{x+2} + \dfrac{B}{(x+2)^2} + \dfrac{C}{(x+2)^3};\; A = 1,\, B = -4,\, C = 4$

$\displaystyle\int \dfrac{1}{x+2}\,dx - 4\int \dfrac{1}{(x+2)^2}\,dx + 4\int \dfrac{1}{(x+2)^3}\,dx = \ln|x+2| + \dfrac{4}{x+2} - \dfrac{2}{(x+2)^2} + C$

32. $\dfrac{2x^2 + 3x + 3}{(x+1)^3} = \dfrac{A}{x+1} + \dfrac{B}{(x+1)^2} + \dfrac{C}{(x+1)^3};\; A = 2,\, B = -1,\, C = 2$

$2\displaystyle\int \dfrac{1}{x+1}\,dx - \int \dfrac{1}{(x+1)^2}\,dx + 2\int \dfrac{1}{(x+1)^3}\,dx = 2\ln|x+1| + \dfrac{1}{x+1} - \dfrac{1}{(x+1)^2} + C$

33. $\dfrac{2x^2 - 1}{(4x-1)(x^2+1)} = \dfrac{A}{4x-1} + \dfrac{Bx+C}{x^2+1};\; A = -14/17,\, B = 12/17,\, C = 3/17$

$\displaystyle\int \dfrac{2x^2 - 1}{4x^3 - x^2 + 4x - 1}\,dx = -\dfrac{7}{34}\ln|4x-1| + \dfrac{6}{17}\ln(x^2+1) + \dfrac{3}{17}\tan^{-1}x + C$

34. $\dfrac{1}{x(x^2 + x + 1)} = \dfrac{A}{x} + \dfrac{Bx+C}{x^2+x+1};\; A = 1,\, B = C = -1$

$\displaystyle\int \dfrac{-x-1}{x^2+x+1}\,dx = -\int \dfrac{x+1}{(x+1/2)^2 + 3/4}\,dx = -\int \dfrac{u+1/2}{u^2+3/4}\,du, \quad u = x + 1/2$

$\qquad\qquad = -\dfrac{1}{2}\ln(u^2 + 3/4) - \dfrac{1}{\sqrt{3}}\tan^{-1} 2u/\sqrt{3} + C_1$

so $\displaystyle\int \dfrac{dx}{x(x^2+x+1)} = \ln|x| - \dfrac{1}{2}\ln(x^2+x+1) - \dfrac{1}{\sqrt{3}}\tan^{-1}\dfrac{2x+1}{\sqrt{3}} + C$

35. $\dfrac{1}{(x+2)(x-2)(x^2+4)} = \dfrac{A}{x+2} + \dfrac{B}{x-2} + \dfrac{Cx+D}{x^2+4};\; A = -1/32,\, B = 1/32,\, C = 0,\, D = -1/8$

$\displaystyle\int \dfrac{dx}{x^4 - 16} = \dfrac{1}{32}\ln\left|\dfrac{x-2}{x+2}\right| - \dfrac{1}{16}\tan^{-1}(x/2) + C$

36. $\dfrac{1}{x(x^2+1)} = \dfrac{A}{x} + \dfrac{Bx+C}{x^2+1};\; A = 1,\, B = -1,\, C = 0$

$\displaystyle\int \dfrac{1}{x^3+x}\,dx = \ln|x| - \dfrac{1}{2}\ln(x^2+1) + C = \dfrac{1}{2}\ln\dfrac{x^2}{x^2+1} + C$

37. $\dfrac{x^3 + 3x^2 + x + 9}{(x^2 + 1)(x^2 + 3)} = \dfrac{Ax + B}{x^2 + 1} + \dfrac{Cx + D}{x^2 + 3}$; $A = 0, B = 3, C = 1, D = 0$

$$\int \dfrac{x^3 + 3x^2 + x + 9}{(x^2 + 1)(x^2 + 3)}\,dx = 3\tan^{-1} x + \dfrac{1}{2}\ln(x^2 + 3) + C$$

38. $\dfrac{x^3 + x^2 + x + 2}{(x^2 + 1)(x^2 + 2)} = \dfrac{Ax + B}{x^2 + 1} + \dfrac{Cx + D}{x^2 + 2}$; $A = D = 0, B = C = 1$

$$\int \dfrac{x^3 + x^2 + x + 2}{(x^2 + 1)(x^2 + 2)}\,dx = \tan^{-1} x + \dfrac{1}{2}\ln(x^2 + 2) + C$$

39. $\dfrac{x^3 - 3x^2 + 2x - 3}{x^2 + 1} = x - 3 + \dfrac{x}{x^2 + 1}$,

$$\int \dfrac{x^3 - 3x^2 + 2x - 3}{x^2 + 1}\,dx = \dfrac{1}{2}x^2 - 3x + \dfrac{1}{2}\ln(x^2 + 1) + C$$

40. $\dfrac{x^4 + 6x^3 + 10x^2 + x}{x^2 + 6x + 10} = x^2 + \dfrac{x}{x^2 + 6x + 10}$,

$$\int \dfrac{x}{x^2 + 6x + 10}\,dx = \int \dfrac{x}{(x + 3)^2 + 1}\,dx = \int \dfrac{u - 3}{u^2 + 1}\,du, \quad u = x + 3$$

$$= \dfrac{1}{2}\ln(u^2 + 1) - 3\tan^{-1} u + C_1$$

so $\displaystyle\int \dfrac{x^4 + 6x^3 + 10x^2 + x}{x^2 + 6x + 10}\,dx = \dfrac{1}{3}x^3 + \dfrac{1}{2}\ln(x^2 + 6x + 10) - 3\tan^{-1}(x + 3) + C$

41. $\dfrac{x^2 + 1}{(x^2 + 2x + 3)^2} = \dfrac{Ax + B}{x^2 + 2x + 3} + \dfrac{Cx + D}{(x^2 + 2x + 3)^2}$; $A = 0, B = 1, C = D = -2$

$$\int \dfrac{x^2 + 1}{(x^2 + 2x + 3)^2}\,dx = \int \dfrac{1}{(x + 1)^2 + 2}\,dx - \int \dfrac{2x + 2}{(x^2 + 2x + 3)^2}\,dx$$

$$= \dfrac{1}{\sqrt{2}}\tan^{-1}\dfrac{x + 1}{\sqrt{2}} + 1/(x^2 + 2x + 3) + C$$

42. $\dfrac{x^5 + x^4 + 4x^3 + 4x^2 + 4x + 4}{(x^2 + 2)^3} = \dfrac{Ax + B}{x^2 + 2} + \dfrac{Cx + D}{(x^2 + 2)^2} + \dfrac{Ex + F}{(x^2 + 2)^3}$;

$A = B = 1, C = D = E = F = 0$

$$\int \dfrac{x + 1}{x^2 + 2}\,dx = \dfrac{1}{2}\ln(x^2 + 2) + \dfrac{1}{\sqrt{2}}\tan^{-1}(x/\sqrt{2}) + C$$

43. let $x = \sin\theta$ to get $\displaystyle\int \frac{1}{x^2 + 4x - 5}dx$,

$$\frac{1}{(x+5)(x-1)} = \frac{A}{x+5} + \frac{B}{x-1}; \ A = -1/6, \ B = 1/6$$

$$-\frac{1}{6}\int \frac{1}{x+5}dx + \frac{1}{6}\int \frac{1}{x-1}dx = \frac{1}{6}\ln\left|\frac{x-1}{x+5}\right| + C = \frac{1}{6}\ln\left|\frac{\sin\theta-1}{\sin\theta+5}\right| + C$$

44. let $x = e^t$ then $\displaystyle\int \frac{e^t}{e^{2t} - 4}dt = \int \frac{1}{x^2 - 4}dx$,

$$\frac{1}{(x+2)(x-2)} = \frac{A}{x+2} + \frac{B}{x-2}; \ A = -1/4, \ B = 1/4$$

$$-\frac{1}{4}\int \frac{1}{x+2}dx + \frac{1}{4}\int \frac{1}{x-2}dx = \frac{1}{4}\ln\left|\frac{x-2}{x+2}\right| + C = \frac{1}{4}\ln\left|\frac{e^t-2}{e^t+2}\right| + C$$

45. let $u = e^x$ to get $\displaystyle\int \frac{dx}{1+e^x} = \int \frac{e^x\,dx}{e^x(1+e^x)} = \int \frac{du}{u(1+u)}$,

$$\frac{1}{u(1+u)} = \frac{A}{u} + \frac{B}{1+u}; \ A = 1, \ B = -1$$

$$\int \frac{du}{u(1+u)} = \ln u - \ln(1+u) + C = \ln\frac{e^x}{1+e^x} + C$$

46. Let $x = \tan\theta$ to get $\displaystyle\int \frac{1}{x^3 - x^2}dx$

$$\frac{1}{x^2(x-1)} = \frac{A}{x} + \frac{B}{x^2} + \frac{C}{x-1}; \ A = -1, \ B = -1, \ C = 1$$

$$-\int \frac{1}{x}dx - \int \frac{1}{x^2}dx + \int \frac{1}{x-1}dx = -\ln|x| + \frac{1}{x} + \ln|x-1| + C$$

$$= \frac{1}{x} + \ln\left|\frac{x-1}{x}\right| + C = \cot\theta + \ln\left|\frac{\tan\theta-1}{\tan\theta}\right| + C = \cot\theta + \ln|1 - \cot\theta| + C$$

47. **(a)** $x^4 + 1 = (x^4 + 2x^2 + 1) - 2x^2 = (x^2 + 1)^2 - 2x^2$
$$= [(x^2 + 1) + \sqrt{2}x][(x^2 + 1) - \sqrt{2}x]$$
$$= (x^2 + \sqrt{2}x + 1)(x^2 - \sqrt{2}x + 1); \ a = \sqrt{2}, b = -\sqrt{2}$$

(b) $\displaystyle\frac{x}{(x^2 + \sqrt{2}x + 1)(x^2 - \sqrt{2}x + 1)} = \frac{Ax + B}{x^2 + \sqrt{2}x + 1} + \frac{Cx + D}{x^2 - \sqrt{2}x + 1};$

$$A = 0, \ B = -\frac{\sqrt{2}}{4}, \ C = 0, \ D = \frac{\sqrt{2}}{4} \text{ so}$$

$$\int_0^1 \frac{x}{x^4+1}dx = -\frac{\sqrt{2}}{4}\int_0^1 \frac{1}{x^2+\sqrt{2}x+1}dx + \frac{\sqrt{2}}{4}\int_0^1 \frac{1}{x^2-\sqrt{2}x+1}dx$$

$$= -\frac{\sqrt{2}}{4}\int_0^1 \frac{1}{(x+\sqrt{2}/2)^2+1/2}dx + \frac{\sqrt{2}}{4}\int_0^1 \frac{1}{(x-\sqrt{2}/2)^2+1/2}dx$$

$$= -\frac{\sqrt{2}}{4}\int_{\sqrt{2}/2}^{1+\sqrt{2}/2} \frac{1}{u^2+1/2}du + \frac{\sqrt{2}}{4}\int_{-\sqrt{2}/2}^{1-\sqrt{2}/2} \frac{1}{u^2+1/2}du$$

$$= -\frac{1}{2}\tan^{-1}\sqrt{2}u\Big]_{\sqrt{2}/2}^{1+\sqrt{2}/2} + \frac{1}{2}\tan^{-1}\sqrt{2}u\Big]_{-\sqrt{2}/2}^{1-\sqrt{2}/2}$$

$$= -\frac{1}{2}\tan^{-1}(\sqrt{2}+1) + \frac{1}{2}\left(\frac{\pi}{4}\right) + \frac{1}{2}\tan^{-1}(\sqrt{2}-1) - \frac{1}{2}\left(-\frac{\pi}{4}\right)$$

$$= \frac{\pi}{4} - \frac{1}{2}[\tan^{-1}(\sqrt{2}+1) - \tan^{-1}(\sqrt{2}-1)]$$

$$= \frac{\pi}{4} - \frac{1}{2}[\tan^{-1}(1+\sqrt{2}) + \tan^{-1}(1-\sqrt{2})]$$

$$= \frac{\pi}{4} - \frac{1}{2}\tan^{-1}\left[\frac{(1+\sqrt{2})+(1-\sqrt{2})}{1-(1+\sqrt{2})(1-\sqrt{2})}\right] \quad \text{(Exercise 16, 8.1)}$$

$$= \frac{\pi}{4} - \frac{1}{2}\tan^{-1}1 = \frac{\pi}{4} - \frac{1}{2}\left(\frac{\pi}{4}\right) = \frac{\pi}{8}$$

48. $A = \displaystyle\int_1^2 \frac{3-x}{x^3+x^2}dx, \quad \frac{3-x}{x^2(x+1)} = \frac{A}{x} + \frac{B}{x^2} + \frac{C}{x+1}; \quad A=-4, B=3, C=4$

$$A = -4\ln|x| - \frac{3}{x} + 4\ln|x+1|\Big]_1^2$$

$$= (-4\ln 2 - \frac{3}{2} + 4\ln 3) - (-4\ln 1 - 3 + 4\ln 2) = \frac{3}{2} - 8\ln 2 + 4\ln 3 = \frac{3}{2} + 4\ln\frac{3}{4}$$

49. $V = \pi\displaystyle\int_0^2 \frac{x^4}{(9-x^2)^2}dx, \quad \frac{x^4}{x^4-18x^2+81} = 1 + \frac{18x^2-81}{x^4-18x^2+81},$

$$\frac{18x^2-81}{(9-x^2)^2} = \frac{18x^2-81}{(x+3)^2(x-3)^2} = \frac{A}{x+3} + \frac{B}{(x+3)^2} + \frac{C}{x-3} + \frac{D}{(x-3)^2};$$

$$A = -\frac{9}{4}, B = \frac{9}{4}, C = \frac{9}{4}, D = \frac{9}{4}$$

$$V = \pi\left[x - \frac{9}{4}\ln|x+3| - \frac{9/4}{x+3} + \frac{9}{4}\ln|x-3| - \frac{9/4}{x-3}\right]_0^2 = \pi\left(\frac{19}{5} - \frac{9}{4}\ln 5\right)$$

50. $\int \dfrac{1}{y^2 + y} dy = \int dx, \quad \dfrac{1}{y(y+1)} = \dfrac{1}{y} - \dfrac{1}{y+1}, \quad \ln|y| - \ln|y+1| = x + C_1,$

$\ln\left|\dfrac{y}{y+1}\right| = x + C_1, \quad \dfrac{y}{y+1} = \pm e^{x+C_1} = \pm e^{C_1} e^x = C_2 e^x,$

$y = C_2 e^x y + C_2 e^x, \quad y(1 - C_2 e^x) = C_2 e^x, \quad y = \dfrac{C_2 e^x}{1 - C_2 e^x} = \dfrac{1}{Ce^{-x} - 1}.$

51. $\int \dfrac{1}{y^2 - 5y + 6} dy = \int dx, \quad \dfrac{1}{(y-3)(y-2)} = \dfrac{1}{y-3} - \dfrac{1}{y-2},$

$\ln|y-3| - \ln|y-2| = x + C_1, \quad \ln\left|\dfrac{y-3}{y-2}\right| = x + C_1, \quad \dfrac{y-3}{y-2} = \pm e^{C_1} e^x = Ce^x,$

$y - 3 = Ce^x y - 2Ce^x, \quad y(1 - Ce^x) = 3 - 2Ce^x, \quad y = \dfrac{3 - 2Ce^x}{1 - Ce^x}.$

52. $\int \dfrac{1}{y^2 - 4y} dy = \int t^2 dt, \quad \dfrac{1}{y(y-4)} = \dfrac{-1/4}{y} + \dfrac{1/4}{y-4},$

$-\dfrac{1}{4}\ln|y| + \dfrac{1}{4}\ln|y-4| = \dfrac{1}{3}t^3 + C_1, \quad \dfrac{1}{4}\ln\left|\dfrac{y-4}{y}\right| = \dfrac{1}{3}t^3 + C_1,$

$\dfrac{y-4}{y} = \pm e^{C_1} e^{4t^3/3} = Ce^{4t^3/3}, \quad y - 4 = Ce^{4t^3/3}y, \quad y = \dfrac{4}{1 - Ce^{4t^3/3}}.$

53. $\int \dfrac{1}{y^2 + y} dy = \int \dfrac{1}{t(t-1)} dt, \quad \dfrac{1}{y(y+1)} = \dfrac{1}{y} - \dfrac{1}{y+1}$ and $\dfrac{1}{t(t-1)} = -\dfrac{1}{t} + \dfrac{1}{t-1},$

$\ln|y| - \ln|y+1| = -\ln|t| + \ln|t-1| + C_1, \quad \ln\left|\dfrac{y}{y+1}\right| = \ln\left|\dfrac{t-1}{t}\right| + C_1,$

$\dfrac{y}{y+1} = C_2 \dfrac{t-1}{t}; \text{ solve for } y \text{ to get } y = \dfrac{C_2(t-1)/t}{1 - C_2(t-1)/t} = \dfrac{1}{Ct/(t-1) - 1} = \dfrac{t-1}{Ct - t + 1}.$

54. **(a)** $\int \dfrac{1}{(a-x)(b-x)} dx = \int k\, dt, \quad \dfrac{1}{(a-x)(b-x)} = \dfrac{1/(b-a)}{a-x} + \dfrac{1/(a-b)}{b-x},$

$-\dfrac{1}{b-a}\ln(a-x) - \dfrac{1}{a-b}\ln(b-x) = kt + C, \quad \dfrac{1}{a-b}\ln\dfrac{a-x}{b-x} = kt + C;$

$x = 0 \text{ when } t = 0 \text{ so } C = \dfrac{1}{a-b}\ln\dfrac{a}{b}, \quad \dfrac{1}{a-b}\ln\dfrac{b(a-x)}{a(b-x)} = kt, \quad t = \dfrac{1}{k(a-b)}\ln\dfrac{b(a-x)}{a(b-x)}.$

(b) $t = \dfrac{1}{(0.3)(0.04)}\ln\dfrac{(0.06)(0.08)}{(0.10)(0.04)} \approx 15.2 \text{ min}$

55. (a) $\displaystyle\int \frac{1}{ay - by^2}\,dy = \int dt,\ \frac{1}{y(a - by)} = \frac{1/a}{y} + \frac{b/a}{a - by},$

$\displaystyle\frac{1}{a}\ln|y| - \frac{1}{a}\ln|a - by| = t + C_1,\ \frac{1}{a}\ln\left|\frac{y}{a - by}\right| = t + C_1,$

$\displaystyle\frac{y}{a - by} = C_2 e^{at},\ y = aC_2 e^{at} - bC_2 e^{at} y,\ y = \frac{aC_2 e^{at}}{1 + bC_2 e^{at}} = \frac{a}{Ce^{-at} + b}.$

(b) $\displaystyle\lim_{t \to +\infty} y = a/b,\ \lim_{t \to -\infty} y = 0$

56. (a) $\displaystyle y = \frac{2}{1 + Ce^{-2t}},\ y = \frac{1}{2}$ when $t = 0$ so $\displaystyle\frac{2}{1 + C} = \frac{1}{2},\ 1 + C = 4,\ C = 3,\ y = \frac{2}{1 + 3e^{-2t}}$

(b)

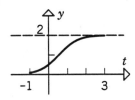

57. (a) $x^3 - 6x^2 + 11x - 6 = (x - 1)(x - 2)(x - 3)$

(b) $x^3 - 3x^2 + x - 20 = (x - 4)(x^2 + x + 5)$

(c) $x^4 - 5x^3 + 7x^2 - 5x + 6 = (x - 2)(x - 3)(x^2 + 1)$

58. (a) $8x^3 + 4x^2 - 2x - 1 = 8(x - 1/2)(x + 1/2)^2$

(b) $6x^4 - 7x^3 + 6x^2 - 1 = 6(x - 1/2)(x + 1/3)(x^2 - x + 1)$

(c) $9x^4 - 56x^3 + 57x^2 + 98x - 24 = 9(x + 1)(x - 3)(x - 4)(x - 2/9)$

59. $x^4 - 3x^3 - 7x^2 + 27x - 18 = (x - 1)(x - 2)(x - 3)(x + 3),$

$\displaystyle\frac{1}{(x - 1)(x - 2)(x - 3)(x + 3)} = \frac{A}{x - 1} + \frac{B}{x - 2} + \frac{C}{x - 3} + \frac{D}{x + 3};$

$A = 1/8,\ B = -1/5,\ C = 1/12,\ D = -1/120$

$\displaystyle\int \frac{dx}{x^4 - 3x^3 - 7x^2 + 27x - 18} = \frac{1}{8}\ln|x - 1| - \frac{1}{5}\ln|x - 2| + \frac{1}{12}\ln|x - 3| - \frac{1}{120}\ln|x + 3| + C$

60. $16x^3 - 4x^2 + 4x - 1 = (4x - 1)(4x^2 + 1),$

$\displaystyle\frac{1}{(4x - 1)(4x^2 + 1)} = \frac{A}{4x - 1} + \frac{Bx + C}{4x^2 + 1};\ A = 4/5,\ B = -4/5,\ C = -1/5$

$\displaystyle\int \frac{dx}{16x^3 - 4x^2 + 4x - 1} = \frac{1}{5}\ln|4x - 1| - \frac{1}{10}\ln(4x^2 + 1) - \frac{1}{10}\tan^{-1}(2x) + C$

61. **(a)** $\sqrt{2}$ is a positive root of $x^2 - 2 = 0$. The only possible positive rational roots of $x^2 - 2 = 0$ are the integers 1 and 2 neither of which satisfies the equation so $\sqrt{2}$ is not rational.

(b) $\sqrt{a}$ is a positive root of $x^2 - a = 0$. The only possible positive rational roots of $x^2 - a = 0$ are the positive integers that divide a. If one of these satisfies the equation then $\sqrt{a}$ is an integer, otherwise $\sqrt{a}$ cannot be rational.

62. **(a)** The symbol $\equiv$ means that the equation is true for all values of x, which is certainly correct if $a_0 = a_1 = \cdots = a_n = 0$. Suppose one or more of the coefficients were not zero, then the equation would be of degree n or less with more than n distinct roots, which is impossible because a polynomial equation of degree m cannot have more than m distinct roots so $a_0 = a_1 = \cdots = a_n = 0$.

(b) The given equation yields $(a_0 - b_0)x^n + (a_1 - b_1)x^{n-1} + \ldots + (a_n - b_n) \equiv 0$ so from part (a) $a_0 - b_0 = a_1 - b_1 = \cdots = a_n - b_n = 0$, $a_0 = b_0$, $a_1 = b_1, \ldots, a_n = b_n$.

EXERCISE SET 9.7

1. $u = \sqrt{x - 2}$, $x = u^2 + 2$, $dx = 2u\,du$

$$\int 2u^2(u^2 + 2)du = 2\int(u^4 + 2u^2)du = \frac{2}{5}u^5 + \frac{4}{3}u^3 + C = \frac{2}{5}(x-2)^{5/2} + \frac{4}{3}(x-2)^{3/2} + C$$

2. $u = \sqrt{x + 1}$, $x = u^2 - 1$, $dx = 2u\,du$; $2\int_1^3 (u^2 - 1)du = 2\left(\frac{2}{3}u^3 - u\right)\Big]_1^3 = \frac{92}{3}$

3. $u = \sqrt{x - 4}$, $x = u^2 + 4$, $dx = 2u\,du$

$$\int_0^2 \frac{2u^2}{u^2 + 4}du = 2\int_0^2\left[1 - \frac{4}{u^2 + 4}\right]du = 2u - 4\tan^{-1}(u/2)\Big]_0^2 = 4 - \pi$$

4. $u = \sqrt{x}$, $x = u^2$, $dx = 2u\,du$

$$2\int_0^3 \frac{u^2}{u^2 + 9}du = 2\int_0^3\left(1 - \frac{9}{u^2 + 9}\right)du = \left(2u - 6\tan^{-1}\frac{u}{3}\right)\Big]_0^3 = 6 - \frac{3}{2}\pi$$

5. $u = 3 + \sqrt{x}$, $x = (u - 3)^2$, $dx = 2(u - 3)du$

$$\int_3^5 \frac{2(u - 3)}{u}du = 2\int_3^5 (1 - 3/u)du = 2u - 6\ln|u|\Big]_3^5 = 4 - 6\ln(5/3)$$

6. $u = \sqrt{x^3 + 1}$, $x^3 = u^2 - 1$, $3x^2\,dx = 2u\,du$

$$\frac{2}{3}\int(u^2 - 1)du = \frac{2}{9}u^3 - \frac{2}{3}u + C = \frac{2}{9}(x^3 + 1)^{3/2} - \frac{2}{3}(x^3 + 1)^{1/2} + C$$

7. $u = \sqrt{x^3 + 1}$, $x^3 = u^2 - 1$, $3x^2dx = 2u\,du$

$$\frac{2}{3}\int u^2(u^2 - 1)du = \frac{2}{3}\int (u^4 - u^2)du = \frac{2}{15}u^5 - \frac{2}{9}u^3 + C = \frac{2}{15}(x^3 + 1)^{5/2} - \frac{2}{9}(x^3 + 1)^{3/2} + C$$

8. $u = \sqrt{x^3 - 1}$, $x^3 = u^2 + 1$, $3x^2dx = 2u\,du$

$$\frac{2}{3}\int \frac{1}{u^2 + 1}du = \frac{2}{3}\tan^{-1}u + C = \frac{2}{3}\tan^{-1}\sqrt{x^3 - 1} + C$$

9. $u = x^{1/6}$, $x = u^6$, $dx = 6u^5du$

$$\int \frac{6u^5}{u^3 + u^2}du = 6\int \frac{u^3}{u + 1}du = 6\int \left[u^2 - u + 1 - \frac{1}{u + 1}\right]du$$

$$= 2x^{1/2} - 3x^{1/3} + 6x^{1/6} - 6\,\ln(x^{1/6} + 1) + C$$

10. $u = x^{1/5}$, $x = u^5$, $dx = 5u^4du$; $\displaystyle\int \frac{5u^4}{u^5 - u^3}du = 5\int \frac{u}{u^2 - 1}du = \frac{5}{2}\ln|x^{2/5} - 1| + C$

11. $u = v^{1/4}$, $v = u^4$, $dv = 4u^3du$; $\displaystyle 4\int \frac{1}{u(1 - u)}du = 4\int \left[\frac{1}{u} + \frac{1}{1 - u}\right]du = 4\ln\frac{v^{1/4}}{|1 - v^{1/4}|} + C$

12. $u = x^{1/3}$, $x = u^3$, $dx = 3u^2du$, $\displaystyle 3\int \frac{u^4}{u^3 + 1}du = 3\int (u - \frac{u}{u^3 + 1})du$,

$$\frac{u}{u^3 + 1} = \frac{1}{(u + 1)(u^2 - u + 1)} = \frac{-1/3}{u + 1} + \frac{(1/3)u + 1/3}{u^2 - u + 1}$$

$$3\int \left(u - \frac{u}{u^3 + 1}\right)du = \int \left(3u + \frac{1}{u + 1} - \frac{u + 1}{u^2 - u + 1}\right)du$$

$$= \frac{3}{2}u^2 + \ln|u + 1| - \frac{1}{2}\ln(u^2 - u + 1) - \sqrt{3}\tan^{-1}\frac{2u - 1}{\sqrt{3}} + C$$

$$= \frac{3}{2}x^{2/3} + \ln|x^{1/3} + 1| - \frac{1}{2}\ln(x^{2/3} - x^{1/3} + 1) - \sqrt{3}\tan^{-1}\frac{2x^{1/3} - 1}{\sqrt{3}} + C$$

13. $u = t^{1/6}$, $t = u^6$, $dt = 6u^5du$

$$6\int \frac{u^3}{u - 1}du = 6\int \left[u^2 + u + 1 + \frac{1}{u - 1}\right]du = 2t^{1/2} + 3t^{1/3} + 6t^{1/6} + 6\,\ln|t^{1/6} - 1| + C$$

14. $u = \sqrt{x}$, $x = u^2$, $dx = 2u\,du$

$$-2\int \frac{u^2 + u}{u - 1}du = -2\int \left(u + 2 + \frac{2}{u - 1}\right)du = -x - 4\sqrt{x} - 4\ln|\sqrt{x} - 1| + C$$

15. $u = \sqrt{1+x^2}$, $x^2 = u^2 - 1$, $2x\,dx = 2u\,du$, $x\,dx = u\,du$

$$\int (u^2 - 1)du = \frac{1}{3}(1+x^2)^{3/2} - (1+x^2)^{1/2} + C$$

16. $u = (x+3)^{1/5}$, $x = u^5 - 3$, $dx = 5u^4 du$

$$5\int (u^8 - 3u^3)du = \frac{5}{9}(x+3)^{9/5} - \frac{15}{4}(x+3)^{4/5} + C$$

17. $z = \sqrt{x}$, $x = z^2$, $dx = 2z\,dz$, $2\int z\sin z\,dz$; use integration by parts:

$u = z$, $dv = \sin z\,dz$, $du = dz$, $v = -\cos z$

$$2\int z\sin z\,dz = 2\left(-z\cos z + \int \cos z\,dz\right) = -2z\cos z + 2\sin z + C$$

so $\int \sin\sqrt{x}\,dx = -2\sqrt{x}\cos\sqrt{x} + 2\sin\sqrt{x} + C$

18. $z = \sqrt{x}$, $x = z^2$, $dx = 2z\,dz$, $2\int ze^z\,dz$; use integration by parts:

$u = z$, $dv = e^z dz$, $du = dz$, $v = e^z$

$$2\int ze^z dz = 2\left(ze^z - \int e^z dz\right) = 2ze^z - 2e^z + C \text{ so } \int e^{\sqrt{x}}dx = 2\sqrt{x}e^{\sqrt{x}} - 2e^{\sqrt{x}} + C$$

19. $u = \sqrt{e^x + 1}$, $e^x = u^2 - 1$, $x = \ln(u^2 - 1)$, $dx = \dfrac{2u}{u^2 - 1}du$

$$\int \frac{2}{u^2 - 1}du = \int \left[\frac{1}{u-1} - \frac{1}{u+1}\right]du = \ln|u-1| - \ln|u+1| + C = \ln\frac{\sqrt{e^x+1}-1}{\sqrt{e^x+1}+1} + C$$

20. $u = \sqrt{e^x - 1}$, $e^x = u^2 + 1$, $x = \ln(u^2 + 1)$, $dx = \dfrac{2u}{u^2 + 1}du$

$$\int_0^1 \frac{2u^2}{u^2 + 1}du = 2\int_0^1 \left(1 - \frac{1}{u^2 + 1}\right)du = (2u - 2\tan^{-1} u)\Big]_0^1 = 2 - \frac{\pi}{2}$$

21. $$\int \frac{1}{1 + \dfrac{2u}{1+u^2} + \dfrac{1-u^2}{1+u^2}}\frac{2}{1+u^2}du = \int \frac{1}{u+1}du = \ln|\tan(x/2) + 1| + C$$

22. $$\int \frac{1}{2 + \dfrac{2u}{1+u^2}}\left(\frac{2}{1+u^2}\right)du = \int \frac{1}{u^2 + u + 1}du$$

$$= \int \frac{1}{(u+1/2)^2 + 3/4}du = \frac{2}{\sqrt{3}}\tan^{-1}\left(\frac{2\tan(x/2) + 1}{\sqrt{3}}\right) + C$$

23. $u = \tan(\theta/2)$, $\displaystyle\int \frac{d\theta}{1-\cos\theta} = \int \frac{1}{u^2}du = -\frac{1}{u} + C = -\cot(\theta/2) + C$,

$$\int_{\pi/2}^{\pi} \frac{d\theta}{1-\cos\theta} = -\cot(\theta/2)\Big]_{\pi/2}^{\pi} = 1$$

24. $u = \tan(x/2)$

$$\int \frac{2}{3u^2 + 8u - 3}du = \frac{2}{3}\int \frac{1}{(u+4/3)^2 - 19/3}du = \frac{2}{3}\int \frac{1}{z^2 - 19/3}dz \quad (z = u + 4/3)$$

$$= \frac{1}{\sqrt{57}}\ln\left|\frac{z - \sqrt{19/3}}{z + \sqrt{19/3}}\right| + C = \frac{1}{\sqrt{57}}\ln\left|\frac{\tan(x/2) + 4/3 - \sqrt{19/3}}{\tan(x/2) + 4/3 + \sqrt{19/3}}\right| + C$$

25. $u = \tan(x/2)$, $2\displaystyle\int \frac{1-u^2}{(3u^2+1)(u^2+1)}du$

$$\frac{1-u^2}{(3u^2+1)(u^2+1)} = \frac{(0)u+2}{3u^2+1} + \frac{(0)u-1}{u^2+1} = \frac{2}{3u^2+1} - \frac{1}{u^2+1},$$

$$\int \frac{\cos x}{2-\cos x}dx = \frac{4}{\sqrt{3}}\tan^{-1}[\sqrt{3}\tan(x/2)] - x + C$$

26. $u = \tan(x/2)$, $\dfrac{1}{2}\displaystyle\int \frac{1-u^2}{u}du = \frac{1}{2}\int(1/u - u)du = \frac{1}{2}\ln|\tan(x/2)| - \frac{1}{4}\tan^2(x/2) + C$

27. **(a)** $\displaystyle\int \sec x\,dx = \int \frac{1}{\cos x}dx = \int \frac{2}{1-u^2}du = \ln\left|\frac{1+u}{1-u}\right| + C = \ln\left|\frac{1+\tan(x/2)}{1-\tan(x/2)}\right| + C$

   (b) $\dfrac{1+\tan(x/2)}{1-\tan(x/2)} = \dfrac{\tan(\pi/4) + \tan(x/2)}{1 - \tan(\pi/4)\tan(x/2)} = \tan(\pi/4 + x/2)$ (trig identity)

   (c) $\dfrac{1+\tan(x/2)}{1-\tan(x/2)} = \dfrac{\cos(x/2) + \sin(x/2)}{\cos(x/2) - \sin(x/2)} = \dfrac{[\cos(x/2) + \sin(x/2)]^2}{\cos^2(x/2) - \sin^2(x/2)}$

$$= \frac{\cos^2(x/2) + 2\sin(x/2)\cos(x/2) + \sin^2(x/2)}{\cos x}$$

$$= \frac{1 + \sin x}{\cos x} = \sec x + \tan x$$

28. **(a)** $\displaystyle\int \csc x\,dx = \int \frac{1}{\sin x}dx = \int 1/u\,du = \ln|\tan(x/2)| + C$, but

$$\ln|\tan(x/2)| = \frac{1}{2}\ln\frac{\sin^2(x/2)}{\cos^2(x/2)} = \frac{1}{2}\ln\frac{(1-\cos x)/2}{(1+\cos x)/2} = \frac{1}{2}\ln\frac{1-\cos x}{1+\cos x}$$

(b) $\dfrac{1}{2}\ln\dfrac{1-\cos x}{1+\cos x} = -\dfrac{1}{2}\ln\dfrac{1+\cos x}{1-\cos x} = -\dfrac{1}{2}\ln\dfrac{(1+\cos x)^2}{\sin^2 x}$

$$= -\dfrac{1}{2}\ln(\csc x + \cot x)^2 = -\ln|\csc x + \cot x|$$

29. Let $u = \tanh(x/2)$ then $\cosh(x/2) = 1/\operatorname{sech}(x/2) = 1/\sqrt{1 - \tanh^2(x/2)} = 1/\sqrt{1 - u^2}$,

$\sinh(x/2) = \tanh(x/2)\cosh(x/2) = u/\sqrt{1 - u^2}$

so $\sinh x = 2\sinh(x/2)\cosh(x/2) = 2u/(1 - u^2)$,

$\cosh x = \cosh^2(x/2) + \sinh^2(x/2) = (1 + u^2)/(1 - u^2)$, $x = 2\tanh^{-1} u$, $dx = [1/(1 - u^2)]du$

$$\int \dfrac{dx}{2\cosh x + \sinh x} = \int \dfrac{1}{u^2 + u + 1}\,du$$

$$= \dfrac{2}{\sqrt{3}}\tan^{-1}\dfrac{2u + 1}{\sqrt{3}} + C = \dfrac{2}{\sqrt{3}}\tan^{-1}\dfrac{2\tanh(x/2) + 1}{\sqrt{3}} + C$$

30. $dx = -(1/u^2)du$, $-\displaystyle\int u\sqrt{4u^2 - 1}\,du = -\dfrac{1}{12}(4u^2 - 1)^{3/2} + C = -\dfrac{(4 - x^2)^{3/2}}{12x^3} + C$

31. $dx = -(1/u^2)du$, $-\displaystyle\int \dfrac{u}{\sqrt{3u^2 - 1}}\,du = -\dfrac{1}{3}\sqrt{3u^2 - 1} + C = -\dfrac{\sqrt{3 - x^2}}{3x} + C$

32. $dx = -(1/u^2)du$, $-\displaystyle\int \dfrac{u}{\sqrt{1 + u^2}}\,du = -\sqrt{1 + u^2} + C = -\dfrac{\sqrt{x^2 + 1}}{x} + C$

33. $dx = -(1/u^2)du$, $-\displaystyle\int u\sqrt{1 - 5u^2}\,du = \dfrac{1}{15}(1 - 5u^2)^{3/2} + C = \dfrac{(x^2 - 5)^{3/2}}{15x^3} + C$

EXERCISE SET 9.8

1. exact value $= 14/3 \approx 4.666666667$
    (a) 4.667600663, $|E_M| \approx 0.000933996$ (b) 4.664795679, $|E_T| \approx 0.001870988$
    (c) 4.666651630, $|E_S| \approx 0.000015037$

2. exact value $= 2$
    (a) 1.998377048, $|E_M| \approx 0.001622952$ (b) 2.003260982, $|E_T| \approx 0.003260982$
    (c) 2.000072698, $|E_S| \approx 0.000072698$

3. exact value $= 2$

    (a) 2.008248408, $|E_M| \approx 0.008248408$ **(b)** 1.983523538, $|E_T| \approx 0.016476462$

    (c) 2.000109517, $|E_S| \approx 0.000109517$

4. exact value $= \sin(1) \approx 0.841470985$

    (a) 0.841821700, $|E_M| \approx 0.000350715$ **(b)** 0.840769642, $|E_T| \approx 0.000701343$

    (c) 0.841471453, $|E_S| \approx 0.000000468$

5. exact value $= e^{-1} - e^{-3} \approx 0.318092373$

    (a) 0.317562837, $|E_M| \approx 0.000529536$ **(b)** 0.319151975, $|E_T| \approx 0.001059602$

    (c) 0.318095187, $|E_S| \approx 0.000002814$

6. exact value $= \dfrac{1}{2} \ln 5 \approx 0.804718956$

    (a) 0.801605339, $|E_M| \approx 0.003113617$ **(b)** 0.811019505, $|E_T| \approx 0.006300549$

    (c) 0.805041497, $|E_S| \approx 0.000322541$

7. $f(x) = \sqrt{x+1}$, $f''(x) = -\dfrac{1}{4}(x+1)^{-3/2}$, $f^{(4)}(x) = -\dfrac{15}{16}(x+1)^{-7/2}$; $K_2 = 1/4$, $K_4 = 15/16$

    (a) $|E_M| \le \dfrac{27}{2400}(1/4) \approx 0.002812500$ **(b)** $|E_T| \le \dfrac{27}{1200}(1/4) \approx 0.005625000$

    (c) $|E_S| \le \dfrac{243}{180 \times 10^4}(15/16) \approx 0.000126563$

8. $f(x) = 1/\sqrt{x}$, $f''(x) = \dfrac{3}{4}x^{-5/2}$, $f^{(4)}(x) = \dfrac{105}{16}x^{-9/2}$; $K_2 = 3/4$, $K_4 = 105/16$

    (a) $|E_M| \le \dfrac{27}{2400}(3/4) \approx 0.008437500$ **(b)** $|E_T| \le \dfrac{27}{1200}(3/4) \approx 0.016875000$

    (c) $|E_S| \le \dfrac{243}{180 \times 10^4}(105/16) \approx 0.000885938$

9. $f(x) = \sin x$, $f''(x) = -\sin x$, $f^{(4)}(x) = \sin x$; $K_2 = K_4 = 1$

    (a) $|E_M| \le \dfrac{\pi^3}{2400}(1) \approx 0.012919282$ **(b)** $|E_T| \le \dfrac{\pi^3}{1200}(1) \approx 0.025838564$

    (c) $|E_S| \le \dfrac{\pi^5}{180 \times 10^4}(1) \approx 0.000170011$

10. $f(x) = \cos x,\ f''(x) = -\cos x,\ f^{(4)}(x) = \cos x;\ K_2 = K_4 = 1$

(a) $|E_M| \le \dfrac{1}{2400}(1) \approx 0.000416667$

(b) $|E_T| \le \dfrac{1}{1200}(1) \approx 0.000833333$

(c) $|E_S| \le \dfrac{1}{180 \times 10^4}(1) \approx 0.000000555$

11. $f(x) = e^{-x},\ f''(x) = f^{(4)}(x) = e^{-x};\ K_2 = K_4 = e^{-1}$

(a) $|E_M| \le \dfrac{8}{2400}(e^{-1}) \approx 0.001226265$

(b) $|E_T| \le \dfrac{8}{1200}(e^{-1}) \approx 0.002452530$

(c) $|E_S| \le \dfrac{32}{180 \times 10^4}(e^{-1}) \approx 0.000006540$

12. $f(x) = 1/(2x+3),\ f''(x) = 8(2x+3)^{-3},\ f^{(4)}(x) = 384(2x+3)^{-5};\ K_2 = 8,\ K_4 = 384$

(a) $|E_M| \le \dfrac{8}{2400}(8) \approx 0.026666667$

(b) $|E_T| \le \dfrac{8}{1200}(8) \approx 0.053333333$

(c) $|E_S| \le \dfrac{32}{180 \times 10^4}(384) \approx 0.006826667$

13. (a) $n > \left[\dfrac{(27)(1/4)}{(24)(5 \times 10^{-4})}\right]^{1/2} \approx 23.7;\ n = 24$

(b) $n > \left[\dfrac{(27)(1/4)}{(12)(5 \times 10^{-4})}\right]^{1/2} \approx 33.5;\ n = 34$

(c) $n > \left[\dfrac{(243)(15/16)}{(180)(5 \times 10^{-4})}\right]^{1/4} \approx 7.1;\ n = 8$

14. (a) $n > \left[\dfrac{(27)(3/4)}{(24)(5 \times 10^{-4})}\right]^{1/2} \approx 41.1;\ n = 42$

(b) $n > \left[\dfrac{(27)(3/4)}{(12)(5 \times 10^{-4})}\right]^{1/2} \approx 58.1;\ n = 59$

(c) $n > \left[\dfrac{(243)(105/16)}{(180)(5 \times 10^{-4})}\right]^{1/4} \approx 11.5;\ n = 12$

15. (a) $n > \left[\dfrac{(\pi^3)(1)}{(24)(10^{-3})}\right]^{1/2} \approx 35.9;\ n = 36$

(b) $n > \left[\dfrac{(\pi^3)(1)}{(12)(10^{-3})}\right]^{1/2} \approx 50.8;\ n = 51$

(c) $n > \left[\dfrac{(\pi^5)(1)}{(180)(10^{-3})}\right]^{1/4} \approx 6.4;\ n = 8$

16. **(a)** $n > \left[\dfrac{(1)(1)}{(24)(10^{-3})}\right]^{1/2} \approx 6.5;\ n = 7$ **(b)** $n > \left[\dfrac{(1)(1)}{(12)(10^{-3})}\right]^{1/2} \approx 9.1;\ n = 10$

(c) $n > \left[\dfrac{(1)(1)}{(180)(10^{-3})}\right]^{1/4} \approx 1.5;\ n = 2$

17. **(a)** $n > \left[\dfrac{(8)(e^{-1})}{(24)(10^{-6})}\right]^{1/2} \approx 350.2;\ n = 351$ **(b)** $n > \left[\dfrac{(8)(e^{-1})}{(12)(10^{-6})}\right]^{1/2} \approx 495.2;\ n = 496$

(c) $n > \left[\dfrac{(32)(e^{-1})}{(180)(10^{-6})}\right]^{1/4} \approx 15.99;\ n = 16$

18. **(a)** $n > \left[\dfrac{(8)(8)}{(24)(10^{-6})}\right]^{1/2} \approx 1632.99;\ n = 1633$ **(b)** $n > \left[\dfrac{(8)(8)}{(12)(10^{-6})}\right]^{1/2} \approx 2309.4;$

$n = 2310$

(c) $n > \left[\dfrac{(32)(384)}{(180)(10^{-6})}\right]^{1/4} \approx 90.9;\ n = 92$

19. **(a)** 0.747130878   **(b)** 0.746210796   **(c)** 0.746824948

20. **(a)** 1.139482279   **(b)** 1.133926122   **(c)** 1.137631378

21. **(a)** 2.129469966   **(b)** 2.130644002   **(c)** 2.129861595

22. **(a)** 2.420452262   **(b)** 2.414290301   **(c)** 2.418388347

23. **(a)** 0.809253858   **(b)** 0.795924733   **(c)** 0.805376152

24. **(a)** 1.549399137   **(b)** 1.526348529   **(c)** 1.536963087

25. **(a)** 3.142425985, $|E_M| \approx 0.000833331$ **(b)** 3.139925989, $|E_T| \approx 0.001666665$
(c) 3.141592614, $|E_S| \approx 0.000000040$

26. **(a)** 3.152411433, $|E_M| \approx 0.010818779$ **(b)** 3.104518326, $|E_T| \approx 0.037074328$
(c) 3.127008159, $|E_S| \approx 0.014584495$

27. $S_{14} = 0.693147984$, $|E_S| \approx 0.000000803 = 8.03 \times 10^{-7}$; the method used in Example 5 results in a value of n which ensures that the magnitude of the error will be less than 10^{-6}, this is not necessarily the *smallest* value of n.

28. **(a)** greater, because the graph of e^{-x^2} is concave up on the interval $(1, 2)$.

   (b) less, because the graph of e^{-x^2} is concave down on the interval $(0, 0.5)$.

29. $f(x) = x \sin x$, $f''(x) = 2 \cos x - x \sin x$, $|f''(x)| \leq 2|\cos x| + |x||\sin x| \leq 2 + 2 = 4$ so $K_2 \leq 4$,

$$n > \left[\frac{(8)(4)}{(24)(10^{-4})} \right]^{1/2} \approx 115.5, \, n = 116.$$

30. $f(x) = e^{\cos x}$, $f''(x) = (\sin^2 x)e^{\cos x} - (\cos x)e^{\cos x}$, $|f''(x)| \leq e^{\cos x}(\sin^2 x + |\cos x|) \leq 2e$ so

$$K_2 \leq 2e, \, n > \left[\frac{(1)(2e)}{(24)(10^{-4})} \right]^{1/2} \approx 47.6, \, n = 48.$$

31. $f(x) = \sqrt{x}$, $f''(x) = -\dfrac{1}{4x^{3/2}}$, $\lim\limits_{x \to 0^+} |f''(x)| = +\infty$

32. $f(x) = \sin \sqrt{x}$, $f''(x) = -\dfrac{\sqrt{x} \sin \sqrt{x} + \cos \sqrt{x}}{4x^{3/2}}$, $\lim\limits_{x \to 0^+} |f''(x)| = +\infty$

33. $L = \displaystyle\int_0^\pi \sqrt{1 + \cos^2 x} \, dx \approx 3.820$ **34.** $L = \displaystyle\int_1^3 \sqrt{1 + 1/x^4} \, dx \approx 2.147$

35.

t(sec)	0	0	10	15	20
v (mi/hr)	0	40	60	73	84
v (ft/sec)	0	58.67	88	107.07	123.2

$$\int_0^{20} v \, dt \approx \frac{20}{(3)(4)}[0 + 4(58.67) + 2(88) + 4(107.07) + 123.2] \approx 1604 \text{ ft}$$

36.

t	0	1	2	3	4	5	6	7	8
a	0	0.01	0.05	0.2	0.4	0.6	0.7	0.6	0

$$\int_0^8 a \, dt \approx \frac{8}{(3)(8)}[0 + 4(0.01) + 2(0.05) + 4(0.2) + 2(0.4) + 4(0.6) + 2(0.7) + 4(0.6) + 0]$$
$$\approx 2.6 \text{ cm/sec}$$

37. $\displaystyle\int_0^{180} v \, dt \approx \frac{180}{(3)(6)}[0.00 + 4(0.03) + 2(0.08) + 4(0.16) + 2(0.27) + 4(0.42) + 0.65] = 37.9 \text{ mi}$

38. $\displaystyle\int_0^{1800} (1/v) dx \approx \frac{1800}{(3)(6)} \left[\frac{1}{3100} + \frac{4}{2908} + \frac{2}{2725} + \frac{4}{2549} + \frac{2}{2379} + \frac{4}{2216} + \frac{1}{2059} \right] \approx 0.71 \text{ sec}$

39. $V = \int_0^{16} \pi r^2 dy = \pi \int_0^{16} r^2 dy \approx \pi \dfrac{16}{(3)(4)}[(8.5)^2 + 4(11.5)^2 + 2(13.8)^2 + 4(15.4)^2 + (16.8)^2]$

$$\approx 9270 \text{ cm}^3 \approx 9.3 \text{ L}$$

40. $A = \int_0^{600} h \, dx \approx \dfrac{600}{(3)(6)}[0 + 4(7) + 2(16) + 4(24) + 2(25) + 4(16) + 0] = 9000 \text{ ft}^2,$

$V = 75A \approx 75(9000) = 675,000 \text{ ft}^3$

SUPPLEMENTARY EXERCISES CHAPTER 9

1. $u = x, \ dv = \cos 2x \, dx, \ du = dx, \ v = \dfrac{1}{2}\sin 2x; \ \int x \cos 2x \, dx = \dfrac{1}{2}x \sin 2x + \dfrac{1}{4}\cos 2x + C$

2. $\dfrac{1}{2}\sin(x^2) + C$

3. $\int (\sec^2 x - 1)\sec x \tan x \, dx = \dfrac{1}{3}\sec^3 x - \sec x + C$

4. $\int (1 - \cos^2 x)\cos^2 x \sin x \, dx = -\dfrac{1}{3}\cos^3 x + \dfrac{1}{5}\cos^5 x + C$

5. $u = \tan 3t, \ \dfrac{1}{3}\int u^2 du = \dfrac{1}{9}\tan^3 3t + C$ 　　 **6.** $\int \csc^2 2x(\csc 2x \cot 2x)dx = -\dfrac{1}{6}\csc^3 2x + C$

7. $\int \dfrac{1 - \cos^2 x}{1 + \cos x} dx = \int (1 - \cos x)dx = x - \sin x + C$

8. $\int \dfrac{2\sin x \cos x}{\cos x(1 + \cos x)} dx = \int \dfrac{2\sin x}{1 + \cos x} dx = -2\ln(1 + \cos x) + C$

9. $\int x^2 \cos^2 x \, dx = \dfrac{1}{2}\int x^2(1 + \cos 2x)dx = \dfrac{1}{2}\int x^2 dx + \dfrac{1}{2}\int x^2 \cos 2x \, dx,$

use integration by parts twice to get

$$\int x^2 \cos 2x \, dx = \dfrac{1}{2}x^2 \sin 2x + \dfrac{1}{2}x \cos 2x - \dfrac{1}{4}\sin 2x + C_1$$

so $\int x^2 \cos^2 x \, dx = \dfrac{1}{6}x^3 + \dfrac{1}{4}(x^2 - 1/2)\sin 2x + \dfrac{1}{4}x \cos 2x + C$

10. $\displaystyle\int \sin^2 2x \cos^2 2x \, dx = \frac{1}{4} \int (2 \sin 2x \cos 2x)^2 dx = \frac{1}{4} \int \sin^2 4x \, dx$

$$= \frac{1}{8} \int (1 - \cos 8x) dx = \frac{1}{8} x - \frac{1}{64} \sin 8x + C$$

11. $\displaystyle\int \cos^{-5} x \sin x \, dx = \frac{1}{4} \cos^{-4} x + C = \frac{1}{4} \sec^4 x + C$

12. Let $u = 2x$, $\displaystyle\frac{1}{2} \int \tan^5 u \, du = \frac{1}{8} \tan^4 2x - \frac{1}{4} \tan^2 2x - \frac{1}{2} \ln|\cos 2x| + C$

13. $\displaystyle\frac{1}{8} \int (1 - \cos 2x)^2 (1 + \cos 2x) dx = \frac{1}{8} \int (1 - \cos 2x) \sin^2 2x \, dx$

$$= \frac{1}{8} \int \sin^2 2x \, dx - \frac{1}{8} \int \sin^2 2x \cos 2x \, dx$$

$$= \frac{1}{16} \int (1 - \cos 4x) dx - \frac{1}{48} \sin^3 2x = \frac{1}{16} x - \frac{1}{64} \sin 4x - \frac{1}{48} \sin^3 2x + C$$

14. $\displaystyle\int \cos^4 x \, dx = \frac{3}{8} x + \frac{1}{4} \sin 2x + \frac{1}{32} \sin 4x + C$ using (5) of 9.3.

15. $\displaystyle\int_0^{\pi/4} \sin 5x \sin 3x \, dx = \frac{1}{2} \int_0^{\pi/4} (\cos 2x - \cos 8x) dx = \frac{1}{4} \sin 2x - \frac{1}{16} \sin 8x \Big]_0^{\pi/4} = 1/4$

16. $\displaystyle\int_{-\pi/10}^0 \sin 2x \cos 3x \, dx = \frac{1}{2} \int_{-\pi/10}^0 (\sin 5x - \sin x) dx$

$$= -\frac{1}{10} \cos 5x + \frac{1}{2} \cos x \Big]_{-\pi/10}^0 = \frac{2}{5} - \frac{1}{2} \cos(\pi/10)$$

17. $\displaystyle\frac{1}{2} \int_0^1 (1 - \cos 2\pi x) dx = \frac{1}{2} x - \frac{1}{4\pi} \sin 2\pi x \Big]_0^1 = 1/2$

18. $\displaystyle\int_0^{\pi/3} (1 - \cos^2 3x) \sin 3x \, dx = -\frac{1}{3} \cos 3x + \frac{1}{9} \cos^3 3x \Big]_0^{\pi/3} = 4/9$

19. $\displaystyle\frac{1}{2} \tan(x^2) \Big]_0^{\sqrt{\pi}/2} = 1/2$

20. $u = 1 + 3 \tan x$, $\displaystyle\frac{1}{3} \int_1^4 u^{-1/2} du = \frac{2}{3} u^{1/2} \Big]_1^4 = 2/3$

21. $u = \cot^{-1} x$, $-\int \sin u\, du = \cos(\cot^{-1} x) + C = x/\sqrt{1+x^2} + C$

22. $\int e^{\tan 3x} \sec^2 3x\, dx = \dfrac{1}{3} e^{\tan 3x} + C$ **23.** $\ln|\sec(e^x) + \tan(e^x)| + C$

24. $u = x$, $dv = \sec^2 3x\, dx$, $du = dx$, $v = \dfrac{1}{3}\tan 3x$, $\int x \sec^2 3x\, dx = \dfrac{1}{3} x \tan 3x + \dfrac{1}{9}\ln|\cos 3x| + C$

25. $u = e^{2x} + 1$, $\dfrac{1}{2}\int u^{-1/2}\, du = \sqrt{e^{2x}+1} + C$

26. $u = e^{2x} + 1$, $\dfrac{1}{2}\int \dfrac{1}{u}\, du = \dfrac{1}{2}\ln(e^{2x}+1) + C$

27. Use integration by parts with $u = e^{3x}$, $dv = \sin 2x\, dx$ to get

$\displaystyle\int e^{3x} \sin 2x\, dx = -\frac{1}{2} e^{3x} \cos 2x + \frac{3}{2}\int e^{3x} \cos 2x\, dx$ and again with

$u = e^{3x}$, $dv = \cos 2x\, dx$ to get $\displaystyle\int e^{3x} \cos 2x\, dx = \frac{1}{2} e^{3x} \sin 2x - \frac{3}{2}\int e^{3x} \sin 2x\, dx$ so, with

$I = \displaystyle\int e^{3x} \sin 2x\, dx$, $I = -\frac{1}{2} e^{3x} \cos 2x + \frac{3}{4} e^{3x} \sin 2x - \frac{9}{4} I$, $I = \frac{1}{13} e^{3x}(3 \sin 2x - 2 \cos 2x) + C$

28. $u = \ln(a^2 + x^2)$, $dv = dx$, $du = \dfrac{2x}{a^2 + x^2}\, dx$, $v = x$

$\displaystyle\int \ln(a^2 + x^2)\, dx = x \ln(a^2 + x^2) - 2\int \frac{x^2}{a^2 + x^2}\, dx$

but $\displaystyle\int \frac{x^2}{a^2 + x^2}\, dx = \int \left(1 - \frac{a^2}{a^2 + x^2}\right) dx = x - a\tan^{-1}(x/a) + C_1$

so $\displaystyle\int \ln(a^2 + x^2)\, dx = x \ln(a^2 + x^2) - 2x + 2a\tan^{-1}(x/a) + C$

29. $u = \sin^{-1}(x/2)$, $dv = dx$, $du = 1/\sqrt{4 - x^2}\, dx$, $v = x$

$\displaystyle\int_1^2 \sin^{-1}(x/2)\, dx = x \sin^{-1}(x/2)\Big]_1^2 - \int_1^2 x(4 - x^2)^{-1/2}\, dx$

$\qquad\qquad = (2)(\pi/2) - (1)(\pi/6) + (4 - x^2)^{1/2}\Big]_1^2 = 5\pi/6 - \sqrt{3}$

30. Rewrite as $\displaystyle\int e^{-2\pi x} \cos 2\pi x\, dx$ then $u = e^{-2\pi x}$, $dv = \cos 2\pi x\, dx$,

$du = -2\pi e^{-2\pi x}\, dx$, $v = \dfrac{1}{2\pi}\sin 2\pi x$

$$\int e^{-2\pi x} \cos 2\pi x \, dx = \frac{1}{2\pi} e^{-2\pi x} \sin 2\pi x + \int e^{-2\pi x} \sin 2\pi x \, dx.$$

For $\int e^{-2\pi x} \sin 2\pi x \, dx$ use $u = e^{-2\pi x}$, $dv = \sin 2\pi x \, dx$ to get

$$\int e^{-2\pi x} \sin 2\pi x \, dx = -\frac{1}{2\pi} e^{-2\pi x} \cos 2\pi x - \int e^{-2\pi x} \cos 2\pi x \, dx \text{ so}$$

$$\int e^{-2\pi x} \cos 2\pi x \, dx = \frac{1}{2\pi} e^{-2\pi x} \sin 2\pi x - \frac{1}{2\pi} e^{-2\pi x} \cos 2\pi x - \int e^{-2\pi x} \cos 2\pi x \, dx,$$

$$\int e^{-2\pi x} \cos 2\pi x \, dx = \frac{1}{4\pi} e^{-2\pi x} (\sin 2\pi x - \cos 2\pi x) + C$$

31. $u = \sin(3 \ln x)$, $dv = dx$, $du = \dfrac{3}{x} \cos(3 \ln x) dx$, $v = x$

$$\int \sin(3 \ln x) dx = x \sin(3 \ln x) - 3 \int \cos(3 \ln x) dx. \text{ Use } u = \cos(3 \ln x), \ dv = dx \text{ to get}$$

$$\int \cos(3 \ln x) dx = x \cos(3 \ln x) + 3 \int \sin(3 \ln x) dx \text{ so}$$

$$\int \sin(3 \ln x) dx = x \sin(3 \ln x) - 3x \cos(3 \ln x) - 9 \int \sin(3 \ln x) dx,$$

$$\int \sin(3 \ln x) dx = \frac{1}{10} x[\sin(3 \ln x) - 3 \cos(3 \ln x)] + C$$

32. $u = x^2$, $dv = xe^{-x^2} dx$, $du = 2x \, dx$, $v = -\dfrac{1}{2} e^{-x^2}$

$$\int x^3 e^{-x^2} dx = -\frac{1}{2} x^2 e^{-x^2} + \int x e^{-x^2} dx = -\frac{1}{2} x^2 e^{-x^2} - \frac{1}{2} e^{-x^2} + C$$

33. $\displaystyle\int x(x^2 - 9)^{-1/2} dx = \sqrt{x^2 - 9} + C$

34. $x = \dfrac{1}{2} \sec \theta$, $dx = \dfrac{1}{2} \sec \theta \tan \theta \, d\theta$

$$\int_{\pi/3}^{\sec^{-1} 4} \tan^2 \theta \, d\theta = \left. \tan \theta - \theta \right]_{\pi/3}^{\sec^{-1} 4} = \tan(\sec^{-1} 4) - \sec^{-1} 4 - \sqrt{3} + \pi/3$$

$$= \sqrt{15} - \sec^{-1} 4 - \sqrt{3} + \pi/3$$

35. $x = 3\sin\theta,\; dx = 3\cos\theta\, d\theta$

$$3\int_{\sin^{-1}(1/3)}^{\pi/2} \frac{\cos^2\theta}{\sin\theta}\, d\theta = 3\int_{\sin^{-1}(1/3)}^{\pi/2} \frac{1 - \sin^2\theta}{\sin\theta}\, d\theta - 3\int_{\sin^{-1}(1/3)}^{\pi/2}(\csc\theta - \sin\theta)d\theta$$

$$= -3\ln|\csc\theta + \cot\theta| + 3\cos\theta\Big]_{\sin^{-1}(1/3)}^{\pi/2}$$

$$= -3\ln(1) + 3\ln|3 + \sqrt{8}| - 3(\sqrt{8}/3) = 3\ln(3 + \sqrt{8}) - \sqrt{8}$$

36. $u = \sin 3x,\; du = 3\cos 3x\, dx$

$$\frac{1}{3}\int_0^1 \frac{1}{\sqrt{4 - u^2}}\, du = \frac{1}{3}\sin^{-1}\frac{u}{2}\Big]_0^1 = \frac{1}{3}(\pi/6) = \pi/18$$

37. $u = \sqrt{2x + 3},\; x = (u^2 - 3)/2,\; dx = u\, du$

$$\frac{1}{4}\int(u^2 - 3)^2 du = \frac{1}{4}\int(u^4 - 6u^2 + 9)du$$

$$= \frac{1}{4}\left(\frac{1}{5}u^5 - 2u^3 + 9u\right) + C = \frac{1}{20}u(u^4 - 10u^2 + 45) + C$$

$$= \frac{1}{20}\sqrt{2x + 3}(4x^2 + 12x + 9 - 20x - 30 + 45) + C$$

$$= \frac{1}{5}(x^2 - 2x + 6)\sqrt{2x + 3} + C$$

38. $u = \sqrt{x},\; du = \dfrac{1}{2\sqrt{x}}dx;\; 2\displaystyle\int \frac{1}{u^2 + 9}\, du = \frac{2}{3}\tan^{-1}\frac{\sqrt{x}}{3} + C$

39. $\dfrac{1}{2}\displaystyle\int \frac{1}{\sqrt{1 - (t + 1/2)^2}}\, dt = \frac{1}{2}\sin^{-1}(t + 1/2) + C$

40. $\displaystyle\int \frac{1}{\sqrt{9 - (x - 3)^2}}\, dx = \sin^{-1}\frac{x - 3}{3} + C$

41. $x = a\sin\theta,\; dx = a\cos\theta\, d\theta;\; \dfrac{1}{a^2}\displaystyle\int \csc^2\theta\, d\theta = -\frac{1}{a^2}\cot\theta + C = -\frac{\sqrt{a^2 - x^2}}{a^2 x} + C$

42. $u = (x^2 + 4)^{1/3},\; x^2 = u^3 - 4,\; 2x\, dx = 3u^2\, du,\; x\, dx = \dfrac{3}{2}u^2\, du$

$$\frac{3}{2}\int(u^3 - 4)u\, du = \frac{3}{2}\int(u^4 - 4u)du = \frac{3}{2}\left(\frac{1}{5}u^5 - 2u^2\right) + C$$

$$= \frac{3}{10}u^2(u^3 - 10) + C = \frac{3}{10}(x^2 + 4)^{2/3}(x^2 - 6) + C$$

43. $x = a\sin\theta,\ dx = a\cos\theta\ d\theta$

$$a^2 \int \cos^2\theta\ d\theta = \frac{1}{2}a^2\theta + \frac{1}{4}a^2\sin 2\theta + C = \frac{1}{2}a^2\sin^{-1}(x/a) + \frac{1}{2}x\sqrt{a^2 - x^2} + C$$

44. $-\frac{1}{3}(a^2 - x^2)^{3/2} + C$

45. $\displaystyle\int \frac{x-2}{\sqrt{4-(x-2)^2}}dx = \int \frac{u}{\sqrt{4-u^2}}du \quad (u = x-2) = -\sqrt{4-u^2} + C = -\sqrt{4x - x^2} + C$

46. $\displaystyle\int_1^3 \frac{1}{(x-1)^2 + 4}dx = \frac{1}{2}\tan^{-1}\frac{x-1}{2}\bigg]_1^3 = \pi/8$

47. $2x^2 + 3x + 1 = (2x+1)(x+1),\ \dfrac{1}{(2x+1)(x+1)} = \dfrac{2}{2x+1} - \dfrac{1}{x+1}$

$$\int \frac{dx}{(2x+1)(x+1)} = \ln\left|\frac{2x+1}{x+1}\right| + C$$

48. $x = 2\tan\theta,\ dx = 2\sec^2\theta\ d\theta$

$$\frac{1}{8}\int \cos^2\theta\ d\theta = \frac{1}{16}\theta + \frac{1}{32}\sin 2\theta + C = \frac{1}{16}\tan^{-1}(x/2) + \frac{x}{8(x^2+4)} + C$$

49. $\dfrac{x+1}{x(x+3)(x-2)} = \dfrac{-1/6}{x} + \dfrac{-2/15}{x+3} + \dfrac{3/10}{x-2}$

$$\int \frac{x+1}{x^3 + x^2 - 6x}dx = -\frac{1}{6}\ln|x| - \frac{2}{15}\ln|x+3| + \frac{3}{10}\ln|x-2| + C$$

50. $\displaystyle\int \frac{x^3+1}{x-2}dx = \int\left(x^2 + 2x + 4 + \frac{9}{x-2}\right)dx = \frac{1}{3}x^3 + x^2 + 4x + 9\ln|x-2| + C$

51. $u = x^3 - 3x,\ \dfrac{1}{3}\displaystyle\int \frac{1}{u}du = \frac{1}{3}\ln|x^3 - 3x| + C$

52. $x^3 - 1 = (x-1)(x^2 + x + 1),$

$$\frac{x-3}{(x-1)(x^2+x+1)} = \frac{-2/3}{x-1} + \frac{(2/3)x + (7/3)}{x^2+x+1}$$

$$\frac{1}{3}\int \frac{2x+7}{x^2+x+1}dx = \frac{1}{3}\int \frac{2x+7}{(x+1/2)^2 + 3/4}dx = \frac{1}{3}\int \frac{2u+6}{u^2+3/4}du \quad (u = x + 1/2)$$

$$= \frac{1}{3}\ln(u^2 + 3/4) + \frac{4}{\sqrt{3}}\tan^{-1}(2u/\sqrt{3}) + C_1$$

so $\displaystyle\int \frac{x-3}{x^3-1}dx = -\frac{2}{3}\ln|x-1| + \frac{1}{3}\ln(x^2 + x + 1) + \frac{4}{\sqrt{3}}\tan^{-1}\frac{2x+1}{\sqrt{3}} + C$

53. $x^4 - 1 = (x+1)(x-1)(x^2+1)$

$$\int \frac{2x^2+5}{x^4-1}dx = \int \left[\frac{-7/4}{x+1} + \frac{7/4}{x-1} + \frac{-3/2}{x^2+1}\right]dx = \frac{7}{4}\ln\left|\frac{x-1}{x\mid 1}\right| - \frac{3}{2}\tan^{-1}x + C$$

54. $\int \frac{x^4 - x^3 - x - 1}{x^3 - x^2}dx = \int \left[x - \frac{x+1}{x^2(x-1)}\right]dx = \int \left[x - \left(\frac{-2}{x} + \frac{-1}{x^2} + \frac{2}{x-1}\right)\right]dx$

$$= \frac{1}{2}x^2 + 2\ln\left|\frac{x}{x-1}\right| - \frac{1}{x} + C$$

55. $\int \frac{dx}{(x^2+4)(x-3)} = \int \left[\frac{(-1/13)x - (3/13)}{x^2+4} + \frac{1/13}{x-3}\right]dx$

$$= -\frac{1}{26}\ln(x^2+4) - \frac{3}{26}\tan^{-1}\frac{x}{2} + \frac{1}{13}\ln|x-3| + C$$

56. $u = x+1,\ \int \frac{u-1}{u^3}du = \int (u^{-2} - u^{-3})du = -u^{-1} + \frac{1}{2}u^{-2} + C = -\frac{1}{x+1} + \frac{1}{2(x+1)^2} + C$

57. $\dfrac{3x^2 + 12x + 2}{(x^2+4)^2} = \dfrac{3}{x^2+4} + \dfrac{12x-10}{(x^2+4)^2} = \dfrac{3}{x^2+4} + \dfrac{12x}{(x^2+4)^2} - \dfrac{10}{(x^2+4)^2}$

$$\int \frac{1}{(x^2+4)^2} = \frac{1}{8}\int \cos^2\theta\,d\theta \quad (x = 2\tan\theta)$$

$$= \frac{1}{16}\theta + \frac{1}{32}\sin 2\theta + C_1 = \frac{1}{16}\tan^{-1}(x/2) + \frac{x}{8(x^2+4)} + C_1$$

so $\displaystyle\int \frac{3x^2 + 12x + 2}{(x^2+4)^2}dx = \frac{3}{2}\tan^{-1}\frac{x}{2} - \frac{6}{x^2+4} - \frac{5}{8}\tan^{-1}\frac{x}{2} - \frac{5x}{4(x^2+4)} + C$

$$= \frac{7}{8}\tan^{-1}\frac{x}{2} - \frac{5x+24}{4(x^2+4)} + C$$

58. $x^4 + 2x^3 + x^2 = x^2(x+1)^2,$

$$\frac{4x+2}{x^2(x+1)^2} = \frac{0}{x} + \frac{2}{x^2} + \frac{0}{x+1} + \frac{-2}{(x+1)^2} = 2/x^2 - 2/(x+1)^2$$

$$\int \frac{4x+2}{x^4 + 2x^3 + x^2}dx = -\frac{2}{x} + \frac{2}{x+1} + C = -\frac{2}{x(x+1)} + C$$

59. $\int \frac{x}{(x+1)^2+4}dx = \int \frac{u-1}{u^2+4}du \quad (u = x+1)$

$$= \frac{1}{2}\ln(u^2+4) - \frac{1}{2}\tan^{-1}\frac{u}{2} + C = \frac{1}{2}\ln(x^2 + 2x + 5) - \frac{1}{2}\tan^{-1}\frac{x+1}{2} + C$$

60. $-\dfrac{3}{2(x^2+9)^2} + C$

61. $u = \sqrt{2}x$, $\dfrac{1}{\sqrt{2}} \displaystyle\int \dfrac{1}{\sqrt{3 - u^2}}\,du = \dfrac{1}{\sqrt{2}}\sin^{-1}\sqrt{2/3}\,x + C$

62. $\displaystyle\int (t^{-1/2} + t^{1/2})\,dt = 2t^{1/2} + \dfrac{2}{3}t^{3/2} + C$

63. $u = \sqrt{t}$, $t = u^2$, $dt = 2u\,du$; $\displaystyle\int \dfrac{2u^2}{u^2 + 1}\,du = 2\int \left[1 - \dfrac{1}{u^2 + 1}\right]du = 2\sqrt{t} - 2\tan^{-1}\sqrt{t} + C$

64. $x = \sin\theta$, $dx = \cos\theta\,d\theta$; $\displaystyle\int \cot^2\theta\,d\theta = -\cot\theta - \theta + C = -\sqrt{1 - x^2}/x - \sin^{-1}x + C$

65. $u = 1 + x^{1/3}$, $x = (u - 1)^3$, $dx = 3(u - 1)^2\,du$

$$3\int_1^2 \dfrac{(u - 1)^4}{u}\,du = 3\int_1^2 \left[u^3 - 4u^2 + 6u - 4 + \dfrac{1}{u}\right]du$$

$$= 3\left[\dfrac{1}{4}u^4 - \dfrac{4}{3}u^3 + 3u^2 - 4u + \ln u\right]_1^2 = -7/4 + 3\ln 2$$

66. $u = x^{1/4}$, $x = u^4$, $dx = 4u^3\,du$

$$4\int \dfrac{u^2}{u + 1}\,du = 4\int \left(u - 1 + \dfrac{1}{u + 1}\right)du = 2x^{1/2} - 4x^{1/4} + 4\ln(x^{1/4} + 1) + C$$

67. $u = \tan(x/2)$, $\tan x = \sin x/\cos x = 2u/(1 - u^2)$

$$\int \dfrac{dx}{1 - \tan x} = \int \dfrac{2u^2 - 2}{(u^2 + 1)(u^2 + 2u - 1)}\,du$$

$$\dfrac{2u^2 - 2}{(u^2 + 1)(u^2 + 2u - 1)} = \dfrac{u + 1}{u^2 + 1} + \dfrac{-u - 1}{u^2 + 2u - 1}$$

$$\int \dfrac{dx}{1 - \tan x} = \dfrac{1}{2}\ln(u^2 + 1) + \tan^{-1}u - \dfrac{1}{2}\ln|u^2 + 2u - 1| + C$$

$$= \tan^{-1}u - \dfrac{1}{2}\ln\left|\dfrac{u^2 + 2u - 1}{u^2 + 1}\right| + C = \tan^{-1}u - \dfrac{1}{2}\ln\left|\dfrac{2u}{1 + u^2} - \dfrac{1 - u^2}{1 + u^2}\right| + C$$

$$= \dfrac{x}{2} - \dfrac{1}{2}\ln|\sin x - \cos x| + C$$

68. $u = \tan(x/2)$, $\displaystyle\int \dfrac{dx}{3\cos x + 5} = \int \dfrac{1}{u^2 + 4}\,du = \dfrac{1}{2}\tan^{-1}\left[\dfrac{1}{2}\tan(x/2)\right] + C$

69. $u = \tan(x/2)$, $\tan x = 2u/(1 - u^2)$

$$\int \dfrac{dx}{\sin x - \tan x} = \dfrac{1}{2}\int \dfrac{u^2 - 1}{u^3}\,du = \dfrac{1}{2}\int (1/u - u^{-3})\,du = \dfrac{1}{2}\ln\left|\tan\dfrac{x}{2}\right| + \dfrac{1}{4}\cot^2\dfrac{x}{2} + C$$

70. $u = \tan(x/2)$, $\sec x = 1/\cos x = (1+u^2)/(1-u^2)$

$$\int_0^{\pi/3} \frac{dx}{5\sec x - 3} = \int_0^{1/\sqrt{3}} \frac{1-u^2}{(u^2+1)(4u^2+1)} du = \int_0^{1/\sqrt{3}} \left(\frac{-2/3}{u^2+1} + \frac{5/3}{4u^2+1} \right) du$$

$$= \left. -\frac{2}{3}\tan^{-1} u + \frac{5}{6}\tan^{-1} 2u \right]_0^{1/\sqrt{3}} = -\pi/9 + \frac{5}{6}\tan^{-1}(2/\sqrt{3})$$

71. $\displaystyle\int \frac{dx}{x^2 - a^2} = \int \left[\frac{1/(2a)}{x-a} + \frac{-1/(2a)}{x+a} \right] dx$

$$= \frac{1}{2a}\ln|x-a| - \frac{1}{2a}\ln|x+a| + C = \frac{1}{2a}\ln\left|\frac{x-a}{x+a}\right| + C$$

72.   **(a)** $\displaystyle L = \int_0^2 \sqrt{1+x^2}\,dx = \int_0^{\tan^{-1} 2} \sec^3 \theta\,d\theta, \quad x = \sec\theta$

$$= \left. \frac{1}{2}\sec\theta\tan\theta + \frac{1}{2}\ln|\sec\theta + \tan\theta| \right]_0^{\tan^{-1} 2} = \sqrt{5} + \frac{1}{2}\ln(\sqrt{5}+2)$$

(b) $\displaystyle L = \int_0^{\pi/4} \sqrt{1+\tan^2 x}\,dx = \int_0^{\pi/4} \sec x\,dx = \ln|\sec x + \tan x| \Big]_0^{\pi/4} = \ln(\sqrt{2}+1)$

73.   **(a)** $\displaystyle A = \int_0^2 \frac{1}{4+x^2}dx = \left. \frac{1}{2}\tan^{-1}\frac{x}{2} \right]_0^2 = \pi/8$

(b) $\displaystyle V = \pi \int_0^2 \frac{1}{(4+x^2)^2}dx = \frac{\pi}{8}\int_0^{\pi/4} \cos^2\theta\,d\theta \quad (x = 2\tan\theta)$

$$= \left. \frac{\pi}{16}\left(\theta + \frac{1}{2}\sin 2\theta \right) \right]_0^{\pi/4} = \pi(\pi+2)/64$$

(c) $\displaystyle V = 2\pi \int_0^2 \frac{x}{4+x^2}dx = \pi\ln(4+x^2) \Big]_0^2 = \pi\ln 2$

74.   **(a)** $u = x^n$, $dv = e^{ax}dx$, $du = nx^{n-1}dx$, $v = \dfrac{1}{a}e^{ax}$

$$\int x^n e^{ax}\,dx = \frac{1}{a}x^n e^{ax} - \frac{n}{a}\int x^{n-1} e^{ax}\,dx$$

(b) $u = x^n$, $dv = \sin ax\,dx$, $du = nx^{n-1}dx$, $v = -\dfrac{1}{a}\cos ax$

$$\int x^n \sin ax\,dx = -\frac{1}{a}x^n \cos ax + \frac{n}{a}\int x^{n-1}\cos ax\,dx.$$

The second formula is obtained in a similar way.

(c) $u = \sin^{n-1} ax,\ dv = \sin ax \cos^m ax\ dx$

$$du = a(n-1)\sin^{n-2} ax \cos ax\ dx,\ v = -\frac{\cos^{m+1} ax}{a(m+1)}$$

$$\int \sin^n ax \cos^m ax\ dx = -\frac{\sin^{n-1} ax \cos^{m+1} ax}{a(m+1)} + \frac{n-1}{m+1}\int \sin^{n-2} ax \cos^{m+2} ax\ dx$$

but $\displaystyle\int \sin^{n-2} ax \cos^{m+2} ax\ dx = \int \sin^{n-2} ax(1-\sin^2 ax)\cos^m ax\ dx$

$$= \int \sin^{n-2} ax \cos^m ax\ dx - \int \sin^n ax \cos^m ax\ dx \text{ so}$$

$$\frac{m+n}{m+1}\int \sin^n ax \cos^m ax\ dx = -\frac{\sin^{n-1} ax \cos^{m+1} ax}{a(m+1)} + \frac{n-1}{m+1}\int \sin^{n-2} ax \cos^m ax\ dx$$

and $\displaystyle\int \sin^n ax \cos^m ax\ dx = -\frac{\sin^{n-1} ax \cos^{m+1} ax}{a(m+n)} + \frac{n-1}{m+n}\int \sin^{n-2} ax \cos^m ax\ dx.$

Similarly, take $u = \cos^{m-1} ax,\ dv = \sin^n ax \cos ax\ dx$ to get the second equality.

75. (a) $\displaystyle\int x^3 e^{2x}\ dx = \frac{1}{2}x^3 e^{2x} - \frac{3}{2}\int x^2 e^{2x}\ dx = \frac{1}{2}x^3 e^{2x} - \frac{3}{2}\left[\frac{1}{2}x^2 e^{2x} - \int x e^{2x}\ dx\right]$

$$= \frac{1}{2}x^3 e^{2x} - \frac{3}{4}x^2 e^{2x} + \frac{3}{2}\left[\frac{1}{2}x e^{2x} - \frac{1}{2}\int e^{2x}\ dx\right]$$

$$= \frac{1}{2}x^3 e^{2x} - \frac{3}{4}x^2 e^{2x} + \frac{3}{4}x e^{2x} - \frac{3}{8}e^{2x} + C$$

(b) $\displaystyle\int_0^{\pi/10} x^2 \sin 5x\ dx = -\frac{1}{5}x^2 \cos 5x\Big]_0^{\pi/10} + \frac{2}{5}\int_0^{\pi/10} x \cos 5x\ dx$

$$= 0 + \frac{2}{5}\left[\frac{1}{5}x \sin 5x\right]_0^{\pi/10} - \frac{2}{25}\int_0^{\pi/10} \sin 5x\ dx$$

$$= \frac{2}{25}(\pi/10) + \frac{2}{125}\cos 5x\Big]_0^{\pi/10} = \pi/125 + \frac{2}{125}(0-1) = (\pi-2)/125$$

(c) $\displaystyle\int \sin^2 x \cos^4 x\ dx = \frac{1}{6}\sin^3 x \cos^3 x + \frac{1}{2}\int \sin^2 x \cos^2 x\ dx$

$$= \frac{1}{6}\sin^3 x \cos^3 x + \frac{1}{2}\left[\frac{1}{4}\sin^3 x \cos x + \frac{1}{4}\int \sin^2 x\ dx\right]$$

$$= \frac{1}{6}\sin^3 x \cos^3 x + \frac{1}{8}\sin^3 x \cos x + \frac{1}{8}\left[-\frac{1}{2}\sin x \cos x + \frac{1}{2}\int dx\right]$$

$$= \frac{1}{6}\sin^3 x \cos^3 x + \frac{1}{8}\sin^3 x \cos x - \frac{1}{16}\sin x \cos x + \frac{x}{16} + C$$

76. **(a)** $u = \ln ax$, $dv = x^n dx$, $du = \dfrac{1}{x} dx$, $v = \dfrac{x^{n+1}}{n+1}$

$$\int x^n \ln ax \, dx = \frac{1}{n+1} x^{n+1} \ln ax - \frac{1}{n+1} \int x^n dx$$

$$= \frac{1}{n+1} x^{n+1} \ln ax - \frac{1}{(n+1)^2} x^{n+1} + C$$

(b) $\displaystyle\int \sec^{n-1} ax (\sec ax \tan ax) dx = \frac{1}{an} \sec^n ax + C$

77. **(a)** $\displaystyle\int \frac{1-\cos^2\theta}{\cos^5\theta} \sin\theta \, d\theta = \int (\cos^{-5}\theta - \cos^{-3}\theta)\sin\theta \, d\theta$

$$= \frac{1}{4}\cos^{-4}\theta - \frac{1}{2}\cos^{-2}\theta + C = \frac{1}{4}\sec^4\theta - \frac{1}{2}\sec^2\theta + C$$

(b) $\displaystyle\int \tan^3\theta \sec^2\theta \, d\theta = \frac{1}{4}\tan^4\theta + C$ but $\dfrac{1}{4}\tan^4\theta = \dfrac{1}{4}(\sec^2\theta - 1)^2 = \dfrac{1}{4}(\sec^4\theta - 2\sec^2\theta + 1)$

so the answers to (a) and (b) differ by 1/4.

78. **(a)** 0.6433   **(b)** 0.6565   **79.** **(a)** 58.9275   **(b)** 54.7328

80. **(a)** 28.4649   **(b)** 26.4386   **81.** **(a)** 1.8277   **(b)** 1.8278

82. 0.35593   **83.** 0.36972

84. **(a)** $\displaystyle\int_0^\pi x f(\sin x) dx = -\int_\pi^0 (\pi - u) f(\sin(\pi - u)) du = \int_0^\pi (\pi - u) f(\sin u) du$

$$= \pi \int_0^\pi f(\sin u) du - \int_0^\pi u f(\sin u) du = \pi \int_0^\pi f(\sin x) dx - \int_0^\pi x f(\sin x) dx,$$

$$2\int_0^\pi x f(\sin x) dx = \pi \int_0^\pi f(\sin x) dx, \quad \int_0^\pi x f(\sin x) dx = \frac{\pi}{2}\int_0^\pi f(\sin x) dx.$$

(b) $\displaystyle\int_0^\pi \frac{x \sin x}{2 - \sin^2 x} dx = \frac{\pi}{2}\int_0^\pi \frac{\sin x}{2 - \sin^2 x} dx = \frac{\pi}{2}\int_0^\pi \frac{\sin x}{1 + \cos^2 x} dx$, let $u = \cos x$,

$$= -\frac{\pi}{2}\int_1^{-1} \frac{1}{1 + u^2} du = \frac{\pi}{2}\tan^{-1} u \Big]_{-1}^1 = \frac{1}{4}\pi^2$$

85. $\displaystyle\int \frac{1}{e^{ax} + 1} dx = \int \frac{e^{-ax}}{1 + e^{-ax}} dx = -\frac{1}{a}\ln(1 + e^{-ax}) + C$

86. $\dfrac{(x-2)^3}{\sqrt{4x - x^2}} = \dfrac{(x-2)^3}{\sqrt{4 - (x-2)^2}}$, let $u = x - 2$ to get $\displaystyle\int \frac{u^3}{\sqrt{4 - u^2}} du$; then let $z = \sqrt{4 - u^2}$,

$u^2 = 4 - z^2$, $2u \, du = -2z \, dz$, $u \, du = -z \, dz$, so

$$\int \frac{u^3}{\sqrt{4-u^2}} du = \int (z^2 - 4) dz = \frac{1}{3} z^3 - 4z + C = \frac{1}{3} (4 - u^2)^{3/2} - 4(4 - u^2)^{1/2} + C$$

$$= \frac{1}{3} (4x - x^2)^{3/2} - 4(4x - x^2)^{1/2} + C$$

87. $\dfrac{\sqrt{1+x} + \sqrt{1-x}}{\sqrt{1+x} - \sqrt{1-x}} = \dfrac{(\sqrt{1+x} + \sqrt{1-x})^2}{2x} = \dfrac{1 + \sqrt{1-x^2}}{x}$

$$\int \left[\frac{1}{x} + \frac{\sqrt{1-x^2}}{x} \right] dx = \int \frac{1}{x} dx + \int \frac{\sqrt{1-x^2}}{x} dx = \ln|x| + \int \frac{u^2}{u^2 - 1} du \quad (u = \sqrt{1-x^2})$$

$$= \ln|x| + \int \left[1 + \frac{1}{u^2 - 1} \right] du = \ln|x| + u + \frac{1}{2} \ln \frac{1-u}{1+u} + C$$

$$= \ln|x| + \sqrt{1-x^2} + \frac{1}{2} \ln \frac{1 - \sqrt{1-x^2}}{1 + \sqrt{1-x^2}} + C$$

$$= \sqrt{1-x^2} + \frac{1}{2} \ln(x^2) + \frac{1}{2} \ln \frac{(1 - \sqrt{1-x^2})^2}{x^2} + C$$

$$= \sqrt{1-x^2} + \ln(1 - \sqrt{1-x^2}) + C$$

88. $\displaystyle\int (\cos^{32} x \sin^{30} x - \cos^{30} x \sin^{32} x) dx = \int \cos^{30} x \sin^{30} x (\cos^2 x - \sin^2 x) dx$

$$= \frac{1}{2^{30}} \int \sin^{30} 2x \cos 2x \, dx = \frac{\sin^{31} 2x}{31(2^{31})} + C$$

89. $x - 1 = 1/u, \; x = 1 + 1/u, \; dx = -(1/u^2) du$

$$\int \frac{\sqrt{x+1}}{(x-1)^{5/2}} dx = - \int \sqrt{2u+1} \, du = -\frac{1}{3} (2u+1)^{3/2} + C = -\frac{1}{3} \left[\frac{x+1}{x-1} \right]^{3/2} + C$$

90. $\displaystyle\int \frac{1}{x^{10}(1+x^{-9})} dx = -\frac{1}{9} \int \frac{1}{u} du = -\frac{1}{9} \ln|u| + C = -\frac{1}{9} \ln|1 + x^{-9}| + C$

91. $\displaystyle\int \frac{1}{x^6(3 + 2x^{-5})} dx = -\frac{1}{10} \int \frac{1}{u} du \quad (u = 3 + 2x^{-5}) = -\frac{1}{10} \ln|u| + C = -\frac{1}{10} \ln|3 + 2x^{-5}| + C$

92. $\displaystyle\int \frac{3x^6 - 2}{x(2x^6 + 5)} dx = \int \frac{3x^5}{2x^6 + 5} dx - 2 \int \frac{1}{x^7(2 + 5x^{-6})} dx = \frac{1}{4} \ln(2x^6 + 5) + \frac{1}{15} \ln(2 + 5x^{-6}) + C$

93. $\displaystyle\int \sqrt{x - \sqrt{x^2 - 4}} \, dx = \frac{1}{\sqrt{2}} \int (\sqrt{x+2} - \sqrt{x-2}) dx = \frac{\sqrt{2}}{3} [(x+2)^{3/2} - (x-2)^{3/2}] + C$

94. $\displaystyle\int_0^1 \sqrt{1+\sqrt{1-x^2}}\,dx = \frac{1}{\sqrt{2}}\int_0^1 (\sqrt{1+x}+\sqrt{1-x})\,dx = \frac{1}{\sqrt{2}}\left[\frac{2}{3}(1+x)^{3/2} - \frac{2}{3}(1-x)^{3/2}\right]_0^1 = \frac{4}{3}$

CHAPTER 10
Improper Integrals; L'Hôpital's Rule

EXERCISE SET 10.1

1. $\displaystyle\lim_{\ell\to+\infty}(-e^{-x})\Big]_0^{\ell} = \lim_{\ell\to+\infty}(-e^{-\ell}+1) = 1$

2. $\displaystyle\lim_{\ell\to+\infty}\left(-\frac{1}{2x^2}\right)\Big]_1^{\ell} = \lim_{\ell\to+\infty}\frac{1}{2}\left(-\frac{1}{\ell^2}+1\right) = \frac{1}{2}$

3. $\displaystyle\lim_{\ell\to+\infty}2\sqrt{x}\,\Big]_1^{\ell} = \lim_{\ell\to+\infty}2(\sqrt{\ell}-1) = +\infty$, divergent

4. $\displaystyle\lim_{\ell\to+\infty}\frac{1}{2}\ln(1+x^2)\Big]_{-1}^{\ell} = \lim_{\ell\to+\infty}\frac{1}{2}[\ln(1+\ell^2)-\ln 2] = +\infty$, divergent

5. $\displaystyle\lim_{\ell\to+\infty}\ln\frac{x-1}{x+1}\Big]_4^{\ell} = \lim_{\ell\to+\infty}\left(\ln\frac{\ell-1}{\ell+1}-\ln\frac{3}{5}\right) = -\ln\frac{3}{5} = \ln\frac{5}{3}$

6. $\displaystyle\lim_{\ell\to+\infty}-\frac{1}{2}e^{-x^2}\Big]_0^{\ell} = \lim_{\ell\to+\infty}\frac{1}{2}\left(-e^{-\ell^2}+1\right) = 1/2$

7. $\displaystyle\lim_{\ell\to+\infty}-\frac{1}{2\ln^2 x}\Big]_e^{\ell} = \lim_{\ell\to+\infty}\left[-\frac{1}{2\ln^2\ell}+\frac{1}{2}\right] = \frac{1}{2}$

8. $\displaystyle\lim_{\ell\to+\infty}2\sqrt{\ln x}\,\Big]_2^{\ell} = \lim_{\ell\to+\infty}(2\sqrt{\ln\ell}-2\sqrt{\ln 2}) = +\infty$, divergent

9. $\displaystyle\lim_{\ell\to+\infty}-\frac{1}{2(x^2+1)}\Big]_a^{\ell} = \lim_{\ell\to+\infty}\left[-\frac{1}{2(\ell^2+1)}+\frac{1}{2(a^2+1)}\right] = \frac{1}{2(a^2+1)}$

10. $\displaystyle\lim_{\ell\to+\infty}\frac{1}{ab}\tan^{-1}\frac{bx}{a}\Big]_0^{\ell} = \lim_{\ell\to+\infty}\frac{1}{ab}\tan^{-1}\frac{b\ell}{a} = \frac{\pi}{2ab}$

11. $\displaystyle\lim_{\ell\to-\infty}-\frac{1}{4(2x-1)^2}\Big]_{\ell}^0 = \lim_{\ell\to-\infty}\frac{1}{4}[-1+1/(2\ell-1)^2] = -1/4$

12. $\displaystyle\lim_{\ell\to-\infty}\frac{1}{2}\tan^{-1}\frac{x}{2}\Big]_\ell^2 = \lim_{\ell\to-\infty}\frac{1}{2}\left[\frac{\pi}{4}-\tan^{-1}\frac{\ell}{2}\right] = \frac{1}{2}[\pi/4-(-\pi/2)] = 3\pi/8$

13. $\displaystyle\lim_{\ell\to-\infty}\frac{1}{3}e^{3x}\Big]_\ell^0 = \lim_{\ell\to-\infty}\left[\frac{1}{3}-\frac{1}{3}e^{3\ell}\right] = \frac{1}{3}$

14. $\displaystyle\lim_{\ell\to-\infty}-\frac{1}{2}\ln(3-2e^x)\Big]_\ell^0 = \lim_{\ell\to-\infty}\frac{1}{2}\ln(3-2e^\ell) = \frac{1}{2}\ln 3$

15. $\displaystyle\int_{-\infty}^{+\infty}x^3\,dx$ converges if $\displaystyle\int_{-\infty}^{0}x^3\,dx$ and $\displaystyle\int_{0}^{+\infty}x^3\,dx$ both converge; it diverges if either (or both)

diverge. $\displaystyle\int_{0}^{+\infty}x^3\,dx = \lim_{\ell\to+\infty}\frac{1}{4}x^4\Big]_0^\ell = \lim_{\ell\to+\infty}\frac{1}{4}\ell^4 = +\infty$ so $\displaystyle\int_{-\infty}^{+\infty}x^3\,dx$ is divergent.

16. $\displaystyle\int_{0}^{+\infty}\frac{x}{\sqrt{x^2+2}}\,dx = \lim_{\ell\to+\infty}\sqrt{x^2+2}\,\Big]_0^\ell = \lim_{\ell\to+\infty}(\sqrt{\ell^2+2}-\sqrt{2}) = +\infty$

so $\displaystyle\int_{-\infty}^{\infty}\frac{x}{\sqrt{x^2+2}}\,dx$ is divergent.

17. $\displaystyle\int_{0}^{+\infty}\frac{x}{(x^2+3)^2}\,dx = \lim_{\ell\to+\infty}-\frac{1}{2(x^2+3)}\Big]_0^\ell = \lim_{\ell\to+\infty}\frac{1}{2}[-1/(\ell^2+3)+1/3] = \frac{1}{6}$,

similarly $\displaystyle\int_{-\infty}^{0}\frac{x}{(x^2+3)^2}\,dx = -1/6$ so $\displaystyle\int_{-\infty}^{\infty}\frac{x}{(x^2+3)^2}\,dx = 1/6+(-1/6) = 0$

18. $\displaystyle\int_{0}^{+\infty}\frac{e^{-t}}{1+e^{-2t}}\,dt = \lim_{\ell\to+\infty}-\tan^{-1}(e^{-t})\Big]_0^\ell = \lim_{\ell\to+\infty}\left[-\tan^{-1}(e^{-\ell})+\frac{\pi}{4}\right] = \frac{\pi}{4}$,

$\displaystyle\int_{-\infty}^{0}\frac{e^{-t}}{1+e^{-2t}}\,dt = \lim_{\ell\to-\infty}-\tan^{-1}(e^{-t})\Big]_\ell^0 = \lim_{\ell\to-\infty}\left[-\frac{\pi}{4}+\tan^{-1}(e^{-\ell})\right] = \frac{\pi}{4}$,

$\displaystyle\int_{-\infty}^{+\infty}\frac{e^{-t}}{1+e^{-2t}}\,dt = \frac{\pi}{4}+\frac{\pi}{4} = \frac{\pi}{2}$

19. $\displaystyle\lim_{\ell\to3+}-\frac{1}{x-3}\Big]_\ell^4 = \lim_{\ell\to3+}\left[-1+\frac{1}{\ell-3}\right] = +\infty$, divergent

20. $\displaystyle\lim_{\ell\to0+}\frac{3}{2}x^{2/3}\Big]_\ell^8 = \lim_{\ell\to0+}\frac{3}{2}(4-\ell^{2/3}) = 6$

21. $\displaystyle\lim_{\ell\to\pi/2-}-\ln(\cos x)\Big]_0^\ell = \lim_{\ell\to\pi/2-}-\ln(\cos\ell) = +\infty$, divergent

22. $\quad \lim\limits_{\ell \to 9^-} -2\sqrt{9-x}\,\Big]_0^\ell = \lim\limits_{\ell \to 9^-} 2(-\sqrt{9-\ell}+3) = 6$

23. $\quad \lim\limits_{\ell \to 1^-} \sin^{-1} x\,\Big]_0^\ell = \lim\limits_{\ell \to 1^-} \sin^{-1}\ell = \pi/2$

24. $\quad \lim\limits_{\ell \to -3^+} -\sqrt{9-x^2}\,\Big]_\ell^1 = \lim\limits_{\ell \to -3^+} (-\sqrt{8}+\sqrt{9-\ell^2}) = -\sqrt{8}$

25. $\quad \lim\limits_{\ell \to \pi/6^-} -\sqrt{1-2\sin x}\,\Big]_0^\ell = \lim\limits_{\ell \to \pi/6^-} (-\sqrt{1-2\sin\ell}+1) = 1$

26. $\quad \lim\limits_{\ell \to \pi/4^-} -\ln(1-\tan x)\,\Big]_0^\ell = \lim\limits_{\ell \to \pi/4^-} -\ln(1-\tan\ell) = +\infty$, divergent

27. $\quad \displaystyle\int_0^2 \frac{dx}{x-2} = \lim\limits_{\ell \to 2^-} \ln|x-2|\,\Big]_0^\ell = \lim\limits_{\ell \to 2^-} (\ln|\ell-2| - \ln 2) = -\infty$, divergent

28. $\quad \displaystyle\int_0^2 \frac{dx}{x^2} = \lim\limits_{\ell \to 0^+} -1/x\,\Big]_\ell^2 = \lim\limits_{\ell \to 0^+}(-1/2 + 1/\ell) = +\infty$ so $\displaystyle\int_{-2}^2 \frac{dx}{x^2}$ is divergent

29. $\quad \displaystyle\int_0^8 x^{-1/3}dx = \lim\limits_{\ell \to 0^+} \frac{3}{2}x^{2/3}\,\Big]_\ell^8 = \lim\limits_{\ell \to 0^+} \frac{3}{2}(4 - \ell^{2/3}) = 6,$

$\quad \displaystyle\int_{-1}^0 x^{-1/3}dx = \lim\limits_{\ell \to 0^-} \frac{3}{2}x^{2/3}\,\Big]_{-1}^\ell = \lim\limits_{\ell \to 0^-} \frac{3}{2}(\ell^{2/3} - 1) = -3/2$

$\quad$ so $\displaystyle\int_{-1}^8 x^{-1/3}dx = 6 + (-3/2) = 9/2$

30. $\quad \displaystyle\int_0^2 \frac{dx}{(x-2)^{2/3}} = \lim\limits_{\ell \to 2^-} 3(x-2)^{1/3}\,\Big]_0^\ell = \lim\limits_{\ell \to 2^-} 3[(\ell-2)^{1/3} - (-2)^{1/3}] = 3\sqrt[3]{2},$

$\quad$ similarly $\displaystyle\int_2^4 \frac{dx}{(x-2)^{2/3}} = \lim\limits_{\ell \to 2^+} 3(x-2)^{1/3}\,\Big]_\ell^4 = 3\sqrt[3]{2}$ so $\displaystyle\int_0^4 \frac{dx}{(x-2)^{2/3}} = 6\sqrt[3]{2}$

31. $\quad$ Define $\displaystyle\int_0^{+\infty} \frac{1}{x^2}dx = \int_0^a \frac{1}{x^2}dx + \int_a^{+\infty} \frac{1}{x^2}dx$ where $a > 0$; take $a = 1$ for convenience,

$\quad \displaystyle\int_0^1 \frac{1}{x^2}dx = \lim\limits_{\ell \to 0^+} (-1/x)\,\Big]_\ell^1 = \lim\limits_{\ell \to 0^+} (1/\ell - 1) = +\infty$ so $\displaystyle\int_0^{+\infty} \frac{1}{x^2}dx$ is divergent.

32. Define $\displaystyle\int_{1}^{+\infty} \frac{dx}{x\sqrt{x^2-1}} = \int_{1}^{a} \frac{dx}{x\sqrt{x^2-1}} + \int_{a}^{+\infty} \frac{dx}{x\sqrt{x^2-1}}$ where $a > 1$, take $a = 2$ for convenience to get

$$\int_{1}^{2} \frac{dx}{x\sqrt{x^2-1}} = \lim_{\ell\to 1^+} \sec^{-1} x \Big]_{\ell}^{2} = \lim_{\ell\to 1^+} (\pi/3 - \sec^{-1}\ell) = \pi/3,$$

$$\int_{2}^{+\infty} \frac{dx}{x\sqrt{x^2-1}} = \lim_{\ell\to +\infty} \sec^{-1} x \Big]_{2}^{\ell} = \pi/2 - \pi/3 \text{ so } \int_{1}^{+\infty} \frac{dx}{x\sqrt{x^2-1}} = \pi/2$$

33. $\displaystyle\int_{0}^{+\infty} \frac{e^{-\sqrt{x}}}{\sqrt{x}} dx = 2\int_{0}^{+\infty} e^{-u} du = 2\lim_{\ell\to +\infty} (-e^{-u}) \Big]_{0}^{\ell} = 2\lim_{\ell\to +\infty} (1 - e^{-\ell}) = 2$

34. $\displaystyle\int_{0}^{+\infty} \frac{dx}{\sqrt{x}(x+4)} = 2\int_{0}^{+\infty} \frac{du}{u^2+4} = 2\lim_{\ell\to +\infty} \frac{1}{2}\tan^{-1}\frac{u}{2} \Big]_{0}^{\ell} = \lim_{\ell\to +\infty} \tan^{-1}\frac{\ell}{2} = \frac{\pi}{2}$

35. $\displaystyle\int_{0}^{+\infty} \frac{e^{-x}}{\sqrt{1-e^{-x}}} dx = \int_{0}^{1} \frac{du}{\sqrt{u}} = \lim_{\ell\to 0^+} 2\sqrt{u} \Big]_{\ell}^{1} = \lim_{\ell\to 0^+} 2(1 - \sqrt{\ell}) = 2$

36. $\displaystyle\int_{0}^{+\infty} \frac{e^{-x}}{\sqrt{1-e^{-2x}}} dx = -\int_{1}^{0} \frac{du}{\sqrt{1-u^2}} = \int_{0}^{1} \frac{du}{\sqrt{1-u^2}} = \lim_{\ell\to 1} \sin^{-1} u \Big]_{0}^{\ell} = \lim_{\ell\to 1} \sin^{-1}\ell = \frac{\pi}{2}$

37. $\displaystyle\int_{0}^{+\infty} e^{-ax} dx = \lim_{\ell\to +\infty} -\frac{1}{a}e^{-ax} \Big]_{0}^{\ell} = \lim_{\ell\to +\infty} \left[-\frac{1}{a}e^{-a\ell} + \frac{1}{a} \right] = \frac{1}{a} = 5, \ a = \frac{1}{5}$

38. $\displaystyle\int_{0}^{+\infty} \frac{dx}{x^2+a^2} = \lim_{\ell\to +\infty} \frac{1}{a}\tan^{-1}(x/a) \Big]_{0}^{\ell} = \lim_{\ell\to +\infty} \frac{1}{a}\tan^{-1}(\ell/a) = \frac{\pi}{2a} = 1, a = \pi/2$

39. $u = \sqrt{x}, \ \displaystyle\int_{0}^{+\infty} \frac{e^{-x}}{\sqrt{x}} dx = 2\int_{0}^{+\infty} e^{-u^2} du = 2(\sqrt{\pi}/2) = \sqrt{\pi}$

40. $u = ax, \ \displaystyle\int_{0}^{+\infty} e^{-a^2 x^2} dx = \frac{1}{a}\int_{0}^{+\infty} e^{-u^2} du = \frac{\sqrt{\pi}}{2a}$

41. $u = \sqrt{x}, \ \displaystyle\int_{0}^{+\infty} \frac{\sin x}{\sqrt{x}} dx = 2\int_{0}^{+\infty} \sin(u^2) du = \sqrt{\pi/2}$

42. Let $a^2 = \dfrac{M}{2RT}$ to get

    (a) $\bar{v} = \dfrac{4}{\sqrt{\pi}} \left(\dfrac{M}{2RT} \right)^{3/2} \dfrac{1}{2} \left(\dfrac{M}{2RT} \right)^{-2} = \dfrac{2}{\sqrt{\pi}}\sqrt{\dfrac{2RT}{M}} = \sqrt{\dfrac{8RT}{\pi M}}$

(b) $v_{rms}^2 = \dfrac{4}{\sqrt{\pi}} \left(\dfrac{M}{2RT}\right)^{3/2} \dfrac{3\sqrt{\pi}}{8} \left(\dfrac{M}{2RT}\right)^{-5/2} = \dfrac{3RT}{M}$ so $v_{rms} = \sqrt{\dfrac{3RT}{M}}$

43. (a) $\displaystyle\int_0^{+\infty} \cos x\, dx = \lim_{\ell\to+\infty} \sin x \Big]_0^{\ell} = \lim_{\ell\to+\infty} \sin \ell$ which does not exist and does not become infinite.

(b) $u = \sqrt{x}$, $\displaystyle\int_0^{+\infty} \dfrac{\cos\sqrt{x}}{\sqrt{x}} dx = 2\int_0^{+\infty} \cos u\, du$; $\displaystyle\int_0^{+\infty} \cos u\, du$ diverges

(c) $u = 1/x$, $\displaystyle\int_0^1 \dfrac{\cos(1/x)}{x^2} dx = -\int_{+\infty}^1 \cos u\, du = \int_1^{+\infty} \cos u\, du$ which diverges

44. $I = \displaystyle\int_0^{\pi/2} \ln(\tan x)dx = -\int_{x/2}^0 \ln[\tan(\pi/2 - u)]du = \int_0^{\pi/2} \ln(\cot u)du$

$= \displaystyle\int_0^{\pi/2} \ln(1/\tan u)du = -\int_0^{\pi/2} \ln(\tan u)du = -I$ so $I = -I, 2I = 0, I = 0$

45. $\displaystyle\lim_{\ell\to+\infty} \int_0^{\ell} e^{-x}\cos x\, dx = \lim_{\ell\to+\infty} \dfrac{1}{2}e^{-x}(\sin x - \cos x) \Big]_0^{\ell} = \lim_{\ell\to+\infty} \dfrac{1}{2}[e^{-\ell}(\sin\ell - \cos\ell) + 1]$

but both $e^{-\ell}\sin\ell$ and $e^{-\ell}\cos\ell \to 0$ as $\ell \to +\infty$ (by the Squeezing Theorem because

$-e^{-\ell} \le e^{-\ell}\sin\ell \le e^{-\ell}$ and $-e^{-\ell} \le e^{-\ell}\cos\ell \le e^{-\ell}$) so $\displaystyle\int_0^{+\infty} e^{-x}\cos x\, dx = 1/2$.

46. If $p = 0$, $\displaystyle\int_0^{+\infty} (1)dx = \lim_{\ell\to+\infty} x \Big]_0^{\ell} = +\infty$,

if $p \ne 0$, $\displaystyle\int_0^{+\infty} e^{px} dx = \lim_{\ell\to+\infty} \dfrac{1}{p}e^{px} \Big]_0^{\ell} = \lim_{\ell\to+\infty} \dfrac{1}{p}(e^{p\ell} - 1) = \begin{cases} -1/p, & p < 0 \\ +\infty, & p > 0 \end{cases}$

47. If $p = 1$, $\displaystyle\int_0^1 \dfrac{dx}{x} = \lim_{\ell\to0^+} \ln x \Big]_{\ell}^1 = +\infty$;

if $p \ne 1$, $\displaystyle\int_0^1 \dfrac{dx}{x^p} = \lim_{\ell\to0^+} \dfrac{x^{1-p}}{1-p} \Big]_{\ell}^1 = \lim_{\ell\to0^+} [(1 - \ell^{1-p})/(1 - p)] = \begin{cases} 1/(1-p), & p < 1 \\ +\infty, & p > 1 \end{cases}$

48. If $p = 1$, $\displaystyle\int_1^{+\infty} \dfrac{dx}{x} = \lim_{\ell\to+\infty} \ln x \Big]_1^{\ell} = +\infty$;

if $p \ne 1$, $\displaystyle\int_1^{+\infty} \dfrac{dx}{x^p} = \lim_{\ell\to+\infty} \dfrac{x^{1-p}}{1-p} \Big]_1^{\ell} = \lim_{\ell\to+\infty} [(\ell^{1-p} - 1)/(1 - p)] = \begin{cases} +\infty, & p < 1 \\ 1/(p - 1), & p > 1 \end{cases}$

49. (a) $\displaystyle\int_{2}^{+\infty}\frac{x}{x^5+1}dx \le \int_{2}^{+\infty}\frac{dx}{x^4} = \lim_{\ell\to+\infty}\left.-\frac{1}{3x^3}\right]_{2}^{\ell} = 1/24$

(b) $\displaystyle\int_{1}^{+\infty}e^{-x^2}dx \le \int_{1}^{+\infty}xe^{-x^2}dx = \lim_{\ell\to+\infty}\left.-\frac{1}{2}e^{-x^2}\right]_{1}^{\ell} = \frac{1}{2}e^{-1}$

50. (a) $\displaystyle\frac{1}{x} \le \frac{\sqrt{x^3+1}}{x}$ for $x \ge 2$, $\displaystyle\int_{2}^{+\infty}\frac{1}{x}dx = \lim_{\ell\to+\infty}\left.\ln x\right]_{2}^{\ell} = +\infty$

(b) $\displaystyle\frac{1}{2x+1} \le \frac{e^x}{2x+1}$ for $x \ge 0$, $\displaystyle\int_{0}^{+\infty}\frac{1}{2x+1}dx = \lim_{\ell\to+\infty}\left.\frac{1}{2}\ln(2x+1)\right]_{0}^{\ell} = +\infty$

51. $A = \displaystyle\int_{0}^{+\infty}e^{-3x}dx = \lim_{\ell\to+\infty}\left.-\frac{1}{3}e^{-3x}\right]_{0}^{\ell} = \lim_{\ell\to+\infty}\frac{1}{3}(1-e^{-3\ell}) = 1/3.$

52. $A = \displaystyle\int_{3}^{+\infty}\frac{8}{x^2-4}dx = \lim_{\ell\to+\infty}\left.2\ln\frac{x-2}{x+2}\right]_{3}^{\ell} = \lim_{\ell\to+\infty}2\left[\ln\frac{\ell-2}{\ell+2} - \ln\frac{1}{5}\right] = 2\ln 5$

53. (a) $V = \displaystyle\int_{1}^{+\infty}\frac{\pi}{x^2}dx = \lim_{\ell\to+\infty}\left.-\pi/x\right]_{1}^{\ell} = \pi,$

(b) $S = \displaystyle\int_{1}^{+\infty}2\pi(1/x)\sqrt{1+1/x^4}dx$, but $\sqrt{1+1/x^4} \ge 1$ if $x \ge 1$ so

$(2\pi/x)\sqrt{1+1/x^4} \ge 2\pi/x$, $\displaystyle\lim_{\ell\to+\infty}\int_{1}^{\ell}(2\pi/x)dx = +\infty$; S is infinite.

54. (a) $V = \pi\displaystyle\int_{0}^{+\infty}e^{-2x}dx = -\frac{\pi}{2}\lim_{\ell\to+\infty}\left.e^{-2x}\right]_{0}^{\ell} = \pi/2$

(b) $S = 2\pi\displaystyle\int_{0}^{+\infty}e^{-x}\sqrt{1+e^{-2x}}dx$, let $u = e^{-x}$ to get

$S = -2\pi\displaystyle\int_{1}^{0}\sqrt{1+u^2}du = 2\pi\int_{0}^{1}\sqrt{1+u^2}du$

$= 2\pi\left[\dfrac{u}{2}\sqrt{1+u^2} + \dfrac{1}{2}\ln|u+\sqrt{1+u^2}|\,\right]_{0}^{1} = \pi\left[\sqrt{2}+\ln(1+\sqrt{2})\right]$

55. $\displaystyle\int\frac{dx}{(r^2+x^2)^{3/2}} = \frac{1}{r^2}\int\cos\theta\,d\theta\,(x = r\tan\theta) = \frac{1}{r^2}\sin\theta + C = \frac{x}{r^2\sqrt{r^2+x^2}} + C$

so $u = \dfrac{2\pi NIr}{k}\displaystyle\lim_{\ell\to+\infty}\left.\frac{x}{r^2\sqrt{r^2+x^2}}\right]_{a}^{\ell} = \frac{2\pi NI}{kr}\lim_{\ell\to+\infty}(\ell/\sqrt{r^2+\ell^2} - a/\sqrt{r^2+a^2})$

$= \dfrac{2\pi NI}{kr}(1 - a/\sqrt{r^2+a^2})$

56. Solve $y = 1/(1 + x^2)$ for x getting

$x = \sqrt{\dfrac{1 - y}{y}}$ and integrate with respect

to y to get $A = \displaystyle\int_0^1 \sqrt{\dfrac{1 - y}{y}}\, dy$

(see figure)

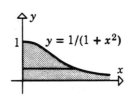

57. (a) $\displaystyle\int_{4000}^{4000+\ell} 9.6 \times 10^{10} x^{-2}\, dx$

(b) $\displaystyle\int_{4000}^{+\infty} 9.6 \times 10^{10} x^{-2}\, dx = \lim_{\ell \to +\infty} -9.6 \times 10^{10}/x \Big]_{4000}^{\ell} = 2.4 \times 10^7$

58. $\mathcal{L}\{e^{2t}\} = \displaystyle\int_0^{+\infty} e^{-st} e^{2t}\, dt = \int_0^{+\infty} e^{-(s-2)t}\, dt = \lim_{\ell \to +\infty} -\frac{1}{s-2} e^{-(s-2)t} \Big]_0^{\ell} = \frac{1}{s-2}$

59. $\mathcal{L}\{1\} = \displaystyle\int_0^{+\infty} e^{-st}\, dt = \lim_{\ell \to +\infty} -\frac{1}{s} e^{-st} \Big]_0^{\ell} = \frac{1}{s}$

60. $\mathcal{L}\{f(t)\} = \displaystyle\int_3^{+\infty} e^{-st}\, dt = \lim_{\ell \to +\infty} -\frac{1}{s} e^{-st} \Big]_3^{\ell} = \frac{e^{-3s}}{s}$

61. $\mathcal{L}\{\sin t\} = \displaystyle\int_0^{+\infty} e^{-st} \sin t\, dt = \lim_{\ell \to +\infty} \frac{e^{-st}}{s^2 + 1}(-s \sin t - \cos t) \Big]_0^{\ell} = \frac{1}{s^2 + 1}$

62. $\mathcal{L}\{\cos t\} = \displaystyle\int_0^{+\infty} e^{-st} \cos t\, dt = \lim_{\ell \to +\infty} \frac{e^{-st}}{s^2 + 1}(-s \cos t - \sin t) \Big]_0^{\ell} = \frac{s}{s^2 + 1}$

63. $2 \displaystyle\int_0^1 \cos(u^2)\, du \approx 1.809$

64. $-2 \displaystyle\int_1^0 \sin(1 - u^2)\, du = 2 \int_0^1 \sin(1 - u^2)\, du \approx 1.187$

65. (a) $\displaystyle\int_0^4 \frac{1}{x^6 + 1}\, dx \approx 1.047; \ \pi/3 \approx 1.047$

(b) $\displaystyle\int_0^{+\infty} \frac{1}{x^6 + 1}\, dx = \int_0^4 \frac{1}{x^6 + 1}\, dx + \int_4^{+\infty} \frac{1}{x^6 + 1}\, dx$ so

$E = \displaystyle\int_4^{+\infty} \frac{1}{x^6 + 1}\, dx < \int_4^{+\infty} \frac{1}{x^6}\, dx = \frac{1}{5(4)^5} < 2 \times 10^{-4}.$

66. **(a)** $\int_0^3 e^{-x^2}\,dx \approx 0.8862$; $\sqrt{\pi}/2 \approx 0.8862$

(b) $\int_0^{+\infty} e^{-x^2}\,dx = \int_0^3 e^{-x^2}\,dx + \int_3^{+\infty} e^{-x^2}\,dx$ so

$$E = \int_3^{+\infty} e^{-x^2}\,dx < \int_3^{+\infty} xe^{-x^2}\,dx = \frac{1}{2}e^{-9} < 7 \times 10^{-5}.$$

EXERCISE SET 10.2

1. $\displaystyle\lim_{x \to 1} \frac{1/x}{1} = 1$

2. $\displaystyle\lim_{x \to 0} \frac{2\cos 2x}{5\cos 5x} = 2/5$

3. $\displaystyle\lim_{x \to 0} \frac{e^x}{\cos x} = 1$

4. $\displaystyle\lim_{x \to 3} \frac{1}{6x - 13} = 1/5$

5. $\displaystyle\lim_{\theta \to 0} \frac{\sec^2 \theta}{1} = 1$

6. $\displaystyle\lim_{t \to 0} \frac{te^t + e^t}{-e^t} = -1$

7. $\displaystyle\lim_{x \to 1} \frac{1/x}{\pi \sec^2 \pi x} = 1/\pi$

8. $\displaystyle\lim_{x \to c} \frac{(1/3)x^{-2/3}}{1} = 1/(3c^{2/3})$

9. $\displaystyle\lim_{x \to \pi^+} \frac{\cos x}{1} = -1$

10. $\displaystyle\lim_{x \to 0^+} \frac{\cos x}{2x} = +\infty$

11. $\displaystyle\lim_{x \to \pi/2^-} \frac{-\sin x}{-(1/2)(\pi/2 - x)^{-1/2}} = \lim_{x \to \pi/2^-} 2(\sin x)\sqrt{\pi/2 - x} = 0$

12. $\displaystyle\lim_{x \to 0^+} \frac{\sin x}{3x^2} = \lim_{x \to 0^+} \frac{\cos x}{6x} = +\infty$

13. $\displaystyle\lim_{x \to 0} \frac{e^x - e^{-x}}{2\sin 2x} = \lim_{x \to 0} \frac{e^x + e^{-x}}{4\cos 2x} = 1/2$

14. $\displaystyle\lim_{x \to 0} \frac{2\sinh x}{2\sin 2x} = \lim_{x \to 0} \frac{\cosh x}{2\cos 2x} = 1/2$

15. $\displaystyle\lim_{x \to 0} \frac{3\cos 3x}{2\cosh 2x} = 3/2$

16. $\displaystyle\lim_{x \to 0} \frac{2e^{-2x}}{2x + 3} = \frac{2}{3}$

17. $\displaystyle\lim_{x \to \pi/2} \frac{2\cos 2x}{8x} = -\frac{1}{2\pi}$

18. $\displaystyle\lim_{x \to 2} \frac{5/(5x - 9)}{3x^2} = \frac{5}{12}$

19. $\displaystyle\lim_{x \to 0} \frac{1 - 1/(x + 1)}{2\sin 2x} = \lim_{x \to 0} \frac{x}{2(x + 1)\sin 2x} = \lim_{x \to 0} \frac{1}{4(x + 1)\cos 2x + 2\sin 2x} = 1/4$

20. $\displaystyle\lim_{x\to0}\frac{1-\dfrac{1}{1+x^2}}{3x^2}=\lim_{x\to0}\frac{1}{3(1+x^2)}=\frac{1}{3}$

21. $\displaystyle\lim_{x\to0}\frac{-2x+2\sin x}{4x^3}=\lim_{x\to0}\frac{-2+2\cos x}{12x^2}=\lim_{x\to0}-\frac{\sin x}{12x}=-1/12$

22. $\displaystyle\lim_{x\to+\infty}\frac{\dfrac{1}{1+3/x}(-3/x^2)}{\cos(2/x)(-2/x^2)}=\lim_{x\to+\infty}\frac{3/2}{(1+3/x)\cos(2/x)}=\frac{3}{2}$

23. $\displaystyle\lim_{x\to0}\frac{x-\sin x}{x^3}=\lim_{x\to0}\frac{1-\cos x}{3x^2}=\lim_{x\to0}\frac{\sin x}{6x}=1/6$

24. $\displaystyle\lim_{x\to-1}\frac{2x}{3/(3x+4)}=-\frac{2}{3}$ **25.** $\displaystyle\lim_{x\to0}\frac{ae^{ax}-be^{bx}}{1}=a-b$

26. $\displaystyle\lim_{x\to0}a^x\ln a=\ln a$

27. $\displaystyle\lim_{x\to0}\frac{1-\sec^2 x}{\cos x-1}=\lim_{x\to0}\frac{\cos^2 x-1}{\cos^2 x(\cos x-1)}=\lim_{x\to0}\frac{\cos x+1}{\cos^2 x}=2$

28. $\displaystyle\lim_{x\to\pi}\frac{2\sin x\cos x}{-3\sin 3x}=\lim_{x\to\pi}\frac{\sin 2x}{-3\sin 3x}=\lim_{x\to\pi}\frac{2\cos 2x}{-9\cos 3x}=2/9$

29. $\displaystyle\lim_{x\to+\infty}\frac{-\dfrac{1}{1+x^2}}{\dfrac{1}{1+1/x^2}\left(-\dfrac{2}{x^3}\right)}=\lim_{x\to+\infty}\frac{x}{2}=+\infty$

30. $\displaystyle\lim_{x\to0^+}\frac{\sec^2 x}{2\sec^2 2x}=1/2$

31. $\displaystyle\lim_{x\to0^+}\frac{-\sin x/\cos x}{-3\sin 3x/\cos 3x}=\lim_{x\to0^+}\frac{\tan x}{3\tan 3x}=\lim_{x\to0^+}\frac{\sec^2 x}{9\sec^2 3x}=1/9$

32. $\displaystyle\lim_{\theta\to0}\frac{2\sin\theta\cos\theta-2\theta\cos(\theta^2)}{4\theta^3}=\lim_{\theta\to0}\frac{\sin 2\theta-2\theta\cos(\theta^2)}{4\theta^3}$

$$=\lim_{\theta\to0}\frac{\cos 2\theta+2\theta^2\sin(\theta^2)-\cos(\theta^2)}{6\theta^2}$$

$$= \lim_{\theta \to 0} \frac{-\sin 2\theta + 2\theta^3 \cos(\theta^2) + 3\theta \sin(\theta^2)}{6\theta}$$

$$= \lim_{\theta \to 0} \frac{-2\cos 2\theta - 4\theta^4 \sin(\theta^2) + 12\theta^2 \cos(\theta^2) + 3\sin(\theta^2)}{6} = -1/3$$

33. **(a)** L'Hôpital's rule does not apply to the problem $\lim\limits_{x \to 1} \dfrac{3x^2 - 2x + 1}{3x^2 - 2x}$ because it is not a $\dfrac{0}{0}$ form

(b) $\lim\limits_{x \to 1} \dfrac{3x^2 - 2x + 1}{3x^2 - 2x} = 2$

34. $\lim\limits_{x \to 1} \dfrac{4x^3 - 12x^2 + 12x - 4}{4x^3 - 9x^2 + 6x - 1} = \lim\limits_{x \to 1} \dfrac{12x^2 - 24x + 12}{12x^2 - 18x + 6} = \lim\limits_{x \to 1} \dfrac{24x - 24}{24x - 18} = 0$

35. $\lim\limits_{x \to 0} \dfrac{k + \cos \ell x}{x^2}$ does not exist if $k \neq -1$ so suppose $k = -1$, then

$\lim\limits_{x \to 0} \dfrac{-1 + \cos \ell x}{x^2} = \lim\limits_{x \to 0} \dfrac{-\ell \sin \ell x}{2x} = \lim\limits_{x \to 0} \dfrac{-\ell^2 \cos \ell x}{2} = -\ell^2/2 = -4$ if $\ell^2 = 8$, $\ell = \pm 2\sqrt{2}$

36. Rewrite as $\lim\limits_{x \to 0} \left[\dfrac{2 + x}{\cos x}\right]\left[\dfrac{\ln(1 - x)}{1 - e^x}\right]$, but $\lim\limits_{x \to 0} \dfrac{2 + x}{\cos x} = 2$

and $\lim\limits_{x \to 0} \dfrac{\ln(1 - x)}{1 - e^x} = \lim\limits_{x \to 0} \dfrac{-1/(1 - x)}{-e^x} = 1$ so $\lim\limits_{x \to 0} \left[\dfrac{2 + x}{\cos x}\right]\left[\dfrac{\ln(1 - x)}{1 - e^x}\right] = (2)(1) = 2$

37. $\lim\limits_{x \to 1} \dfrac{\ln x}{x^4 - 1} = \lim\limits_{x \to 1} \dfrac{1/x}{4x^3} = \dfrac{1}{4}$; $\lim\limits_{x \to 1} \sqrt{\dfrac{\ln x}{x^4 - 1}} = \sqrt{\lim\limits_{x \to 1} \dfrac{\ln x}{x^4 - 1}} = \dfrac{1}{2}$

38. $\lim\limits_{x \to 0} \dfrac{x^2}{1 - e^{-3x^2}} = \lim\limits_{x \to 0} \dfrac{1}{3e^{-3x^2}} = \dfrac{1}{3}$;

$\lim\limits_{x \to 0^+} \dfrac{x}{\sqrt{1 - e^{-3x^2}}} = \lim\limits_{x \to 0^+} \sqrt{\dfrac{x^2}{1 - e^{-3x^2}}} = \sqrt{\lim\limits_{x \to 0^+} \dfrac{x^2}{1 - e^{-3x^2}}} = \dfrac{1}{\sqrt{3}}$,

$\lim\limits_{x \to 0^-} \dfrac{x}{\sqrt{1 - e^{-3x^2}}} = \lim\limits_{x \to 0^-} -\sqrt{\dfrac{x^2}{1 - e^{-3x^2}}} = -\sqrt{\lim\limits_{x \to 0^-} \dfrac{x^2}{1 - e^{-3x^2}}} = -\dfrac{1}{\sqrt{3}}$

39. $\lim\limits_{x \to +\infty} \dfrac{\ln\left(\dfrac{x + 1}{x - 1}\right)}{1/x} = \lim\limits_{x \to +\infty} \dfrac{-2/(x^2 - 1)}{-1/x^2} = \lim\limits_{x \to +\infty} \dfrac{2x^2}{x^2 - 1} = \lim\limits_{x \to +\infty} \dfrac{4x}{2x} = 2$

40. **(a)** Apply the rule to get $\lim\limits_{x \to 0} \dfrac{-\cos(1/x) + 2x \sin(1/x)}{\cos x}$ which does not exist (nor is it $\pm\infty$)

(b) Rewrite as $\lim\limits_{x \to 0}\left[\dfrac{x}{\sin x}\right][x\sin(1/x)]$, but $\lim\limits_{x \to 0}\dfrac{x}{\sin x} = \lim\limits_{x \to 0}\dfrac{1}{\cos x} = 1$ and $\lim\limits_{x \to 0} x\sin(1/x) = 0$

thus $\lim\limits_{x \to 0}\left[\dfrac{x}{\sin x}\right][x\sin(1/x)] = (1)(0) = 0$

41. $\lim\limits_{x \to 0+}\dfrac{\sin(1/x)}{(\sin x)/x}$, $\lim\limits_{x \to 0+}\dfrac{\sin x}{x} = 1$ but $\lim\limits_{x \to 0+}\sin(1/x)$ does not exist because $\sin(1/x)$ oscillates

between -1 and 1 as $x \to +\infty$, so $\lim\limits_{x \to 0+}\dfrac{x\sin(1/x)}{\sin x}$ does not exist.

42. (a) $\displaystyle\int_1^x \frac{1}{t^{1-k}}dt = \int_1^x t^{k-1}dt = \frac{t^k}{k}\bigg]_1^x = \frac{x^k-1}{k}$

(b) If $k \to 0$, then $\displaystyle\int_1^x \frac{1}{t^{1-k}}dt$ would seem to approach $\displaystyle\int_1^x \frac{1}{t}dt = \ln t\bigg]_1^x = \ln x$

(c) $\lim\limits_{k \to 0}\dfrac{x^k-1}{k} = \lim\limits_{k \to 0} x^k \ln x = \ln x$

43. $T(\theta) = \dfrac{1}{2}\sin\theta(1 - \cos\theta),$

$S(\theta) = \dfrac{1}{2}(\theta - \sin\theta),$

$\lim\limits_{\theta \to 0+}\dfrac{T(\theta)}{S(\theta)} = \lim\limits_{\theta \to 0+}\dfrac{\sin\theta - \sin\theta\cos\theta}{\theta - \sin\theta}$

$\qquad = \lim\limits_{\theta \to 0+}\dfrac{\cos\theta + \sin^2\theta - \cos^2\theta}{1 - \cos\theta}$

$\qquad = \lim\limits_{\theta \to 0+}\dfrac{\cos\theta - \cos 2\theta}{1 - \cos\theta}$

$\qquad = \lim\limits_{\theta \to 0+}\dfrac{-\sin\theta + 2\sin 2\theta}{\sin\theta}$

$\qquad = \lim\limits_{\theta \to 0+}\dfrac{-\cos\theta + 4\cos 2\theta}{\cos\theta} = 3$

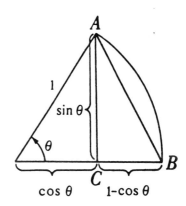

EXERCISE SET 10.3

1. $\lim\limits_{x \to +\infty}\dfrac{1/x}{1} = 0$

2. $\lim\limits_{x \to +\infty}\dfrac{3e^{3x}}{2x} = \lim\limits_{x \to +\infty}\dfrac{9e^{3x}}{2} = +\infty$

3. $\lim\limits_{x \to 0+}\dfrac{-\csc^2 x}{1/x} = \lim\limits_{x \to 0+}\dfrac{-x}{\sin^2 x} = \lim\limits_{x \to 0+}\dfrac{-1}{2\sin x\cos x} = -\infty$

4. $\displaystyle\lim_{x\to0^+}\frac{-1/x}{(-1/x^2)e^{1/x}}=\lim_{x\to0^+}\frac{x}{e^{1/x}}=0$

5. $\displaystyle\lim_{x\to+\infty}\frac{1+\ln x}{1+1/x}=+\infty$

6. $\displaystyle\lim_{x\to+\infty}\frac{3x^2-2}{12x^2}=\lim_{x\to+\infty}\frac{6x}{24x}=1/4$

7. $\displaystyle\lim_{x\to+\infty}\frac{100x^{99}}{e^x}=\lim_{x\to+\infty}\frac{(100)(99)x^{98}}{e^x}=\cdots=\lim_{x\to+\infty}\frac{(100)(99)(98)\cdots(1)}{e^x}=0$

8. $\displaystyle\lim_{x\to0^+}\frac{\cos x/\sin x}{\sec^2 x/\tan x}=\lim_{x\to0^+}\cos^2 x=1$

9. $\displaystyle\lim_{x\to+\infty}xe^{-x}=\lim_{x\to+\infty}\frac{x}{e^x}=\lim_{x\to+\infty}\frac{1}{e^x}=0$

10. $\displaystyle\lim_{x\to\pi}(x-\pi)\tan(x/2)=\lim_{x\to\pi}\frac{x-\pi}{\cot(x/2)}=\lim_{x\to\pi}\frac{1}{-(1/2)\csc^2(x/2)}=-2$

11. $\displaystyle\lim_{x\to+\infty}x\sin(\pi/x)=\lim_{x\to+\infty}\frac{\sin(\pi/x)}{1/x}=\lim_{x\to+\infty}\frac{(-\pi/x^2)\cos(\pi/x)}{-1/x^2}=\lim_{x\to+\infty}\pi\cos(\pi/x)=\pi$

12. $\displaystyle\lim_{x\to0^+}\tan x\ln x=\lim_{x\to0^+}\frac{\ln x}{\cot x}=\lim_{x\to0^+}\frac{1/x}{-\csc^2 x}=\lim_{x\to0^+}\frac{-\sin^2 x}{x}=\lim_{x\to0^+}\frac{-2\sin x\cos x}{1}=0$

13. $\displaystyle\lim_{x\to+\infty}x(e^{\sin(2/x)}-1)=\lim_{x\to+\infty}\frac{e^{\sin(2/x)}-1}{1/x}=\lim_{x\to+\infty}\frac{(-2/x^2)e^{\sin(2/x)}}{-1/x^2}=\lim_{x\to+\infty}2e^{\sin(2/x)}=2$

14. $y=x^{1/(1-x)}$, $\displaystyle\lim_{x\to1}\ln y=\lim_{x\to1}\frac{\ln x}{1-x}=\lim_{x\to1}-\frac{1}{x}=-1$, $\displaystyle\lim_{x\to1}y=e^{-1}$

15. $y=(1-3/x)^x$, $\displaystyle\lim_{x\to+\infty}\ln y=\lim_{x\to+\infty}\frac{\ln(1-3/x)}{1/x}=\lim_{x\to+\infty}\frac{-3}{1-3/x}=-3$, $\displaystyle\lim_{x\to+\infty}y=e^{-3}$

16. $y=(1+2x)^{-3/x}$, $\displaystyle\lim_{x\to0}\ln y=\lim_{x\to0}-\frac{3\ln(1+2x)}{x}=\lim_{x\to0}-\frac{6}{1+2x}=-6$, $\displaystyle\lim_{x\to0}y=e^{-6}$

17. $y=(e^x+x)^{1/x}$, $\displaystyle\lim_{x\to0}\ln y=\lim_{x\to0}\frac{\ln(e^x+x)}{x}=\lim_{x\to0}\frac{e^x+1}{e^x+x}=2$, $\displaystyle\lim_{x\to0}y=e^2$

18. $y=(1+a/x)^{bx}$, $\displaystyle\lim_{x\to+\infty}\ln y=\lim_{x\to+\infty}\frac{b\ln(1+a/x)}{1/x}=\lim_{x\to+\infty}\frac{ab}{1+a/x}=ab$, $\displaystyle\lim_{x\to+\infty}y=e^{ab}$

19. $y=(1+1/x^2)^x$

$\displaystyle\lim_{x\to+\infty}\ln y=\lim_{x\to+\infty}\frac{\ln(1+1/x^2)}{1/x}=\lim_{x\to+\infty}\frac{2x}{x^2+1}=\lim_{x\to+\infty}\frac{1}{x}=0$, $\displaystyle\lim_{x\to+\infty}y=e^0=1$

20. $y = \left(\dfrac{x+1}{x+2}\right)^x$

$$\lim_{x\to+\infty} \ln y = \lim_{x\to+\infty} \frac{\ln \dfrac{x+1}{x+2}}{1/x} = \lim_{x\to+\infty} -\frac{x^2}{(x+1)(x+2)} = -1, \; \lim_{x\to+\infty} y = e^{-1}$$

21. $y = (1+1/x)^{x^2}$

$$\lim_{x\to+\infty} \ln y = \lim_{x\to+\infty} \frac{\ln(1+1/x)}{1/x^2} = \lim_{x\to+\infty} \frac{x^2}{2(x+1)} = \lim_{x\to+\infty} x = +\infty, \; \lim_{x\to+\infty} y = +\infty$$

22. $y = (1+\sin 2x)^{1/x}$, $\displaystyle\lim_{x\to0} \ln y = \lim_{x\to0} \frac{\ln(1+\sin 2x)}{x} = \lim_{x\to0} \frac{2\cos 2x}{1+\sin 2x} = 2$, $\displaystyle\lim_{x\to0} y = e^2$

23. $y = (2-x)^{\tan(\pi x/2)}$, $\displaystyle\lim_{x\to1} \ln y = \lim_{x\to1} \frac{\ln(2-x)}{\cot(\pi x/2)} = \lim_{x\to1} \frac{2\sin^2(\pi x/2)}{\pi(2-x)} = 2/\pi$, $\displaystyle\lim_{x\to1} y = e^{2/\pi}$

24. $y = [\cos(2/x)]^{x^2}$, $\displaystyle\lim_{x\to+\infty} \ln y = \lim_{x\to+\infty} \frac{\cos(2/x)}{1/x^2} = \lim_{x\to+\infty} -\frac{\sin(2/x)}{1/x} = -2$, $\displaystyle\lim_{x\to0} y = e^{-2}$

25. $y = x^{\sin x}$, $\displaystyle\lim_{x\to0+} \ln y = \lim_{x\to0+} \frac{\ln x}{\csc x} = \lim_{x\to0+} \frac{1/x}{-\csc x \cot x} = \lim_{x\to0+} \left(-\frac{\sin x}{x}\right)\tan x = 0$,

$\displaystyle\lim_{x\to0+} y = e^0 = 1$

26. $y = x^x$, $\displaystyle\lim_{x\to0+} \ln y = \lim_{x\to0+} \frac{\ln x}{1/x} = \lim_{x\to0+} -x = 0$, $\displaystyle\lim_{x\to0+} y = 1$

27. $y = (\sin x)^{3/\ln x}$, $\displaystyle\lim_{x\to0+} \ln y = \lim_{x\to0+} \frac{3\ln\sin x}{\ln x} = \lim_{x\to0+} (3\cos x)\frac{x}{\sin x} = 3$, $\displaystyle\lim_{x\to0+} y = e^3$

28. $y = (e^{2x}-1)^{1/\ln x}$, $\displaystyle\lim_{x\to0+} \ln y = \lim_{x\to0+} \frac{\ln(e^{2x}-1)}{\ln x} = \lim_{x\to0+} \frac{2xe^{2x}}{e^{2x}-1} = \lim_{x\to0+} (2x+1) = 1$,

$\displaystyle\lim_{x\to0+} y = e$

29. $y = (\tan x)^{\cos x}$, $\displaystyle\lim_{x\to\pi/2-} \ln y = \lim_{x\to\pi/2-} \frac{\ln\tan x}{\sec x} = \lim_{x\to\pi/2-} \frac{\sec^2 x/\tan x}{\sec x \tan x} = \lim_{x\to\pi/2-} \frac{\cos x}{\sin^2 x} = 0$,

$\displaystyle\lim_{x\to\pi/2-} y = e^0 = 1$

30. $y = (\ln x)^{1/x}$, $\displaystyle\lim_{x\to+\infty} \ln y = \lim_{x\to+\infty} \frac{\ln(\ln x)}{x} = \lim_{x\to+\infty} \frac{1}{x\ln x} = 0$, $\displaystyle\lim_{x\to+\infty} y = 1$

31. $y = (1 + x^2)^{1/\ln x}$

$$\lim_{x \to +\infty} \ln y = \lim_{x \to +\infty} \frac{\ln(1 + x^2)}{\ln x} = \lim_{x \to +\infty} \frac{2x^2}{1 + x^2} = \lim_{x \to +\infty} 2 = 2, \ \lim_{x \to +\infty} y = e^2$$

32. $y = (3^x + 5^x)^{1/x}, \ \lim_{x \to +\infty} \ln y = \lim_{x \to +\infty} \frac{\ln(3^x + 5^x)}{x} = \lim_{x \to +\infty} \frac{3^x \ln 3 + 5^x \ln 5}{3^x + 5^x}$

$$= \lim_{x \to +\infty} \frac{(3/5)^x \ln 3 + \ln 5}{(3/5)^x + 1} = \ln 5, \ \lim_{x \to +\infty} y = e^{\ln 5} = 5$$

33. $\lim_{\theta \to 0} \left(\frac{1 + \cos \theta}{1 - \cos^2 \theta} - \frac{2}{\sin^2 \theta} \right) = \lim_{\theta \to 0} \frac{\cos \theta - 1}{\sin^2 \theta} = \lim_{\theta \to 0} \frac{-\sin \theta}{2 \sin \theta \cos \theta} = -1/2$

34. $\lim_{x \to 0} \frac{1 - \cos 3x}{x^2} = \lim_{x \to 0} \frac{3 \sin 3x}{2x} = \lim_{x \to 0} \frac{9}{2} \cos 3x = \frac{9}{2}$

35. $\lim_{x \to 0} \left(\frac{1}{\sin x} - \frac{1}{x} \right) = \lim_{x \to 0} \frac{x - \sin x}{x \sin x} = \lim_{x \to 0} \frac{1 - \cos x}{x \cos x + \sin x} = \lim_{x \to 0} \frac{\sin x}{2 \cos x - x \sin x} = 0$

36. $\lim_{x \to 0} \frac{e^x - 1 - x}{xe^x - x} = \lim_{x \to 0} \frac{e^x - 1}{xe^x + e^x - 1} = \lim_{x \to 0} \frac{e^x}{xe^x + 2e^x} = 1/2$

37. $\lim_{x \to 0} \left(\frac{\cos x}{\sin x} - \frac{1}{\sin x} \right) = \lim_{x \to 0} \frac{\cos x - 1}{\sin x} = \lim_{x \to 0} \frac{-\sin x}{\cos x} = 0$

38. $\lim_{x \to +\infty} \ln \frac{x}{1 + x} = \lim_{x \to +\infty} \ln \frac{1}{1/x + 1} = \ln(1) = 0$

39. $\lim_{x \to +\infty} [x - \ln(x^2 + 1)] = \lim_{x \to +\infty} [\ln e^x - \ln(x^2 + 1)] = \lim_{x \to +\infty} \ln \frac{e^x}{x^2 + 1},$

$$\lim_{x \to +\infty} \frac{e^x}{x^2 + 1} = \lim_{x \to +\infty} \frac{e^x}{2x} = \lim_{x \to +\infty} \frac{e^x}{2} = +\infty \text{ so } \lim_{x \to +\infty} [x - \ln(x^2 + 1)] = +\infty$$

40. $\lim_{x \to +\infty} [\ln e^x - \ln(1 + 2e^x)] = \lim_{x \to +\infty} \ln \frac{e^x}{1 + 2e^x} = \lim_{x \to +\infty} \ln \frac{1}{e^{-x} + 2} = \ln \frac{1}{2}$

41. $\lim_{x \to 0^+} \frac{\cot x}{\cot 2x} = \lim_{x \to 0^+} \frac{\tan 2x}{\tan x} = \lim_{x \to 0^+} \frac{2 \sec^2 2x}{\sec^2 x} = 2$

42. $\lim_{x \to \pi/2^-} \frac{4 \sec^2 x}{\sec x \tan x} = \lim_{x \to \pi/2^-} \frac{4}{\sin x} = 4$

43. In each case, apply L'Hôpital's rule n times.

(a) $\displaystyle\lim_{x\to+\infty}\frac{x^n}{e^x} = \cdots = \lim_{x\to+\infty}\frac{n(n-1)(n-2)\cdots(1)}{e^x} = 0$

(b) $\displaystyle\lim_{x\to+\infty}\frac{e^x}{x^n} = \cdots = \lim_{x\to+\infty}\frac{e^x}{n(n-1)(n-2)\cdots(1)} = +\infty$

44. (a) $\displaystyle\lim_{x\to+\infty}\frac{\ln x}{x^n} = \lim_{x\to+\infty}\frac{1/x}{nx^{n-1}} = \lim_{x\to+\infty}\frac{1}{nx^n} = 0$

(b) $\displaystyle\lim_{x\to+\infty}\frac{x^n}{\ln x} = \lim_{x\to+\infty}\frac{nx^{n-1}}{1/x} = \lim_{x\to+\infty}nx^n = +\infty$

45. (a) 0 (b) $+\infty$ (c) 0 (d) $-\infty$

  (e) $+\infty$ (f) $+\infty$ (g) $-\infty$ (h) $-\infty$

46. $\displaystyle\lim_{x\to+\infty}(e^x - x^2) = \lim_{x\to+\infty}x^2(e^x/x^2 - 1)$, but $\displaystyle\lim_{x\to+\infty}\frac{e^x}{x^2} = \lim_{x\to+\infty}\frac{e^x}{2x} = \lim_{x\to+\infty}\frac{e^x}{2} = +\infty$

so $\displaystyle\lim_{x\to+\infty}(e^x/x^2 - 1) = +\infty$ and thus $\displaystyle\lim_{x\to+\infty}x^2(e^x/x^2 - 1) = +\infty$

47. Let $y = x^x$, $\displaystyle\lim_{x\to+\infty}y = +\infty$ and

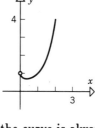

$\displaystyle\lim_{x\to0^+}y = 1$. Use logarithmic differentiation to get $dy/dx = x^x(1 + \ln x)$
so $dy/dx = 0$ when $x = e^{-1}$, $dy/dx < 0$
if $x < e^{-1}$, $dy/dx > 0$ if $x > e^{-1}$,
and $dy/dx \to -\infty$ as $x \to 0^+$. Also,
$d^2y/dx^2 = x^x[1/x + (1 + \ln x)^2] > 0$ for $x > 0$ so the curve is always concave up.

48. Let $y = \dfrac{\tan x}{x}$, $\displaystyle\lim_{x\to0}y = 1$ and

$\displaystyle\lim_{x\to\pi/2^-}y = \lim_{x\to\pi/2^-}y = +\infty$.

$\dfrac{\tan(-x)}{(-x)} = \dfrac{\tan x}{x}$ so the graph is

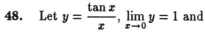

symmetric about the y-axis.

$dy/dx = (x\sec^2 x - \tan x)/x^2$,

$\displaystyle\lim_{x\to0}\frac{dy}{dx} = \lim_{x\to0}\frac{x\sec^2 x - \tan x}{x^2} = \lim_{x\to0}\sec^2 x \tan x = 0.$

$$\frac{x\sec^2 x - \tan x}{x^2} = \frac{x - \sin x \cos x}{x^2 \cos^2 x} = \frac{2x - \sin 2x}{x^2 \cos^2 x}$$

so $dy/dx > 0$ for $0 < x < \pi/2$ because $\sin 2x < 2x$ for $x > 0$. By symmetry, $dy/dx < 0$ for $-\pi/2 < x < 0$.

49. $\displaystyle\int \ln x\, dx = x \ln x - x + C,$

$$\int_0^1 \ln x\, dx = \lim_{\ell \to 0+} \int_\ell^1 \ln x\, dx = \lim_{\ell \to 0+} (x \ln x - x)\Big]_\ell^1 = \lim_{\ell \to 0+}(-1 - \ell\ln\ell + \ell),$$

but $\displaystyle\lim_{\ell \to 0+} \ell\ln\ell = \lim_{\ell \to 0+} \frac{\ln\ell}{1/\ell} = \lim_{\ell \to 0+}(-\ell) = 0$ so $\displaystyle\int_0^1 \ln x\, dx = -1$

50. $\displaystyle\int \frac{\ln x}{x^2} dx = -\frac{\ln x}{x} - \frac{1}{x} + C,$

$$\int_1^{+\infty} \frac{\ln x}{x^2} dx = \lim_{\ell \to +\infty} \int_1^\ell \frac{\ln x}{x^2} dx = \lim_{\ell \to +\infty}\left(-\frac{\ln x}{x} - \frac{1}{x}\right)\Big]_1^\ell = \lim_{\ell \to +\infty}\left(-\frac{\ln\ell}{\ell} - \frac{1}{\ell} + 1\right),$$

but $\displaystyle\lim_{\ell \to +\infty} \frac{\ln\ell}{\ell} = \lim_{\ell \to +\infty} \frac{1}{\ell} = 0$ so $\displaystyle\int_1^{+\infty} \frac{\ln x}{x^2} = 1$

51. $\displaystyle\int xe^{-3x}\, dx = -\frac{1}{3} xe^{-3x} - \frac{1}{9}e^{-3x} + C,$

$$\int_0^{+\infty} xe^{-3x}\, dx = \lim_{\ell \to +\infty} \int_0^\ell xe^{-3x}\, dx = \lim_{\ell \to +\infty}\left(-\frac{1}{3} xe^{-3x} - \frac{1}{9}e^{-3x}\right)\Big]_0^\ell$$

$$= \lim_{\ell \to +\infty}\left(-\frac{1}{3}\ell e^{-3\ell} - \frac{1}{9}e^{-3\ell} + \frac{1}{9}\right),$$

but $\displaystyle\lim_{\ell \to +\infty} \ell e^{-3\ell} = \lim_{\ell \to +\infty} \frac{\ell}{e^{3\ell}} = \lim_{\ell \to +\infty} \frac{1}{3e^{3\ell}} = 0$ so $\displaystyle\int_0^{+\infty} xe^{-3x}\, dx = 1/9$

52. $\displaystyle A = \int_e^{+\infty} \frac{\ln x - 1}{x^2} dx = \lim_{\ell \to +\infty} -\frac{\ln x}{x}\Big]_e^\ell = \lim_{\ell \to +\infty}\left(\frac{1}{e} - \frac{\ln\ell}{\ell}\right),$ but $\displaystyle\lim_{\ell \to +\infty} \frac{\ln\ell}{\ell} = \lim_{\ell \to +\infty} \frac{1}{\ell} = 0$

so $A = 1/e$.

53. $\displaystyle V = 2\pi \int_0^{+\infty} xe^{-x}\, dx = 2\pi \lim_{\ell \to +\infty} -e^{-x}(x+1)\Big]_0^\ell = 2\pi \lim_{\ell \to +\infty} [1 - e^{-\ell}(\ell+1)],$

but $\displaystyle\lim_{\ell \to +\infty} e^{-\ell}(\ell+1) = \lim_{\ell \to +\infty} \frac{\ell+1}{e^\ell} = \lim_{\ell \to +\infty} \frac{1}{e^\ell} = 0$ so $V = 2\pi$.

54. **(a)** $\displaystyle\int_1^\ell e^{t^2}\, dt \geq \int_1^\ell e^t\, dt = e^\ell - e,$ but $\displaystyle\lim_{\ell \to +\infty}(e^\ell - e) = +\infty$ so $\displaystyle\lim_{\ell \to +\infty} \int_1^\ell e^{t^2}\, dt = +\infty.$

(b) $\displaystyle \lim_{x \to +\infty} \frac{\int_1^x e^{t^2}\,dt}{x} = \lim_{x \to +\infty} \frac{e^{x^2}}{1} = +\infty.$

55. (a) $\displaystyle \int_0^\ell \sqrt{1+t^3}\,dt \geq \int_0^\ell t^{3/2}\,dt = \frac{2}{5}t^{5/2}\Big]_0^\ell = \frac{2}{5}\ell^{5/2},$

$\displaystyle \lim_{\ell \to +\infty} \int_0^\ell t^{3/2}\,dt = \lim_{\ell \to +\infty} \frac{2}{5}\ell^{5/2} = +\infty$ so $\displaystyle \int_0^{+\infty} \sqrt{1+t^3}\,dt = +\infty$

(b) $\displaystyle \lim_{x \to +\infty} \frac{2\sqrt{1+8x^3}}{(5/2)x^{3/2}} = \lim_{x \to +\infty} \frac{4}{5}\sqrt{1/x^3 + 8} = 8\sqrt{2}/5$

56. (a) $\displaystyle \int_0^\ell \sqrt{3+e^{-2x}}\,dx \geq \int_0^\ell \sqrt{3}\,dx = \sqrt{3}\ell,\ \lim_{\ell \to +\infty} \int_0^\ell \sqrt{3}\,dx = \lim_{\ell \to +\infty} \sqrt{3}\ell = +\infty$ so

$\displaystyle \int_0^{+\infty} \sqrt{3+e^{-2x}}\,dx = +\infty$

(b) $\displaystyle f_{\text{ave}} = \frac{1}{a}\int_0^a \sqrt{3+e^{-2x}}\,dx,$

$\displaystyle \lim_{a \to +\infty} f_{\text{ave}} = \lim_{a \to +\infty} \frac{\int_0^a \sqrt{3+e^{-2x}}\,dx}{a} = \lim_{a \to +\infty} \sqrt{3+e^{-2a}} = \sqrt{3}$

57. $\displaystyle \lim_{x \to +\infty} \frac{1+2\cos 2x}{1}$ does not exist, nor is it $\pm\infty$; $\displaystyle \lim_{x \to +\infty} \frac{x+\sin 2x}{x} = \lim_{x \to +\infty}\left(1+\frac{\sin 2x}{x}\right) = 1.$

58. $\displaystyle \lim_{x \to +\infty} \frac{2-\cos x}{3+\cos x}$ does not exist, nor is it $\pm\infty$; $\displaystyle \lim_{x \to +\infty} \frac{2x-\sin x}{3x+\sin x} = \lim_{x \to +\infty} \frac{2-(\sin x)/x}{3+(\sin x)/x} = \frac{2}{3}.$

59. $\displaystyle \lim_{x \to +\infty} (2+x\cos x + \sin x)$ does not exist, nor is it $\pm\infty$; $\displaystyle \lim_{x \to +\infty} \frac{x(2+\sin x)}{x+1} = \lim_{x \to +\infty} \frac{2+\sin x}{1+1/x},$
which does not exist because $\sin x$ oscillates between -1 and 1 as $x \to +\infty$.

60. $\displaystyle \lim_{x \to +\infty}\left(\frac{1}{x} + \frac{1}{2}\cos x + \frac{\sin x}{2x}\right)$ does not exist, nor is it $\pm\infty$;

$\displaystyle \lim_{x \to +\infty} \frac{x(2+\sin x)}{x^2+1} = \lim_{x \to +\infty} \frac{2+\sin x}{x+1/x} = 0.$

61. (a) $t = 1/x, x = 1/t,$

$\displaystyle \lim_{x \to +\infty} x\left(k^{1/x} - 1\right) = \lim_{t \to 0^+} \frac{k^t - 1}{t} = \lim_{t \to 0^+} = \frac{e^{t\ln k} - 1}{t} = \lim_{t \to 0^+} (\ln k)e^{t\ln k} = \ln k$

(b) $1024 = 2^{10}$ so enter the value of k, press the square root key ten times, subtract 1, and
multiply the result by 1024: with $k = 0.3$ we get -1.203265293 ($\ln 0.3 \approx -1.203972804$),
with $k = 2$ we get 0.693381829 ($\ln 2 \approx 0.693147181$)

62. **(a)** $\displaystyle\lim_{x\to\pi/2}(\pi/2-x)\tan x = \lim_{x\to\pi/2}\frac{\pi/2-x}{\cot x} = \lim_{x\to\pi/2}\frac{-1}{-\csc^2 x} = \lim_{x\to\pi/2}\sin^2 x = 1$

(b) $\displaystyle\lim_{x\to\pi/2}\left(\frac{1}{\pi/2-x}-\tan x\right) = \lim_{x\to\pi/2}\left(\frac{1}{\pi/2-x}-\frac{\sin x}{\cos x}\right) = \lim_{x\to\pi/2}\frac{\cos x-(\pi/2-x)\sin x}{(\pi/2-x)\cos x}$

$$= \lim_{x\to\pi/2}\frac{-(\pi/2-x)\cos x}{-(\pi/2-x)\sin x-\cos x}$$

$$= \lim_{x\to\pi/2}\frac{(\pi/2-x)\sin x+\cos x}{-(\pi/2-x)\cos x+2\sin x} = 0$$

(c) $1/(\pi/2-1.57)\approx 1255.765856,\,\tan 1.57\approx 1255.765591;\,1/(\pi/2-1.57)-\tan 1.57\approx 0.000265$

63. $u=t/\sqrt{x},\,x=t^2/u^2,$

$$\lim_{x\to+\infty}xf(t/\sqrt{x}) = \lim_{u\to0+}t^2\frac{f(u)}{u^2} = t^2\lim_{u\to0+}\frac{f'(u)}{2u} = t^2\lim_{u\to0+}\frac{f''(u)}{2} = \frac{1}{2}at^2$$

64. $\displaystyle\lim_{x\to+\infty}\frac{\ln f(x)}{\ln g(x)} = \lim_{x\to+\infty}\frac{f'(x)/f(x)}{g'(x)/g(x)} = \lim_{x\to+\infty}\frac{g(x)}{f(x)}\frac{f'(x)}{g'(x)}$

$$= \left[\lim_{x\to+\infty}\frac{g(x)}{f(x)}\right]\left[\lim_{x\to+\infty}\frac{f'(x)}{g'(x)}\right] = \left[\lim_{x\to+\infty}\frac{g'(x)}{f'(x)}\right]\frac{b}{a} = \frac{a}{b}\frac{b}{a} = 1$$

65. $\displaystyle\mathcal{L}\{t\} = \int_0^{+\infty}te^{-st}dt = \left[-\frac{1}{s}te^{-st}-\frac{1}{s^2}e^{-st}\right]_0^{+\infty}$, but

$\displaystyle\lim_{t\to+\infty}te^{-st}=0$ and $\displaystyle\lim_{t\to+\infty}e^{-st}=0$ so $\mathcal{L}\{t\}=1/s^2$.

66. $\displaystyle\mathcal{L}\{t^2\} = \int_0^{+\infty}t^2e^{-st}dt = \left[-\frac{1}{s}t^2e^{-st}-\frac{2}{s}te^{-st}-\frac{2}{s^3}e^{-st}\right]_0^{+\infty}$, but

$\displaystyle\lim_{t\to+\infty}t^2e^{-st}=0,\,\lim_{t\to+\infty}te^{-st}=0,$ and $\displaystyle\lim_{t\to+\infty}e^{-st}=0$ so $\mathcal{L}\{t^2\}=2/s^3$.

67. **(a)** $y=x^{\frac{\ln a}{1+\ln x}},$

$$\lim_{x\to0+}\ln y = \lim_{x\to0+}\frac{(\ln a)\ln x}{1+\ln x} = \lim_{x\to0+}\frac{(\ln a)/x}{1/x} = \lim_{x\to0+}\ln a = \ln a,\,\lim_{x\to0+}y = e^{\ln a} = a$$

(b) same as part (a) with $x\to+\infty$

(c) $y=(x+1)^{\frac{\ln a}{x}},\,\displaystyle\lim_{x\to0}\ln y = \lim_{x\to0}\frac{(\ln a)\ln(x+1)}{x} = \lim_{x\to0}\frac{\ln a}{x+1} = \ln a,\,\lim_{x\to0}y = e^{\ln a} = a$

68. **(a)** $\displaystyle\Gamma(1) = \int_0^{+\infty}e^{-t}dt = \lim_{\ell\to+\infty}-e^{-t}\Big]_0^{\ell} = \lim_{\ell\to+\infty}(-e^{-\ell}+1) = 1$

(b) $\Gamma(x+1) = \displaystyle\int_0^{+\infty} t^x e^{-t}\,dt$; let $u = t^x$, $dv = e^{-t}\,dt$ to get

$$\Gamma(x+1) = -t^x e^{-t}\Big]_0^{+\infty} + x\int_0^{+\infty} t^{x-1}e^{-t}\,dt = -t^x e^{-t}\Big]_0^{+\infty} + x\Gamma(x)$$

$\displaystyle\lim_{t\to+\infty} t^x e^{-t} = \lim_{t\to+\infty}\frac{t^x}{e^t} = 0$ (by multiple applications of L'Hôpital's rule)

so $\Gamma(x+1) = x\Gamma(x)$.

(c) $\Gamma(2) = (1)\Gamma(1) = (1)(1) = 1$, $\Gamma(3) = 2\Gamma(2) = (2)(1) = 2$, $\Gamma(4) = 3\Gamma(3) = (3)(2) = 6$

(d) $\Gamma\left(\dfrac{1}{2}\right) = \displaystyle\int_0^{+\infty} t^{-1/2}e^{-t}\,dt = 2\int_0^{+\infty} e^{-u^2}\,du$ (with $u = \sqrt{t}$) $= 2(\sqrt{\pi}/2) = \sqrt{\pi}$.

(e) $\Gamma\left(\dfrac{3}{2}\right) = \dfrac{1}{2}\Gamma\left(\dfrac{1}{2}\right) = \dfrac{1}{2}\sqrt{\pi}$, $\Gamma\left(\dfrac{5}{2}\right) = \dfrac{3}{2}\Gamma\left(\dfrac{3}{2}\right) = \dfrac{3}{4}\sqrt{\pi}$.

69. (a) $t = -\ln x, x = e^{-t}, dx = -e^{-t}\,dt$,

$$\int_0^1 (\ln x)^n\,dx = -\int_{+\infty}^0 (-t)^n e^{-t}\,dt = (-1)^n\int_0^{+\infty} t^n e^{-t}\,dt = (-1)^n\Gamma(n+1).$$

(b) $t = x^n, x = t^{1/n}, dx = (1/n)t^{1/n-1}\,dt$,

$$\int_0^{+\infty} e^{-x^n}\,dx = (1/n)\int_0^{+\infty} t^{1/n-1}e^{-t}\,dt = (1/n)\Gamma(1/n) = \Gamma(1/n+1).$$

SUPPLEMENTARY EXERCISES CHAPTER 10

1. $\displaystyle\int_0^{+\infty}\frac{dx}{x^2+4} = \lim_{\ell\to+\infty}\frac{1}{2}\tan^{-1}(x/2)\Big]_0^\ell = \lim_{\ell\to+\infty}\frac{1}{2}\tan^{-1}(\ell/2) = \pi/4$,

$\displaystyle\int_\ell^0\frac{dx}{x^2+4} = \lim_{\ell\to-\infty}\frac{1}{2}\tan^{-1}(x/2)\Big]_\ell^0 = \pi/4$ so $\displaystyle\int_{-\infty}^{+\infty}\frac{dx}{x^2+4} = \pi/2$

2. $\displaystyle\lim_{\ell\to4+} -\ln|4-x|\Big]_\ell^6 = \lim_{\ell\to4+}(-\ln 2 + \ln|4-\ell|) = +\infty$, diverges

3. $\displaystyle\lim_{\ell\to1-} -\sqrt{1-x^2}\Big]_0^\ell = \lim_{\ell\to1-}(-\sqrt{1-\ell^2}+1) = 1$

4. $\displaystyle\lim_{\ell\to5-}\sin^{-1}(x/5)\Big]_0^\ell = \pi/2$

5. $\displaystyle\int_0^1 x^{-2/3}\,dx = \lim_{\ell\to0+} 3x^{1/3}\Big]_\ell^1 = 3$, $\displaystyle\int_{-1}^0 x^{-2/3}\,dx = \lim_{\ell\to0-} 3x^{1/3}\Big]_{-1}^\ell = 3$, $\displaystyle\int_{-1}^1 x^{-2/3}\,dx = 6$

6. $\displaystyle\lim_{\ell\to\pi/2-}\ \tan x\ \Big]_0^\ell = +\infty$, diverges

7. $\displaystyle\lim_{\ell\to+\infty}\ -\frac{1}{2}e^{-x^2}\ \Big]_0^\ell = \lim_{\ell\to+\infty}\frac{1}{2}(-e^{-\ell^2}+1)=1/2,$

$\displaystyle\lim_{\ell\to-\infty}\ -\frac{1}{2}e^{-x^2}\ \Big]_\ell^0 = \lim_{\ell\to-\infty}\frac{1}{2}(-1+e^{-\ell^2})=-1/2,$ so $\displaystyle\int_{-\infty}^{+\infty}xe^{-x^2}dx = 1/2-1/2=0$

8. $\displaystyle\lim_{\ell\to-\infty}\ (xe^x-e^x)\ \Big]_\ell^0 = \lim_{\ell\to-\infty}(-1-\ell e^\ell + e^\ell)=-1$ because

$\displaystyle\lim_{\ell\to-\infty}\ell e^\ell = \lim_{\ell\to-\infty}\frac{\ell}{e^{-\ell}}=\lim_{\ell\to-\infty}\frac{1}{-e^{-\ell}}=0$ and $\displaystyle\lim_{\ell\to-\infty}e^\ell=0$

9. $\displaystyle\lim_{\ell\to0+}\ln|\sin x|\ \Big]_\ell^{\pi/2} = \lim_{\ell\to0+}-\ln|\sin\ell|=+\infty$, diverges

10. $\displaystyle\int_0^{+\infty}x^{-5}dx = \int_0^1 x^{-5}dx + \int_1^{+\infty}x^{-5}dx,\ \int_0^1 x^{-5}dx = \lim_{\ell\to0+}-1/(4x^4)\ \Big]_\ell^1 = +\infty$ so

$\displaystyle\int_0^{+\infty}x^{-5}dx$ is divergent.

11. $\displaystyle\lim_{\ell\to+\infty}\ -1/\ln x\ \Big]_e^\ell = \lim_{\ell\to+\infty}(-1/\ln\ell + 1)=1$

12. $\displaystyle\lim_{\ell\to0+}\left(\frac{2}{3}x^{3/2}\ln x - \frac{4}{9}x^{3/2}\right)\Big]_\ell^1 = \lim_{\ell\to0+}\left(-\frac{4}{9}-\frac{2}{3}\ell^{3/2}\ln\ell + \frac{4}{9}\ell^{3/2}\right)=-4/9$ because

$\displaystyle\lim_{\ell\to0+}\ell^{3/2}\ln\ell = \lim_{\ell\to0+}\frac{\ln\ell}{\ell^{-3/2}}=\lim_{\ell\to0+}\frac{1/\ell}{(-3/2)\ell^{-5/2}}=\lim_{\ell\to0+}-\frac{2}{3}\ell^{3/2}=0$ and $\displaystyle\lim_{\ell\to0+}\ell^{3/2}=0.$

13. $\displaystyle\lim_{\ell\to+\infty}\ \tan^{-1}(x+1)\ \Big]_e^\ell = \lim_{\ell\to+\infty}[\tan^{-1}(\ell+1)-\tan^{-1}(1)]=\pi/2-\pi/4=\pi/4.$

14. $\displaystyle\lim_{\ell\to0+}\ -2e^{-\sqrt{x}}\ \Big]_\ell^4 = \lim_{\ell\to0+}2(-e^{-2}+e^{-\sqrt{\ell}})=2(1-e^{-2})$

15. If $n=-1$ then $\displaystyle\int_0^1\frac{\ln x}{x}dx = \lim_{\ell\to0+}\frac{1}{2}(\ln x)^2\ \Big]_\ell^1 = -\infty$ so the integral diverges. If $n\ne-1$ then

$\displaystyle\int_0^1 x^n\ln x\ dx = \lim_{\ell\to0+}\left[\frac{x^{n+1}}{n+1}\ln x - \frac{x^{n+1}}{(n+1)^2}\right]_\ell^1 = \lim_{\ell\to0+}\left[-\frac{1}{(n+1)^2}-\frac{\ell^{n+1}}{n+1}\ln\ell + \frac{\ell^{n+1}}{(n+1)^2}\right]$

If $n < -1$ then $n+1 < 0$, $\lim\limits_{\ell \to 0+} \ell^{n+1} \ln \ell = -\infty$ and $\lim_{\ell \to 0+} \ell^{n+1} = +\infty$ so the integral diverges.

If $n > -1$ then $\lim\limits_{\ell \to 0+} \ell^{n+1} \ln \ell = \lim\limits_{\ell \to 0+} \dfrac{\ln \ell}{\ell^{-(n+1)}} = \lim\limits_{\ell \to 0+} -\dfrac{\ell^{n+1}}{n+1} = 0$ and $\lim_{\ell \to 0+} \ell^{n+1} = 0$ so the integral converges to $-1/(n+1)^2$.

16. $\lim\limits_{x \to 1} \dfrac{1/x}{1} = 1$

17. $\lim\limits_{x \to 0} \dfrac{3xe^{3x} + e^{3x} - 1}{2 \sin 2x} = \lim\limits_{x \to 0} \dfrac{9xe^{3x} + 6e^{3x}}{4 \cos 2x} = 3/2$

18. $\lim\limits_{x \to +\infty} \dfrac{1/(x \ln x)}{1/(2\sqrt{x})} = \lim\limits_{x \to +\infty} \dfrac{2}{\sqrt{x} \ln x} = 0$

19. $\lim\limits_{x \to 0+} \dfrac{e^{1/x}}{1/x^2} = \lim\limits_{x \to 0+} \dfrac{(-1/x^2)e^{1/x}}{-2/x^3} = \lim\limits_{x \to 0+} \dfrac{e^{1/x}}{2/x} = \lim\limits_{x \to 0+} \dfrac{(-1/x^2)e^{1/x}}{-2/x^2} = \lim\limits_{x \to 0+} (1/2)e^{1/x} = +\infty$

20. $\lim\limits_{x \to +\infty} \dfrac{(x^2 + x) - x^2}{\sqrt{x^2 + x} + x} = \lim\limits_{x \to +\infty} \dfrac{x}{\sqrt{x^2 + x} + x} = \lim\limits_{x \to +\infty} \dfrac{1}{\sqrt{1 + 1/x} + 1} = 1/2$

21. $\lim\limits_{x \to 0-} x^2 e^{1/x} = (0)(0) = 0$

22. $y = (1 - x)^{2/x}$, $\lim\limits_{x \to 0-} \ln y = \lim\limits_{x \to 0-} \dfrac{2 \ln(1 - x)}{x} = \lim\limits_{x \to 0-} \dfrac{-2}{1 - x} = -2$, $\lim\limits_{x \to 0-} y = e^{-2}$

23. $\lim\limits_{\theta \to 0} \left(\dfrac{1}{\theta \sin \theta} - \dfrac{1}{\theta^2} \right) = \lim\limits_{\theta \to 0} \dfrac{\theta - \sin \theta}{\theta^2 \sin \theta} = \lim\limits_{\theta \to 0} \dfrac{1 - \cos \theta}{\theta^2 \cos \theta + 2\theta \sin \theta}$

$$= \lim\limits_{\theta \to 0} \dfrac{\sin \theta}{-\theta^2 \sin \theta + 4\theta \cos \theta + 2 \sin \theta}$$

$$= \lim\limits_{\theta \to 0} \dfrac{\cos \theta}{-\theta^2 \cos \theta - 6\theta \sin \theta + 6 \cos \theta} = 1/6$$

24. $\lim\limits_{x \to 0} \dfrac{1 - 1/(1 + x^2)}{4x^3} = \lim\limits_{x \to 0} \dfrac{1}{4x(1 + x^2)}$, which does not exist

25. $\lim\limits_{x \to 2} \dfrac{1 - e^{x-2}}{2\pi \sin 2\pi x} = \lim\limits_{x \to 2} \dfrac{-e^{x-2}}{4\pi^2 \cos 2\pi x} = -1/(4\pi^2)$

26. $\lim\limits_{x \to 0} \dfrac{9^x \ln 9 - 3^x \ln 3}{1} = \ln 9 - \ln 3 = \ln 3$

27. $\lim\limits_{x \to 0} \dfrac{\sin(x^2)}{2x \cos(x^2)} = \lim\limits_{x \to 0} \dfrac{2x \cos(x^2)}{-4x^2 \sin(x^2) + 2 \cos(x^2)} = 0$

28. $y = x^{1/x}$, $\displaystyle\lim_{x\to+\infty} \ln y = \lim_{x\to+\infty} \frac{\ln x}{x} = \lim_{x\to+\infty} \frac{1}{x} = 0$, $\displaystyle\lim_{x\to+\infty} y = e^0 = 1$

29. $\displaystyle\lim_{x\to+\infty} \frac{3(\ln x)^2}{x} = \lim_{x\to+\infty} \frac{6\ln x}{x} = \lim_{x\to+\infty} \frac{6}{x} = 0$

30. $y = \left(\dfrac{x}{x-3}\right)^x$, $\displaystyle\lim_{x\to+\infty} \ln y = \lim_{x\to+\infty} \frac{\ln \dfrac{x}{x-3}}{1/x} = \lim_{x\to+\infty} \frac{3x}{x-3} = 3$, $\displaystyle\lim_{x\to+\infty} y = e^3$

31. $y = (1+x)^{\ln x}$, $\displaystyle\lim_{x\to0+} \ln y = \lim_{x\to0+} \ln x \ln(1+x) = \lim_{x\to0+} \frac{\ln(1+x)}{1/\ln x}$

$$= \lim_{x\to0+} \frac{1/(1+x)}{-1/[x(\ln x)^2]} = \lim_{x\to0+} \frac{-x(\ln x)^2}{1+x},$$

but $\displaystyle\lim_{x\to0+} x(\ln x)^2 = \lim_{x\to0+} \frac{(\ln x)^2}{1/x} = \lim_{x\to0+} \frac{(2\ln x)/x}{-1/x^2}$

$$= \lim_{x\to0+} \frac{2\ln x}{-1/x} = \lim_{x\to0+} \frac{2/x}{-1/x^2} = \lim_{x\to0+} (-2x) = 0$$

so $\displaystyle\lim_{x\to0+} \frac{-x(\ln)^2}{1+x} = \frac{0}{1} = 0$ and $\displaystyle\lim_{x\to0+} y = e^0 = 1$

32. $A = \displaystyle\int_0^{+\infty} (e^{-x} - e^{-2x})dx = \lim_{\ell\to+\infty} \left(-e^{-x} + \frac{1}{2}e^{-2x}\right)\Big]_0^{\ell}$

$$= \lim_{\ell\to+\infty} \left(-e^{-\ell} + \frac{1}{2}e^{-2\ell} + \frac{1}{2}\right) = 1/2$$

33.   **(a)** $A = \displaystyle\int_8^{+\infty} x^{-2/3}dx = \lim_{\ell\to+\infty} 3x^{1/3}\Big]_8^{\ell} = +\infty$

   (b) $V = \displaystyle\int_8^{+\infty} \pi x^{-4/3}dx = \lim_{\ell\to+\infty} -3\pi x^{-1/3}\Big]_8^{\ell} = 3\pi/2$

34.   **(a)** $A = \displaystyle\int_0^1 x^{-1/3}dx = \lim_{\ell\to0+} \frac{3}{2}x^{2/3}\Big]_{\ell}^1 = 3/2$

   (b) $V = \displaystyle\int_0^1 \pi x^{-2/3}dx = \lim_{\ell\to0+} 3\pi x^{1/3}\Big]_{\ell}^1 = 3\pi$

35. $f(x) = \sqrt{x - x^2} - \sin^{-1}\sqrt{x} = \sqrt{x(1-x)} - \sin^{-1}\sqrt{x}$, the domain of f is $0 \le x \le 1$,

$f'(x) = \dfrac{1}{2}(x - x^2)^{-1/2}(1 - 2x) - \dfrac{1}{\sqrt{1-x}}(\dfrac{1}{2}x^{-1/2}) = -\dfrac{x}{\sqrt{x - x^2}},$

$$1 + [f'(x)]^2 = 1 + \frac{x^2}{x - x^2} = \frac{1}{1-x},$$

$$L = \int_0^1 \frac{1}{\sqrt{1-x}} dx = \lim_{\ell \to 1^-} -2\sqrt{1-x} \Big]_0^\ell = \lim_{\ell \to 1^-} 2(-\sqrt{1-\ell} + 1) = 2$$

CHAPTER 11
Infinite Series

EXERCISE SET 11.1

1. $1/3, 2/4, 3/5, 4/6, 5/7, \ldots$; $\displaystyle\lim_{n \to +\infty} \frac{n}{n+2} = 1$, converges

2. $1/3, 4/5, 9/7, 16/9, 25/11, \ldots$; $\displaystyle\lim_{n \to +\infty} \frac{n^2}{2n+1} = +\infty$, diverges

3. $2, 2, 2, 2, 2, \ldots$; $\displaystyle\lim_{x \to +\infty} 2 = 2$, converges

4. $\ln 1, \ln \dfrac{1}{2}, \ln \dfrac{1}{3}, \ln \dfrac{1}{4}, \ln \dfrac{1}{5}, \ldots$; $\displaystyle\lim_{x \to +\infty} \ln(1/n) = -\infty$, diverges

5. $\dfrac{\ln 1}{1}, \dfrac{\ln 2}{2}, \dfrac{\ln 3}{3}, \dfrac{\ln 4}{4}, \dfrac{\ln 5}{5}, \ldots$; $\displaystyle\lim_{x \to +\infty} \frac{\ln n}{n} = \lim_{x \to +\infty} \frac{1}{n} = 0$, converges

6. $\sin \pi, 2\sin(\pi/2), 3\sin(\pi/3), 4\sin(\pi/4), 5\sin(\pi/5), \ldots$;
   $\displaystyle\lim_{n \to +\infty} n \sin(\pi/n) = \lim_{n \to +\infty} \frac{\sin(\pi/n)}{1/n} = \lim_{n \to +\infty} \frac{(-\pi/n^2)\cos(\pi/n)}{-1/n^2} = \pi$, converges

7. $0, 2, 0, 2, 0, \ldots$; diverges

8. $1, -1/4, 1/9, -1/16, 1/25, \ldots$; $\displaystyle\lim_{n \to +\infty} \frac{(-1)^{n+1}}{n^2} = 0$, converges

9. $-1, 16/9, -54/28, 128/65, -250/126, \ldots$; diverges because odd-numbered terms approach -2, even-numbered terms approach 2.

10. $1/2, 2/4, 3/8, 4/16, 5/32, \ldots$; $\displaystyle\lim_{n \to +\infty} \frac{n}{2^n} = \lim_{n \to +\infty} \frac{1}{2^n \ln 2} = 0$, converges

11. $6/2, 12/8, 20/18, 30/32, 42/50, \ldots$; $\displaystyle\lim_{n \to +\infty} \frac{1}{2}(1 + 1/n)(1 + 2/n) = 1/2$, converges

12. $\pi/4, \pi^2/4^2, \pi^3/4^3, \pi^4/4^4, \pi^5/4^5, \ldots$; $\displaystyle\lim_{n \to +\infty} (\pi/4)^n = 0$, converges

13. $\cos(3), \cos(3/2), \cos(1), \cos(3/4), \cos(3/5), \ldots$; $\displaystyle\lim_{n \to +\infty} \cos(3/n) = 1$, converges

14. $0, -1, 0, 1, 0, \ldots$; diverges

15. e^{-1}, $4e^{-2}$, $9e^{-3}$, $16e^{-4}$, $25e^{-5}$, ...; $\displaystyle\lim_{x\to+\infty} x^2 e^{-x} = \lim_{x\to+\infty} \frac{x^2}{e^x} = 0$, so $\displaystyle\lim_{n\to+\infty} n^2 e^{-n} = 0$, converges

16. 1, $\sqrt{10} - 2$, $\sqrt{18} - 3$, $\sqrt{28} - 4$, $\sqrt{40} - 5$, ...;

$\displaystyle\lim_{n\to+\infty} (\sqrt{n^2 + 3n} - n) = \lim_{n\to+\infty} \frac{3n}{\sqrt{n^2 + 3n} + n} = \lim_{n\to+\infty} \frac{3}{\sqrt{1 + 3/n} + 1} = \frac{3}{2}$, converges

17. 2, $(5/3)^2$, $(6/4)^3$, $(7/5)^4$, $(8/6)^5$, ...; let $y = \left[\dfrac{x+3}{x+1}\right]^x$, converges because

$\displaystyle\lim_{x\to+\infty} \ln y = \lim_{x\to+\infty} \frac{\ln \dfrac{x+3}{x+1}}{1/x} = \lim_{x\to+\infty} \frac{2x^2}{(x+1)(x+3)} = 2$, so $\displaystyle\lim_{n\to+\infty} \left[\frac{n+3}{n+1}\right]^n = e^2$

18. -1, 0, $(1/3)^3$, $(2/4)^4$, $(3/5)^5$, ...; let $y = (1 - 2/x)^x$, converges because

$\displaystyle\lim_{x\to+\infty} \ln y = \lim_{x\to+\infty} \frac{\ln(1 - 2/x)}{1/x} = \lim_{x\to+\infty} \frac{-2}{1 - 2/x} = -2$, $\displaystyle\lim_{n\to+\infty} (1 - 2/n)^n = \lim_{x\to+\infty} y = e^{-2}$

19. $\left\{\dfrac{2n-1}{2n}\right\}_{n=1}^{+\infty}$; $\displaystyle\lim_{n\to+\infty} \frac{2n-1}{2n} = 1$, converges

20. $\left\{\dfrac{n-1}{n^2}\right\}_{n=1}^{+\infty}$; $\displaystyle\lim_{n\to+\infty} \frac{n-1}{n^2} = 0$, converges

21. $\{1/3^n\}_{n=1}^{+\infty}$; $\lim_{n\to+\infty} 1/3^n = 0$, converges

22. $\{(-1)^n n\}_{n=1}^{+\infty}$; diverges because odd-numbered terms tend toward $-\infty$, even-numbered terms tend toward $+\infty$.

23. $\left\{\dfrac{1}{n} - \dfrac{1}{n+1}\right\}_{n=1}^{+\infty}$; $\displaystyle\lim_{n\to+\infty} \left(\frac{1}{n} - \frac{1}{n+1}\right) = 0$, converges

24. $\{3/2^{n-1}\}_{n=1}^{+\infty}$; $\displaystyle\lim_{n\to+\infty} 3/2^{n-1} = 0$, converges

25. $\{\sqrt{n+1} - \sqrt{n+2}\}_{n=1}^{+\infty}$; converges because

$\displaystyle\lim_{n\to+\infty} (\sqrt{n+1} - \sqrt{n+2}) = \lim_{n\to+\infty} \frac{(n+1) - (n+2)}{\sqrt{n+1} + \sqrt{n+2}} = \lim_{n\to+\infty} \frac{-1}{\sqrt{n+1} + \sqrt{n+2}} = 0$

26. $\{(-1)^{n+1}/3^{n+4}\}_{n=1}^{+\infty}$; $\displaystyle\lim_{n\to+\infty} (-1)^{n+1}/3^{n+4} = 0$, converges

27. **(a)** $\sqrt{6}, \sqrt{6+\sqrt{6}}, \sqrt{6+\sqrt{6+\sqrt{6}}}$

(b) $\lim\limits_{n\to+\infty} a_{n+1} = \lim\limits_{n\to+\infty} \sqrt{6+a_n}$, $L = \sqrt{6+L}$, $L^2 - L - 6 = 0$, $(L-3)(L+2) = 0$, $L = -2$
(reject, because the terms in the sequence are positive) or $L = 3$; $\lim\limits_{n\to+\infty} a_n = 3$.

28. $\lim\limits_{n\to+\infty} a_{n+1} = \lim\limits_{n\to+\infty} \dfrac{1}{2}(a_n + k/a_n)$, $L = \dfrac{1}{2}(L + k/L)$, $L^2 = k$, $L = \sqrt{k}$; $\lim\limits_{n\to+\infty} a_n = \sqrt{k}$.

29. **(a)** $1, 1, 2, 3, 5, 8, 13, 21$

(b) $a_{n+2}/a_{n+1} = a_n/a_{n+1} + 1 = 1/(a_{n+1}/a_n) + 1$,
$\lim\limits_{n\to+\infty}(a_{n+2}/a_{n+1}) = \lim\limits_{n\to+\infty}[1/(a_{n+1}/a_n) + 1]$, with $L = \lim\limits_{n\to+\infty}(a_{n+1}/a_n)$, $L = 1/L + 1$,
$L^2 - L - 1 = 0$, $L = (1 \pm \sqrt{5})/2$ so $L = (1 + \sqrt{5})/2$ because the limit cannot be negative.

30. **(a)** $a_n = \begin{cases} n, & n \text{ odd} \\ 1/2^n, & n \text{ even} \end{cases}$ **(b)** $a_n = \begin{cases} 1/n, & n \text{ odd} \\ 1/(n+1), & n \text{ even} \end{cases}$

31. **(a)** $1, \dfrac{1}{4} + \dfrac{2}{4}, \dfrac{1}{9} + \dfrac{2}{9} + \dfrac{3}{9}, \dfrac{1}{16} + \dfrac{2}{16} + \dfrac{3}{16} + \dfrac{4}{16}, \cdots = 1, 3/4, 2/3, 5/8, \cdots$

(b) $a_n = \dfrac{1}{n^2}(1 + 2 + \cdots + n) = \dfrac{1}{n^2}\dfrac{1}{2}n(n+1) = \dfrac{1}{2}\dfrac{n+1}{n}$, $\lim\limits_{n\to+\infty} a_n = 1/2$

32. **(a)** $1, \dfrac{1}{8} + \dfrac{4}{8}, \dfrac{1}{27} + \dfrac{4}{27} + \dfrac{9}{27}, \dfrac{1}{64} + \dfrac{4}{64} + \dfrac{9}{64} + \dfrac{16}{64}, \cdots = 1, 5/8, 14/27, 15/32, \cdots$

(b) $a_n = \dfrac{1}{n^3}(1^2 + 2^2 + \cdots + n^2) = \dfrac{1}{n^3}\dfrac{1}{6}n(n+1)(2n+1) = \dfrac{1}{6}\dfrac{(n+1)(2n+1)}{n^2}$,
$\lim\limits_{x\to+\infty} a_n = \lim\limits_{x\to+\infty}\dfrac{1}{6}(1 + 1/n)(2 + 1/n) = 1/3$

33. $\left|\dfrac{1}{n} - 0\right| = \dfrac{1}{n} < \epsilon$ if $n > 1/\epsilon$

(a) $1/\epsilon = 1/0.5 = 2$, $N = 3$ **(b)** $1/\epsilon = 1/0.1 = 10$, $N = 11$
(c) $1/\epsilon = 1/0.001 = 1000$, $N = 1001$

34. $\left|\dfrac{n}{n+1} - 1\right| = \dfrac{1}{n+1} < \epsilon$ if $n + 1 > 1/\epsilon$, $n > 1/\epsilon - 1$

(a) $1/\epsilon - 1 = 1/0.25 - 1 = 3$, $N = 4$ **(b)** $1/\epsilon - 1 = 1/0.1 - 1 = 9$, $N = 10$
(c) $1/\epsilon - 1 = 1/0.001 - 1 = 999$, $N = 1000$

35. **(a)** $\left|\dfrac{1}{n} - 0\right| = \dfrac{1}{n} < \epsilon$ if $n > 1/\epsilon$, choose any $N > 1/\epsilon$.

(b) $\left|\dfrac{n}{n+1} - 1\right| = \dfrac{1}{n+1} < \epsilon$ if $n > 1/\epsilon - 1$, choose any $N > 1/\epsilon - 1$.

36. Let $f(x) = 1/(1+x)$, $0 \le x \le 1$. Take $\Delta x_k = 1/n$ and $x_k^* = (k-1)/n$ then

$$a_n = \sum_{k=0}^{n-1} \frac{1}{1+(k/n)}(1/n) = \sum_{k=1}^{n} \frac{1}{1+(k-1)/n}(1/n) = \sum_{k=1}^{n} \frac{1}{1+x_k^*}\Delta x_k$$

so $\displaystyle \lim_{n \to +\infty} a_n = \int_0^1 \frac{1}{1+x}dx = \ln(1+x)\Big]_0^1 = \ln 2$

37. **(a)** Let s_n denote the length of each of the n sides of the polygon, then

$$\sin(\pi/n) = \frac{s_n/2}{r}$$
$$s_n = 2r\sin(\pi/n)$$
$$p_n = ns_n = 2rn\sin(\pi/n)$$

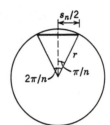

(b) $\displaystyle \lim_{n \to +\infty} 2rn\sin(\pi/n) = \lim_{n \to +\infty} \frac{2r\sin(\pi/n)}{1/n}$

$$= \lim_{n \to +\infty} 2\pi r\cos(\pi/n) = 2\pi r$$

38. If $|r| < 1$ then $\displaystyle \lim_{n \to +\infty} r^n = 0$; if $r > 1$ then $\displaystyle \lim_{n \to +\infty} r^n = +\infty$, if $r < -1$ then r^n oscillates between positive and negative values that grow in magnitude so $\displaystyle \lim_{n \to +\infty} r^n$ does not exist for $|r| > 1$; if $r = 1$ then $\displaystyle \lim_{n \to +\infty} 1^n = 1$; if $r = -1$ then $(-1)^n$ oscillates between -1 and 1 so $\displaystyle \lim_{n \to +\infty} (-1)^n$ does not exist.

39. Let $y = (2^x + 3^x)^{1/x}$,

$$\lim_{x \to +\infty} \ln y = \lim_{x \to +\infty} \frac{\ln(2^x + 3^x)}{x} = \lim_{x \to +\infty} \frac{2^x \ln 2 + 3^x \ln 3}{2^x + 3^x} = \lim_{x \to +\infty} \frac{(2/3)^x \ln 2 + \ln 3}{(2/3)^x + 1} = \ln 3$$

so $\displaystyle \lim_{x \to +\infty} (2^n + 3^n)^{1/n} = e^{\ln 3} = 3$

EXERCISE SET 11.2

1. $a_n - a_{n+1} = \dfrac{1}{n} - \dfrac{1}{n+1} = \dfrac{1}{n(n+1)} > 0$ for $n \ge 1$, so decreasing.

2. $a_n - a_{n+1} = (1 - \frac{1}{n}) - (1 - \frac{1}{n+1}) = -\frac{1}{n(n+1)} < 0$ for $n \geq 1$, so increasing.

3. $a_n - a_{n+1} = \frac{n}{2n+1} - \frac{n+1}{2n+3} = -\frac{1}{(2n+1)(2n+3)} < 0$ for $n \geq 1$, so increasing.

4. $a_n - a_{n+1} = \frac{n}{4n-1} - \frac{n+1}{4n+3} = \frac{1}{(4n-1)(4n+3)} > 0$ for $n \geq 1$, so decreasing.

5. $a_n - a_{n+1} = (n - 2^n) - (n + 1 - 2^{n+1}) = 2^n - 1 > 0$ for $n \geq 1$, so decreasing.

6. $a_n - a_{n+1} = (n - n^2) - [(n+1) - (n+1)^2] = 2n > 0$ for $n \geq 1$, so decreasing.

7. $\frac{a_{n+1}}{a_n} = \frac{(n+1)/(2n+3)}{n/(2n+1)} = \frac{(n+1)(2n+1)}{n(2n+3)} = \frac{2n^2 + 3n + 1}{2n^2 + 3n} > 1$ for $n \geq 1$, so increasing.

8. $\frac{a_{n+1}}{a_n} = \frac{(n+1)/2^{n+1}}{n/2^n} = \frac{n+1}{2n} = \frac{1}{2} + \frac{1}{2n} \leq 1$ for $n \geq 1$, so nonincreasing.

9. $\frac{a_{n+1}}{a_n} = \frac{(n+1)e^{-(n+1)}}{ne^{-n}} = (1 + 1/n)e^{-1} < 1$ for $n \geq 1$, so decreasing.

10. $\frac{a_{n+1}}{a_n} = \frac{(n+1)^2/3^{n+1}}{n^2/3^n} = \frac{(n+1)^2}{3n^2}, \frac{(n+1)^2}{3n^2} > 1$ for $n = 1$, $\frac{(n+1)^2}{3n^2} < 1$ for $n \geq 2$,
so not monotone.

11. $\frac{a_{n+1}}{a_n} = \frac{2^{n+1}/(n+1)!}{2^n/n!} = \frac{2^{n+1}}{2^n} \cdot \frac{n!}{(n+1)!} = \frac{2}{n+1} \leq 1$ for $n \geq 1$, so nonincreasing.

12. $\frac{a_{n+1}}{a_n} = \frac{e^{n+1}/(n+1)!}{e^n/n!} = \frac{e}{n+1}, \frac{e}{n+1} > 1$ for $n = 1$, $\frac{e}{n+1} < 1$ for $n \geq 2$, so not monotone.

13. $\frac{a_{n+1}}{a_n} = \frac{(n+1)!}{3^{n+1}} \cdot \frac{3^n}{n!} = \frac{n+1}{3}, \frac{n+1}{3} \leq 1$ for $n = 1$ and 2, $\frac{n+1}{3} > 1$ for $n \geq 3$,
so not monotone.

14. $\frac{a_{n+1}}{a_n} = \frac{(n+1)^2/(n+1)!}{n^2/n!} = \frac{n+1}{n^2}, \frac{n+1}{n^2} > 1$ for $n = 1$, $\frac{n+1}{n^2} < 1$ for $n \geq 2$,
so not monotone.

15. $\frac{a_{n+1}}{a_n} = \frac{10^{n+1}}{(2n+2)!} \cdot \frac{(2n)!}{10^n} = \frac{10}{(2n+2)(2n+1)} < 1$ for $n \geq 1$, so decreasing.

16. $\dfrac{a_{n+1}}{a_n} = \dfrac{2^{n+1}}{1+2^{n+1}} \cdot \dfrac{1+2^n}{2^n} = \dfrac{2+2^{n+1}}{1+2^{n+1}} = 1 + \dfrac{2^{n+1}}{1+2^{n+1}} > 1$ for $n \geq 1$, so increasing.

17. $\dfrac{a_{n+1}}{a_n} = \dfrac{(n+1)^{n+1}}{(n+1)!} \cdot \dfrac{n!}{n^n} = \dfrac{(n+1)^n}{n^n} = (1+1/n)^n > 1$ for $n \geq 1$, so increasing.

18. $\dfrac{a_{n+1}}{a_n} = \dfrac{10^{n+1}}{2^{(n+1)^2}} \cdot \dfrac{2^{n^2}}{10^n} = \dfrac{10}{2^{2n+1}}, \dfrac{10}{2^{2n+1}} > 1$ for $n = 1$, $\dfrac{10}{2^{2n+1}} < 1$ for $n \geq 2$, so not monotone.

19. $f(x) = x/(2x+1)$, $f'(x) = 1/(2x+1)^2 > 0$ for $x \geq 1$, so increasing.

20. $f(x) = 3 - 1/x$, $f'(x) = 1/x^2 > 0$ for $x \geq 1$, so increasing.

21. $f(x) = 1/(x + \ln x)$, $f'(x) = -\dfrac{1+1/x}{(x+\ln x)^2} < 0$ for $x \geq 1$, so decreasing.

22. $f(x) = xe^{-2x}$, $f'(x) = (1-2x)e^{-2x} < 0$ for $x \geq 1$, so decreasing.

23. $f(x) = \dfrac{\ln(x+2)}{x+2}$, $f'(x) = \dfrac{1-\ln(x+2)}{(x+2)^2} < 0$ for $x \geq 1$, so decreasing.

24. $f(x) = \tan^{-1} x$, $f'(x) = 1/(1+x^2) > 0$ for $x \geq 1$, so increasing.

25. $a_{n+1}/a_n = (n+1)/(5n) < 1$ for $n \geq 1$ so decreasing; 0 is a lower bound of $n/5^n$ for $n \geq 1$ so the sequence converges.

26. $\dfrac{a_{n+1}}{a_n} = \dfrac{2^{n+1}(n+1)!}{2^n(n+2)!} = \dfrac{2}{n+2} < 1$ for $n \geq 1$ so decreasing; 0 is a lower bound of $2^n/(n+1)!$ so the sequence converges.

27. Let $f(x) = x - 1/x$, then $f'(x) = 1 + 1/x^2 > 0$ so increasing; $n - 1/n$ has no upper bound so the sequence diverges.

28. Let $f(x) = \cos\dfrac{\pi}{2x}$, then $f'(x) = \dfrac{\pi}{2x^2}\sin\dfrac{\pi}{2x} > 0$ for $x \geq 1$ so increasing; 1 is an upper bound of $\cos\dfrac{\pi}{2n}$ for $n \geq 1$ so the sequence converges.

29. Let $f(x) = 2 + 1/x$, then $f'(x) = -1/x^2 < 0$ for $x \geq 1$ so decreasing; 2 is a lower bound because $2 + 1/n \geq 2$ for $n \geq 1$ so the sequence converges.

30. Let $f(x) = (4x-1)/(5x+2)$, then $f'(x) = 13/(5x+2)^2 > 0$ for $x \geq 1$ so increasing; $4/5$ is an upper bound because $(4n-1)/(5n+2) < (4n)/(5n) = 4/5$ so the sequence converges.

31. **(a)** We can discard the first two terms without affecting the convergence or the limit. This leaves the sequence $1, \dfrac{1}{2}, \dfrac{1}{3}, \ldots, \dfrac{1}{n}, \ldots$ Because $\lim\limits_{n \to +\infty} \dfrac{1}{n} = 0$, this is also the limit of the given sequence.

    (b) Discard the first four terms, leaving $1, 2, 3, \ldots, n, \ldots$; $\lim\limits_{n \to +\infty} n = +\infty$ so the limit does not exist.

32. **(a)** $a_{n+1}/a_n = 100/(n+1)$; $a_{n+1}/a_n \geq 1$ for $1 \leq n \leq 99$, $a_{n+1}/a_n < 1$ for $n \geq 100$, so the sequence is not monotone.

    (b) The sequence is convergent because it is decreasing for $n \geq 100$ and 0 is a lower bound.

33. $\dfrac{a_{n+1}}{a_n} = \dfrac{3^{n+1}(1+3^{2n})}{3^n(1+3^{2n+2})} = \dfrac{3(1+3^{2n})}{1+3^{2n+2}} < \dfrac{3(1+3^{2n})}{3^{2n+2}} = \dfrac{1}{3^{2n+1}} + \dfrac{1}{3} < 1$ for $n \geq 1$ so decreasing.

34. $\dfrac{a_{n+1}}{a_n} = \dfrac{1 \cdot 3 \cdot 5 \cdots (2n-1)(2n+1)n!}{1 \cdot 3 \cdot 5 \cdots (2n-1)(n+1)!} = \dfrac{2n+1}{n+1} > 1$ for $n \geq 1$ so increasing.

35. **(a)** $\sqrt{2}, \sqrt{2+\sqrt{2}}, \sqrt{2+\sqrt{2+\sqrt{2}}}$

    (b) $a_1 = \sqrt{2} < 2$ so $a_2 = \sqrt{2+a_1} < \sqrt{2+2} = 2$, $a_3 = \sqrt{2+a_2} < \sqrt{2+2} = 2$, and so on indefinitely.

    (c) $a_{n+1}^2 - a_n^2 = (2+a_n) - a_n^2 = 2 + a_n - a_n^2 = (2-a_n)(1+a_n)$

    (d) $a_n > 0$ and, from part (a), $a_n < 2$ so $2 - a_n > 0$ and $1 + a_n > 0$ thus, from part (c), $a_{n+1}^2 - a_n^2 > 0$, $a_{n+1} - a_n > 0$, $a_{n+1} > a_n$; $\{a_n\}$ is an increasing sequence.

    (e) The sequence is increasing and has 2 as an upper bound so it must converge to a limit L, $\lim\limits_{n \to +\infty} a_{n+1} = \lim\limits_{n \to +\infty} \sqrt{2+a_n}$, $L = \sqrt{2+L}$, $L^2 - L - 2 = 0$, $(L-2)(L+1) = 0$ thus $\lim\limits_{n \to +\infty} a_n = 2$.

36. **(a)** $\sqrt{3}, \sqrt{3\sqrt{3}}, \sqrt{3\sqrt{3\sqrt{3}}}$ (or $3^{1/2}, 3^{3/4}, 3^{7/8}$)

    (b) $a_1 = \sqrt{3} < 3$ so $a_2 = \sqrt{3a_1} < \sqrt{3(3)} = 3$, $a_3 = \sqrt{3a_2} < \sqrt{3(3)} = 3$, and so on indefinitely.

    (c) $a_{n+1}^2 - a_n^2 = 3a_n - a_n^2 = a_n(3 - a_n)$

    (d) $a_n > 0$ and, from part (a), $a_n < 3$ so, from part (c), $a_{n+1}^2 - a_n^2 > 0$, $a_{n+1} - a_n > 0$, $a_{n+1} > a_n$.

    (e) The sequence is increasing and has 3 as an upper bound so it must converge to a limit L, $\lim\limits_{n \to +\infty} a_{n+1} = \lim\limits_{n \to +\infty} \sqrt{3a_n}$, $L = \sqrt{3L}$, $L^2 - 3L = 0$, $L(L-3) = 0$ thus $\lim\limits_{n \to +\infty} a_n = 3$.

37. **(a)** If $\{a_n\}_{n=1}^{+\infty}$ is nonincreasing then $a_n \geq a_{n+1}$ for all n, thus $-a_n \leq -a_{n+1}$ so $\{-a_n\}_{n=1}^{+\infty}$ is nondecreasing.

(b) From part (a), $\{-a_n\}_{n=1}^{+\infty}$ is nondecreasing so Theorem 11.2.2 applies. Suppose there is a finite constant M_1 such that $-a_n \leq M_1$ and $\lim\limits_{n\to+\infty}(-a_n) = L_1 \leq M_1$, then $a_n \geq -M_1$, and $\lim\limits_{n\to+\infty} a_n = -L_1 \geq -M_1$; part (a) of Theorem 11.2.3 follows by letting $M = -M_1$ and $L = -L_1$. Suppose no such constant exists, then $\lim\limits_{n\to+\infty}(-a_n) = +\infty$ so $\lim\limits_{n\to+\infty} a_n = -\infty$.

38. **(a)** The altitudes of the rectangles are $\ln k$ for $k = 2$ to n, and their bases all have length 1 so the sum of their areas is $\ln 2 + \ln 3 + \cdots + \ln n = \ln(2 \cdot 3 \cdots n) = \ln n!$. $\int_1^n \ln x\, dx$ is the area under the curve $y = \ln x$ for x in the interval $[1, n]$, $\int_1^{n+1} \ln x\, dx$ is the area for x in the interval $[1, n+1]$ so, from the figure, $\int_1^n \ln x\, dx < \ln n! < \int_1^{n+1} \ln x\, dx$.

(b) $\int_1^n \ln x\, dx = (x \ln x - x)]_1^n = n \ln n - n + 1$ and $\int_1^{n+1} \ln x\, dx = (n+1)\ln(n+1) - n$ so, from part (a), $n \ln n - n + 1 < \ln n! < (n+1)\ln(n+1) - n$, $e^{n \ln n - n + 1} < n! < e^{(n+1)\ln(n+1) - n}$, $e^{n \ln n} e^{1-n} < n! < e^{(n+1)\ln(n+1)} e^{-n}$, $\dfrac{n^n}{e^{n-1}} < n! < \dfrac{(n+1)^{n+1}}{e^n}$.

39. From part (b) of Exercise 38, $\left[\dfrac{n^n}{e^{n-1}}\right]^{1/n} < \sqrt[n]{n!} < \left[\dfrac{(n+1)^{n+1}}{e^n}\right]^{1/n}$,

$\dfrac{n}{e^{1-1/n}} < \sqrt[n]{n!} < \dfrac{(n+1)^{1+1/n}}{e}$, $\dfrac{1}{e^{1-1/n}} < \dfrac{\sqrt[n]{n!}}{n} < \dfrac{(1+1/n)(n+1)^{1/n}}{e}$,

but $\dfrac{1}{e^{1-1/n}} \to \dfrac{1}{e}$ and $\dfrac{(1+1/n)(n+1)^{1/n}}{e} \to \dfrac{1}{e}$ as $n \to +\infty$ so $\lim\limits_{n\to+\infty} \dfrac{\sqrt[n]{n!}}{n} = \dfrac{1}{e}$.

40. $n! > \dfrac{n^n}{e^{n-1}}$, $\sqrt[n]{n!} > \dfrac{n}{e^{1-1/n}}$, $\lim\limits_{n\to+\infty} \dfrac{n}{e^{1-1/n}} = +\infty$ so $\lim\limits_{n\to+\infty} \sqrt[n]{n!} = +\infty$.

41. **(a)** $\dfrac{a_{n+1}}{a_n} = \dfrac{(n+1)^{n+1}}{(n+1)! e^{n+1}} \cdot \dfrac{n! e^n}{n^n} = \dfrac{(1+1/n)^n}{e} < 1$ for $n \geq 1$ because $(1+1/n)^n < e$ for $n \geq 1$.

(b) Yes, because it is decreasing and bounded below by 0.

EXERCISE SET 11.3

1. **(a)** $s_1 = 2$, $s_2 = 12/5$, $s_3 = 62/25$, $s_4 = 312/125$

    $s_n = \dfrac{2 - 2(1/5)^n}{1 - 1/5} = \dfrac{5}{2} - \dfrac{5}{2}(1/5)^n$, $\lim\limits_{n \to +\infty} s_n = 5/2$, converges

    (b) $\dfrac{1}{(k+1)(k+2)} = \dfrac{1}{k+1} - \dfrac{1}{k+2}$, $s_1 = 1/6$, $s_2 = 1/4$, $s_3 = 3/10$, $s_4 = 1/3$ $s_n = \dfrac{1}{2} - \dfrac{1}{n+2}$,

    $\lim\limits_{n \to +\infty} s_n = 1/2$, converges

    (c) $s_1 = 1/4$, $s_2 = 3/4$, $s_3 = 7/4$, $s_4 = 15/4$

    $s_n = \dfrac{(1/4) - (1/4)2^n}{1 - 2} = -\dfrac{1}{4} + \dfrac{1}{4}(2^n)$, $\lim\limits_{n \to +\infty} s_n = +\infty$, diverges

2. geometric, $a = 1/5$, $r = 1/5$, sum $= \dfrac{1/5}{1 - 1/5} = 1/4$

3. geometric, $a = 1$, $r = -3/4$, sum $= \dfrac{1}{1 - (-3/4)} = 4/7$

4. geometric, $a = (2/3)^3$, $r = 2/3$, sum $= \dfrac{(2/3)^3}{1 - 2/3} = 8/9$

5. geometric, $a = 7$, $r = -1/6$, sum $= \dfrac{7}{1 + 1/6} = 6$

6. geometric, $r = 4$, diverges   7. geometric, $r = -3/2$, diverges

8. $s_n = \sum\limits_{k=1}^{n} \left(\dfrac{1}{k+3} - \dfrac{1}{k+4} \right) = \dfrac{1}{4} - \dfrac{1}{n+4}$, $\lim\limits_{n \to +\infty} s_n = 1/4$

9. $s_n = \sum\limits_{k=1}^{n} \left(\dfrac{1}{k+2} - \dfrac{1}{k+3} \right) = \dfrac{1}{3} - \dfrac{1}{n+3}$, $\lim\limits_{n \to +\infty} s_n = 1/3$

10. $s_n = \sum\limits_{k=1}^{n} \left(\dfrac{1}{2^k} - \dfrac{1}{2^{k+1}} \right) = \dfrac{1}{2} - \dfrac{1}{2^{n+1}}$, $\lim\limits_{n \to +\infty} s_n = 1/2$

11. $s_n = \sum\limits_{k=1}^{n} \left(\dfrac{1/3}{3k-1} - \dfrac{1/3}{3k+2} \right) = \dfrac{1}{6} - \dfrac{1/3}{3n+2}$, $\lim\limits_{n \to +\infty} s_n = 1/6$

12. $s_n = \sum\limits_{k=2}^{n+1}\left[\dfrac{1/2}{k-1}-\dfrac{1/2}{k+1}\right] = \dfrac{1}{2}\left[\sum\limits_{k=2}^{n+1}\dfrac{1}{k-1}-\sum\limits_{k=2}^{n+1}\dfrac{1}{k+1}\right]$

$= \dfrac{1}{2}\left[\sum\limits_{k=2}^{n+1}\dfrac{1}{k-1}-\sum\limits_{k=4}^{n+3}\dfrac{1}{k-1}\right] = \dfrac{1}{2}\left[1+\dfrac{1}{2}-\dfrac{1}{n+1}-\dfrac{1}{n+2}\right]$; $\lim\limits_{n\to+\infty} s_n = \dfrac{3}{4}$

13. $\sum\limits_{k=1}^{\infty}\dfrac{4^{k+2}}{7^{k-1}} = \sum\limits_{k=1}^{\infty}64\left(\dfrac{4}{7}\right)^{k-1}$; geometric, $a=64$, $r=4/7$, sum $=\dfrac{64}{1-4/7}=448/3$

14. geometric, $a=1$, $r=e/\pi$, sum $=\dfrac{1}{1-e/\pi}=\pi/(\pi-e)$

15. geometric, $a=-1/2$, $r=-1/2$, sum $=\dfrac{-1/2}{1+1/2}=-1/3$

16. $\sum\limits_{k=3}^{\infty}\dfrac{5}{k-2} = \sum\limits_{k=1}^{\infty}5/k$ so each term is larger than the corresponding term of the harmonic series $\sum\limits_{k=1}^{\infty}1/k$. The n-th partial sum of $\sum\limits_{k=1}^{\infty}5/k$ is larger than the n-th partial sum of $\sum\limits_{k=1}^{\infty}1/k$ so the partial sums of $\sum\limits_{k=1}^{\infty}5/k$ have no upper bound, the series diverges.

17. $0.4444\cdots = 0.4+0.04+0.004+\cdots = \dfrac{0.4}{1-0.1}=4/9$

18. $0.9999\cdots = 0.9+0.09+0.009+\cdots = \dfrac{0.9}{1-0.1}=1$

19. $5.373737\cdots = 5+0.37+0.0037+0.000037+\cdots = 5+\dfrac{0.37}{1-0.01}=5+37/99=532/99$

20. $0.159159159\cdots = 0.159+0.000159+0.000000159+\cdots = \dfrac{0.159}{1-0.001}=159/999=53/333$

21. $0.782178217821\cdots = 0.7821+0.00007821+0.000000007821+\cdots$

$= \dfrac{0.7821}{1-0.0001}=7821/9999=869/1111$

22. $0.451141414\cdots = 0.451+0.00014+0.0000014+0.000000014+\cdots$

$= 0.451+\dfrac{0.00014}{1-0.01}=44663/99000$

23. $s_n = \ln \dfrac{1}{2} + \ln \dfrac{2}{3} + \ln \dfrac{3}{4} + \cdots + \ln \dfrac{n}{n+1} = \ln \left(\dfrac{1}{2} \cdot \dfrac{2}{3} \cdot \dfrac{3}{4} \cdots \dfrac{n}{n+1} \right) = \ln \dfrac{1}{n+1} = -\ln(n+1),$

$\displaystyle \lim_{n \to +\infty} s_n = -\infty$, series diverges.

24. $d = 10 + 2 \cdot \dfrac{3}{4} \cdot 10 + 2 \cdot \dfrac{3}{4} \cdot \dfrac{3}{4} \cdot 10 + 2 \cdot \dfrac{3}{4} \cdot \dfrac{3}{4} \cdot \dfrac{3}{4} \cdot 10 + \cdots$

$= 10 + 20 \left(\dfrac{3}{4} \right) + 20 \left(\dfrac{3}{4} \right)^2 + 20 \left(\dfrac{3}{4} \right)^3 + \cdots = 10 + \dfrac{20(3/4)}{1 - 3/4} = 10 + 60 = 70$ meters

25. $\ln 1 - 1/k^2 = \ln \dfrac{k^2 - 1}{k^2} = \ln \dfrac{(k-1)(k+1)}{k^2} = \ln \dfrac{k-1}{k} + \ln \dfrac{k+1}{k} = \ln \dfrac{k-1}{k} - \ln \dfrac{k}{k+1},$

$s_n = \displaystyle\sum_{k=2}^{n+1} \left[\ln \dfrac{k-1}{k} - \ln \dfrac{k}{k+1} \right]$

$= \left(\ln \dfrac{1}{2} - \ln \dfrac{2}{3} \right) + \left(\ln \dfrac{2}{3} - \ln \dfrac{3}{4} \right) + \left(\ln \dfrac{3}{4} - \ln \dfrac{4}{5} \right) + \cdots + \left(\ln \dfrac{n}{n+1} - \ln \dfrac{n+1}{n+2} \right)$

$= \ln \dfrac{1}{2} - \ln \dfrac{n+1}{n+2}, \displaystyle\lim_{n \to +\infty} s_n = \ln \dfrac{1}{2} = -\ln 2$

26. $\dfrac{\sqrt{k+1} - \sqrt{k}}{\sqrt{k^2 + k}} = \dfrac{\sqrt{k+1} - \sqrt{k}}{\sqrt{k}\sqrt{k+1}} = \dfrac{1}{\sqrt{k}} - \dfrac{1}{\sqrt{k+1}},$

$s_n = \displaystyle\sum_{k=1}^{n} \left(\dfrac{1}{\sqrt{k}} - \dfrac{1}{\sqrt{k+1}} \right)$

$= \left(\dfrac{1}{\sqrt{1}} - \dfrac{1}{\sqrt{2}} \right) + \left(\dfrac{1}{\sqrt{2}} - \dfrac{1}{\sqrt{3}} \right) + \left(\dfrac{1}{\sqrt{3}} - \dfrac{1}{\sqrt{4}} \right) + \cdots + \left(\dfrac{1}{\sqrt{n}} - \dfrac{1}{\sqrt{n+1}} \right)$

$= 1 - \dfrac{1}{\sqrt{n+1}}; \displaystyle\lim_{n \to +\infty} s_n = 1$

27. $s_n = (1 - 1/3) + (1/2 - 1/4) + (1/3 - 1/5) + (1/4 - 1/6) + \cdots + [1/n - 1/(n+2)]$

$= (1 + 1/2 + 1/3 + \cdots + 1/n) - (1/3 + 1/4 + 1/5 + \cdots + 1/(n+2))$

$= 3/2 - 1/(n+1) - 1/(n+2), \displaystyle\lim_{n \to +\infty} s_n = 3/2$

28. **(a)** $\dfrac{2^k A}{3^k - 2^k} + \dfrac{2^k B}{3^{k+1} - 2^{k+1}} = \dfrac{2^k \left(3^{k+1} - 2^{k+1} \right) A + 2^k \left(3^k - 2^k \right) B}{\left(3^k - 2^k \right) \left(3^{k+1} - 2^{k+1} \right)}$

$= \dfrac{\left(3 \cdot 6^k - 2 \cdot 2^{2k} \right) A + \left(6^k - 2^{2k} \right) B}{\left(3^k - 2^k \right) \left(3^{k+1} - 2^{k+1} \right)} = \dfrac{(3A + B)6^k - (2A + B)2^{2k}}{\left(3^k - 2^k \right) \left(3^{k+1} - 2^{k+1} \right)}$

so $3A + B = 1$ and $2A + B = 0$, $A = 1$ and $B = -2$.

(b) $s_n = \sum_{k=1}^{n} \left[\dfrac{2^k}{3^k - 2^k} - \dfrac{2^{k+1}}{3^{k+1} - 2^{k+1}} \right] = \sum_{k=1}^{n} (a_k - a_{k+1})$ where $a_k = \dfrac{2^k}{3^k - 2^k}$.

But $s_n = (a_1 - a_2) + (a_2 - a_3) + (a_3 - a_4) + \cdots + (a_n - a_{n+1})$ which is a telescoping sum,

$s_n = a_1 - a_{n+1} = 2 - \dfrac{2^{n+1}}{3^{n+1} - 2^{n+1}}, \quad \lim_{n \to +\infty} s_n = \lim_{n \to +\infty} \left[2 - \dfrac{(2/3)^{n+1}}{1 - (2/3)^{n+1}} \right] = 2.$

29. $s_n = \sum_{k=1}^{n} \dfrac{1}{(2k-1)(2k+1)} = \sum_{k=1}^{n} \left[\dfrac{1/2}{2k-1} - \dfrac{1/2}{2k+1} \right] = \dfrac{1}{2} \left[\sum_{k=1}^{n} \dfrac{1}{2k-1} - \sum_{k=1}^{n} \dfrac{1}{2k+1} \right]$

$= \dfrac{1}{2} \left[\sum_{k=1}^{n} \dfrac{1}{2k-1} - \sum_{k=2}^{n+1} \dfrac{1}{2k-1} \right] = \dfrac{1}{2} \left[1 - \dfrac{1}{2n+1} \right]; \quad \lim_{n \to +\infty} s_n = \dfrac{1}{2}$

30. $s_n = \sum_{k=1}^{n} \dfrac{1}{k(k+2)} = \sum_{k=1}^{n} \left[\dfrac{1/2}{k} - \dfrac{1/2}{k+1} \right] = \dfrac{1}{2} \left[\sum_{k=1}^{n} \dfrac{1}{k} - \sum_{k=1}^{n} \dfrac{1}{k+2} \right]$

$= \dfrac{1}{2} \left[\sum_{k=1}^{n} \dfrac{1}{k} - \sum_{k=3}^{n+2} \dfrac{1}{k} \right] = \dfrac{1}{2} \left[1 + \dfrac{1}{2} - \dfrac{1}{n+1} - \dfrac{1}{n+2} \right]; \quad \lim_{n \to +\infty} s_n = \dfrac{3}{4}$

31. **(a)** $\sum_{k=0}^{\infty} (-1)^k x^k = 1 - x + x^2 - x^3 + \cdots = \dfrac{1}{1 - (-x)} = \dfrac{1}{1+x}$ if $|-x| < 1, |x| < 1, -1 < x < 1.$

(b) $\sum_{k=0}^{\infty} (x-3)^k = 1 + (x-3) + (x-3)^2 + \cdots = \dfrac{1}{1 - (x-3)} = \dfrac{1}{4-x}$ if $|x-3| < 1, 2 < x < 4.$

(c) $\sum_{k=0}^{\infty} (-1)^k x^{2k} = 1 - x^2 + x^4 - x^6 + \cdots = \dfrac{1}{1 - (-x^2)} = \dfrac{1}{1+x^2}$ if $|-x^2| < 1, |x| < 1,$
$-1 < x < 1.$

32. Geometric series, $a = x, r = -x^2$. Converges for $|-x^2| < 1, |x| < 1; \ S = \dfrac{x}{1 - (-x^2)} = \dfrac{x}{1+x^2}.$

33. Geometric series, $a = 1/x^2, r = 2/x$. Converges for $|2/x| < 1, |x| > 2;$

$S = \dfrac{1/x^2}{1 - 2/x} = \dfrac{1}{x^2 - 2x}.$

34. Geometric series, $a = e^{-x}, r = e^{-x}$. Converges for $|e^{-x}| < 1, e^{-x} < 1, e^x > 1, x > 0;$

$S = \dfrac{e^{-x}}{1 - e^{-x}} = \dfrac{1}{e^x - 1}.$

35. Geometric series, $a = \sin x$, $r = -\dfrac{1}{2}\sin x$. Converges for $\left| -\dfrac{1}{2}\sin x \right| < 1$, $|\sin x| < 2$, so converges for all values of x. $S = \dfrac{\sin x}{1 + \dfrac{1}{2}\sin x} = \dfrac{2\sin x}{2 + \sin x}$.

36. $0.a_1 a_2 \cdots a_n 9999 \cdots = 0.a_1 a_2 \cdots a_n + 0.9\,(10^{-n}) + 0.09\,(10^{-n}) + \cdots$

$$= 0.a_1 a_2 \cdots a_n + \dfrac{0.9\,(10^{-n})}{1 - 0.1} = 0.a_1 a_2 \cdots a_n + 10^{-n}$$

$$= 0.a_1 a_2 \cdots (a_n + 1) = 0.a_1 a_2 \cdots (a_n + 1)\,0000 \cdots$$

37. $a_2 = \dfrac{1}{2}a_1 + \dfrac{1}{2}$, $a_3 = \dfrac{1}{2}a_2 + \dfrac{1}{2} = \dfrac{1}{2^2}a_1 + \dfrac{1}{2^2} + \dfrac{1}{2}$, $a_4 = \dfrac{1}{2}a_3 + \dfrac{1}{2} = \dfrac{1}{2^3}a_1 + \dfrac{1}{2^3} + \dfrac{1}{2^2} + \dfrac{1}{2}$,

$a_5 = \dfrac{1}{2}a_4 + \dfrac{1}{2} = \dfrac{1}{2^4}a_1 + \dfrac{1}{2^4} + \dfrac{1}{2^3} + \dfrac{1}{2^2} + \dfrac{1}{2}, \cdots, a_n = \dfrac{1}{2^{n-1}}a_1 + \dfrac{1}{2^{n-1}} + \dfrac{1}{2^{n-2}} + \cdots + \dfrac{1}{2}$,

$$\lim_{n\to+\infty} a_n = \lim_{n\to+\infty} \dfrac{a_1}{2^{n-1}} + \sum_{n=1}^{\infty}\left(\dfrac{1}{2}\right)^n = 0 + \dfrac{1/2}{1 - 1/2} = 1$$

38. $P_0 P_1 = a\sin\theta$,

$P_1 P_2 = a\sin\theta\cos\theta$,

$P_2 P_3 = a\sin\theta\cos^2\theta$

$P_3 P_4 = a\sin\theta\cos^3\theta, \cdots$

(see figure)

Each sum is a geometric series.

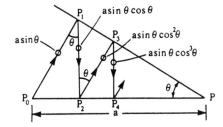

(a) $P_0 P_1 + P_1 P_2 + P_2 P_3 + \cdots = a\sin\theta + a\sin\theta\cos\theta + a\sin\theta\cos^2\theta + \cdots$

$$= \dfrac{a\sin\theta}{1 - \cos\theta}$$

(b) $P_0 P_1 + P_2 P_3 + P_4 P_5 + \cdots = a\sin\theta + a\sin\theta\cos^2\theta + a\sin\theta\cos^4\theta + \cdots$

$$= \dfrac{a\sin\theta}{1 - \cos^2\theta} = \dfrac{a\sin\theta}{\sin^2\theta} = a\csc\theta$$

(c) $P_1 P_2 + P_3 P_4 + P_5 P_6 + \cdots = a\sin\theta\cos\theta + a\sin\theta\cos^3\theta + \cdots$

$$= \dfrac{a\sin\theta\cos\theta}{1 - \cos^2\theta} = \dfrac{a\sin\theta\cos\theta}{\sin^2\theta} = a\cot\theta.$$

39. By inspection, $\dfrac{\theta}{2} - \dfrac{\theta}{4} + \dfrac{\theta}{8} - \dfrac{\theta}{16} + \cdots = \dfrac{\theta/2}{1 - (-1/2)} = \theta/3$

40. $A_1 + A_2 + A_3 + \cdots = 1 + 1/2 + 1/4 + \cdots = \dfrac{1}{1 - (1/2)} = 2$

41. The series converges to $1/(1 - x)$ only if $-1 < x < 1$.

EXERCISE SET 11.4

1. $\displaystyle\sum_{k=1}^{\infty} \frac{1}{2^k} = \frac{1/2}{1 - 1/2} = 1; \quad \sum_{k=1}^{\infty} \frac{1}{4^k} = \frac{1/4}{1 - 1/4} = 1/3; \quad \sum_{k=1}^{\infty} \left(\frac{1}{2^k} + \frac{1}{4^k} \right) = 1 + 1/3 = 4/3$

2. $\displaystyle\sum_{k=1}^{\infty} \frac{1}{5^k} = \frac{1/5}{1 - 1/5} = 1/4; \quad \sum_{k=1}^{\infty} \frac{1}{k(k+1)} = 1 \quad \text{(Example 4, 11.3)};$

$\displaystyle\sum_{k=1}^{\infty} \left[\frac{1}{5^k} - \frac{1}{k(k+1)} \right] = 1/4 - 1 = -3/4$

3. $\displaystyle\sum_{k=2}^{\infty} \frac{1}{k^2 - 1} = \sum_{k=2}^{\infty} \left[\frac{1/2}{k-1} - \frac{1/2}{k+1} \right],$

$s_n = \dfrac{1}{2} \left[\left(1 - \dfrac{1}{3} \right) + \left(\dfrac{1}{2} - \dfrac{1}{4} \right) + \left(\dfrac{1}{3} - \dfrac{1}{5} \right) + \cdots + \left(\dfrac{1}{n} - \dfrac{1}{n+2} \right) \right]$

$\qquad = \dfrac{1}{2} \left[\left(1 + \dfrac{1}{2} + \dfrac{1}{3} + \cdots + \dfrac{1}{n} \right) - \left(\dfrac{1}{3} + \dfrac{1}{4} + \dfrac{1}{5} + \cdots + \dfrac{1}{n+2} \right) \right]$

$\qquad = \dfrac{3}{4} - \dfrac{1}{2} \left(\dfrac{1}{n+1} + \dfrac{1}{n+2} \right),$

$\displaystyle\sum_{k=2}^{\infty} \frac{1}{k^2 - 1} = \lim_{n \to +\infty} s_n = 3/4; \quad \sum_{k=2}^{\infty} \frac{7}{10^{k-1}} = \frac{7/10}{1 - 1/10} = 7/9;$

so $\displaystyle\sum_{k=2}^{\infty} \left[\frac{1}{k^2 - 1} - \frac{7}{10^{k-1}} \right] = 3/4 - 7/9 = -1/36$

4. $\displaystyle\sum_{k=1}^{\infty} \frac{7}{3^k} = \frac{7/3}{1 - 1/3} = 7/2; \quad \sum_{k=1}^{\infty} \frac{6}{(k+3)(k+4)} = \sum_{k=1}^{\infty} \left[\frac{6}{k+3} - \frac{6}{k+4} \right]$

so $s_n = \dfrac{6}{4} - \dfrac{6}{n+4}$ thus $\displaystyle\sum_{k=1}^{\infty} \frac{6}{(k+3)(k+4)} = \lim_{n \to +\infty} s_n = 3/2;$

$\displaystyle\sum_{k=1}^{\infty} \left[\frac{7}{3^k} + \frac{6}{(k+3)(k+4)} \right] = 7/2 + 3/2 = 5$

5. **(a)** $p = 3$, converges   **(b)** $p = 1/2$, diverges
   (c) $p = 1$, diverges   **(d)** $p = 2/3$, diverges
   (e) $p = 4/3$, converges   **(f)** $p = 1/4$, diverges
   (g) $p = 5/3$, converges   **(h)** $p = \pi$, converges

6. **(a)** $\displaystyle \lim_{k \to +\infty} \frac{k+1}{k+2} = 1$ **(b)** $\displaystyle \lim_{k \to +\infty} \ln k = +\infty$

7. **(a)** $\displaystyle \lim_{k \to +\infty} \frac{k^2 + k + 3}{2k^2 + 1} = \frac{1}{2}$ **(b)** $\displaystyle \lim_{k \to +\infty} \left(1 + \frac{1}{k}\right)^k = e$

8. **(a)** $\displaystyle \lim_{k \to +\infty} \cos k\pi$ does not exist   **(b)** $\displaystyle \lim_{k \to +\infty} \frac{e^k}{k} = +\infty$

9. $\displaystyle \sum_{k=1}^{\infty} \frac{1}{k+6} = \sum_{k=7}^{\infty} \frac{1}{k}$, diverges because the harmonic series diverges.

10. $\displaystyle \sum_{k=1}^{\infty} \frac{3}{5k} = \sum_{k=1}^{\infty} \frac{3}{5}\left(\frac{1}{k}\right)$, diverges because the harmonic series diverges.

11. $\displaystyle \int_{1}^{+\infty} \frac{1}{5x+2} = \lim_{\ell \to +\infty} \frac{1}{5} \ln(5x+2) \bigg]_{1}^{\ell} = +\infty$, the series diverges by the integral test.

12. $\displaystyle \int_{1}^{+\infty} \frac{x}{1+x^2} dx = \lim_{\ell \to +\infty} \frac{1}{2} \ln(1+x^2) \bigg]_{1}^{\ell} = +\infty$, the series diverges by the integral test.

13. $\displaystyle \int_{1}^{+\infty} \frac{1}{1+9x^2} dx = \lim_{\ell \to +\infty} \frac{1}{3} \tan^{-1} 3x \bigg]_{1}^{\ell} = \frac{1}{3}\left(\pi/2 - \tan^{-1} 3\right)$, the series converges by the integral test.

14. $\displaystyle \int_{1}^{+\infty} (4+2x)^{-3/2} dx = \lim_{\ell \to +\infty} -1/\sqrt{4+2x} \bigg]_{1}^{\ell} = 1/\sqrt{6}$, the series converges by the integral test.

15. $\displaystyle \sum_{k=1}^{\infty} \frac{1}{\sqrt{k+5}} = \sum_{k=6}^{\infty} \frac{1}{\sqrt{k}}$, diverges because the p-series with $p = 1/2 \leq 1$ diverges.

16. $\displaystyle \lim_{k \to +\infty} \frac{1}{e^{1/k}} = 1$, the series diverges because $\displaystyle \lim_{k \to +\infty} u_k \neq 0$.

17. $\int_1^{+\infty} (2x-1)^{-1/3} dx = \lim_{\ell \to +\infty} \frac{3}{4}(2x-1)^{2/3}\Big]_1^\ell = +\infty$, the series diverges by the integral test.

18. $\int_3^{+\infty} \frac{\ln x}{x} = \lim_{\ell \to +\infty} \frac{1}{2}(\ln x)^2\Big]_3^\ell = +\infty$, the series diverges by the integral test.

19. $\lim_{k \to +\infty} \frac{k}{\ln(k+1)} = \lim_{k \to +\infty} \frac{1}{1/(k+1)} = +\infty$, the series diverges because $\lim_{k \to +\infty} u_k \neq 0$.

20. $\int_1^{+\infty} xe^{-x^2} dx = \lim_{\ell \to +\infty} -\frac{1}{2}e^{-x^2}\Big]_1^\ell = e^{-1}/2$, the series converges by the integral test.

21. $\int_1^{+\infty} \frac{[\ln(x+1)]^{-2}}{x+1} dx = \lim_{\ell \to +\infty} -1/\ln(x+1)\Big]_1^\ell = 1/\ln 2$, the series converges by the integral test.

22. $\lim_{k \to +\infty} \frac{k^2+1}{k^2+3} = 1 \neq 0$, the series diverges.

23. $\lim_{k \to +\infty} (1+1/k)^{-k} = 1/e \neq 0$, the series diverges.

24. $\int_1^{+\infty} \frac{1}{\sqrt{x^2+1}} dx = \lim_{\ell \to +\infty} \sinh^{-1} x.\Big]_1^\ell = +\infty$, the series diverges by the integral test.

25. $\int_1^{+\infty} \frac{\tan^{-1} x}{1+x^2} dx = \lim_{\ell \to +\infty} \frac{1}{2}\left(\tan^{-1} x\right)^2\Big]_1^\ell = 3\pi^2/32$, the series converges by the integral test.

26. $\int_1^{+\infty} \text{sech}^2 x \, dx = \lim_{\ell \to +\infty} \tanh x\Big]_1^\ell = 1 - \tanh(1)$, the series converges by the integral test.

27. $\sum_{k=5}^{\infty} 7k^{-p} = \sum_{k=5}^{\infty} 7\left(\frac{1}{k^p}\right)$, converges because a p-series with $p > 1$ converges.

28. $\sum_{k=1}^{\infty} 7(k+5)^{-p} = \sum_{k=6}^{\infty} 7\left(\frac{1}{k^p}\right)$, diverges because a p-series with $p \leq 1$ diverges.

29. $\lim_{k \to +\infty} k^2 \sin^2(1/k) = 1 \neq 0$, the series diverges.

30. $\displaystyle\int_1^{+\infty} x^2 e^{-x^3}\,dx = \lim_{\ell\to+\infty} -\frac{1}{3}e^{-x^3}\Big]_1^{\ell} = e^{-1}/3$, the series converges by the integral test.

31. Use the integral test with $\displaystyle\int_2^{+\infty}\frac{dx}{x(\ln x)^p}$ to get $\displaystyle\lim_{\ell\to+\infty}\ln(\ln x)\Big]_2^{\ell} = +\infty$ if $p = 1$,

$$\lim_{\ell\to+\infty}\frac{(\ln x)^{1-p}}{1-p}\Big]_2^{\ell} = \begin{cases} +\infty & \text{if } p < 1 \\[2mm] \dfrac{1}{(p-1)(\ln 2)^{p-1}} & \text{if } p > 1 \end{cases}$$

32. Use the integral test with $\displaystyle\int_3^{+\infty}\frac{dx}{x(\ln x)[\ln(\ln x)]^p}$ to get

$$\lim_{\ell\to+\infty}\ln[\ln(\ln x)]\Big]_3^{\ell} = +\infty \text{ if } p = 1,\quad \lim_{\ell\to+\infty}\frac{[\ln(\ln x)]^{1-p}}{1-p}\Big]_3^{\ell} = \begin{cases} +\infty & \text{if } p < 1, \\[2mm] \dfrac{1}{(p-1)[\ln(\ln 3)]^{p-1}} & \text{if } p > 1 \end{cases}$$

33. Suppose $\Sigma(u_k + v_k)$ converges then so does $\Sigma[(u_k + v_k) - u_k]$, but $\Sigma[(u_k + v_k) - u_k] = \Sigma v_k$ so Σv_k converges which contradicts the assumption that Σv_k diverges. Suppose $\Sigma(u_k - v_k)$ converges then so does $\Sigma[u_k - (u_k - v_k)] = \Sigma v_k$ which leads to the same contradiction as before.

34. Let $u_k = 2/k$ and $v_k = 1/k$ then both $\Sigma(u_k + v_k)$ and $\Sigma(u_k - v_k)$ diverge; let $u_k = 1/k$ and $v_k = -1/k$ then $\Sigma(u_k + v_k)$ converges; let $u_k = v_k = 1/k$ then $\Sigma(u_k - v_k)$ converges.

35. **(a)** diverges because $\displaystyle\sum_{k=1}^{\infty}(2/3)^{k-1}$ converges and $\displaystyle\sum_{k=1}^{\infty}1/k$ diverges.

(b) diverges because $\displaystyle\sum_{k=1}^{\infty}\frac{k^2}{1+k^2}$ diverges and $\displaystyle\sum_{k=1}^{\infty}\frac{1}{k(k+1)}$ converges.

(c) diverges because $\displaystyle\sum_{k=1}^{\infty}1/(3k+2)$ diverges and $\displaystyle\sum_{k=1}^{\infty}1/k^{3/2}$ converges.

(d) converges because both $\displaystyle\sum_{k=2}^{\infty}\frac{1}{k(\ln k)^2}$ and $\displaystyle\sum_{k=2}^{\infty}1/k^2$ converge.

36. If $\displaystyle S = \sum_{k=1}^{\infty}u_k$ and $\displaystyle s_n = \sum_{k=1}^{n}u_k$, then $\displaystyle S - s_n = \sum_{k=n+1}^{\infty}u_k$. Interpret $u_k,\ k = n+1, n+2, \cdots$, as the areas of inscribed or circumscribed rectangles with height u_k and base of length one for the curve $y = f(x)$ to obtain the result.

37. **(a)** $s_{10} \approx 1.1975$; let $f(x) = \dfrac{1}{x^3}$, then $\displaystyle\int_{10}^{+\infty} \dfrac{1}{x^3}dx = \dfrac{1}{200} = 0.0050$ and

$$\int_{11}^{+\infty} \dfrac{1}{x^3}dx = \dfrac{1}{242} \approx 0.0041 \text{ so } 1.2016 < S < 1.2026$$

(b) $\displaystyle\int_{n}^{+\infty} \dfrac{1}{x^3}dx = \dfrac{1}{2n^2} < 10^{-3}, n > \sqrt{500} \approx 22.4; n = 23.$

38. **(a)** $s_6 \approx 1.08112$; let $f(x) = \dfrac{1}{x^4}$, then $\displaystyle\int_{6}^{+\infty} \dfrac{1}{x^4}dx = \dfrac{1}{648} \approx 0.00154$ and

$$\int_{7}^{+\infty} \dfrac{1}{x^4}dx = \dfrac{1}{1029} \approx 0.00097 \text{ so } 1.08209 < S < 1.08267 \ (\pi^4/90 \approx 1.08232).$$

(b) $\displaystyle\int_{n}^{+\infty} \dfrac{1}{x^4}dx = \dfrac{1}{3n^3} < 10^{-5}, n > (10^5/3)^{1/3} \approx 32.2; n = 33.$

39. **(a)** Let $F(x) = \dfrac{1}{x}$, then $\displaystyle\int_{1}^{n} \dfrac{1}{x}dx = \ln n$ and $\displaystyle\int_{1}^{n+1} \dfrac{1}{x}dx = \ln(n+1)$, $u_1 = 1$ so
$\ln(n+1) < s_n < 1 + \ln n$; $\ln(1,000,001) < s_{1,000,000} < 1 + \ln(1,000,000)$,
$13 < s_{1,000,000} < 15.$

(b) $s_n > \ln(n+1) \geq 100, n \geq e^{100} - 1 \approx 2.688 \times 10^{43}; n = 2.69 \times 10^{43}$

40. **(a)** Let $f(x) = \dfrac{1}{\sqrt{x}}$, then $\displaystyle\int_{1}^{n} \dfrac{1}{\sqrt{x}}dx = 2\sqrt{n} - 2$ and $\displaystyle\int_{1}^{n+1} \dfrac{1}{\sqrt{x}}dx = 2\sqrt{n+1} - 2$, $u_1 = 1$ so
$2\sqrt{n+1} - 2 < s_n < 2\sqrt{n} - 1$; $2\sqrt{10,001} - 2 < s_{10,000} < 2\sqrt{10,000} - 1$,
$198 < s_{10,000} < 199.$

(b) $s_n > 2\sqrt{n+1} - 2 \geq 100, n \geq (51)^2 - 1 = 2600; n = 2600$

EXERCISE SET 11.5

1. $\rho = \displaystyle\lim_{k \to +\infty} \dfrac{3^{k+1}/(k+1)!}{3^k/k!} = \lim_{k \to +\infty} \dfrac{3}{k+1} = 0$, the series converges.

2. $\rho = \displaystyle\lim_{k \to +\infty} \dfrac{4^{k+1}/(k+1)^2}{4^k/k^2} = \lim_{k \to +\infty} \dfrac{4k^2}{(k+1)^2} = 4$, the series diverges.

3. $\rho = \displaystyle\lim_{k \to +\infty} \dfrac{k}{k+1} = 1$, the result is inconclusive.

4. $\rho = \displaystyle\lim_{k \to +\infty} \dfrac{(k+1)(1/2)^{k+1}}{k(1/2)^k} = \lim_{k \to +\infty} \dfrac{k+1}{2k} = 1/2$, the series converges.

5. $\rho = \lim\limits_{k \to +\infty} \dfrac{(k+1)!/(k+1)^3}{k!/k^3} = \lim\limits_{k \to +\infty} \dfrac{k^3}{(k+1)^2} = +\infty$, the series diverges.

6. $\rho = \lim\limits_{k \to +\infty} \dfrac{(k+1)/[(k+1)^2+1]}{k/(k^2+1)} = \lim\limits_{k \to +\infty} \dfrac{(k+1)(k^2+1)}{k(k^2+2k+2)} = 1$, the result is inconclusive.

7. $\rho = \lim\limits_{k \to +\infty} \dfrac{3k+2}{2k-1} = 3/2$, the series diverges.

8. $\rho = \lim\limits_{k \to +\infty} k/100 = +\infty$, the series diverges.

9. $\rho = \lim\limits_{k \to +\infty} \dfrac{k^{1/k}}{5} = 1/5$, the series converges.

10. $\rho = \lim\limits_{k \to +\infty} (1 + e^{-k}) = 1$, the result is inconclusive.

11. ratio test, $\rho = \lim\limits_{k \to +\infty} \dfrac{2k^3}{(k+1)^3} = 2$, diverges

12. converges (p-series with $p = 2$)

13. ratio test, $\rho = \lim\limits_{k \to +\infty} 7/(k+1) = 0$, converges

14. diverges (integral test)

15. ratio test, $\rho = \lim\limits_{k \to +\infty} \dfrac{(k+1)^2}{5k^2} = 1/5$, converges

16. ratio test, $\rho = \lim\limits_{k \to +\infty} (10/3)(k+1) = +\infty$, diverges

17. ratio test, $\rho = \lim\limits_{k \to +\infty} e^{-1}(k+1)^{50}/k^{50} = e^{-1} < 1$, converges

18. diverges (integral test using $\displaystyle\int_2^\infty \dfrac{x^2}{x^3+1}dx$)

19. root test, $\rho = \lim\limits_{k \to +\infty} k^{1/k}(2/3) = 2/3$, converges

20. root test, $\rho = \lim\limits_{k \to +\infty} k = +\infty$, diverges

21. diverges (integral test)

22. ratio test, $\rho = \lim\limits_{k \to +\infty} \dfrac{2(k^3 + 1)}{(k+1)^3 + 1} = 2$, diverges

23. root test, $\rho = \lim\limits_{k \to +\infty} 4/(7k - 1) = 0$, converges

24. ratio test, $\rho = \lim\limits_{k \to +\infty} \dfrac{2(k+1)^2}{(2k+4)(2k+3)} = 1/2$, converges

25. ratio test, $\rho = \lim\limits_{k \to +\infty} \dfrac{(k+1)^2}{(2k+2)(2k+1)} = 1/4$, converges

26. converges (integral test)

27. integral test, $\displaystyle\int_1^{+\infty} \dfrac{dx}{1 + \sqrt{x}} = \lim\limits_{\ell \to +\infty} 2[\sqrt{x} - \ln(1 + \sqrt{x})]_1^\ell = +\infty$, diverges

28. ratio test, $\rho = \lim\limits_{k \to +\infty} (1 + 1/k)^{-k} = 1/e < 1$, converges

29. ratio test, $\rho = \lim\limits_{k \to +\infty} \dfrac{\ln(k+1)}{e \ln k} = \lim\limits_{k \to +\infty} \dfrac{k}{e(k+1)} = 1/e < 1$, converges

30. ratio test, $\rho = \lim\limits_{k \to +\infty} \dfrac{k+1}{e^{2k+1}} = \lim\limits_{k \to +\infty} \dfrac{1}{2e^{2k+1}} = 0$, converges

31. ratio test, $\rho = \lim\limits_{k \to +\infty} \dfrac{k+5}{4(k+1)} = 1/4$, converges

32. root test, $\rho = \lim\limits_{k \to +\infty} \left(\dfrac{k}{k+1}\right)^k = \lim\limits_{k \to +\infty} \dfrac{1}{(1 + 1/k)^k} = 1/e$, converges

33. $u_k = \dfrac{k!}{1 \cdot 3 \cdot 5 \cdots (2k-1)}$, by the ratio test $\rho = \lim\limits_{k \to +\infty} \dfrac{k+1}{2k+1} = 1/2$; converges

34. $u_k = \dfrac{1 \cdot 3 \cdot 5 \cdots (2k-1)}{(2k-1)!}$, by the ratio test $\rho = \lim\limits_{k \to +\infty} \dfrac{1}{2k} = 0$; converges

35. $u_k = \dfrac{(k+1)!}{1 \cdot 4 \cdot 7 \cdots (3k-2)}$, by the ratio test $\rho = \lim\limits_{k \to +\infty} \dfrac{k+2}{3k+1} = \dfrac{1}{3}$; converges

36. By the root test, $\rho = \lim\limits_{k \to +\infty} \dfrac{\alpha}{(k^{1/k})^\alpha} = \dfrac{\alpha}{1^\alpha} = \alpha$, the series converges if $\alpha < 1$ and diverges

if $\alpha > 1$. If $\alpha = 1$ then the series is $\displaystyle\sum_{k=1}^{\infty} 1/k$ which diverges.

37.   **(a)** $\displaystyle\lim_{x\to+\infty} \ln y = \lim_{x\to+\infty} \frac{\ln(\ln x)}{x} = \lim_{x\to+\infty}\frac{1}{x\ln x} = 0$ so $\displaystyle\lim_{x\to+\infty} y = e^0 = 1 = \lim_{k\to+\infty}(\ln k)^{1/k}$

     (b) $\displaystyle\rho = \lim_{k\to+\infty}\frac{1}{3}(\ln k)^{1/k} = 1/3$

     (c) $\displaystyle\rho = \lim_{k\to+\infty}\frac{\ln(k+1)}{3\ln k} = \lim_{k\to+\infty}\frac{k}{3(k+1)} = 1/3$

38. Consider the series $\displaystyle\sum_{k=1}^{\infty} k!/k^k$. By the ratio test, $\displaystyle\rho = \lim_{k\to+\infty}\frac{k^k}{(k+1)^k} = \lim_{k\to+\infty}\frac{1}{(1+1/k)^k} = 1/e$

  so the series converges. By Theorem 11.4.1, $\displaystyle\lim_{k\to+\infty} k!/k^k = 0$.

39. The result follows trivially if $a = 0$ so suppose $a \neq 0$ and consider the series $\displaystyle\sum_{k=1}^{\infty} a^k/k!$.

  By the ratio test, $\displaystyle\rho = \lim_{k\to+\infty}\frac{a}{k+1} = 0$ so the series converges for every real number a and

  hence $\displaystyle\lim_{k\to+\infty} a^k/k! = 0$.

40.   **(a)** If r_k is decreasing for $k \geq n+1$, then $r_{n+m} < r_{n+1}$ for $m \geq 2$ and

$$u_{n+m} = u_{n+1}\frac{u_{n+2}}{u_{n+1}}\frac{u_{n+3}}{u_{n+2}}\cdots\frac{u_{n+m}}{u_{n+m-1}} = u_{n+1}r_{n+1}r_{n+2}\cdots r_{n+m-1} < r_{n+1}^{m-1}u_{n+1} \text{ for}$$

$$m \geq 3 \text{ so } u_{n+1} + u_{n+2} + u_{n+3} + \cdots < u_{n+1} + r_{n+1}u_{n+1} + r_{n+1}^2 u_{n+1} + \cdots = \frac{u_{n+1}}{1 - r_{n+1}}$$

     (b) If r_k is increasing for $k \geq n+1$, then $r_{n+m} < \rho$ for $m \geq 1$ and

$$u_{n+m} = u_{n+1}r_{n+1}r_{n+2}\cdots r_{n+m-1} < \rho^{m-1}u_{n+1} \text{ for } m \geq 2$$

$$\text{so } u_{n+1} + u_{n+2} + u_{n+3} + \cdots < u_{n+1} + \rho u_{n+1} + \rho^2 u_{n+1} + \cdots = \frac{u_{n+1}}{1 - \rho}.$$

41.   **(a)** $s_5 \approx 1.71667$, $r_k = \dfrac{1}{k+1}$ which is decreasing for $k \geq 6$ and $r_6 < 1$; $u_6 = 1/6!$, $r_6 = 1/7$,

$$S - s_5 < \frac{1/6!}{1 - 1/7} < 0.00163.$$

     (b) $u_{n+1} = \dfrac{1}{(n+1)!}$, $r_{n+1} = \dfrac{1}{n+2}$, $\dfrac{u_{n+1}}{1 - r_{n+1}} = \dfrac{n+2}{(n+1)(n+1)!} \leq 10^{-5}$ if $n = 8$.

42.   **(a)** $s_8 \approx 0.74928$, $r_k = \dfrac{k+1}{3k}$ which is decreasing for $k \geq 9$ and $r_9 < 1$; $u_9 = 9/3^9$, $r_9 = 10/27$,

$$S - s_8 < \frac{9/3^9}{1 - 10/27} < 0.00073.$$

     (b) $u_{n+1} = \dfrac{n+1}{3^{n+1}}$, $r_{n+1} = \dfrac{n+2}{3(n+1)}$, $\dfrac{u_{n+1}}{1 - r_{n+1}} = \dfrac{(n+1)^2}{3^n(2n+1)} \leq 10^{-5}$ if $n = 13$.

43. **(a)** $s_7 \approx 0.69226$, $r_k = \dfrac{k}{2(k+1)}$ which is increasing for $k \geq 8$ and $\rho = \lim\limits_{k \to +\infty} r_k = 1/2$,

$u_8 = 1/[(8)(2^8)]$, $S - s_7 < \dfrac{1/2^{11}}{1 - 1/2} < 0.00098$.

(b) $u_{n+1} = \dfrac{1}{(n+1)2^{n+1}}$, $\dfrac{u_{n+1}}{1-\rho} = \dfrac{1}{(n+1)2^n} \leq 10^{-5}$ if $n = 13$.

44. **(a)** $s_4 \approx 0.43946$, $r_k = \dfrac{\sqrt{k}}{3\sqrt{k}+1}$ which is increasing for $k \geq 5$ and $\rho = \lim\limits_{k \to +\infty} r_k = 1/3$,

$u_5 = 1/(\sqrt{5}\,3^5)$, $S - s_4 < \dfrac{1/(\sqrt{5}\,3^5)}{1 - 1/3} < 0.00277$.

(b) $u_{n+1} = \dfrac{1}{\sqrt{n+1}\,3^{n+1}}$, $\dfrac{u_{n+1}}{1-\rho} = \dfrac{1}{2\sqrt{n+1}\,(3^n)} < 10^{-5}$ if $n = 9$.

EXERCISE SET 11.6

1. $\dfrac{1}{3^k+5} < \dfrac{1}{3^k}$, $\displaystyle\sum_{k=1}^{\infty} \dfrac{1}{3^k}$ converges

2. $\dfrac{2}{k^4+k} < \dfrac{2}{k^4}$, $\displaystyle\sum_{k=1}^{\infty} \dfrac{2}{k^4}$ converges

3. $\dfrac{1}{5k^2-k} \leq \dfrac{1}{5k^2-k^2} = \dfrac{1}{4k^2}$, $\displaystyle\sum_{k=1}^{\infty} \dfrac{1}{4k^2}$ converges

4. $\dfrac{k}{8k^3+2k^2-1} < \dfrac{k}{8k^3-1} \leq \dfrac{k}{8k^3-k^3} = \dfrac{1}{7k^2}$, $\displaystyle\sum_{k=1}^{\infty} \dfrac{1}{7k^2}$ converges

5. $\dfrac{2^k-1}{3^k+2k} < \dfrac{2^k}{3^k} = (2/3)^k$, $\displaystyle\sum_{k=1}^{\infty}(2/3)^k$ converges

6. $\dfrac{5\sin^2 k}{k!} < \dfrac{5}{k!}$, $\displaystyle\sum_{k=1}^{\infty} \dfrac{5}{k!}$ converges

7. $\dfrac{3}{k-1/4} > \dfrac{3}{k}$, $\displaystyle\sum_{k=1}^{\infty} 3/k$ diverges

8. $\dfrac{1}{\sqrt{k+8}} \geq \dfrac{1}{\sqrt{k+8k}} = \dfrac{1}{3\sqrt{k}}$, $\displaystyle\sum_{k=1}^{\infty} \dfrac{1}{3\sqrt{k}}$ diverges

9. $\dfrac{9}{\sqrt{k}+1} \geq \dfrac{9}{\sqrt{k}+\sqrt{k}} = \dfrac{9}{2\sqrt{k}}$, $\displaystyle\sum_{k=1}^{\infty} \dfrac{9}{2\sqrt{k}}$ diverges

10. $\dfrac{k+1}{k^2-k} > \dfrac{k}{k^2} = \dfrac{1}{k}, \displaystyle\sum_{k=2}^{\infty} 1/k$ diverges

11. $\dfrac{k^{4/3}}{8k^2+5k+1} \geq \dfrac{k^{4/3}}{8k^2+5k^2+k^2} = \dfrac{1}{14k^{2/3}}, \displaystyle\sum_{k=1}^{\infty} \dfrac{1}{14k^{2/3}}$ diverges

12. $\dfrac{k^{-1/2}}{2+\sin^2 k} > \dfrac{k^{-1/2}}{2k^{1/2}+k^{1/2}} = \dfrac{1}{3k}, \displaystyle\sum_{k=1}^{\infty} \dfrac{1}{3k}$ diverges

13.   compare with the convergent series $\displaystyle\sum_{k=1}^{\infty} 1/k^5$, $\rho = \displaystyle\lim_{k \to +\infty} \dfrac{4k^7-2k^6+6k^5}{8k^7+k-8} = 1/2$, converges

14.   compare with the divergent series $\displaystyle\sum_{k=1}^{\infty} 1/k$, $\rho = \displaystyle\lim_{k \to +\infty} \dfrac{k}{9k+6} = 1/9$, diverges.

15.   compare with the convergent series $\displaystyle\sum_{k=1}^{\infty} 5/3^k$, $\rho = \displaystyle\lim_{k \to +\infty} \dfrac{3^k}{3^k+1} = 1$, converges

16.   compare with the divergent series $\displaystyle\sum_{k=1}^{\infty} 1/k$, $\rho = \displaystyle\lim_{k \to +\infty} \dfrac{k^2(k+3)}{(k+1)(k+2)(k+5)} = 1$, diverges

17.   compare with the divergent series $\displaystyle\sum_{k=1}^{\infty} \dfrac{1}{k^{2/3}}$,

$\rho = \displaystyle\lim_{k \to +\infty} \dfrac{k^{2/3}}{(8k^2-3k)^{1/3}} = \displaystyle\lim_{k \to +\infty} \dfrac{1}{(8-3/k)^{1/3}} = 1/2$, diverges

18.   compare with the convergent series $\displaystyle\sum_{k=1}^{\infty} 1/k^{17}$,

$\rho = \displaystyle\lim_{k \to +\infty} \dfrac{k^{17}}{(2k+3)^{17}} = \displaystyle\lim_{k \to +\infty} \dfrac{1}{(2+3/k)^{17}} = 1/2^{17}$, converges

19. $\dfrac{1}{k^3+2k+1} < \dfrac{1}{k^3}, \displaystyle\sum_{k=1}^{\infty} 1/k^3$ converges so $\displaystyle\sum_{k=1}^{\infty} \dfrac{1}{k^3+2k+1}$ converges by the comparison test

20. limit comparison test, compare with the divergent series $\sum\limits_{k=1}^{\infty} 1/k^{2/5}$,

$$\rho = \lim_{k \to +\infty} \frac{k^{2/5}}{(3+k)^{2/5}} = \lim_{k \to +\infty} \frac{1}{(3/k+1)^{2/5}} = 1, \text{ diverges}$$

21. $\dfrac{1}{9k-2} > \dfrac{1}{9k}, \sum\limits_{k=1}^{\infty} \dfrac{1}{9k}$ diverges so $\sum\limits_{k=1}^{\infty} \dfrac{1}{9k-2}$ diverges by the comparison test

22. diverges by the integral test

23. limit comparison test, compare with the convergent series $\sum\limits_{k=1}^{\infty} 1/k^{5/2}$,

$$\rho = \lim_{k \to +\infty} \frac{k^3}{k^3+1} = 1, \text{ converges}$$

24. $\dfrac{4}{2+k3^k} < \dfrac{4}{k3^k}, \sum\limits_{k=1}^{\infty} \dfrac{4}{k3^k}$ converges (ratio test) so $\sum\limits_{k=1}^{\infty} \dfrac{4}{2+k3^k}$ converges by the comparison test

25. limit comparison test, compare with the divergent series $\sum\limits_{k=1}^{\infty} 1/k$,

$$\rho = \lim_{k \to +\infty} \frac{k}{\sqrt{k^2+k}} = 1, \text{ diverges}$$

26. $\dfrac{2+(-1)^k}{5^k} \le \dfrac{3}{5^k}, \sum\limits_{k=1}^{\infty} 3/5^k$ converges so $\sum\limits_{k=1}^{\infty} \dfrac{2+(-1)^k}{5^k}$ converges

27. limit comparison test, compare with the convergent series $\sum\limits_{k=1}^{\infty} 1/k^{5/2}$,

$$\rho = \lim_{k \to +\infty} \frac{k^3+2k^{5/2}}{k^3+3k^2+3k} = 1, \text{ converges}$$

28. $\dfrac{4+|\cos k|}{k^3} < \dfrac{5}{k^3}, \sum\limits_{k=1}^{\infty} 5/k^3$ converges so $\sum\limits_{k=1}^{\infty} \dfrac{4+|\cos k|}{k^3}$ converges

29. diverges because $\lim\limits_{k \to +\infty} \dfrac{1}{4+2^{-k}} = 1/4 \ne 0$

30. $\displaystyle\sum_{k=1}^{\infty}\frac{\sqrt{k}\ln k}{k^3+1}=\sum_{k=2}^{\infty}\frac{\sqrt{k}\ln k}{k^3+1}$ because $\ln 1=0$, $\dfrac{\sqrt{k}\ln k}{k^3+1}<\dfrac{k\ln k}{k^3}=\dfrac{\ln k}{k^2}$,

$\displaystyle\int_{2}^{+\infty}\frac{\ln x}{x^2}dx=\lim_{\ell\to+\infty}\left.\left(-\frac{\ln x}{x}-\frac{1}{x}\right)\right]_{2}^{\ell}=\frac{1}{2}(\ln 2+1)$ so $\displaystyle\sum_{k=2}^{\infty}\frac{\ln k}{k^2}$ converges and so does $\displaystyle\sum_{k=1}^{\infty}\frac{\sqrt{k}\ln k}{k^3+1}$.

31. $\dfrac{\tan^{-1}k}{k^2}<\dfrac{\pi/2}{k^2}$, $\displaystyle\sum_{k=1}^{\infty}\frac{\pi/2}{k^2}$ converges so $\displaystyle\sum_{k=1}^{\infty}\frac{\tan^{-1}k}{k^2}$ converges

32. $\dfrac{5^k+k}{k!+3}<\dfrac{5^k+5^k}{k!}=\dfrac{2\left(5^k\right)}{k!}$, $\displaystyle\sum_{k=1}^{\infty}2\left(\frac{5^k}{k!}\right)$ converges (ratio test) so $\displaystyle\sum_{k=1}^{\infty}\frac{5^k+k}{k!+3}$ converges

33. $\displaystyle\sum_{k=1}^{\infty}\frac{\ln k}{k\sqrt{k}}=\sum_{k=2}^{\infty}\frac{\ln k}{k\sqrt{k}}$ because $\ln 1=0$,

$\displaystyle\int_{2}^{+\infty}\frac{\ln x}{x^{3/2}}dx=\lim_{\ell\to+\infty}\left[-\frac{2\ln x}{x^{1/2}}-\frac{4}{x^{1/2}}\right]_{2}^{\ell}=\sqrt{2}(\ln 2+2)$ so $\displaystyle\sum_{k=2}^{\infty}\frac{\ln k}{k^{3/2}}$ converges.

34. $\dfrac{\cos(1/k)}{k^2}<\dfrac{1}{k^2}$, $\displaystyle\sum_{k=1}^{\infty}\frac{1}{k^2}$ converges so $\displaystyle\sum_{k=1}^{\infty}\frac{\cos(1/k)}{k^2}$ converges.

35. $\displaystyle\rho=\lim_{k\to+\infty}\frac{1-\cos(1/k)}{1/k^2}$, but

$\displaystyle\lim_{x\to+\infty}\frac{1-\cos(1/x)}{1/x^2}=\lim_{x\to+\infty}\frac{(-1/x^2)\sin(1/x)}{-2/x^3}=\lim_{x\to+\infty}\frac{\sin(1/x)}{2(1/x)}=1/2$, so $\rho=1/2$;

the series converges.

36. $\displaystyle\rho=\lim_{k\to+\infty}\frac{\sin(\pi/k)}{\pi/k}=1$ and $\displaystyle\sum_{k=1}^{\infty}\pi/k$ diverges

37. $\dfrac{\ln k}{k^2}<\dfrac{\sqrt{k}}{k^2}=\dfrac{1}{k^{3/2}}$, $\displaystyle\sum_{k=1}^{\infty}\frac{1}{k^{3/2}}$ converges so $\displaystyle\sum_{k=1}^{\infty}\frac{\ln k}{k^2}$ converges

38. $\dfrac{1}{(\ln k)^2}>\dfrac{1}{k}$, $\displaystyle\sum_{k=2}^{\infty}\frac{1}{k}$ diverges so $\displaystyle\sum_{k=2}^{\infty}\frac{1}{(\ln k)^2}$ diverges

39. limit comparison test, compare with $\displaystyle\sum_{k=1}^{\infty} 1/k^p$,

$$\rho = \lim_{k \to +\infty} \frac{k^p}{(a+bk)^p} = \lim_{k \to +\infty} \frac{1}{(a/k+b)^p} = 1/b^p, \text{ converges for } p > 1.$$

40. **(a)** $k^k = k \cdot k \cdot k \cdots k > k(k-1)(k-2) \cdots (1) = k!, \; k^{-k} = 1/k^k < 1/k!,$

$\displaystyle\sum_{k=1}^{\infty} 1/k!$ converges (ratio test) so $\displaystyle\sum_{k=1}^{\infty} k^{-k}$ converges

(b) $\rho = \displaystyle\lim_{k \to +\infty} k^{-1} = 0$

41. Compare with the convergent series $\displaystyle\sum_{k=1}^{\infty} 1/k!, \; \rho = \lim_{k \to +\infty} \frac{(k+1)^2 k!}{(k+2)!} = \lim_{k \to +\infty} \frac{k+1}{k+2} = 1,$
converges

42. $1 + 1/3 + 1/5 + 1/7 + \cdots = \displaystyle\sum_{k=1}^{\infty} \frac{1}{2k-1}$, compare with the divergent series $\displaystyle\sum_{k=1}^{\infty} 1/k$,

$$\rho = \lim_{k \to +\infty} \frac{k}{2k-1} = 1/2, \text{ diverges}$$

43. $k! = k(k-1)(k-2) \cdots (2)(1) \geq 2 \cdot 2 \cdot 2 \cdots 2 \cdot 1 = 2^{k-1}, \; 1/k! \leq 1/2^{k-1}, \; \displaystyle\sum_{k=1}^{\infty} 1/2^{k-1}$ converges

so $\displaystyle\sum_{k=1}^{\infty} 1/k!$ converges

44. **(a)** if $\displaystyle\lim_{k \to +\infty} (a_k/b_k) = 0$ then for $k \geq K$, $a_k/b_k < 1$, $a_k < b_k$ so $\sum a_k$ converges by the comparison test.

(b) if $\displaystyle\lim_{k \to +\infty} (a_k/b_k) = +\infty$ then for $k \geq K$, $a_k/b_k > 1$, $a_k > b_k$ so $\sum a_k$ diverges by the comparison test.

EXERCISE SET 11.7

1. converges

2. converges

3. diverges because $\displaystyle\lim_{k \to +\infty} a_k = \lim_{k \to +\infty} \frac{k+1}{3k+1} = 1/3 \neq 0$

4. converges

5. converges

6. converges

7. $\rho = \lim\limits_{k \to +\infty} \dfrac{(3/5)^{k+1}}{(3/5)^k} = 3/5$, converges absolutely

8. $\rho = \lim\limits_{k \to +\infty} \dfrac{2}{k+1} = 0$, converges absolutely

9. $\rho = \lim\limits_{k \to +\infty} \dfrac{3k^2}{(k+1)^2} = 3$, diverges

10. $\rho = \lim\limits_{k \to +\infty} \dfrac{k+1}{5k} = 1/5$, converges absolutely

11. $\rho = \lim\limits_{k \to +\infty} \dfrac{(k+1)^3}{ek^3} = 1/e$, converges absolutely

12. $\rho = \lim\limits_{k \to +\infty} \dfrac{(k+1)^{k+1}k!}{(k+1)!k^k} = \lim\limits_{k \to +\infty} (1+1/k)^k = e$, diverges

13.   conditionally convergent, $\displaystyle\sum_{k=1}^{\infty} \dfrac{(-1)^{k+1}}{3k}$ converges by the alternating series test but $\displaystyle\sum_{k=1}^{\infty} \dfrac{1}{3k}$, diverges

14.   absolutely convergent, $\displaystyle\sum_{k=1}^{\infty} \dfrac{1}{k^{4/3}}$ converges

15.   divergent, $\lim\limits_{k \to +\infty} a_k \neq 0$

16.   absolutely convergent, ratio test for absolute convergence

17. $\displaystyle\sum_{k=1}^{\infty} \dfrac{\cos k\pi}{k} = \sum_{k=1}^{\infty} \dfrac{(-1)^k}{k}$ is conditionally convergent, $\displaystyle\sum_{k=1}^{\infty} \dfrac{(-1)^k}{k}$ converges by the alternating series test but $\displaystyle\sum_{k=1}^{\infty} 1/k$ diverges.

18.   conditionally convergent, $\displaystyle\sum_{k=3}^{\infty} \dfrac{(-1)^k \ln k}{k}$ converges by the alternating series test but $\displaystyle\sum_{k=3}^{\infty} \dfrac{\ln k}{k}$ diverges (integral test).

19.   absolutely convergent, $\displaystyle\sum_{k=1}^{\infty} \left[\dfrac{k+2}{3k-1}\right]^k$ converges by the root test.

20. absolutely convergent, $\displaystyle\sum_{k=1}^{\infty} \frac{1}{k^2+1}$ converges (compare with $\sum 1/k^2$)

21. conditionally convergent, $\displaystyle\sum_{k=1}^{\infty}(-1)^{k+1}\frac{k+2}{k(k+3)}$ converges by the alternating series test but

$\displaystyle\sum_{k=1}^{\infty}\frac{k+2}{k(k+3)}$ diverges (limit comparison test with $\sum 1/k$)

22. conditionally convergent, $\displaystyle\sum_{k=1}^{\infty}\frac{(-1)^{k+1}k^2}{k^3+1}$ converges by the alternating series test but $\displaystyle\sum_{k=1}^{\infty}\frac{k^2}{k^3+1}$ diverges

23. $\displaystyle\sum_{k=1}^{\infty}\sin(k\pi/2) = 1+0-1+0+1+0-1+0+\cdots$, divergent ($\displaystyle\lim_{k\to+\infty}\sin(k\pi/2)$ does not exist)

24. absolutely convergent, $\displaystyle\sum_{k=1}^{\infty}\frac{|\sin k|}{k^3}$ converges (compare with $\sum 1/k^3$)

25. conditionally convergent, $\displaystyle\sum_{k=2}^{\infty}\frac{(-1)^k}{k\ln k}$ converges by the alternating series test but $\displaystyle\sum_{k=2}^{\infty}\frac{1}{k\ln k}$ diverges (integral test)

26. conditionally convergent, $\displaystyle\sum_{k=1}^{\infty}\frac{(-1)^k}{\sqrt{k(k+1)}}$ converges by the alternating series test but

$\displaystyle\sum_{k=1}^{\infty}\frac{1}{\sqrt{k(k+1)}}$ diverges (limit comparison test with $\sum 1/k$)

27. absolutely convergent, $\displaystyle\sum_{k=2}^{\infty}(1/\ln k)^k$ converges by the root test

28. conditionally convergent, $\displaystyle\sum_{k=1}^{\infty}\frac{(-1)^{k+1}}{\sqrt{k+1}+\sqrt{k}}$ converges by the alternating series test but

$\displaystyle\sum_{k=1}^{\infty}\frac{1}{\sqrt{k+1}+\sqrt{k}}$ diverges (limit comparison test with $\sum 1/\sqrt{k}$)

29. conditionally convergent, let $f(x) = \dfrac{x^2+1}{x^3+2}$ then $f'(x) = \dfrac{x(4-3x-x^3)}{(x^3+2)^2} \le 0$ for $x \ge 2$ so

$\{a_k\}_{k=2}^{+\infty} = \left\{\dfrac{k^2+1}{k^3+2}\right\}_{k=2}^{+\infty}$ is nonincreasing, $\lim\limits_{k\to+\infty} a_k = 0$; the series converges by the alternat-

ing series test but $\sum\limits_{k=2}^{\infty} \dfrac{k^2+1}{k^3+2}$ diverges (limit comparison test with $\sum 1/k$)

30. $\sum\limits_{k=1}^{\infty} \dfrac{k\cos k\pi}{k^2+1} = \sum\limits_{k=1}^{\infty} \dfrac{(-1)^k k}{k^2+1}$ is conditionally convergent, $\sum\limits_{k=1}^{\infty} \dfrac{(-1)^k k}{k^2+1}$ converges by the alternat-

ing series test but $\sum\limits_{k=1}^{\infty} \dfrac{k}{k^2+1}$ diverges

31. $|\text{error}| < a_8 = 1/8 = 0.125$ **32.** $|\text{error}| < a_6 = 1/6! < 0.0014$

33. $|\text{error}| < a_{100} = 1/\sqrt{100} = 0.1$ **34.** $|\text{error}| < a_4 = 1/(5\ln 5) < 0.125$

35. $|\text{error}| < 0.0001$ if $a_{n+1} \le 0.0001$, $1/(n+1) \le 0.0001$, $n+1 \ge 10{,}000$, $n \ge 9{,}999$; $n = 9{,}999$

36. $|\text{error}| < 0.00001$ if $a_{n+1} \le 0.00001$, $1/(n+1)! \le 0.00001$, $(n+1)! \ge 100{,}000$. But $8! = 40{,}320$, $9! = 362{,}880$ so $(n+1)! \ge 100{,}000$ if $n+1 \ge 9$, $n \ge 8$; $n = 8$.

37. $|\text{error}| < 0.005$ if $a_{n+1} \le 0.005$, $1/\sqrt{n+1} \le 0.005$, $\sqrt{n+1} \ge 200$, $n+1 \ge 40{,}000$, $n \ge 39{,}999$; $n = 39{,}999$

38. $|\text{error}| < 0.1$ if $a_{n+1} \le 0.1$, $1/[(n+2)\ln(n+2)] \le 0.1$, $(n+2)\ln(n+2) \ge 10$. But $5\ln 5 \approx 8.05$ and $6\ln 6 \approx 10.75$ so $(n+2)\ln(n+2) \ge 10$ if $n+2 \ge 6$, $n \ge 4$; $n = 4$

39. $a_k = \dfrac{3}{2^{k+1}}$, $|\text{error}| < a_{11} = \dfrac{3}{2^{12}} < 0.00074$; $s_{10} \approx 0.4995$; $S = \dfrac{3/4}{1-(-1/2)} = 0.5$.

40. $a_k = \left(\dfrac{2}{3}\right)^{k-1}$, $|\text{error}| < a_{11} = \left(\dfrac{2}{3}\right)^{10} < 0.01734$; $s_{10} \approx 0.5896$; $S = \dfrac{1}{1-(-2/3)} = 0.6$.

41. $a_k = \dfrac{1}{(2k-1)!}$, $a_{n+1} = \dfrac{1}{(2n+1)!} \le 10^{-4}$, $(2n+1)! \ge 10{,}000$, $2n+1 \ge 8$, $n \ge 3.5$; $n = 4$. $s_4 \approx 0.84147$, $\sin(1) \approx 0.841470985$.

42. $a_k = \dfrac{1}{(2k-2)!}$, $a_{n+1} = \dfrac{1}{(2n)!} \le 10^{-4}$, $(2n)! \ge 10{,}000$, $2n \ge 8$, $n \ge 4$; $n = 4$. $s_4 \approx 0.54028$, $\cos(1) \approx 0.540302306$.

43. $a_k = \dfrac{1}{k2^k}$, $a_{n+1} = \dfrac{1}{(n+1)2^{n+1}} \le 10^{-4}$, $(n+1)2^{n+1} \ge 10,000$, $n+1 \ge 10$, $n \ge 9$; $n = 9$.

$s_9 \approx 0.40553$, $\ln\dfrac{3}{2} \approx 0.405465108$.

44. $a_k = \dfrac{1}{(2k-1)^5 + 4(2k-1)}$, $a_{n+1} = \dfrac{1}{(2n+1)^5 + 4(2n+1)} \le 10^{-4}$,

$(2n+1)^5 + 4(2n+1) \ge 10,000$, $2n+1 \ge 7$, $n \ge 3$; $n = 3$. $s_3 \approx 0.19640$, $\pi/16 \approx 0.196349541$.

45. (a) $a_k = \dfrac{1}{k^2}$, $a_{n+1} = \dfrac{1}{(n+1)^2} \le 5 \times 10^{-3}$, $(n+1)^2 \ge 200$, $n \ge 14$; $n = 14$

(b) $s_{10} \approx 0.817962176$, $\pi^2/12 \approx 0.822467033$, $|\text{error}| \approx 0.004504858$

46. (a) $a_k = \dfrac{1}{2k-1}$, $a_{n+1} = \dfrac{1}{2n+1} \le 10^{-2}$, $2n+1 \ge 100$, $n \ge 49.5$; $n = 50$

(b) $s_{26} \approx 0.775786328$, $\pi/4 \approx 0.785398163$, $|\text{error}| \approx 0.009611835$

47. Suppose $\Sigma|a_k|$ converges, then $\lim\limits_{k\to+\infty} |a_k| = 0$ so $|a_k| < 1$ for $k \ge K$ and thus $|a_k|^2 < |a_k|$, $a_k^2 < |a_k|$ hence Σa_k^2 converges by the comparison test.

48. $a_k = 1/k$, for example

49. Suppose $a_1 - a_2 + a_3 - a_4 + \cdots + (-1)^{k+1}a_k + \cdots$ satisfies (a) and (b) of Theorem 11.7.1, then the series converges and by Theorem 11.4.3b so does $-\left(a_1 - a_2 + a_3 - a_4 + \cdots + (-1)^{k+1}a_k + \cdots\right)$ which equals $-a_1 + a_2 - a_3 + a_4 - \cdots + (-1)^k a_k + \cdots$

50. (a) Consider the series $\Sigma|u_k|$ then by the ratio test $\lim\limits_{k\to+\infty} |u_{k+1}|/|u_k| = \rho < 1$ thus $\Sigma|u_k|$ converges and by Theorem 11.7.4 so does Σu_k.

(b) Pattern the proof along the same lines as that for Theorem 11.5.2, part (b), to show that $\lim\limits_{k\to+\infty} |u_k| \ne 0$ so that $\lim\limits_{k\to+\infty} u_k \ne 0$.

(c) Consider $\sum 1/k$ and $\sum 1/k^2$.

51. $\left(1 - \dfrac{1}{2} - \dfrac{1}{4}\right) + \left(\dfrac{1}{3} - \dfrac{1}{6} - \dfrac{1}{8}\right) + \left(\dfrac{1}{5} - \dfrac{1}{10} - \dfrac{1}{12}\right) + \cdots$

$= \left(\dfrac{1}{2} - \dfrac{1}{4}\right) + \left(\dfrac{1}{6} - \dfrac{1}{8}\right) + \left(\dfrac{1}{10} - \dfrac{1}{12}\right) + \cdots = \dfrac{1}{2}\left(1 - \dfrac{1}{2} + \dfrac{1}{3} - \dfrac{1}{4} + \dfrac{1}{5} - \dfrac{1}{6} + \cdots\right) = S/2$

52. $\dfrac{1}{\sqrt{4k-3}} + \dfrac{1}{\sqrt{4k-1}} - \dfrac{1}{\sqrt{2k}} > \dfrac{1}{\sqrt{4k}} + \dfrac{1}{\sqrt{4k}} - \dfrac{1}{\sqrt{2k}} = \dfrac{1}{\sqrt{k}} - \dfrac{1}{\sqrt{2}\sqrt{k}} = \dfrac{1 - 1/\sqrt{2}}{\sqrt{k}}$, but

$\displaystyle\sum_{k=1}^{\infty} \dfrac{1 - 1/\sqrt{2}}{\sqrt{k}} = +\infty$, so the rearranged series diverges to $+\infty$ by the comparison test.

53. $1 + \dfrac{1}{3^2} + \dfrac{1}{5^2} + \cdots = \left[1 + \dfrac{1}{2^2} + \dfrac{1}{3^2} + \cdots\right] - \left[\dfrac{1}{2^2} + \dfrac{1}{4^2} + \dfrac{1}{6^2} + \cdots\right]$

$= \dfrac{\pi^2}{6} - \dfrac{1}{2^2}\left[1 + \dfrac{1}{2^2} + \dfrac{1}{3^2} + \cdots\right] = \dfrac{\pi^2}{6} - \dfrac{1}{4}\dfrac{\pi^2}{6} = \dfrac{\pi^2}{8}$

54. $1 + \dfrac{1}{3^4} + \dfrac{1}{5^4} + \cdots = \left[1 + \dfrac{1}{2^4} + \dfrac{1}{3^4} + \cdots\right] - \left[\dfrac{1}{2^4} + \dfrac{1}{4^4} + \dfrac{1}{6^4} + \cdots\right]$

$= \dfrac{\pi^4}{90} - \dfrac{1}{2^4}\left[1 + \dfrac{1}{2^4} + \dfrac{1}{3^4} + \cdots\right] = \dfrac{\pi^4}{90} - \dfrac{1}{16}\dfrac{\pi^4}{90} = \dfrac{\pi^4}{96}$

55. $1 - \dfrac{1}{2^2} + \dfrac{1}{3^2} - \cdots = \left[1 + \dfrac{1}{2^2} + \dfrac{1}{3^2} + \cdots\right] - 2\left[\dfrac{1}{2^2} + \dfrac{1}{4^2} + \dfrac{1}{6^2} + \cdots\right]$

$= \dfrac{\pi^2}{6} - \dfrac{2}{2^2}\left[1 + \dfrac{1}{2^2} + \dfrac{1}{3^2} + \cdots\right] = \dfrac{\pi^2}{6} - \dfrac{1}{2}\dfrac{\pi^2}{6} = \dfrac{\pi^2}{12}$

56. **(a)** The distance d from the starting point is

$d = 180 - \dfrac{180}{2} + \dfrac{180}{3} - \cdots - \dfrac{180}{1000} = 180\left[1 - \dfrac{1}{2} + \dfrac{1}{4} - \cdots - \dfrac{1}{1000}\right].$

From Theorem 11.7.2, $1 - \dfrac{1}{2} + \dfrac{1}{4} - \cdots - \dfrac{1}{1000}$ differs from $\ln 2$ by less than $1/1001$ so $180(\ln 2 - 1/1001) < d < 180(\ln 2 + 1/1001),\ 124.58 < d < 124.95.$

(b) The total distance s traveled is $s = 180 + \dfrac{180}{2} + \dfrac{180}{3} + \cdots + \dfrac{180}{1000}$, from inequality (4) in Section 11.4

$$\int_1^{1001} \dfrac{180}{x}dx < s < 180 + \int_1^{1000} \dfrac{180}{x}dx$$
$$180\ln 1001 < s < 180(1 + \ln 1000)$$
$$1243 < s < 1424$$

EXERCISE SET 11.8

1. $\rho = \lim\limits_{k \to +\infty} \dfrac{k+1}{k+2}|x| = |x|$, the series converges if $|x| < 1$ and diverges if $|x| > 1$. If $x = -1$, $\sum\limits_{k=0}^{\infty} \dfrac{(-1)^k}{k+1}$ converges by the alternating series test; if $x = 1$, $\sum\limits_{k=0}^{\infty} \dfrac{1}{k+1}$ diverges. The radius of convergence is 1, the interval of convergence is $[-1, 1)$.

2. $\rho = \lim\limits_{k \to +\infty} 3|x| = 3|x|$, the series converges if $3|x| < 1$ or $|x| < 1/3$ and diverges if $|x| > 1/3$. If

$x = -1/3$, $\sum\limits_{k=0}^{\infty}(-1)^k$ diverges, if $x = 1/3$, $\sum\limits_{k=0}^{\infty}(1)$ diverges. The radius of convergence is $1/3$, the interval of convergence is $(-1/3, 1/3)$.

3. $\rho = \lim\limits_{k \to +\infty} \dfrac{|x|}{k+1} = 0$, the radius of convergence is $+\infty$, the interval is $(-\infty, +\infty)$.

4. $\rho = \lim\limits_{k \to +\infty} \dfrac{k+1}{2}|x| = +\infty$, the radius of convergence is 0, the series converges only if $x = 0$.

5. $\rho = \lim\limits_{k \to +\infty} \dfrac{5k^2|x|}{(k+1)^2} = 5|x|$, converges if $|x| < 1/5$ and diverges if $|x| > 1/5$. If $x = -1/5$,

$\sum\limits_{k=1}^{\infty} \dfrac{(-1)^k}{k^2}$ converges; if $x = 1/5$, $\sum\limits_{k=1}^{\infty} 1/k^2$ converges. Radius of convergence is $1/5$, interval of convergence is $[-1/5, 1/5]$.

6. $\rho = \lim\limits_{k \to +\infty} \dfrac{\ln k}{\ln(k+1)}|x| = |x|$, the series converges if $|x| < 1$ and diverges if $|x| > 1$. If $x = -1$,

$\sum\limits_{k=2}^{\infty} \dfrac{(-1)^k}{\ln k}$ converges; if $x = 1$, $\sum\limits_{k=2}^{\infty} 1/\ln k$ diverges (compare to $\sum \dfrac{1}{\sqrt{k}}$, see hint to Exercise 37, 11.6). Radius of convergence is 1, interval of convergence is $[-1, 1)$.

7. $\rho = \lim\limits_{k \to +\infty} \dfrac{k|x|}{k+2} = |x|$, converges if $|x| < 1$, diverges if $|x| > 1$. If $x = -1$, $\sum\limits_{k=1}^{\infty} \dfrac{(-1)^k}{k(k+1)}$

converges; if $x = 1$, $\sum\limits_{k=1}^{\infty} \dfrac{1}{k(k+1)}$ converges. Radius of convergence is 1, interval of convergence is $[-1, 1]$.

8. $\rho = \lim\limits_{k \to +\infty} 2\dfrac{k+1}{k+2}|x| = 2|x|$, converges if $|x| < 1/2$, diverges if $|x| > 1/2$. If $x = -1/2$,

$\sum\limits_{k=0}^{\infty} \dfrac{-1}{2(k+1)}$ diverges; if $x = 1/2$, $\sum\limits_{k=0}^{\infty} \dfrac{(-1)^k}{2(k+1)}$ converges. Radius of convergence is $1/2$, interval of convergence is $(-1/2, 1/2]$.

9. $\rho = \lim\limits_{k \to +\infty} \dfrac{\sqrt{k}}{\sqrt{k+1}}|x| = |x|$, converges if $|x| < 1$, diverges if $|x| > 1$. If $x = -1$, $\sum\limits_{k=1}^{\infty} \dfrac{-1}{\sqrt{k}}$

diverges; if $x = 1$, $\sum\limits_{k=1}^{\infty} \dfrac{(-1)^{k-1}}{\sqrt{k}}$ converges. Radius of convergence is 1, interval of convergence is $(-1, 1]$.

10. $\rho = \lim\limits_{k \to +\infty} \dfrac{|x|^2}{(2k+2)(2k+1)} = 0$, radius of convergence is $+\infty$, interval of convergence is $(-\infty, +\infty)$.

11. $\rho = \lim\limits_{k \to +\infty} \dfrac{|x|^2}{(2k+3)(2k+2)} = 0$, radius of convergence is $+\infty$, interval of convergence is $(-\infty, +\infty)$.

12. $\rho = \lim\limits_{k \to +\infty} \dfrac{k^{3/2}|x|^3}{(k+1)^{3/2}} = |x|^3$, converges if $|x| < 1$, diverges if $|x| > 1$. If $x = -1$, $\sum\limits_{k=0}^{\infty} \dfrac{1}{k^{3/2}}$

converges; if $x = 1$, $\sum\limits_{k=0}^{\infty} \dfrac{(-1)^k}{k^{3/2}}$ converges. Radius of convergence is 1, interval of convergence is $[-1, 1]$.

13. $\rho = \lim\limits_{k \to +\infty} \dfrac{3|x|}{k+1} = 0$, radius of convergence is $+\infty$, interval of convergence is $(-\infty, +\infty)$.

14. $\rho = \lim\limits_{k \to +\infty} \dfrac{k(\ln k)^2|x|}{(k+1)[\ln(k+1)]^2} = |x|$, converges if $|x| < 1$, diverges if $|x| > 1$. If $x = -1$,

$\sum\limits_{k=2}^{\infty} \dfrac{-1}{k(\ln k)^2}$ converges; if $x = 1$, $\sum\limits_{k=2}^{\infty} \dfrac{(-1)^{k+1}}{k(\ln k)^2}$ converges. Radius of convergence is 1, interval of convergence is $[-1, 1]$.

15. $\rho = \lim\limits_{k \to +\infty} \dfrac{1+k^2}{1+(k+1)^2}|x| = |x|$, converges if $|x| < 1$, diverges if $|x| > 1$. If $x = -1$, $\sum\limits_{k=0}^{\infty} \dfrac{(-1)^k}{1+k^2}$

converges; if $x = 1$, $\sum\limits_{k=0}^{\infty} \dfrac{1}{1+k^2}$ converges. Radius of convergence is 1, interval of convergence is $[-1, 1]$.

16. $\rho = \lim\limits_{k \to +\infty} \dfrac{1}{2}|x - 3| = \dfrac{1}{2}|x - 3|$, converges if $|x - 3| < 2$, diverges if $|x - 3| > 2$. If $x = 1$,

$\sum\limits_{k=0}^{\infty} (-1)^k$ diverges; if $x = 5$, $\sum\limits_{k=0}^{\infty} 1$ diverges. Radius of convergence is 2, interval of convergence is $(1, 5)$.

17. $\rho = \lim\limits_{k \to +\infty} \dfrac{k|x+1|}{k+1} = |x+1|$, converges if $|x+1| < 1$, diverges if $|x+1| > 1$. If $x = -2$, $\sum\limits_{k=1}^{\infty} \dfrac{-1}{k}$

diverges; if $x = 0$, $\sum\limits_{k=1}^{\infty} \dfrac{(-1)^{k+1}}{k}$ converges. Radius of convergence is 1, interval of convergence is $(-2, 0]$.

18. $\rho = \lim\limits_{k \to +\infty} \dfrac{(k+1)^2}{(k+2)^2}|x-4| = |x-4|$, converges if $|x-4| < 1$, diverges if $|x-4| > 1$. If $x = 3$,

$\sum\limits_{k=0}^{\infty} 1/(k+1)^2$ converges; if $x = 5$, $\sum\limits_{k=0}^{\infty}(-1)^k/(k+1)^2$ converges. Radius of convergence is 1, interval of convergence is $[3, 5]$.

19. $\rho = \lim\limits_{k \to +\infty} (3/4)|x+5| = \dfrac{3}{4}|x+5|$, convergence if $|x+5| < 4/3$, diverges if $|x+5| > 4/3$. If

$x = -19/3$, $\sum\limits_{k=0}^{\infty}(-1)^k$ diverges; if $x = -11/3$, $\sum\limits_{k=0}^{\infty} 1$ diverges. Radius of convergence is 4/3, interval of convergence is $(-19/3, -11/3)$.

20. $\rho = \lim\limits_{k \to +\infty} \dfrac{(2k+3)(2k+2)k^3}{(k+1)^3}|x-2| = +\infty$, radius of convergence is 0, series converges only at $x = 2$.

21. $\rho = \lim\limits_{k \to +\infty} \dfrac{k^2+4}{(k+1)^2+4}|x+1|^2 = |x+1|^2$, converges if $|x+1| < 1$, diverges if $|x+1| > 1$. If

$x = -2$, $\sum\limits_{k=1}^{\infty} \dfrac{(-1)^{3k+1}}{k^2+4}$ converges; if $x = 0$, $\sum\limits_{k=1}^{\infty} \dfrac{(-1)^k}{k^2+4}$ converges. Radius of convergence is 1, interval of convergence is $[-2, 0]$.

22. $\rho = \lim\limits_{k \to +\infty} \dfrac{k \ln(k+1)}{(k+1)\ln k}|x-3| = |x-3|$, converges if $|x-3| < 1$, diverges if $|x-3| > 1$. If $x = 2$,

$\sum\limits_{k=1}^{\infty} \dfrac{(-1)^k \ln k}{k}$ converges; if $x = 4$, $\sum\limits_{k=1}^{\infty} \dfrac{\ln k}{k}$ diverges. Radius of convergence is 1, interval of convergence is $[2, 4)$.

23. $\rho = \lim\limits_{k \to +\infty} \dfrac{\pi|x-1|^2}{(2k+3)(2k+2)} = 0$, radius of convergence $+\infty$, interval of convergence $(-\infty, +\infty)$.

24. $\rho = \lim\limits_{k \to +\infty} \dfrac{1}{16}|2x-3| = \dfrac{1}{16}|2x-3|$, converges if $\dfrac{1}{16}|2x-3| < 1$ or $|x-3/2| < 8$, diverges

if $|x-3/2| > 8$. If $x = -13/2$, $\sum\limits_{k=0}^{\infty}(-1)^k$ diverges; if $x = 19/2$, $\sum\limits_{k=0}^{\infty} 1$ diverges. Radius of convergence is 8, interval of convergence is $(-13/2, 19/2)$.

25. $x + \dfrac{1}{2}x^2 + \dfrac{3}{14}x^3 + \dfrac{3}{35}x^4 + \cdots$; $\rho = \lim\limits_{k \to +\infty} \dfrac{k+1}{3k+1}|x| = \dfrac{1}{3}|x|$, converges if $\dfrac{1}{3}|x| < 1$, $|x| < 3$ so $R = 3$.

26. $-x^3 + \dfrac{2}{3}x^5 - \dfrac{2}{5}x^7 + \dfrac{8}{35}x^9 - \cdots$; $\rho = \displaystyle\lim_{k \to +\infty} \dfrac{k+1}{2k+1}|x|^2 = \dfrac{1}{2}|x|^2$, converges if $\dfrac{1}{2}|x|^2 < 1$, $|x|^2 < 2$, $|x| < \sqrt{2}$ so $R = \sqrt{2}$.

27. $x + \dfrac{3}{2}x^2 + \dfrac{5}{8}x^3 + \dfrac{7}{48}x^4 + \cdots$; $\rho = \displaystyle\lim_{k \to +\infty} \dfrac{2k+1}{(2k)(2k-1)}|x| = 0$ so $R = +\infty$.

28. $\rho = \displaystyle\lim_{k \to +\infty} \sqrt[k]{|u_k|} = \lim_{k \to +\infty} \dfrac{|x|}{\ln k} = 0$, the series converges absolutely for all x so the interval of convergence is $(-\infty, +\infty)$.

29. By the ratio test for absolute convergence, $\rho = \displaystyle\lim_{k \to +\infty} \dfrac{|x-a|}{b} = \dfrac{|x-a|}{b}$; converges if $|x-a| < b$,

diverges if $|x-a| > b$. If $x = a-b$, $\displaystyle\sum_{k=0}^{\infty}(-1)^k$ diverges; if $x = a+b$, $\displaystyle\sum_{k=0}^{\infty}1$ diverges. The interval of convergence is $(a-b, a+b)$.

30. By the ratio test for absolute convergence,

$\rho = \displaystyle\lim_{k \to +\infty} \dfrac{(pk+p)!(k!)^p}{(pk)![(k+1)!]^p}|x|$

$= \displaystyle\lim_{k \to +\infty} \dfrac{(pk+p)(pk+p-1)(pk+p-2)\cdots(pk+p-[p-1])}{(k+1)^p}|x|$

$= \displaystyle\lim_{k \to +\infty} p\left(p - \dfrac{1}{k+1}\right)\left(p - \dfrac{2}{k+1}\right)\cdots\left(p - \dfrac{p-1}{k+1}\right)|x| = p^p|x|$,

converges if $|x| < 1/p^p$, diverges if $|x| > 1/p^p$. Radius of convergence is $1/p^p$.

31. By the ratio test for absolute convergence,

$\rho = \displaystyle\lim_{k \to +\infty} \dfrac{(k+1+p)!k!(k+q)!}{(k+p)!(k+1)!(k+1+q)!}|x| = \lim_{k \to +\infty} \dfrac{k+1+p}{(k+1)(k+1+q)}|x| = 0$,

radius of convergence is $+\infty$.

32. By the root test for absolute convergence,

$\rho = \displaystyle\lim_{k \to +\infty} |c_k|^{1/k}|x| = L|x|$, $L|x| < 1$ if $|x| < 1/L$ so the radius of convergence is $1/L$.

33. By assumption $\displaystyle\sum_{k=0}^{\infty} c_k x^k$ converges if $|x| < R$ so $\displaystyle\sum_{k=0}^{\infty} c_k x^{2k} = \sum_{k=0}^{\infty} c_k(x^2)^k$ converges if $|x^2| < R$,

$|x| < \sqrt{R}$. Thus $\displaystyle\sum_{k=0}^{\infty} c_k x^{2k}$ has radius of convergence $\sqrt{R}$.

34. The assumption is that $\displaystyle\sum_{k=0}^{\infty} c_k R^k$ is convergent and $\displaystyle\sum_{k=0}^{\infty} c_k(-R)^k$ is divergent. Suppose that $\displaystyle\sum_{k=0}^{\infty} c_k R^k$ is absolutely convergent then $\displaystyle\sum_{k=0}^{\infty} c_k(-R)^k$ is also absolutely convergent and hence convergent because $|c_k R^k| = |c_k(-R)^k|$, which contradicts the assumption that $\displaystyle\sum_{k=0}^{\infty} c_k(-R)^k$ is divergent so $\displaystyle\sum_{k=0}^{\infty} c_k R^k$ must be conditionally convergent.

EXERCISE SET 11.9

1. $1 - 2x + 2x^2 - \dfrac{4}{3}x^3 + \dfrac{2}{3}x^4$

2. $1 - x + x^2 - x^3 + x^4$

3. $2x - \dfrac{4}{3}x^3$

4. $1 + x - \dfrac{1}{3}x^3 - \dfrac{1}{6}x^4$

5. $x + \dfrac{1}{3}x^3$

6. $1 + 2x - x^2 + x^3$

7. $x + x^2 + \dfrac{1}{2}x^3 + \dfrac{1}{6}x^4$

8. $x - \dfrac{1}{3}x^3$

9. $1 + \dfrac{1}{2}x^2 + \dfrac{5}{24}x^4$

10. $1 + \dfrac{1}{2}x - \dfrac{1}{8}x^2 + \dfrac{1}{16}x^3 - \dfrac{5}{128}x^4$

11. $\ln 3 + \dfrac{2}{3}x - \dfrac{2}{9}x^2 + \dfrac{8}{81}x^3 - \dfrac{4}{81}x^4$

12. $x + \dfrac{1}{6}x^3$

13. $e + e(x-1) + \dfrac{e}{2}(x-1)^2 + \dfrac{e}{6}(x-1)^3$

14. $(x-1) - \dfrac{1}{2}(x-1)^2 + \dfrac{1}{3}(x-1)^3$

15. $2 + \dfrac{1}{4}(x-4) - \dfrac{1}{64}(x-4)^2 + \dfrac{1}{512}(x-4)^3$

16. $11 - 31(x+2) + 24(x+2)^2 - 8(x+2)^3$

17. $\dfrac{\sqrt{2}}{2} - \dfrac{\sqrt{2}}{2}(x - \pi/4) - \dfrac{\sqrt{2}}{4}(x - \pi/4)^2 + \dfrac{\sqrt{2}}{12}(x - \pi/4)^3$

18. $\sqrt{3} + 4(x - \pi/3) + 4\sqrt{3}(x - \pi/3)^2 + \dfrac{40}{3}(x - \pi/3)^3$

19. $-\dfrac{\sqrt{3}}{2} + \dfrac{\pi}{2}(x + 1/3) + \dfrac{\sqrt{3}\pi^2}{4}(x + 1/3)^2 - \dfrac{\pi^3}{12}(x + 1/3)^3$

20. $1 + \dfrac{1}{2}(x - \pi/2)^2$

21. $\dfrac{\pi}{4} + \dfrac{1}{2}(x - 1) - \dfrac{1}{4}(x - 1)^2 + \dfrac{1}{12}(x - 1)^3$

22. $\dfrac{5}{4} + \dfrac{3}{4}(x - \ln 2) + \dfrac{5}{8}(x - \ln 2)^2 + \dfrac{1}{8}(x - \ln 2)^3$

23. $f^{(k)}(x) = (-1)^k e^{-x},\; f^{(k)}(0) = (-1)^k;\; \displaystyle\sum_{k=0}^{\infty} \dfrac{(-1)^k}{k!} x^k$

24. $f^{(k)}(x) = a^k e^{ax},\; f^{(k)}(0) = a^k;\; \displaystyle\sum_{k=0}^{\infty} \dfrac{a^k}{k!} x^k$

25. $f^{(k)}(x) = \dfrac{(-1)^k k!}{(1 + x)^{k+1}},\; f^{(k)}(0) = (-1)^k k!;\; \displaystyle\sum_{k=0}^{\infty}(-1)^k x^k$

26. $f^{(k)}(x) = (k + x)e^x,\; f^{(k)}(0) = k;\; \displaystyle\sum_{k=0}^{\infty} \dfrac{k}{k!} x^k = \sum_{k=1}^{\infty} \dfrac{1}{(k-1)!} x^k$

27. $f^{(0)}(0) = 0;$ for $k \geq 1,\; f^{(k)}(x) = \dfrac{(-1)^{k+1}(k-1)!}{(1+x)^k},\; f^{(k)}(0) = (-1)^{k+1}(k-1)!;\; \displaystyle\sum_{k=1}^{\infty} \dfrac{(-1)^{k+1}}{k} x^k$

28. $f^{(k)}(0) = 0$ if k is even, $f^{(k)}(0)$ is alternately π^k and $-\pi^k$ if k is odd;

$$\sum_{k=0}^{\infty} \dfrac{f^{(k)}(0)}{k!} x^k = \pi x - \dfrac{\pi^3}{3!}x^3 + \dfrac{\pi^5}{5!}x^5 - \cdots = \sum_{k=0}^{\infty} \dfrac{(-1)^k \pi^{2k+1}}{(2k+1)!} x^{2k+1}$$

29. $f^{(k)}(0) = 0$ if k is odd, $f^{(k)}(0)$ is alternately $1/2^k$ and $-1/2^k$ if k is even.

$$\sum_{k=0}^{\infty} \dfrac{f^{(k)}(0)}{k!} x^k = 1 - \dfrac{1}{2^2 2!}x^2 + \dfrac{1}{2^4 4!}x^4 - \cdots = \sum_{k=0}^{\infty} \dfrac{(-1)^k}{2^{2k}(2k)!} x^{2k}$$

30. $f^{(k)}(0) = 0$ if k is even, $f^{(k)}(0) = 1$ if k is odd;

$$\sum_{k=0}^{\infty} \dfrac{f^{(k)}(0)}{k!} x^k = x + \dfrac{1}{3!}x^3 + \dfrac{1}{5!}x^5 + \cdots = \sum_{k=0}^{\infty} \dfrac{1}{(2k+1)!} x^{2k+1}$$

31. $f^{(k)}(0) = 0$ if k is odd, $f^{(k)}(0) = 1$ if k is even;

$$\sum_{k=0}^{\infty} \dfrac{f^{(k)}(0)}{k!} x^k = 1 + \dfrac{1}{2!}x^2 + \dfrac{1}{4!}x^4 + \cdots = \sum_{k=0}^{\infty} \dfrac{1}{(2k)!} x^{2k}$$

32. $f^{(k)}(x) = \dfrac{(-1)^k k!}{x^{k+1}}$, $f^{(k)}(3) = \dfrac{(-1)^k k!}{3^{k+1}}$; $\displaystyle\sum_{k=0}^{\infty} \dfrac{(-1)^k}{3^{k+1}}(x-3)^k$

33. $f^{(k)}(x) = \dfrac{(-1)^k k!}{x^{k+1}}$, $f^{(k)}(-1) = -k!$; $\displaystyle\sum_{k=0}^{\infty}(-1)(x+1)^k$

34. $f^{(k)}(x) = e^x$, $f^{(k)}(2) = e^2$; $\displaystyle\sum_{k=0}^{\infty} \dfrac{e^2}{k!}(x-2)^k$

35. $f^{(0)}(1) = 0$; for $k \geq 1$, $f^{(k)}(x) = \dfrac{(-1)^{k+1}(k-1)!}{x^k}$, $f^{(k)}(1) = (-1)^{k+1}(k-1)!$;

$\displaystyle\sum_{k=1}^{\infty} \dfrac{(-1)^{k+1}}{k}(x-1)^k$

36. $f^{(k)}(\pi/2) = 0$ if k is even, $f^{(k)}(\pi/2)$ is alternately -1 and 1 if k is odd;

$\displaystyle\sum_{k=0}^{\infty} \dfrac{f^{(k)}(\pi/2)}{k!}(x-\pi/2)^k = -(x-\pi/2) + \dfrac{1}{3!}(x-\pi/2)^3 - \cdots = \sum_{k=0}^{\infty} \dfrac{(-1)^{k+1}}{(2k+1)!}(x-\pi/2)^{2k+1}$

37. $f^{(k)}(1/2) = 0$ if k is odd, $f^{(k)}(1/2)$ is alternately π^k and $-\pi^k$ if k is even;

$\displaystyle\sum_{k=0}^{\infty} \dfrac{f^{(k)}(1/2)}{k!}(x-1/2)^k = 1 - \dfrac{\pi^2}{2!}(x-1/2)^2 + \dfrac{\pi^4}{4!}(x-1/2)^4 - \cdots$

$$= \sum_{k=0}^{\infty} \dfrac{(-1)^k \pi^{2k}}{(2k)!}(x-1/2)^{2k}$$

38. $f^{(k)}(x) = \dfrac{(-1)^k k!}{(x+2)^{k+1}}$, $f^{(k)}(3) = \dfrac{(-1)^k k!}{5^{k+1}}$; $\displaystyle\sum_{k=0}^{\infty} \dfrac{(-1)^k}{5^{k+1}}(x-3)^k$

39. $f^{(k)}(\ln 4) = 15/8$ for k even, $f^{(k)}(\ln 4) = 17/8$ for k odd, which can be written as

$f^{(k)}(\ln 4) = \dfrac{16 - (-1)^k}{8}$; $\displaystyle\sum_{k=0}^{\infty} \dfrac{16 - (-1)^k}{8k!}(x-\ln 4)^k$

40. $p_n(x) = \displaystyle\sum_{k=0}^{n} \dfrac{f^{(k)}(a)}{k!}(x-a)^k$

$p_n'(x) = \displaystyle\sum_{k=1}^{n} \dfrac{f^{(k)}(a)}{k!}k(x-a)^{k-1} = \sum_{k=1}^{n} \dfrac{f^{(k)}(a)}{(k-1)!}(x-a)^{k-1}$

$$p_n''(x) = \sum_{k=2}^{n} \frac{f^{(k)}(a)}{(k-1)!}(k-1)(x-a)^{k-2} = \sum_{k=2}^{n} \frac{f^{(k)}(a)}{(k-2)!}(x-a)^{k-2}$$

$$\vdots$$

$$p_n^{(j)}(x) = \sum_{k=j}^{n} \frac{f^{(k)}(a)}{(k-j)!}(x-a)^{k-j} \text{ for } j = 0, 1, 2, \cdots, n \text{ so } p_n^{(j)}(a) = \frac{f^{(j)}(a)}{0!} = f^{(j)}(a)$$

EXERCISE SET 11.10

1. $f^{(6)}(x) = 2^6 e^{2x}$, $R_5(x) = \dfrac{2^6 e^{2c}}{6!} x^6$

2. $f^{(9)}(x) = -\sin x$, $R_8(x) = -\dfrac{\sin c}{9!} x^9$

3. $f^{(5)}(x) = -5!/(x+1)^6$, $R_4(x) = -\dfrac{1}{(c+1)^6} x^5$

4. $f^{(3)}(x) = 2\sec^4 x + 4\sec^2 x \tan^2 x$, $R_2(x) = \dfrac{2\sec^4 c + 4\sec^2 c \tan^2 c}{3!} x^3$

5. $f^{(4)}(x) = (4+x)e^x$, $R_3(x) = \dfrac{(4+c)e^c}{4!} x^4$

6. $f^{(6)}(x) = -5!/(1+x)^6$, $R_5(x) = -\dfrac{1}{6(1+c)^6} x^6$

7. $f^{(3)}(x) = -\dfrac{2(1-3x^2)}{(1+x^2)^3}$, $R_2(x) = -\dfrac{1-3c^2}{3(1+c^2)^3} x^3$

8. $f^{(7)}(x) = \cosh x$, $R_6(x) = \dfrac{\cosh c}{7!} x^7$

9. $f^{(4)}(x) = -\dfrac{15}{16} x^{-7/2}$, $R_3(x) = -\dfrac{5}{128c^{7/2}}(x-4)^4$

10. $f^{(6)}(x) = 6!/x^7$, $R_5(x) = \dfrac{1}{c^7}(x-1)^6$

11. $f^{(5)}(x) = \cos x$, $R_4(x) = \dfrac{\cos c}{5!}(x-\pi/6)^5$

12. $f^{(3)}(x) = \pi^3 \sin \pi x$, $R_2(x) = \dfrac{\pi^3 \sin \pi c}{3!}(x-1/2)^3$

13. $f^{(6)}(x) = 7!/(1+x)^8$, $R_5(x) = \dfrac{7}{(1+c)^8}(x+2)^6$

14. $f^{(2)}(x) = \csc^3 x + \csc x \cot^2 x$, $R_1(x) = \dfrac{1}{2}(\csc^3 c + \csc c \cot^2 c)(x - \pi/2)^2$

15. $f^{(n+1)}(x) = (n+1)!/(1-x)^{n+2}$, $R_n(x) = \dfrac{1}{(1-c)^{n+2}}x^{n+1}$

16. $f^{(n+1)}(x) = (-1)^{n+1}e^{-x}$, $R_n(x) = \dfrac{(-1)^{n+1}e^{-c}}{(n+1)!}x^{n+1}$

17. $f^{(n+1)}(x) = 2^{n+1}e^{2x}$, $R_n(x) = \dfrac{2^{n+1}e^{2c}}{(n+1)!}x^{n+1}$

18. $f^{(n+1)}(x) = \dfrac{(-1)^n n!}{(1+x)^{n+1}}$, $R_n(x) = \dfrac{(-1)^n}{(n+1)(1+c)^{n+1}}x^{n+1}$

19. $f(x) = \cos x$, $f^{(n+1)}(x) = \pm \sin x$ or $\pm \cos x$, $|f^{(n+1)}(x)| \le 1$,

$|R_n(x)| = \dfrac{|f^{(n+1)}(c)|}{(n+1)!}|x|^{n+1} \le \dfrac{|x|^{n+1}}{(n+1)!}$, $\lim\limits_{n \to +\infty} \dfrac{|x|^{n+1}}{(n+1)!} = 0$, by the Squeezing Theorem

$\lim\limits_{n \to +\infty} |R_n(x)| = 0$ so $\lim\limits_{n \to +\infty} R_n(x) = 0$ for all x.

20. $f(x) = \sin x$, $f^{(n+1)}(x) = \pm \sin x$ or $\pm \cos x$, $|f^{(n+1)}(x)| \le 1$,

$|R_n(x)| = \dfrac{|f^{(n+1)}(c)|}{(n+1)!}|x - \pi/4|^{n+1} \le \dfrac{|x - \pi/4|^{n+1}}{(n+1)!}$, $\lim\limits_{n \to +\infty} \dfrac{|x - \pi/4|^{n+1}}{(n+1)!} = 0$,

by the Squeezing Theorem $\lim\limits_{n \to +\infty} |R_n(x)| = 0$ so $\lim\limits_{n \to +\infty} R_n(x) = 0$ for all x.

21. $f(x) = e^x$, $f^{(n+1)}(x) = e^x$, $|R_n(x)| = \dfrac{e^c}{(n+1)!}|x - 1|^{n+1}$. If $x \ge 1$, $e^c \le e^x$,

$|R_n(x)| \le e^x \dfrac{|x-1|^{n+1}}{(n+1)!}$, $\lim\limits_{n \to +\infty} e^x \dfrac{|x-1|^{n+1}}{(n+1)!} = e^x(0) = 0$ so $\lim\limits_{n \to +\infty} R_n(x) = 0$.

If $x < 1$, $e^c < e$, $|R_n(x)| < e\dfrac{|x-1|^{n+1}}{(n+1)!}$ and again $\lim\limits_{n \to +\infty} R_n(x) = 0$.

22. **(a)** $f(x) = \ln(1+x)$, $f^{(n+1)}(x) = \dfrac{(-1)^n n!}{(1+x)^{n+1}}$. For $0 \le x \le 1$, $|R_n(x)| = \dfrac{x^{n+1}}{(n+1)(1+c)^{n+1}}$

and $c \ge 0$ so $(1+c)^{n+1} \ge 1$, $|R_n(x)| \le \dfrac{x^{n+1}}{n+1}$, $\lim\limits_{n \to +\infty} \dfrac{x^{n+1}}{n+1} = 0$ because $0 \le x \le 1$ thus

$\lim\limits_{n \to +\infty} R_n(x) = 0$.

23. $f(x) = e^x$, $f^{(n+1)}(x) = e^x$, $|R_n(x)| = \dfrac{e^c}{(n+1)!}|x - a|^{n+1}$. If $x \geq a$, $e^c \leq e^x$,

$|R_n(x)| \leq e^x \dfrac{|x - a|^{n+1}}{(n+1)!}$, $\displaystyle\lim_{n \to +\infty} e^x \dfrac{|x - a|^{n+1}}{(n+1)!} = e^x(0) = 0$ so $\displaystyle\lim_{n \to +\infty} R_n(x) = 0$.

If $x < a$, $e^c < e^a$, $|R_n(x)| < e^a \dfrac{|x - a|^{n+1}}{(n+1)!}$ and again $\displaystyle\lim_{n \to +\infty} R_n(x) = 0$.

24. $f(x) = \sin x$, $f^{(n+1)}(x) = \pm \sin x$ or $\pm \cos x$, $|f^{(n+1)}(x)| \leq 1$,

$|R_n(x)| = \dfrac{|f^{(n+1)}(c)|}{(n+1)!}|x - a|^{n+1} \leq \dfrac{|x - a|^{n+1}}{(n+1)!}$, $\displaystyle\lim_{n \to +\infty} \dfrac{|x - a|^{n+1}}{(n+1)!} = 0$ so $\displaystyle\lim_{n \to +\infty} R_n(x) = 0$

for all x.

25. $f(x) = \cos x$, $f^{(n+1)}(x) = \pm \sin x$ or $\pm \cos x$, $|f^{(n+1)}(x)| \leq 1$,

$|R_n(x)| = \dfrac{|f^{(n+1)}(c)|}{(n+1)!}|x - a|^{n+1} \leq \dfrac{|x - a|^{n+1}}{(n+1)!}$, $\displaystyle\lim_{n \to +\infty} \dfrac{|x - a|^{n+1}}{(n+1)!} = 0$ so $\displaystyle\lim_{n \to +\infty} R_n(x) = 0$

for all x.

26. $f^{(0)}(x) = (1+x)^m$, $f^{(k)}(x) = m(m-1)(m-2)\cdots(m-k+1)(1+x)^{m-k}$ for $k \geq 1$, $f^{(0)}(0) = 1$,
$f^{(k)}(0) = m(m-1)(m-2)\cdots(m-k+1)$, so the Maclaurin series for $(1+x)^m$ is

$$1 + mx + \frac{m(m-1)}{2!}x^2 + \cdots + \frac{m(m-1)(m-2)\cdots(m-k+1)}{k!}x^k + \cdots$$

27. $1 - 2x + 2x^2 - \dfrac{4}{3}x^3 + \cdots$; $(-\infty, +\infty)$

28. $x^2\left(1 + x + \dfrac{1}{2!}x^2 + \dfrac{1}{3!}x^3 + \cdots\right) = x^2 + x^3 + \dfrac{1}{2!}x^4 + \dfrac{1}{3!}x^5 + \cdots$; $(-\infty, +\infty)$

29. $x\left(1 - x + \dfrac{1}{2!}x^2 - \dfrac{1}{3!}x^3 + \cdots\right) = x - x^2 + \dfrac{1}{2!}x^3 - \dfrac{1}{3!}x^4 + \cdots$; $(-\infty, +\infty)$

30. $1 + x^2 + \dfrac{1}{2!}x^4 + \dfrac{1}{3!}x^6 + \cdots$; $(-\infty, +\infty)$

31. $2x - \dfrac{2^3}{3!}x^3 + \dfrac{2^5}{5!}x^5 - \dfrac{2^7}{7!}x^7 + \cdots$; $(-\infty, +\infty)$

32. $1 - \dfrac{2^2}{2!}x^2 + \dfrac{2^4}{4!}x^4 - \dfrac{2^6}{6!}x^6 + \cdots$; $(-\infty, +\infty)$

33. $x^2\left(1 - \dfrac{1}{2!}x^2 + \dfrac{1}{4!}x^4 - \dfrac{1}{6!}x^6 + \cdots\right) = x^2 - \dfrac{1}{2!}x^4 + \dfrac{1}{4!}x^6 - \dfrac{1}{6!}x^8 + \cdots$; $(-\infty, +\infty)$

34. $x^2 - \dfrac{1}{3!}x^6 + \dfrac{1}{5!}x^{10} - \dfrac{1}{7!}x^{14} + \cdots;\ (-\infty, +\infty)$

35. $\dfrac{1}{2}\left[1 - \left(1 - \dfrac{2^2}{2!}x^2 + \dfrac{2^4}{4!}x^4 - \dfrac{2^6}{6!}x^6 + \cdots\right)\right] = x^2 - \dfrac{2^3}{4!}x^4 + \dfrac{2^5}{6!}x^6 - \dfrac{2^7}{8!}x^8 + \cdots;\ (-\infty, +\infty)$

36. $\dfrac{1}{2}\left[1 + \left(1 - \dfrac{2^2}{2!}x^2 + \dfrac{2^4}{4!}x^4 - \dfrac{2^6}{6!}x^6 + \cdots\right)\right] = 1 - x^2 + \dfrac{2^3}{4!}x^4 - \dfrac{2^5}{6!}x^6 + \cdots;\ (-\infty, +\infty)$

37. $-x^2 - \dfrac{1}{2}x^4 - \dfrac{1}{3}x^6 - \dfrac{1}{4}x^8 - \cdots;\ (-1, 1)$

38. $2x - 2x^2 + \dfrac{8}{3}x^3 - 4x^4 + \cdots;\ (-1/2, 1/2]$

39. $1 + 4x^2 + 16x^4 + 64x^6 + \cdots;\ (-1/2, 1/2)$

40. $x\left(1 + x + x^2 + x^3 + \cdots\right) = x + x^2 + x^3 + x^4 + \cdots;\ (-1, 1)$

41. $x^2\left(1 - 3x + 9x^2 - 27x^3 + \cdots\right) = x^2 - 3x^3 + 9x^4 - 27x^5 + \cdots;\ (-1/3, 1/3)$

42. $x\left(1 - x^2 + x^4 - x^6 + \cdots\right) = x - x^3 + x^5 - x^7 + \cdots;\ (-1, 1)$

43. $x\left(2x + \dfrac{2^3}{3!}x^3 + \dfrac{2^5}{5!}x^5 + \dfrac{2^7}{7!}x^7 + \cdots\right) = 2x^2 + \dfrac{2^3}{3!}x^4 + \dfrac{2^5}{5!}x^6 + \dfrac{2^7}{7!}x^8 + \cdots;\ (-\infty, +\infty)$

44. $1 + \dfrac{1}{2!}x^4 + \dfrac{1}{4!}x^8 + \dfrac{1}{6!}x^{12} + \cdots;\ (-\infty, +\infty)$

45. $1 + \dfrac{3}{2}x - \dfrac{9}{8}x^2 + \dfrac{27}{16}x^3 - \cdots;\ (-1/3, 1/3)$

46. $1 + \dfrac{1}{2}x^2 - \dfrac{1}{8}x^4 + \dfrac{1}{16}x^6 - \cdots;\ (-1, 1)$

47. $(1 - 2x)^{-2} = 1 + 4x + 12x^2 + 32x^3 + \cdots;\ (-1/2, 1/2)$

48. $x(1 + 2x)^{-3} = x - 6x^2 + 24x^3 - 80x^4 + \cdots;\ (-1/2, 1/2)$

49. $x(1 - x^2)^{-1/2} = x + \dfrac{1}{2}x^3 + \dfrac{3}{8}x^5 + \dfrac{5}{16}x^7 + \cdots;\ (-1, 1)$

50. $x - \dfrac{3}{2}x^3 + \dfrac{3}{8}x^5 + \dfrac{1}{16}x^7 + \cdots;\ (-1, 1)$

51. $\dfrac{1}{x} = \dfrac{1}{1+(x-1)} = \dfrac{1}{1-[-(x-1)]} = \displaystyle\sum_{k=0}^{\infty}[-(x-1)]^k = \sum_{k=0}^{\infty}(-1)^k(x-1)^k$ which is valid for

$-1 < -(x-1) < 1,\, 0 < x < 2$

52. If $x \geq 0$, then $\cos\sqrt{x} = 1 - \dfrac{(\sqrt{x})^2}{2!} + \dfrac{(\sqrt{x})^4}{4!} - \dfrac{(\sqrt{x})^6}{6!} + \cdots = 1 - \dfrac{x}{2!} + \dfrac{x^2}{4!} - \dfrac{x^3}{6!} + \cdots$; if $x \leq 0$,

then $\cosh(\sqrt{-x}) = 1 + \dfrac{(\sqrt{-x})^2}{2!} + \dfrac{(\sqrt{-x})^4}{4!} + \dfrac{(\sqrt{-x})^6}{6!} + \cdots = 1 - \dfrac{x}{2!} + \dfrac{x^2}{4!} - \dfrac{x^3}{6!} + \cdots$.

53. $(1+x)^m = \dbinom{m}{0} + \displaystyle\sum_{k=1}^{\infty}\dbinom{m}{k}x^k = \sum_{k=0}^{\infty}\dbinom{m}{k}x^k$

54. $e^2 - 1$ **55.** $\sin\pi = 0$

56. $\cos e$ **57** $e^{-\ln 3} = 1/3$

58. (a) $\dfrac{1}{1-x^2} = 1 + (x^2) + (x^2)^2 + (x^2)^3 + \cdots = 1 + x^2 + x^4 + x^6 + \cdots$

$\dfrac{x}{1-x^2} = x\left(1 + x^2 + x^4 + x^6 + \cdots\right) = x + x^3 + x^5 + x^7 + \cdots$

(b) $\dfrac{f^{(5)}(0)}{5!} = 1$ so $f^{(5)}(0) = 5! = 120$, $\dfrac{f^{(6)}(0)}{6!} = 0$ so $f^{(6)}(0) = 0$

59. (a) $\cos 2x = 1 - \dfrac{(2x)^2}{2!} + \dfrac{(2x)^4}{4!} - \dfrac{(2x)^6}{6!} + \cdots = 1 - 2x^2 + \dfrac{2}{3}x^4 - \dfrac{4}{45}x^6 + \cdots$,

$x^2\cos 2x = x^2 - 2x^4 + \dfrac{2}{3}x^6 - \dfrac{4}{45}x^8 + \cdots$

(b) $\dfrac{f^{(5)}(0)}{5!} = 0$ so $f^{(5)}(0) = 0$

60. (a) $f'(0) = \displaystyle\lim_{h\to 0}\dfrac{f(h) - f(0)}{h} = \lim_{h\to 0}\dfrac{e^{-1/h^2}}{h}$, let $t = 1/h$ then $h = 1/t$ and

$\displaystyle\lim_{h\to 0+}\dfrac{e^{-1/h^2}}{h} = \lim_{t\to+\infty}te^{-t^2} = \lim_{t\to+\infty}\dfrac{t}{e^{t^2}} = \lim_{t\to+\infty}\dfrac{1}{2te^{t^2}} = 0$, similarly $\displaystyle\lim_{h\to 0-}\dfrac{e^{-1/h^2}}{h} = 0$

so $f'(0) = 0$.

(b) The Maclaurin series is $0 + (0)x + (0)x^2 + \cdots = 0$, but $f(0) = 0$ and $f(x) > 0$ if $x \neq 0$ so the series converges to $f(x)$ only at the point $x = 0$.

EXERCISE SET 11.11

1. (a) $3/(n+1)! < 0.5 \times 10^{-5}$, $n = 9$ **(b)** $3/(n+1)! < 0.5 \times 10^{-10}$, $n = 13$

2. $|R_n(-1)| = \dfrac{e^c}{(n+1)!}(1)^{n+1} < \dfrac{1}{(n+1)!} < 0.5 \times 10^{-3}$ if $n = 6$, so

$e^{-1} \approx 1 - 1 + \dfrac{1}{2!} - \dfrac{1}{3!} + \dfrac{1}{4!} - \dfrac{1}{5!} + \dfrac{1}{6!} \approx 0.368$

3. $|R_n(1/2)| = \dfrac{e^c}{(n+1)!}(1/2)^{n+1} < \dfrac{2}{(n+1)!}\dfrac{1}{2^{n+1}} = \dfrac{1}{2^n(n+1)!} < 0.5 \times 10^{-4}$ if $n = 5$

so $\sqrt{e} = e^{0.5} \approx 1 + 0.5 + \dfrac{(0.5)^2}{2!} + \dfrac{(0.5)^3}{3!} + \dfrac{(0.5)^4}{4!} + \dfrac{(0.5)^5}{5!}$, $\sqrt{e} \approx 1.6487$

4. $4° = \pi/45$ radians, $|R_n(\pi/45)| \leq \dfrac{(\pi/45)^{n+1}}{(n+1)!} < 0.5 \times 10^{-5}$ if $n = 3$,

$\sin 4° \approx (\pi/45) - \dfrac{(\pi/45)^3}{3!} \approx 0.06976$

5. $|R_n(\pi/20)| \leq \dfrac{(\pi/20)^{n+1}}{(n+1)!} < 0.5 \times 10^{-4}$ if $n = 3$, $\cos(\pi/20) \approx 1 - \dfrac{(\pi/20)^2}{2!} \approx 0.9877$

6. Expand about $\pi/2$ to get $\sin x = 1 - \dfrac{1}{2!}(x - \pi/2)^2 + \dfrac{1}{4!}(x - \pi/2)^4 - \cdots$, $85° = 17\pi/36$ radians,

$|R_n(x)| \leq \dfrac{|x - \pi/2|^{n+1}}{(n+1)!}$, $|R_n(17\pi/36)| \leq \dfrac{|17\pi/36 - \pi/2|^{n+1}}{(n+1)!} = \dfrac{(\pi/36)^{n+1}}{(n+1)!} < 0.5 \times 10^{-4}$

if $n = 3$, $\sin 85° \approx 1 - \dfrac{1}{2}(-\pi/36)^2 \approx 0.9962$

7. Expand about $\pi/3$ to get $\cos x = \dfrac{1}{2} - \dfrac{\sqrt{3}}{2}(x - \pi/3) - \dfrac{1}{4}(x - \pi/3)^2 + \cdots$, $58° = 29\pi/90$ radians,

$|R_n(x)| \leq \dfrac{|x - \pi/3|^{n+1}}{(n+1)!}$, $|R_n(29\pi/90)| \leq \dfrac{|29\pi/90 - \pi/3|^{n+1}}{(n+1)!} = \dfrac{(\pi/90)^{n+1}}{(n+1)!} < 0.5 \times 10^{-4}$

if $n = 2$, $\cos 58° \approx \dfrac{1}{2} - \dfrac{\sqrt{3}}{2}(-\pi/90) - \dfrac{1}{4}(-\pi/90)^2 \approx 0.5299$

8. Expand about $\pi/6$ to get $\sin x = \dfrac{1}{2} + \dfrac{\sqrt{3}}{2}(x - \pi/6) - \dfrac{1}{4}(x - \pi/6)^2 - \dfrac{\sqrt{3}}{12}(x - \pi/6)^3 + \cdots$,

$35° = 7\pi/36$ radians, $|R_n(x)| \leq \dfrac{|x - \pi/6|^{n+1}}{(n+1)!}$,

$|R_n(7\pi/36)| \leq \dfrac{|7\pi/36 - \pi/6|^{n+1}}{(n+1)!} = \dfrac{(\pi/36)^{n+1}}{(n+1)!} < 0.5 \times 10^{-4}$ if $n = 3$,

$\sin 35° \approx \dfrac{1}{2} + \dfrac{\sqrt{3}}{2}(\pi/36) - \dfrac{1}{4}(\pi/36)^2 - \dfrac{\sqrt{3}}{12}(\pi/36)^3 \approx 0.5736$

9. Let $x = 1/9$ in series (16) to get $\ln 1.25 \approx 0.223$

10. Let $x = 1/2$ in series (16) to get $\ln 3 \approx 1.0986$

11. $(0.1)^3/3 < 0.5 \times 10^{-3}$ so $\tan^{-1}(0.1) \approx 0.100$ to three decimal place accuracy.

12. $|R_n(0.5)| = \dfrac{|f^{n+1}(c)|}{(n+1)!}(0.5)^{n+1}$ where $f^{(n+1)}(c) = \sinh c$ or $\cosh c$ for $0 < c < 0.5$,

but $\sinh c < \cosh c < \cosh 0.5$, and $\cosh 0.5 = \dfrac{1}{2}\left(e^{0.5} + e^{-0.5}\right) < \dfrac{1}{2}(2+1) = 1.5$

so $|R_n(0.5)| < \dfrac{1.5(0.5)^{n+1}}{(n+1)!} \leq 0.5 \times 10^{-3}$ if $n = 4$, $\sinh 0.5 \approx 0.5 + \dfrac{(0.5)^3}{3!} \approx 0.521$

13. $|R_n(0.1)| = \dfrac{|f^{(n+1)}(c)|}{(n+1)!}(0.1)^{n+1}$ where $f^{(n+1)}(c) = \sinh c$ or $\cosh c$ for $0 < c < 0.1$, but

$\sinh c < \cosh c < \cosh 0.1$, and $\cosh 0.1 = \dfrac{1}{2}\left(e^{0.1} + e^{-0.1}\right) < \dfrac{1}{2}(2+1) = 1.5$

so $|R_n(0.1)| < \dfrac{1.5(0.1)^{n+1}}{(n+1)!} \leq 0.5 \times 10^{-4}$ if $n = 3$, $\cosh 0.1 \approx 1 + \dfrac{(0.1)^2}{2!} \approx 1.0050$

14. Expand about 27 to get the series $\sqrt[3]{x} = 3 + \dfrac{1}{3^3}(x-27) - \dfrac{1}{3^7}(x-27)^2 + \dfrac{5}{3^{12}}(x-27)^3 - \cdots$

which is alternating after the first term. Let $x = 28$ to get $\sqrt[3]{28} = 3 + \dfrac{1}{3^3} - \dfrac{1}{3^7} + \dfrac{5}{3^{12}} - \cdots$,

but $1/3^7 < 0.5 \times 10^{-3}$ so $\sqrt[3]{28} \approx 3 + 1/3^3 \approx 3.037$

15. $\sin x = x - \dfrac{x^3}{3!} + (0)x^4 + R_4(x)$, $|R_4(x)| \leq \dfrac{|x|^5}{5!} < 0.5 \times 10^{-3}$ if $|x|^5 < 0.06$, $|x| < (0.06)^{1/5} \approx 0.569$

16. $|R_2(x)| = \dfrac{e^c}{3!}|x|^3$. If $x > 0$ then $e^c < e^x$, $|R_2(x)| < \dfrac{e^x x^3}{3!} < 0.0005$, $e^x x^3 < 0.003$ if $x < 0.137$

(by trial and error with a hand calculator). If $x < 0$ then $e^c < 1$, $|R_2(x)| < \dfrac{|x|^3}{3!} < 0.0005$,

$|x|^3 < 0.003$, $x^3 > -0.003$, $x > -(0.003)^{1/3} \approx -0.144$, so $-0.144 < x < 0.137$.

17. $\cos x = 1 - \dfrac{x^2}{2!} + \dfrac{x^4}{4!} + (0)x^5 + R_5(x)$, $|R_5(x)| \leq \dfrac{|x|^6}{6!} \leq \dfrac{(0.2)^6}{6!} < 9 \times 10^{-8}$

18. $f''(x) = -1/(1+x)^2$, $|R_1(x)| = \dfrac{|x|^2}{2(1+c)^2}$ but $c > -0.01$ if $|x| < 0.01$

so $(1+c)^2 > (1-0.01)^2 = (0.99)^2$ and $|R_1(x)| < \dfrac{(0.01)^2}{2(0.99)^2} < 5.11 \times 10^{-5}$

19. **(a)** $\ln 2 = 1 - 1/2 + 1/3 - 1/4 + \cdots$, $|\text{error}| < 1/(n+1) \leq 0.5 \times 10^{-6}$ if $n + 1 \geq 2 \times 10^6$,
$n \geq 1,999,999$; $n = 1,999,999$

(b) Let $f(x) = \ln\dfrac{1+x}{1-x} = \ln(1+x) - \ln(1-x)$, $f^{(n+1)}(c) = n!\left[\dfrac{(-1)^n}{(1+c)^{n+1}} + \dfrac{1}{(1-c)^{n+1}}\right]$,

$$|f^{n+1}(c)| \le n!\left[\dfrac{1}{(1+c)^{n+1}} + \dfrac{1}{(1-c)^{n+1}}\right]$$

$$< n!\left[\dfrac{1}{(1+0)^{n+1}} + \dfrac{1}{(1-1/3)^{n+1}}\right] \text{ for } 0 < c < 1/3$$

$$= n![1 + 1/(2/3)^{n+1}],$$

$$|R_n(1/3)| < [1 + 1/(2/3)^{n+1}]\dfrac{(1/3)^{n+1}}{n+1} = (1/3^{n+1} + 1/2^{n+1})/(n+1) \le 0.5 \times 10^{-6}$$

if $n \ge 16$ so 8 <u>terms</u> in series (16) are sufficient to assure six decimal place accuracy (even powers of x have zero coefficients).

20. Show that $\tan(\tan^{-1}1/2 + \tan^{-1}1/3) = 1$,

$$\tan(\tan^{-1}1/2 + \tan^{-1}1/3) = \dfrac{\tan(\tan^{-1}1/2) + \tan(\tan^{-1}1/3)}{1 - [\tan(\tan^{-1}1/2)][\tan(\tan^{-1}1/3)]} = \dfrac{1/2 + 1/3}{1 - (1/2)(1/3)} = 1$$

21. $(1/2)^9/9! < 0.5 \times 10^{-3}$ and $(1/3)^7/7! < 0.5 \times 10^{-3}$ so

$$\tan^{-1}1/2 \approx 1/2 - \dfrac{(1/2)^3}{3} + \dfrac{(1/2)^5}{5} - \dfrac{(1/2)^7}{7} \approx 0.463$$

$$\tan^{-1}1/3 \approx 1/3 - \dfrac{(1/3)^3}{3} + \dfrac{(1/3)^5}{5} \approx 0.322, \ \pi \approx 4(0.463 + 0.322) = 3.140$$

EXERCISE SET 11.12

1. **(a)** $\dfrac{d}{dx}\left(1 + x + x^2/2! + x^3/3! + \cdots\right) = 1 + x + x^2/2! + \cdots = e^x$

   (b) $\displaystyle\int \left(1 + x + x^2/2! + \cdots\right) dx = \left(x + x^2/2! + x^3/3! + \cdots\right) + C_1$

   $$= \left(1 + x + x^2/2! + x^3/3! + \cdots\right) + C_1 - 1 = e^x + C$$

2. **(a)** $\dfrac{d}{dx}\left(1 - x^2/2! + x^4/4! - x^6/6! + \cdots\right) = -x + x^3/3! - x^5/5! + \cdots$

   $$= -\left(x - x^3/3! + x^5/5! - \cdots\right) = -\sin x$$

   (b) $\displaystyle\int \left(x - x^3/3! + x^5/5! - \cdots\right) dx = \left(x^2/2! - x^4/4! + x^6/6! - \cdots\right) + C_1$

   $$= -\left(1 - x^2/2! + x^4/4! - x^6/6! + \cdots\right) + C_1 + 1$$

   $$= -\cos x + C$$

3. **(a)** $\dfrac{d}{dx}\left(x + x^3/3! + x^5/5! + \cdots\right) = 1 + x^2/2! + x^4/4! + \cdots = \cosh x$

    (b) $\displaystyle\int \left(x + x^3/3! + x^5/5! + \cdots\right) dx = \left(x^2/2! + x^4/4! + x^6/6! + \cdots\right) + C_1$

$$= \left(1 + x^2/2! + x^4/4! + x^6/6! + \cdots\right) + C_1 - 1$$
$$= \cosh x + C$$

4. **(a)** $\dfrac{d}{dx}\left(x - x^2/2! + x^3/3! - \cdots\right) = 1 - x + x^2 - \cdots = 1/(1+x)$

    (b) $\displaystyle\int \left(1 - x + x^2 - \cdots\right) dx = \left(x - x^2/2 + x^3/3 - \cdots\right) + C = \ln(1+x) + C$

5. $1/(1+x)^2 = \dfrac{d}{dx}\left[-\dfrac{1}{1+x}\right] = \dfrac{d}{dx}\left[-\displaystyle\sum_{k=0}^{\infty}(-1)^k x^k\right]$

$$= \dfrac{d}{dx}\left[\sum_{k=0}^{\infty}(-1)^{k+1}x^k\right] = \sum_{k=1}^{\infty}(-1)^{k+1}k x^{k-1}$$

6. $\dfrac{x}{(1-x)^2} = x\dfrac{d}{dx}\left[\dfrac{1}{1-x}\right] = x\dfrac{d}{dx}\left[\displaystyle\sum_{k=0}^{\infty}x^k\right] = x\left[\sum_{k=1}^{\infty}k x^{k-1}\right] = \sum_{k=1}^{\infty}k x^k$

7. $\ln\dfrac{1}{1-x} = -\ln(1-x) = \displaystyle\int \dfrac{1}{1-x}dx - C = \int \left[\sum_{k=0}^{\infty}x^k\right] dx - C$

$$= \sum_{k=0}^{\infty}\dfrac{x^{k+1}}{k+1} - C = \sum_{k=1}^{\infty}\dfrac{x^k}{k} - C, \ln\dfrac{1}{1-0} = 0 \text{ so } C = 0.$$

8. $x = \dfrac{1}{3}, S = \dfrac{1/3}{(1-1/3)^2} = \dfrac{3}{4}$ **9.** $x = 1/4, S = \ln\dfrac{1}{1-1/4} = \ln\dfrac{4}{3}$

10. $f(x) = xe^x = x + x^2 + \dfrac{x^3}{2!} + \dfrac{x^4}{3!} + \cdots = \displaystyle\sum_{k=0}^{\infty}\dfrac{x^{k+1}}{k!}$,

$$f'(x) = (x+1)e^x = 1 + 2x + \dfrac{3x^2}{2!} + \dfrac{4x^3}{3!} + \cdots = \sum_{k=0}^{\infty}\dfrac{k+1}{k!}x^k; \sum_{k=0}^{\infty}\dfrac{k+1}{k!} = f'(1) = 2e.$$

11. $f(x) = \dfrac{1}{1-x} = \displaystyle\sum_{k=0}^{\infty}x^k, \ f'(x) = \dfrac{1}{(1-x)^2} = \sum_{k=1}^{\infty}k x^{k-1}$,

$$f''(x) = \dfrac{2}{(1-x)^3} = \sum_{k=2}^{\infty}k(k-1)x^{k-2} = 2 + 6x + 12x^2 + 20x^3 + \cdots$$

12. $f(x) = \dfrac{1}{1-x} = 1 + x + x^2 + x^3 + \cdots = \displaystyle\sum_{k=0}^{\infty} x^k,$

$f'(x) = \dfrac{1}{(1-x)^2} = 1 + 2x + 3x^2 + 4x^3 + \cdots = \displaystyle\sum_{k=1}^{\infty} kx^{k-1},$

$g(x) = xf'(x) = \dfrac{x}{(1-x)^2} = x + 2x^2 + 3x^3 + 4x^4 + \cdots = \displaystyle\sum_{k=1}^{\infty} kx^k,$

$g'(x) = \dfrac{1+x}{(1-x)^3} = 1 + 4x + 9x^2 + 16x^3 + \cdots = \displaystyle\sum_{k=1}^{\infty} k^2 x^{k-1},$

$F(x) = xg'(x) = \dfrac{x + x^2}{(1-x)^3} = x + 4x^2 + 9x^3 + 16x^4 + \cdots = \displaystyle\sum_{k=1}^{\infty} k^2 x^k;$

$\displaystyle\sum_{k=1}^{\infty} \dfrac{k^2}{4^k} = F(1/4) = \dfrac{1/4 + (1/4)^2}{(1 - 1/4)^3} = \dfrac{20}{27}.$

13. **(a)** $\rho = \displaystyle\lim_{k \to +\infty} \dfrac{|x|^{k+2}}{k+2} \cdot \dfrac{k+1}{|x|^{k+1}} = |x| \lim_{k \to +\infty} \dfrac{k+1}{k+2} = |x|;$ converges if $|x| < 1.$

(b) $f'(x) = \displaystyle\sum_{k=0}^{\infty} (-1)^k x^k,$ converges on $(-1, 1)$

(c) $f'(x) = \dfrac{1}{1+x}$ so $f(x) = \ln(1+x) + C$ for x in $(-1, 1),$ let $x = 0$ to find that $C = 0,$ thus $f(x) = \ln(1+x).$

14. $\displaystyle\int_0^1 \sin\left(x^2\right) dx = \int_0^1 \left(x^2 - x^6/3! + x^{10}/5! - x^{14}/7! + \cdots\right) dx$

$= \dfrac{1}{3}x^3 - \dfrac{1}{7 \cdot 3!}x^7 + \dfrac{1}{11 \cdot 5!}x^{11} - \dfrac{1}{15 \cdot 7!}x^{15} + \cdots \Bigg]_0^1$

$= \dfrac{1}{3} - \dfrac{1}{7 \cdot 3!} + \dfrac{1}{11 \cdot 5!} - \dfrac{1}{15 \cdot 7!} + \cdots,$

but $\dfrac{1}{15 \cdot 7!} < 0.5 \times 10^{-3}$ so $\displaystyle\int_0^1 \sin(x^2) dx \approx \dfrac{1}{3} - \dfrac{1}{7 \cdot 3!} + \dfrac{1}{11 \cdot 5!} \approx 0.310$

15. $\displaystyle\int_0^1 \cos\sqrt{x}\, dx = \int_0^1 \left(1 - x/2! + x^2/4! - x^3/6! + \cdots\right) dx$

$= x - \dfrac{1}{2 \cdot 2!}x^2 + \dfrac{1}{3 \cdot 4!}x^3 - \dfrac{1}{4 \cdot 6!}x^4 + \cdots \Bigg]_0^1 = 1 - \dfrac{1}{2 \cdot 2!} + \dfrac{1}{3 \cdot 4!} - \dfrac{1}{4 \cdot 6!} + \cdots,$

but $\dfrac{1}{4 \cdot 6!} < 0.5 \times 10^{-3}$ so $\displaystyle\int_0^1 \cos\sqrt{x}\, dx \approx 1 - \dfrac{1}{2 \cdot 2!} + \dfrac{1}{3 \cdot 4!} \approx 0.764$

16. $\displaystyle\int_0^{0.1} \frac{\sin x}{x}\,dx = \int_0^{0.1}\left(1 - x^2/3! + x^4/5! - \cdots\right)dx$

$$= x - \frac{1}{3\cdot 3!}x^3 + \frac{1}{5\cdot 5!}x^5 - \cdots \Big]_0^{0.1} = 0.1 - \frac{(0.1)^3}{3\cdot 3!} + \frac{(0.1)^5}{5\cdot 5!} - \cdots,$$

but $\dfrac{(0.1)^3}{3\cdot 3!} < 0.5\times 10^{-3}$ so $\displaystyle\int_0^{0.1}\frac{\sin x}{x}\,dx \approx 0.100$

17. $\displaystyle\int_0^{1/2}\frac{dx}{1+x^4} = \int_0^{1/2}\left(1 - x^4 + x^8 - \cdots\right)dx$

$$= x - \frac{1}{5}x^5 + \frac{1}{9}x^9 - \cdots \Big]_0^{1/2} = 1/2 - \frac{(1/2)^5}{5} + \frac{(1/2)^9}{9} - \cdots,$$

but $\dfrac{(1/2)^9}{9} < 0.5\times 10^{-3}$ so $\displaystyle\int_0^{1/2}\frac{dx}{1+x^4} \approx 1/2 - \frac{(1/2)^5}{5} \approx 0.494$

18. $\displaystyle\int_0^{1/2}\tan^{-1}\left(2x^2\right)dx = \int_0^{1/2}\left(2x^2 - 8x^6/3 + 32x^{10}/5 - \cdots\right)dx$

$$= \frac{2}{3}x^3 - \frac{8}{21}x^7 + \frac{32}{55}x^{11} - \cdots \Big]_0^{1/2}$$

$$= \frac{2}{3}(1/2)^3 - \frac{8}{21}(1/2)^7 + \frac{32}{55}(1/2)^{11} - \cdots,$$

but $\dfrac{32}{55}(1/2)^{11} < 0.5\times 10^{-3}$ so $\displaystyle\int_0^{1/2}\tan^{-1}(2x^2)dx \approx \frac{2}{3}(1/2)^3 - \frac{8}{21}(1/2)^7 \approx 0.080$

19. $\displaystyle\int_0^{0.1} e^{-x^3}dx = \int_0^{0.1}\left(1 - x^3 + x^6/2! - \cdots\right)dx$

$$= x - \frac{1}{4}x^4 + \frac{1}{7\cdot 2!}x^7 - \cdots \Big]_0^{0.1} = 0.1 - \frac{1}{4}(0.1)^4 + \frac{1}{7\cdot 2!}(0.1)^7 - \cdots,$$

but $\dfrac{1}{4}(0.1)^4 < 0.5\times 10^{-3}$ so $\displaystyle\int_0^{0.1} e^{-x^3}dx \approx 0.100$

20. $\displaystyle\int_0^{0.2}\left(1+x^4\right)^{1/3}dx = \int_0^{0.2}\left(1 + x^4/3 - x^8/9 + \cdots\right)dx$

$$= x + \frac{1}{15}x^5 - \frac{1}{81}x^9 + \cdots \Big]_0^{0.2} = 0.2 + \frac{1}{15}(0.2)^5 - \frac{1}{81}(0.2)^9 + \cdots,$$

but $\dfrac{1}{15}(0.2)^5 < 0.5\times 10^{-3}$ so $\displaystyle\int_0^{0.2}(1+x^4)^{1/3}dx \approx 0.200$

21. $\displaystyle\int_0^{1/2}(1+x^2)^{-1/4}dx = \int_0^{1/2}\left(1 - \frac{1}{4}x^2 + \frac{5}{32}x^4 - \frac{15}{128}x^6 + \cdots\right)dx$

$$= x - \frac{1}{12}x^3 + \frac{1}{32}x^5 - \frac{15}{896}x^7 + \cdots\bigg]_0^{1/2}$$

$$= 1/2 - \frac{1}{12}(1/2)^3 + \frac{1}{32}(1/2)^5 - \frac{15}{896}(1/2)^7 + \cdots,$$

but $\dfrac{15}{896}(1/2)^7 < 0.5\times10^{-3}$ so $\displaystyle\int_0^{1/2}(1+x^2)^{-1/4}dx \approx 1/2 - \frac{1}{12}(1/2)^3 + \frac{1}{32}(1/2)^5 \approx 0.491$

22. $x^4e^x = x^4\left(1 + x + x^2/2! + x^3/3! + \cdots\right) = x^4 + x^5 + x^6/2! + x^7/3! + \cdots$

23. $e^{-x^2}\cos x = \left(1 - x^2 + \dfrac{x^4}{2!} - \dfrac{x^6}{3!} + \cdots\right)\left(1 - \dfrac{x^2}{2!} + \dfrac{x^4}{4!} - \dfrac{x^6}{6!} + \cdots\right)$

$$= 1 - \frac{3}{2}x^2 + \frac{25}{24}x^4 - \frac{331}{720}x^6 + \cdots$$

24. $\dfrac{x^2}{1+x^4} = x^2\left(\dfrac{1}{1+x^4}\right) = x^2\left(1 - x^4 + x^8 - x^{12} + \cdots\right) = x^2 - x^6 + x^{10} - x^{14} + \cdots$

25. $\dfrac{\sin x}{e^x} = e^{-x}\sin x = \left(1 - x + \dfrac{x^2}{2!} - \dfrac{x^3}{3!} + \dfrac{x^4}{4!} - \cdots\right)\left(x - \dfrac{x^3}{3!} + \dfrac{x^5}{5!} - \cdots\right)$

$$= x - x^2 + \frac{1}{3}x^3 - \frac{1}{30}x^5 + \cdots$$

26. $\tanh x = \dfrac{\sinh x}{\cosh x} = \dfrac{x + x^3/3! + x^5/5! + x^7/7! + \cdots}{1 + x^2/2! + x^4/4! + x^6/6! + \cdots}$

$$= x - \frac{1}{3}x^3 + \frac{2}{15}x^5 - \frac{17}{315}x^7 + \cdots \text{ (by long division)}$$

27. $x\ln\left(1-x^2\right) = x\left(-x^2 - \dfrac{1}{2}x^4 - \dfrac{1}{3}x^6 - \dfrac{1}{4}x^8 - \cdots\right) = -x^3 - \dfrac{1}{2}x^5 - \dfrac{1}{3}x^7 - \dfrac{1}{4}x^9 - \cdots$

28. $\dfrac{\ln(1+x)}{1-x} = \dfrac{1}{1-x}\ln(1+x) = \left(1 + x + x^2 + x^3 + \cdots\right)\left(x - \dfrac{1}{2}x^2 + \dfrac{1}{3}x^3 - \dfrac{1}{4}x^4 + \cdots\right)$

$$= x + \frac{1}{2}x^2 + \frac{5}{6}x^3 + \frac{7}{12}x^4 + \cdots$$

29. $x^2e^{4x}\sqrt{1+x} = x^2\left(1 + 4x + 8x^2 + \dfrac{32}{3}x^3 + \cdots\right)\left(1 + \dfrac{1}{2}x - \dfrac{1}{8}x^2 + \dfrac{1}{16}x^3 + \cdots\right)$

$$= x^2\left(1 + \frac{9}{2}x + \frac{79}{8}x^2 + \frac{683}{48}x^3 + \cdots\right) = x^2 + \frac{9}{2}x^3 + \frac{79}{8}x^4 + \frac{683}{48}x^5 + \cdots$$

30. $\displaystyle\lim_{x\to 0}\frac{\sin x}{x}=\lim_{x\to 0}\left(1-x^2/3!+x^4/5!-\cdots\right)=1$

31. **(a)** $\displaystyle\frac{1-\cos x}{\sin x}=\frac{1-\left(1-x^2/2!+x^4/4!-x^6/6!+\cdots\right)}{x-x^3/3!+x^5/5!-\cdots}$

$$=\frac{x^2/2!-x^4/4!+x^6/6!-\cdots}{x-x^3/3!+x^5/5!-\cdots}=\frac{x/2!-x^3/4!+x^5/6!-\cdots}{1-x^2/3!+x^4/5!-\cdots},x\neq 0$$

$$\lim_{x\to 0}\frac{1-\cos x}{\sin x}=\frac{0}{1}=0$$

(b) $\displaystyle\ln\sqrt{1+x}-\sin 2x=\frac{1}{2}\ln(1+x)-\sin 2x$

$$=\frac{1}{2}\left(x-\frac{1}{2}x^2+\frac{1}{3}x^3-\cdots\right)-\left(2x-\frac{4}{3}x^3+\frac{4}{15}x^5-\cdots\right)$$

$$=-\frac{3}{2}x-\frac{1}{4}x^2+\frac{3}{2}x^3+\cdots,$$

$$\lim_{x\to 0}\frac{\ln\sqrt{1+x}-\sin 2x}{x}=\lim_{x\to 0}\left(-\frac{3}{2}-\frac{1}{4}x+\frac{3}{2}x^2+\cdots\right)=-3/2$$

32. **(a)** $\displaystyle\sin^{-1}x=\int(1-x^2)^{-1/2}dx-C=\int\left(1+\frac{1}{2}x^2+\frac{3}{8}x^4+\frac{5}{16}x^6+\cdots\right)dx-C$

$$=\left(x+\frac{1}{6}x^3+\frac{3}{40}x^5+\frac{5}{112}x^7+\cdots\right)-C,\sin^{-1}0=0\text{ so }C=0$$

(b) $\displaystyle(1-x^2)^{-1/2}=1+\sum_{k=1}^{\infty}\frac{(-1/2)(-3/2)(-5/2)\cdots(-1/2-k+1)}{k!}(-x^2)^k$

$$=1+\sum_{k=1}^{\infty}\frac{(-1)^k(1/2)^k(1)(3)(5)\cdots(2k-1)}{k!}(-1)^k x^{2k}$$

$$=1+\sum_{k=1}^{\infty}\frac{1\cdot 3\cdot 5\cdots(2k-1)}{2^k k!}x^{2k}$$

$$\sin^{-1}x=x+\sum_{k=1}^{\infty}\frac{1\cdot 3\cdot 5\cdots(2k-1)}{2^k k!(2k+1)}x^{2k+1}$$

(c) $R=1$

33. **(a)** $\displaystyle\sinh^{-1}x=\int(1+x^2)^{-1/2}\,dx-C=\int\left(1-\frac{1}{2}x^2+\frac{3}{8}x^4-\frac{5}{16}x^6+\cdots\right)dx-C$

$$=\left(x-\frac{1}{6}x^3+\frac{3}{40}x^5-\frac{5}{112}x^7+\cdots\right)-C,$$

$\sinh^{-1}0=0$ so $C=0$

(b) $(1+x^2)^{-1/2} = 1 + \sum_{k=1}^{\infty} \frac{(-1/2)(-3/2)(-5/2)\cdots(-1/2-k+1)}{k!}(x^2)^k$

$$= 1 + \sum_{k=1}^{\infty}(-1)^k \frac{1\cdot 3 \cdot 5 \cdots (2k-1)}{2^k k!} x^{2k},$$

$$\sinh^{-1} x = x + \sum_{k=1}^{\infty}(-1)^k \frac{1\cdot 3 \cdot 5 \cdots (2k-1)}{2^k k!(2k+1)} x^{2k+1}$$

(c) $R = 1$

34. If $\sum_{k=0}^{\infty} a_k x^k = \sum_{k=0}^{\infty} b_k x^k$ for x in $(-r,\ r)$ then $\sum_{k=0}^{\infty}(a_k - b_k)x^k = 0$ so by Theorem 11.12.3

$\sum_{k=0}^{\infty}(a_k - b_k)x^k$ is the Taylor series for $f(x) = 0$ about 0 and hence $a_k - b_k = 0$,

$a_k = b_k$ for all k.

SUPPLEMENTARY EXERCISES CHAPTER 11

1. $L = 0$ **2.** $L = e^0 = 1$

3. $L = 0 - 0 = 0$ **4.** $\sin \pi n = 0$ for all n so $L = 0$

5. $\sin[(2n-1)\pi/2]$ is alternately 1 and -1 so the limit does not exist

6. $L = 0$

7. $a_n = (-1)^n/e^n$ is alternating; $a_n = e^{1/n}$ is decreasing;

$a_n = \dfrac{1}{\sqrt{n}} - \dfrac{1}{\sqrt{n+1}} = \dfrac{\sqrt{n+1} - \sqrt{n}}{\sqrt{n}\sqrt{n+1}} = \dfrac{1}{\sqrt{n}\sqrt{n+1}\left(\sqrt{n+1} + \sqrt{n}\right)}$ is decreasing;

$a_n = \sin \pi n = 0$ is nondecreasing; $a_n = \sin[(2n-1)\pi/2]$ is alternating;

$a_n = \dfrac{n+1}{n(n+2)}$, let $f(x) = \dfrac{x+1}{x^2 + 2x}$ then $f'(x) = -\dfrac{x^2 + 2x + 2}{(x^2 + 2x)^2} < 0$ if $x \geq 1$ so a_n is decreasing.

8. a_n is increasing because $f'(x) > 0$, $a_n \leq 1 - e^{-x} < 1$ so $\{a_n\}$ converges by Theorem 11.2.2a.

9. **(a)** $\sum_{k=0}^{\infty} \left(\pi/q^2\right)^k$ is a geometric series which converges for $\pi/q^2 < 1$, $q^2 > \pi$, $|q| > \sqrt{\pi}$

(b) $\sum_{k=1}^{\infty} 1/k^{3q}$ is a p-series with $p = 3q$, converges for $3q > 1$, $q > 1/3$

(c) $\displaystyle\sum_{k=2}^{\infty} 1/(k \ln q) = \sum_{k=2}^{\infty}(1/\ln q)(1/k)$ diverges for all q because $\displaystyle\sum_{k=2}^{\infty} 1/k$ diverges

(d) $\displaystyle\sum_{k=2}^{\infty}(1/\ln q)^k$ is a geometric series which converges for $|1/\ln q| < 1$, $|\ln q| > 1$,

$q > e$ or $0 < q < e^{-1}$

10. **(a)** If $q = 1$, $\displaystyle\int_2^{+\infty} \frac{1}{x \ln x}\,dx = \lim_{\ell\to+\infty} \ln(\ln x)\Big]_2^{\ell} = +\infty$, the series diverges. If $q \neq 1$,

$$\int_2^{+\infty} \frac{1}{x}(\ln x)^{-q}\,dx = \lim_{\ell\to+\infty} \frac{(\ln x)^{1-q}}{1-q}\Big]_2^{\ell} = \begin{cases} +\infty & q < 1 \\[2mm] \dfrac{l}{(q-1)(\ln 2)^{q-1}}, & q > 1 \end{cases}$$

so the series converges for $q > 1$.

(b) $(2 + \cos x)/x^2$ is not a decreasing function. The series converges because

$(2 + \cos k)/k^2 \leq 3/k^2$ and $\displaystyle\sum_{k=1}^{\infty} 3/k^2$ converges.

11. **(a)** $1.3636\cdots = 1 + \displaystyle\sum_{k=1}^{\infty} 36(0.01)^k$

(b) $1.3636\cdots = 1 + \dfrac{0.36}{1 - 0.01} = 1 + 36/99 = 1 + 4/11 = 15/11$

12. **(a)** $\dfrac{2k-1}{3k^2-k} \geq \dfrac{2k-k}{3k^2} = \dfrac{1}{3k}$, $\displaystyle\sum_{k=1}^{\infty} 1/(3k)$ diverges so $\displaystyle\sum_{k=1}^{\infty} \dfrac{2k-1}{3k^2-k}$ diverges.

(b) $\dfrac{2k+1}{3k^2+k} > \dfrac{2k}{3k^2+k^2} = \dfrac{1}{2k}$, $\displaystyle\sum_{k=1}^{\infty} 1/(2k)$ diverges so $\displaystyle\sum_{k=1}^{\infty} \dfrac{2k+1}{3k^2+k}$ diverges.

(c) $\dfrac{2k-1}{3k^3-k^2} < \dfrac{2k}{3k^3-k^3} = 1/k^2$, $\displaystyle\sum_{k=1}^{\infty} 1/k^2$ converges so $\displaystyle\sum_{k=1}^{\infty} \dfrac{2k-1}{3k^3-k^2}$ converges.

(d) $\dfrac{2k+1}{3k^3+k^2} < \dfrac{2k+k}{3k^3} = 1/k^2$, $\displaystyle\sum_{k=1}^{\infty} 1/k^2$ converges so $\displaystyle\sum_{k=1}^{\infty} \dfrac{2k+1}{3k^3+k^2}$ converges.

13. **(a)** $\dfrac{1}{6}\left[\displaystyle\sum_{k=1}^{\infty}\left(\dfrac{1}{3}\right)^k + \sum_{k=1}^{\infty}\left(\dfrac{1}{2}\right)^k\right] = \dfrac{1}{6}\left[\dfrac{1/3}{1-1/3} + \dfrac{1/2}{1-1/2}\right] = 1/4$

(b) $\displaystyle\sum_{k=2}^{\infty} \ln\frac{k+1}{k} = \sum_{k=2}^{\infty}[\ln(k+1) - \ln k]$,

$s_n = [\ln 3 - \ln 2] + [\ln 4 - \ln 3] + \cdots + [\ln(n+2) - \ln(n+1)]$

$= \ln(n+2) - \ln 2$, $\displaystyle\lim_{n\to+\infty} s_n = +\infty$, diverges

    (c) $s_n = [1^{-1/2} - 2^{-1/2}] + [2^{-1/2} - 3^{-1/2}] + \cdots + [n^{-1/2} - (n+1)^{-1/2}]$

                $= 1 - (n+1)^{-1/2}$, $\lim\limits_{n \to +\infty} s_n = 1$

14.   converges (geometric series, $a = 1$, $r = e^{-1}$)

15.   converges (integral test, $\displaystyle\int_1^\infty xe^{-x^2}\,dx$ converges)

16.   diverges (limit comparison test with $\Sigma 1/k$, $\rho = 1$)

17.   converges (comparison test, $\dfrac{\sqrt{k}}{k^2 + 7} < \dfrac{\sqrt{k}}{k^2} = \dfrac{1}{k^{3/2}}$)

18.   diverges $\left(\lim\limits_{k \to +\infty} \left(\dfrac{k}{k+1}\right)^k = \lim\limits_{k \to +\infty} \dfrac{1}{(1 + 1/k)^k} = 1/e \neq 0\right)$

19.   converges (ratio test, $\rho = 0$)   **20.**   converges (ratio test, $\rho = 0$)

21.   diverges (root test, $\rho = (5/2)^3 > 1$)   **22.**   diverges $\left(\lim\limits_{k \to +\infty} |u_k| = 1 \neq 0\right)$

23.   absolutely convergent (comparison test, $2^k/(3^k + 1) < 2^k/3^k = (2/3)^k$, $\Sigma(2/3)^k$ is a convergent geometric series)

24.   conditionally convergent (the series converges by the alternating series test but $\sum 1/(2k+1)$ diverges)

25.   diverges $\left(\lim\limits_{k \to +\infty} |u_k| = \lim\limits_{k \to +\infty} \dfrac{1}{2}(3/2)^k = +\infty\right)$

26.   **(a)** $1/[(n+1)^2 + 1] \le 0.0001$, $(n+1)^2 \ge 9999$, $n + 1 \ge 100$, $n \ge 99$; take $n = 99$

        (b) $1/(5^{n+1} + 1) \le 0.00005$, $5^{n+1} + 1 \ge 20,000$, $5^{n+1} \ge 19,999$, $(n+1)\ln 5 \ge \ln 19,999$,

             $n \ge \dfrac{\ln 19,999}{\ln 5} - 1 \approx 5.15$; take $n = 6$

27. $\rho = \lim\limits_{k \to +\infty} \dfrac{k^{3/2}|x - 1|}{(k+1)^{3/2}} = |x - 1|$, converges if $|x - 1| < 1$, diverges if $|x - 1| > 1$.

     If $x = 0$, $\displaystyle\sum_{k=1}^{\infty} \dfrac{(-1)^k}{k^{3/2}}$ converges; if $x = 2$, $\displaystyle\sum_{k=1}^{\infty} \dfrac{1}{k^{3/2}}$ converges. $R = 1$, interval of

     convergence $[0,2]$.

28. $\rho = \lim\limits_{k \to +\infty} \dfrac{k|2x|}{k+1} = |2x|$, converges if $|x| < 1/2$, diverges if $|x| > 1/2$. If $x = -1/2$,

$\sum\limits_{k=1}^{\infty} \dfrac{(-1)^k}{3k}$ converges; if $x = 1/2$, $\sum\limits_{k=1}^{\infty} 1/(3k)$ diverges. $R = 1/2$, interval of convergence

$[-1/2, 1/2)$.

29. $\rho = \lim\limits_{k \to +\infty} \dfrac{k|1-x|^2}{4(k+1)} = \dfrac{1}{4}|1-x|^2$, converges if $|x-1|^2 < 4$, $|x-1| < 2$; diverges if $|x-1| > 2$.

If $x = -1$, $\sum\limits_{k=1}^{\infty} 1/k$ diverges; if $x = 3$, $\sum\limits_{k=1}^{\infty} 1/k$ diverges. $R = 2$, interval of convergence $(-1, 3)$.

30. $\rho = \lim\limits_{k \to +\infty} \dfrac{(k+1)^2|x-2|}{k^2(k+1)} = 0$, $R = +\infty$, interval of convergence $(-\infty, +\infty)$.

31. $\rho = \lim\limits_{k \to +\infty} \dfrac{1}{5}(k+1)|x-1| = +\infty$, $R = 0$, converges only for $x = 1$.

32. $\rho = \lim\limits_{k \to +\infty} \dfrac{2k+1}{2k+3}|x| = |x|$, converges if $|x| < 1$, diverges if $|x| > 1$. If $x = -1$,

$\sum\limits_{k=1}^{\infty} \dfrac{(-1)^k}{2k+1}$ converges; if $x = 1$, $\sum\limits_{k=1}^{\infty} 1/(2k+1)$ diverges. $R = 1$, interval of convergence $[-1, 1)$.

33. (a) $(x-2) - \dfrac{1}{2}(x-2)^2 + \dfrac{1}{3}(x-2)^3$

(b) $R_3(x) = -\dfrac{(x-2)^4}{4(c-1)^4}$, c between 2 and x

(c) $|R_3(x)| = \dfrac{|x-2|^4}{4|c-1|^4} < \dfrac{|3/2-2|^4}{4|3/2-1|^4} = 1/4$

34. (a) $1 + x/2 + x^2/8 + x^3/48 + x^4/384$ (b) $R_4(x) = \dfrac{e^{c/2}x^5}{2^5 5!}$, c between 0 and x

(c) $|R_4(x)| = \dfrac{e^{c/2}|x|^5}{2^5 5!} < \dfrac{1}{2^5 5!} < 0.000261$

35. (a) $1 + \dfrac{1}{2}(x-1) - \dfrac{1}{8}(x-1)^2$ (b) $R_2(x) = \dfrac{(x-1)^3}{16c^{5/2}}$, c between 1 and x

(c) $|R_2(x)| = \dfrac{|x-1|^3}{16c^{5/2}} < \dfrac{|4/9-1|^3}{16(4/9)^{5/2}} = \dfrac{(5/9)^3}{16(2/3)^5} < 0.0814$

36. **(a)** $\dfrac{1}{a-x} = \dfrac{1}{a}\left[\dfrac{1}{1-x/a}\right] = \dfrac{1}{a}\sum\limits_{k=0}^{\infty}(x/a)^k = \sum\limits_{k=0}^{\infty}\dfrac{x^k}{a^{k+1}}$, converges if $|x/a| < 1$,

$|x| < |a|$ so $R = |a|$

(b) $\dfrac{1}{3+x} = \dfrac{1}{3}\left[\dfrac{1}{1+x/3}\right] = \dfrac{1}{3}\sum\limits_{k=0}^{\infty}(-1)^k(x/3)^k = \sum\limits_{k=0}^{\infty}(-1)^k\dfrac{x^k}{3^{k+1}}$, $R = 3$

(c) $\dfrac{2x}{4+x^2} = \dfrac{x}{2}\left[\dfrac{1}{1+x^2/4}\right] = \dfrac{x}{2}\sum\limits_{k=0}^{\infty}(-1)^k(x^2/4)^k = \sum\limits_{k=0}^{\infty}(-1)^k(x/2)^{2k+1}$,

converges if $x^2/4 < 1$, $x^2 < 4$, $|x| < 2$ so $R = 2$

(d) $\dfrac{1}{(1-x)(2-x)} = \dfrac{1}{1-x} - \dfrac{1}{2-x} = \dfrac{1}{1-x} - \dfrac{1}{2}\left[\dfrac{1}{1-x/2}\right]$

$= \sum\limits_{k=0}^{\infty}x^k - \dfrac{1}{2}\sum\limits_{k=0}^{\infty}(x/2)^k = \sum\limits_{k=0}^{\infty}(1-2^{-k-1})x^k$,

the series for $1/(1-x)$ converges if $|x| < 1$ and that for $1/(2-x)$ if $|x| < 2$ so both will converge if $|x| < 1$ thus $R = 1$

37. $\ln(a+x) = \ln a(1+x/a) = \ln a + \ln(1+x/a) = \ln a + \sum\limits_{k=0}^{\infty}(-1)^k\dfrac{(x/a)^{k+1}}{k+1}$,

converges if $|x/a| < 1$, $|x| < |a| = a$ so $R = a$

38. **(a)** $e^x = e^{a+(x-a)} = e^a e^{x-a} = e^a\sum\limits_{k=0}^{\infty}\dfrac{(x-a)^k}{k!} = \sum\limits_{k=0}^{\infty}\dfrac{e^a(x-a)^k}{k!}$

(b) $\sin x = \sin[a+(x-a)] = \sin a\cos(x-a) + \cos a\sin(x-a)$

$= (\sin a)\sum\limits_{k=0}^{\infty}(-1)^k\dfrac{(x-a)^{2k}}{(2k)!} + (\cos a)\sum\limits_{k=0}^{\infty}(-1)^k\dfrac{(x-a)^{2k+1}}{(2k+1)!}$

(c) $\dfrac{1}{x} = \dfrac{1}{a+(x-a)} = \dfrac{1}{a}\left[\dfrac{1}{1+(x-a)/a}\right]$

$= \dfrac{1}{a}\sum\limits_{k=0}^{\infty}(-1)^k\dfrac{(x-a)^k}{a^k} = \sum\limits_{k=0}^{\infty}(-1)^k\dfrac{(x-a)^k}{a^{k+1}}$, $a \neq 0$

39. $1/(9+x)^{1/2} = \dfrac{1}{3}(1+x/9)^{-1/2} = \dfrac{1}{3}\left[1 + \sum\limits_{k=1}^{\infty}(-1)^k\dfrac{1\cdot3\cdot5\cdots(2k-1)}{2^k\,k!}(x/9)^k\right]$,

converges if $|x/9| < 1$, $|x| < 9$ so $R = 9$

40. $f(x) = e^{\tan x}$, $f'(x) = e^{\tan x}\sec^2 x$, $f''(x) = e^{\tan x}\left(2\sec^2 x\tan x + \sec^4 x\right)$, $f(0) = 1$, $f'(0) = 1$,

$f''(0) = 1$ so the Maclaurin series is $1 + x + x^2/2 + \cdots$

41. $\sec x = 1/\cos x = 1/(1 - x^2/2! + x^4/4! - \cdots) = 1 + x^2/2 + 5x^4/24 + \cdots$

42. $\dfrac{\sin x}{e^x + x} = \dfrac{x - x^3/3! + x^5/5! - \cdots}{(1 + x + x^2/2! + \cdots) + x} = \dfrac{x - x^3/3! + x^5/5! - \cdots}{1 + 2x + x^2/2! + \cdots} = x - 2x^2 + \dfrac{10}{3}x^3 + \cdots$

43. $[\cos x]^{1/2} = \left[1 - x^2/2! + x^4/4! - \cdots\right]^{1/2} = \left[1 + \left(-x^2/2! + x^4/4! - \cdots\right)\right]^{1/2}$

$$= 1 + \frac{1}{2}\left(-x^2/2! + x^4/4! - \cdots\right) - \frac{1}{8}\left(-x^2/2! + x^4/4! - \cdots\right)^2 + \cdots$$

$$= 1 - x^2/4 - x^4/96 + \cdots$$

44. $e^x \ln(1 - x) = \left(1 + x + x^2/2! + \cdots\right)\left(-x - x^2/2 - x^3/3 - \cdots\right) = -x - 3x^2/2 - 4x^3/3 + \cdots$

45. $f(x) = \ln(1 + \sin x)$, $f'(x) = \dfrac{\cos x}{1 + \sin x}$, $f''(x) = -\dfrac{1}{1 + \sin x}$, $f'''(x) = \dfrac{\cos x}{(1 + \sin x)^2}$;

$f(0) = 0$, $f'(0) = 1$, $f''(0) = -1$, $f'''(0) = 1$; $\ln(1 + \sin x) = x - \dfrac{1}{2}x^2 + \dfrac{1}{6}x^3 + \cdots$

46. $\dfrac{1 - \cos 3x}{x^2} = \dfrac{1}{x^2}\left[1 - \left(1 - \dfrac{9x^2}{2!} + \dfrac{81x^4}{4!} - \cdots\right)\right] = \dfrac{9}{2!} - \dfrac{81x^2}{4!} + \cdots$; $\displaystyle\lim_{x \to 0} \dfrac{1 - \cos 3x}{x^2} = \dfrac{9}{2}$

47. $\dfrac{\ln(1 - 2x)}{x} = \dfrac{1}{x}\left(-2x - 2x^2 - \dfrac{8}{3}x^3 - \cdots\right) = -2 - 2x - \dfrac{8}{3}x^2 - \cdots$, $\displaystyle\lim_{x \to 0} \dfrac{\ln(1 - 2x)}{x} = -2$

48. $\cos x = 1 - x^2/2 + (0)x^3 + R_3(x)$, $|R_3(x)| \le \dfrac{|x|^4}{4!} < \dfrac{(0.1)^4}{4!} < 0.5 \times 10^{-5}$, so 5 decimal

place accuracy is guaranteed.

49. $\sin x = x - x^3/3! + x^5/5! + (0)x^6 + R_6(x)$, $|R_6(x)| \le \dfrac{|x|^7}{7!} < 6 \times 10^{-4}$ if $|x|^7 < 3.024$,

$|x| < (3.024)^{1/7} \approx 1.17$

50. $\cos x = 1 - x^2/2! + x^4/4! - \cdots$, $|R_n(x)| \le \dfrac{|x|^{n+1}}{(n+1)!}$, $10° = \pi/18$ radians,

$|R_n(\pi/18)| \le \dfrac{(\pi/18)^{n+1}}{(n+1)!} < 0.5 \times 10^{-3}$ if $n = 3$, $\cos 10° \approx 1 - (\pi/18)^2/2 \approx 0.985$

51. $\displaystyle\int_0^1 \frac{1-e^{-t/2}}{t}dt - \int_0^1 \frac{\left[1-\left(1-\dfrac{t}{2}+\dfrac{t^2}{8}-\dfrac{t^3}{48}+\dfrac{t^4}{384}-\dfrac{t^5}{3840}+\cdots\right)\right]}{t}dt$

$$= \int_0^1 \left(\frac{1}{2}-\frac{t}{8}+\frac{t^2}{48}-\frac{t^3}{384}+\frac{t^4}{3840}-\cdots\right)dt$$

$$= \frac{t}{2}-\frac{t^2}{16}+\frac{t^3}{144}-\frac{t^4}{1436}+\frac{t^5}{19200}-\cdots\Bigg]_0^1$$

$$= 1/2 - 1/16 + 1/144 - 1/1436 + 1/19200 - \cdots,$$

but $1/19200 < 0.5 \times 10^{-3}$ so $\displaystyle\int_0^1 \frac{1-e^{-t/2}}{t}dt \approx 1/2 - 1/16 + 1/144 - 1/1436 \approx 0.444$

52. $\displaystyle\int_0^1 \frac{\sin x}{\sqrt{x}}dx = \int_0^1 x^{-1/2}(x - x^3/3! + x^5/5! - x^7/7! + \cdots)dx$

$$= \int_0^1 \left(x^{1/2} - \frac{1}{3!}x^{5/2} + \frac{1}{5!}x^{9/2} - \frac{1}{7!}x^{13/2} + \cdots\right)dx$$

$$= \frac{2}{3}x^{3/2} - \frac{2}{7\cdot 3!}x^{7/2} + \frac{2}{11\cdot 5!}x^{11/2} - \frac{2}{15\cdot 7!}x^{15/2} + \cdots\Bigg]_0^1$$

$$= \frac{2}{3} - \frac{2}{7\cdot 3!} + \frac{2}{11\cdot 5!} - \frac{2}{15\cdot 7!} + \cdots,$$

but $2/(15\cdot 7!) < 0.5 \times 10^{-3}$ so $\displaystyle\int_0^1 \frac{\sin x}{\sqrt{x}}dx \approx \frac{2}{3} - \frac{2}{7\cdot 3!} + \frac{2}{11\cdot 5!} \approx 0.621$

53. $\displaystyle y' = \sum_{n=1}^{\infty}\frac{k^n x^{n-1}}{(n-1)!} = \sum_{n=0}^{\infty}\frac{k^{n+1}x^k}{n!} = k\sum_{n=0}^{\infty}\frac{k^n x^k}{n!} = ky$, so $y' - ky = 0$

CHAPTER 12
Topics In Analytic Geometry

EXERCISE SET 12.2

1.

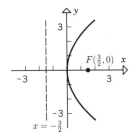

2.

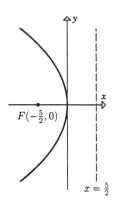

3.

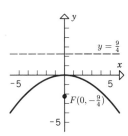

4.

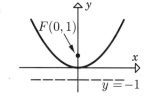

5. $y^2 = (12/5)x$

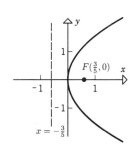

6. $x^2 = 40y$

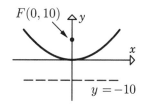

7.

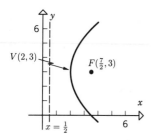

8.

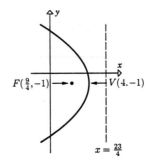

9.

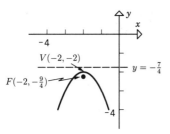

10.

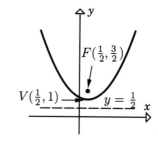

11. $(x - 2)^2 = -2(y - 5/2)$

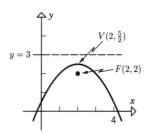

12. $(y - 3)^2 = 2(x + 4)$

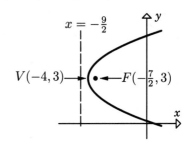

13. $(y - 2)^2 = x + 2$

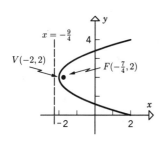

14. $(x + 1)^2 = \frac{1}{4}(y - 1)$

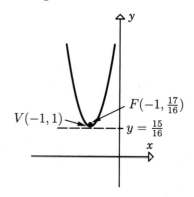

15. $(y-1)^2 = x+1$

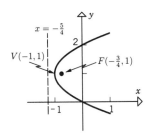

16. $(x+2)^2 = -(y-5)$

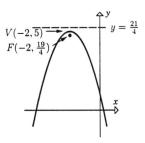

17. $y^2 = 4px$, $p = 3$, $y^2 = 12x$

18. $x^2 = -4py$, $p = 4$, $x^2 = -16y$

19. $y^2 = -4px$, $p = 7$, $y^2 = -28x$

20. $x^2 = -4py$, $p = 1/2$, $x^2 = -2y$

21. $y^2 = ax$, $2^2 = a(2)$, $a = 2$, $y^2 = 2x$

22. $x^2 = ay$, $(-1)^2 = a(3)$, $a = 1/3$, $x^2 = y/3$

23. $x^2 = -4py$, $p = 3$, $x^2 = -12y$

24. $y^2 = 4px$, $p = 6$, $y^2 = 24x$

25. $y^2 = a(x-h)$, $4 = a(3-h)$ and $9 = a(2-h)$, solve simultaneously to get $h = 19/5$, $a = -5$ so $y^2 = -5(x - 19/5)$

26. $x^2 = a(y-k)$, $4 = a(-1-h)$ and $16 = a(5-k)$, solve simultaneously to get $k = -3$, $a = 2$ so $x^2 = 2(y+3)$

27. The vertex is half way between the focus and directrix so the vertex is at $(3/2, 0)$ and $p = 3/2$, $y^2 = 6(x - 3/2)$.

28. The focus is 3 units to the left of the vertex so $p = 3$, $(y+5)^2 = -12(x-4)$.

29. The vertex is 3 units above the directrix so $p = 3$, $(x-1)^2 = 12(y-1)$.

30. The vertex is half way between the focus and directrix so the vertex is at $(2, 4)$, the focus is 3 units to the left of the vertex so $p = 3$, $(y-4)^2 = -12(x-2)$

31. $(x-5)^2 = a(y+3)$, $(9-5)^2 = a(5+3)$ so $a = 2$, $(x-5)^2 = 2(y+3)$

32. $PF = PD$, $\sqrt{(x-2)^2 + (y-1)^2} = \dfrac{|x+y+1|}{\sqrt{2}}$,

$x^2 - 4x + 4 + y^2 - 2y + 1 = (x^2 + y^2 + 1 + 2xy + 2x + 2y)/2$,

$x^2 - 2xy + y^2 - 10x - 6y + 9 = 0$

33. (a) $y = Ax^2 + Bx + C$; use $(0,3)$, $(2,0)$ and $(3,2)$ to get the system of equations $C = 3$, $9A + 3B + C = 2$, and $4A + 2B + C = 0$ which when solved yields $A = 7/6$, $B = -23/6$, $C = 3$ so $y = \dfrac{7}{6}x^2 - \dfrac{23}{6}x + 3$.

(b) $x = Ay^2 + By + C$; $9A + 3B + C = 0$, $4A + 2B + C = 3$, and $C = 2$. Solve to get $A = -7/6$, $B = 17/6$, $C = 2$ so $x = -\dfrac{7}{6}y^2 + \dfrac{17}{6}y + 2$

34. $y = \dfrac{1}{4p}x^2$, $dy/dx = \dfrac{1}{2p}x$, $dy/dx\Big|_{x=x_0} = \dfrac{1}{2p}x_0$, the tangent line at (x_0, y_0) is

$y - y_0 = \dfrac{x_0}{2p}(x - x_0) = \dfrac{x_0}{2p}x - \dfrac{x_0^2}{2p}$ but $\dfrac{x_0^2}{2p} = 2y_0$ because (x_0, y_0) is on the parabola

$y = \dfrac{1}{4p}x^2$ so the tangent line is $y - y_0 = \dfrac{x_0}{2p}x - 2y_0$, $y = \dfrac{x_0}{2p}x - y_0$.

35. Complete the square to get $\left(x + \dfrac{B}{2A}\right)^2 = \dfrac{1}{A}\left(y - C + \dfrac{B^2}{4A}\right)$ so the vertex is at

$\left(-\dfrac{B}{2A}, \dfrac{4AC - B^2}{4A}\right)$, the focus is at $\left(-\dfrac{B}{2A}, \dfrac{4AC - B^2 + 1}{4A}\right)$, and the directrix is

$y = \dfrac{4AC - B^2 - 1}{4A}$.

36. (a) $(x - b/2)^2 = a(y - h)$, but $(0,0)$ is on the parabola so $b^2/4 = -ah$, $a = -\dfrac{b^2}{4h}$,

$(x - b/2)^2 = -\dfrac{b^2}{4h}(y - h)$

(b) From part (a), $y = -\dfrac{4h}{b^2}(x - b/2)^2 + h$, $A = \displaystyle\int_0^b \left[-\dfrac{4h}{b^2}(x - b/2)^2 + h\right]dx = \dfrac{2}{3}bh$

37. $y = ax^2 + b$, $(20,0)$ and $(10,12)$ are on the curve so $400a + b = 0$ and $100a + b = 12$. Solve for b to get $b = 16 =$ height of arch.

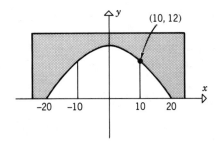

38. Let R be the radius of a circle C' that is tangent to both C and L; draw the line L' parallel to L and at a distance r from it (see diagram). The center of C' is equidistant from the center of C and the line L' (the common distance is $r + R$). The focus is the center of C and the directrix is the line L'.

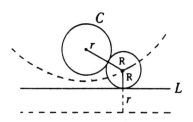

39. Let (x_0, y_0) be a point on the parabola $y^2 = 4px$, then
$$PF = \sqrt{(x_0 - p)^2 + y_0^2} = \sqrt{x_0^2 - 2px_0 + p^2 + 4px_0} = \sqrt{(x_0 + p)^2}$$
so $PF = x_0 + p$ where $x_0 \geq 0$ and PF is a minimum when $x_0 = 0$ (the vertex).

40. Let $p =$ distance (in millions of miles) between the vertex (closest point) and the focus F,

then $PD = PF$, $2p + 20 = 40$,

$p = 10$ million miles.

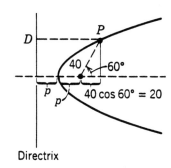

Directrix

41. Use an xy-coordinate system so that $y^2 = 4px$ is an equation of the parabola, then $(1, 1/2)$ is a point on the curve so $(1/2)^2 = 4p(1)$, $p = 1/16$. The light source should be placed at the focus which is $1/16$ ft. from the vertex.

42. Similar to proof in text.   **43.** Similar to proof in text.

44. Use the result from Exercise 34 with $x = 0$ to show that the tangent line at P intersects the y-axis at $-y_0$. $QF = \sqrt{(p + y_0)^2} = p + y_0$ and

$PF = \sqrt{x_0^2 + (y_0 - p)^2} = \sqrt{4py_0 + y_0^2 - 2py_0 + p^2} = \sqrt{(y_0 + p)^2} = y_0 + p$ thus $PF = QF$ so triangle PQF is isosceles and angle $PQF = \beta$, but angle $PQF = \alpha$ therefore $\alpha = \beta$.

EXERCISE SET 12.3

1. $c^2 = 16 - 9 = 7, c = \sqrt{7}$

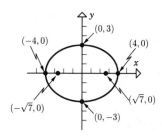

2. $c^2 = 25 - 4 = 21, c = \sqrt{21}$

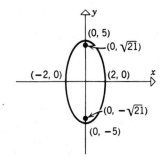

3. $\dfrac{x^2}{1} + \dfrac{y^2}{9} = 1$

$c^2 = 9 - 1 = 8, c = \sqrt{8}$

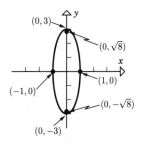

4. $\dfrac{x^2}{9} + \dfrac{y^2}{4} = 1$

$c^2 = 9 - 4 = 5, c = \sqrt{5}$

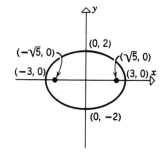

5. $\dfrac{x^2}{2} + \dfrac{y^2}{2/3} = 1$

$c^2 = 2 - 2/3 = 4/3, c = 2/\sqrt{3}$

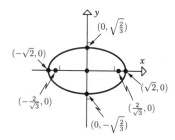

6. $\dfrac{x^2}{1/16} + \dfrac{y^2}{1/4} = 1$

$c^2 = 1/4 - 1/16 = 3/16, c = \sqrt{3}/4$

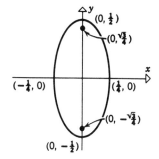

7. $\dfrac{(x-1)^2}{16} + \dfrac{(y-3)^2}{9} = 1$

$c^2 = 16 - 9 = 7, c = \sqrt{7}$

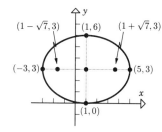

8. $\dfrac{(x+3)^2}{16} + \dfrac{(y-5)^2}{4} = 1$

$c^2 = 16 - 4 = 12, c = 2\sqrt{3}$

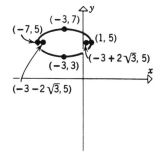

9. $\dfrac{(x+2)^2}{4} + \dfrac{(y+1)^2}{3} = 1$

$c^2 = 4 - 3 = 1, c = 1$

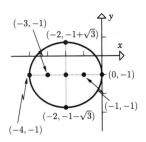

10. $\dfrac{x^2}{4} + \dfrac{(y+2)^2}{9} = 1$

$c^2 = 9 - 4 = 5, c = \sqrt{5}$

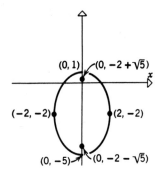

11. $\dfrac{(x+1)^2}{9} + \dfrac{(y-1)^2}{1} = 1$

$c^2 = 9 - 1 = 8, c = \sqrt{8}$

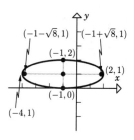

12. $\dfrac{(x+1)^2}{4} + \dfrac{(y-3)^2}{9} = 1$

$c^2 = 9 - 4 = 5, c = \sqrt{5}$

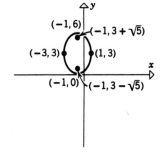

13. $\dfrac{(x+1)^2}{4} + \dfrac{(y-5)^2}{16} = 1$

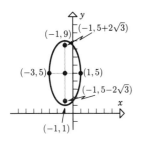

14. $\dfrac{(x-2)^2}{9} + \dfrac{(y+3)^2}{5} = 1$

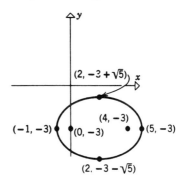

15. $x^2/9 + y^2/4 = 1$

16. $x^2 + y^2/5 = 1$

17. $a = 26/2 = 13$, $c = 5$, $b^2 = a^2 - c^2 = 169 - 25 = 144$; $x^2/169 + y^2/144 = 1$

18. $b = 8$, $c = 6$, $a^2 = b^2 + c^2 = 64 + 36 = 100$; $x^2/64 + y^2/100 = 1$

19. $c = 1$, $a^2 = b^2 + c^2 = 2 + 1 = 3$; $x^2/3 + y^2/2 = 1$

20. $c = 3$, $b^2 = a^2 - c^2 = 16 - 9 = 7$; $x^2/16 + y^2/7 = 1$

21. $b^2 = 16 - 12 = 4$; $x^2/16 + y^2/4 = 1$ and $x^2/4 + y^2/16 = 1$

22. $a^2 = 9 + 16 = 25$; $x^2/25 + y^2/9 = 1$ and $x^2/9 + y^2/25 = 1$

23. $a = 6$, $(2, 3)$ satisfies $x^2/36 + y^2/b^2 = 1$ so $4/36 + 9/b^2 = 1$, $b^2 = 81/8$; $x^2/36 + y^2/(81/8) = 1$

24. Substitute $(3, 2)$ and $(1, 6)$ into $x^2/A + y^2/B = 1$ to get $9/A + 4/B = 1$ and $1/A + 36/B = 1$ which yields $A = 10$, $B = 40$; $x^2/10 + y^2/40 = 1$

25. The center is midway between the foci so it is at $(1, 3)$ thus $c = 1$, $b = 1$, $a^2 = 1 + 1 = 2$; $(x-1)^2 + (y-3)^2/2 = 1$

26. The center is at $(2, -1)$ thus $c = 2$, $a = 3$, $b^2 = 9 - 4 = 5$; $(x-2)^2/5 + (y+1)^2/9 = 1$

27. $(4, 1)$ and $(4, 5)$ are the foci so the center is at $(4, 3)$ thus $c = 2$, $a = 12/2 = 6$, $b^2 = 36 - 4 = 32$; $(x-4)^2/32 + (y-3)^2/36 = 1$

28. $(0,0)$ and $(1,1)$ are the foci, use the definition of an ellipse to get

$\sqrt{x^2 + y^2} + \sqrt{(x-1)^2 + (y-1)^2} = 4$, transpose the first radical to the right side of the equation and square both sides and simplify to get $4\sqrt{x^2 + y^2} = x + y + 7$, square both sides and simplify to get $15x^2 - 2xy + 15y^2 - 14x - 14y - 49 = 0$.

29. Substitute $x = 8 - 2y$ into $x^2 + 4y^2 = 40$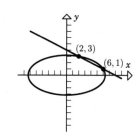
to get $y^2 - 4y + 3 = 0$ which yields
$y = 1, 3$. Substitute these into
$x = 8 - 2y$ to get $x = 6, 2$ so the
points of intersection are $(2, 3)$ and $(6, 1)$.

30. Substitute $y^2 = 2x$ into $x^2 + 2y^2 = 12$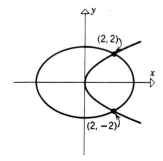
to get $x^2 + 4x - 12 = 0$, $x = 2, -6$.
Use $y^2 = 2x$ to get $y = \pm 2$ when $x = 2$
and no solutions when $x = -6$. The
points of intersection are $(2, 2)$ and $(2, -2)$.

31. Substitute $x^2 = 20 - y^2$ into $x^2 + 9y^2 = 36$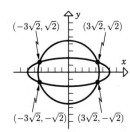
to get $y^2 = 2$, $y = \pm\sqrt{2}$. Use
$x^2 = 20 - y^2$ to get $x = \pm 3\sqrt{2}$ when
$y = \sqrt{2}$ or $-\sqrt{2}$. The points of intersection are $(3\sqrt{2}, \sqrt{2})$, $(3\sqrt{2}, -\sqrt{2})$,
$(-3\sqrt{2}, \sqrt{2})$, and $(-3\sqrt{2}, -\sqrt{2})$.

32. Eliminate y to get $x^2 = 1$, $x = \pm 1$ and substitute into either of the given equations to get $y = \pm 2\sqrt{5}/3$ when $x = 1$ or -1. The points of intersection are $(1, 2\sqrt{5}/3)$, $(1, -2\sqrt{5}/3)$, $(-1, 2\sqrt{5}/3)$, and $(-1, -2\sqrt{5}/3)$.

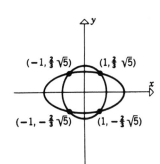

33. Use implicit differentiation on $x^2 + 4y^2 = 8$ to get $\dfrac{dy}{dx}\Big|_{(x_0, y_0)} = -\dfrac{x_0}{4y_0}$ where (x_0, y_0) is the point of tangency, but $-x_0/(4y_0) = -1/2$ because the slope of the line is $-1/2$ so $x_0 = 2y_0$. (x_0, y_0) is on the ellipse so $x_0^2 + 4y_0^2 = 8$ which when solved with $x_0 = 2y_0$ yields the points of tangency $(2, 1)$ and $(-2, -1)$. Substitute these into the equation of the line to get $k = \pm 4$.

34. By implicit differentiation, $\dfrac{dy}{dx}\Big|_{(x_0, y_0)} = -\dfrac{b^2}{a^2}\dfrac{x_0}{y_0}$ if $y_0 \neq 0$, the tangent line is

$$y - y_0 = -\frac{b^2}{a^2}\frac{x_0}{y_0}(x - x_0), \quad a^2 y_0 y - a^2 y_0^2 = -b^2 x_0 x + b^2 x_0^2, \quad b^2 x_0 x + a^2 y_0 y = b^2 x_0^2 + a^2 y_0^2,$$ but (x_0, y_0) is on the ellipse so $b^2 x_0^2 + a^2 y_0^2 = a^2 b^2$ thus the tangent line is $b^2 x_0 x + a^2 y_0 y = a^2 b^2$, $x_0 x / a^2 + y_0 y / b^2 = 1$. If $y_0 = 0$ then $x_0 = \pm a$ and the tangent lines are $x = \pm a$ which also follow from $x_0 x / a^2 + y_0 y / b^2 = 1$.

35. $y = (b/a)\sqrt{a^2 - x^2}$ is the upper half of the ellipse,

$$A = 4\int_0^a \frac{b}{a}\sqrt{a^2 - x^2}\,dx = \frac{4b}{a}\int_0^a \sqrt{a^2 - x^2}\,dx = \frac{4b}{a}\left(\frac{1}{4}\pi a^2\right) = \pi ab$$

36. **(a)** $V = 2\displaystyle\int_0^a \pi y^2\,dx = 2\pi\frac{b^2}{a^2}\int_0^a (a^2 - x^2)\,dx = \frac{4}{3}\pi ab^2$

(b) $V = 2\displaystyle\int_0^b x^2\,dy = 2\pi\frac{a^2}{b^2}\int_0^b (b^2 - y^2)\,dy = \frac{4}{3}\pi a^2 b$

37. $y = \dfrac{b}{a}\sqrt{a^2 - x^2}$, $\dfrac{dy}{dx} = -\dfrac{b}{a}\dfrac{x}{\sqrt{a^2 - x^2}}$, $1 + \left(\dfrac{dy}{dx}\right)^2 = \dfrac{a^4 - c^2 x^2}{a^2(a^2 - x^2)}$,

$S = 2(2\pi) \displaystyle\int_0^a y\sqrt{1 + (dy/dx)^2}\, dx = 4\pi \int_0^a \dfrac{b}{a}\sqrt{a^2 - x^2}\dfrac{\sqrt{a^4 - c^2 x^2}}{a\sqrt{a^2 - x^2}}\, dx$

$= \dfrac{4\pi b}{a^2}\displaystyle\int_0^a \sqrt{a^4 - c^2 x^2}\, dx = \dfrac{4\pi b}{a^2 c}\int_0^{ac}\sqrt{a^4 - u^2}\, du \quad (u = cx)$

$= \dfrac{4\pi b}{a^2 c}\left[\dfrac{u}{2}\sqrt{a^4 - u^2} + \dfrac{a^4}{2}\sin^{-1}\dfrac{u}{a^2}\right]_0^{ac} = \dfrac{4\pi b}{a^2 c}\left[\dfrac{1}{2}ac\sqrt{a^4 - a^2 c^2} + \dfrac{1}{2}a^4\sin^{-1}\dfrac{c}{a}\right]$

$= 2\pi ab\left[\dfrac{b}{a} + \dfrac{a}{c}\sin^{-1}\dfrac{c}{a}\right].$

38. $x = \dfrac{a}{b}\sqrt{b^2 - y^2}$, $\dfrac{dx}{dy} = -\dfrac{a}{b}\dfrac{y}{\sqrt{b^2 - y^2}}$, $1 + \left(\dfrac{dx}{dy}\right)^2 = \dfrac{b^4 + c^2 y^2}{b^2(b^2 - y^2)}$,

$S = 2(2\pi)\displaystyle\int_0^b x\sqrt{1 + (dx/dy)^2}\, dy = 4\pi \int_0^b \dfrac{a}{b}\sqrt{b^2 - y^2}\dfrac{\sqrt{b^4 + c^2 y^2}}{b\sqrt{b^2 - y^2}}\, dy$

$= \dfrac{4\pi a}{b^2}\displaystyle\int_0^b \sqrt{b^4 + c^2 y^2}\, dy = \dfrac{4\pi a}{b^2 c}\int_0^{bc}\sqrt{b^4 + u^2}\, du \quad (u = cy)$

$= \dfrac{4\pi a}{b^2 c}\left[\dfrac{u}{2}\sqrt{b^4 + u^2} + \dfrac{b^4}{2}\ln|u + \sqrt{b^4 + u^2}|\right]_0^{bc}$

$= \dfrac{4\pi a}{b^2 c}\left[\dfrac{1}{2}ab^2 c + \dfrac{1}{2}b^4\ln\dfrac{a + c}{b}\right] = 2\pi ab\left[\dfrac{a}{b} + \dfrac{b}{c}\ln\dfrac{a + c}{b}\right].$

39. Use $\dfrac{x^2}{9} + \dfrac{y^2}{4} = 1$, $x = \dfrac{3}{2}\sqrt{4 - y^2}$,

$V = \displaystyle\int_{-2}^{-2+h}(2)(3/2)\sqrt{4 - y^2}(18)dy = 54\int_{-2}^{-2+h}\sqrt{4 - y^2}\, dy$

$= 54\left[\dfrac{y}{2}\sqrt{4 - y^2} + 2\sin^{-1}\dfrac{y}{2}\right]_{-2}^{-2+h} = 27\left[4\sin^{-1}\dfrac{h - 2}{2} + (h - 2)\sqrt{4h - h^2} + 2\pi\right]$

40. With xy-axes as shown in the diagram, points on the arch satisfy the equation $x^2/625 + y^2/b^2 = 1$ where b is the height of the arch. But $(15, 14)$ is on the curve so $225/625 + 196/b^2 = 1$, $b = 17.5$ feet.

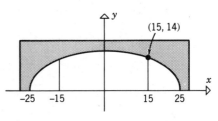

41. The vertex in the first quadrant is at the point where $y = x > 0$ so $x^2/a^2 + x^2/b^2 = 1$, $x^2 = a^2b^2/(a^2 + b^2)$, $x = ab/\sqrt{a^2 + b^2}$. $A = (2x)^2 = 4x^2 = 4a^2b^2/(a^2 + b^2)$.

42. Open the compass to the length of half the major axis, place the point of the compass at an end of the minor axis and draw arcs that cross the major axis to both sides of the center of the ellipse. Place the tacks where the arcs intersect the major axis.

43. $\sqrt{(x-4)^2 + y^2} = \dfrac{4}{5}\left|\dfrac{25}{4} - x\right|$, $x^2 - 8x + 16 + y^2 = \dfrac{16}{25}\left(\dfrac{625}{16} - \dfrac{25}{2}x + x^2\right)$,

$9x^2 + 25y^2 = 225$, $x^2/25 + y^2/9 = 1$; center: $(0,0)$, major axis: 10, minor axis: 6

44. In the $x'y'$-plane an equation of the circle is $x'^2 + y'^2 = r^2$ where r is the radius of the cylinder. Let $P(x, y)$ be a point on the curve in the xy-plane, then $x' = x\cos\theta$ and $y' = y$ so $x^2\cos^2\theta + y^2 = r^2$ which is an equation of an ellipse in the xy-plane.

45. $L = 2a = \sqrt{D^2 + p^2D^2} = D\sqrt{1 + p^2}$ (see figure),

so $a = \dfrac{1}{2}D\sqrt{1 + p^2}$, but $b = \dfrac{1}{2}D$,

$T = c = \sqrt{a^2 - b^2}$

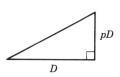

$\qquad = \sqrt{\dfrac{1}{4}D^2(1 + p^2) - \dfrac{1}{4}D^2} = \dfrac{1}{2}pD.$

46. Use $\dfrac{x^2}{81/4} + \dfrac{y^2}{4} = 1$ as the equation of the ellipse,

(a) The cross sectional area is $A(x) = (2y)^2 = 4y^2$ so

$$V = 2\int_0^{9/2} (4y^2)dx = 32\int_0^{9/2} (1 - 4x^2/81)dx = 96 \text{ cubic units.}$$

(b) The cross sectional area is $A(y) = \sqrt{3}x^2$ so

$$V = 2\int_0^2 (\sqrt{3}x^2)dy = \dfrac{81\sqrt{3}}{8}\int_0^2 (4 - y^2)dy = 54\sqrt{3} \text{ cubic units.}$$

47. (a) $0 < c < a$ so $0 < c/a < 1$, $0 < e < 1$.

(b) $c = 3$, $e = c/a = 3/a = 3/5$ so $a = 5$, $b^2 = a^2 - c^2 = 25 - 9 = 16$, $x^2/16 + y^2/25 = 1$.

(c) c approaches a as e approaches 1 so $b = \sqrt{a^2 - c^2}$ approaches 0; the ellipse flattens and approaches the major axis.

(d) c approaches 0 as e approaches 0 so b approaches a; the ellipse widens and approaches a circle of radius a.

48. **(a)** Draw a diagram to see that the smallest distance is $a - c$ and the largest is $a + c$ so
$$\frac{a-c}{a+c} = \frac{59}{61}, \frac{1-c/a}{1+c/a} = \frac{59}{61}, \frac{1-e}{1+e} = \frac{59}{61} \text{ which when solved for } e \text{ yields } e = 1/60.$$

(b) From part (a), $e = \dfrac{c}{a} = \dfrac{1}{60}$ so $c = \dfrac{1}{60}a$. The smallest distance is
$$a - c = a - \frac{1}{60}a = \frac{59}{60}a = \frac{59}{60}(93) = 91.45 \text{ million miles.}$$

49. Let R be the radius of a circle C that
is tangent to both C_1 and C_2. The distances
between the center of C and the centers
of C_1 and C_2 are, respectively,
$r_1 + R$ and $r_2 - R$ (see accompanying
diagram). Their sum is
$(r_1 + R) + (r_2 - R) = r_1 + r_2$ which is
a constant so the centers lie on an
ellipse with foci at the centers of C_1
and C_2. The length of the major axis is

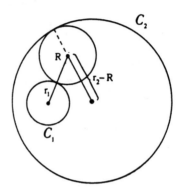

$2a = r_1 + r_2$; the center of the ellipse is at the midpoint of the line segment that joins the
centers of C_1 and C_2.

50. By implicit differentiation, $m = \dfrac{dy}{dx}\Big|_{P(x_0,y_0)} = -\dfrac{b^2}{a^2}\dfrac{x_0}{y_0}$ if $y_0 \neq 0$. Let m_1 and m_2 be the
slopes of the lines through P and the foci at $(-c, 0)$ and $(c, 0)$ respectively, then
$m_1 = y_0/(x_0 + c)$ and $m_2 = y_0/(x_0 - c)$. For P in the first quadrant,
$$\tan \alpha = \frac{m - m_2}{1 + mm_2} = \frac{-(b^2x_0)/(a^2y_0) - y_0/(x_0 - c)}{1 - (b^2x_0)/[a^2(x_0 - c)]}$$
$$= \frac{-b^2x_0^2 - a^2y_0^2 + b^2cx_0}{[(a^2 - b^2)x_0 - a^2c]\,y_0} = \frac{-a^2b^2 + b^2cx_0}{(c^2x_0 - a^2c)y_0} = \frac{b^2}{cy_0}$$

similarly $\tan(\pi - \beta) = \dfrac{m - m_1}{1 + mm_1} = -\dfrac{b^2}{cy_0} = -\tan\beta$ so $\tan\alpha = \tan\beta$, $\alpha = \beta$. The proof for the
case $y_0 = 0$ follows trivially. By symmetry, the result holds for P in the other three quadrants
as well.

51. Similar to derivation in text.

EXERCISE SET 12.4

1. $c^2 = a^2 + b^2 = 16 + 4 = 20, c = 2\sqrt{5}$

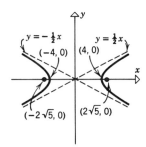

2. $c^2 = a^2 + b^2 = 9 + 25 = 34, c = \sqrt{34}$

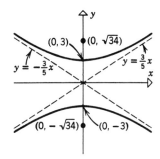

3. $y^2/4 - x^2/9 = 1$
  $c^2 = 4 + 9 = 13, c = \sqrt{13}$

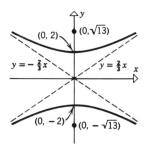

4. $x^2/25 - y^2/16 = 1$
  $c^2 = 25 + 16 = 41, c = \sqrt{41}$

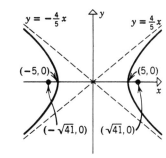

5. $x^2/1 - y^2/8 = 1$
  $c^2 = 1 + 8 = 9, c = 3$

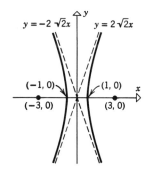

6. $y^2/9 - x^2/3 = 1$
  $c^2 = 9 + 3 = 12, c = 2\sqrt{3}$

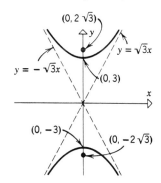

7. $c^2 = 1 + 1 = 2, c = \sqrt{2}$

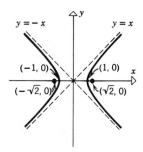

8. $y^2/(1/4) - x^2/(1/4) = 1$
$c^2 = 1/4 + 1/4 = 1/2, c = \sqrt{2}/2$

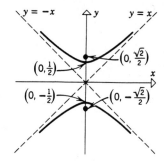

9. $c^2 = 9 + 4 = 13, c = \sqrt{13}$

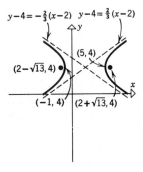

10. $c^2 = 3 + 5 = 8, c = 2\sqrt{2}$

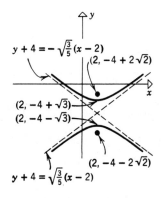

11. $(y+3)^2/36 - (x+2)^2/4 = 1$
$c^2 = 36 + 4 = 40, c = 2\sqrt{10}$

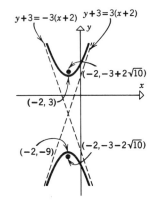

12. $(x+1)^2/1 - (y-3)^2/2 = 1$
$c^2 = 1 + 2 = 3, c = \sqrt{3}$

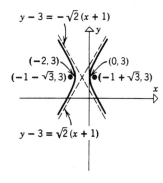

13. $(x+1)^2/4 - (y-1)^2/1 = 1$
$c^2 = 4 + 1 = 5, c = \sqrt{5}$

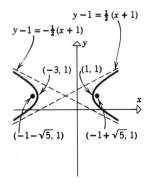

14. $(y-3)^2/4 - (x+2)^2/9 = 1$
$c^2 = 4 + 9 = 13, c = \sqrt{13}$

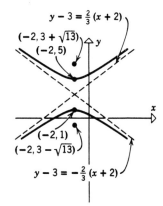

15. $(x-1)^2/4 - (y+3)^2/64 = 1$
$c^2 = 4 + 64 = 68, c = 2\sqrt{17}$

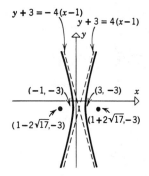

16. $(y+5)^2/9 - (x+2)^2/36 = 1$
$c^2 = 9 + 36 = 45, c = 3\sqrt{5}$

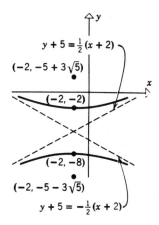

17. $a = 2, c = 3, b^2 = 9 - 4 = 5; x^2/4 - y^2/5 = 1$

18. $a = 3, c = 5, b^2 = 25 - 9 = 16; y^2/9 - x^2/16 = 1$

19. $a = 1, b/a = 2, b = 2; x^2 - y^2/4 = 1$ **20.** $a = 3, a/b = 1, b = 3; y^2/9 - x^2/9 = 1$

21. vertices along x-axis: $b/a = 3/2$ so $a = 8/3; x^2/(64/9) - y^2/16 = 1$
vertices along y-axis: $a/b = 3/2$ so $a = 6; y^2/36 - x^2/16 = 1$

22. $c = 5, a/b = 2$ and $a^2 + b^2 = 25$, solve to get $a^2 = 20, b^2 = 5; y^2/20 - x^2/5 = 1$

23. The form of the equation is $y^2/a^2 - x^2/b^2$ because $(5, 9)$ is above the asymptote $y = x$, $a/b = 1$ and $81/a^2 - 25/b^2 = 1$, solve to get $a^2 = b^2 = 56; y^2/56 - x^2/56 = 1$

24. foci along the x-axis: $b/a = 3/4$ and $a^2 + b^2 = 25$, solve to get $a^2 = 16, b^2 = 9; x^2/16 - y^2/9 = 1$
foci along the y-axis: $a/b = 3/4$ and $a^2 + b^2 = 25$ which results in $y^2/9 - x^2/16 = 1$

25. $a = 2$ so $x^2/4 - y^2/b^2 = 1$, $(4, 2)$ is on the curve so $4 - 4/b^2 = 1$, $b^2 = 4/3; x^2/4 - y^2/(4/3) = 1$

26. $c = 3, b/a = 2$ and $a^2 + b^2 = 9$ so $a^2 = 9/5, b^2 = 36/5; x^2/(9/5) - y^2/(36/5) = 1$

27. the center is at $(2, -3), a = 2, c = 3, b^2 = 9 - 4 = 5; (x-2)^2/4 - (y+3)^2/5 = 1$

28. the center is at $(1, -2), a = 2, c = 10, b^2 = 100 - 4 = 96; (y+2)^2/4 - (x-1)^2/96 = 1$

29. the center is at $(6, 4), a = 4, c = 5, b^2 = 25 - 16 = 9; (x-6)^2/16 - (y-4)^2/9 = 1$

30. The asymptotes intersect at $(1/2, 2)$ which is the center, $(y-2)^2/a^2 - (x-1/2)^2/b^2 = 1$ is the form of the equation because $(0,0)$ is below the asymptote $y = 2x + 1$, $4/a^2 - (1/4)/b^2 = 1$ and $a/b = 2$ which yields $a^2 = 3$, $b^2 = 3/4$; $(y-2)^2/3 - (x-1/2)^2/(3/4) = 1$.

31. From the definition of a hyperbola, $\left| \sqrt{(x-1)^2 + (y-1)^2} - \sqrt{x^2 + y^2} \right| = 1$,

$\sqrt{(x-1)^2 + (y-1)^2} - \sqrt{x^2 + y^2} = \pm 1$, transpose the second radical to the right hand side of the equation and square and simplify to get $\pm 2\sqrt{x^2 + y^2} = -2x - 2y + 1$, square and simplify again to get $8xy - 4x - 4y + 1 = 0$.

32. Use the definition of a hyperbola to get $\sqrt{(x-4)^2 - (y+3)^2} - \sqrt{(x+2)^2 + (y-5)^2} = \pm 6$, follow the procedure used in the solution to Exercise 31 to get $24xy - 7y^2 - 24x - 10y + 161 = 0$.

33. Substitute $x = 2y + 20$ into
$x^2 - 4y^2 = 36$ to get $y = -91/20$,
so $x = 2(-91/20) + 20 = 109/10$.
The curves intersect at $(109/10, -91/20)$.

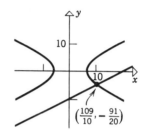

34. Substitute $x^2 = y/2$ into $y^2 - 8x^2 = 5$
to get $y^2 - 4y - 5 = 0$; $y = -1, 5$.
Use $x^2 = y/2$ to find that there is
no solution if $y = -1$ and that $x = \pm\sqrt{5/2}$
if $y = 5$. The curves intersect at
$(\sqrt{5/2}, 5)$ and $(-\sqrt{5/2}, 5)$.

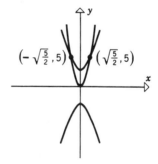

35. Eliminate x to get $y^2 = 1$, $y = \pm 1$.
Use either equation to find that
$x = \pm 2$ if $y = 1$ or if $y = -1$.
The curves intersect at $(2, 1)$,
$(2, -1)$, $(-2, 1)$, and $(-2, -1)$.

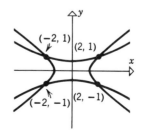

36. Add both equations to get $x^2 = 4$,
$x = \pm 2$. Use either equation to find
that $y = \pm\sqrt{3}$ if $x = 2$ or if $x = -2$.
The curves intersect at $(2, \sqrt{3})$, $(2, -\sqrt{3})$,
$(-2, \sqrt{3})$, $(-2, -\sqrt{3})$.

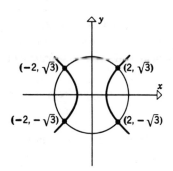

37. Let (x, y) be the coordinates of the point, use the formula for the distance between a point and a line to get $(|mx - y|/\sqrt{m^2 + 1})(|mx + y|/\sqrt{m^2 + 1}) = k^2$, $|m^2 x^2 - y^2|/(m^2 + 1) = k^2$ so $m^2 x^2 - y^2 = \pm k^2(m^2 + 1)$ which are hyperbolas with $y = \pm mx$ as asymptotes.

38. By implicit differentiation, $\dfrac{dy}{dx}\bigg|_{(x_0, y_0)} = \dfrac{b^2}{a^2}\dfrac{x_0}{y_0}$ if $y_0 \neq 0$, the tangent line is

$y - y_0 = \dfrac{b^2}{a^2}\dfrac{x_0}{y_0}(x - x_0)$, $b^2 x_0 x - a^2 y_0 y = b^2 x_0^2 - a^2 y_0^2 = a^2 b^2$, $x_0 x/a^2 - y_0 y/b^2 = 1$. If $y_0 = 0$

then $x_0 = \pm a$ and the tangent lines are $x = \pm a$ which also follow from $x_0 x/a^2 - y_0 y/b^2 = 1$.

39. Let (x_0, y_0) be one of the points then $dy/dx\big|_{(x_0, y_0)} = 4x_0/y_0$, the tangent line is

$y = (4x_0/y_0)x + 4$, but (x_0, y_0) is on both the line and the curve which leads to
$4x_0^2 - y_0^2 + 4y_0 = 0$ and $4x_0^2 - y_0^2 = 36$, solve to get $x_0 = \pm 3\sqrt{13}/2$, $y_0 = -9$.

40. **(a)** $V = \displaystyle\int_a^c \pi y^2 \, dx = \pi\dfrac{b^2}{a^2}\int_a^c (x^2 - a^2)\,dx = \dfrac{\pi}{3}\dfrac{b^2}{a^2}(c^3 - 3a^2 c + 2a^3)$.

(b) Use shells to get $V = 2\pi\displaystyle\int_a^c x(2y)\,dx = 4\pi\dfrac{b}{a}\int_a^c x\sqrt{x^2 - a^2}\,dx$

$= \dfrac{4}{3}\pi\dfrac{b}{a}(c^2 - a^2)^{3/2} = \dfrac{4}{3}\pi\dfrac{b^4}{a}$ because $c^2 = a^2 + b^2$.

41. Let (x_0, y_0) be such a point. The foci are at $(-\sqrt{5}, 0)$ and $(\sqrt{5}, 0)$, the lines are perpendicular if the product of their slopes is -1 so $\dfrac{y_0}{x_0 + \sqrt{5}}\cdot\dfrac{y_0}{x_0 - \sqrt{5}} = -1$, $y_0^2 = 5 - x_0^2$ and $4x_0^2 - y_0^2 = 4$. Solve to get $x_0 = \pm 3/\sqrt{5}$, $y_0 = \pm 4/\sqrt{5}$. The coordinates are $(\pm 3/\sqrt{5}, 4/\sqrt{5})$, $(\pm 3/\sqrt{5}, -4/\sqrt{5})$.

42. $\sqrt{(x - 5)^2 + y^2} = \dfrac{5}{3}\left|x - \dfrac{9}{5}\right|$, $x^2 - 10x + 25 + y^2 = \dfrac{25}{9}\left(x^2 - \dfrac{18}{5}x + \dfrac{81}{25}\right)$, $16x^2 - 9y^2 = 144$ which is a hyperbola.

43.   **(a)** $c > a$ so $c/a > 1$, $e > 1$.

       (b) $c = 5$, $e = c/a = 5/a = 5/3$ so $a = 3$, $b^2 = c^2 - a^2 = 25 - 9 = 16$, $x^2/9 - y^2/16 = 1$.

       (c) c approaches a as e approaches 1 so $b = \sqrt{c^2 - a^2}$ approaches 0; the hyperbola flattens and approaches the focal axis, excluding the segment between the vertices.

       (d) c approaches $+\infty$ as e approaches $+\infty$ so b approaches $+\infty$; the hyperbola approaches the lines that are perpendicular to the focal axis at the vertices.

44.   Let R be the radius of a circle C that is tangent to both C_1 and C_2. The distances between the center of C and the centers of C_1 and C_2 are, respectively, $r_1 + R$ and $r_2 + R$ (see diagram). Their difference is

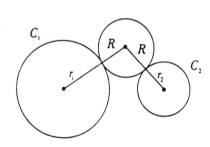

$(r_1 + R) - (r_2 + R) = r_1 - r_2$ which is a positive constant (assuming that $r_1 > r_2$)

so the centers lie on a branch of a hyperbola whose foci are the centers of C_1 and C_2. The center of the hyperbola is the midpoint of the line segment that joins the centers of C_1 and C_2.

45.   Let d_1 and d_2 be the distances of the first and second observers, respectively, from the point where the gun was fired, and let v be the speed of sound. Then $t = $ (time for sound to reach the second observer) $-$ (time for sound to reach the first observer) $= d_2/v - d_1/v$ so $d_2 - d_1 = vt$. For constant v and t the difference of distances, d_2 and d_1 is constant so the gun was fired somewhere on a branch of a hyperbola whose foci are where the observers are.

46.   Transpose the second radical to the right side of the equation, square and simplify to get $\sqrt{(x + c)^2 + y^2} = -\dfrac{c}{a}x - a$. Square again and simplify to get $\dfrac{x^2}{a^2} + \dfrac{y^2}{a^2 - c^2} = 1$ which, by virtue of (1), can be written as $\dfrac{x^2}{a^2} - \dfrac{y^2}{b^2} = 1$.

47.   Similar to the derivation in the text.

48.   Let $P(x_0, y_0)$ be in the third quadrant. Suppose $y_0 \neq 0$ and let $m = $ slope of the tangent line at P, $m_1 = $ slope of the line through P and $(-c, 0)$, $m_2 = $ slope of the line through P and $(c, 0)$ then $m = \dfrac{dy}{dx}\bigg|_{(x_0, y_0)} = (b^2 x_0)/(a^2 y_0)$, $m_1 = y_0/(x_0 + c)$, $m_2 = y_0/(x_0 - c)$. Use $\tan \alpha = (m_1 - m)/(1 + m_1 m)$ and $\tan \beta = (m - m_2)/(1 + m m_2)$ to get $\tan \alpha = \tan \beta = -b^2/(c y_0)$ so $\alpha = \beta$. If $y_0 = 0$ the result follows trivially and by symmetry the result holds for P in the other three quadrants as well.

49. **(a)** Use $x^2/a^2 + y^2/b^2 = 1$ and $x^2/A^2 - y^2/B^2$ as the equations of the ellipse and hyperbola. If (x_0, y_0) is a point of intersection then $b^2 x_0^2 + a^2 y_0^2 = a^2 b^2$ and $B^2 x_0^2 - A^2 y_0^2 = A^2 B^2$, solve to get

$$x_0^2 = \frac{a^2 A^2 (b^2 + B^2)}{a^2 B^2 + A^2 b^2} \qquad \text{and} \qquad y_0^2 = \frac{b^2 B^2 (a^2 - A^2)}{a^2 B^2 + A^2 b^2} \tag{1}$$

From Exercises 34 (Section 12.3) and 38 the slopes of the tangent lines to the ellipse and hyperbola at (x_0, y_0) are, respectively, $-\dfrac{b^2}{a^2}\dfrac{x_0}{y_0}$ and $\dfrac{B^2}{A^2}\dfrac{x_0}{y_0}$ so their product is $-\dfrac{b^2 B^2 x_0^2}{a^2 A^2 y_0^2}$ which, using (1), gives $-\dfrac{b^2 + B^2}{a^2 - A^2}$. The ellipse and hyperbola have the same foci so $c^2 = a^2 - b^2 = A^2 + B^2$, $a^2 - A^2 = b^2 + B^2$, $(b^2 + B^2)/(a^2 - A^2) = 1$, thus the product of the slopes of the tangent lines is -1 and the lines are perpendicular.

(b) From the figure,
$$2(\alpha + \beta) = 180° \text{ so } \alpha + \beta = 90°.$$

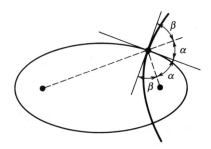

EXERCISE SET 12.5

1. **(a)** $\sin\theta = \sqrt{3}/2$, $\cos\theta = 1/2$

$x' = (-2)(1/2) + (6)(\sqrt{3}/2) = -1 + 3\sqrt{3}$, $y' = -(-2)(\sqrt{3}/2) + 6(1/2) = 3 + \sqrt{3}$

(b) $x = \dfrac{1}{2}x' - \dfrac{\sqrt{3}}{2}y' = \dfrac{1}{2}(x' - \sqrt{3}y')$, $y = \dfrac{\sqrt{3}}{2}x' + \dfrac{1}{2}y' = \dfrac{1}{2}(\sqrt{3}x' + y')$

$$\sqrt{3}\left[\frac{1}{2}(x' - \sqrt{3}y')\right]\left[\frac{1}{2}(\sqrt{3}x' + y')\right] + \left[\frac{1}{2}(\sqrt{3}x' + y')\right]^2 = 6$$

$$\frac{\sqrt{3}}{4}(\sqrt{3}x'^2 - 2x'y' - \sqrt{3}y'^2) + \frac{1}{4}(3x'^2 + 2\sqrt{3}x'y' + y'^2) = 6$$

$$\frac{3}{2}x'^2 - \frac{1}{2}y'^2 = 6, \quad \frac{x'^2}{4} - \frac{y'^2}{12} = 1$$

(c)

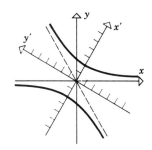

2. (a) $\sin\theta = 1/2$, $\cos\theta = \sqrt{3}/2$

$x' = (1)(\sqrt{3}/2) + (-\sqrt{3})(1/2) = 0$, $y' = -(1)(1/2) + (-\sqrt{3})(\sqrt{3}/2) = -2$

(b) $x = \dfrac{\sqrt{3}}{2}x' - \dfrac{1}{2}y' = \dfrac{1}{2}(\sqrt{3}x' - y')$, $y = \dfrac{1}{2}x' + \dfrac{\sqrt{3}}{2}y' = \dfrac{1}{2}(x' + \sqrt{3}y')$

$2\left[\dfrac{1}{2}(\sqrt{3}x' - y')\right]^2 + 2\sqrt{3}\left[\dfrac{1}{2}(\sqrt{3}x' - y')\right]\left[\dfrac{1}{2}(x' + \sqrt{3}y')\right] = 3$

$\dfrac{1}{2}(3x'^2 - 2\sqrt{3}x'y' + y'^2) + \dfrac{\sqrt{3}}{2}(\sqrt{3}x'^2 + 2x'y' - \sqrt{3}y'^2) = 3$

$3x'^2 - y'^2 = 3$, $x'^2/1 - y'^2/3 = 1$

(c)

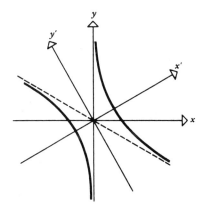

3. $\cot 2\theta = (0 - 0)/1 = 0$, $2\theta = 90°$, $\theta = 45°$

$x = (\sqrt{2}/2)(x' - y')$, $y = (\sqrt{2}/2)(x' + y')$

$y'^2/18 - x'^2/18 = 1$, hyperbola

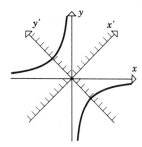

4. $\cot 2\theta = (1-1)/(-1) = 0$, $\theta = 45°$

    $x = (\sqrt{2}/2)(x' - y')$, $y = (\sqrt{2}/2)(x' + y')$

    $x'^2/4 + y'^2/(4/3) = 1$, ellipse

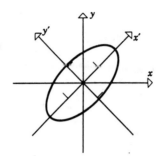

5. $\cot 2\theta = [1 - (-2)]/4 = 3/4$

    $\cos 2\theta = 3/5$

    $\sin \theta = \sqrt{(1 - 3/5)/2} = 1/\sqrt{5}$

    $\cos \theta = \sqrt{(1 + 3/5)/2} = 2/\sqrt{5}$

    $x = (1/\sqrt{5})(2x' - y')$

    $y = (1/\sqrt{5})(x' + 2y')$

    $x'^2/3 - y'^2/2 = 1$, hyperbola

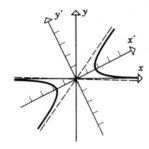

6. $\cot 2\theta = (31 - 21)/(10\sqrt{3}) = 1/\sqrt{3}$,

    $2\theta = 60°$, $\theta = 30°$

    $x = (1/2)(\sqrt{3}x' - y')$,

    $y = (1/2)(x' + \sqrt{3}y')$

    $x'^2/4 + y'^2/9 = 1$, ellipse

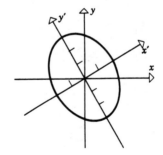

7. $\cot 2\theta = (1 - 3)/(2\sqrt{3}) = -1/\sqrt{3}$,

    $2\theta = 120°$, $\theta = 60°$

    $x = (1/2)(x' - \sqrt{3}y')$

    $y = (1/2)(\sqrt{3}x' + y')$

    $y' = x'^2$, parabola

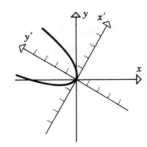

8. $\cot 2\theta = (34 - 41)/(-24) = 7/24$

$\cos 2\theta = 7/25$

$\sin\theta = \sqrt{(1 - 7/25)/2} = 3/5$

$\cos\theta = \sqrt{(1 + 7/25)/2} = 4/5$

$x = (1/5)(4x' - 3y')$,

$y = (1/5)(3x' + 4y')$

$x'^2 + y'^2/(1/2) = 1$, ellipse

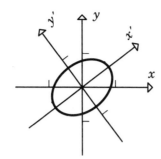

9. $\cot 2\theta = (9 - 16)/(-24) = 7/24$

$\cos 2\theta = 7/25$,

$\sin\theta = 3/5$, $\cos\theta = 4/5$

$x = (1/5)(4x' - 3y')$,

$y = (1/5)(3x' + 4y')$

$y'^2 = 4(x' - 1)$, parabola

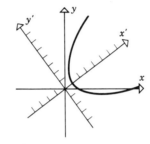

10. $\cot 2\theta = (5 - 5)/(-6) = 0$,

$\theta = 45°$

$x = (\sqrt{2}/2)(x' - y')$,

$y = (\sqrt{2}/2)(x' + y')$,

$x'^2/8 + (y' + 1)^2/2 = 1$, ellipse

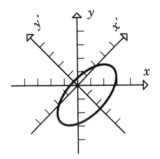

11. $\cot 2\theta = (52 - 73)/(-72) = 7/24$

$\cos 2\theta = 7/25$, $\sin\theta = 3/5$,

$\cos\theta = 4/5$

$x = (1/5)(4x' - 3y')$,

$y = (1/5)(3x' + 4y')$

$(x' + 1)^2/4 + y'^2 = 1$, ellipse

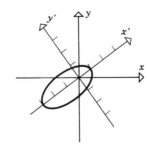

12. $\cot 2\theta = [6 - (-1)]/24 = 7/24$
       $\cos 2\theta = 7/25, \qquad \sin\theta = 3/5,$
         $\cos\theta = 4/5$
            $x = (1/5)(4x' - 3y'),$
            $y = (1/5)(3x' + 4y')$
      $(y' - 7/5)^2/3 - (x' + 1/5)^2/2 = 1,$
      hyperbola

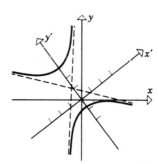

13.   Let $x = x'\cos\theta - y'\sin\theta$, $y = x'\sin\theta + y'\cos\theta$ then $x^2 + y^2 = r^2$ becomes
$(\sin^2\theta + \cos^2\theta)x'^2 + (\sin^2\theta + \cos^2\theta)y'^2 = r^2$, $x'^2 + y'^2 = r^2$. Under a rotation transformation the center of the circle stays at the origin of both coordinate systems.

14.   Multiply the first equation through by $\cos\theta$ and the second by $\sin\theta$ and add to get
$x\cos\theta + y\sin\theta = (\cos^2\theta + \sin^2\theta)x' = x'$. Multiply the first by $-\sin\theta$ and the second by $\cos\theta$ and add to get y'.

15. $x' = (\sqrt{2}/2)(x + y)$, $y' = (\sqrt{2}/2)(-x + y)$ which when substituted into $3x'^2 + y'^2 = 6$ yields
$x^2 + xy + y^2 = 3$.

16.   From (5), $x = \dfrac{1}{2}(\sqrt{3}x' - y')$ and $y = \dfrac{1}{2}(x' + \sqrt{3}y')$ so $y = x^2$ becomes

     $\dfrac{1}{2}(x' + \sqrt{3}y') = \dfrac{1}{4}(\sqrt{3}x' - y')^2$; simplify to get $3x'^2 - 2\sqrt{3}x'y' + y'^2 - 2x' - 2\sqrt{3}y' = 0$.

17. $\sqrt{x} + \sqrt{y} = 1$, $\sqrt{x} = 1 - \sqrt{y}$, $x = 1 - 2\sqrt{y} + y$, $2\sqrt{y} = 1 - x + y$, $4y = 1 + x^2 + y^2 - 2x + 2y - 2xy$,
$x^2 - 2xy + y^2 - 2x - 2y + 1 = 0$. $\cot 2\theta = \dfrac{1-1}{2} = 0$, $2\theta = \pi/2$, $\theta = \pi/4$. Let $x = x'/\sqrt{2} - y'/\sqrt{2}$,
$y = x'/\sqrt{2} + y'/\sqrt{2}$ to get $2y'^2 - 2\sqrt{2}x' + 1 = 0$, which is a parabola. From $\sqrt{x} + \sqrt{y} = 1$ we
see that $0 \le x \le 1$ and $0 \le y \le 1$, so the graph is just a portion of a parabola.

18.   Let $x = x'\cos\theta - y'\sin\theta$ and $y = x'\sin\theta + y'\cos\theta$ in (7), expand and add all the coefficients
of the terms that contain $x'y'$ to get B'.

19.   Use (9) to express $B' - 4A'C'$ in terms of A, B, C, and θ, then simplify.

20.   Use (9) to express $A' + C'$ in terms of A, B, C, and θ and then simplify.

21. $\cot 2\theta = (A - C)/B = 0$ if $A = C$ so $2\theta = 90°$, $\theta = 45°$.

22. If $F = 0$ then $x^2 + Bxy = 0$, $x(x + By) = 0$ so $x = 0$ or $x - By = 0$ which are lines that intersect at $(0,0)$. Suppose $F \neq 0$, rotate through an angle θ where $\cot 2\theta = 1/B$ eliminating the cross product term to get $A'x'^2 + C'y'^2 + F' = 0$. From (9),

$A' = \cos^2 \theta + B \cos \theta \sin \theta = \cos \theta (\cos \theta + B \sin \theta)$ and

$C' = \sin^2 \theta - B \sin \theta \cos \theta = \sin \theta (\sin \theta - B \cos \theta)$ so

$A'C' = \sin \theta \cos \theta [\sin \theta \cos \theta - B(\cos^2 \theta - \sin^2 \theta) - B^2 \sin \theta \cos \theta]$

$$= \frac{1}{2} \sin 2\theta \left[\frac{1}{2} \sin 2\theta - B \cos 2\theta - \frac{1}{2} B^2 \sin 2\theta \right] = \frac{1}{4} \sin^2 2\theta [1 - 2B \cot 2\theta - B^2]$$

$$= \frac{1}{4} \sin^2 2\theta [1 - 2B(1/B) - B^2] = -\frac{1}{4} \sin^2 2\theta (1 + B^2) < 0$$

thus A' and C' have unlike signs so the graph is a hyperbola.

23. $B^2 - 4AC = (-1)^2 - 4(1)(1) = -3 < 0$; ellipse, point, or no graph

24. $B^2 - 4AC = (4)^2 - 4(1)(-2) = 24 > 0$; hyperbola or pair of intersecting lines

25. $B^2 - 4AC = (2\sqrt{3})^2 - 4(1)(3) = 0$; parabola, line, pair of parallel lines, or no graph

26. $B^2 - 4AC = (24)^2 - 4(6)(-1) = 600 > 0$; hyperbola or pair of intersecting lines

27. $B^2 - 4AC = (-24)^2 - 4(34)(41) = -5000 < 0$; ellipse, point, or no graph

28. **(a)** $(x - y)(x + y) = 0$
$y = x$ or $y = -x$
(two intersecting lines)

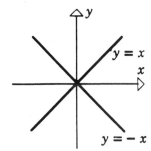

(b) $x^2 + 3y^2 = -7$ which has no real solutions, no graph

(c) $8x^2 + 7y^2 = 0$

$x = 0$ and $y = 0$,

(a point)

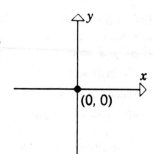

(d) $(x - y)^2 = 0$,

$y = x$

(a line)

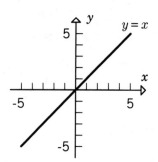

(e) $(3x + 2y)^2 = 36$,

$3x + 2y = 6$ or $3x + 2y = -6$

(a pair of parallel lines)

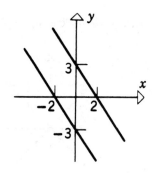

(f) $(x - 1)^2 + (y - 2)^2 = 0$,

the point $(1, 2)$

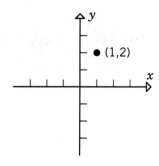

29. Part (b): from (18), $A'C' < 0$ so A' and C' have opposite signs. By multiplying (19) through by -1, if necessary, assume that $A' < 0$ and $C' > 0$ so (19) can be written as

$(x' - h)^2/C' - (y' - k)^2/|A'| = K$. If $K \neq 0$ then the graph is a hyperbola (divide both sides by K), if $K = 0$ then we get the pair of intersecting lines $(x' - h)/\sqrt{C'} = \pm(y' - k)/\sqrt{|A'|}$.

Part (c): from (18), $A'C' = 0$ so either $A' = 0$ or $C' = 0$ but not both (this would imply that $A = B = C = 0$ which results in (14) being linear). Suppose $A' \neq 0$ and $C' = 0$ then complete the square to get $(x' - h)^2 = -\dfrac{E'}{A'}y' + K$. If $E' \neq 0$ the graph is a parabola, if $E' = 0$ and $K = 0$ the graph is the line $x' = h$, if $E' = 0$ and $K > 0$ the graph is the pair of parallel lines $x' = h \pm \sqrt{K}$, if $E' = 0$ and $K < 0$ there is no graph.

SUPPLEMENTARY EXERCISES CHAPTER 12

1. parabola, $(y - 3)^2 = -12(x + 2)$, $p = 3$; vertex $(-2, 3)$, focus $(-5, 3)$, directrix $x = 1$.

2. hyperbola, $y^2/(1/4) - x^2/1 = 1$, $a = 1/2$, $b = 1$, $c = \sqrt{5}/2$; center $(0, 0)$, foci $(0, \pm\sqrt{5}/2)$, vertices $(0, \pm 1/2)$, asymptotes $y = \pm x/2$.

3. ellipse, $(x + 2)^2/4 + (y - 1)^2/9$, $a = 3$, $b = 2$, $c = \sqrt{5}$; center $(-2, 1)$, foci $(-2, 1 \pm \sqrt{5})$, major axis 6, minor axis 4.

4. ellipse, $(x-3)^2/1 + (y-1)^2/(1/4) = 1$, $a = 1$, $b = 1/2$, $c = \sqrt{3}/2$; center $(3, 1)$, foci $(3 \pm \sqrt{3}/2, 1)$, major axis 2, minor axis 1.

5. hyperbola, $(x - 2)^2/9 - (y - 1)^2/1 = 1$, $a = 3$, $b = 1$, $c = \sqrt{10}$, center $(2, 1)$, foci $(2 \pm \sqrt{10}, 1)$, vertices $(-1, 1)$ and $(5, 1)$, asymptotes $y - 1 = \pm(x - 2)/3$.

6. parabola, $(x + 1)^2 = 4(y + 2)$, $p = 1$; vertex $(-1, -2)$, focus $(-1, -1)$, directrix $y = -3$.

7. parabola, $(y - 1)^2 = (-3/2)(x - 3)$, $p = 3/8$; vertex $(3, 1)$, focus $(21/8, 1)$, directrix $x = 27/8$.

8. hyperbola, $(y - 2)^2/4 - x^2/1 = 1$, $a = 2$, $b = 1$, $c = \sqrt{5}$; center $(0, 2)$, foci $(0, 2 \pm \sqrt{5})$, vertices $(0, 0)$ and $(0, 4)$, asymptotes $y - 2 = \pm 2x$.

9. $p = 4$; $(y - 3)^2 = 16(x - 1)$.

10. center $(2, 3)$, $c = 4$, $a = 12/2 = 6$, $b^2 = 20$; $(x - 2)^2/20 + (y - 3)^2/36 = 1$.

11. center $(0, 0)$, $c = 5$, $a = 6/2 = 3$, $b^2 = 16$, $y^2/9 - x^2/16 = 1$.

12. $(y - 1)^2 = a(x - 2)$, $(-2)^2 = a(1)$, $a = 4$; $(y - 1)^2 = 4(x - 2)$.

13. center $(0,0)$, $c = 3$, $a = 10/2 = 5$, $b^2 = 16$; $x^2/25 + y^2/16 = 1$.

14. center $(0,0)$, $a = 2$, $a/b = 3$ oo $b - 2/3$; $y^2/4 - x^2/(4/9) = 1$.

15. The curve is a parabola with focus at $(3,4)$ and directrix $y = 2$ so the vertex is at $(3,3)$ and $p = 1$; $(x - 3)^2 = 4(y - 3)$.

16. center $(-1,2)$, $a = 2$, asymptotes $y = \pm(b/a)x$ where $(b/a)(-b/a) = -1$ because the asymptotes are perpendicular so $-b^2/a^2 = -1$, $b^2 = a^2 = 4$; $(x + 1)^2/4 - (y - 2)^2/4 = 1$.

17.

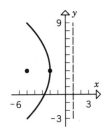

18.

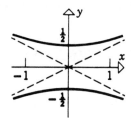

19.

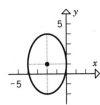

20.

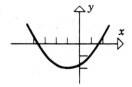

21. $\cot 2\theta = (3 - 3)/(-2) = 0$, $\theta = 45°$; use $x = (\sqrt{2}/2)(x' - y')$, $y = (\sqrt{2}/2)(x' + y')$ to get $x'^2/2 + y'^2/1 = 1$; ellipse.

22. $\cot 2\theta = (7 - 1)/(-8) = -3/4$ so $\cos 2\theta = -3/5$, $\sin \theta = \sqrt{(1 + 3/5)/2} = 2/\sqrt{5}$, $\cos \theta = \sqrt{(1 - 3/5)/2} = 1/\sqrt{5}$, $\theta = \tan^{-1} 2$; use $x = (1/\sqrt{5})(x' - 2y')$, $y = (1/\sqrt{5})(2x' + y')$ to get $y'^2/1 - x'^2/9 = 1$; hyperbola.

23. $\cot 2\theta = (11 - 1)/(10\sqrt{3}) = 1/\sqrt{3}$, $\theta = 30°$; use $x = (1/2)(\sqrt{3}x' - y')$, $y = (1/2)(x' + \sqrt{3}y')$ to get $x'^2/(1/4) - y'^2/1 = 1$; hyperbola.

24. $\cot 2\theta = (1 - 4)/4 = -3/4$, $\sin \theta = 2/\sqrt{5}$, $\cos \theta = 1/\sqrt{5}$, $\theta = \tan^{-1} 2$; use $x = (1/\sqrt{5})(x' - 2y')$, $y = (1/\sqrt{5})(2x' + y')$ to get $y' = -x'^2$; parabola.

25. $\cot 2\theta = (16 - 9)/(-24) = -7/24$, $\cos 2\theta = -7/25$, $\sin \theta = \sqrt{(1 + 7/25)/2} = 4/5$,

$\cos \theta = \sqrt{(1 - 7/25)/2} = 3/5$, $\theta = \tan^{-1}(4/3)$; use $x = (1/5)(3x' - 4y')$, $y = (1/5)(4x' + 3y')$

to get $y'^2 = 4(x' - 1)$; parabola.

26. $\cot 2\theta = (73 - 52)/(-72) = -7/24$, $\sin \theta = 4/5$, $\cos \theta = 3/5$, $\theta = \tan^{-1}(4/3)$; use

$x = (1/5)(3x' - 4y')$, $y = (1/5)(4x' + 3y')$ to get $x'^2/4 + y'^2/1 = 1$; ellipse

27.

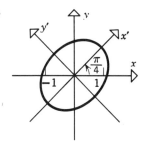

28.

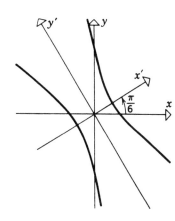

29.

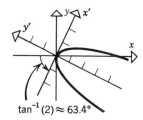

30. **(a)** $\cot 2\theta = 0$, $\theta = 45°$

     (b) $\theta = \tan^{-1}(3/4)$, $\sin \theta = 3/5$, $\cos \theta = 4/5$; use $x = (1/5)(4x' - 3y')$, $y = (1/5)(3x' + 4y')$ to

        get $\dfrac{12}{25}x'^2 + \dfrac{7}{25}x'y' - \dfrac{12}{25}y'^2 + \dfrac{1}{5}x' - \dfrac{7}{5}y' = 1$; $A = C = 0$, $B = 1$, $A' = 12/25$, $B' = 7/25$,

        $C' = -12/25$ so $A' + C' = 0 = A + C$, $B'^2 - 4A'C' = 1 = B^2 - 4AC$.

31. **(a)** $PF = \sqrt{x^2 + y^2}$, $PD = |x - k|$, so $PF = ePD$ yields

$$\sqrt{x^2 + y^2} = e|x - k|$$
$$x^2 + y^2 = e^2(x^2 - 2kx + k^2)$$
$$(1 - e^2)x^2 + 2e^2 kx + y^2 = e^2 k^2$$

$$(1-e^2)\left[x^2+\frac{2e^2k}{1-e^2}x+\frac{e^4k^2}{(1-e^2)^2}\right]+y^2=e^2k^2+\frac{e^4k^2}{1-e^2}=\frac{e^2k^2}{1-e^2}$$

$$(1-e^2)\left(x+\frac{e^2k}{1-e^2}\right)^2+y^2=\frac{e^2k}{1-e^2}$$

$$\frac{(x+e^2k/(1-e^2))^2}{e^2k^2/(1-e^2)^2}+\frac{y^2}{e^2k^2/(1-e^2)}=1; \qquad (1)$$

let $c=\dfrac{e^2k}{1-e^2}$, $a^2=\dfrac{e^2k^2}{(1-e^2)^2}$, and $b^2=\dfrac{e^2k^2}{1-e^2}$ to get $\dfrac{(x+c)^2}{a^2}+\dfrac{y^2}{b^2}=1.$

(b) If $e>1$, then $e^2-1>0$, rewrite (1) as $\dfrac{(x-e^2k/(e^2-1))^2}{e^2k^2/(e^2-1)^2}-\dfrac{y^2}{e^2k^2/(e^2-1)}=1$, then

with $c=\dfrac{e^2k}{e^2-1}$, $a^2=\dfrac{e^2k^2}{(e^2-1)^2}$, and $b^2=\dfrac{e^2k^2}{e^2-1}$ we get $\dfrac{(x-c)^2}{a^2}-\dfrac{y^2}{b^2}=1.$

32. **(a)** $a^2-b^2=\dfrac{e^2k^2}{(1-e^2)^2}-\dfrac{e^2k^2}{1-e^2}=\dfrac{e^2k^2[1-(1-e^2)]}{(1-e^2)^2}=\dfrac{e^4k^2}{(1-e^2)^2}=c^2$ so c is the distance

between the center of the ellipse and the foci; the center of the ellipse is $(-c,0)$ thus one focus is c units to the right of the center, which is the point F.

(b) $a^2+b^2=\dfrac{e^2k^2}{(e^2-1)^2}+\dfrac{e^2k^2}{e^2-1}=\dfrac{e^2k^2[1+(e^2-1)]}{(e^2-1)^2}=\dfrac{e^4k^2}{(e^2-1)^2}=c^2$ so c is the distance

between the center of the hyperbola and the foci; the center of the hyperbola is $(c,0)$, thus one focus is c units to the left of the center, which is the point F.

(c) In either case, $\dfrac{c^2}{a^2}=\dfrac{e^4k^2/(1-e^2)^2}{e^2k^2/(1-e^2)^2}=e^2$ so $\dfrac{c}{a}=e.$

CHAPTER 13
Polar Coordinates And Parametric Equations

EXERCISE SET 13.1

1.

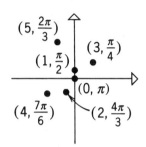

2.

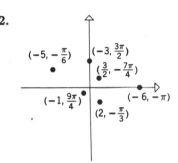

3.   **(a)** $(3\sqrt{3}, 3)$ **(b)** $(-7/2, 7\sqrt{3}/2)$ **(c)** $(4\sqrt{2}, 4\sqrt{2})$
      (d) $(5, 0)$ **(e)** $(-7\sqrt{3}/2, 7/2)$ **(f)** $(0, 0)$

4.   **(a)** $(-4\sqrt{2}, -4\sqrt{2})$ **(b)** $(7\sqrt{2}/2, -7\sqrt{2}/2)$ **(c)** $(3\sqrt{3}, 3)$
      (d) $(0, 0)$ **(e)** $(0, -2)$ **(f)** $(-5, 0)$

5.   **(a)** $(5, \pi)$ **(b)** $(4, 11\pi/6)$ **(c)** $(2, 3\pi/2)$
      (d) $(8\sqrt{2}, 5\pi/4)$ **(e)** $(6, 2\pi/3)$ **(f)** $(\sqrt{2}, \pi/4)$

6.   **(a)** $(5, \pi)$ **(b)** $(4, -\pi/6)$ **(c)** $(2, -\pi/2)$
      (d) $(8\sqrt{2}, -3\pi/4)$ **(e)** $(6, 2\pi/3)$ **(f)** $(\sqrt{2}, \pi/4)$

7.   **(a)** $(-5, 0)$ **(b)** $(-4, 5\pi/6)$ **(c)** $(-2, \pi/2)$
      (d) $(-8\sqrt{2}, \pi/4)$ **(e)** $(-6, 5\pi/3)$ **(f)** $(-\sqrt{2}, 5\pi/4)$

8.   **(a)** $(2, 5\pi/6)$ **(b)** $(-2, 11\pi/6)$ **(c)** $(2, -7\pi/6)$ **(d)** $(-2, -\pi/6)$

9. $x^2 + y^2 = 4$; circle   **10.** $x^2 + y^2 = 9$; circle

11. $y = 4$; horizontal line   **12.** $r \cos\theta = 5$, $x = 5$; vertical line

13. $r^2 = 3r\cos\theta$, $x^2 + y^2 = 3x$, $(x - 3/2)^2 + y^2 = 9/4$; circle

14. $r^2 = 2r \sin \theta$, $x^2 + y^2 = 2y$, $x^2 + (y-1)^2 = 1$; circle

15. $r^2(2 \sin \theta \cos \theta) = 8$, $2(r \sin \theta)(r \cos \theta) = 8$, $xy = 4$; hyperbola

16. $r^2(\cos^2 \theta - \sin^2 \theta) = 9$, $(r \cos \theta)^2 - (r \sin \theta)^2 = 9$; $x^2 - y^2 = 9$; hyperbola

17. $r + r \sin \theta = 2$, $r = 2 - y$, $r^2 = (2-y)^2$, $x^2 + y^2 = 4 - 4y + y^2$, $x^2 + 4y = 4$; parabola

18. $2r - r \cos \theta = 6$, $2r = x + 6$, $4r^2 = (x+6)^2$, $4(x^2 + y^2) = x^2 + 12x + 36$, $3x^2 + 4y^2 - 12x = 36$; ellipse

19. $3r \cos \theta + 2r \sin \theta = 6$, $3x + 2y = 6$; line

20. $r = \dfrac{1}{\cos \theta} \dfrac{\sin \theta}{\cos \theta}$, $r \cos^2 \theta = \sin \theta$, $r^2 \cos^2 \theta = r \sin \theta$, $x^2 = y$; parabola

21. $r \cos \theta = 7$ 22. $r \sin \theta = -3$ 23. $r = 3$ 24. $r = \sqrt{5}$

25. $r^2 - 6r \sin \theta = 0$, $r = 6 \sin \theta$ 26. $r^2 + 4r \cos \theta = 0$, $r = -4 \cos \theta$

27. $r^2 \cos^2 \theta = 9r \sin \theta$, $r = 9 \dfrac{\sin \theta}{\cos^2 \theta} = 9 \tan \theta \sec \theta$

28. $r^2 \cos^2 \theta - r^2 \sin^2 \theta = 4$, $r^2(\cos^2 \theta - \sin^2 \theta) = 4$, $r^2 \cos 2\theta = 4$

29. $4(r \cos \theta)(r \sin \theta) = 9$, $4r^2 \sin \theta \cos \theta = 9$, $r^2 \sin 2\theta = 9/2$

30. $r^4 = 16(r^2 \cos^2 \theta - r^2 \sin^2 \theta)$, $r^2 = 16 \cos 2\theta$

31. $r^4 = 2r^2 \sin \theta \cos \theta$, $r^2 = \sin 2\theta$

32. $r^4 \cos^2 \theta = r^2 \sin^2 \theta$, $r^2 = \tan^2 \theta$, $r = \tan \theta$

33. $(r-1)(r-2) = 0$, $r = 1$ or $r = 2$; the graph consists of the concentric circles $r = 1$ and $r = 2$.

34.

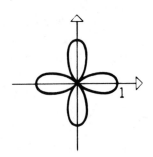

35.

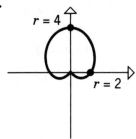

36.

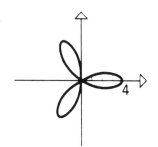

37.

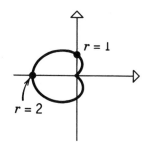

38. Let (x_1, y_1) and (x_2, y_2) be the corresponding rectangular coordinates of the points (r_1, θ_1) and (r_2, θ_2) then

$$d = \sqrt{(x_2 - x_1)^2 + (y_2 - y_1)^2} = \sqrt{(r_2 \cos \theta_2 - r_1 \cos \theta_1)^2 + (r_2 \sin \theta_2 - r_1 \sin \theta_1)^2}$$

$$= \sqrt{r_1^2 + r_2^2 - 2r_1 r_2(\cos \theta_1 \cos \theta_2 + \sin \theta_1 \sin \theta_2)} = \sqrt{r_1^2 + r_2^2 - 2r_1 r_2 \cos(\theta_1 - \theta_2)}.$$

39. $r^2 = ar \sin \theta + br \cos \theta$, $x^2 + y^2 = ay + bx$ which is a circle.

40. $A = \dfrac{1}{2} h r_1$, but

$h = r_2 \sin(\theta_2 - \theta_1)$ so

$A = \dfrac{1}{2} r_1 r_2 \sin(\theta_2 - \theta_1).$

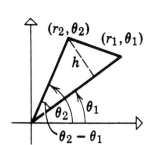

41. (r, θ) and $(-r, \theta + \pi)$ are polar coordinates of the same point so if $r < 0$ then $-r > 0$ and $x = (-r) \cos(\theta + \pi) = (-r)(-\cos \theta) = r \cos \theta$, $y = (-r) \sin(\theta + \pi) = (-r)(-\sin \theta) = r \sin \theta$.

42. The coordinates (r_1, θ_1) and (r_2, θ_2) satisfy the equation so they are on the graph. Use the trigonometric identity $\sin(\alpha - \beta) = \sin \alpha \cos \beta - \cos \alpha \sin \beta$ in the first two terms of the equation to get $r \cos \theta (r_2 \sin \theta_2 - r_1 \sin \theta_1) + r \sin \theta (r_1 \cos \theta_1 - r_2 \cos \theta_2) + r_1 r_2 \sin(\theta_1 - \theta_2) = 0$, $(r_2 \sin \theta_2 - r_1 \sin \theta_1)x + (r_1 \cos \theta_1 - r_2 \cos \theta_2)y + r_1 r_2 \sin(\theta_1 - \theta_2) = 0$ which is the equation of a line in rectangular coordinates.

EXERCISE SET 13.2

1.

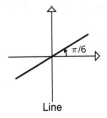

Line

2.

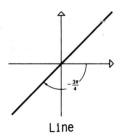

Line

3.

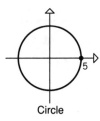

Circle

4.

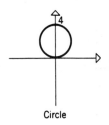

Circle

5.

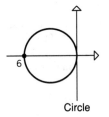

Circle

6.

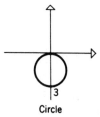

Circle

7.

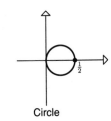

Circle

8.

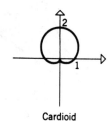

Cardioid

9.

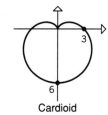

Cardioid

10.

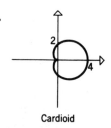

Cardioid

11.

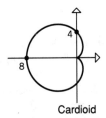

Cardioid

12.

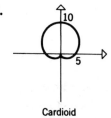

Cardioid

13.

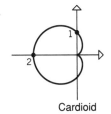

Cardioid

14.

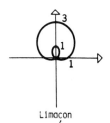

Limaçon

15.

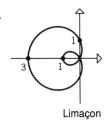

Limaçon

16.

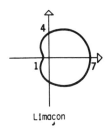

Limaçon

17.

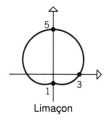

Limaçon

18.

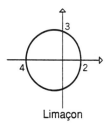

Limaçon

19.

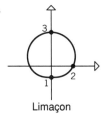

Limaçon

20.

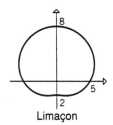

Limaçon

21.

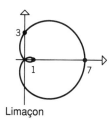

Limaçon

22.

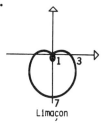

Limaçon

23.

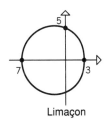

Limaçon

24.

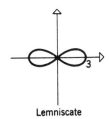

Lemniscate

25.

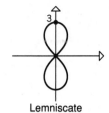

Lemniscate

26.

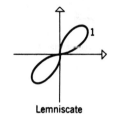

Lemniscate

27.

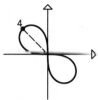

Lemniscate

28.

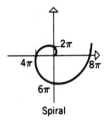

Spiral

29.

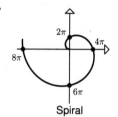

Spiral

30.

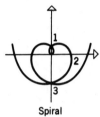

Spiral

31.

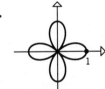

Four-petal rose

32.

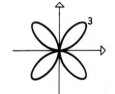

Four-petal rose

33.

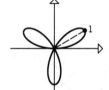

Three-petal rose

34.

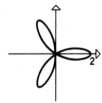

Three-petal rose

35.

Eight-petal rose

36.

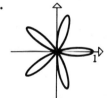

Five-petal rose

37. $r^2 = 4\cos\theta + 4r\sin\theta$,
$x^2 + y^2 = 4x + 4y$,
$(x-2)^2 + (y-2)^2 = 8$

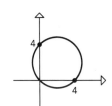

38.

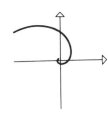

39.

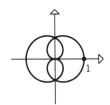

40.

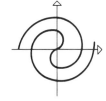

41.   Note that $r \to \pm\infty$ as θ approches
odd multiples of $\pi/2$;
$x = r\cos\theta = 4\tan\theta\cos\theta = 4\sin\theta$,
$y = r\sin\theta = 4\tan\theta\sin\theta$
so $x \to \pm 4$ and $y \to \pm\infty$ as
θ approaches odd multiples of $\pi/2$.

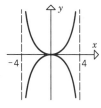

42.   Note that $r \to \pm\infty$ as θ approaches
odd multiples of $\pi/2$;
$x = r\cos\theta = (2 + 2\sec\theta)\cos\theta = 2\cos\theta + 2$,
$y = r\sin\theta = (2 + 2\sec\theta)\sin\theta = 2\sin\theta + 2\tan\theta$
so $x \to 2$ and $y \to \pm\infty$ as
θ approaches odd multiples of $\pi/2$.

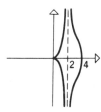

43. Note that $r \to \pm\infty$ as θ approaches
     odd multiples of $\pi/2$;
     $x = r\cos\theta = (2\sin\theta\tan\theta)\cos\theta = 2\sin^2\theta$,
     $y = r\sin\theta = (2\sin\theta\tan\theta)\sin\theta = 2\sin^2\theta\tan\theta$
     so $x \to 2$ and $y \to \pm\infty$ as
     θ approaches odd multiples of $\pi/2$.

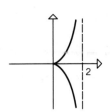

44. $\displaystyle\lim_{\theta\to0+} y = \lim_{\theta\to0+}\frac{\sin\theta}{\theta} = 1$

45. $\displaystyle\lim_{\theta\to0+} y = \lim_{\theta\to0+}\frac{\sin\theta}{\sqrt{\theta}} = 0$

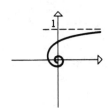

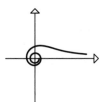

46. $\displaystyle\lim_{\theta\to0+} y = \lim_{\theta\to0+}\frac{\sin\theta}{\theta^2} = +\infty$

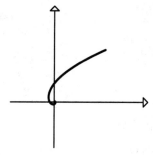

47. $y = r\sin\theta = (1+\cos\theta)\sin\theta = \sin\theta + \sin\theta\cos\theta$,
     $dy/d\theta = \cos\theta - \sin^2\theta + \cos^2\theta = 2\cos^2\theta + \cos\theta - 1 = (2\cos\theta - 1)(\cos\theta + 1)$
     $dy/d\theta = 0$ if $\cos\theta = 1/2$ or if $\cos\theta = -1$; $\theta = \pi/3$ or π.
     If $\theta = 0, \pi/3, \pi$, then $y = 0, 3\sqrt{3}/4, 0$ so the maximum value of y is $3\sqrt{3}/4$.

48. (a) $y = r\sin\theta = \dfrac{\sin\theta}{\sqrt{\theta}}, \dfrac{dy}{d\theta} = \dfrac{2\theta\cos\theta - \sin\theta}{2\theta^{3/2}}$; $\dfrac{dy}{d\theta} = 0$ if $2\theta\cos\theta - \sin\theta = 0$, $\tan\theta = 2\theta$.

     (b) Let $f(\theta) = \tan\theta - 2\theta$, then $\theta_{n+1} = \theta_n - \dfrac{f(\theta_n)}{f'(\theta_n)}$ yields $\theta = 1.1656$ to 4 decimal place
         accuracy.

(c) $y_{\max} \approx \dfrac{\sin(1.1656)}{\sqrt{1.1656}} \approx 0.85$

49. $y = r \sin \theta = \cos 2\theta \sin \theta$, $dy/d\theta = \cos 2\theta \cos \theta - 2 \sin 2\theta \sin \theta$, use the identities
$\cos 2\theta = 1 - 2 \sin^2 \theta$ and $\sin 2\theta = 2 \sin \theta \cos \theta$ to get $dy/d\theta = \cos \theta (1 - 6 \sin^2 \theta)$, $dy/d\theta = 0$
for $0 \le \theta \le \pi/4$ if $\sin^2 \theta = 1/6$, $\sin \theta = 1/\sqrt{6}$ where y attains its maximum value of
$y = \cos 2\theta \sin \theta = (1 - 2 \sin^2 \theta) \sin \theta = [1 - 2(1/6)](1/\sqrt{6}) = \sqrt{6}/9$ so the width of the
petal is $2y = 2\sqrt{6}/9$.

50. $y = r \sin \theta = \cos n\theta \sin \theta$, $dy/d\theta = \cos n\theta \cos \theta - n \sin n\theta \sin \theta = 0$ if $n \sin n\theta \sin \theta = \cos n\theta \cos \theta$,
$n \tan n\theta \tan \theta = 1$.

51. $x = r \cos \theta = (1 + \cos \theta) \cos \theta = \cos \theta + \cos^2 \theta$,
$dx/d\theta = -\sin \theta - 2 \sin \theta \cos \theta = -\sin \theta (1 + 2 \cos \theta)$,
$dx/d\theta = 0$ if $\sin \theta = 0$ or if $\cos \theta = -1/2$; $\theta = 0$, $2\pi/3$, or π. If $\theta = 0$, $2\pi/3$, π, then
$x = 2, -1/4, 0$ so the minimum value of x is $-1/4$.

52. $x = r \cos \theta = (a + b \cos \theta) \cos \theta = a \cos \theta + b \cos^2 \theta$,
$\dfrac{dx}{d\theta} = -a \sin \theta - 2b \sin \theta \cos \theta = -\sin \theta (a + 2b \cos \theta)$; $\dfrac{dx}{d\theta} = 0$ for $0 < \theta < \pi$ when $\cos \theta = -\dfrac{a}{2b}$ if
$a < 2b$. By the first derivative test there is a relative minimum at this value of θ, which is also
the absolute minimum on $[0, \pi]$ because there is only one critical point in $(0, \pi)$. If $\cos \theta = -\dfrac{a}{2b}$
then $x = a \left(-\dfrac{a}{2b} \right) + b \left(-\dfrac{a}{2b} \right)^2 = -\dfrac{a^2}{4b}$. If $a \ge 2b$ then there are no critical points in $(0, \pi)$ so
the minimum must occur at an endpoint of the interval $[0, \pi]$. If $\theta = 0$ then $x = a + b$, if $\theta = \pi$
then $x = b - a$; the minimum value of x is $b - a$ for $a \ge 2b$.

53. For the directrix to the left of the pole (see figure)

$\dfrac{r}{k + r \cos \theta} = e$, $r = ek + re \cos \theta$,

$r(1 - e \cos \theta) = ek$ so $r = \dfrac{ek}{1 - e \cos \theta}$.

If the directrix is to the right of the pole,

then $r/(k - r \cos \theta) = e$ and it follows that

$r = ek/(1 + e \cos \theta)$.

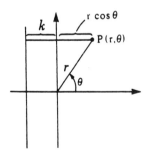

54. Draw a diagram like that shown in the solution to Exercise 53 to see that if the directrix is
below the pole, then $r/(k + r \sin \theta) = e$, $r = ek/(1 - e \sin \theta)$; if the directrix is above the pole
then $r/(k - r \sin \theta) = e$, $r = ek/(1 + e \sin \theta)$.

55. $r = \dfrac{3/2}{1 - \cos \theta}, e = 1$

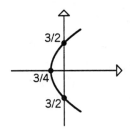

56. $r = \dfrac{5/3}{1 + \sin \theta}, e = 1$

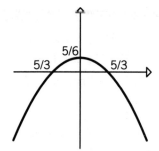

57. $r = \dfrac{3/2}{1 + \frac{1}{2}\sin \theta}, e = 1/2$

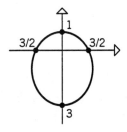

58. $r = \dfrac{4/3}{1 - \frac{2}{3}\cos \theta}, e = 2/3$

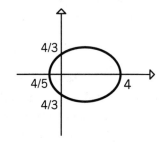

59. $r = \dfrac{2}{1 + \frac{3}{2}\cos \theta}, e = 3/2$

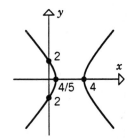

60. $r = \dfrac{1}{1 - \frac{4}{3}\sin \theta}, e = 4/3$

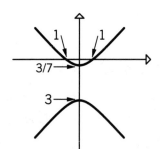

61. The graph of $r = f(\theta + \alpha)$ is the graph of $r = f(\theta)$ rotated α radians clockwise about the pole if $\alpha > 0$, $|\alpha|$ radians counterclockwise if $\alpha < 0$.

62. Let $r = a \sin n\theta$ (the proof for $r = a \cos n\theta$ is similar). If θ starts at 0, then θ would have to increase by some positive integer multiple of π radians in order to reach the starting point and begin to retrace the curve. Let (r, θ) be the coordinates of a point P on the curve for $0 \leq \theta < 2\pi$. Now $a \sin n(\theta + 2\pi) = a \sin(n\theta + 2\pi n) = a \sin n\theta = r$ so P is reached again with coordinates $(r, \theta + 2\pi)$ thus the curve is traced out either exactly once or exactly twice for $0 \leq \theta < 2\pi$. If for $0 \leq \theta < \pi$, $P(r, \theta)$ is reached again with coordinates $(-r, \theta + \pi)$ then the curve is traced out exactly once for $0 \leq \theta < \pi$, otherwise exactly once for $0 \leq \theta < 2\pi$. But

$$a \sin n(\theta + \pi) = a \sin(n\theta + n\pi) = \begin{cases} a \sin n\theta, & n \text{ even} \\ -a \sin n\theta, & n \text{ odd} \end{cases}$$

so the curve is traced out exactly once for $0 \leq \theta < 2\pi$ if n is even, and exactly once for $0 \leq \theta < \pi$ if n is odd.

EXERCISE SET 13.3

1. $\displaystyle A = \int_{\pi/6}^{\pi/3} \frac{1}{2}\theta^2 \, d\theta = 7\pi^3/1296$

2. $\displaystyle A = \int_0^{\pi/2} \frac{1}{2}(1 + \sin \theta)^2 \, d\theta = 3\pi/8 + 1$

3. $\displaystyle A = 2 \int_0^{\pi} \frac{1}{2}(2 + 2\cos \theta)^2 \, d\theta = 6\pi$

4. $\displaystyle A = 2 \int_0^{\pi} \frac{1}{2}[16 - (2 - 2\cos \theta)^2] \, d\theta = 10\pi$

5. $\displaystyle A = 2 \int_{\pi/6}^{\pi/2} \frac{1}{2}[25 \sin^2 \theta - (2 + \sin \theta)^2] \, d\theta = 8\pi/3 + \sqrt{3}$

6. $\displaystyle A = 2 \int_{2\pi/3}^{\pi} \frac{1}{2}(1 + 2\cos \theta)^2 \, d\theta = \pi - 3\sqrt{3}/2$

7. $\displaystyle A = 2 \int_0^{\pi/3} \frac{1}{2}[(2 + 2\cos \theta)^2 - 9] \, d\theta = 9\sqrt{3}/2 - \pi$

8. $\displaystyle A = \int_0^{\pi} \frac{1}{2}(4a^2 \sin^2 \theta) \, d\theta = \pi a^2$

9. $\displaystyle A = 2 \int_0^{\pi/2} \frac{1}{2}\sin 2\theta \, d\theta = 1$

10. $\displaystyle A = 2 \int_0^{\pi/4} \frac{1}{2}(16 \sin^2 \theta) \, d\theta = 2\pi - 4$

11. $\displaystyle A = 6 \int_0^{\pi/6} \frac{1}{2}(16 \cos^2 3\theta) \, d\theta = 4\pi$

12. $\displaystyle A = 8 \int_0^{\pi/8} \frac{1}{2}(4a^2 \cos^2 2\theta - 2a^2) \, d\theta = 2a^2$

13. $A = 2 \left[\int_0^{\pi/3} \frac{1}{2}(1 + \cos\theta)^2 d\theta + \int_{\pi/3}^{\pi/2} \frac{1}{2}(9\cos^2\theta)d\theta \right] = 5\pi/4$

14. $A = 2 \left[\int_0^{2\pi/3} \frac{1}{2}(1/2 + \cos\theta)^2 d\theta - \int_{2\pi/3}^{\pi} \frac{1}{2}(1/2 + \cos\theta)^2 d\theta \right] = (\pi + 3\sqrt{3})/4$

15. $A = 2 \int_0^{\cos^{-1}(3/5)} \frac{1}{2}(100 - 36\sec^2\theta)d\theta = 100\cos^{-1}(3/5) - 48$

16. $A = \int_0^{2\pi} \frac{1}{2}a^2(1 + \sin\theta)^2 d\theta - \pi(a/2)^2 = 5\pi a^2/4$

17. $A = \int_0^{\pi/2} \frac{1}{2}a^2\sec^4(\theta/2)d\theta = 4a^2/3$

18. $A = 2 \int_0^{\pi/3} \frac{1}{2} \left[(2 + 2\cos\theta)^2 - \frac{9}{4}\sec^2\theta \right] d\theta = 2\pi + \frac{9}{4}\sqrt{3}$

19. $A = \int_0^{\pi} \frac{9}{2}e^{-4\theta} d\theta = \frac{9}{8}(1 - e^{-4\pi})$

20. $A = \int_1^3 \frac{2}{\theta^2} d\theta = 4/3$

    21. $A = \int_{1/9}^4 \frac{1}{2}\frac{1}{\theta} d\theta = \ln 6$

22. (a) r is not real for $\pi/4 < \theta < 3\pi/4$ and $5\pi/4 < \theta < 7\pi/4$

    (b) $A = 4 \int_0^{\pi/4} \frac{1}{2}a^2\cos 2\theta \, d\theta = a^2$

23. $A = 4 \int_0^{\pi/6} \frac{1}{2}(4\cos 2\theta - 2)d\theta = 2\sqrt{3} - 2\pi/3$

24. $A = \int_{2\pi}^{4\pi} \frac{1}{2}a^2\theta^2 \, d\theta - \int_0^{2\pi} \frac{1}{2}a^2\theta^2 \, d\theta = 8\pi^3 a^2$

25. (a) $x = r\cos\theta$ and $y = r\sin\theta$ so $r^3\cos^3\theta - r^2\sin\theta\cos\theta + r^3\sin^3\theta = 0$, $r^2[r(\cos^3\theta + \sin^3\theta) - \sin\theta\cos\theta] = 0$, $r = \sin\theta\cos\theta/(\cos^3\theta + \sin^3\theta)$.

    (b) Divide numerator and denominator of the expression in part (a) by $\cos^3\theta$ to get $r = \sec\theta\tan\theta/(1 + \tan^3\theta)$. The loop is traced out for $0 \le \theta \le \pi/2$ so

$$A = \frac{1}{2}\int_0^{\pi/2} r^2 d\theta = \frac{1}{2}\int_0^{\pi/2} \frac{\sec^2\theta \tan^2\theta}{(1+\tan^3\theta)^2}d\theta, \text{ let } u = 1+\tan^3\theta \text{ to get}$$

$$A = \frac{1}{6}\int_1^{+\infty} \frac{1}{u^2}du = -\frac{1}{6}\frac{1}{u}\Big]_1^{+\infty} = \frac{1}{6}.$$

26. The area enclosed by $r = 2f(\theta)$ is $\dfrac{1}{2}\displaystyle\int_\alpha^\beta [2f(\theta)]^2 d\theta = 4\left[\dfrac{1}{2}\displaystyle\int_\alpha^\beta f^2(\theta)d\theta\right]$ where $\dfrac{1}{2}\displaystyle\int_\alpha^\beta f^2(\theta)d\theta$

is the area enclosed by $r = f(\theta)$.

EXERCISE SET 13.4

1. **(a)**

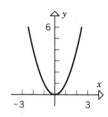

2.

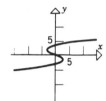

    (b) $y = x^2$

3. $\cos^2 t + \sin^2 t = 1;$
   $x^2 + y^2 = 1$

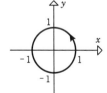

4. $\cos t = x - 1, \ \sin t = 3 - y;$
   $(x-1)^2 + (y-3)^2 = 1$

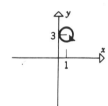

5. $t = (x + 4)/3;$
   $y = 2x + 10$

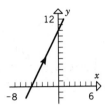

6. $t = x + 3;$
   $y = 3x + 2, -3 \leq x \leq 0$

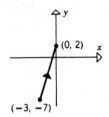

7. $\cos t = x/2, \ \sin t = y/5;$
   $x^2/4 + y^2/25 = 1$

8. $t = x^2;$
   $y = 2x^2 + 4, \ x \geq 0$

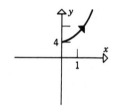

9. $\cos t = (x - 3)/2, \sin t = (y - 2)/4;$
   $(x - 3)^2/4 + (y - 2)^2/16 = 1$

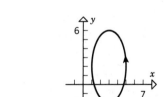

10. $\cosh t = x/2, \sinh t = y/4;$
   $x^2/4 - y^2/16 = 1, \ x \geq 2$

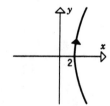

11. $\sin 2\pi t = x/4,\ \cos 2\pi t = y/4$;
$x^2/16 + y^2/16 = 1$

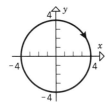

12. $\sec^2 t - \tan^2 t = 1$;
$x^2 - y^2 = 1, x \leq -1$ and $y \geq 0$

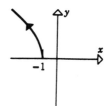

13. $\cos 2t = 1 - 2\sin^2 t$;
$x = 1 - 2y^2, -1 \leq y \leq 1$

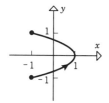

14. $t = (x - 3)/4$;
$y = (x - 3)^2 - 9$

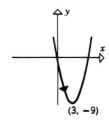

15. $y = \ln t^2 = \ln x, x \geq 1$

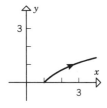

16. $y = \dfrac{4}{3}x + \dfrac{5}{3}$,
$-2 < x \leq 1, -1 < y \leq 3$

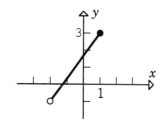

17. $x = 3y^2 - 1,$
        $-1 < x \leq 2, 0 < y \leq 1$

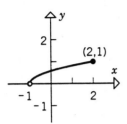

18. $y = x - 1,$
        $x \geq 1, y \geq 0$

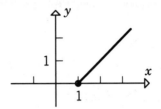

19. $x/2 + y/3 = 1,$
        $0 \leq x \leq 2, 0 \leq y \leq 3$

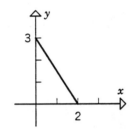

20. $x^2 - y^2 = 1,$
        $x \geq 1, -\infty < y < +\infty$

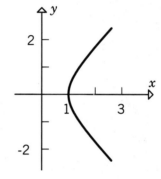

21. $y = 1 - x^2$,
$-1 \le x \le 1, 0 \le y \le 1$

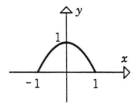

22. $x = \frac{1}{2}y^2 - 1$,
$-1 \le x \le 1, -2 \le y \le 2$

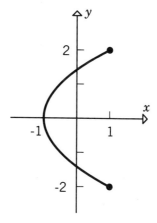

23. $x + (y - 1)^2 = 1$,
$0 \le x \le 1, 0 \le y \le 2$

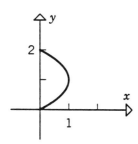

24. $y = 1 - 2x^2$
$-1 \le x \le 1, -1 \le y \le 1$

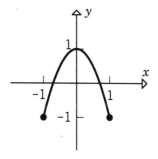

25. $x^2 + y^2 = 1$,
$\cos 1 \le x < 1, 0 < y \le \sin 1$

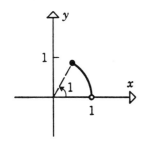

26. $P(x, \sqrt{a^2 - x^2})$ is on the semicircle for $-a \leq x \leq a$,

$t = \sqrt{(x + a)^2 + (a^2 - x^2)} - \sqrt{2ax + 2a^2}$, solve for x to get $x = \dfrac{t^2}{2a} - a$ so

$y = \sqrt{a^2 - x^2} = \dfrac{t\sqrt{4a^2 - t^2}}{2a}$ for $0 \leq t \leq 2a$.

27. $(x_0, \sqrt{x_0})$ is on the curve for $x_0 \geq 0$. $y' = 1/(2\sqrt{x})$; the tangent line at $(x_0, \sqrt{x_0})$ is

$y - \sqrt{x_0} = (x - x_0)/(2\sqrt{x_0})$, which crosses the x-axis at $x = -x_0 = t$ so $x_0 = -t$ hence

$x = -t$, $y = \sqrt{-t}$ for $t \leq 0$.

28. $dy/dx = \dfrac{8}{2t}$, $dy/dx\big|_{t=2} = 2$

29. $dy/dx = \dfrac{\cos t}{-\sin t} = -\cot t$, $dy/dx\big|_{t=3\pi/4} = 1$

30. $dy/dx = \dfrac{5}{1} = 5$, $dy/dx\big|_{t=1} = 5$

31. $dy/dx = \dfrac{2}{1/(2\sqrt{t})} = 4\sqrt{t}$, $dy/dx\big|_{t=9} = 12$

32. $dy/dx = \dfrac{\sec^2 \theta}{\sec \theta \tan \theta} = \csc \theta$, $dy/dx\big|_{\theta=\pi/3} = 2/\sqrt{3}$

33. $dy/dx = \dfrac{6\pi \cos 2\pi s}{-8\pi \sin 2\pi s} = -\dfrac{3}{4} \cot 2\pi s$, $dy/dx\big|_{s=-1/4} = 0$

34. $dy/dx = \dfrac{\sinh t}{\cosh t} = \tanh t$, $dy/dx\big|_{t=0} = 0$

35. $dy/dx = \dfrac{t^2}{t} = t$, $d^2y/dx^2 = \dfrac{1}{t}$, $d^2y/dx^2\big|_{t=2} = 1/2$

36. $dy/dx = \dfrac{\cos \phi}{-\sin \phi} = -\cot \phi$, $d^2y/dx^2 = \dfrac{\csc^2 \phi}{-\sin \phi} = -\csc^3 \phi$, $d^2y/dx^2\big|_{\phi=\pi/4} = -2\sqrt{2}$

37. $dy/dx = \dfrac{2}{1/(2\sqrt{t})} = 4\sqrt{t}$, $d^2y/dx^2 = \dfrac{2/\sqrt{t}}{1/(2\sqrt{t})} = 4$, $d^2y/dx^2\big|_{t=1} = 4$

38. $dy/dx = \dfrac{\sec^2 t}{\sec t \tan t} = \csc t$, $d^2y/dx^2 = \dfrac{-\csc t \cot t}{\sec t \tan t} = -\cot^3 t$, $d^2y/dx^2\big|_{t=\pi/3} = -1/(3\sqrt{3})$

39. $(dx/dt)^2 + (dy/dt)^2 = (4)^2 + (3)^2 = 25$, $L = \int_0^2 5\,dt = 10$

40. $(dx/dt)^2 + (dy/dt)^2 = (-3\cos^2 t \sin t)^2 + (3\sin^2 t \cos t)^2 = 9\sin^2 t \cos^2 t$,

$L = \int_0^{\pi/2} 3\sin t \cos t\,dt = 3/2$

41. $(dx/dt)^2 + (dy/dt)^2 = (t^2)^2 + (t)^2 = t^2(t^2 + 1)$, $L = \int_0^1 t(t^2 + 1)^{1/2}\,dt = (2\sqrt{2} - 1)/3$

42. $(dx/dt)^2 + (dy/dt)^2 = t^2(t^2 + 1)$, $L = \int_{-1}^0 |t|(t^2 + 1)^{1/2}\,dt = \int_{-1}^0 (-t)(t^2 + 1)^{1/2}\,dt = \dfrac{(2\sqrt{2} - 1)}{3}$

43. $(dx/dt)^2 + (dy/dt)^2 = (-2\sin 2t)^2 + (2\cos 2t)^2 = 4$, $L = \int_0^{\pi/2} 2\,dt = \pi$

44. $(dx/dt)^2 + (dy/dt)^2 = (2e^t \cos t)^2 + (-2e^t \sin t)^2 = 4e^{2t}$, $L = \int_1^4 2e^t\,dt = 2(e^4 - e)$

45. $(dx/dt)^2 + (dy/dt)^2 = [2(1 + t)]^2 + [3(1 + t)^2]^2 = (1 + t)^2[4 + 9(1 + t)^2]$,

$L = \int_0^1 (1 + t)[4 + 9(1 + t)^2]^{1/2}\,dt = (80\sqrt{10} - 13\sqrt{13})/27$

46. $(dx/dt)^2 + (dy/dt)^2 = [e^t(\cos t - \sin t)]^2 + [e^t(\cos t + \sin t)]^2 = 2e^{2t}$,

$L = \int_0^{\pi/2} \sqrt{2}e^t\,dt = \sqrt{2}(e^{\pi/2} - 1)$

47. $(dx/dt)^2 + (dy/dt)^2 = [a(1 - \cos t)]^2 + [a\sin t]^2 = 2a^2(1 - \cos t) = 4a^2 \sin^2(t/2)$,

$L = \int_0^{2\pi} 2a\sin(t/2)\,dt = 8a$

48. $(dx/dt)^2 + (dy/dt)^2 = (-a\sin t)^2 + (b\cos t)^2 = a^2 \sin^2 t + b^2 \cos^2 t$

$= a^2(1 - \cos^2 t) + b^2 \cos^2 t = a^2 - (a^2 - b^2)\cos^2 t$

$= a^2 \left[1 - \dfrac{a^2 - b^2}{a^2}\cos^2 t\right] = a^2[1 - e^2 \cos^2 t]$,

$L = \int_0^{2\pi} a\sqrt{1 - e^2 \cos^2 t}\,dt = 4a \int_0^{\pi/2} \sqrt{1 - e^2 \cos^2 t}\,dt$

49. **(a)** $(dx/dt)^2 + (dy/dt)^2 = 4\sin^2 t + \cos^2 t = 4\sin^2 t + (1 - \sin^2 t) = 1 + 3\sin^2 t$,

$$L = \int_0^{2\pi} \sqrt{1 + 3\sin^2 t}\, dt = 4\int_0^{\pi/2} \sqrt{1 + 3\sin^2 t}\, dt$$

(b) 9.69

(c) distance traveled $= \displaystyle\int_{1.5}^{4.8} \sqrt{1 + 3\sin^2 t}\, dt \approx 5.16$ cm

50. $x = r\cos\theta = 2\cos 2\theta \cos\theta$, $y = r\sin\theta = 2\cos 2\theta \sin\theta$

51. $x = (2 + 3\sin\theta)\cos\theta$, $y = (2 + 3\sin\theta)\sin\theta$

52. $dy/dx = \dfrac{16t - 2}{2} = 8t - 1$; for $t = 1$, $dy/dx = 7$, $(x, y) = (6, 10)$;

$y - 10 = 7(x - 6)$, $y = 7x - 32$

53. $dy/dx = \dfrac{-e^{-t}}{e^t} = -e^{-2t}$; for $t = 2$, $dy/dx = -e^{-4}$, $(x, y) = (e^2, e^{-2})$;

$y - e^{-2} = -e^{-4}(x - e^2)$, $y = -e^{-4}x + 2e^{-2}$

54. $dy/dx = \dfrac{4\cos t}{-2\sin t} = -2\cot t$

(a) $dy/dx = 0$ if $\cot t = 0$, $t = \pi/2 + n\pi$ for $n = 0, \pm 1, \cdots$

(b) $dx/dy = -\dfrac{1}{2}\tan t = 0$ if $\tan t = 0$, $t = n\pi$ for $n = 0, \pm 1, \cdots$

55. $dy/dx = \dfrac{2t + 1}{6t^2 - 30t + 24} = \dfrac{2t + 1}{6(t - 1)(t - 4)}$

(a) $dy/dx = 0$ if $t = -1/2$

(b) $dx/dy = \dfrac{6(t - 1)(t - 4)}{2t + 1} = 0$ if $t = 1, 4$

56. If $y = 4$ then $t^2 = 4$, $t = \pm 2$, $x = 0$ for $t = \pm 2$ so $(0, 4)$ is reached when $t = \pm 2$.
$dy/dx = 2t/(3t^2 - 4)$. For $t = 2$, $dy/dx = 1/2$ and for $t = -2$, $dy/dx = -1/2$. The tangent lines are $y = \pm x/2 + 4$.

57. If $x = 3$ then $t^2 - 3t + 5 = 3$, $t^2 - 3t + 2 = 0$, $(t - 1)(t - 2) = 0$, $t = 1$ or 2. If $t = 1$ or 2 then $y = 1$ so $(3, 1)$ is reached when $t = 1$ or 2. $dy/dx = (3t^2 + 2t - 10)/(2t - 3)$. For $t = 1$, $dy/dx = 5$, the tangent line is $y - 1 = 5(x - 3)$, $y = 5x - 14$. For $t = 2$, $dy/dx = 6$, the tangent line is $y - 1 = 6(x - 3)$, $y = 6x - 17$.

58. $2x\dfrac{dx}{dt} + 2y\dfrac{dy}{dt} = 0$, $\dfrac{dy}{dt} = -\dfrac{x}{y}\dfrac{dx}{dt}$ so at $(4,3)$, $\dfrac{dy}{dt} = -\dfrac{4}{3}(8) = -32/3$

59. Assuming that $a \neq 0$ and $b \neq 0$, eliminate the parameter to get $(x-h)^2/a^2 + (y-k)^2/b^2 = 1$. If $|a| = |b|$ the curve is a circle with center (h,k) and radius $|a|$; if $|a| \neq |b|$ the curve is an ellipse with center (h,k) and major axis parallel to the x-axis when $|a| > |b|$ or major axis parallel to the y-axis when $|a| < |b|$.

60. Refer to the diagram to get

$b\theta = a\phi$, $\theta = a\phi/b$ but $\theta - \alpha = \phi + \pi/2$

so $\alpha = \theta - \phi - \pi/2 = (a/b - 1)\phi - \pi/2$

$x = (a-b)\cos\phi - b\sin\alpha$

$\quad = (a-b)\cos\phi + b\cos\left(\dfrac{a-b}{b}\right)\phi,$

$y = (a-b)\sin\phi - b\cos\alpha$

$\quad = (a-b)\sin\phi - b\sin\left(\dfrac{a-b}{b}\right)\phi.$

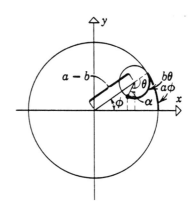

61. **(a)**

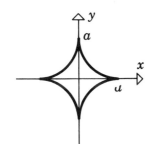

(b) Use $b = a/4$ in the equations of Exercise 60 to get $x = \dfrac{3}{4}a\cos\phi + \dfrac{1}{4}a\cos 3\phi$,

$y = \dfrac{3}{4}a\sin\phi - \dfrac{1}{4}a\sin 3\phi$; but trigonometric identities yield $\cos 3\phi = 4\cos^3\phi - 3\cos\phi$,

$\sin 3\phi = 3\sin\phi - 4\sin^3\phi$ so $x = a\cos^3\phi$, $y = a\sin^3\phi$.

(c) From the result in part (b), $\cos\phi = (x/a)^{1/3}$, $\sin\phi = (y/a)^{1/3}$ so

$(x/a)^{2/3} + (y/a)^{2/3} = 1$, $x^{2/3} + y^{2/3} = a^{2/3}$

62. $x' = 2t$, $y' = 2$, $(x')^2 + (y')^2 = 4t^2 + 4$

$$S = 2\pi \int_0^4 (2t)\sqrt{4t^2 + 4}\,dt = 8\pi \int_0^4 t\sqrt{t^2 + 1}\,dt = \frac{8\pi}{3}(17\sqrt{17} - 1)$$

63. $x' = e^t(\cos t - \sin t)$, $y' = e^t(\cos t + \sin t)$, $(x')^2 + (y')^2 = 2e^{2t}$

$$S = 2\pi \int_0^{\pi/2} (e^t \sin t)\sqrt{2e^{2t}}\,dt = 2\sqrt{2}\pi \int_0^{\pi/2} e^{2t} \sin t\,dt$$

$$= 2\sqrt{2}\pi \left[\frac{1}{5}e^{2t}(2\sin t - \cos t)\right]_0^{\pi/2} = \frac{2\sqrt{2}}{5}\pi(2e^\pi + 1)$$

64. $x' = -2\sin t \cos t$, $y' = 2\sin t \cos t$, $(x')^2 + (y')^2 = 8\sin^2 t \cos^2 t$

$$S = 2\pi \int_0^{\pi/2} \cos^2 t\sqrt{8\sin^2 t \cos^2 t}\,dt = 4\sqrt{2}\pi \int_0^{\pi/2} \cos^3 t \sin t\,dt = \sqrt{2}\pi$$

65. $x' = 1$, $y' = 4t$, $(x')^2 + (y')^2 = 1 + 16t^2$, $S = 2\pi \int_0^1 t\sqrt{1 + 16t^2}\,dt = \frac{\pi}{24}(17\sqrt{17} - 1)$

66. $x' = -r\sin t$, $y' = r\cos t$, $(x')^2 + (y')^2 = r^2$, $S = 2\pi \int_0^\pi r\sin t\sqrt{r^2}\,dt = 2\pi r^2 \int_0^\pi \sin t\,dt = 4\pi r^2$

67. $\dfrac{dx}{d\phi} = a(1 - \cos\phi)$, $\dfrac{dy}{d\phi} = a\sin\phi$, $\left(\dfrac{dx}{d\phi}\right)^2 + \left(\dfrac{dy}{d\phi}\right)^2 = 2a^2(1 - \cos\phi)$

$$S = 2\pi \int_0^{2\pi} a(1 - \cos\phi)\sqrt{2a^2(1 - \cos\phi)}\,d\phi = 2\sqrt{2}\pi a^2 \int_0^{2\pi} (1 - \cos\phi)^{3/2}d\phi,$$

but $1 - \cos\phi = 2\sin^2\dfrac{\phi}{2}$ so $(1 - \cos\phi)^{3/2} = 2\sqrt{2}\sin^3\dfrac{\phi}{2}$ for $0 \le \phi \le \pi$ and, taking advantage of

the symmetry of the cycloid, $S = 16\pi a^2 \displaystyle\int_0^\pi \sin^3\dfrac{\phi}{2}d\phi = 64\pi a^2/3$

EXERCISE SET 13.5

1. $\theta = \pi/3$; $dr/d\theta = -\sqrt{3}$, $r = 1$, $\tan\theta = \sqrt{3}$, $m = \dfrac{1 + (\sqrt{3})(-\sqrt{3})}{-\sqrt{3} + (-\sqrt{3})} = 1/\sqrt{3}$

2. $\theta = \pi/4$; $dr/d\theta = \sqrt{2}/2$, $r = 1 + \sqrt{2}/2$, $\tan\theta = 1$,

$$m = \dfrac{(1 + \sqrt{2}/2) + (1)(\sqrt{2}/2)}{-(1 + \sqrt{2}/2)(1) + (\sqrt{2}/2)} = -1 - \sqrt{2}$$

3. $\theta = 2$; $dr/d\theta = -1/4$, $r = 1/2$, $\tan \theta = \tan 2$, $m = \dfrac{1/2 + (\tan 2)(-1/4)}{-(1/2)\tan 2 + (-1/4)} = \dfrac{\tan 2 - 2}{2\tan 2 + 1}$

4. $\theta = \pi/6$; $dr/d\theta = 4\sqrt{3}a$, $r = 2a$, $\tan \theta = 1/\sqrt{3}$, $m = \dfrac{2a + (1/\sqrt{3})(4\sqrt{3}a)}{-2a(1/\sqrt{3}) + 4\sqrt{3}a} = 3\sqrt{3}/5$

5. $\theta = 3\pi/4$; $dr/d\theta = -3\sqrt{2}/2$, $r = \sqrt{2}/2$, $\tan \theta = -1$, $m = \dfrac{\sqrt{2}/2 + (-1)(-3\sqrt{2}/2)}{-(\sqrt{2}/2)(-1) + (-3\sqrt{2}/2)} = -2$

6. $\theta = \pi$; $dr/d\theta = 3$, $r = 4$, $\tan \theta = 0$, $m = \dfrac{4 + (0)(3)}{-4(0) + (3)} = 4/3$

7. $\theta = \pi/2$; $dr/d\theta = 3$, $r = 3$, $\tan \psi = 1$ 8. $\theta = 1$; $dr/d\theta = 2$, $r = 2$, $\tan \psi = 1$

9. $\theta = \pi$, $dr/d\theta = -5$, $r = 0$, $\tan \psi = 0$

10. $\theta = 3\pi/4$, $dr/d\theta = 2$, $r = -1$, $\tan \psi = -1/2$

11. $\theta = 5\pi/6$; $dr/d\theta = -2\sqrt{3}$, $r = 1$, $\tan \psi = -1/(2\sqrt{3})$

12. $\theta = \pi/3$; $dr/d\theta = 2/3$, $r = \sqrt{3}/3$, $\tan \psi = \sqrt{3}/2$

13. $r^2 + (dr/d\theta)^2 = (e^{3\theta})^2 + (3e^{3\theta})^2 = 10e^{6\theta}$, $L = \displaystyle\int_0^2 \sqrt{10}e^{3\theta}\,d\theta = \sqrt{10}(e^6 - 1)/3$

14. $r^2 + (dr/d\theta)^2 = a^2 + 0^2 = a^2$, $L = \displaystyle\int_0^{2\pi} a\,d\theta = 2\pi a$

15. $r^2 + (dr/d\theta)^2 = (2a\cos\theta)^2 + (-2a\sin\theta)^2 = 4a^2$, $L = \displaystyle\int_0^{\pi} 2a\,d\theta = 2\pi a$

16. $r^2 + (dr/d\theta)^2 = [\sin^2(\theta/2)]^2 + [\sin(\theta/2)\cos(\theta/2)]^2 = \sin^2(\theta/2)$, $L = \displaystyle\int_0^{\pi} \sin(\theta/2)\,d\theta = 2$

17. $r^2 + (dr/d\theta)^2 = (a\theta^2)^2 + (2a\theta)^2 = a^2\theta^2(\theta^2 + 4)$,

    $L = \displaystyle\int_0^{\pi} a\theta(\theta^2 + 4)^{1/2}\,d\theta = \dfrac{a}{3}[(\pi^2 + 4)^{3/2} - 8]$

18. $r^2 + (dr/d\theta)^2 = [\sin^3(\theta/3)]^2 + [\sin^2(\theta/3)\cos(\theta/3)]^2 = \sin^4(\theta/3)$,

    $L = \displaystyle\int_0^{\pi/2} \sin^2(\theta/3)\,d\theta = (2\pi - 3\sqrt{3})/8$

19. $r^2 + (dr/d\theta)^2 = [a(1 - \cos\theta)]^2 + [a\sin\theta]^2 = 4a^2\sin^2(\theta/2)$, $L = 2\displaystyle\int_0^\pi 2a\sin(\theta/2)d\theta = 8a$

20. **(a)** $r^2 + (dr/d\theta)^2 = (e^{-a\theta})^2 + (-ae^{-a\theta})^2 = (1 + a^2)e^{-2a\theta}$,

$$L = \int_0^{\theta_0} \sqrt{1 + a^2}\, e^{-a\theta}\, d\theta = \frac{\sqrt{1 + a^2}}{a}(1 - e^{-a\theta_0})$$

(b) $\displaystyle\lim_{\theta_0 \to +\infty} L = \sqrt{1 + a^2}/a$

21. **(a)** $r^2 + (dr/d\theta)^2 = (\cos n\theta)^2 + (-n\sin n\theta)^2 = \cos^2 n\theta + n^2\sin^2 n\theta$
$$= (1 - \sin^2 n\theta) + n^2\sin^2 n\theta = 1 + (n^2 - 1)\sin^2 n\theta,$$

$$L = 2\int_0^{\pi/(2n)} \sqrt{1 + (n^2 - 1)\sin^2 n\theta}\, d\theta$$

(b) $L = 2\displaystyle\int_0^{\pi/4} \sqrt{1 + 3\sin^2 2\theta}\, d\theta \approx 2.42$

22. If $r = 2f(\theta)$, then $r^2 + (dr/d\theta)^2 = 4f(\theta) + 4[f'(\theta)]^2 = 4(f(\theta) + [f'(\theta)]^2)$ so the length of

$r = 2f(\theta)$ is $2\displaystyle\int_\alpha^\beta \sqrt{f(\theta) + [f'(\theta)]^2}\, d\theta$ where $\displaystyle\int_\alpha^\beta \sqrt{f(\theta) + [f'(\theta)]^2}\, d\theta$ is the length of $r = f(\theta)$.

23. **(a)** $\dfrac{dr}{dt} = 2$ and $\dfrac{d\theta}{dt} = 0.5$ so $\dfrac{dr}{d\theta} = \dfrac{dr/dt}{d\theta/dt} = \dfrac{2}{0.5} = 4$, $r = 4\theta + C$, $r = 10$ when $\theta = 0$ so
$10 = C, r = 4\theta + 10$.

(b) $r^2 + (dr/d\theta)^2 = (4\theta + 10)^2 + 16$, during the first 5 seconds the rod rotates through an

angle of $(0.5)(5) = 2.5$ radians so $L = \displaystyle\int_0^{2.5} \sqrt{(4\theta + 10)^2 + 16}\, d\theta$, let $u = 4\theta + 10$ to get

$$L = \frac{1}{4}\int_{10}^{20} \sqrt{u^2 + 16}\, du = \frac{1}{4}\left[\frac{u}{2}\sqrt{u^2 + 16} + 8\ln\left|u + \sqrt{u^2 + 16}\right|\right]_{10}^{20}$$

$$= \frac{1}{4}\left[10\sqrt{416} - 5\sqrt{116} + 8\ln\frac{20 + \sqrt{416}}{10 + \sqrt{116}}\right] \approx 38.9\text{ mm}$$

24. $dx/d\theta = -a\sin\theta(1 + 2\cos\theta)$, $dy/d\theta = a(2\cos\theta - 1)(\cos\theta + 1)$.

(a) horizontal if $dy/d\theta = 0$ and $dx/d\theta \neq 0$. $dy/d\theta = 0$ when $\cos\theta = 1/2$ or $\cos\theta = -1$ so
$\theta = \pi/3, 5\pi/3$, or π; $dx/d\theta \neq 0$ for $\theta = \pi/3$ and $5\pi/3$. For the singular point $\theta = \pi$ we
find that $\displaystyle\lim_{\theta \to \pi} dy/dx = 0$. There is a horizontal tangent at $\theta = \pi/3, \pi$, and $5\pi/3$.

(b) vertical if $dy/d\theta \neq 0$ and $dx/d\theta = 0$. $dx/d\theta = 0$ when $\sin\theta = 0$ or $\cos\theta = -1/2$ so $\theta = 0$,
π, $2\pi/3$, or $4\pi/3$; $dy/d\theta \neq 0$ for $\theta = 0, 2\pi/3$, and $4\pi/3$. The singular point $\theta = \pi$ was
discussed in part (a). There is a vertical tangent at $\theta = 0, 2\pi/3$, and $4\pi/3$.

25. $dx/d\theta = 4\sin^2\theta - \sin\theta - 2$, $dy/d\theta = \cos\theta(1 - 4\sin\theta)$. $dy/d\theta = 0$ when $\cos\theta = 0$ or $\sin\theta = 1/4$ so $\theta = \pi/2$, $3\pi/2$, $\sin^{-1}(1/4)$, or $\pi - \sin^{-1}(1/4)$; $dx/d\theta \neq 0$ at these points so there is a horizontal tangent at each one.

26. Let $\alpha = \psi_2 - \psi_1$ then $\tan\alpha = \tan(\psi_2 - \psi_1) = \dfrac{\tan\psi_2 - \tan\psi_1}{1 + \tan\psi_1\tan\psi_2}$.

If $0 \leq \alpha < \pi/2$ then $\beta = \alpha$, $\tan\beta = \tan\alpha = |\tan\alpha|$; if $-\pi/2 < \alpha < 0$ then $\beta = -\alpha$, $\tan\beta = -\tan\alpha = |\tan\alpha|$; if $\pi/2 < \alpha < \pi$ then $\beta = \pi - \alpha$, $\tan\beta = \tan(\pi - \alpha) = |\tan\alpha|$; if $-\pi < \alpha < -\pi/2$ then $\beta = \pi + \alpha$, $\tan\beta = \tan\alpha = |\tan\alpha|$. In all cases,

$$\tan\beta = \left|\frac{\tan\psi_2 - \tan\psi_1}{1 + \tan\psi_1\tan\psi_2}\right|.$$

27. $(\sqrt{3}/2, \pi/6)$ satisfies both equations so it is a point of intersection.

$$\tan\psi_1 = \frac{r}{dr/d\theta} = \frac{\sin 2\theta}{2\cos 2\theta} = \frac{1}{2}\tan 2\theta, \quad \tan\psi_2 = \frac{r}{dr/d\theta} = \frac{\cos\theta}{-\sin\theta} = -\cot\theta, \text{ at } \theta = \pi/6,$$

$\tan\psi_1 = \sqrt{3}/2$ and $\tan\psi_2 = -\sqrt{3}$ so $\tan\beta = \left|\dfrac{-\sqrt{3} - \sqrt{3}/2}{1 + (\sqrt{3}/2)(-\sqrt{3})}\right| = 3\sqrt{3}$, $\beta = \tan^{-1} 3\sqrt{3}$.

28. $\cos\theta = 1 - \cos\theta$ if $2\cos\theta = 1$ so $\cos\theta = 1/2$, $\theta = \pi/3$ and $5\pi/3$. The curves intersect at $(1/2, \pi/3)$ and $(1/2, 5\pi/3)$ (draw a graph to see that the curves also intersect at the origin, at which point the tangent lines are perpendicular). $\tan\psi_1 = -\cot\theta$, $\tan\psi_2 = (1 - \cos\theta)/\sin\theta$.

At $\theta = \pi/3$, $\tan\psi_1 = -1/\sqrt{3}$ and $\tan\psi_2 = 1/\sqrt{3}$ so $\tan\beta = \sqrt{3}$, $\beta = 60°$.

At $\theta = 5\pi/3$, $\tan\psi_1 = 1/\sqrt{3}$ and $\tan\psi_2 = -1/\sqrt{3}$ so $\tan\beta = \sqrt{3}$, $\beta = 60°$.

29. $\tan\psi = r/(dr/d\theta) = e^{a\theta}/(ae^{a\theta}) = 1/a$ so ψ is a constant.

30. Suppose (r_0, θ_0) satisfies both equations then at (r_0, θ_0), $\tan\psi_1 = -\dfrac{1 + \cos\theta_0}{\sin\theta_0}$

and $\tan\psi_2 = \dfrac{1 - \cos\theta_0}{\sin\theta_0}$. But $\cot(\psi_2 - \psi_1) = \dfrac{1 + \cot\psi_1\cot\psi_2}{\cot\psi_1 - \cot\psi_2}$,

$$1 + \cot\psi_1\cot\psi_2 = 1 + \left(-\frac{\sin\theta_0}{1 + \cos\theta_0}\right)\left(\frac{\sin\theta_0}{1 - \cos\theta_0}\right) = 1 - \frac{\sin^2\theta_0}{1 - \cos^2\theta_0} = 1 - 1 = 0$$

and $\cot\psi_1 - \cot\psi_2 \neq 0$ thus $\cot(\psi_2 - \psi_1) = 0$, $\psi_2 - \psi_1 = \pm\pi/2$ so the tangent lines are perpendicular.

SUPPLEMENTARY EXERCISES CHAPTER 13

1. **(a)** $(1, \sqrt{3})$ **(b)** $(0, -2)$ **(c)** $(0, 0)$
   (d) $(-1, 1)$ **(e)** $(-3, 0)$ **(f)** $(3/5, -4/5)$

2. **(a)** **(i)** $(2, 7\pi/6)$ **(ii)** $(2, -5\pi/6)$ **(iii)** $(-2, \pi/6)$
   (b) **(i)** $(3, \pi)$ **(ii)** $(3, \pi)$ **(iii)** $(-3, 0)$
   (c) **(i)** $(\sqrt{2}, 7\pi/4)$ **(ii)** $(\sqrt{2}, -\pi/4)$ **(iii)** $(-\sqrt{2}, 3\pi/4)$

3. **(a)**   **(b)**

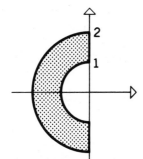 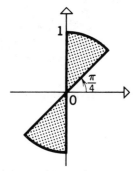

4. $r = 2/(1 - \cos\theta)$, $r - r\cos\theta = 2$, $r - x = 2$, $r = x + 2$, $r^2 = (x + 2)^2$, $x^2 + y^2 = x^2 + 4x + 4$, $y^2 = 4x + 4$; parabola.

5. $r^2 \sin 2\theta = 1$, $r^2(2\sin\theta\cos\theta) = 1$, $2(r\sin\theta)(r\cos\theta) = 1$, $2yx = 1$; hyperbola.

6. $r = \pi/2$, $r^2 = \pi^2/4$, $x^2 + y^2 = \pi^2/4$; circle.

7. $r = -4\csc\theta$, $r = -4/\sin\theta$, $r\sin\theta = -4$, $y = -4$, line.

8. $r = 6/(3 - \sin\theta)$, $3r - r\sin\theta = 6$, $3r - y = 6$, $3r = y + 6$, $9r^2 = (y + 6)^2$, $9(x^2 + y^2) = y^2 + 12y + 36$, $9x^2 + 8y^2 - 12y = 36$; ellipse.

9. $\theta = \pi/3$, $\tan\theta = \sqrt{3}$, $y = \sqrt{3}x$; line.

10. $r = 2\sin\theta + 3\cos\theta$, $r^2 = 2r\sin\theta + 3r\cos\theta$, $x^2 + y^2 = 2y + 3x$; circle.

11. $r = 0$, $x = 0$ and $y = 0$; point.   12. $x^2 + y^2 = kx$, $r^2 = kr\cos\theta$, $r = k\cos\theta$

13. $x = -3$, $r\cos\theta = -3$

14. $y^2 = 4x$, $(r \sin \theta)^2 = 4r \cos \theta$, $r \sin^2 \theta = 4 \cos \theta$, $r = 4 \csc \theta \cot \theta$

15. $y = 3x$, $\tan \theta = 3$, $\theta = \tan^{-1} 3$

16.

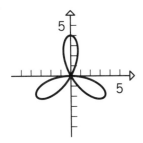

17.

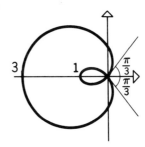

18.

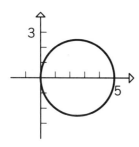

19.

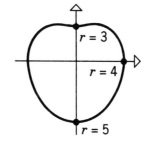

20.

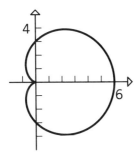

21.

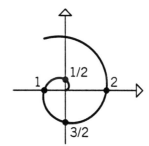

22.

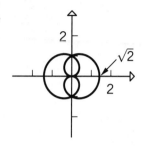

23.

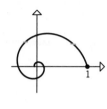

24. $3\cos\theta = 1 + \cos\theta$,

$\cos\theta = 1/2$, $\theta = \pm\pi/3$.

The curves intersect at

$(3/2, \pi/3)$, $(3/2, -\pi/3)$,

and also at the origin

(see sketch).

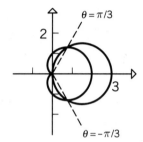

25. $a\cos 2\theta = a/2$, $\cos 2\theta = 1/2$;

one solution is $2\theta = \pi/3$, $\theta = \pi/6$

and from the symmetry of the graphs

the others are $\theta = -\pi/6$, $\pm\pi/3$, $\pm 2\pi/3$,

$\pm 5\pi/6$. The points of intersection are

$(a/2, \pm\pi/6)$, $(a/2, \pm\pi/3)$, $(a/2, \pm 2\pi/3)$,

$(a/2, \pm 5\pi/6)$.

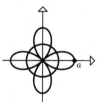

26. By inspection of the graphs, the

curves intersect at $(2, \pi/2)$ and

the origin.

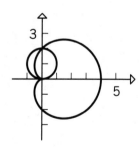

27. **(a)** $A = 2\left[\dfrac{1}{2}\displaystyle\int_0^{\pi/3}(1+\cos\theta)^2 d\theta + \dfrac{1}{2}\displaystyle\int_{\pi/3}^{\pi/2}(3\cos\theta)^2 d\theta\right]$

$= \displaystyle\int_0^{\pi/3}(1+\cos\theta)^2 d\theta + \displaystyle\int_{\pi/3}^{\pi/2}9\cos^2\theta\, d\theta$

(b) $r^2 + (dr/d\theta)^2 = (1+\cos\theta)^2 + (-\sin\theta)^2 = 2(1+\cos\theta), \; L = 2\displaystyle\int_{\pi/3}^{\pi}\sqrt{2(1+\cos\theta)}\,d\theta$

28. **(a)** $A = 8\displaystyle\int_0^{\pi/6}\dfrac{1}{2}[(a\cos 2\theta)^2 - (a/2)^2]d\theta = 4a^2\displaystyle\int_0^{\pi/6}(\cos^2 2\theta - 1/4)d\theta$

(b) $r^2 + (dr/d\theta)^2 = (a\cos 2\theta)^2 + (-2a\sin 2\theta)^2 = a^2(\cos^2 2\theta + 4\sin^2 2\theta),$

$L = 8\displaystyle\int_{\pi/6}^{\pi/4}a\sqrt{\cos^2 2\theta + 4\sin^2 2\theta}\,d\theta$

29. **(a)** $A = \displaystyle\int_{\pi/2}^{\pi}\dfrac{1}{2}[(2\sin\theta)^2 - (2+2\cos\theta)^2]d\theta = 2\displaystyle\int_{\pi/2}^{\pi}[\sin^2\theta - (1+\cos\theta)^2]d\theta$

(b) $r^2 + (dr/d\theta)^2 = (2\sin\theta)^2 + (2\cos\theta)^2 = 4, \; L = \displaystyle\int_0^{\pi/2}2d\theta$

30. $A = \displaystyle\int_0^{\pi/3}\dfrac{1}{2}(a\sin 3\theta)^2 d\theta = \dfrac{a^2}{2}\displaystyle\int_0^{\pi/3}\sin^2 3\theta\, d\theta = \pi a^2/12$

31. $A = 4\displaystyle\int_0^{\pi/6}\dfrac{1}{2}(2a^2\cos 2\theta - a^2)d\theta = 2a^2\displaystyle\int_0^{\pi/6}(2\cos 2\theta - 1)d\theta = a^2(\sqrt{3} - \pi/3)$

32. $A = 4a^2\displaystyle\int_0^{\pi/6}(\cos^2 2\theta - 1/4)d\theta = a^2(\pi/6 + \sqrt{3}/4)$

33. $A = 2\displaystyle\int_{\pi/2}^{\pi}[\sin^2\theta - (1+\cos\theta)^2]d\theta = 2\displaystyle\int_{\pi/2}^{\pi}(-1 - 2\cos\theta - \cos 2\theta)d\theta = 4 - \pi$

34. **(a)** Eliminate the parameter to get
$x = 3 - (y-2)^2, \; (y-2)^2 = -(x-3)$
for $-6 \le x \le 3$ and $2 \le y \le 5$.

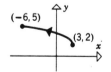

(b) $dy/dx = \dfrac{1}{-2t} = -\dfrac{1}{2}t^{-1}, \; d^2y/dx^2 = \dfrac{(1/2)t^{-2}}{-2t} = -\dfrac{1}{4}t^{-3}$; at $t_0 = 1$, $dy/dx = -1/2$ and
$d^2y/dx^2 = -1/4$, $x = 2$, $y = 3$ so the tangent line is $y - 3 = (-1/2)(x-2)$, $y = -x/2 + 4$.

35. **(a)** eliminate the parameter to get
$(x-1)^2/9 + (y+1)^2/4 = 1$ for
$-2 \le x \le 4$ and $-1 \le y \le 1$.

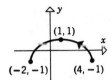

    (b) $dy/dx = \dfrac{2\cos\theta}{-3\sin\theta} = -\dfrac{2}{3}\cot\theta$, $d^2y/dx^2 = \dfrac{(2/3)\csc^2\theta}{-3\sin\theta} = -\dfrac{2}{9}\csc^3\theta$; at $\theta_0 = \pi/2$,
$dy/dx = 0$ and $d^2y/dx^2 = -2/9$, $x = 1$, $y = 1$ so the tangent line is $y = 1$.

36. **(a)** Eliminate the parameter to get
$y^2 - x^2/4 = 1$ for $-\infty < x < +\infty$
and $y \ge 1$.

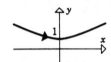

    (b) $dy/dx = \dfrac{\sec\theta\tan\theta}{2\sec^2\theta} = \dfrac{1}{2}\sin\theta$, $d^2y/dx^2 = \dfrac{(1/2)\cos\theta}{2\sec^2\theta} = \dfrac{1}{4}\cos^3\theta$; at $\theta_0 = \pi/3$,
$dy/dx = \sqrt{3}/4$ and $d^2y/dx^2 = 1/32$, $x = 2\sqrt{3}$, $y = 2$ so the tangent line is
$y - 2 = (\sqrt{3}/4)(x - 2\sqrt{3})$, $y = \sqrt{3}x/4 + 1/2$.

37. **(a)** Eliminate the parameter to get
$y = \ln(1/x) = -\ln x$ for
$1 \le x \le e^{-1}$ and $0 \le y \le 1$.

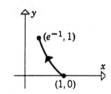

    (b) $dy/dx = \dfrac{1/t}{-1/t^2} = -t$, $d^2y/dx^2 = \dfrac{-1}{-1/t^2} = t^2$; at $t_0 = 2$, $dy/dx = -2$ and $d^2y/dx^2 = 4$,
$x = 1/2$, $y = \ln 2$ so the tangent line is $y - \ln 2 = -2(x - 1/2)$, $y = -2x + 1 + \ln 2$.

38. $(dx/dt)^2 + (dy/dt)^2 = (6t^2)^2 + (6t)^2 = 36t^2(t^2+1)$,
$$L = \int_{-4}^{4} 6|t|\sqrt{t^2+1}\,dt = 12\int_{0}^{4} t(t^2+1)^{1/2}dt = 4(17^{3/2} - 1)$$

39. $(dx/dt)^2 + (dy/dt)^2 = (-2\tan 2t)^2 + 2^2 = 4\sec^2 2t$, $L = \displaystyle\int_{0}^{\pi/6} 2\sec 2t\,dt = \ln(2 + \sqrt{3})$

40. $(dx/dt)^2 + (dy/dt)^2 = (-3\sin t)^2 + (3\cos t)^2 = 9,\ L = \int_0^{\pi} 3dt = 3\pi$

41. $(dx/dt)^2 + (dy/dt)^2 = (6t)^2 + (3t^2-3)^2 = (3t^2+3)^2,\ L = \int_0^1 (3t^2+3)dt = 4$

42. $(dx/dt)^2 + (dy/dt)^2 = (\sin t)^2 + (1-\cos t)^2 = 4\sin^2(t/2),$

   $L = \int_{-\pi}^{\pi} 2|\sin(t/2)|dt = 4\int_0^{\pi} \sin(t/2)dt = 8$

43. $r^2 + (dr/d\theta)^2 = (e^\theta)^2 + (e^\theta)^2 = 2e^{2\theta},\ L = \int_0^{2\pi} \sqrt{2}\,e^\theta d\theta = \sqrt{2}(e^{2\pi}-1)$

44. $dx/dt = -4t,\ dy/dt = 3t^2 - 3$

   (a)   horizontal when $dy/dt = 0$ and $dx/dt \neq 0$; $3t^2 - 3 = 0$, $t^2 = 1$, $t = \pm 1$ so (x,y) is $(-2,3)$
   or $(-2,7)$.

   (b)   vertical when $dx/dt = 0$ and $dy/dt \neq 0$; $-4t = 0$, $t = 0$ so (x,y) is $(0,5)$.

45. $dx/dt = -2\cos t,\ dy/dt = 1 - 2\sin t$

   (a)   horizontal when $dy/dt = 0$ and $dx/dt \neq 0$; $1 - 2\sin t = 0$, $\sin t = 1/2$, $t = \pi/6,\ 5\pi/6$ so
   (x,y) is $(0, \pi/6 + \sqrt{3})$ or $(0, 5\pi/6 - \sqrt{3})$.

   (b)   vertical when $dx/dt = 0$ and $dy/dt \neq 0$; $-2\cos t = 0$, $\cos t = 0$, $t = \pi/2$ so (x,y) is
   $(-1, \pi/2)$.

46. $dx/dt = 1/t,\ dy/dt = 2t - 4$

   (a)   horizontal when $dy/dt = 0$ and $dx/dt \neq 0$; $2t - 4 = 0$, $t = 2$ so (x,y) is $(\ln 2, -4)$.

   (b)   vertical when $dx/dt = 0$ and $dy/dt \neq 0$; $1/t = 0$ has no solution so the instantaneous
   direction of motion is never vertical.

47. $dy/dx = (2t-4)/(1/t) = 2t^2 - 4t,\ d^2y/dx^2 = (4t-4)/(1/t) = 4t(t-1)$. For $t > 0$, $d^2y/dx^2 = 0$
   when $t = 1$ and d^2y/dx^2 changes sign there so an inflection point occurs at $t = 1$.

48.   **(a)**   Let $x = t$, then $y = 2t + 3$.

   (b) $(x-2)^2 + (y/2)^2 = 1$, let $x - 2 = \cos t$ and $y/2 = \sin t$ to get $x = 2 + \cos t$, $y = 2\sin t$

49. $r = 2(1 + \cos\theta),\ dr/d\theta = -2\sin\theta$. When $\theta = \pi/2$, $\sin\theta = 1$, $\cos\theta = 0$, $r = 2$, $dr/d\theta = -2$ so
   $m = [(2)(0) + (1)(-2)]/[-(2)(1) + (0)(-2)] = 1$ and $\tan\psi = 2/(-2) = -1$, $\psi = 3\pi/4$.

50. $\tan \psi = r/(dr/d\theta) = (4\sin\theta)/(4\cos\theta) = \tan\theta$ so $\psi = \theta$ if $0 \le \theta < \pi$,

$$\tan\phi = \frac{8\sin\theta\cos\theta}{4(\cos^2\theta - \sin^2\theta)} - \frac{\sin 2\theta}{\cos 2\theta} = \tan 2\theta \text{ so } \phi = 2\theta \text{ if } 0 < \theta < \pi/2.$$

CHAPTER 14
Three-Dimensional Space; Vectors

EXERCISE SET 14.1

1. **(a)** $d = \sqrt{(2-0)^2 + (1-0)^2 + (3-0)^2} = \sqrt{4+1+9} = \sqrt{14}$; midpoint $(1, 1/2, 3/2)$
    (b) $d = \sqrt{(4-5)^2 + (1-2)^2 + (6-3)^2} = \sqrt{1+1+9} = \sqrt{11}$; midpoint $(9/2, 3/2, 9/2)$
    (c) $d = \sqrt{(3+2)^2 + (0+1)^2 + (5-3)^2} = \sqrt{23+1+4} = \sqrt{30}$; midpoint $(1/2, -1/2, 4)$
    (d) $d = \sqrt{(4+1)^2 + (3+1)^2 + (-2+3)^2} = \sqrt{25+16+1} = \sqrt{42}$; midpoint $(3/2, 1, -5/2)$

2. vertices: $(2,2,\pm 2)$, $(2,-2,\pm 2)$, $(-2,2,\pm 2)$, $(-2,-2,\pm 2)$

3. vertices: $(4,2,-2)$, $(4,2,1)$, $(4,1,1)$, $(4,1,-2)$, $(-6,1,1)$, $(-6,2,1)$, $(-6,2,-2)$, $(-6,1,-2)$

4. each side has length $\sqrt{14}$ so the triangle is equilateral.

5. **(a)** the sides have lengths 7, 14, and $7\sqrt{5}$; it is a right triangle because the sides satisfy the Pythagorean theorem, $(7\sqrt{5})^2 = 7^2 + 14^2$.
    (b) $(2,1,6)$ is the vertex of the $90°$ angle because it is opposite the longest side (the hypotenuse).
    (c) area $= (1/2)(\text{altitude})(\text{base}) = (1/2)(7)(14) = 49$

6. **(a)** 3   **(b)** 2   **(c)** 5

    (d) $\sqrt{(2)^2 + (-3)^2} = \sqrt{13}$ **(e)** $\sqrt{(-5)^2 + (-3)^2} = \sqrt{34}$ **(f)** $\sqrt{(-5)^2 + (2)^2} = \sqrt{29}$

7. The distance to the z-axis is the distance between (x_0, y_0, z_0) and $(0, 0, z_0)$ which is $\sqrt{x_0^2 + y_0^2}$; similarly, the distance to the x-axis is $\sqrt{y_0^2 + z_0^2}$ and the distance to the y-axis is $\sqrt{x_0^2 + z_0^2}$.

8. $x^2 + y^2 + z^2 = 64$ 9. $(x+2)^2 + (y-4)^2 + (z+1)^2 = 36$

10. $(x-5)^2 + (y+2)^2 + (z-4)^2 = 7$ 11. $x^2 + (y-1)^2 + z^2 = 9$

12. $(x+3)^2 + (y-5)^2 + (z+4)^2 = r^2$,
    (a) $r^2 = 4^2 = 16$ **(b)** $r^2 = 5^2 = 25$ **(c)** $r^2 = 3^2 = 9$

13. $(x-2)^2 + (y+1)^2 + (z+3)^2 = r^2$,
    (a) $r^2 = 3^2 = 9$ **(b)** $r^2 = 1^2 = 1$ **(c)** $r^2 = 2^2 = 4$

14. $(x - 1)^2 + y^2 + (z + 1)^2 = 16$

15. $r = \dfrac{1}{2}\sqrt{(-1 - 0)^2 + (2 - 2)^2 + (1 - 3)^2} = \dfrac{1}{2}\sqrt{5}$, center $(-1/2, 2, 2)$,
    $(x + 1/2)^2 + (y - 2)^2 + (z - 2)^2 = 5/4$

16. $r = \sqrt{(-1 - 0)^2 + (3 - 0)^2 + (2 - 0)^2} = \sqrt{14}$, $(x + 1)^2 + (y - 3)^2 + (z - 2)^2 = 14$

17. $r = \sqrt{(7 - 3)^2 + (2 + 2)^2 + (1 - 4)^2} = \sqrt{41}$, $(x - 3)^2 + (y + 2)^2 + (z - 4)^2 = 41$

18. $r = |[\text{distance between } (-3, 5, -4) \text{ and } (0, 0, 0)] \pm 1| = \sqrt{50} \pm 1$,
    $(x + 3)^2 + (y - 5)^2 + (z + 4)^2 = r^2 = (\sqrt{50} \pm 1)^2 = 51 \pm 10\sqrt{2}$

19. $r = |[\text{distance between } (0,0,0) \text{ and } (3, -2, 4)] \pm 1| = \sqrt{29} \pm 1$,
    $x^2 + y^2 + z^2 = r^2 = (\sqrt{29} \pm 1)^2 = 30 \pm 2\sqrt{29}$

20. $(x - 1)^2 + (y - 3)^2 + (z - 4)^2 = 25$; sphere, $C(1, 3, 4)$, $r = 5$

21. $(x + 5)^2 + (y + 2)^2 + (z + 1)^2 = 49$; sphere, $C(-5, -2, -1)$, $r = 7$

22. $x^2 + (y - 1/2)^2 + z^2 = 1/4$; sphere, $C(0, 1/2, 0)$, $r = 1/2$

23. $(x - 1/2)^2 + (y - 3/4)^2 + (z + 5/4)^2 = 54/16$; sphere, $C(1/2, 3/4, -5/4)$, $r = 3\sqrt{6}/4$

24. $(x + 1)^2 + (y - 1)^2 + (z + 1)^2 = 0$; the point $(-1, 1, -1)$

25. $(x - 3/2)^2 + (y + 2)^2 + (z - 4)^2 = -11/4$; no graph

26. Complete the square to get $x^2 + (y - 1)^2 + (z + 3)^2 = 16$; center $(0, 1, -3)$, radius 4. The distance between $P(1, 1, 1)$ and the center is $\sqrt{17} > 4$ so P is outside the sphere. The largest distance is $\sqrt{17} + 4$, the smallest is $\sqrt{17} - 4$.

27. Complete the square to get $(x + 1)^2 + (y - 1)^2 + (z - 2)^2 = 9$; center $(-1, 1, 2)$, radius 3. The distance between the origin and the center is $\sqrt{6} < 3$ so the origin is inside the sphere. The largest distance is $3 + \sqrt{6}$, the smallest is $3 - \sqrt{6}$.

28. $(x - 1)^2 + y^2 + (z + 4)^2 \leq 25$; all points on and inside the sphere of radius 5 with center at $(1, 0, -4)$.

29. $(y + 3)^2 + (z - 2)^2 > 16$; all points outside the circular cylinder $(y + 3)^2 + (z - 2)^2 = 16$.

30. $\sqrt{(x-1)^2 + (y+2)^2 + z^2} = 2\sqrt{x^2 + (y-1)^2 + (z-1)^2}$, square and simplify to get
$3x^2 + 3y^2 + 3z^2 + 2x - 12y - 8z + 3 = 0$, then complete the square to get
$(x + 1/3)^2 + (y - 2)^2 + (z - 4/3)^2 = 44/9$; center $(-1/3, 2, 4/3)$, radius $2\sqrt{11}/3$.

31. Let r be the radius of a styrofoam sphere. The distance from the origin to the center of the bowling ball is equal to the sum of the distance from the origin to the center of the styrofoam sphere nearest the origin and the distance between the center of this sphere and the center of the bowling ball so $\sqrt{3}R = \sqrt{3}r + r + R$, $(\sqrt{3} + 1)r = (\sqrt{3} - 1)R$, $r = \dfrac{\sqrt{3} - 1}{\sqrt{3} + 1}R = (2 - \sqrt{3})R$.

32. (a) 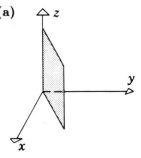   (b) 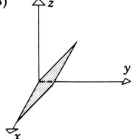   (c)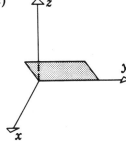

33. (a) 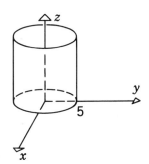   (b) 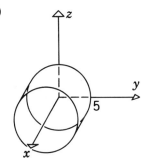   (c)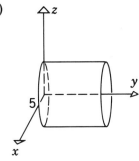

34. (a) 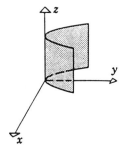   (b) 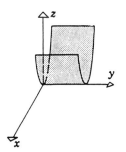   (c)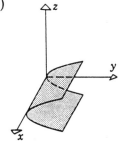

35. **(a)**

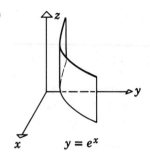

$y = e^x$

(b)

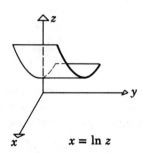

$x = \ln z$

(c)

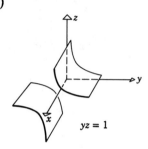

$yz = 1$

36. **(a)**

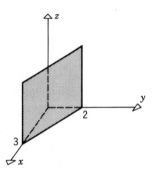

(b)

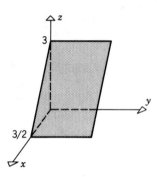

37. **(a)**

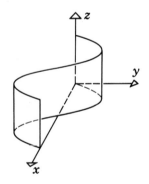

(b)

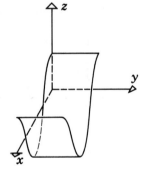

38. (a)

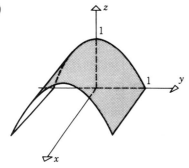

(b)

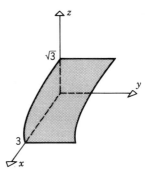

39. (a)

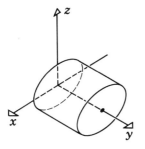

(b)

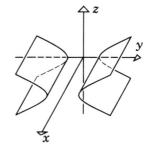

40.   **(a)** $(x - a)^2 + (z - a)^2 = a^2$ **(b)** $(x - a)^2 + (y - a)^2 = a^2$

   (c) $(y - a)^2 + (z - a)^2 = a^2$

41. $(a \sin \phi \cos \theta)^2 + (a \sin \phi \sin \theta)^2 + (a \cos \phi)^2 = a^2 \sin^2 \phi \cos^2 \theta + a^2 \sin^2 \phi \sin^2 \theta + a^2 \cos^2 \phi$

$$= a^2 \sin^2 \phi (\cos^2 \theta + \sin^2 \theta) + a^2 \cos^2 \phi$$

$$= a^2 \sin^2 \phi + a^2 \cos^2 \phi = a^2 (\sin^2 \phi + \cos^2 \phi) = a^2$$

42.   **(a)**   Complete the square to get $(x + G/2)^2 + (y + H/2)^2 + (z + I/2)^2 = K/4$, so the equation represents a sphere when $K > 0$, a point when $K = 0$, and no graph when $K < 0$.

   (b) $C(-G/2, -H/2, -I/2)$, $r = \sqrt{K}/2$

EXERCISE SET 14.2

1.

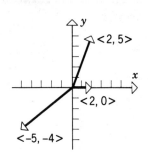

2.

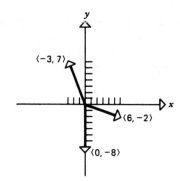

3.

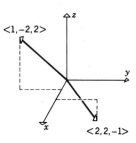

4.

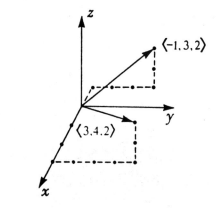

5.

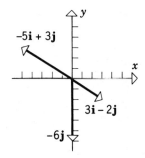

6.

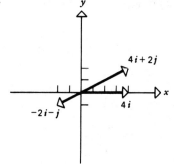

7.

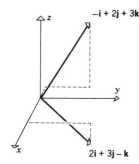

8.

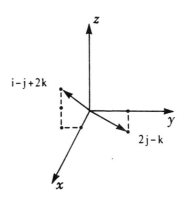

9. (a) $\langle 2-3, 8-5 \rangle = \langle -1, 3 \rangle$ (b) $\langle 0-7, 0-(-2) \rangle = \langle -7, 2 \rangle$
    (c) $\langle -4-(-6), -1-(-2) \rangle = \langle 2, 1 \rangle$ (d) $\langle -8-0, 7-0 \rangle = \langle -8, 7 \rangle$

10. (a) $\langle 4-1, 1-3 \rangle = \langle 3, -2 \rangle$ (b) $\langle 0-6, 0-(-4) \rangle = \langle -6, 4 \rangle$
    (c) $\langle -3-(-8), -2-(-1) \rangle = \langle 5, -1 \rangle$ (d) $\langle -3, -5 \rangle$

11. (a) $\langle -3, 6, 1 \rangle$ (b) $\langle 1, -3, -5 \rangle$ **12.** (a) $\langle -1, 6, 1 \rangle$ (b) $\langle 5, 0, 0 \rangle$

13. Let (x, y) be the terminal point, then $x - 1 = 3$, $x = 4$ and $y - (-2) = -2$, $y = -4$.
    The terminal point is $(4, -4)$.

14. Let (x, y) be the terminal point, then $x - 2 = 7$, $x = 9$ and $y - (-1) = 6$, $y = 5$.
    The terminal point is $(9,5)$.

15. Let (x, y) be the initial point, then $2 - x = -2$, $x = 4$ and $0 - y = 4$, $y = -4$.
    The initial point is $(4, -4)$.

16. Let (x, y, z) be the terminal point, then $x + 2 = 1$, $y - 1 = 2$, and $z - 4 = -3$ so $x = -1$,
    $y = 3$, and $z = 1$. The terminal point is $(-1, 3, 1)$.

17. Let (x, y, z) be the initial point, then $5 - x = -3$, $-y = 1$, and $-1 - z = 2$ so $x = 8$,
    $y = -1$, and $z = -3$. The initial point is $(8, -1, -3)$.

18. (a) $\langle -3, 4 \rangle$ (b) $\langle 26, 4 \rangle$ (c) $\langle -2, 2 \rangle$
    (d) $\langle -39, -12 \rangle$ (e) $\langle -38, 5 \rangle$ (f) $\langle -1, 0 \rangle$

19. (a) $-5\mathbf{i} - 2\mathbf{j}$ (b) $8\mathbf{i} + 10\mathbf{j}$ (c) $-2\mathbf{i} + 4\mathbf{j}$
    (d) $40\mathbf{i} + 36\mathbf{j}$ (e) $-20\mathbf{i} + 22\mathbf{j}$ (f) $-8\mathbf{i} - 8\mathbf{j}$

20. **(a)** $\langle 1, -2, 0 \rangle$
(b) $\langle 28, 0, -14 \rangle + \langle 3, 3, 9 \rangle = \langle 31, 3, -5 \rangle$
(c) $\langle 3, -1, -5 \rangle$
(d) $3(\langle 2, -1, 3 \rangle - \langle 28, 0, -14 \rangle) = 3\langle -26, -1, 17 \rangle = \langle -78, -3, 51 \rangle$
(e) $\langle -12, 0, 6 \rangle - \langle 8, 8, 24 \rangle = \langle -20, -8, -18 \rangle$
(f) $\langle 8, 0, -4 \rangle - \langle 3, 0, 6 \rangle = \langle 5, 0, -10 \rangle$

21. **(a)** $-\mathbf{i} + 4\mathbf{j} - 2\mathbf{k}$ **(b)** $18\mathbf{i} + 12\mathbf{j} - 6\mathbf{k}$ **(c)** $-\mathbf{i} - 5\mathbf{j} - 2\mathbf{k}$
(d) $40\mathbf{i} - 4\mathbf{j} - 4\mathbf{k}$ **(e)** $-2\mathbf{i} - 16\mathbf{j} - 18\mathbf{k}$ **(f)** $-\mathbf{i} + 13\mathbf{j} - 2\mathbf{k}$

22. **(a)** $\|\mathbf{v}\| = \sqrt{9 + 16} = 5$ **(b)** $\|\mathbf{v}\| = \sqrt{1 + 49} = 5\sqrt{2}$ **(c)** $\|\mathbf{v}\| = \sqrt{0 + 9} = 3$

23. **(a)** $\|\mathbf{v}\| = \sqrt{1 + 1} = \sqrt{2}$ **(b)** $\|\mathbf{v}\| = \sqrt{4 + 0} = 2$ **(c)** $\|\mathbf{v}\| = \sqrt{2 + 7} = 3$

24. **(a)** $\|\mathbf{v}\| = \sqrt{3}$ **(b)** $\|\mathbf{v}\| = \sqrt{21}$ **25.** **(a)** $\|\mathbf{v}\| = \sqrt{14}$ **(b)** $\|\mathbf{v}\| = 3$

26. **(a)** $\|\langle 2, -2 \rangle\| = 2\sqrt{2}$ **(b)** $\sqrt{10} + \sqrt{2}$
(c) $2\|\mathbf{u}\| + 2\|\mathbf{v}\| = 2\sqrt{10} + 2\sqrt{2}$ **(d)** $\|\langle 0, -18 \rangle\| = 18$

27. **(a)** $\|\langle 5, 4 \rangle\| = \sqrt{41}$ **(b)** $2 + 5 = 7$
(c) $3\|\mathbf{u}\| + 4\|\mathbf{v}\| = 3\sqrt{29} + 8$ **(d)** $\|\langle -3, -9 \rangle\| = 3\sqrt{10}$
(e) $\frac{1}{5}\langle 3, 4 \rangle = \langle 3/5, 4/5 \rangle$ **(f)** 1

28. **(a)** $\|\mathbf{u} + \mathbf{v}\| = \|\langle 2, 0, -1 \rangle\| = \sqrt{5}$ **(b)** $\|\mathbf{u}\| + \|\mathbf{v}\| = \sqrt{5} + \sqrt{2}$
(c) $\|3\mathbf{u}\| = 3\|\mathbf{u}\| = 3\sqrt{5}$ **(d)** $\|2\mathbf{u} - 3\mathbf{v}\| = \|\langle 4, -5, 3 \rangle\| = 5\sqrt{2}$

29. **(a)** $\|\mathbf{u} + \mathbf{v}\| = \|2\mathbf{i} - 2\mathbf{j} + 2\mathbf{k}\| = 2\sqrt{3}$ **(b)** $\|\mathbf{u}\| + \|\mathbf{v}\| = \sqrt{14} + \sqrt{2}$
(c) $\| -2\mathbf{u}\| + 2\|\mathbf{v}\| = 2\sqrt{14} + 2\sqrt{2}$ **(d)** $\|3\mathbf{u} - 5\mathbf{v} + \mathbf{w}\| = \| -12\mathbf{j} + 2\mathbf{k}\| = 2\sqrt{37}$
(e) $(1/\sqrt{6})\mathbf{i} + (1/\sqrt{6})\mathbf{j} - (2/\sqrt{6})\mathbf{k}$ **(f)** 1

30. $\mathbf{u} - 2\mathbf{x} = \mathbf{x} - \mathbf{w} + 3\mathbf{v}, \ 3\mathbf{x} = \mathbf{u} + \mathbf{w} - 3\mathbf{v}, \ \mathbf{x} = \frac{1}{3}(\mathbf{u} + \mathbf{w} - 3\mathbf{v}) = \langle 2/3, 2/3 \rangle$

31. $6\mathbf{x} = 2\mathbf{u} - \mathbf{v} - \mathbf{w} = \langle -4, 6 \rangle, \mathbf{x} = \langle -2/3, 1 \rangle$

32. $\mathbf{u} = \langle -5, 8 \rangle, \mathbf{v} = \langle 7, -11 \rangle$

33. $\mathbf{u} = \frac{5}{7}\mathbf{i} + \frac{2}{7}\mathbf{j} + \frac{1}{7}\mathbf{k}, \ \mathbf{v} = \frac{8}{7}\mathbf{i} - \frac{1}{7}\mathbf{j} - \frac{4}{7}\mathbf{k}$

34. Take **w** as the diagonal of a parallelogram with **u** and **v** along adjacent sides as shown. Then **w** can be written as the sum $c_1\mathbf{u} + c_2\mathbf{v}$.

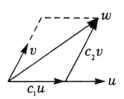

35. Take **z** as the diagonal of a parallelepiped with **u**, **v**, and **w** along its edges as shown. Then **z** can be written as the sum $c_1\mathbf{u} + c_2\mathbf{v} + c_3\mathbf{w}$.

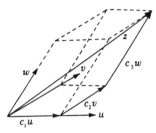

36. $c_1\mathbf{u} + c_2\mathbf{v} = (2c_1 + 4c_2)\mathbf{i} + (-c_1 + 2c_2)\mathbf{j} = -4\mathbf{j}$, so $2c_1 + 4c_2 = 0$ and $-c_1 + 2c_2 = -4$ which gives $c_1 = 2$, $c_2 = -1$.

37. $c_1\mathbf{u} + c_2\mathbf{v} = \langle c_1 - 2c_2, -3c_1 + 6c_2 \rangle = \langle 3, 5 \rangle$, so $c_1 - 2c_2 = 3$ and $-3c_1 + 6c_2 = 5$ which has no solution.

38. Equate corresponding components to get the system of equations $c_1 + 3c_2 = -1$, $2c_2 + c_3 = 1$, and $c_1 + c_3 = 5$. Solve to get $c_1 = 2$, $c_2 = -1$, and $c_3 = 3$.

39. Equate corresponding components to get the system of equations $c_1 + 3c_2 + 4c_3 = 2$, $-c_1 - c_3 = 1$, and $c_2 + c_3 = -1$. From the second and third equations, $c_1 = -1 - c_3$ and $c_2 = -1 - c_3$; substitute these into the first equation to get $-4 = 2$, which is nonsense so the system has no solution.

40. $\|k\mathbf{v}\| = |k|\,\|\mathbf{v}\| = |k|5 = 3$, $|k| = 3/5$, $k = \pm 3/5$

42. $\|-1 + 4\mathbf{j}\| = \sqrt{17}$ so the required vector is $(-1/\sqrt{17})\,\mathbf{i} + (4/\sqrt{17})\,\mathbf{j}$

43. $\|3\mathbf{i} - 4\mathbf{j}\| = 5$ so the required vector is $-\dfrac{1}{5}(3\mathbf{i} - 4\mathbf{j}) = -\dfrac{3}{5}\mathbf{i} + \dfrac{4}{5}\mathbf{j}$

44. $\|2\mathbf{i} - \mathbf{j} - 2\mathbf{k}\| = 3$ so the required vector is $\dfrac{2}{3}\mathbf{i} - \dfrac{1}{3}\mathbf{j} - \dfrac{2}{3}\mathbf{k}$

45. $\|6\mathbf{i} - 4\mathbf{j} + 2\mathbf{k}\| = 2\sqrt{14}$ so the required vector is $-(3\mathbf{i} - 2\mathbf{j} + \mathbf{k})/\sqrt{14}$

46. $\overrightarrow{AB} = 4\mathbf{i} - 3\mathbf{j}$, $\|\overrightarrow{AB}\| = 5$ so the required vector is $\dfrac{4}{5}\mathbf{i} - \dfrac{3}{5}\mathbf{j}$

47. $\overrightarrow{AB} = 4\mathbf{i} + \mathbf{j} - \mathbf{k}$, $\|\overrightarrow{AB}\| = 3\sqrt{2}$ so the required vector is $(4\mathbf{i} + \mathbf{j} - \mathbf{k})/(3\sqrt{2})$

48. $3\mathbf{v} = -6\mathbf{i} + 9\mathbf{j}$ 　　　　　　　　　　　　　**49.** $-\dfrac{1}{2}\mathbf{v} = \langle -3/2, 2\rangle$

50. $2\mathbf{v} = \langle 14, 0, -12\rangle$ 　　　　　　　　　　　**51.** $-2\mathbf{v} = 6\mathbf{i} - 8\mathbf{j} - 2\mathbf{k}$

52. $\|\mathbf{r}\| = \sqrt{x^2 + y^2} = 1$, circle of radius 1 and center at $(0,0)$.

53. $\|\mathbf{r} - \mathbf{r}_0\| = \|\langle x - x_0,\, y - y_0\rangle\| = \sqrt{(x - x_0)^2 + (y - y_0)^2} = 1$, circle of radius 1 and center at (x_0, y_0).

54. The sum of the distances between (x, y) and the points (x_1, y_1), (x_2, y_2) is the constant k so the set consists of all points on the ellipse with foci at (x_1, y_1) and (x_2, y_2), and major axis of length k.

55. **(a)** $\|\mathbf{r}\| = \sqrt{x^2 + y^2 + z^2} = 2$, sphere of radius 2 with center at $(0,0,0)$.

　　　(b) $\|\mathbf{r} - \mathbf{r}_0\| = \sqrt{(x - x_0)^2 + (y - y_0)^2 + (z - z_0)^2} = 3$, sphere of radius 3 with center at (x_0, y_0, z_0).

　　　(c) $\|\mathbf{r} - \mathbf{r}_0\| = \sqrt{(x - x_0)^2 + (y - y_0)^2 + (z - z_0)^2} \le 1$, all points on or inside the sphere of radius 1 with center at (x_0, y_0, z_0).

56. Choose two points on the line, for example $P_1(0, 2)$ and $P_2(1, 5)$ then $\overrightarrow{P_1 P_2} = \langle 1, 3\rangle$ is parallel to the line, $\|\langle 1, 3\rangle\| = \sqrt{10}$, so $\langle 1/\sqrt{10}, 3/\sqrt{10}\rangle$ and $\langle -1/\sqrt{10}, -3/\sqrt{10}\rangle$ are unit vectors parallel to the line.

57. **(a)** Choose two points on the line, for example $P_1(0, 4)$ and $P_2(1, 3)$ then $\overrightarrow{P_1 P_2} = \langle 1, -1\rangle$ is parallel to the line, $\|\langle 1, -1\rangle\| = \sqrt{2}$ so $\langle 1/\sqrt{2}, -1/\sqrt{2}\rangle$ and $\langle -1/\sqrt{2}, 1/\sqrt{2}\rangle$ are unit vectors parallel to the line.

　　　(b) Pick any line that is perpendicular to the line $x + y = 4$, for example $y = x$, and proceed as in part (a) to get $\langle 1/\sqrt{2}, 1/\sqrt{2}\rangle$ and $\langle -1/\sqrt{2}, -1/\sqrt{2}\rangle$.

58. Let $R(x, y)$ be the required point then

$$\overrightarrow{PR} = \frac{3}{4}\,\overrightarrow{PQ},\ \langle x - 2,\, y - 3\rangle = \frac{3}{4}\langle 5, -7\rangle = \langle 15/4,\, -21/4\rangle \text{ so } x - 2 = 15/4,\ x = 23/4 \text{ and }$$
$y - 3 = -21/4$, $y = -9/4$. The point is $(23/4,\, -9/4)$.

59. Let $R(x,y)$ be the required point then $\overrightarrow{QR} = 3/4\,\overrightarrow{QP}$,

$\langle x-7,\ y+4\rangle = 3/4\langle -5,7\rangle = \langle -15/4,\ 21/4\rangle$ so $x-7 = -15/4$, $x = 13/4$ and $y+4 = 21/4$, $y = 5/4$. The point is $(13/4,\ 21/4)$.

60. $\langle\cos 135°,\ \sin 135°\rangle = \langle -1/\sqrt{2}, 1/\sqrt{2}\rangle$

61. **(a)** $\langle\cos(\pi/3),\ \sin(\pi/3)\rangle = \langle 1/2,\ \sqrt{3}/2\rangle$
(b) $4\langle\cos(3\pi/4),\ \sin(3\pi/4)\rangle = \langle -2\sqrt{2},\ 2\sqrt{2}\rangle$

62. $\|(\mathbf{i}+\mathbf{j}) + (\mathbf{i}-2\mathbf{j})\| = \|2\mathbf{i}-\mathbf{j}\| = \sqrt{5}$

63. Let A, B, C be the vertices $(0,0)$, $(1,3)$, $(2,4)$ and D the fourth vertex (x,y). For the parallelogram ABCD, $\overrightarrow{AD} = \overrightarrow{BC}$, $\langle x,y\rangle = \langle 1,1\rangle$ so $x = 1$, $y = 1$ and D is at $(1,1)$. For the parallelogram ACBD, $\overrightarrow{AD} = \overrightarrow{CB}$, $\langle x,y\rangle = \langle -1,-1\rangle$ so $x = -1$, $y = -1$ and D is at $(-1,-1)$.

64. Place $\mathbf{u}$ and $\mathbf{v}$ tip to tail so that $\mathbf{u}+\mathbf{v}$ is the vector from the initial point of $\mathbf{u}$ to the terminal point of $\mathbf{v}$. The shortest distance between two points is along the line joining these points so $\|\mathbf{u}+\mathbf{v}\| \le \|\mathbf{u}\| + \|\mathbf{v}\|$.

65. Use an analytic approach as illustrated in the text.

66. Use an analytic approach as illustrated in the text.

67. Draw the triangles with sides formed by the vectors $\mathbf{u}$, $\mathbf{v}$, $\mathbf{u}+\mathbf{v}$ and $k\mathbf{u}$, $k\mathbf{v}$, $k\mathbf{u}+k\mathbf{v}$. By similar triangles, $k(\mathbf{u}+\mathbf{v}) = k\mathbf{u}+k\mathbf{v}$.

68. Let $\mathbf{a}$, $\mathbf{b}$, $\mathbf{c}$, $\mathbf{d}$ be vectors along the sides of the quadrilateral and A, B, C, D the corresponding midpoints, then

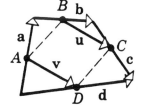

$\mathbf{u} = \dfrac{1}{2}\mathbf{b} + \dfrac{1}{2}\mathbf{c}$ and

$\mathbf{v} = \dfrac{1}{2}\mathbf{d} - \dfrac{1}{2}\mathbf{a}$ but $\mathbf{d} = \mathbf{a}+\mathbf{b}+\mathbf{c}$ so

$\mathbf{v} = \dfrac{1}{2}(\mathbf{a}+\mathbf{b}+\mathbf{c}) - \dfrac{1}{2}\mathbf{a} = \dfrac{1}{2}\mathbf{b} + \dfrac{1}{2}\mathbf{c} = \mathbf{u}$

thus ABCD is a parallelogram because sides AD and BC are equal and parallel.

69. Let **a**, **b**, **c** be vectors along the sides of the triangle and A,B the midpoints of **a** and **b**, then

$$u = \frac{1}{2}a - \frac{1}{2}b = \frac{1}{2}(a - b) = \frac{1}{2}c$$

so **u** is parallel to **c** and half as long.

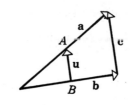

70. The sum is **0** (see diagram)

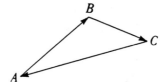

71. $\overrightarrow{AB} = \overrightarrow{AM} + \overrightarrow{MB}$,

$\overrightarrow{AC} = \overrightarrow{AM} + \overrightarrow{MC}$; add to get

$\overrightarrow{AB} + \overrightarrow{AC} = 2\,\overrightarrow{AM} + \overrightarrow{MB} + \overrightarrow{MC}$ but

$\overrightarrow{MB} = -\,\overrightarrow{MC}$ so $\overrightarrow{AB} + \overrightarrow{AC} = 2\,\overrightarrow{AM}$.

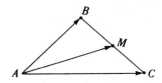

72. $\overrightarrow{AB} = \overrightarrow{AM} + \overrightarrow{MN} + \overrightarrow{NB}$,

$\overrightarrow{CD} = \overrightarrow{CM} + \overrightarrow{MN} + \overrightarrow{ND}$ where

$\overrightarrow{AM} = -\,\overrightarrow{CM}$ and $\overrightarrow{NB} = -\,\overrightarrow{ND}$;

add to get $\overrightarrow{AB} + \overrightarrow{CD} = 2\,\overrightarrow{MN}$

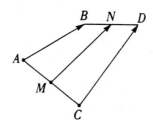

73. $\overrightarrow{AB} = \overrightarrow{AM} + \overrightarrow{MN} + \overrightarrow{NB}$,

$\overrightarrow{AD} = \overrightarrow{AM} + \overrightarrow{MN} + \overrightarrow{ND}$,

$\overrightarrow{CB} = \overrightarrow{CM} + \overrightarrow{MN} + \overrightarrow{NB}$,

$\overrightarrow{CD} = \overrightarrow{CM} + \overrightarrow{MN} + \overrightarrow{ND}$, where

$\overrightarrow{AM} = -\,\overrightarrow{CM}$ and $\overrightarrow{NB} = -\,\overrightarrow{ND}$;

add to get

$\overrightarrow{AB} + \overrightarrow{AD} + \overrightarrow{CB} + \overrightarrow{CD} = 4\,\overrightarrow{MN}$

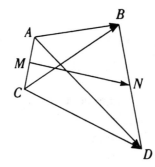

74. $\overrightarrow{AP} = t\,\overrightarrow{PB}$, $\mathbf{r} - \mathbf{a} = t(\mathbf{b} - \mathbf{r})$, solve for $\mathbf{r}$ to get $\mathbf{r} = \dfrac{\mathbf{a} + t\mathbf{b}}{1 + t}$

75. $\displaystyle\sum_{k=1}^{n} \overrightarrow{PP_k} = \sum_{k=1}^{n}(\mathbf{r}_k - \mathbf{r}) = \sum_{k=1}^{n}\mathbf{r}_k - \sum_{k=1}^{n}\mathbf{r} = \sum_{k=1}^{n}\mathbf{r}_k - n\mathbf{r} = 0$, $\mathbf{r} = \dfrac{1}{n}\sum_{k=1}^{n}\mathbf{r}_k$.

76. (a) $\mathbf{r}_1 = \mathbf{i} + \mathbf{j}$, $\mathbf{r}_2 = 3\mathbf{i} + 3\mathbf{j}$, $\mathbf{r}_3 = 5\mathbf{i}$, $\mathbf{r} = \dfrac{1}{3}\displaystyle\sum_{k=1}^{3}\mathbf{r}_k = 3\mathbf{i} + \dfrac{4}{3}\mathbf{j}$; centroid is at $(3, 4/3)$.

77. (a) $\mathbf{r}_1 = -\mathbf{i} + 2\mathbf{j}$, $\mathbf{r}_2 = 2\mathbf{i} + 3\mathbf{j}$, $\mathbf{r}_3 = 5\mathbf{i} - 2\mathbf{j}$, $\mathbf{r}_4 = -\mathbf{j}$, $\mathbf{r} = \dfrac{1}{4}\displaystyle\sum_{k=1}^{4}\mathbf{r}_k = \dfrac{3}{2}\mathbf{i} + \dfrac{1}{2}\mathbf{j}$;

   centroid is at $(3/2, 1/2)$.

EXERCISE SET 14.3

1. (a) $(1)(6) + (2)(-8) = -10$ (b) $(-7)(0) + (-3)(1) = -3$
   (c) $(1)(8) + (-3)(-2) + (7)(-2) = 0$ (d) $(-3)(4) + (1)(2) + (2)(-5) = -20$

2. (a) $\cos\theta = (-10)/[(\sqrt{5})(10)] = -1/\sqrt{5}$
   (b) $\cos\theta = (-3)/[(\sqrt{58})(1)] = -3/\sqrt{58}$
   (c) $\cos\theta = 0$
   (d) $\cos\theta = (-20)/[(\sqrt{14})(\sqrt{45})] = -20/(3\sqrt{70})$

3. (a) $\mathbf{u} \cdot \mathbf{v} = -34 < 0$, obtuse   (b) $\mathbf{u} \cdot \mathbf{v} = 6 > 0$, acute
   (c) $\mathbf{u} \cdot \mathbf{v} = -1 < 0$, obtuse   (d) $\mathbf{u} \cdot \mathbf{v} = 0$, orthogonal

4. (a) $(12/13)\mathbf{i} - (8/13)\mathbf{j}$ (b) $\langle 0, 0\rangle$
   (c) $-(80/13)\mathbf{i} - (16/13)\mathbf{k}$ (d) $\langle 32/89, 12/89, 16/89\rangle$

5. (a) $(14/13)\mathbf{i} + (21/13)\mathbf{j}$ (b) $\langle 2, 6\rangle$
   (c) $-(11/13)\mathbf{i} + \mathbf{j} + (55/13)\mathbf{k}$ (d) $\langle -32/89, -12/89, 73/89\rangle$

6. Use formula (9) of this section to get
   (a) $2/5$ (b) $6/\sqrt{5}$ (c) 2 (d) $37/7$

8. By inspection, $2\mathbf{i} + 3\mathbf{j}$ is orthogonal to $3\mathbf{i} - 2\mathbf{j}$, $\|2\mathbf{i} + 3\mathbf{j}\| = \sqrt{13}$ so $\pm(2\mathbf{i} + 3\mathbf{j})/\sqrt{13}$ are the desired vectors.

9. **(a)** $\langle 1,2 \rangle \cdot (\langle 28, -14 \rangle + \langle 6,0 \rangle) = \langle 1,2 \rangle \cdot \langle 34, -14 \rangle = 6$

  (b) $\|6\mathbf{w}\| = 6\|\mathbf{w}\| = 36$ **(c)** $24\sqrt{5}$ **(d)** $24\sqrt{5}$

10. **(a)** The dot product of a vector $\mathbf{u}$ and a scalar $\mathbf{v} \cdot \mathbf{w}$ is not defined.

  (b) The sum of a scalar $\mathbf{u} \cdot \mathbf{v}$ and a vector $\mathbf{w}$ is not defined.

  (c) $\mathbf{u} \cdot \mathbf{v}$ is not a vector.

  (d) The dot product of a scalar k and a vector $\mathbf{u} + \mathbf{v}$ is not defined.

11. Let A, B, and C be the vertices $(-1,0)$, $(2,-1)$, and $(1,4)$ with corresponding interior angles α, β, and γ, then

$$\cos \alpha = \frac{\overrightarrow{AB} \cdot \overrightarrow{AC}}{\|\overrightarrow{AB}\|\,\|\overrightarrow{AC}\|} = \frac{\langle 3,-1 \rangle \cdot \langle 2,4 \rangle}{\sqrt{10}\sqrt{20}} = 1/(5\sqrt{2})$$

$$\cos \beta = \frac{\overrightarrow{BA} \cdot \overrightarrow{BC}}{\|\overrightarrow{BA}\|\,\|\overrightarrow{BC}\|} = \frac{\langle -3,1 \rangle \cdot \langle -1,5 \rangle}{\sqrt{10}\sqrt{26}} = 4/\sqrt{65}$$

$$\cos \gamma = \frac{\overrightarrow{CA} \cdot \overrightarrow{CB}}{\|\overrightarrow{CA}\|\,\|\overrightarrow{CB}\|} = \frac{\langle -2,-4 \rangle \cdot \langle 1,-5 \rangle}{\sqrt{20}\sqrt{26}} = 9/\sqrt{130}$$

12. By inspection, $3\mathbf{i} - 4\mathbf{j}$ is orthogonal to and has the same length as $4\mathbf{i} + 3\mathbf{j}$

  so $\mathbf{u}_1 = (4\mathbf{i} + 3\mathbf{j}) + (3\mathbf{i} - 4\mathbf{j}) = 7\mathbf{i} - \mathbf{j}$ and $\mathbf{u}_2 = (4\mathbf{i} + 3\mathbf{j}) + (-1)(3\mathbf{i} - 4\mathbf{j}) = \mathbf{i} + 7\mathbf{j}$ each make an angle of $45°$ with $4\mathbf{i} + 3\mathbf{j}$; unit vectors in the directions of $\mathbf{u}_1$ and $\mathbf{u}_2$ are $(7\mathbf{i} - \mathbf{j})/\sqrt{50}$ and $(\mathbf{i} + 7\mathbf{j})/\sqrt{50}$.

13. $\overrightarrow{AB} = \langle 1,3,-2 \rangle$, $\overrightarrow{BC} = \langle 4,-2,-1 \rangle$, $\overrightarrow{AB} \cdot \overrightarrow{BC} = 0$ so $\overrightarrow{AB}$ and $\overrightarrow{BC}$ are orthogonal; it is a right triangle with the right angle at vertex B.

14. $\overrightarrow{AB} \cdot \overrightarrow{AP} = [2\mathbf{i} + \mathbf{j} + 2\mathbf{k}] \cdot [(k-1)\mathbf{i} + (k+1)\mathbf{j} + (k-3)\mathbf{k}]$

  $= 2(k-1) + (k+1) + 2(k-3) = 5k - 7 = 0, k = 7/5.$

15. **(a)** $\mathbf{r} \cdot \mathbf{r}_0 = x_0 x + y_0 y = 0$ where $\mathbf{r}$ is perpendicular to $\mathbf{r}_0$; the line through the origin and perpendicular to $\mathbf{r}_0$.

  (b) $(\mathbf{r} - \mathbf{r}_0) \cdot \mathbf{r}_0 = x_0(x - x_0) + y_0(y - y_0) = 0$ where the vector from (x_0, y_0) to (x, y) is perpendicular to $\mathbf{r}_0$; the line through (x_0, y_0) and perpendicular to $\mathbf{r}_0$.

  (c) $\mathbf{r} \cdot (\mathbf{r} - \mathbf{r}_0) = x(x - x_0) + y(y - y_0) = (x - x_0/2)^2 + (y - y_0/2)^2 - x_0^2/4 - y_0^2/4 = 0$; circle with center at the midpoint of $\mathbf{r}_0$ and radius $\|\mathbf{r}_0\|/2$.

16. If $\mathbf{a} \cdot \mathbf{b} = \mathbf{a} \cdot \mathbf{c}$ then $\mathbf{a} \cdot \mathbf{b} - \mathbf{a} \cdot \mathbf{c} = 0$, $\mathbf{a} \cdot (\mathbf{b} - \mathbf{c}) = 0$, which implies that $\mathbf{a}$ and $\mathbf{b} - \mathbf{c}$ are orthogonal, it does not follow that $\mathbf{b} = \mathbf{c}$.

17. (a) $\mathbf{a} \cdot \mathbf{b} = 0$, $4k + 3 = 0$, $k = -3/4$

(b) Use $\mathbf{a} \cdot \mathbf{b} = \|\mathbf{a}\| \, \|\mathbf{b}\| \cos\theta$ to get $4k + 3 = \sqrt{k^2 + 1}\,(5) \cos(\pi/4)$, $4k + 3 = 5\sqrt{k^2 + 1}/\sqrt{2}$
Square both sides and rearrange to get $7k^2 + 48k - 7 = 0$, $(7k - 1)(k + 7) = 0$ so $k = -7$ (invalid) or $k = 1/7$.

(c) Proceed as in (b) with $\theta = \pi/6$ to get $11k^2 - 96k + 39 = 0$ and use the quadratic formula to get $k = \left(48 \pm 25\sqrt{3}\right)/11$.

(d) If $\mathbf{a}$ and $\mathbf{b}$ are parallel then $\theta = 0$ or π so $\mathbf{a} \cdot \mathbf{b} = \pm\|\mathbf{a}\| \, \|\mathbf{b}\|$, $4k + 3 = \pm 5\sqrt{k^2 + 1}$, $9k^2 - 24k + 16 = 0$, $(3k - 4)^2 = 0$, $k = 4/3$.

18. (a) $\|\mathbf{u}\| = \sqrt{3}$ so $\cos\alpha = \cos\beta = 1/\sqrt{3}$, $\cos\gamma = -1/\sqrt{3}$, $\alpha = \beta = 55°$, $\gamma = 125°$

(b) $\|\mathbf{u}\| = 3$ so $\cos\alpha = 2/3$, $\cos\beta = -2/3$, $\cos\gamma = 1/3$, $\alpha = 48°$, $\beta = 132°$, $\gamma = 71°$

(c) $\|\mathbf{u}\| = 7$ so $\cos\alpha = 3/7$, $\cos\beta = -2/7$, $\cos\gamma = -6/7$, $\alpha = 65°$, $\beta = 107°$, $\gamma = 149°$

(d) $\|\mathbf{u}\| = 5$, $\cos\alpha = 3/5$, $\cos\beta = 0$, $\cos\gamma = -4/5$, $\alpha = 53°$, $\beta = 90°$, $\gamma = 143°$

19. $\cos^2\alpha + \cos^2\beta + \cos^2\gamma = \dfrac{u_1^2}{\|\mathbf{u}\|^2} + \dfrac{u_2^2}{\|\mathbf{u}\|^2} + \dfrac{u_3^2}{\|\mathbf{u}\|^2} = \left(u_1^2 + u_2^2 + u_3^2\right)/\|\mathbf{u}\|^2 = \|\mathbf{u}\|^2/\|\mathbf{u}\|^2 = 1$

20. Let $\mathbf{u}_1 = \|\mathbf{u}_1\|\langle\cos\alpha_1, \cos\beta_1, \cos\gamma_1\rangle$, $\mathbf{u}_2 = \|\mathbf{u}_2\|\langle\cos\alpha_2, \cos\beta_2, \cos\gamma_2\rangle$,

$\mathbf{u}_1$ and $\mathbf{u}_2$ are perpendicular if and only if $\mathbf{u}_1 \cdot \mathbf{u}_2 = 0$ so

$\|\mathbf{u}_1\| \, \|\mathbf{u}_2\|(\cos\alpha_1 \cos\alpha_2 + \cos\beta_1 \cos\beta_2 + \cos\gamma_1 \cos\gamma_2) = 0$,

$\cos\alpha_1 \cos\alpha_2 + \cos\beta_1 \cos\beta_2 + \cos\gamma_1 \cos\gamma_2 = 0$.

21. (a) $D = |3 - 8 + 7|/\sqrt{9 + 16} = 2/5$ (b) $D = |-6 + 5 - 1|/\sqrt{4 + 1} = 2/\sqrt{5}$

(c) $D = |4 + 6 - 8|/\sqrt{4 + 1} = 2/\sqrt{5}$

22. (a) $\overrightarrow{AP} = -4\mathbf{i} + 2\mathbf{k}$, $\overrightarrow{AB} = -3\mathbf{i} + 2\mathbf{j} - 4\mathbf{k}$, $\|\text{proj}_{\overrightarrow{AB}} \overrightarrow{AP}\| = |\overrightarrow{AP} \cdot \overrightarrow{AB}|/\|\overrightarrow{AB}\| = 4/\sqrt{29}$.

(b) $\|\overrightarrow{AP}\| = \sqrt{20}$, $\sqrt{20 - 16/29} = \sqrt{564/29}$

23. (a) $\overrightarrow{AP} = 2\mathbf{i} + 2\mathbf{j} + 3\mathbf{k}$, $\overrightarrow{AB} = -2\mathbf{i} + \mathbf{j} + 2\mathbf{k}$, $\|\text{proj}_{\overrightarrow{AB}} \overrightarrow{AP}\| = |\overrightarrow{AP} \cdot \overrightarrow{AB}|/\|\overrightarrow{AB}\| = 4/3$

(b) $\|\overrightarrow{AP}\| = \sqrt{17}$, $\sqrt{17 - 16/9} = \sqrt{137/3}$

24. $W = \mathbf{F} \cdot \overrightarrow{PQ}$

$= \|\mathbf{F}\|\,\|\overrightarrow{PQ}\|\cos 45°$

$= (50)(100)\left(\sqrt{2}/2\right)$

$= 2500\sqrt{2} \text{ N} \cdot \text{m}$

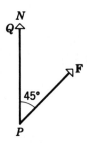

25.   Let P and Q be the points $(1,3)$ and $(4,7)$ then $\overrightarrow{PQ} = 3\mathbf{i} + 4\mathbf{j}$ so $W = \mathbf{F} \cdot \overrightarrow{PQ} = -12$ ft·lb.

26. $\mathbf{u} + \mathbf{v}$ and $\mathbf{u} - \mathbf{v}$ are vectors along the diagonals,

$(\mathbf{u} + \mathbf{v}) \cdot (\mathbf{u} - \mathbf{v}) = \mathbf{u} \cdot \mathbf{u} - \mathbf{u} \cdot \mathbf{v} + \mathbf{v} \cdot \mathbf{u} - \mathbf{v} \cdot \mathbf{v} = \|\mathbf{u}\|^2 - \|\mathbf{v}\|^2$ so $(\mathbf{u} + \mathbf{v}) \cdot (\mathbf{u} - \mathbf{v}) = 0$

if and only if $\|\mathbf{u}\| = \|\mathbf{v}\|$.

27.   The diagonals have lengths $\|\mathbf{u} + \mathbf{v}\|$ and $\|\mathbf{u} - \mathbf{v}\|$ but

$\|\mathbf{u} + \mathbf{v}\|^2 = (\mathbf{u} + \mathbf{v}) \cdot (\mathbf{u} + \mathbf{v}) = \|\mathbf{u}\|^2 + 2\mathbf{u} \cdot \mathbf{v} + \|\mathbf{v}\|^2$, and

$\|\mathbf{u} - \mathbf{v}\|^2 = (\mathbf{u} - \mathbf{v}) \cdot (\mathbf{u} + \mathbf{v}) = \|\mathbf{u}\|^2 - 2\mathbf{u} \cdot \mathbf{v} + \|\mathbf{v}\|^2$. If the parallelogram is a rectangle then
$\mathbf{u} \cdot \mathbf{v} = 0$ so $\|\mathbf{u} + \mathbf{v}\|^2 = \|\mathbf{u} - \mathbf{v}\|^2$; the diagonals are equal. If the diagonals are equal, then
$4\mathbf{u} \cdot \mathbf{v} = 0$, $\mathbf{u} \cdot \mathbf{v} = 0$ so $\mathbf{u}$ is perpendicular to $\mathbf{v}$ and hence the parallelogram is a rectangle.

28. $\|\mathbf{u} + \mathbf{v}\|^2 = (\mathbf{u} + \mathbf{v}) \cdot (\mathbf{u} + \mathbf{v}) = \|\mathbf{u}\|^2 + 2\mathbf{u} \cdot \mathbf{v} + \|\mathbf{v}\|^2$ and

$\|\mathbf{u} - \mathbf{v}\|^2 = (\mathbf{u} - \mathbf{v}) \cdot (\mathbf{u} - \mathbf{v}) = \|\mathbf{u}\|^2 - 2\mathbf{u} \cdot \mathbf{v} + \|\mathbf{v}\|^2$, add to get

$\|\mathbf{u} + \mathbf{v}\|^2 + \|\mathbf{u} - \mathbf{v}\|^2 = 2\|\mathbf{u}\|^2 + 2\|\mathbf{v}\|^2$

29. $\|\mathbf{u} + \mathbf{v}\|^2 = (\mathbf{u} + \mathbf{v}) \cdot (\mathbf{u} + \mathbf{v}) = \|\mathbf{u}\|^2 + 2\mathbf{u} \cdot \mathbf{v} + \|\mathbf{v}\|^2$ and

$\|\mathbf{u} - \mathbf{v}\|^2 = (\mathbf{u} - \mathbf{v}) \cdot (\mathbf{u} - \mathbf{v}) = \|\mathbf{u}\|^2 - 2\mathbf{u} \cdot \mathbf{v} + \|\mathbf{v}\|^2$, subtract to get

$\|\mathbf{u} + \mathbf{v}\|^2 - \|\mathbf{u} - \mathbf{v}\|^2 = 4\mathbf{u} \cdot \mathbf{v}$, the result follows by dividing both sides by 4.

30.   Let k be the length of an edge and
introduce a coordinate system as
shown in the figure, then

$\mathbf{d} = \langle k, k, k \rangle, \mathbf{f} = \langle k, k, 0 \rangle$,

$\cos\theta = \dfrac{\mathbf{d} \cdot \mathbf{f}}{\|\mathbf{d}\|\,\|\mathbf{f}\|} = \dfrac{2k^2}{\left(k\sqrt{3}\right)\left(k\sqrt{2}\right)} = 2/\sqrt{6}$

so $\theta = \cos^{-1}(2/\sqrt{6}) \approx 35°$

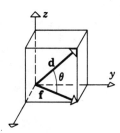

31. With the cube as shown in the diagram, and a the length of each edge,
$\mathbf{d_1} = a\mathbf{i} + a\mathbf{j} + a\mathbf{k}$, $\mathbf{d_2} = a\mathbf{i} + a\mathbf{j} - a\mathbf{k}$,
$\cos\theta = (\mathbf{d_1} \cdot \mathbf{d_2}) / (\|\mathbf{d_1}\| \, \|\mathbf{d_2}\|) = 1/3$,
$\theta \approx 71°$

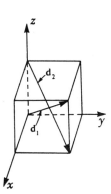

32. Take $\mathbf{i}, \mathbf{j}$, and $\mathbf{k}$ along adjacent edges of the box, then $10\mathbf{i} + 15\mathbf{j} + 25\mathbf{k}$ is along a diagonal, and a unit vector in this direction is $\dfrac{2}{\sqrt{38}}\mathbf{i} + \dfrac{3}{\sqrt{38}}\mathbf{j} + \dfrac{5}{\sqrt{38}}\mathbf{k}$. The direction cosines are $\cos\alpha = 2/\sqrt{38}$, $\cos\beta = 3/\sqrt{38}$, and $\cos\gamma = 5/\sqrt{38}$ so $\alpha \approx 71°$, $\beta \approx 61°$, and $\gamma \approx 36°$.

33. $\mathbf{v} = c_1\mathbf{v_1} + c_2\mathbf{v_2} + c_3\mathbf{v_3}$ so $\mathbf{v} \cdot \mathbf{v_i} = c_i\mathbf{v_i} \cdot \mathbf{v_i}$ because $\mathbf{v_i} \cdot \mathbf{v_j} = 0$ if $i \neq j$,
thus $\mathbf{v} \cdot \mathbf{v_i} = c_i\|\mathbf{v_i}\|^2$, $c_i = \mathbf{v} \cdot \mathbf{v_i}/\|\mathbf{v_i}\|^2$ for $i = 1, 2, 3$.

34. $\mathbf{v_1} \cdot \mathbf{v_2} = \mathbf{v_1} \cdot \mathbf{v_3} = \mathbf{v_2} \cdot \mathbf{v_3} = 0$ so they are mutually perpendicular. Let $\mathbf{v} = \mathbf{i} - \mathbf{j} + \mathbf{k}$, then
$c_1 = \dfrac{\mathbf{v} \cdot \mathbf{v_1}}{\|\mathbf{v_1}\|^2} = \dfrac{3}{7}, c_2 = \dfrac{\mathbf{v} \cdot \mathbf{v_2}}{\|\mathbf{v_2}\|^2} = -\dfrac{1}{3}$, and $c_3 = \dfrac{\mathbf{v} \cdot \mathbf{v_3}}{\|\mathbf{v_3}\|^2} = \dfrac{1}{21}$.

35. If $\mathbf{v}$ is orthogonal to $\mathbf{w_1}$ and $\mathbf{w_2}$ then $\mathbf{v} \cdot \mathbf{w_1} = \mathbf{v} \cdot \mathbf{w_2} = 0$,
$\mathbf{v} \cdot (k_1\mathbf{w_1} + k_2\mathbf{w_2}) = k_1\mathbf{v} \cdot \mathbf{w_1} + k_2\mathbf{v} \cdot \mathbf{w_2} = k_1(0) + k_2(0) = 0$ so $\mathbf{v}$ is orthogonal to $k_1\mathbf{w_1} + k_2\mathbf{w_2}$ for all scalars k_1 and k_2.

36. Let α be the angle between $\mathbf{u}$ and $\mathbf{w}$, and β the angle between $\mathbf{v}$ and $\mathbf{w}$.
$\mathbf{u} \cdot \mathbf{w} = \mathbf{u} \cdot (\ell\mathbf{u} + k\mathbf{v}) = \ell\|\mathbf{u}\|^2 + k\mathbf{u} \cdot \mathbf{v} = k^2\ell + k\mathbf{u} \cdot \mathbf{v}$,
$\cos\alpha = (\mathbf{u} \cdot \mathbf{w})/(\|\mathbf{u}\| \, \|\mathbf{w}\|) = (k^2\ell + k\mathbf{u} \cdot \mathbf{v})/(\|\mathbf{w}\|) = (k\ell + \mathbf{u} \cdot \mathbf{v})/\|\mathbf{w}\|$; similarly,
$\cos\beta = (\mathbf{v} \cdot \mathbf{w})/(\|\mathbf{v}\| \, \|\mathbf{w}\|) = (k\ell + \mathbf{u} \cdot \mathbf{v})/\|\mathbf{w}\|$ so $\cos\alpha = \cos\beta$, $\alpha = \beta$.

EXERCISE SET 14.4

1. $\langle 7, 10, 9 \rangle$ **2.** $-\mathbf{i} - 2\mathbf{j} - 7\mathbf{k}$ **3.** $\langle -4, -6, -3 \rangle$ **4.** $\mathbf{i} + 2\mathbf{j} - 4\mathbf{k}$

5. (a) $\mathbf{v} \times \mathbf{w} = \langle -23, 7, -1 \rangle, \mathbf{u} \times (\mathbf{v} \times \mathbf{w}) = \langle -20, -67, -9 \rangle$
    (b) $\mathbf{u} \times \mathbf{v} = \langle -10, -14, 2 \rangle, (\mathbf{u} \times \mathbf{v}) \times \mathbf{w} = \langle -78, 52, -26 \rangle$
    (c) $\mathbf{v} - 2\mathbf{w} = \langle -2, -7, -3 \rangle, \mathbf{u} \times (\mathbf{v} - 2\mathbf{w}) = \langle 24, 0, -16 \rangle$

(d) $(\mathbf{u} \times \mathbf{v}) - 2\mathbf{w} = \langle -10, -14, 2 \rangle - \langle 2, 8, 10 \rangle = \langle -12, -22, -8 \rangle$

(e) $(\mathbf{u} \times \mathbf{v}) \times (\mathbf{v} \times \mathbf{w}) = \langle -10, -14, 2 \rangle \times \langle -23, 7, -1 \rangle = \langle 0, -56, -392 \rangle$

(f) $(\mathbf{v} \times \mathbf{w}) \times (\mathbf{u} \times \mathbf{v}) = \langle 0, 56, 392 \rangle$

6. (a) $\mathbf{u} \times \mathbf{v} = 12\mathbf{i} + 30\mathbf{j} - 6\mathbf{k}$ (or any scalar multiple)

(b) $\mathbf{u} \times \mathbf{v} = \langle -2, 0, 2 \rangle$ (or any scalar multiple)

9. A vector parallel to the yz-plane must be perpendicular to $\mathbf{i}$;
$\mathbf{i} \times (3\mathbf{i} - \mathbf{j} + 2\mathbf{k}) = -2\mathbf{j} - \mathbf{k}$, $\| -2\mathbf{j} - \mathbf{k} \| = \sqrt{5}$, the unit vectors are $\pm (2\mathbf{j} + \mathbf{k})/\sqrt{5}$.

10. $\|\mathbf{u} \times \mathbf{v}\| = \|\mathbf{u}\| \, \|\mathbf{v}\| \sin \theta$, $\mathbf{u} \cdot \mathbf{v} = \|\mathbf{u}\| \, \|\mathbf{v}\| \cos \theta$; divide to get $\tan \theta = \dfrac{\|\mathbf{u} \times \mathbf{v}\|}{\mathbf{u} \cdot \mathbf{v}}$

11. $(\mathbf{u} + \mathbf{v}) \times (\mathbf{u} - \mathbf{v}) = \mathbf{u} \times \mathbf{u} - \mathbf{u} \times \mathbf{v} + \mathbf{v} \times \mathbf{u} - \mathbf{v} \times \mathbf{v} = 2\mathbf{v} \times \mathbf{u}$ because $\mathbf{u} \times \mathbf{u} = \mathbf{v} \times \mathbf{v} = 0$
and $-\mathbf{u} \times \mathbf{v} = \mathbf{v} \times \mathbf{u}$.

12. (a) $A = \|\mathbf{u} \times \mathbf{v}\| = \| -7\mathbf{i} - \mathbf{j} + 3\mathbf{k} \| = \sqrt{59}$

(b) $A = \|\mathbf{u} \times \mathbf{v}\| = \| -6\mathbf{i} + 4\mathbf{j} + 7\mathbf{k} \| = \sqrt{101}$

13. (a) $A = \dfrac{1}{2} \| \overrightarrow{PQ} \times \overrightarrow{PR} \| = \dfrac{1}{2} \| \langle -1, -5, 2 \rangle \times \langle 2, 0, 3 \rangle \| = \dfrac{1}{2} \| \langle -15, 7, 10 \rangle \| = \sqrt{374}/2$

(b) $A = \dfrac{1}{2} \| \overrightarrow{PQ} \times \overrightarrow{PR} \| = \dfrac{1}{2} \| \langle -1, 4, 8 \rangle \times \langle 5, 2, 12 \rangle \| = \dfrac{1}{2} \| \langle 32, 52, -22 \rangle \| = 9\sqrt{13}$

14. $\sin \theta = \dfrac{\|\mathbf{a} \times \mathbf{b}\|}{\|\mathbf{a}\| \, \|\mathbf{b}\|} = \dfrac{\|36\mathbf{i} - 24\mathbf{j}\|}{(7)(7)} = 12\sqrt{13}/49$

15. (a) $\overrightarrow{AB} = -\mathbf{i} + 2\mathbf{j} + 2\mathbf{k}$, $\overrightarrow{AC} = \mathbf{i} + \mathbf{j} - \mathbf{k}$, $\overrightarrow{AB} \times \overrightarrow{AC} = -4\mathbf{i} + \mathbf{j} - 3\mathbf{k}$, area $= \dfrac{1}{2} \| \overrightarrow{AB} \times \overrightarrow{AC} \| = \sqrt{26}/2$

(b) area $= \dfrac{1}{2} h \| \overrightarrow{AB} \| = \dfrac{3}{2} h = \dfrac{1}{2} \sqrt{26}$, $h = \sqrt{26}/3$

16. From the diagram
$$d = \|\mathbf{u}\| \sin \theta = \dfrac{\|\mathbf{u}\| \, \|\mathbf{v}\| \sin \theta}{\|\mathbf{v}\|} = \dfrac{\|\mathbf{u} \times \mathbf{v}\|}{\|\mathbf{v}\|}$$

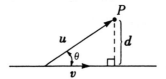

17. (a) $\mathbf{u} = \overrightarrow{AP} = -4\mathbf{i} + 2\mathbf{k}$, $\mathbf{v} = \overrightarrow{AB} = -3\mathbf{i} + 2\mathbf{j} - 4\mathbf{k}$, $\mathbf{u} \times \mathbf{v} = -4\mathbf{i} - 22\mathbf{j} - 8\mathbf{k}$;
distance $= \|\mathbf{u} \times \mathbf{v}\| / \|\mathbf{v}\| = 2\sqrt{141}/29$

(b) $\mathbf{u} = \overrightarrow{AP} = 2\mathbf{i} + 2\mathbf{j} + 3\mathbf{k}$, $\mathbf{v} = \overrightarrow{AB} = -2\mathbf{i} + \mathbf{j} + 2\mathbf{k}$, $\mathbf{u} \times \mathbf{v} = \mathbf{i} - 10\mathbf{j} + 6\mathbf{k}$;
distance $= \|\mathbf{u} \times \mathbf{v}\| / \|\mathbf{v}\| = \sqrt{137}/3$

18. $\mathbf{u} \times \mathbf{v}$ is perpendicular to the plane determined by $\mathbf{u}$ and $\mathbf{v}$, $(\mathbf{u} \times \mathbf{v}) \times \mathbf{w}$ is perpendicular to $\mathbf{u} \times \mathbf{v}$ and hence in the plane of $\mathbf{u}$ and $\mathbf{v}$, and perpendicular to $\mathbf{w}$ so the unit vectors are

$$\pm \frac{(\mathbf{u} \times \mathbf{v}) \times \mathbf{w}}{\|(\mathbf{u} \times \mathbf{v}) \times \mathbf{w}\|} = \pm \left(\frac{6}{7}\mathbf{i} - \frac{3}{7}\mathbf{j} - \frac{2}{7}\mathbf{k} \right).$$

19. ambiguous (needs parentheses)

20. 29   **21.** 80   **22.** -3 **23.** 1

24.   (a) $\mathbf{u} \cdot (\mathbf{w} \times \mathbf{v}) = -\mathbf{u} \cdot (\mathbf{v} \times \mathbf{w}) = -3$ (b) $(\mathbf{v} \times \mathbf{w}) \cdot \mathbf{u} = \mathbf{u} \cdot (\mathbf{v} \times \mathbf{w}) = 3$
       (c) $\mathbf{w} \cdot (\mathbf{u} \times \mathbf{v}) = \mathbf{u} \cdot (\mathbf{v} \times \mathbf{w}) = 3$ (d) $\mathbf{v} \cdot (\mathbf{u} \times \mathbf{w}) = \mathbf{u} \cdot (\mathbf{w} \times \mathbf{v}) = -3$
       (e) $(\mathbf{u} \times \mathbf{w}) \cdot \mathbf{v} = \mathbf{v} \cdot (\mathbf{u} \times \mathbf{w}) = \mathbf{u} \cdot (\mathbf{w} \times \mathbf{v}) = -3$
       (f) $\mathbf{v} \cdot (\mathbf{w} \times \mathbf{w}) = 0$ because $\mathbf{w} \times \mathbf{w} = 0$

25.   (a) $V = |\mathbf{a} \cdot (\mathbf{b} \times \mathbf{c})| = |-16| = 16$ (b) $V = |\mathbf{a} \cdot (\mathbf{b} \times \mathbf{c})| = |45| = 45$

26.   (a) $\mathbf{u} \cdot (\mathbf{v} \times \mathbf{w}) = 0$, yes   (b) $\mathbf{u} \cdot (\mathbf{v} \times \mathbf{w}) = 0$, yes
       (c) $\mathbf{u} \cdot (\mathbf{v} \times \mathbf{w}) = 245$, no

27.   (a) $V = |\mathbf{a} \cdot (\mathbf{b} \times \mathbf{c})| = |-9| = 9$
       (b) $A = \|\mathbf{a} \times \mathbf{c}\| = \|3\mathbf{i} - 8\mathbf{j} + 7\mathbf{k}\| = \sqrt{122}$
       (c) $\mathbf{b} \times \mathbf{c} = -3\mathbf{i} - \mathbf{j} + 2\mathbf{k}$ is perpendicular to the plane determined by $\mathbf{b}$ and $\mathbf{c}$; let θ be the angle between $\mathbf{a}$ and $\mathbf{b} \times \mathbf{c}$ then

$$\cos\theta = \frac{\mathbf{a} \cdot (\mathbf{b} \times \mathbf{c})}{\|\mathbf{a}\| \, \|\mathbf{b} \times \mathbf{c}\|} = \frac{-9}{\sqrt{14}\sqrt{14}} = -9/14$$

       so the acute angle ϕ that $\mathbf{a}$ makes with the plane determined by $\mathbf{b}$ and $\mathbf{c}$ is
       $\phi = \theta - \pi/2 = \sin^{-1}(9/14)$.

28. $\mathbf{n} = \overrightarrow{AB} \times \overrightarrow{AC} = \langle 1, 1, -3 \rangle \times \langle -1, 3, -1 \rangle = \langle 8, 4, 4 \rangle$ (or any nonzero scalar multiple)

29.   (a) $(\mathbf{u}+k\mathbf{v}) \times \mathbf{v} = \mathbf{u} \times \mathbf{v} + k\mathbf{v} \times \mathbf{v} = \mathbf{u} \times \mathbf{v} + k(0) = \mathbf{u} \times \mathbf{v}$
       (b) $\mathbf{u} \cdot \mathbf{v} \times \mathbf{z} = \mathbf{u} \cdot (\mathbf{v} \times \mathbf{z}) = \mathbf{z} \cdot (\mathbf{u} \times \mathbf{v})$ from formula (9)

$$= (\mathbf{u} \times \mathbf{v}) \cdot \mathbf{z} = \mathbf{u} \times \mathbf{v} \cdot \mathbf{z}$$

30.   (a) $\mathbf{v} \times \mathbf{w}$ is perpendicular to the plane determined by $\mathbf{v}$ and $\mathbf{w}$, but $\mathbf{u} \times (\mathbf{v} \times \mathbf{w})$ is perpendicular to $\mathbf{v} \times \mathbf{w}$ and must therefore lie in the plane determined by $\mathbf{v}$ and $\mathbf{w}$.
       (b) Similar to (a).

31. Part (b): let $\mathbf{u} = \langle u_1, u_2, u_3 \rangle$, $\mathbf{v} = \langle v_1, v_2, v_3 \rangle$, and $\mathbf{w} = \langle w_1, w_2, w_3 \rangle$; show that $\mathbf{u} \times (\mathbf{v} + \mathbf{w})$ and $(\mathbf{u} \times \mathbf{v}) + (\mathbf{u} \times \mathbf{w})$ are the same.

Part (c): $(\mathbf{u} + \mathbf{v}) \times \mathbf{w} = -[\mathbf{w} \times (\mathbf{u} + \mathbf{v})]$ from part (a)
$= -[(\mathbf{w} \times \mathbf{u}) + (\mathbf{w} \times \mathbf{v})]$ from part (b)
$= (\mathbf{u} \times \mathbf{w}) + (\mathbf{v} \times \mathbf{w})$ from part (a)

32. Let $\mathbf{u} = \langle u_1, u_2, u_3 \rangle$ and $\mathbf{v} = \langle v_1, v_2, v_3 \rangle$; show that $k(\mathbf{u} \times \mathbf{v})$, $(k\mathbf{u}) \times \mathbf{v}$, and $\mathbf{u} \times (k\mathbf{v})$ are all the same; parts (e) and (f) are proved in a similar fashion.

33. Let $\mathbf{x} = x_1\mathbf{i} + x_2\mathbf{j} + x_3\mathbf{k}$ and $\mathbf{y} = y_1\mathbf{i} + y_2\mathbf{j} + y_3\mathbf{k}$. If $\mathbf{z} = \mathbf{i}$ then both $\mathbf{x} \times (\mathbf{y} \times \mathbf{i})$ and $(\mathbf{x} \cdot \mathbf{i})\mathbf{y} - (\mathbf{x} \cdot \mathbf{y})\mathbf{i}$ can be shown to be the same. The cases $\mathbf{z} = \mathbf{j}$ and $\mathbf{z} = \mathbf{k}$ are treated the same way. Finally, for $\mathbf{z} = z_1\mathbf{i} + z_2\mathbf{j} + z_3\mathbf{k}$,

$$\mathbf{x} \times (\mathbf{y} \times \mathbf{z}) = \mathbf{x} \times (z_1\mathbf{y} \times \mathbf{i} + z_2\mathbf{y} \times \mathbf{j} + z_3\mathbf{y} \times \mathbf{k})$$
$$= z_1[\mathbf{x} \times (\mathbf{y} \times \mathbf{i})] + z_2[\mathbf{x} \times (\mathbf{y} \times \mathbf{j})] + z_3[\mathbf{x} \times (\mathbf{y} \times \mathbf{k})]$$
$$= z_1[(\mathbf{x} \cdot \mathbf{i})\mathbf{y} - (\mathbf{x} \cdot \mathbf{y})\mathbf{i}] + z_2[(\mathbf{x} \cdot \mathbf{j})\mathbf{y} - (\mathbf{x} \cdot \mathbf{y})\mathbf{j}] + z_3[(\mathbf{x} \cdot \mathbf{k})\mathbf{y} - (\mathbf{x} \cdot \mathbf{y})\mathbf{k}]$$
$$= [\mathbf{x} \cdot (z_1\mathbf{i} + z_2\mathbf{j} + z_3\mathbf{k})]\mathbf{y} - (\mathbf{x} \cdot \mathbf{y})(z_1\mathbf{i} + z_2\mathbf{j} + z_3\mathbf{k}) = (\mathbf{x} \cdot \mathbf{z})\mathbf{y} - (\mathbf{x} \cdot \mathbf{y})\mathbf{z}$$

34. $-8\mathbf{i} - 8\mathbf{k}$

35. If $\mathbf{a}$, $\mathbf{b}$, $\mathbf{c}$, and $\mathbf{d}$ lie in the same plane then $\mathbf{a} \times \mathbf{b}$ and $\mathbf{c} \times \mathbf{d}$ are parallel so $(\mathbf{a} \times \mathbf{b}) \times (\mathbf{c} \times \mathbf{d}) = 0$

36. Take $\mathbf{b}$ and $\mathbf{c}$ as sides of the (triangular) base, then area of base $= \frac{1}{2}\|\mathbf{b} \times \mathbf{c}\|$ and

height $= \|\text{proj}_{\mathbf{b} \times \mathbf{c}}\mathbf{a}\| = \dfrac{|\mathbf{a} \cdot (\mathbf{b} \times \mathbf{c})|}{\|\mathbf{b} \times \mathbf{c}\|}$ so $V = \dfrac{1}{3}$ (area of base) (height) $= \dfrac{1}{6}|\mathbf{a} \cdot (\mathbf{b} \times \mathbf{c})|$

37. (a) $\overrightarrow{PQ} = \langle 3, -1, -3 \rangle, \overrightarrow{PR} = \langle 2, -2, 1 \rangle, \overrightarrow{PS} = \langle 4, -4, 3 \rangle$.
$V = \dfrac{1}{6}|\overrightarrow{PQ} \cdot (\overrightarrow{PR} \times \overrightarrow{PS})| = \dfrac{1}{6}|-4| = 2/3$.

(b) $\overrightarrow{PQ} = \langle 1, 2, -1 \rangle, \overrightarrow{PR} = \langle 3, 4, 0 \rangle, \overrightarrow{PS} = \langle -1, -3, 4 \rangle$.
$V = \dfrac{1}{6}|\overrightarrow{PQ} \cdot (\overrightarrow{PR} \times \overrightarrow{PS})| = \dfrac{1}{6}|-3| = 1/2$.

EXERCISE SET 14.5

1. $\overrightarrow{P_1P_2} = \langle 2, 3 \rangle$ so $x = 3 + 2t$, $y = -2 + 3t$

2. $\overrightarrow{P_1P_2} = \langle -3, -5 \rangle$ so $x = -3t$, $y = 1 - 5t$

3. $\overrightarrow{P_1P_2} = \langle 0, 2 \rangle$ so $x = 4$, $y = 1 + 2t$

4. $\overrightarrow{P_1P_2} = \langle -2, 5 \rangle$ so $x = 5 - 2t$, $y = 2 + 5t$

5. $\overrightarrow{P_1P_2} = \langle -3, 6, 1 \rangle$ so $x = 5 - 3t$, $y = -2 + 6t$, $z = 1 + t$

6. $\overrightarrow{P_1P_2} = \langle 0, 0, -3 \rangle$ so $x = -1$, $y = 3$, $z = 5 - 3t$

7. $\overrightarrow{P_1P_2} = \langle -1, 6, 1 \rangle$ so $x = -t$, $y = 6t$, $z = t$

8. $\overrightarrow{P_1P_2} = \langle -5, -1, -5 \rangle$ so $x = 4 - 5t$, $y = -t$, $z = 7 - 5t$

9. Exercise 1 with $0 \le t \le 1$.   **10.** Exercise 2 with $0 \le t \le 1$.

11. Exercise 3 with $0 \le t \le 1$.   **12.** Exercise 4 with $0 \le t \le 1$.

13. Exercise 5 with $0 \le t \le 1$.   **14.** Exercise 6 with $0 \le t \le 1$.

15. Exercise 7 with $0 \le t \le 1$.   **16.** Exercise 8 with $0 \le t \le 1$.

17. $x = -5 + 2t$, $y = 2 - 3t$ **18.** $x = t$, $y = 3 - 2t$

19. $2x + 2yy' = 0$, $y' = -x/y = -(3)/(-4) = 3/4$, $\mathbf{v} = 4\mathbf{i} + 3\mathbf{j}$; $x = 3 + 4t$, $y = -4 + 3t$

20. $y' = 2x = 2(-2) = -4$, $\mathbf{v} = \mathbf{i} - 4\mathbf{j}$; $x = -2 + t$, $y = 4 - 4t$

21. $x = -1 + 3t$, $y = 2 - 4t$, $z = 4 + t$ **22.** $x = 2 - t$, $y = -1 + 2t$, $z = 5 + 7t$

23. The line is parallel to the vector $\langle 2, -1, 2 \rangle$ so $x = -2 + 2t$, $y = -t$, $z = 5 + 2t$.

24. The line is parallel to the vector $\langle 1, 1, 0 \rangle$ so $x = t$, $y = t$, $z = 0$.

25. The line is parallel to the vector $\langle 1, 0, 0 \rangle$ so $x = 3 + t$, $y = 7$, $z = 0$.

26. **(a)** $y = 2 - t = 0$; $t = 2$ so $x = 1 + 3(2) = 7$
(b) $x = 1 + 3t = 0$; $t = -1/3$ so $y = 2 - (-1/3) = 7/3$

27. $3 + 4t = 4t^2$, $4t^2 - 4t - 3 = 0$, $(2t + 1)(2t - 3) = 0$; $t = -1/2, 3/2$. If $t = -1/2$, then $x = -1$, $y = 1$; if $t = 3/2$, then $x = 3$, $y = 9$. The points of intersection are $(-1, 1)$ and $(3,9)$.

28. **(a)** $z = 0$ when $t = 4$ so the point is $(7,7,0)$

    (b) $y = 0$ when $t = -3$ so the point is $(-7,0,7)$

    (c) $x = 0$ when $t = 1/2$ so the point is $(0,7/2,7/2)$

29. **(a)** $z = 0$ when $t = 3$ so the point is $(-2,10,0)$

    (b) $y = 0$ when $t = -2$ so the point is $(-2,0,-5)$

    (c) x is always -2 so the line does not intersect the yz-plane

30. $2(3t) + 3(-1 + 2t) = 6$, $12t = 9$; $t = 3/4$. The point of intersection is $(5/4, 9/4, 1/2)$

31. $(1+t)^2 + (3-t)^2 = 16$, $t^2 - 2t - 3 = 0$, $(t+1)(t-3) = 0$; $t = -1, 3$. The points of intersection are $(0,4,-2)$ and $(4,0,6)$.

32. The line is parallel to the vector $\langle x_1 - x_0, y_1 - y_0, z_1 - z_0 \rangle$ so $x = x_0 + (x_1 - x_0)t$, $y = y_0 + (y_1 - y_0)t$, $z = z_0 + (z_1 - z_0)t$

33. The line is parallel to the vector $\langle a, b, c \rangle$ so $x = x_1 + at$, $y = y_1 + bt$, $z = z_1 + ct$

34. Solve each of the given parametric equations for t to get $t = (x - x_0)/a$, $t = (y - y_0)/b$, $t = (z - z_0)/c$ so (x, y, z) is on the line if and only if $(x - x_0)/a = (y - y_0)/b = (z - z_0)/c$

35. The lines intersect if we can find values of t_1 and t_2 that satisfy the equations $2 + t_1 = 2 + t_2$, $2 + 3t_1 = 3 + 4t_2$, and $3 + t_1 = 4 + 2t_2$. Solutions of the first two of these equations are $t_1 = -1$, $t_2 = -1$ which also satisfy the third equation so the lines intersect at $(1, -1, 2)$.

36. Solve the equations $-1 + 4t_1 = -13 + 12t_2$, $3 + t_1 = 1 + 6t_2$, and $1 = 2 + 3t_2$. The third equation yields $t_2 = -1/3$ which when substituted into the first and second equations gives $t_1 = -4$ in both cases; the lines intersect at $(-17, -1, 1)$.

37. The lines are parallel, respectively, to the vectors $\langle 7, 1, -3 \rangle$ and $\langle -1, 0, 2 \rangle$. These vectors are not parallel so the lines are not parallel. The system of equations $1 + 7t_1 = 4 - t_2$, $3 + t_1 = 6$, and $5 - 3t_1 = 7 + 2t_2$ has no solution so the lines do not intersect.

38. The vectors $\langle 8, -8, 10 \rangle$ and $\langle 8, -3, 1 \rangle$ are not parallel so the lines are not parallel. The lines do not intersect because the system of equations $2 + 8t_1 = 3 + 8t_2$, $6 - 8t_1 = 5 - 3t_2$, $10t_1 = 6 + t_2$ has no solution.

39. The points lie on the same line if $\overrightarrow{P_1 P_2}$ is parallel to $\overrightarrow{P_2 P_3}$.

    (a) $\overrightarrow{P_1 P_2} = \langle 3, -7, -7 \rangle$, $\overrightarrow{P_2 P_3} = \langle -9, -7, -3 \rangle$; these vectors are not parallel so the points do not lie on the same line.

    (b) $\overrightarrow{P_1 P_2} = \langle 2, -4, -4 \rangle$, $\overrightarrow{P_2 P_3} = \langle 1, -2, -2 \rangle$; $\overrightarrow{P_1 P_2} = 2 \overrightarrow{P_2 P_3}$ so the vectors are parallel and the points lie on the same line.

40. The vectors from $(0,2,3)$ to $(k_1, 1, k_2)$ must be parallel to the vector from $(0,2,3)$ to $(2,7,5)$ so $\langle k_1, -1, k_2 - 3 \rangle = t\langle 2, 5, 2 \rangle = \langle 2t, 5t, 2t \rangle$ for some value of t. Equate the second component of these vectors to get $-1 = 5t$, $t = -1/5$ so $k_1 = 2(-1/5) = -2/5$ and $k_2 - 3 = 2(-1/5)$, $k_2 = 13/5$.

41. Let the desired point be $P(x_0, y_0, z_0)$, then $\overrightarrow{P_1 P} = (2/3)\, \overrightarrow{P_1 P_2}$, $\langle x_0 - 1, y_0 - 4, z_0 + 3 \rangle = (2/3)\langle 0, 1, 2 \rangle = \langle 0, 2/3, 4/3 \rangle$; equate corresponding components to get $x_0 = 1$, $y_0 = 14/3$, $z_0 = -5/3$.

42. **(a)** The lines are parallel, respectively, to the vectors $\mathbf{v}_1 = \langle -2, 1, -1 \rangle$ and $\mathbf{v}_2 = \langle -4, 2, -2 \rangle$; $\mathbf{v}_2 = 2\mathbf{v}_1$, $\mathbf{v}_1$ and $\mathbf{v}_2$ are parallel so the lines are parallel.

    (b) The lines are not parallel because the vectors $\langle 3, -2, 3 \rangle$ and $\langle 9, -6, 8 \rangle$ are not parallel.

43. Show that two different points on one line lie on the other line. For example, with $t = 0$ and 1 in the equations for the first line we find that $(3,1)$ and $(2,3)$ are on the line. These points are also on the second line for $t = 4/3$ and 1.

44. Following the method illustrated in the solution to Exercise 43 with $t = 0$ and 1 we find that $(1, -2, 0)$ and $(4, -1, 2)$ are on the first line and also on the second line for $t = 1/2$ and 0.

45. **(a)** $\langle x, y \rangle = \langle 2, -1 \rangle + t\langle -7, 4 \rangle$ **(b)** $\langle x, y \rangle = \langle 0, 3 \rangle + t\langle 4, 0 \rangle$

46. **(a)** $\langle x, y, z \rangle = \langle 3, -1, 2 \rangle + t\langle -3, 2, -1 \rangle$ **(b)** $\langle x, y, z \rangle = \langle 2, 4, 1 \rangle + t\langle 0, -5, 0 \rangle$

47. The line segment joining the points $(1,0)$ and $(-3, 6)$.

48. The line segment joining the points $(-2, 1, 4)$ and $(7, 1, 1)$.

49. $(3,0,1)$ is on the line $(t = 0)$ so $\mathbf{u} = -5\mathbf{i} + \mathbf{j}$, $\mathbf{v} = -\mathbf{i} + \mathbf{j} + 2\mathbf{k}$, $\mathbf{u} \times \mathbf{v} = 2\mathbf{i} + 10\mathbf{j} - 4\mathbf{k}$; distance $= \|\mathbf{u} \times \mathbf{v}\| / \|\mathbf{v}\| = 2\sqrt{5}$.

50. $(2, -1, 0)$ is on the line $(t = 0)$ so $\mathbf{u} = -\mathbf{i} + 5\mathbf{j} - 3\mathbf{k}$, $\mathbf{v} = \mathbf{i} - \mathbf{j} + 3\mathbf{k}$, $\mathbf{u} \times \mathbf{v} = 12\mathbf{i} - 4\mathbf{k}$; distance $= \|\mathbf{u} \times \mathbf{v}\| / \|\mathbf{v}\| = 4\sqrt{10/11}$.

51. The vectors $\mathbf{v}_1 = -\mathbf{i} + 2\mathbf{j} + \mathbf{k}$ and $\mathbf{v}_2 = 2\mathbf{i} - 4\mathbf{j} - 2\mathbf{k}$ are parallel to the lines, $\mathbf{v}_2 = -2\mathbf{v}_1$ so $\mathbf{v}_1$ and $\mathbf{v}_2$ are parallel. Let $t = 0$ to get the points $P(2, 0, 1)$ and $Q(1, 3, 5)$ on the first and second lines, respectively. Let $\mathbf{u} = \overrightarrow{PQ} = -\mathbf{i} + 3\mathbf{j} + 4\mathbf{k}$, $\mathbf{v} = \frac{1}{2}\mathbf{v}_2 = \mathbf{i} - 2\mathbf{j} - \mathbf{k}$; $\mathbf{u} \times \mathbf{v} = 5\mathbf{i} + 3\mathbf{j} - \mathbf{k}$, distance $= \|\mathbf{u} \times \mathbf{v}\| / \|\mathbf{v}\| = \sqrt{35/6}$.

52. The vectors $\mathbf{v}_1 = 2\mathbf{i} + 4\mathbf{j} - 6\mathbf{k}$ and $\mathbf{v}_2 = 3\mathbf{i} + 6\mathbf{j} - 9\mathbf{k}$ are parallel to the lines, $\mathbf{v}_2 = (3/2)\mathbf{v}_1$ so $\mathbf{v}_1$ and $\mathbf{v}_2$ are parallel. Let $t = 0$ to get the points $P(0, 3, 2)$ and $Q(1, 0, 0)$ on the first and second lines, respectively. Let $\mathbf{u} = \overrightarrow{PQ} = \mathbf{i} - 3\mathbf{j} - 2\mathbf{k}$, $\mathbf{v} = \frac{1}{2}\mathbf{v}_1 = \mathbf{i} + 2\mathbf{j} - 3\mathbf{k}$; $\mathbf{u} \times \mathbf{v} = 13\mathbf{i} + \mathbf{j} + 5\mathbf{k}$, distance $= \|\mathbf{u} \times \mathbf{v}\|/\|\mathbf{v}\| = \sqrt{195/14}$.

53. **(a)** Let $t = 3$ and $t = -2$, respectively, in the equations for L_1 and L_2.

   (b) $\mathbf{u} = 2\mathbf{i} - \mathbf{j} - 2\mathbf{k}$ and $\mathbf{v} = \mathbf{i} + 3\mathbf{j} - \mathbf{k}$ are parallel to L_1 and L_2,
   $\cos\theta = \mathbf{u} \cdot \mathbf{v}/(\|\mathbf{u}\| \, \|\mathbf{v}\|) = 1/(3\sqrt{11})$, $\theta \approx 84°$.

   (c) $\mathbf{u} \times \mathbf{v} = 7\mathbf{i} + 7\mathbf{k}$ is perpendicular to both L_1 and L_2, and hence so is $\mathbf{i} + \mathbf{k}$, thus $x = 7 + t$, $y = -1$, $z = -2 + t$.

54. **(a)** Let $t = 1/2$ and $t = 1$, respectively, in the equations for L_1 and L_2.

   (b) $\mathbf{u} = 4\mathbf{i} - 2\mathbf{j} + 2\mathbf{k}$ and $\mathbf{v} = \mathbf{i} - \mathbf{j} + 4\mathbf{k}$ are parallel to L_1 and L_2,
   $\cos\theta = \mathbf{u} \cdot \mathbf{v}/(\|\mathbf{u}\| \, \|\mathbf{v}\|) = 14/\sqrt{432}$, $\theta \approx 48°$.

   (c) $\mathbf{u} \times \mathbf{v} = -6\mathbf{i} - 14\mathbf{j} - 2\mathbf{k}$ is perpendicular to both L_1 and L_2, and hence so is $3\mathbf{i} + 7\mathbf{j} + \mathbf{k}$, thus $x = 2 + 3t$, $y = 7t$, $z = 3 + t$.

55. $(0,1,2)$ is on the given line $(t = 0)$ so $\mathbf{u} = \mathbf{j} - \mathbf{k}$ is a vector from this point to the point $(0,2,1)$, $\mathbf{v} = 2\mathbf{i} - \mathbf{j} + \mathbf{k}$ is parallel to the given line. $\mathbf{u} \times \mathbf{v} = -2\mathbf{j} - 2\mathbf{k}$, and hence $\mathbf{w} = \mathbf{j} + \mathbf{k}$, is perpendicular to both lines so $\mathbf{v} \times \mathbf{w} = -2\mathbf{i} - 2\mathbf{j} + 2\mathbf{k}$, and hence $\mathbf{i} + \mathbf{j} - \mathbf{k}$, is parallel to the line we seek. Thus $x = t$, $y = 2 + t$, $z = 1 - t$ are parametric equations of the line.

56. $(-2,4,2)$ is on the given line $(t = 0)$ so $\mathbf{u} = 5\mathbf{i} - 3\mathbf{j} - 4\mathbf{k}$ is a vector from this point to the point $(3,1,-2)$, $\mathbf{v} = 2\mathbf{i} + 2\mathbf{j} + \mathbf{k}$ is parallel to the given line. $\mathbf{u} \times \mathbf{v} = 5\mathbf{i} - 13\mathbf{j} + 16\mathbf{k}$ is perpendicular to both lines so $\mathbf{v} \times (\mathbf{u} \times \mathbf{v}) = 45\mathbf{i} - 27\mathbf{j} - 36\mathbf{k}$, and hence $5\mathbf{i} - 3\mathbf{j} - 4\mathbf{k}$ is parallel to the line we seek. Thus $x = 3 + 5t$, $y = 1 - 3t$, $z = -2 - 4t$ are parametric equations of the line.

57. **(a)** When $t = 0$ the particles are at $(4,1,2)$ and $(0,1,1)$ so the distance between them is $\sqrt{4^2 + 0^2 + 1^2} = \sqrt{17}$ cm.

   (b) At any time t the distance D between the particles is
   $D = \sqrt{[t - (4 - t)]^2 + [(1 + t) - (1 + 2t)]^2 + [(1 + 2t) - (2 + t)]^2} = \sqrt{6t^2 - 18t + 17}$,
   $dD/dt = (6t - 9)/\sqrt{6t^2 - 18t + 17} = 0$ when $t = 3/2$; the minimum
   distance is $\sqrt{6(3/2)^2 - 18(3/2) + 17} = \sqrt{14}/2$ cm.

EXERCISE SET 14.6

1. $(x - 2) + 4(y - 6) + 2(z - 1) = 0$, $x + 4y + 2z = 28$

2. $-(x + 1) + 7(x + 1) + 6(z - 2) = 0$, $-x + 7y + 6z = 6$

3. $z = 0$ 　　　　　　　　　　　4. $2x - 3y - 4z = 0$

5. Denote the given points by P_1, P_2, and P_3, respectively, then $\overrightarrow{P_1P_2} \times \overrightarrow{P_1P_3}$ is a normal to the plane.

(a) $\overrightarrow{P_1P_2} \times \overrightarrow{P_1P_3} = \langle 2, 1, 2 \rangle \times \langle 3, -1, -2 \rangle = \langle 0, 10, -5 \rangle$, for convenience choose $\langle 0, 2, -1 \rangle$ which is also normal to the plane. Use any of the given points to get $2y - z = 1$

(b) $\overrightarrow{P_1P_2} \times \overrightarrow{P_1P_3} = \langle -1, -1, -2 \rangle \times \langle -4, 1, 1 \rangle = \langle 1, 9, -5 \rangle$, $x + 9y - 5z = 16$

6. (a) no, because $\langle 3, -2, 1 \rangle$ and $\langle 6, -4, 3 \rangle$ are not parallel

(b) yes, because $\langle 2, -8, -6 \rangle$ and $\langle -1, 4, 3 \rangle$ are parallel

(c) yes, because $\langle 4, -1, -2 \rangle$ and $\langle 1, -1/4, -1/2 \rangle$ are parallel

7. (a) yes, because $\langle 2, -1, -4 \rangle$ and $\langle 3, 2, 1 \rangle$ are perpendicular

(b) no, because $\langle 1, 2, 3 \rangle$ and $\langle 1, -1, 2 \rangle$ are not perpendicular

8. (a) no, because $\langle 1, -1, 3 \rangle$ and $\langle 2, 0, 1 \rangle$ are not perpendicular

(b) yes, because $\langle 3, -2, 1 \rangle$ and $\langle 4, 5, -2 \rangle$ are perpendicular

9. (a) yes, because $\langle 2, 1, -1 \rangle$ and $\langle 4, 2, -2 \rangle$ are parallel

(b) no, because $\langle -1, 1, -3 \rangle$ and $\langle 2, 2, 0 \rangle$ are not parallel

10. (a) $3t - 2t + t - 5 = 0$, $t = 5/2$ so $x = y = z = 5/2$, the point of intersection is $(5/2, 5/2, 5/2)$

(b) $(1 + t) - (-1 + 3t) + 4(2 + 4t) = 7$, $t = -3/14$ so $x = 1 - 3/14 = 11/14$, $y = -1 - 9/14 = -23/14$, $z = 2 - 12/14 = 8/7$, the point is $(11/14, -23/14, 8/7)$

(c) $2(2 - t) + (3 + t) + t = 1$ has no solution so the line and plane do not intersect

11. (a) $\mathbf{n}_1 = \langle 1, 0, 0 \rangle$, $\mathbf{n}_2 = \langle 2, -1, 1 \rangle$, $\mathbf{n}_1 \cdot \mathbf{n}_2 = 2$ so

$$\cos\theta = \frac{\mathbf{n}_1 \cdot \mathbf{n}_2}{\|\mathbf{n}_1\| \, \|\mathbf{n}_2\|} = \frac{2}{\sqrt{1}\sqrt{6}} = 2/\sqrt{6}, \theta = \cos^{-1}(2/\sqrt{6}) \approx 35°$$

(b) $\mathbf{n}_1 = \langle 1, 2, -2 \rangle$, $\mathbf{n}_2 = \langle 6, -3, 2 \rangle$, $\mathbf{n}_1 \cdot \mathbf{n}_2 = -4$ so

$$\cos\theta = \frac{(-\mathbf{n}_1) \cdot \mathbf{n}_2}{\| -\mathbf{n}_1\| \, \|\mathbf{n}_2\|} = \frac{4}{(3)(7)} = 4/21, \theta = \cos^{-1}(4/21) \approx 79°$$

12. $\langle 1, 2, -1 \rangle$ is parallel to the line and hence normal to the plane $x + 2y - z = 10$

13. (a) $z = 0$ (b) $y = 0$ (c) $x = 0$

14. (a) $z = z_0$ (b) $x = x_0$ (c) $y = y_0$

15. $\langle 4, -2, 7 \rangle$ is normal to the desired plane and $(0,0,0)$ is a point on it; $4x - 2y + 7z = 0$

16. $\mathbf{v} = \langle 3, 2, -1 \rangle$ is parallel to the line and $\mathbf{n} = \langle 1, -2, 1 \rangle$ is normal to the given plane so $\mathbf{v} \times \mathbf{n} = \langle 0, -4, -8 \rangle$ is normal to the desired plane. Let $t = 0$ in the line to get $(-2, 4, 3)$ which is also a point on the desired plane, use this point and (for convenience) the normal $\langle 0, 1, 2 \rangle$ to find that $y + 2z = 10$.

17. Find two points P_1 and P_2 on the line of intersection of the given planes and then find an equation of the plane that contains P_1, P_2, and the given point $P_0(-1, 4, 2)$. Let (x_0, y_0, z_0) be on the line of intersection of the given planes then $4x_0 - y_0 + z_0 - 2 = 0$ and $2x_0 + y_0 - 2z_0 - 3 = 0$, eliminate y_0 by addition of the equations to get $6x_0 - z_0 - 5 = 0$; if $x_0 = 0$ then $z_0 = -5$, if $x_0 = 1$ then $z_0 = 1$. Substitution of these values of x_0 and z_0 into either of the equations of the planes gives the corresponding values $y_0 = -7$ and $y_0 = 3$ so $P_1(0, -7, -5)$ and $P_2(1, 3, 1)$ are on the line of intersection of the planes. $\overrightarrow{P_0 P_1} \times \overrightarrow{P_0 P_2} = \langle 4, -13, 21 \rangle$ is normal to the desired plane whose equation is $4x - 13y + 21z = -14$.

18. Denote the points by A, B, C, and D, respectively. The points lie in the same plane if $\overrightarrow{AB} \times \overrightarrow{AC}$ and $\overrightarrow{AB} \times \overrightarrow{AD}$ are parallel. $\overrightarrow{AB} \times \overrightarrow{AC} = \langle 0, -10, 5 \rangle$, $\overrightarrow{AB} \times \overrightarrow{AD} = \langle 0, 16, -8 \rangle$, these vectors are parallel because $\langle 0, -10, 5 \rangle = (-10/16)\langle 0, 16, -8 \rangle$.

19. The line is parallel to the line of intersection of the planes if it is parallel to both planes. Normals to the given planes are $\mathbf{n}_1 = \langle 1, -4, 2 \rangle$ and $\mathbf{n}_2 = \langle 2, 3, -1 \rangle$ so $\mathbf{n}_1 \times \mathbf{n}_2 = \langle -2, 5, 11 \rangle$ is parallel to the line of intersection of the planes and hence parallel to the desired line whose equations are $x = 5 - 2t$, $y = 5t$, $z = -2 + 11t$.

20. $\mathbf{n}_1 = \langle 2, -1, 1 \rangle$ and $\mathbf{n}_2 = \langle 1, 1, -2 \rangle$ are normals to the given planes,

$\mathbf{n}_1 \times \mathbf{n}_2 = \langle 1, 5, 3 \rangle$ is normal to the desired plane whose equation is $x + 5y + 3z = -6$.

21. $\mathbf{n}_1 = \langle 2, 1, 1 \rangle$ and $\mathbf{n}_2 = \langle 1, 2, 1 \rangle$ are normals to the given planes, $\mathbf{n}_1 \times \mathbf{n}_2 = \langle -1, -1, 3 \rangle$ so $\langle 1, 1, -3 \rangle$ is normal to the desired plane whose equation is $x + y - 3z = 6$.

22. $\mathbf{n} = \langle 4, -1, 3 \rangle$ is normal to the given plane, $\overrightarrow{P_1 P_2} = \langle 3, -1, -1 \rangle$ is parallel to the line,

$\mathbf{n} \times \overrightarrow{P_1 P_2} = \langle 4, 13, -1 \rangle$ is normal to the desired plane whose equation is $4x + 13y - z = 1$.

23. $\mathbf{v}_1 = \langle 1, 2, -1 \rangle$ and $\mathbf{v}_2 = \langle -1, -2, 1 \rangle$ are parallel, respectively, to the given lines and to each other so the lines are parallel. Let $t = 0$ to find the points $P_1(-2, 3, 4)$ and $P_2(3, 4, 0)$ that lie, respectively, on the given lines. $\mathbf{v}_1 \times \overrightarrow{P_1 P_2} = \langle -7, -1, -9 \rangle$ so $\langle 7, 1, 9 \rangle$ is normal to the desired plane whose equation is $7x + y + 9z = 25$.

24. Let $t = 0$ and $t = 1$ to get the points $P_1(-1, 0, -4)$ and $P_2(0, 1, -2)$ that lie on the line. Denote the given point by P_0, then $\overrightarrow{P_0 P_1} \times \overrightarrow{P_0 P_2} = \langle 7, -1, -3 \rangle$ is normal to the desired plane whose equation is $7x - y - 3z = 5$.

25. The plane is the perpendicular bisector of the line segment that joins $P_1(2, -1, 1)$ and $P_2(3, 1, 5)$. The midpoint of the line segment is $(5/2, 0, 3)$ and $\overrightarrow{P_1P_2} = \langle 1, 2, 4 \rangle$ is normal to the plane so an equation is $x + 2y + 4z = 29/2$.

26. $\mathbf{n}_1 = \langle 2, -1, 1 \rangle$ and $\mathbf{n}_2 = \langle 0, 1, 1 \rangle$ are normals to the given planes, $\mathbf{n}_1 \times \mathbf{n}_2 = \langle -2, -2, 2 \rangle$ so $\mathbf{n} = \langle 1, 1, -1 \rangle$ is parallel to the line of intersection of the planes. $\mathbf{v} = \langle 3, 1, 2 \rangle$ is parallel to the given line, $\mathbf{v} \times \mathbf{n} = \langle -3, 5, 2 \rangle$ so $\langle 3, -5, -2 \rangle$ is normal to the desired plane. Let $t = 0$ to find the point $(0,1,0)$ that lies on the given line and hence on the desired plane. An equation of the plane is $3x - 5y - 2z = -5$.

27. $\mathbf{v} = \langle 0, 1, 1 \rangle$ is parallel to the line.

    (a) $\mathbf{n} = \langle 6, 4, -4 \rangle$ is normal to the plane, $\mathbf{v} \cdot \mathbf{n} = 0$ so the line is parallel to the plane because $\mathbf{v}$ and $\mathbf{n}$ are perpendicular. $(0,0,0)$ lies on the line and the plane so the entire line must lie in the plane.

    (b) $\mathbf{n} = \langle 5, -3, 3 \rangle$ is normal to the plane, $\mathbf{v} \cdot \mathbf{n} = 0$ so the line is parallel to the plane. $(0,0,0)$ is on the line, $(0, 0, 1/3)$ is on the plane. The line is below the plane because $(0,0,0)$ is below $(0, 0, 1/3)$.

    (c) $\mathbf{n} = \langle 6, 2, -2 \rangle$, $\mathbf{v} \cdot \mathbf{n} = 0$ so the line is parallel to the plane. $(0,0,0)$ is on the line, $(0, 0, -3/2)$ is on the plane. The line is above the plane because $(0,0,0)$ is above $(0, 0, -3/2)$.

28. The system $4t_1 - 1 = 12t_2 - 13$, $t_1 + 3 = 6t_2 + 1$, $1 = 3t_2 + 2$ has the solution $t_1 = -4$, $t_2 = -1/3$ so $(-17, -1, 1)$ is the point of intersection. $\mathbf{v}_1 = \langle 4, 1, 0 \rangle$ and $\mathbf{v}_2 = \langle 12, 6, 3 \rangle$ are parallel to the lines, $\mathbf{v}_1 \times \mathbf{v}_2 = \langle 3, -12, 12 \rangle$ so $\langle 1, -4, 4 \rangle$ is normal to the desired plane whose equation is $x - 4y + 4z = -9$.

29.   **(a)** $\mathbf{n}_1 = \langle -2, 3, 7 \rangle$ and $\mathbf{n}_2 = \langle 1, 2, -3 \rangle$ are normals to the planes, $\mathbf{n}_1 \times \mathbf{n}_2 = \langle -23, 1, -7 \rangle$ is parallel to the line of intersection. Let $z = 0$ in both equations and solve for x and y to get $x = -11/7$, $y = -12/7$ so $(-11/7, -12/7, 0)$ is on the line whose equations are $x = -11/7 - 23t$, $y = -12/7 + t$, $z = -7t$

    (b) Similar to part (a) with $\mathbf{n}_1 = \langle 3, -5, 2 \rangle$, $\mathbf{n}_2 = \langle 0, 0, 1 \rangle$, $\mathbf{n}_1 \times \mathbf{n}_2 = \langle -5, -3, 0 \rangle$. $z = 0$ so $3x - 5y = 0$, let $x = 0$ then $y = 0$ and $(0,0,0)$ is on the line whose equations are $x = -5t$, $y = -3t$, $z = 0$.

30. The intercepts correspond to the points $A(a,0,0)$, $B(0, b, 0)$, and $C(0, 0, c)$. $\overrightarrow{AB} \times \overrightarrow{AC} = \langle bc, ac, ab \rangle$ is normal to the plane so $bcx + acy + abz = abc$ or $x/a + y/b + z/c = 1$.

31. $D = |2(1) - 2(-2) + (3) - 4| / \sqrt{4 + 4 + 1} = 5/3$

32. $D = |3(0) + 6(1) - 2(5) - 5| / \sqrt{9 + 36 + 4} = 9/7$

33. $D = |20(7) - 4(2) - 5(-1)| / \sqrt{400 + 16 + 25} = 137/21$

34. $(0,0,7/4)$ is on the first plane so $D = |4(0) - 6(0) + 8(7/4) - 3|/\sqrt{16 + 36 + 64} = 11/\sqrt{116}$

35. $(0,0,0)$ is on the first plane so $D = |6(0) \quad 3(0) \quad 3(0) - 5|/\sqrt{36 + 9 + 9} - 5/\sqrt{54}$

36. $(0,0,1)$ is on the first plane so $D = |(0) + (0) + (1) + 1|/\sqrt{1 + 1 + 1} = 2/\sqrt{3}$

37. $(1,3,5)$ and $(4,6,7)$ are on L_1 and L_2, respectively. $\mathbf{v}_1 = \langle 7, 1, -3 \rangle$ and $\mathbf{v}_2 = \langle -1, 0, 2 \rangle$ are parallel to L_1 and L_2, $\mathbf{v}_1 \times \mathbf{v}_2 = \langle 2, -11, 1 \rangle$ so the plane $2x - 11y + z + 51 = 0$ contains L_2, $D = |2(1) - 11(3) + (5) + 51|/\sqrt{4 + 121 + 1} = 25/\sqrt{126}$

38. $(3,4,1)$ and $(0,3,0)$ are on L_1 and L_2, respectively. $\mathbf{v}_1 = \langle -1, 4, 2 \rangle$ and $\mathbf{v}_2 = \langle 1, 0, 2 \rangle$ are parallel to L_1 and L_2, $\mathbf{v}_1 \times \mathbf{v}_2 = \langle 8, 4, -4 \rangle = 4\langle 2, 1, -1 \rangle$ so $2x + y - z - 3 = 0$ contains L_2, $D = |2(3) + (4) - (1) - 3|/\sqrt{4 + 1 + 1} = \sqrt{6}$.

39. $(2,6,0)$ and $(3,5,6)$ are on L_1 and L_2, respectively. $\mathbf{v}_1 = \langle 4, -4, 5 \rangle$ and $\mathbf{v}_2 = \langle 8, -3, 1 \rangle$ are parallel to L_1 and L_2, $\mathbf{v}_1 \times \mathbf{v}_2 = \langle 11, 36, 20 \rangle$ so $11x + 36y + 20z - 333 = 0$ contains L_2,

$$D = |11(2) + 36(6) + 20(0) - 333|/\sqrt{121 + 1296 + 400} = 95/\sqrt{1817}.$$

40. $\mathbf{v} = \langle 1, 2, -1 \rangle$ is parallel to the line, $\mathbf{n} = \langle 2, -2, -2 \rangle$ is normal to the plane, $\mathbf{v} \cdot \mathbf{n} = 0$ so $\mathbf{v}$ is parallel to the plane because $\mathbf{v}$ and $\mathbf{n}$ are perpendicular. $(-1, 3, 0)$ is on the line so $D = |2(-1) - 2(3) - 2(0) + 3|/\sqrt{4 + 4 + 4} = 5/\sqrt{12}$

41. $\mathbf{n}_1 = \langle a_1, b_1, c_1 \rangle$ and $\mathbf{n}_2 = \langle a_2, b_2, c_2 \rangle$ are normals to the planes, the planes are perpendicular if and only if their normals are perpendicular so $\mathbf{n}_1 \cdot \mathbf{n}_2 = 0$, $a_1 a_2 + b_1 b_2 + c_1 c_2 = 0$.

42. **(a)** $\mathbf{r} \cdot \mathbf{r}_0 = x_0 x + y_0 y + z_0 z = 0$ where $\mathbf{r}$ is perpendicular to $\mathbf{r}_0$; the plane through the origin and perpendicular to $\mathbf{r}_0$.

(b) $(\mathbf{r} - \mathbf{r}_0) \cdot \mathbf{r}_0 = x_0 (x - x_0) + y_0 (y - y_0) + z_0 (z - z_0) = 0$ where the vector from (x_0, y_0, z_0) to (x, y, z) is perpendicular to $\mathbf{r}_0$; the plane through (x_0, y_0, z_0) and perpendicular to $\mathbf{r}_0$.

43. The distance between $(2, 1, -3)$ and the plane is $|2 - 3(1) + 2(-3) - 4|/\sqrt{1 + 9 + 4} = 11/\sqrt{14}$ which is the radius of the sphere; an equation is $(x - 2)^2 + (y - 1)^2 + (z + 3)^2 = 121/14$.

44. The vector $2\mathbf{i} + \mathbf{j} - \mathbf{k}$ is normal to the plane and hence parallel to the line so parametric equations of the line are $x = 3 + 2t$, $y = 1 + t$, $z = -t$. Substitution into the equation of the plane yields $2(3+2t) + (1+t) - (-t) = 0$, $t = -7/6$; the point of intersection is $(2/3, -1/6, 7/6)$.

EXERCISE SET 14.7

1. **(a)** $4x^2 + y^2 = 4$; ellipse   **(b)** $y^2 + z^2 = 3$; circle   **(c)** $4x^2 + z^2 = 3$; ellipse

2. **(a)** $9x^2 - y^2 = 9$; hyperbola   **(b)** $y^2 - 4z^2 = 27$; hyperbola   **(c)** $9x^2 + 4z^2 = 25$; ellipse

3. **(a)** $9x^2 - z^2 = 16$; hyperbola   **(b)** $y^2 + z^2 = 20$; circle   **(c)** $9x^2 - y^2 = 20$; hyperbola

4. **(a)** $4y^2 - 9z^2 = 0$; two lines   **(b)** $9z^2 - x^2 = 4$; hyperbola   **(c)** $x^2 + 4y^2 = 9$; ellipse

5. **(a)** $z = 4y^2$; parabola   **(b)** $z = 9x^2 + 16$; parabola   **(c)** $9x^2 + 4y^2 = 4$; ellipse

6. **(a)** $z = x^2$; parabola   **(b)** $z = 1 - 4y^2$; parabola   **(c)** $x^2 - 4y^2 = 4$; hyperbola

7.

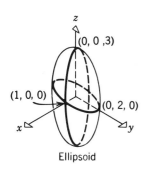

Ellipsoid

8.

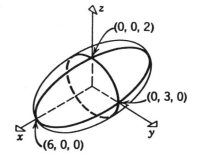

Ellipsoid

9.

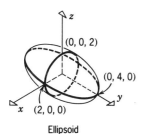

Ellipsoid

10.

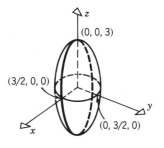

Ellipsoid

11.

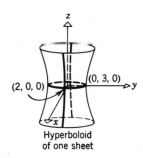

Hyperboloid
of one sheet

12.

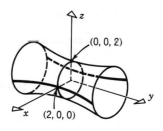

Hyperboloid
of one sheet

13.

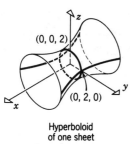

Hyperboloid
of one sheet

14.

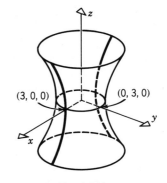

Hyperboloid
of one sheet

15.

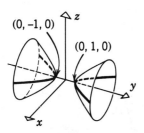

Hyperboloid
of two sheets

16.

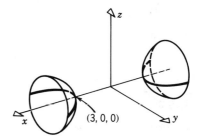

Hyperboloid
of two sheets

17.

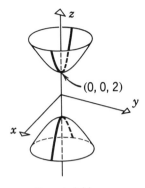

$(0, 0, 2)$

Hyperboloid
of two sheets

18.

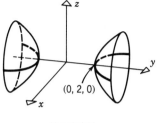

$(0, 2, 0)$

Hyperboloid
of two sheets

19.

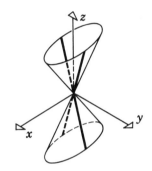

Elliptic cone

20.

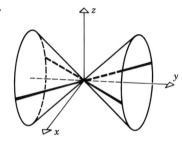

Circular cone

21.

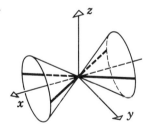

Circular cone

22.

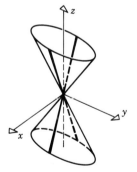

Elliptic cone

23.

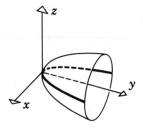

Circular paraboloid

24.

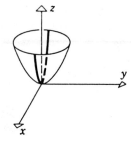

Circular paraboloid

25.

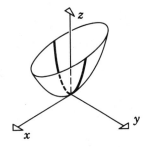

Elliptic paraboloid

26.

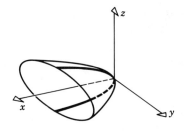

Elliptic paraboloid

27.

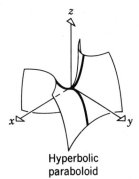

Hyperbolic
paraboloid

28.

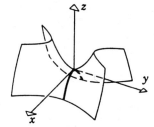

Hyperbolic paraboloid

29. **(a)**

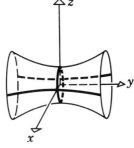

Hyperboloid
of one sheet

(b)

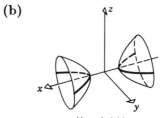

Hyperboloid
of two sheets

(c)

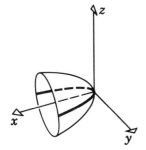

Paraboloid

(d)

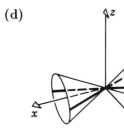

Cone

(e)

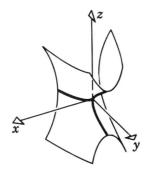

Hyperbolic
paraboloid

(f)

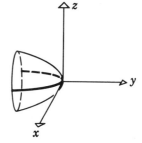

Paraboloid

30.

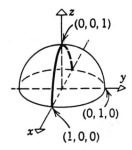

31.

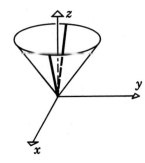

32.

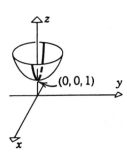

33.

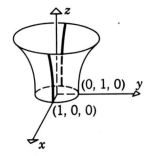

34.

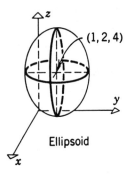

Ellipsoid

35.

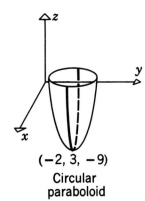

Circular
paraboloid

36.

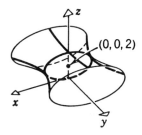

Hyperboloid of
one sheet

37.

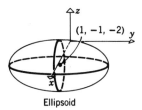

Ellipsoid

38.

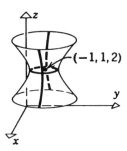

Hyperboloid of
one sheet

39.

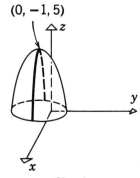

Circular
paraboloid

45. $x^2 + y^2 = 4 - x^2 - y^2, x^2 + y^2 = 2$; circle

46. $x^2 + y^2 = 1 - 4x^2 - y^2, 5x^2 + 2y^2 = 1$; ellipse

47. $x^2 + y^2 = 2x, x^2 + y^2 - 2x = 0$; circle

48. $4 - x^2 - y^2 = y^2, x^2 + 2y^2 = 4$; ellipse

49. $x^2 + y^2 = (y+1)^2, y = \frac{1}{2}x^2 - \frac{1}{2}$; parabola

50. $x^2 + y^2 = (2\sqrt{y})^2, x^2 + y^2 - 4y = 0$; circle

51. $x^2 + y^2 + 4(\sqrt{x})^2 = 5, x^2 + y^2 + 4x = 5$ for $x \geq 0$; circular arc

52. $x^2 + 2y^2 + x^2 = 2, x^2 + y^2 = 1$; circle

53. **(a)** $z = k^2/9 + y^2/4$, $y^2 = 4(z - k^2/9)$ so $4p = 4$, $p = 1$; the focus is at $(k, 0, k^2/9 + 1)$ and the vertex is at $(k, 0, k^2/9)$.

(b) $k = x^2/9 + y^2/4$, $x^2/(9k) + y^2/(4k) = 1$ so $a = 3\sqrt{k}$, $b = 2\sqrt{k}$, $c = \sqrt{5k}$; the foci are at $(\pm\sqrt{5k}, 0, k)$, the endpoints of the major axis are $(\pm 3\sqrt{k}, 0, k)$, and the endpoints of the minor axis are $(0, \pm 2\sqrt{k}, k)$.

54. Each slice perpendicular to the z-axis for $|z| < c$ is an ellipse whose equation is

$$\frac{x^2}{a^2} + \frac{y^2}{b^2} = \frac{c^2 - z^2}{c^2}, \text{ or } \frac{x^2}{(a^2/c^2)(c^2 - z^2)} + \frac{y^2}{(b^2/c^2)(c^2 - z^2)} = 1, \text{ the area of which is}$$

$$\pi\left(\frac{a}{c}\sqrt{c^2 - z^2}\right)\left(\frac{b}{c}\sqrt{c^2 - z^2}\right) = \pi\frac{ab}{c^2}(c^2 - z^2) \text{ so } V = 2\int_0^c \pi\frac{ab}{c^2}(c^2 - z^2)\, dz = \frac{4}{3}\pi abc.$$

55. $|z - (-1)| = \sqrt{x^2 + y^2 + (z - 1)^2}$, $z^2 + 2z + 1 = x^2 + y^2 + z^2 - 2z + 1$, $z = (x^2 + y^2)/4$; paraboloid.

56. $|z + 1| = 2\sqrt{x^2 + y^2 + (z - 1)^2}$, $z^2 + 2z + 1 = 4(x^2 + y^2 + z^2 - 2z + 1)$,

$$4x^2 + 4y^2 + 3z^2 - 10z + 3 = 0, \quad \frac{x^2}{4/3} + \frac{y^2}{4/3} + \frac{(z - 5/3)^2}{16/9} = 1; \text{ ellipsoid, center at } (0, 0, 5/3).$$

57. **(a)** $(3 + t)^2 - (2 + t)^2 = 5 + 2t$ and $(3 + t)^2 - (2 - t)^2 = 5 + 10t$ so both lines lie completely on the surface $z = x^2 - y^2$.

(b) $(x_0 + t)^2 - (y_0 + at)^2 = x_0^2 - y_0^2 + 2(x_0 - ay_0)t + (1 - a^2)t^2 = z_0 + bt$ if $z_0 = x_0^2 - y_0^2$, $2(x_0 - ay_0) = b$, and $1 - a^2 = 0$. But $z_0 = x_0^2 - y_0^2$ because (x_0, y_0, z_0) is on the surface so it remains to find a and b so that $2(x_0 - ay_0) = b$ and $1 - a^2 = 0$. Solve the second equation to get $a = \pm 1$ so $b = 2(x_0 - y_0)$ and $b = 2(x_0 + y_0)$.

58. **(a)** $\left(2 + \frac{3}{5}t\right)^2 + \left(1 + \frac{4}{5}t\right)^2 - (2 + t)^2 = 1$ and $(2 + t)^2 + (1)^2 - (2 + t)^2 = 1$ so both lines lie completely on the surface.

(b) $(x_0 + at)^2 + (y_0 + bt)^2 - (z_0 + t)^2$
$$= (x_0^2 + y_0^2 - z_0^2) + 2(ax_0 + by_0 - z_0)t + (a^2 + b^2 - 1)t^2 = 1$$
if $x_0^2 + y_0^2 - z_0^2 = 1$, $ax_0 + by_0 - z_0 = 0$, and $a^2 + b^2 - 1 = 0$. But $x_0^2 + y_0^2 - z_0^2 = 1$ because (x_0, y_0, z_0) is on the surface so it remains to find a and b so that $ax_0 + by_0 = z_0$ and $a^2 + b^2 = 1$. Square $by_0 = z_0 - ax_0$, replace b^2 by $1 - a^2$, and rearrange to get $(x_0^2 + y_0^2)a^2 - 2x_0z_0a + z_0^2 - y_0^2 = 0$, then use the relationship $x_0^2 + y_0^2 - z_0^2 = 1$ to rewrite as $(z_0^2 + 1)a^2 - 2x_0z_0a + x_0^2 - 1 = 0$. Next, use the quadratic formula to solve for a:

$$a = \frac{2x_0z_0 \pm \sqrt{4x_0^2z_0^2 - 4(z_0^2 + 1)(x_0^2 - 1)}}{2(z_0^2 + 1)}$$

$$= \frac{x_0z_0 \pm \sqrt{z_0^2 - x_0^2 + 1}}{z_0^2 + 1} = \frac{x_0z_0 \pm \sqrt{y_0^2}}{z_0^2 + 1} = \frac{x_0z_0 \pm |y_0|}{z_0^2 + 1}.$$

If $y_0 \neq 0$, then $b = \dfrac{z_0 - ax_0}{y_0}$; if $y_0 = 0$, then from $ax_0 + by_0 = z_0$ we get $a = \dfrac{z_0}{x_0}$, and

from $b^2 = 1 - a^2 = \dfrac{x_0^2 - z_0^2}{x_0^2} = \dfrac{1}{x_0^2}$ we get $b = \pm\dfrac{1}{|x_0|}$.

EXERCISE SET 14.8

1. **(a)** $(8, \pi/6, -4)$ **(b)** $\left(5\sqrt{2}, 3\pi/4, 6\right)$ **(c)** $(2, \pi/2, 0)$
   (d) $(8, 5\pi/3, 6)$ **(e)** $(2, 7\pi/4, 1)$ **(f)** $(0, 0, 1)$

2. **(a)** $(2\sqrt{3}, 2, 3)$ **(b)** $\left(-4\sqrt{2}, 4\sqrt{2}, -2\right)$ **(c)** $(5, 0, 4)$
   (d) $(-7, 0, -9)$ **(e)** $\left(3, -3\sqrt{3}, 7\right)$ **(f)** $(0, 1, 0)$

3. $\rho = \sqrt{x^2 + y^2 + z^2}$, $\tan\theta = y/x$, $\cos\phi = z/\rho$
   (a) $\left(2\sqrt{2}, \pi/3, 3\pi/4\right)$ **(b)** $(2, 7\pi/4, \pi/4)$ **(c)** $(6, \pi/2, \pi/3)$
   (d) $(10, 5\pi/6, \pi/2)$ **(e)** $\left(8\sqrt{2}, \pi/4, \pi/6\right)$ **(f)** $\left(2\sqrt{2}, 5\pi/3, 3\pi/4\right)$

4. **(a)** $\left(5\sqrt{6}/4, 5\sqrt{2}/4, 5\sqrt{2}/2\right)$ **(b)** $(7, 0, 0)$
   (c) $(0, 0, 1)$ **(d)** $(0, -2, 0)$
   (e) $\left(-\sqrt{2}/4, \sqrt{6}/4, -\sqrt{2}/2\right)$ **(f)** $\left(3\sqrt{2}/4, -3\sqrt{2}/4, -3\sqrt{3}/2\right)$

5. $\rho = \sqrt{r^2 + z^2}$, $\theta = \theta$, $\tan\phi = r/z$
   (a) $\left(2\sqrt{3}, \pi/6, \pi/6\right)$ **(b)** $\left(\sqrt{2}, \pi/4, 3\pi/4\right)$ **(c)** $(2, 3\pi/4, \pi/2)$
   (d) $\left(4\sqrt{3}, 1, 2\pi/3\right)$ **(e)** $\left(4\sqrt{2}, 5\pi/6, \pi/4\right)$ **(f)** $\left(2\sqrt{2}, 0, 3\pi/4\right)$

6. **(a)** $\left(5\sqrt{3}/2, \pi/4, -5/2\right)$ **(b)** $(0, 7\pi/6, -1)$ **(c)** $(0, 0, 3)$
   (d) $(4, \pi/6, 0)$ **(e)** $(0, \pi/2, 5)$ **(f)** $\left(3\sqrt{2}, 0, -3\sqrt{2}\right)$

7.

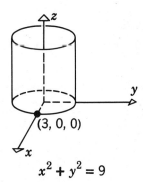

(3, 0, 0)

$$x^2 + y^2 = 9$$

8.

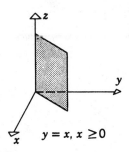

$$y = x, x \geq 0$$

9.

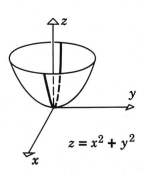

$$z = x^2 + y^2$$

10.

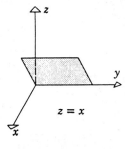

$$z = x$$

11.

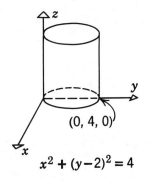

(0, 4, 0)

$$x^2 + (y-2)^2 = 4$$

12.

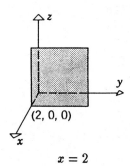

(2, 0, 0)

$$x = 2$$

13.

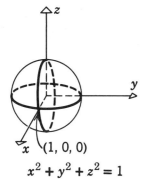

(1, 0, 0)

$$x^2 + y^2 + z^2 = 1$$

14.

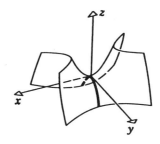

$$z = r^2 \left(\cos^2 - \sin^2 \theta\right)$$
$$= (r\cos\theta)^2 - (r\sin\theta)^2 = x^2 - y^2$$

15.

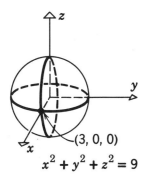

(3, 0, 0)

$$x^2 + y^2 + z^2 = 9$$

16.

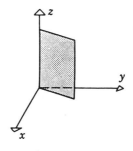

$$y/x = \tan(\pi/3) = \sqrt{3}, \ y = \sqrt{3}x, \ x \geq 0$$

17.

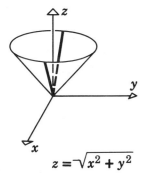

$$z = \sqrt{x^2 + y^2}$$

$$r/z = \tan\phi = 1, z = r = \sqrt{x^2 + y^2}$$

18.

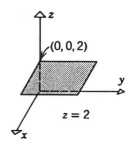

(0, 0, 2)

$$z = 2$$

$$\rho\cos\phi = 2, z = 2$$

19.

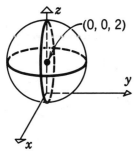

$$x^2 + y^2 + (z - 2)^2 = 4$$

$\rho = 4\cos\phi, \rho^2 = 4\rho\cos\phi$
$x^2 + y^2 + z^2 = 4z$
$x^2 + y^2 + (z - 2)^2 = 4$

20.

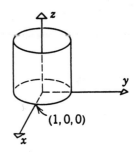

$\rho\sin\phi = 1, r = 1, x^2 + y^2 = 1$

21.

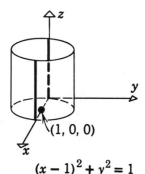

$$(x - 1)^2 + y^2 = 1$$

$\rho\sin\phi = 2\cos\theta$
$r = 2\cos\theta, r^2 = 2r\cos\theta$
$x^2 + y^2 = 2x, (x - 1)^2 + y^2 = 1$

22.

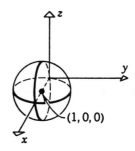

$\rho = 2\sin\phi\cos\theta, \rho^2 = 2\rho\sin\phi\cos\theta$
$x^2 + y^2 + z^2 = 2x, (x - 1)^2 + y^2 + z^2 = 1$

23.   **(a)** $z = 3$ **(b)** $\rho\cos\phi = 3, \rho = 3\sec\phi$

24.   **(a)** $r\sin\theta = 2, r = 2\csc\theta$ **(b)** $\rho\sin\phi\sin\theta = 2, \rho = 2\csc\phi\csc\theta$

25.   **(a)** $z = 3r^2$ **(b)** $\rho\cos\phi = 3\rho^2\sin^2\phi, \rho = \dfrac{1}{3}\csc\phi\cot\phi$

26.   **(a)** $z = \sqrt{3}r$ **(b)** $\rho\cos\phi = \sqrt{3}\rho\sin\phi, \tan\phi = \dfrac{1}{\sqrt{3}}, \phi = \dfrac{\pi}{6}$

27.   **(a)** $r = 2$ **(b)** $\rho\sin\phi = 2, \rho = 2\csc\phi$

28. **(a)** $r^2 - 6r\sin\theta = 0$, $r = 6\sin\theta$ $\qquad\qquad$ **(b)** $\rho\sin\phi = 6\sin\theta$, $\rho = 6\sin\theta\csc\phi$

29. **(a)** $r^2 + z^2 = 9$ $\qquad\qquad\qquad\qquad$ **(b)** $\rho = 3$

30. **(a)** $z^2 = r^2\cos^2\theta - r^2\sin^2\theta = r^2(\cos^2\theta - \sin^2\theta)$, $z^2 = r^2\cos 2\theta$
$\quad$ **(b)** Use the result in part (a) with $r = \rho\sin\phi$, $z = \rho\cos\phi$ to get $\rho^2\cos^2\phi = \rho^2\sin^2\phi\cos 2\theta$,
$\qquad$ $\cos^2\phi = \cos 2\theta$

31. **(a)** $2r\cos\theta + 3r\sin\theta + 4z = 1$
$\quad$ **(b)** $2\rho\sin\phi\cos\theta + 3\rho\sin\phi\sin\theta + 4\rho\cos\phi = 1$

32. **(a)** $r^2 - z^2 = 1$
$\quad$ **(b)** Use the result of part (a) with $r = \rho\sin\phi$, $z = \rho\cos\phi$ to get $\rho^2\sin^2\phi - \rho^2\cos^2\phi = 1$,
$\qquad$ $\rho^2\cos 2\phi = -1$

33. **(a)** $r^2\cos^2\theta = 16 - z^2$
$\quad$ **(b)** $x^2 = 16 - z^2$, $x^2 + y^2 + z^2 = 16 + y^2$, $\rho^2 = 16 + \rho^2\sin^2\phi\sin^2\theta$, $\rho^2\left(1 - \sin^2\phi\sin^2\theta\right) = 16$

34. **(a)** $r^2 + z^2 = 2z$ $\qquad\qquad\qquad\qquad$ **(b)** $\rho^2 = 2\rho\cos\phi$, $\rho = 2\cos\phi$

35. All points on or above the paraboloid $z = x^2 + y^2$, that are also on or below the plane $z = 4$

36. A right circular cylindrical solid of height 3 and radius 1

37. All points on or between concentric spheres of radii 1 and 3

38. All points on or above the cone $\phi = \pi/6$, that are also on or below the sphere $\rho = 2$

39. $\theta = \pi/6$, $\phi = \pi/6$, spherical $(4000, \pi/6, \pi/6)$, rectangular $\left(1000\sqrt{3}, 1000, 2000\sqrt{3}\right)$

40. **(a)** $y = r\sin\theta = a\sin\theta$ but $az = a\sin\theta$ so $\qquad\qquad$ **(b)**
$\qquad$ $y = az$, which is a plane that contains
$\qquad$ the curve of intersection of $z = \sin\theta$ and
$\qquad$ the circular cylinder $r = a$. From Exercise
$\qquad$ 44, Section 12.3, the curve of intersection
$\qquad$ of a plane and a circular cylinder is an ellipse.

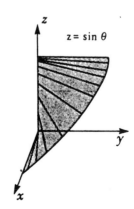

41.

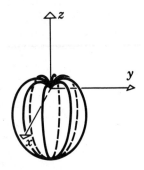

SUPPLEMENTARY EXERCISES CHAPTER 14

1. (a) $\overrightarrow{P_1P_2} = (5-2)\mathbf{i} + (-1-3)\mathbf{j} = 3\mathbf{i} - 4\mathbf{j}$, $\|\overrightarrow{P_1P_2}\| = 5$

    (b) $\overrightarrow{P_1P_2} = (1-2)\mathbf{i} + (3+1)\mathbf{j} = -\mathbf{i} + 4\mathbf{j}$, $\|\overrightarrow{P_1P_2}\| = \sqrt{17}$

2. The slope of the line $x + y = -1$ is -1 so the slope of a line perpendicular to it is 1 thus $\mathbf{i} + \mathbf{j}$ is a vector perpendicular to the given line, $\|\mathbf{i} + \mathbf{j}\| = \sqrt{2}$ so $(\mathbf{i}+\mathbf{j})/\sqrt{2}$ is a vector of length 1 that is perpendicular to the given line, another such vector is $-(\mathbf{i}+\mathbf{j})/\sqrt{2}$.

3. $-(3\mathbf{i} - 4\mathbf{j}) = -3\mathbf{i} + 4\mathbf{j}$

4. Let $\mathbf{v}$ be the desired vector, then $\|\mathbf{v}\| = \|\mathbf{i}\| = 1$ and $\phi = 0 + \theta = \theta$ so $\mathbf{v} = \cos\theta\mathbf{i} + \sin\theta\mathbf{j}$.

5. $4\mathbf{i} + 3\mathbf{j}$ is the vector from $(1,2)$ to $(5,5)$ so the desired vector is $(3/5)(4\mathbf{i} + 3\mathbf{j})$

6. $dy/dx = 2x$, the slope of the tangent at $(-1,1)$ is $2(-1) = -2$ so the vector $\mathbf{i} - 2\mathbf{j}$ is parallel to the tangent, $\|\mathbf{i} - 2\mathbf{j}\| = \sqrt{5}$ so $2(\mathbf{i} - 2\mathbf{j})/\sqrt{5}$ is a vector of length 2 that is parallel to the tangent, another such vector is $-2(\mathbf{i} - 2\mathbf{j})/\sqrt{5}$.

7. $12\cos 120°\mathbf{i} + 12\sin 120°\mathbf{j} = -6\mathbf{i} + 6\sqrt{3}\mathbf{j}$

8. $c_1\langle -2, 5\rangle + 3c_2\langle 1, 3\rangle = \langle -2c_1, 5c_1\rangle + \langle 3c_2, 9c_2\rangle = \langle -2c_1 + 3c_2, 5c_1 + 9c_2\rangle$ so $-2c_1 + 3c_2 = -6$ and $5c_1 + 9c_2 = -51$, solve to get $c_1 = -3$, $c_2 = -4$.

9. $3\mathbf{u} - (\mathbf{i} + \mathbf{j}) = \mathbf{i} + \mathbf{u}$, $2\mathbf{u} = 2\mathbf{i} + \mathbf{j}$, $\mathbf{u} = \mathbf{i} + (1/2)\mathbf{j}$

10. If $3\mathbf{u} - 4\mathbf{v} = 3\mathbf{v} - 2\mathbf{u}$ then $\mathbf{v} = (5/7)\mathbf{u}$, $3\mathbf{u} - 4\mathbf{v} = (3 - 20/7)\mathbf{u} = (1/7)\mathbf{u} = \langle 1, 2\rangle$, $\mathbf{u} = \langle 7, 14\rangle$, $\mathbf{v} = (5/7)\langle 7, 14\rangle = \langle 5, 10\rangle$.

11.   The effect of $\mathbf{F}_1$ and $\mathbf{F}_2$ is the same as the effect of $\mathbf{F}_1 + \mathbf{F}_2 = -\mathbf{i} - 5\mathbf{j}$ acting at the point, to cancel the effect a force $\mathbf{F}_3 = -(\mathbf{F}_1 + \mathbf{F}_2) = \mathbf{i} + 5\mathbf{j}$ must be applied at the point.

12.   Let $S(x,y)$ be the fourth vertex, then $\overrightarrow{PS} = \overrightarrow{QR}$, $\langle x - 3, y - 4 \rangle = \langle 4, 1 \rangle$, so $x - 3 = 4$ and $y - 4 = 1$, $x = 7$ and $y = 5$.

13.   **(a)** $\sqrt{6}$ **(b)** -3 **(c)** $\langle 5, -5, -5 \rangle$
       (d) $\langle -5, 5, 5 \rangle$ **(e)** $5\sqrt{3}/2$ **(f)** $\langle -1, 8, -9 \rangle$

14.   **(a)** 3 **(b)** -15 **(c)** $\langle 2, 11, 10 \rangle$
       (d) $\langle -2, -11, -10 \rangle$ **(e)** $15/2$ **(f)** $\langle -3, -14, 16 \rangle$

15.   **(a)** $2/3$ **(b)** $2/5$ **(c)** $\cos^{-1}(-2/15)$ **(d)** $3/5, -4/5, 0$

16.   **(a)** $1/\sqrt{2}$ **(b)** 1 **(c)** $3\pi/4$ **(d)** $0, -1, 0$

17.   Both sides reduce to $2\mathbf{i} - 2\mathbf{j} + \mathbf{k}$

18. $\mathbf{v} = 5\langle \cos 60°, \cos 120°, \cos 135° \rangle = \langle 5/2, -5/2, -5/\sqrt{2} \rangle$

19. $\langle -3/\sqrt{2}, 0, 3/\sqrt{2} \rangle$

20.   **(a)** Let $M(m_1, m_2, m_3)$ be the midpoint, then $\overrightarrow{PM} = (1/2)\,\overrightarrow{PQ}$,
              $\langle m_1 - 6, m_2 - 5, m_3 - 7 \rangle = \langle 1/2, -1, 1 \rangle$, equate corresponding components to get
              $m_1 = 13/2$, $m_2 = 4$, $m_3 = 8$ so the midpoint is $(13/2, 4, 8)$.
       (b) $\overrightarrow{PQ} = \langle 1, -2, 2 \rangle$, $\| \overrightarrow{PQ} \| = 3$, $\cos \alpha = 1/3$, $\cos \beta = -2/3$, $\cos \gamma = 2/3$

21.   **(a)** $\text{proj}_{\mathbf{v}}\mathbf{u} = \dfrac{\mathbf{u} \cdot \mathbf{v}}{\|\mathbf{v}\|^2}\mathbf{v} = \dfrac{(-3)}{6}(\mathbf{i} + \mathbf{j} + 2\mathbf{k}) = -\dfrac{1}{2}\mathbf{i} - \dfrac{1}{2}\mathbf{j} - \mathbf{k}$
       (b) $\mathbf{u} - \text{proj}_{\mathbf{v}}\mathbf{u} = \dfrac{3}{2}\mathbf{i} + \dfrac{5}{2}\mathbf{j} - 2\mathbf{k}$

22.   With $\mathbf{u} = \mathbf{i}$ and $\mathbf{a} = 3\mathbf{i} - 2\mathbf{j} + \mathbf{k}$, $\text{proj}_{\mathbf{a}}\mathbf{u} = \dfrac{\mathbf{u} \cdot \mathbf{a}}{\|\mathbf{a}\|^2}\mathbf{a} = \dfrac{3}{14}(3\mathbf{i} - 2\mathbf{j} + \mathbf{k})$.

23. $\cos^2 \alpha + \cos^2 \beta + \cos^2 \gamma = 1$, let $\alpha = 50°$, $\beta = 70°$,
       $\cos^2 \gamma = 1 - \cos^2(50°) - \cos^2(70°) \approx 0.46985$, $\gamma \approx 62°$.

24. $\overrightarrow{OA} \cdot \overrightarrow{AB} = 0$, $\langle 0, a, a \rangle \cdot \langle -3, 4 - a, 2 - a \rangle = 0$, $6a - 2a^2 = 0$, $a = 0$ or 3.

25.   **(a)** $(\mathbf{u} + \mathbf{v}) \cdot (\mathbf{u} - \mathbf{v}) = 0$, $\mathbf{u} \cdot \mathbf{u} - \mathbf{u} \cdot \mathbf{v} + \mathbf{v} \cdot \mathbf{u} - \mathbf{v} \cdot \mathbf{v} = 0$, $\|\mathbf{u}\|^2 - \|\mathbf{v}\|^2 = 0$, $\|\mathbf{u}\| = \|\mathbf{v}\|$

      (b) $(\mathbf{a} \cdot \mathbf{b})^2 + \|\mathbf{a} \times \mathbf{b}\|^2 = (\|\mathbf{a}\| \, \|\mathbf{b}\| \cos\theta)^2 + (\|\mathbf{a}\| \, \|\mathbf{b}\| \sin\theta)^2$

$$= \|\mathbf{a}\|^2 \|\mathbf{b}\|^2 (\cos^2\theta + \sin^2\theta) = \|\mathbf{a}\|^2 \|\mathbf{b}\|^2$$

26. $\overrightarrow{PQ} = 2\overrightarrow{PM}$, $\langle q_1 - 1, q_2 - 2, q_3 - 3 \rangle = \langle 4, -6, 4 \rangle$, $q_1 = 5$, $q_2 = -4$, $q_3 = 7$ so Q has coordinates $(5, -4, 7)$.

27. $\mathbf{a} \times \mathbf{b} = \langle 5, 7, -1 \rangle$ is orthogonal to both $\mathbf{a}$ and $\mathbf{b}$, $\|\mathbf{a} \times \mathbf{b}\| = 5\sqrt{3}$ so $\pm\langle 1/\sqrt{3},\, 7/(5\sqrt{3}),\, -1/(5\sqrt{3}) \rangle$ are unit vectors orthogonal to both $\mathbf{a}$ and $\mathbf{b}$.

28. $2x + y + 2z = 2$ is an equation of the plane containing A, B, and C so $D = |2(2) + (3) + 2(4) - 2|/\sqrt{4 + 1 + 4} = 13/3$.

29. The plane contains $\overrightarrow{AB}$ and is parallel to $\mathbf{v}$ thus $\mathbf{v} \times \overrightarrow{AB}$ is normal to the plane,

     $\mathbf{v} \times \overrightarrow{AB} = \langle 5, -5, -5 \rangle$ so $\langle 1, -1, -1 \rangle$ is also a normal to the plane whose equation is $x - y - z = -4$.

30. $\mathbf{n}_1 = \langle 2, -3, 0 \rangle$ and $\mathbf{n}_2 = \langle 3, -1, -4 \rangle$ are normals to the given planes so $\mathbf{n}_1 \times \mathbf{n}_2 = \langle 12, 8, 7 \rangle$ is normal to the desired plane whose equation is $12x + 8y + 7z = 25$.

31. $\overrightarrow{PQ} \times \overrightarrow{PR} = \langle 1, 2, -1 \rangle \times \langle 1, 0, 1 \rangle = \langle 2, -2, -2 \rangle$ is normal to the plane and hence so is $\langle 1, -1, -1 \rangle$, an equation of the plane is $x - y - z = -1$.

32. The intercepts correspond to the points $A(2, 0, 0)$, $B(0, -3, 0)$ and $C(0, 0, 10)$;

     $\overrightarrow{AB} \times \overrightarrow{AC} = \langle -30, 20, -6 \rangle$ is normal to the plane and hence so is $\langle 15, -10, 3 \rangle$, an equation of the plane is $15x - 10y + 3z = 30$.

33.   **(a)** Parametric equations of L are $x = 1 + 3t$, $y = 2 - t$, $z = 8 - 4t$. If Q is on L then for some t_0, $k = 1 + 3t_0$, $3 = 2 - t_0$, $\ell = 8 - 4t_0$. The second of these equations yields $t_0 = -1$ so $k = -2$, $\ell = 12$.

      (b) Use parametric equations in part (a) for L, solve the system $1 + 3t_1 = -8 - 3t_2$, $2 - t_1 = 5 + t_2$, $8 - 4t_1 = 0$ to get $t_1 = 2$, $t_2 = -5$ so L' intersects L at $(7, 0, 0)$.

      (c) An equation of the plane is $3x - 2y + 6z = 6$, use the parametric equations in part (a) to get $3(1 + 3t) - 2(2 - t) + 6(8 - 4t) = 6$, $t = 41/13$ so L intersects the plane at $(136/13, -15/13, -60/13)$.

34.   **(a)** $\mathbf{v}_1 = \langle 2, 1, 2 \rangle$ and $\mathbf{v}_2 = \langle -1, -2, 2 \rangle$ are parallel, respectively, to L_1 and L_2. $\mathbf{v}_1 \cdot \mathbf{v}_2 = 0$ so the lines are perpendicular in the sense that $\mathbf{v}_1$ and $\mathbf{v}_2$ are perpendicular.

(b) $(1, -3/2, -1)$ and $(4, 3, -4)$ are points on L_1 and L_2, respectively, so parametric equations are $L_1 : x = 1 + 2t, y = -3/2 + t, z = -1 + 2t$; $L_2 : x = 4 - t, y = 3 - 2t, z = -4 + 2t$

(c) Solve the system $1 + 2t_1 = 4 - t_2, -3/2 + t_1 = 3 - 2t_2, -1 + 2t_1 = -4 + 2t_2$ to get $t_1 = 1/2, t_2 = 2$ so the lines intersect at $(2, -1, 0)$.

35. **(a)** $\overrightarrow{P_1 P_2} = \langle 2, 3, -3 \rangle$, use P_1 to get $x = 1 + 2t, y = -1 + 3t, z = 2 - 3t$.

(b) $\overrightarrow{P_1 P_2} = \langle 0, 5, -7 \rangle$, use P_1 to get $x = 1, y = -3 + 5t, z = 4 - 7t$.

36. **(a)** $\overrightarrow{AB} \times \overrightarrow{AC} = \langle 1, -2, -2 \rangle \times \langle -2, -1, -2 \rangle = \langle 2, 6, -5 \rangle$

(b) area $= \| \overrightarrow{AB} \times \overrightarrow{AC} \| / 2 = \sqrt{65}/2$

(c) volume $= | \overrightarrow{AD} \cdot (\overrightarrow{AB} \times \overrightarrow{AC}) | = |\langle 1, 2, -3 \rangle \cdot \langle 2, 6, -5 \rangle| = 29$

(d) $\overrightarrow{AB} \times \overrightarrow{AC}$ is normal to the plane so $2x + 6y - 5z + 14 = 0$ is an equation of the plane. The distance from D to the plane is $|2(2) + 6(1) - 5(-1) + 14| / \sqrt{4 + 36 + 25} = 29/\sqrt{65}$.

37. **(a)** $\mathbf{n}_1 = \langle 2, 1, -1 \rangle$ and $\mathbf{n}_2 = \langle 1, 2, 1 \rangle$ are normals to the planes so $\mathbf{n}_1 \times \mathbf{n}_2 = \langle 3, -3, 3 \rangle$ is parallel to the line of intersection and hence so is $\langle 1, -1, 1 \rangle$. To find a point on the line of intersection, let $x = 0$ in the equations of the planes to get $y - z = 3$ and $2y + z = 3$ which yield $y = 2, z = -1$ so $(0, 2, -1)$ is on the line whose equations are $x = t, y = 2 - t, z = -1 + t$.

(b) $\mathbf{n}_1 \cdot \mathbf{n}_2 = 3 > 0$ so $\cos \theta = \dfrac{\mathbf{n}_1 \cdot \mathbf{n}_2}{\|\mathbf{n}_1\| \|\mathbf{n}_2\|} = \dfrac{3}{\sqrt{6}\sqrt{6}} = 1/2, \theta = 60°$.

38. **(a)** the region outside the ellipsoid $x^2/36 + y^2/4 + z^2/9 = 1$

(b) Complete the square to get $(x - 3)^2 + (y + 1)^2 + z^2 < 16$ which is the region inside the sphere of radius 4 centered at $(3, -1, 0)$.

39. **(a)** the region above the elliptic paraboloid $z = 4x^2 + 9y^2$

(b) the point $(0,0,0)$

40. **(a)** The portion of the elliptic cylinder $y^2/4 + z^2 = 1$ that extends from $x = 0$ to $x = 2$.

(b) Complete the square to get $9(x + 2)^2 + 4(y - 1)^2 = -20$ which has no real solutions.

41. $z^2 = \dfrac{x^2}{(36/100)} + \dfrac{y^2}{(36/225)}$, elliptic cone

42. $y = z^2 - x^2$, hyperbolic paraboloid   **43.** $x^2 + y^2/16 + z^2/25 = 1$, ellipsoid

44. $x^2 - y^2/4 + z^2 = 1$, hyperboloid of one sheet

45. $x^2/25 + y^2/4 - z^2/16 = -1$, hyperboloid of two sheets

46. (a) $(x-3)^2 + 4(y+1)^2 - (z-2)^2 = 9$, hyperboloid of one sheet centered at $(3,-1,2)$
  (b) $(x+3)^2 + (y-2)^2 + (z+6)^2 = 49$, the sphere of radius 7 centered at $(-3,2,-6)$

47. $W = \mathbf{F} \cdot \overrightarrow{PQ} = (3\mathbf{i} - 4\mathbf{j} + \mathbf{k}) \cdot (\mathbf{i} - \mathbf{j} + 6\mathbf{k}) = 13$ ft · lb

48. $W = (\mathbf{F}_1 + \mathbf{F}_2) \cdot \overrightarrow{PQ} = (2\mathbf{i} - \mathbf{j} + 3\mathbf{k}) \cdot (\mathbf{i} + 4\mathbf{j} - 3\mathbf{k}) = -11$ ft · lb

49. (a) $(1,1,1)$ (b) $(\sqrt{3}, \pi/4, \tan^{-1}\sqrt{2})$

50. (a) (i) $(2\sqrt{2}, \pi/4, 2\sqrt{6})$ (ii) $(4\sqrt{2}, \pi/4, \pi/6)$ (b) (i) $(2, \pi/3, 0)$ (ii) $(2, \pi/3, \pi/2)$

51. (a) $z = r^2(\cos^2\theta - \sin^2\theta)$, $z = x^2 - y^2$ (b) $(\rho\sin\phi\cos\theta)(\rho\cos\phi) = 1$, $xz = 1$

52. (a)
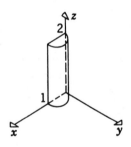

(b)
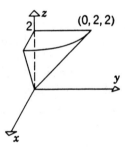

(c)
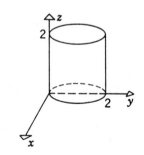

(d)
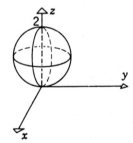

CHAPTER 15
Vector-Valued Functions

EXERCISE SET 15.1

1. $(-\infty, +\infty)$; $\mathbf{r}(\pi) = -\mathbf{i} - 3\pi\mathbf{j}$.

2. $[-1/3, +\infty)$; $\mathbf{r}(1) = \langle 2, 1 \rangle$

3. $[2, +\infty)$; $\mathbf{r}(3) = -\mathbf{i} - \ln 3\mathbf{j} + \mathbf{k}$.

4. $[-1, 1)$; $\mathbf{r}(0) = \langle 2, 0, 0 \rangle$

5. $\mathbf{r} = 3\cos t\mathbf{i} + (t + \sin t)\mathbf{j}$

6. $\mathbf{r} = (t^2 + 1)\mathbf{i} + e^{-2t}\mathbf{j}$

7. $\mathbf{r} = 2t\mathbf{i} + 2\sin 3t\mathbf{j} + 5\cos 3t\mathbf{k}$.

8. $\mathbf{r} = t\sin t\mathbf{i} + \ln t\mathbf{j} + \cos^2 t\mathbf{k}$

9. $x = 3t^2$, $y = -2$, $z = 0$.

10. $x = \sin^2 t$, $y = 1 - \cos 2t$, $z = 0$

11. $x = 2t - 1$, $y = -3\sqrt{t}$, $z = \sin 3t$.

12. $x = te^{-t}$, $y = 0$, $z = -5t^2$

13. The line in 2-space through the point $(2, 0)$ and parallel to the vector $-3\mathbf{i} - 4\mathbf{j}$.

14. The circle of radius 3 in the xy-plane, with center at the origin.

15. The line in 3-space through the point $(0, -3, 1)$ and parallel to the vector $2\mathbf{i} + 3\mathbf{k}$.

16. The circle of radius 2 in the plane $x = 3$, with center at $(3, 0, 0)$.

17. An ellipse in the plane $z = -1$, center at $(0, 0, -1)$, major axis of length 6 parallel to x-axis, minor axis of length 4 parallel to y-axis.

18. A parabola in the plane $x = -2$, vertex at $(-2, 0, -1)$, opening upward.

19. The line is parallel to the vector $-2\mathbf{i} + 3\mathbf{j}$; the slope is $-3/2$.

20. $x = 3 + 2t = 0$, $t = -3/2$ so $y = 5(-3/2) = -15/2$

21. $y = 0$ in the xz-plane so $1 - 2t = 0$, $t = 1/2$ thus $x = 2 + 1/2 = 5/2$ and $z = 3(1/2) = 3/2$; the coordinates are $(5/2, 0, 3/2)$.

22. $x = t$, $y = 1 + 2t$, $z = -3t$ so $3(t) - (1 + 2t) - (-3t) = 2$, $t = 3/4$; the point of intersection is $(3/4, 5/2, -9/4)$.

23. $x = 2$

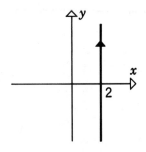

24. $y = 2x + 10$

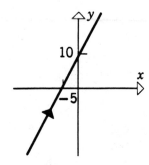

25. $(x - 1)^2 + (y - 3)^2 = 1$

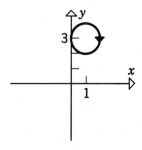

26. $x^2/4 + y^2/25 = 1$

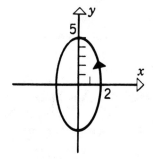

27. $x^2 - y^2 = 1,\ x \geq 1$

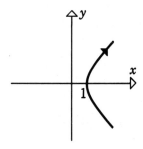

28. $y = 2x^2 + 4,\ x \geq 0$

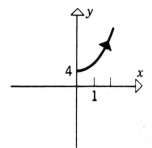

29.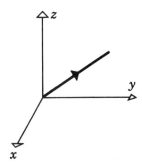

30.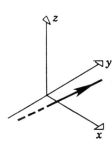

31.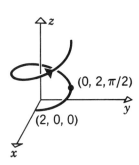

$(0, 2, \pi/2)$

$(2, 0, 0)$

32.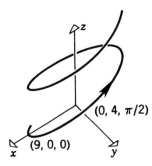

$(0, 4, \pi/2)$

$(9, 0, 0)$

33.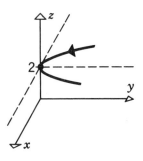

2

34.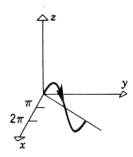

π

2π

35. $x^2 + y^2 = (t \sin t)^2 + (t \cos t)^2 = t^2(\sin^2 t + \cos^2 t) = t^2 = z$

36. $x - y + z + 1 = t - (1+t)/t + (1-t^2)/t + 1 = [t^2 - (1+t) + (1-t^2) + t]/t = 0$

37. $x = \sin t$, $y = 2 \cos t$, $z = \sqrt{3} \sin t$ so $x^2 + y^2 + z^2 = \sin^2 t + 4 \cos^2 t + 3 \sin^2 t = 4$ and $z = \sqrt{3}x$;
it is the curve of intersection of the sphere $x^2 + y^2 + z^2 = 4$ and the plane $z = \sqrt{3}x$, which is
a circle with center at $(0,0,0)$ and radius 2.

38. $x = 3\cos t$, $y = 3\sin t$, $z = 3\sin t$ so $x^2 + y^2 = 9\cos^2 t + 9\sin^2 t = 9$ and $z = y$; it is the curve of intersection of the circular cylinder $x^2 + y^2 = 9$ and the plane $z = y$, which is an ellipse with major axis of length $6\sqrt{2}$ and minor axis of length 6.

39. The helix makes one turn as t varies from 0 to 2π so $z = c(2\pi) = 3$, $c = 3/(2\pi)$.

40. $0.2t = 10$, $t = 50$; the helix has made one revolution when $t = 2\pi$ so when $t = 50$ it has made $50/(2\pi) = 25/\pi \approx 7.96$ revolutions.

41. $x^2 + y^2 = t^2 \cos^2 t + t^2 \sin^2 t = t^2$, $\sqrt{x^2 + y^2} = t = z$; a conical helix.

42. The curve wraps around an elliptic cylinder with axis along the z-axis; an elliptical helix.

43. The plane is parallel to a line on the surface of the cone and does not go through the vertex so the curve of intersection is a parabola. Eliminate z to get $y+2 = \sqrt{x^2 + y^2}$, $(y+2)^2 = x^2 + y^2$, $y = x^2/4 - 1$; let $x = t$, then $y = t^2/4 - 1$ and $z = t^2/4 + 1$.

44. Eliminate x to get $z = (-2)^2 + y^2 = y^2 + 4$ so the curve of intersection is a parabola. Let $y = t$, then $x = -2$, $y = t$, $z = t^2 + 4$ are parametric equations of the curve.

45. Let $x = 3\cos t$ and $y = 3\sin t$, then $z = 9\cos^2 t$.

46. $z = 4 - (x^2 + y^2) = 4 - 1 = 3$ so the curve of intersection is a circle in the plane $z = 3$. Let $x = \cos t$, $y = \sin t$, $z = 3$.

47. $x^2 + 4y^2 = 2x$, $(x-1)^2 + 4y^2 = 1$; let $x = 1 + \cos t$, $y = \dfrac{1}{2}\sin t$, $z = 2 + 2\cos t$.

48. $\sqrt{x^2 + y^2} = 2\sqrt{y}$, $x^2 + y^2 = 4y$, $x^2 + (y-2)^2 = 4$; let $x = 2\cos t$, $y = 2 + 2\sin t$, $z = 2\sqrt{2 + 2\sin t}$.

EXERCISE SET 15.2

1. $9\mathbf{i} + 6\mathbf{j}$

2. $\langle \sqrt{2}/2, \sqrt{2}/2 \rangle$

3. $\mathbf{j}$

4. $\langle 1/3, 0 \rangle$

5. $2\mathbf{i} - 3\mathbf{j} + 4\mathbf{k}$

6. $\langle -1, e^{-\pi}, \sqrt{\pi} \rangle$

7. $\dfrac{\pi}{2}\mathbf{i} + \mathbf{k}$

8. $\langle 3, 1/2, \sin 2 \rangle$

9. $\displaystyle\lim_{t \to \pi/2} \mathbf{r}(t) = 3\mathbf{i} - \pi\mathbf{j} = \mathbf{r}(\pi/2)$

10. $\displaystyle\lim_{t \to 1} \mathbf{r}(t) = 5\mathbf{i} - 2\mathbf{j} + e^2\mathbf{k} = \mathbf{r}(1)$

11. $\mathbf{r}'(t) = 5\mathbf{i} + (1 - 2t)\mathbf{j}$

12. $\mathbf{r}'(t) = \sin t\mathbf{j}$

13. $-\dfrac{1}{t^2}\mathbf{i} + \sec^2 t\,\mathbf{j} + 2e^{2t}\mathbf{k}$

14. $\mathbf{r}'(t) = \dfrac{1}{1+t^2}\mathbf{i} + (\cos t - t\sin t)\mathbf{j} - \dfrac{1}{2\sqrt{t}}\mathbf{k}$

15. $\mathbf{r}'(t) = \langle 1, 2t\rangle,$
$\mathbf{r}'(2) = \langle 1, 4\rangle,$
$\mathbf{r}(2) = \langle 2, 4\rangle$

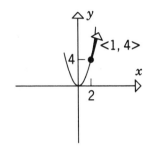

16. $\mathbf{r}'(t) = (-\sin t)\mathbf{i} + (\cos t)\mathbf{j},$
$\mathbf{r}'(3\pi/4) = -(\sqrt{2}/2)\mathbf{i} - (\sqrt{2}/2)\mathbf{j},$
$\mathbf{r}(3\pi/4) = -(\sqrt{2}/2)\mathbf{i} + (\sqrt{2}/2)\mathbf{j}$

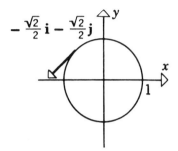

17. $\mathbf{r}'(t) = \langle -e^{-t}, 2e^{2t}\rangle,$
$\mathbf{r}'(\ln 2) = \langle -1/2, 8\rangle,$
$\mathbf{r}(\ln 2) = \langle 1/2, 4\rangle$

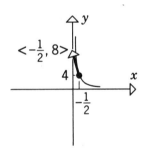

18. $\mathbf{r}'(t) = (-2\sin 2t)\mathbf{i} - (4\cos t)\mathbf{j},$
$\mathbf{r}'(\pi) = 4\mathbf{j},$
$\mathbf{r}(\pi) = \mathbf{i}$

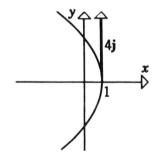

19. $\mathbf{r}'(t) = 2\cos t\mathbf{i} - 2\sin t\mathbf{k}$,
$\mathbf{r}'(\pi/2) = -2\mathbf{k}$,
$\mathbf{r}(\pi/2) = 2\mathbf{i} + \mathbf{j}$

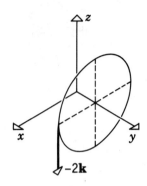

20. $\mathbf{r}'(t) = -\sin t\mathbf{i} + \cos t\mathbf{j} + \mathbf{k}$,
$$\mathbf{r}'(\pi/4) = -\frac{1}{\sqrt{2}}\mathbf{i} + \frac{1}{\sqrt{2}}\mathbf{j} + \mathbf{k},$$
$$\mathbf{r}(\pi/4) = \frac{1}{\sqrt{2}}\mathbf{i} + \frac{1}{\sqrt{2}}\mathbf{j} + \frac{\pi}{4}\mathbf{k}$$

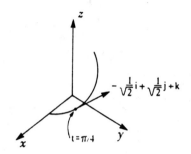

21. $\mathbf{r}'(t) = \mathbf{j} - 2t\mathbf{k}$
$\mathbf{r}'(1) = \mathbf{j} - 2\mathbf{k}$,
$\mathbf{r}(1) = 3\mathbf{i} + \mathbf{j} + \mathbf{k}$

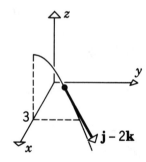

22. $\mathbf{r}'(t) = \mathbf{i} + 2\mathbf{j} + 2t\mathbf{k}$,
$\mathbf{r}'(2) = \mathbf{i} + 2\mathbf{j} + 4\mathbf{k}$,
$\mathbf{r}(2) = 2\mathbf{i} + 4\mathbf{j} + 4\mathbf{k}$

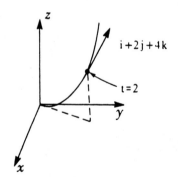

23. $\mathbf{r}'(t) = 2t\mathbf{i} - \dfrac{1}{t}\mathbf{j}$, $\mathbf{r}'(1) = 2\mathbf{i} - \mathbf{j}$, $\mathbf{r}(1) = \mathbf{i} + 2\mathbf{j}$; $x = 1 + 2t$, $y = 2 - t$, $z = 0$.

24. $\mathbf{r}'(t) = 2e^{2t}\mathbf{i} + 6\sin 3t\mathbf{j}$, $\mathbf{r}'(0) = 2\mathbf{i}$, $\mathbf{r}(0) = \mathbf{i} - 2\mathbf{j}$; $x = 1 + 2t$, $y = -2$, $z = 0$.

25. $\mathbf{r}'(t) = -2\pi\sin\pi t\mathbf{i} + 2\pi\cos\pi t\mathbf{j} + 3\mathbf{k}$, $\mathbf{r}'(1/3) = -\sqrt{3}\,\pi\mathbf{i} + \pi\mathbf{j} + 3\mathbf{k}$,
$\mathbf{r}(1/3) = \mathbf{i} + \sqrt{3}\,\mathbf{j} + \mathbf{k}$; $x = 1 - \sqrt{3}\,\pi t$, $y = \sqrt{3} + \pi t$, $z = 1 + 3t$.

26. $\mathbf{r}'(t) = \frac{1}{t}\mathbf{i} - e^{-t}\mathbf{j} + 3t^2\mathbf{k}$, $\mathbf{r}'(2) = \frac{1}{2}\mathbf{i} - e^{-2}\mathbf{j} + 12\mathbf{k}$,

     $\mathbf{r}(2) = \ln 2\mathbf{i} + e^{-2}\mathbf{j} + 8\mathbf{k}$; $x = \ln 2 + \frac{1}{2}t$, $y = e^{-2} - e^{-2}t$, $z = 8 + 12t$.

27. $\mathbf{r}'(t) = 2\mathbf{i} + \dfrac{3}{2\sqrt{3t+4}}\mathbf{j}$, $t = 0$ at P_0 so $\mathbf{r}'(0) = 2\mathbf{i} + \frac{3}{4}\mathbf{j}$,

     $\mathbf{r}(0) = -\mathbf{i} + 2\mathbf{j}$; $\mathbf{r} = (-\mathbf{i} + 2\mathbf{j}) + t(2\mathbf{i} + \frac{3}{4}\mathbf{j})$.

28. $\mathbf{r}'(t) = -4\sin t\mathbf{i} - 3\mathbf{j}$, $t = \pi/3$ at P_0 so $\mathbf{r}'(\pi/3) = -2\sqrt{3}\mathbf{i} - 3\mathbf{j}$,

     $\mathbf{r}(\pi/3) = 2\mathbf{i} - \pi\mathbf{j}$; $\mathbf{r} = (2\mathbf{i} - \pi\mathbf{j}) + t(-2\sqrt{3}\mathbf{i} - 3\mathbf{j})$.

29. $\mathbf{r}'(t) = 2t\mathbf{i} + \dfrac{1}{(t+1)^2}\mathbf{j} - 2t\mathbf{k}$, $t = -2$ at P_0 so $\mathbf{r}'(-2) = -4\mathbf{i} + \mathbf{j} + 4\mathbf{k}$,

     $\mathbf{r}(0) = 4\mathbf{i} + \mathbf{j}$; $\mathbf{r} = (4\mathbf{i} + \mathbf{j}) + t(-4\mathbf{i} + \mathbf{j} + 4\mathbf{k})$.

30. $\mathbf{r}'(t) = \cos t\mathbf{i} + \sinh t\mathbf{j} + \dfrac{1}{1+t^2}\mathbf{k}$, $t = 0$ at P_0 so $\mathbf{r}'(0) = \mathbf{i} + \mathbf{k}$, $\mathbf{r}(0) = \mathbf{j}$; $\mathbf{r} = (\mathbf{i} + \mathbf{k}) + t\mathbf{j}$.

31. $\mathbf{r}' = 3\cos t\mathbf{i} + 2\sin t\mathbf{j} + \mathbf{k}$, $\mathbf{r}'(\pi/2) = 2\mathbf{j} + \mathbf{k}$, $\mathbf{r}(\pi/2) = 3\mathbf{i} + \dfrac{\pi}{2}\mathbf{k}$; $2\mathbf{j} + \mathbf{k}$ is normal to the plane,

     and $(3, 0, \pi/2)$ is on the plane so an equation of the plane is $2y + z = \pi/2$.

32. $\mathbf{r}' = 6t\mathbf{i} + \dfrac{1}{2\sqrt{t+5}}\mathbf{j} - 2\mathbf{k}$, $t = -1$ at P so $\mathbf{r}'(-1) = -6\mathbf{i} + \dfrac{1}{4}\mathbf{j} - 2\mathbf{k}$; $\mathbf{r}'(-1)$ is normal to the

     plane, and $(3, 2, 2)$ is on the plane, so an equation of the plane is $-6x + \dfrac{1}{4}y - 2z = -\dfrac{43}{2}$, or

     $24x - y + 8z = 86$.

33.   **(a)** $2t - t^2 - 3t = -2$, $t^2 + t - 2 = 0$, $(t+2)(t-1) = 0$ so $t = -2, 1$. The points of intersection

        are $(-2, 4, 6)$ and $(1, 1, -3)$.

     (b) $\mathbf{r}' = \mathbf{i} + 2t\mathbf{j} - 3\mathbf{k}$; $\mathbf{r}'(-2) = \mathbf{i} - 4\mathbf{j} - 3\mathbf{k}$, $\mathbf{r}'(1) = \mathbf{i} + 2\mathbf{j} - 3\mathbf{k}$, and $\mathbf{n} = 2\mathbf{i} - \mathbf{j} + \mathbf{k}$ is normal

        to the plane. Let θ be the acute angle, then

        for $t = -2$: $\cos\theta = |\mathbf{n} \cdot \mathbf{r}'|/(\|\mathbf{n}\|\,\|\mathbf{r}'\|) = 3/\sqrt{156}$, $\theta \approx 76°$;

        for $t = 1$: $\cos\theta = |\mathbf{n} \cdot \mathbf{r}'|/(\|\mathbf{n}\|\,\|\mathbf{r}'\|) = 3/\sqrt{84}$, $\theta \approx 71°$.

34. $\mathbf{r}' = -2e^{-2t}\mathbf{i} - \sin t\mathbf{j} + 3\cos t\mathbf{k}$, $t = 0$ at the point $(1, 1, 0)$ so $\mathbf{r}'(0) = -2\mathbf{i} + 3\mathbf{k}$ and hence the

     tangent line is $x = 1 - 2t$, $y = 1$, $z = 3t$. But $x = 0$ in the yz-plane so $1 - 2t = 0$, $t = 1/2$.

     The point of intersection is $(0, 1, 3/2)$.

35. $\mathbf{r}_1(1) = \mathbf{r}_2(2) = \mathbf{i} + \mathbf{j} + 3\mathbf{k}$ so the graphs intersect at P; $\mathbf{r}_1'(t) = 2t\mathbf{i} + \mathbf{j} + 9t^2\mathbf{k}$ and

     $\mathbf{r}_2'(t) = \mathbf{i} + \frac{1}{2}t\mathbf{j} - \mathbf{k}$ so $\mathbf{r}_1'(1) = 2\mathbf{i} + \mathbf{j} + 9\mathbf{k}$ and $\mathbf{r}_2'(2) = \mathbf{i} + \mathbf{j} - \mathbf{k}$ are tangent to the graphs at P,

     thus $\cos\theta = \dfrac{\mathbf{r}_1'(1) \cdot \mathbf{r}_2'(2)}{\|\mathbf{r}_1'(1)\|\,\|\mathbf{r}_2'(2)\|} = \dfrac{6}{\sqrt{86}\sqrt{3}}$, $\theta = \cos^{-1}(6/\sqrt{258}) \approx 68°$.

36. $r_1(0) = r_2(-1) = 2i + j + 3k$ so the graphs intersect at P; $r_1'(t) = -2e^{-t}i - (\sin t)j + 2tk$ and $r_2'(t) = -i + 2tj + 3t^2k$ so $r_1'(0) = -2i$ and $r_2'(-1) = -i - 2j + 3k$ are tangent to the graphs at P, thus $\cos\theta = \dfrac{r_1'(0) \cdot r_2'(-1)}{\|r_1'(0)\| \, \|r_2'(-1)\|} = \dfrac{1}{\sqrt{14}}$, $\theta \approx 74°$.

37. Eliminate the parameter to get $y = x^2$ for both graphs; $r_1'(t) = i + 2tj$ which is never **0**, but $r_2'(t) = 3t^2i + 6t^5j = 0$ when $t = 0$.

38. Note that $r_2(t) = r_1(t^3)$ to see that the graphs are the same; $r_1'(t) = -\sin ti + \cos tj + k$ which is never **0**, but $r_2'(t) = -3t^2\sin(t^3)i + 3t^2\cos(t^3)j + 3t^2k = 0$ when $t = 0$.

39. $r' = 3t^2i + (6t - 2)j + 2tk$; smooth

40. $r' = -2t\sin(t^2)i + 2t\cos(t^2)j - e^{-t}k$; smooth

41. $r' = (1 - t)e^{-t}i + (2t - 2)j - \pi\sin(\pi t)k$; not smooth, $r'(1) = 0$

42. $r' = \pi\cos(\pi t)i + (2 - 1/t)j + (2t - 1)k$; not smooth, $r'(1/2) = 0$

43. (a) $7t^6$

    (b) $12(t\tan t + 1)\sec t - (\sin t)/t - (\cos t)\ln t$

44. (a) $18t^5i - 10t^4j$

    (b) $(t\cos t + \sin t)i + (4 + 4\ln t + 3\sec^2 t)j + 8tk$

45. $(dr/dt)(dt/du) = (i + 2tj)(4) = 4i + 8tj = 4i + 8(4u + 1)j$

46. $(dr/dt)(dt/du) = \langle -3\sin t, 3\cos t\rangle(\pi) = \langle -3\pi\sin\pi u, \, 3\pi\cos\pi u\rangle$

47. $(dr/dt)(dt/du) = (e^t i - 4e^{-t}j)(2u) = 2ue^{u^2}i - 8ue^{-u^2}j$

48. (a) $r(t) \cdot r'(t) = (a\cos ti + a\sin tj) \cdot (-a\sin ti + a\cos tj) = 0$

    (b) $r(t)$ is the position vector for a circle whose center is at the origin so $r(t)$ lies along a radius, $r'(t)$ is tangent to the circle at the tip of $r(t)$ so $r(t)$ and $r'(t)$ are perpendicular.

49. $\dfrac{d}{dt}[r(t) \times r'(t)] = r(t) \times r''(t) + r'(t) \times r'(t) = r(t) \times r''(t) + 0 = r(t) \times r''(t)$

50. $\dfrac{d}{dt}[u \cdot (v \times w)] = u \cdot \dfrac{d}{dt}[v \times w] + \dfrac{du}{dt} \cdot [v \times w] = u \cdot \left(v \times \dfrac{dw}{dt} + \dfrac{dv}{dt} \times w\right) + \dfrac{du}{dt} \cdot [v \times w]$

$$= u \cdot \left[v \times \dfrac{dw}{dt}\right] + u \cdot \left[\dfrac{dv}{dt} \times w\right] + \dfrac{du}{dt} \cdot [v \times w]$$

51. In Exercise 50, write each triple scalar product as a determinant.

52. $\|\mathbf{r}\|^2 = \mathbf{r} \cdot \mathbf{r}$ so $\dfrac{d}{dt}\|\mathbf{r}\|^2 = \dfrac{d}{dt}(\mathbf{r} \cdot \mathbf{r})$, $2\|\mathbf{r}\|\dfrac{d}{dt}(\|\mathbf{r}\|) = \mathbf{r} \cdot \dfrac{d\mathbf{r}}{dt} + \dfrac{d\mathbf{r}}{dt} \cdot \mathbf{r} = 2\mathbf{r} \cdot \mathbf{r}'$, $\dfrac{d}{dt}(\|\mathbf{r}\|) = \dfrac{\mathbf{r} \cdot \mathbf{r}'}{\|\mathbf{r}\|}$.

53. $\dfrac{d}{dt}\left[\dfrac{1}{\|\mathbf{r}\|}\mathbf{r}\right] = \dfrac{1}{\|\mathbf{r}\|}\mathbf{r}' + \mathbf{r}\dfrac{d}{dt}[\|\mathbf{r}\|^{-1}] = \dfrac{1}{\|\mathbf{r}\|}\mathbf{r}' + \mathbf{r}(-\|\mathbf{r}\|^{-2})\dfrac{d}{dt}[\|\mathbf{r}\|] = \dfrac{1}{\|\mathbf{r}\|}\mathbf{r}' - \dfrac{\mathbf{r} \cdot \mathbf{r}'}{\|\mathbf{r}\|^3}\mathbf{r}$

54. Let $\mathbf{c} = c_1\mathbf{i} + c_2\mathbf{j}$, $\mathbf{r}(t) = x(t)\mathbf{i} + y(t)\mathbf{j}$, $\mathbf{r}_1(t) = x_1(t)\mathbf{i} + y_1(t)\mathbf{j}$, $\mathbf{r}_2(t) = x_2(t)\mathbf{i} + y_2(t)\mathbf{j}$ and use Theorem 15.2.2 and properties of derivatives.

55. Let $\mathbf{r}_1(t) = x_1(t)\mathbf{i} + y_1(t)\mathbf{j} + z_1(t)\mathbf{k}$ and $\mathbf{r}_2(t) = x_2(t)\mathbf{i} + y_2(t)\mathbf{j} + z_2(t)\mathbf{k}$, in both (6) and (7); show that the left and right members of the equalities are the same.

56. If $\mathbf{r}'(t) = \mathbf{0}$, then $x'(t) = 0$ and $y'(t) = 0$; both x and y are constant on the interval so $\mathbf{r}$ is constant on the interval.

57. Let $\mathbf{r}(t) = x(t)\mathbf{i} + y(t)\mathbf{j}$ and use Theorem 15.2.2 and the chain rule.

58. Let $\mathbf{r}(t) = x(t)\mathbf{i} + y(t)\mathbf{j}$, $\mathbf{r}_1(t) = x_1(t)\mathbf{i} + y_1(t)\mathbf{j}$, and $\mathbf{r}_2(t) = x_2(t)\mathbf{i} + y_2(t)\mathbf{j}$, then use (1) and the results in Theorem 2.5.1.

59. Let $\mathbf{r}(t) = x(t)\mathbf{i} + y(t)\mathbf{j}$ and use (1) and the conditions for $\mathbf{r}$ to be continuous at t_0.

EXERCISE SET 15.3

1. $3t\mathbf{i} + 2t^2\mathbf{j} + \mathbf{C}$

2. $(\sin t)\mathbf{i} - (\cos t)\mathbf{j} + \mathbf{C}$

3. $\left\langle \dfrac{1}{3}\sin 3t, \dfrac{1}{3}\cos 3t \right\rangle \Big]_0^{\pi/3} = \langle 0, -2/3 \rangle$

4. $\left(\dfrac{1}{3}t^3\mathbf{i} + \dfrac{1}{4}t^4\mathbf{j} \right) \Big]_0^1 = \dfrac{1}{3}\mathbf{i} + \dfrac{1}{4}\mathbf{j}$

5. $\left(\dfrac{2}{3}t^{3/2}\mathbf{i} + 2t^{1/2}\mathbf{j} \right) \Big]_1^9 = \dfrac{52}{3}\mathbf{i} + 4\mathbf{j}$

6. $(-t\cos t + \sin t)\mathbf{i} + t\mathbf{j} + \mathbf{C}$

7. $\langle (t-1)e^t, t(\ln t - 1) \rangle + \mathbf{C}$

8. $\displaystyle\int_0^2 \sqrt{t^2 + t^4}\,dt = \int_0^2 t(1 + t^2)^{1/2}\,dt = (5\sqrt{5} - 1)/3$

9. $(t^3/3)\mathbf{i} - t^2\mathbf{j} + \ln|t|\mathbf{k} + \mathbf{C}$

10. $\langle -e^{-t}, e^t, t^3 \rangle + \mathbf{C}$

11. $\frac{1}{2}(e^2 - 1)\mathbf{i} + (1 - e^{-1})\mathbf{j} + \frac{1}{2}\mathbf{k}$

12. $\left\langle -\frac{2}{5}(3 - t)^{5/2}, \frac{2}{5}(3 + t)^{5/2}, t \right\rangle\Big]_{-3}^{3} = \langle 72\sqrt{6}/5, 72\sqrt{6}/5, 6 \rangle$

13. **(a)** $\mathbf{F} = 3t\mathbf{i} - 2\mathbf{j} - 3t^2\mathbf{k}$

    (b) $\displaystyle\int_0^2 \mathbf{F} \cdot (d\mathbf{r}/dt)dt = \int_0^2 (3t + 12t)dt = \int_0^2 15t\, dt = 30$

14. $\mathbf{r}(t) = \displaystyle\int \mathbf{r}'(t)dt = \frac{1}{3}t^3\mathbf{i} + t^2\mathbf{j} + \mathbf{C}$, $\mathbf{r}(0) = \mathbf{C} = \mathbf{i} + \mathbf{j}$, $\mathbf{r}(t) = (\frac{1}{3}t^3 + 1)\mathbf{i} + (t^2 + 1)\mathbf{j}$

15. $\mathbf{r}(t) = \displaystyle\int \mathbf{r}'(t)dt = (\sin t)\mathbf{i} - (\cos t)\mathbf{j} + \mathbf{C}$,

    $\mathbf{r}(0) = -\mathbf{j} + \mathbf{C} = \mathbf{i} - \mathbf{j}$ so $\mathbf{C} = \mathbf{i}$ and $\mathbf{r}(t) = (1 + \sin t)\mathbf{i} - (\cos t)\mathbf{j}$.

16. $\mathbf{r}'(t) = \displaystyle\int \mathbf{r}''(t)dt = t\mathbf{i} + e^t\mathbf{j} + \mathbf{C}_1$, $\mathbf{r}'(0) = \mathbf{j} + \mathbf{C}_1 = \mathbf{j}$ so $\mathbf{C}_1 = 0$ and $\mathbf{r}'(t) = t\mathbf{i} + e^t\mathbf{j}$.

    $\mathbf{r}(t) = \displaystyle\int \mathbf{r}'(t)dt = \frac{1}{2}t^2\mathbf{i} + e^t\mathbf{j} + \mathbf{C}_2$, $\mathbf{r}(0) = \mathbf{j} + \mathbf{C}_2 = 2\mathbf{i}$ so $\mathbf{C}_2 = 2\mathbf{i} - \mathbf{j}$ and

    $\mathbf{r}(t) = \left(\frac{1}{2}t^2 + 2\right)\mathbf{i} + (e^t - 1)\mathbf{j}$.

17. $\mathbf{r}'(t) = \displaystyle\int \mathbf{r}''(t)dt = 4t^3\mathbf{i} - 2t\mathbf{j} + \mathbf{C}_1$, $\mathbf{r}'(0) = \mathbf{C}_1 = 0$, $\mathbf{r}'(t) = 4t^3\mathbf{i} - 2t\mathbf{j}$

    $\mathbf{r}(t) = \displaystyle\int \mathbf{r}'(t)dt = t^4\mathbf{i} - t^2\mathbf{j} + \mathbf{C}_2$, $\mathbf{r}(0) = \mathbf{C}_2 = 2\mathbf{i} - 4\mathbf{j}$, $\mathbf{r}(t) = (t^4 + 2)\mathbf{i} - (t^2 + 4)\mathbf{j}$

18. $\mathbf{r}(t) = \displaystyle\int \mathbf{r}'(t)dt = -\frac{1}{2}e^{-2t}\mathbf{i} + \sin t\mathbf{j} - t\mathbf{k} + \mathbf{C}$,

    $\mathbf{r}(0) = -\frac{1}{2}\mathbf{i} + \mathbf{C} = 3\mathbf{j} + 2\mathbf{k}$ so $\mathbf{C} = \frac{1}{2}\mathbf{i} + 3\mathbf{j} + 2\mathbf{k}$;

    $\mathbf{r}(t) = \frac{1}{2}(1 - e^{-2t})\mathbf{i} + (3 + \sin t)\mathbf{j} + (2 - t)\mathbf{k}$.

19. $\mathbf{r}(t) = \displaystyle\int \mathbf{r}'(t)dt = 2t\mathbf{i} + \frac{1}{2}\ln(t^2 + 1)\mathbf{j} + \frac{1}{2}t^2\mathbf{k} + \mathbf{C}$,

    $\mathbf{r}(1) = 2\mathbf{i} + \frac{1}{2}\ln 2\mathbf{j} + \frac{1}{2}\mathbf{k} + \mathbf{C} = 0$ so $\mathbf{C} = -2\mathbf{i} - \frac{1}{2}\ln 2\mathbf{j} - \frac{1}{2}\mathbf{k}$ and

    $\mathbf{r}(t) = 2(t - 1)\mathbf{i} + \frac{1}{2}\ln\frac{t^2 + 1}{2}\mathbf{j} + \frac{1}{2}(t^2 - 1)\mathbf{k}$.

20. $\mathbf{r}'(t) = \displaystyle\int \mathbf{r}''(t)dt = -2\cos 2t\mathbf{i} + 3t^2\mathbf{j} - e^{-t}\mathbf{k} + \mathbf{C}_1,$

$\mathbf{r}'(0) = -2\mathbf{i} - \mathbf{k} + \mathbf{C}_1 = \mathbf{k}$ so $\mathbf{C}_1 = 2\mathbf{i} + 2\mathbf{k}$ and $\mathbf{r}'(t) = (2 - 2\cos 2t)\mathbf{i} + 3t^2\mathbf{j} + (2 - e^{-t})\mathbf{k},$

$\mathbf{r}(t) = \displaystyle\int \mathbf{r}'(t)dt = (2t - \sin 2t)\mathbf{i} + t^3\mathbf{j} + (2t + e^{-t})\mathbf{k} + \mathbf{C}_2,$

$\mathbf{r}(0) = \mathbf{k} + \mathbf{C}_2 = 2\mathbf{i}$ so $\mathbf{C}_2 = 2\mathbf{i} - \mathbf{k}$ and $\mathbf{r}(t) = (2 + 2t - \sin 2t)\mathbf{i} + t^3\mathbf{j} + (2t - 1 + e^{-t})\mathbf{k}.$

21. $\mathbf{r}'(t) = 3\mathbf{i} - 2\mathbf{j} + \mathbf{k},\ \|\mathbf{r}'(t)\| = \sqrt{14},\ L = \displaystyle\int_3^4 \sqrt{14}\,dt = \sqrt{14}$

22. $\mathbf{r}'(t) = -3\sin t\mathbf{i} + 3\cos t\mathbf{j} + \mathbf{k},\ \|\mathbf{r}'(t)\| = \sqrt{10},\ L = \displaystyle\int_0^{2\pi} \sqrt{10}\,dt = 2\pi\sqrt{10}$

23. $\mathbf{r}'(t) = 3t^2\mathbf{i} + \mathbf{j} + \sqrt{6}\,t\mathbf{k},\ \|\mathbf{r}'(t)\| = 3t^2 + 1,\ L = \displaystyle\int_1^3 (3t^2 + 1)dt = 28$

24. $(dx/dt)^2 + (dy/dt)^2 + (dz/dt)^2 = (-3\cos^2 t\sin t)^2 + (3\sin^2 t\cos t)^2 + 0^2 = 9\sin^2 t\cos^2 t,$

$L = \displaystyle\int_0^{\pi/2} 3\sin t\cos t\,dt = 3/2$

25. $\mathbf{r}'(t) = \langle e^t, -e^{-t}, \sqrt{2}\rangle,\ \|\mathbf{r}'(t)\| = e^t + e^{-t},\ L = \displaystyle\int_0^1 (e^t + e^{-t})dt = e - e^{-1}$

26. $(dx/dt)^2 + (dy/dt)^2 + (dz/dt)^2 = 1/4 + (1-t)/4 + (1+t)/4 = 3/4,\ L = \displaystyle\int_{-1}^1 (\sqrt{3}/2)dt = \sqrt{3}$

27. $dx/dt = -a\sin t,\ dy/dt = a\cos t,\ dz/dt = c,$

$L = \displaystyle\int_0^{t_0} \sqrt{a^2\sin^2 t + a^2\cos^2 t + c^2}\,dt = \int_0^{t_0} \sqrt{a^2 + c^2}\,dt = t_0\sqrt{a^2 + c^2}$

28.   Represent the helix by $x = a\cos t,\ y = a\sin t,\ z = ct$ with $a = 6.25$ and $c = 10/\pi$, so that the radius of the helix is the distance from the axis of the cylinder to the center of the copper tubing, and the helix makes one turn in a distance of 20 in. $(t = 2\pi)$. From Exercise 27 the length of the helix is $2\pi\sqrt{6.25^2 + (10/\pi)^2} \approx 44$ in.

29. $x = 3u - 2,\ y = 4u + 3,\ (dx/du)^2 + (dy/du)^2 = 25,$

$s = \displaystyle\int_0^t 5du = 5t$ so $t = s/5,\ x = (3/5)s - 2,\ y = (4/5)s + 3.$

30. $x = 3\cos 2u$, $y = 3\sin 2u$, $(dx/du)^2 + (dy/du)^2 = 36$,

$s = \int_0^t 6\,du = 6t$ so $t = s/6$, $x = 3\cos(s/3)$, $y = 3\sin(s/3)$ for $0 \le s \le 6\pi$.

31. $x = 3 + \cos u$, $y = 2 + \sin u$, $(dx/du)^2 + (dy/du)^2 = 1$,

$s = \int_0^t du = t$ so $t = s$, $x = 3 + \cos s$, $y = 2 + \sin s$ for $0 \le s \le 2\pi$.

32. $x = \cos^3 u$, $y = \sin^3 u$, $(dx/du)^2 + (dy/du)^2 = 9\sin^2 u \cos^2 u$,

$s = \int_0^t 3\sin u \cos u\,du = \frac{3}{2}\sin^2 t$ so $\sin t = (2s/3)^{1/2}$, $\cos t = (1 - 2s/3)^{1/2}$,

$x = (1 - 2s/3)^{3/2}$, $y = (2s/3)^{3/2}$ for $0 \le s \le 3/2$.

33. $x = u^3/3$, $y = u^2/2$, $(dx/du)^2 + (dy/du)^2 = u^2(u^2 + 1)$,

$s = \int_0^t u(u^2 + 1)^{1/2}\,du = \frac{1}{3}[(t^2 + 1)^{3/2} - 1]$ so $t = [(3s + 1)^{2/3} - 1]^{1/2}$,

$x = \frac{1}{3}[(3s + 1)^{2/3} - 1]^{3/2}$, $y = \frac{1}{2}[(3s + 1)^{2/3} - 1]$ for $s \ge 0$.

34. $x = (1 + u)^2$, $y = (1 + u)^3$, $(dx/du)^2 + (dy/du)^2 = (1 - u)^2[4 + 9(1 + u)^2]$,

$s = \int_0^t (1 + u)[4 + 9(1 + u)^2]^{1/2}\,du = \frac{1}{27}([4 + 9(1 + t)^2]^{3/2} - 13\sqrt{13})$ so

$1 + t = \frac{1}{3}[(27s + 13\sqrt{13})^{2/3} - 4]^{1/2}$, $x = \frac{1}{9}[(27s + 13\sqrt{13})^{2/3} - 4]$,

$y = \frac{1}{27}[(27s + 13\sqrt{13})^{2/3} - 4]^{3/2}$ for $0 \le s \le (80\sqrt{10} - 13\sqrt{13})/27$.

35. $x = e^u \cos u$, $y = e^u \sin u$, $(dx/du)^2 + (dy/du)^2 = 2e^{2u}$, $s = \int_0^t \sqrt{2}\,e^u\,du = \sqrt{2}(e^t - 1)$ so

$t = \ln(s/\sqrt{2} + 1)$, $x = (s/\sqrt{2} + 1)\cos[\ln(s/\sqrt{2} + 1)]$, $y = (s/\sqrt{2} + 1)\sin[\ln(s/\sqrt{2} + 1)]$
for $0 \le s \le \sqrt{2}(e^{\pi/2} - 1)$.

36. $x = \sin(e^u)$, $y = \cos(e^u)$, $z = \sqrt{3}e^u$,

$(dx/du)^2 + (dy/du)^2 + (dz/du)^2 = 4e^{2u}$, $s = \int_0^t 2e^u\,du = 2(e^t - 1)$ so

$e^t = 1 + s/2$; $x = \sin(1 + s/2)$, $y = \cos(1 + s/2)$, $z = \sqrt{3}(1 + s/2)$ for $s \ge 0$.

37. $x = u \cos u$, $y = u \sin u$, $z = \dfrac{2}{3}\sqrt{2}\, u^{3/2}$,

$(dx/du)^2 + (dy/du)^2 + (dz/du)^2 = u^2 + 2u + 1 = (u+1)^2$, $s = \displaystyle\int_0^t (u+1)du = \dfrac{1}{2}t^2 + t$ so

$t = \sqrt{2s+1} - 1$, $x = (\sqrt{2s+1} - 1)\cos(\sqrt{2s+1} - 1)$, $y = (\sqrt{2s+1} - 1)\sin(\sqrt{2s+1} - 1)$,

$z = \dfrac{2}{3}\sqrt{2}[\sqrt{2s+1} - 1]^{3/2}$ for $s \geq 0$.

38. $x = au - a\sin u$, $y = a - a\cos u$, $(dx/du)^2 + (dy/du)^2 = 4a^2 \sin^2(u/2)$,

$s = \displaystyle\int_0^t 2a\sin(u/2)du = 4a[1 - \cos(t/2)]$ so $\cos(t/2) = 1 - s/(4a)$, $t = 2\cos^{-1}[1 - s/(4a)]$,

$\cos t = 2\cos^2(t/2) - 1 = 2[1 - s/(4a)]^2 - 1$,

$\sin t = 2\sin(t/2)\cos(t/2) = 2(1 - [1 - s/(4a)]^2)^{1/2}(2[1 - s/(4a)]^2 - 1)$,

$x = 2a\cos^{-1}[1 - s/(4a)] - 2a(1 - [1 - s/(4a)]^2)^{1/2}(2[1 - s/(4a)]^2 - 1)$,

$y = 2a - 2a[1 - s/(4a)]^2$ for $0 \leq s \leq 8a$.

39. $x = a\cos u$, $y = a\sin u$, $z = cu$, $(dx/du)^2 + (dy/du)^2 + (dz/du)^2 = a^2 + c^2 = w^2$,

$s = \displaystyle\int_0^t w\, du = wt$ so $t = s/w$; $x = a\cos(s/w)$, $y = a\sin(s/w)$, $z = cs/w$ for $s \geq 0$.

40. $|s| = \|\mathbf{r} - \mathbf{r}_0\| = \|t\mathbf{v}\| = |t|\,\|\mathbf{v}\|$; if the direction of s is the same as t, then $s = t\|\mathbf{v}\|$, $t = s/\|\mathbf{v}\|$
so $\mathbf{r} = \mathbf{r}_0 + s\mathbf{v}/\|\mathbf{v}\|$.

41.   **(a)** $x = OB + CP = a\cos\theta + a\theta\sin\theta$,
             $y = AB - AC = a\sin\theta - a\theta\cos\theta$.

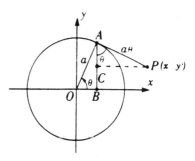

       (b) $x = a(\cos u + u\sin u)$, $y = a(\sin u - u\cos u)$,
            $dx/du = au\cos u$, $dy/du = au\sin u$,
            $(dx/dy)^2 + (dy/du)^2 = a^2u^2$,

            $s = \displaystyle\int_0^\theta au\, du = \dfrac{1}{2}a\theta^2$ so $\theta = \sqrt{2s/a}$,

            $x = a(\cos\sqrt{2s/a} + \sqrt{2s/a}\sin\sqrt{2s/a})$,
            $y = a(\sin\sqrt{2s/a} - \sqrt{2s/a}\cos\sqrt{2s/a})$ for $s \geq 0$.

42. $\dfrac{dx}{dt} = \cos\theta\dfrac{dr}{dt} - r\sin\theta\dfrac{d\theta}{dt}$, $\dfrac{dy}{dt} = \sin\theta\dfrac{dr}{dt} + r\cos\theta\dfrac{d\theta}{dt}$,

$\left(\dfrac{dx}{dt}\right)^2 + \left(\dfrac{dy}{dt}\right)^2 + \left(\dfrac{dz}{dt}\right)^2 = \left(\dfrac{dr}{dt}\right)^2 + r^2\left(\dfrac{d\theta}{dt}\right)^2 + \left(\dfrac{dz}{dt}\right)^2.$

43. (a) $(dr/dt)^2 + r^2(d\theta/dt)^2 + (dz/dt)^2 = 9e^{4t}$, $L = \int_0^{\ln 2} 3e^{2t}dt = \frac{3}{2}e^{2t}\Big]_0^{\ln 2} = 9/2.$

  (b) $(dr/dt)^2 + r^2(d\theta/dt)^2 + (dz/dt)^2 = 5t^2 + t^4 = t^2(5+t^2)$,

  $L = \int_1^2 t(5+t^2)^{1/2}dt = 9 - 2\sqrt{6}.$

44. $\dfrac{dx}{dt} = \sin\phi\cos\theta\dfrac{d\rho}{dt} + \rho\cos\phi\cos\theta\dfrac{d\phi}{dt} - \rho\sin\phi\sin\theta\dfrac{d\theta}{dt},$

  $\dfrac{dy}{dt} = \sin\phi\sin\theta\dfrac{d\rho}{dt} + \rho\cos\phi\sin\theta\dfrac{d\phi}{dt} + \rho\sin\phi\cos\theta\dfrac{d\theta}{dt}, \dfrac{dz}{dt} = \cos\phi\dfrac{d\rho}{dt} - \rho\sin\phi\dfrac{d\phi}{dt},$

  $\left(\dfrac{dx}{dt}\right)^2 + \left(\dfrac{dy}{dt}\right)^2 + \left(\dfrac{dz}{dt}\right)^2 = \left(\dfrac{d\rho}{dt}\right)^2 + \rho^2\sin^2\phi\left(\dfrac{d\theta}{dt}\right)^2 + \rho^2\left(\dfrac{d\phi}{dt}\right)^2.$

45. (a) $(d\rho/dt)^2 + \rho^2\sin^2\phi(d\theta/dt)^2 + \rho^2(d\phi/dt)^2 = 3e^{-2t}$, $L = \int_0^2 \sqrt{3}e^{-t}dt = \sqrt{3}(1 - e^{-2}).$

  (b) $(d\rho/dt)^2 + \rho^2\sin^2\phi(d\theta/dt)^2 + \rho^2(d\phi/dt)^2 = 5$, $L = \int_1^5 \sqrt{5}dt = 4\sqrt{5}.$

46. Similar to proof of part (a).

47. Let $\mathbf{R}(t) = X(t)\mathbf{i} + Y(t)\mathbf{j}$ and $\mathbf{r}(t) = x(t)\mathbf{i} + y(t)\mathbf{j}$ where $X'(t) = x(t)$; $Y'(t) = y(t)$ and use Definition 15.3.1 and properties of indefinite and definite integrals.

48. Let $\mathbf{r}(t) = x(t)\mathbf{i} + y(t)\mathbf{j}$, $\mathbf{r}_1(t) = x_1(t)\mathbf{i} + y_1(t)\mathbf{j}$ and $\mathbf{r}_2(t) = x_2(t)\mathbf{i} + y_2(t)\mathbf{j}$, then use Definition 15.3.1 and properties of indefinite integrals.

EXERCISE SET 15.4

1. $\mathbf{r}'(t) = -5\sin t\mathbf{i} + 5\cos t\mathbf{j}$, $\|\mathbf{r}'(t)\| = 5$

  $\mathbf{T}(t) = -\sin t\mathbf{i} + \cos t\mathbf{j}$, $\mathbf{T}'(t) = -\cos t\mathbf{i} - \sin t\mathbf{j}$;

  $\mathbf{T}(\pi/3) = -\dfrac{\sqrt{3}}{2}\mathbf{i} + \dfrac{1}{2}\mathbf{j}$, $\mathbf{T}'(\pi/3) = -\dfrac{1}{2}\mathbf{i} - \dfrac{\sqrt{3}}{2}\mathbf{j}$, $\mathbf{N}(\pi/3) = -\dfrac{1}{2}\mathbf{i} - \dfrac{\sqrt{3}}{2}\mathbf{j}.$

2. $\mathbf{r}'(t) = 2\mathbf{i} + 8t\mathbf{j}$, $\|\mathbf{r}'(t)\| = 2\sqrt{1 + 16t^2}$, $\mathbf{T}(t) = (1 + 16t^2)^{-1/2}(\mathbf{i} + 4t\mathbf{j})$,
$\mathbf{T}'(t) = (1 + 16t^2)^{-1/2}(4\mathbf{j}) - 16t(1 + 16t^2)^{-3/2}(\mathbf{i} + 4t\mathbf{j})$;
$\mathbf{T}(1) = \dfrac{1}{\sqrt{17}}\mathbf{i} + \dfrac{4}{\sqrt{17}}\mathbf{j}$, $\mathbf{T}'(1) = \dfrac{4}{17\sqrt{17}}(-4\mathbf{i} + \mathbf{j})$, $\mathbf{N}(1) = -\dfrac{4}{\sqrt{17}}\mathbf{i} + \dfrac{1}{\sqrt{17}}\mathbf{j}$.

3. $\mathbf{r}'(t) = 2t\mathbf{i} + \mathbf{j}$, $\|\mathbf{r}'(t)\| = \sqrt{4t^2 + 1}$, $\mathbf{T}(t) = (4t^2 + 1)^{-1/2}(2t\mathbf{i} + \mathbf{j})$,
$\mathbf{T}'(t) = (4t^2 + 1)^{-1/2}(2\mathbf{i}) - 4t(4t^2 + 1)^{-3/2}(2t\mathbf{i} + \mathbf{j})$;
$\mathbf{T}(1) = \dfrac{2}{\sqrt{5}}\mathbf{i} + \dfrac{1}{\sqrt{5}}\mathbf{j}$, $\mathbf{T}'(1) = \dfrac{2}{5\sqrt{5}}(\mathbf{i} - 2\mathbf{j})$, $\mathbf{N}(1) = \dfrac{1}{\sqrt{5}}\mathbf{i} - \dfrac{2}{\sqrt{5}}\mathbf{j}$.

4. $\mathbf{r}'(t) = e^t\mathbf{i} - e^{-t}\mathbf{j}$, $\|\mathbf{r}'(t)\| = \sqrt{e^{2t} + e^{-2t}}$, $\mathbf{T}(t) = (e^{2t} + e^{-2t})^{-1/2}(e^t\mathbf{i} - e^{-t}\mathbf{j})$,
$\mathbf{T}'(t) = (e^{2t} + e^{-2t})^{-1/2}(e^t\mathbf{i} + e^{-t}\mathbf{j}) - (e^{2t} - e^{-2t})(e^{2t} + e^{-2t})^{-3/2}(e^t\mathbf{i} - e^{-t}\mathbf{j})$,
$\mathbf{T}(0) = \dfrac{1}{\sqrt{2}}\mathbf{i} - \dfrac{1}{\sqrt{2}}\mathbf{j}$, $\mathbf{T}'(0) = \dfrac{1}{\sqrt{2}}(\mathbf{i} + \mathbf{j}) = \mathbf{N}(0)$.

4. (Continued)

$$N = \frac{1}{\sqrt{2}}\mathbf{i} + \frac{1}{\sqrt{2}}\mathbf{j}$$

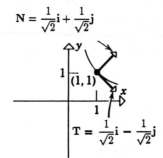

5. $\mathbf{r}'(t) = t\mathbf{i} + t^2\mathbf{j}$, $\mathbf{T}(t) = (t^2 + t^4)^{-1/2}(t\mathbf{i} + t^2\mathbf{j})$,

$\mathbf{T}'(t) = (t^2 + t^4)^{-1/2}(\mathbf{i} + 2t\mathbf{j}) - (t + 2t^3)(t^2 + t^4)^{-3/2}(t\mathbf{i} + t^2\mathbf{j})$;

$\mathbf{T}(1) = \frac{1}{\sqrt{2}}\mathbf{i} + \frac{1}{\sqrt{2}}\mathbf{j}$, $\mathbf{T}'(1) = \frac{1}{2\sqrt{2}}(-\mathbf{i} + \mathbf{j})$, $\mathbf{N}(1) = -\frac{1}{\sqrt{2}}\mathbf{i} + \frac{1}{\sqrt{2}}\mathbf{j}$.

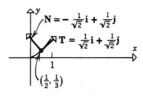

6. $\mathbf{r}'(t) = \frac{1}{t}\mathbf{i} + \mathbf{j}$, $\|\mathbf{r}'(t)\| = \frac{\sqrt{1 + t^2}}{t}$, $\mathbf{T}(t) = (1 + t^2)^{-1/2}(\mathbf{i} + t\mathbf{j})$,

$\mathbf{T}'(t) = (1 + t^2)^{-1/2}(\mathbf{j}) - t(1 + t^2)^{-3/2}(\mathbf{i} + t\mathbf{j})$; $\mathbf{T}(e) = \frac{1}{\sqrt{1 + e^2}}\mathbf{i} + \frac{e}{\sqrt{1 + e^2}}\mathbf{j}$,

$\mathbf{T}'(e) = \frac{1}{(1 + e^2)^{3/2}}(-e\mathbf{i} + \mathbf{j})$, $\mathbf{N}(e) = -\frac{e}{\sqrt{1 + e^2}}\mathbf{i} + \frac{1}{\sqrt{1 + e^2}}\mathbf{j}$.

$$N = -\frac{e}{\sqrt{1 + e^2}}\mathbf{i} + \frac{1}{\sqrt{1 + e^2}}\mathbf{j} \qquad T = \frac{1}{\sqrt{1 + e^2}}\mathbf{i} + \frac{e}{\sqrt{1 + e^2}}\mathbf{j}$$

$(1, e)$

7. $\mathbf{r}'(t) = -4\sin t\mathbf{i} + 9\cos t\mathbf{j}$, $\mathbf{T}(t) = (16\sin^2 t + 81\cos^2 t)^{-1/2}(-4\sin t\mathbf{i} + 9\cos t\mathbf{j})$,

   $\mathbf{T}'(t) = (16\sin^2 t + 81\cos^2 t)^{-1/2}(-4\cos t\mathbf{i} - 9\sin t\mathbf{j})$

   $\qquad + 65\sin t\cos t(16\sin^2 t + 81\cos^2 t)^{-3/2}(-4\sin t\mathbf{i} + 9\cos t\mathbf{j})$;

   $\mathbf{T}(\pi/4) = -\dfrac{4}{\sqrt{97}}\mathbf{i} + \dfrac{9}{\sqrt{97}}\mathbf{j}$, $\mathbf{T}'(\pi/4) = \dfrac{72}{97\sqrt{97}}(-9\mathbf{i} - 4\mathbf{j})$, $\mathbf{N}(\pi/4) = -\dfrac{9}{\sqrt{97}}\mathbf{i} - \dfrac{4}{\sqrt{97}}\mathbf{j}$.

   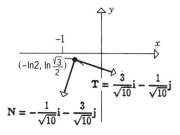

8. $\mathbf{r}'(t) = \cot t\mathbf{i} - \tan t\mathbf{j}$, $\|\mathbf{r}'(t)\| = \sqrt{\cot^2 t + \tan^2 t}$, $\mathbf{T}(t) = (\cot^2 t + \tan^2 t)^{-1/2}(\cot t\mathbf{i} - \tan t\mathbf{j})$,

   $\mathbf{T}'(t) = (\cot^2 t + \tan^2 t)^{-1/2}(-\csc^2 t\mathbf{i} - \sec^2 t\mathbf{j})$

   $\qquad - (-\cot t\csc^2 t + \tan t\sec^2 t)(\cot^2 t + \tan^2 t)^{-3/2}(\cot t\mathbf{i} - \tan t\mathbf{j})$,

   $\mathbf{T}(\pi/6) = \dfrac{3}{\sqrt{10}}\mathbf{i} - \dfrac{1}{\sqrt{10}}\mathbf{j}$, $\mathbf{T}'(\pi/6) = \dfrac{4\sqrt{3}}{5\sqrt{10}}(-\mathbf{i} - 3\mathbf{j})$, $\mathbf{N}(\pi/6) = -\dfrac{1}{\sqrt{10}}\mathbf{i} - \dfrac{3}{\sqrt{10}}\mathbf{j}$.

9. $\mathbf{r}'(t) = -4\sin t\mathbf{i} + 4\cos t\mathbf{j} + \mathbf{k}$, $\mathbf{T}(t) = \dfrac{1}{\sqrt{17}}(-4\sin t\mathbf{i} + 4\cos t\mathbf{j} + \mathbf{k})$,

   $\mathbf{T}'(t) = \dfrac{1}{\sqrt{17}}(-4\cos t\mathbf{i} - 4\sin t\mathbf{j})$, $\mathbf{T}(\pi/2) = -\dfrac{4}{\sqrt{17}}\mathbf{i} + \dfrac{1}{\sqrt{17}}\mathbf{k}$

   $\mathbf{T}'(\pi/2) = -\dfrac{4}{\sqrt{17}}\mathbf{j}$, $\mathbf{N}(\pi/2) = -\mathbf{j}$.

10. $\mathbf{r}'(t) = e^t\mathbf{i} - e^{-t}\mathbf{j} + \mathbf{k}$, $\mathbf{T}(t) = (e^{2t} + e^{-2t} + 1)^{-1/2}(e^t\mathbf{i} - e^{-t}\mathbf{j} + \mathbf{k})$,

    $\mathbf{T}'(t) = (e^{2t} + e^{-2t} + 1)^{-1/2}(e^t\mathbf{i} + e^{-t}\mathbf{j}) - (e^{2t} - e^{-2t})(e^{2t} + e^{-2t} + 1)^{-3/2}(e^t\mathbf{i} - e^{-t}\mathbf{j} + \mathbf{k})$,

    $\mathbf{T}(0) = \dfrac{1}{\sqrt{3}}\mathbf{i} - \dfrac{1}{\sqrt{3}}\mathbf{j} + \dfrac{1}{\sqrt{3}}\mathbf{k}$, $\mathbf{T}'(0) = \dfrac{1}{\sqrt{3}}(\mathbf{i} + \mathbf{j})$, $\mathbf{N}(0) = \dfrac{1}{\sqrt{2}}\mathbf{i} + \dfrac{1}{\sqrt{2}}\mathbf{j}$.

11. $\mathbf{r}'(t) = \mathbf{i} + t\mathbf{j} + t^2\mathbf{k}$, $\mathbf{T}(t) = (1 + t^2 + t^4)^{-1/2}(\mathbf{i} + t\mathbf{j} + t^2\mathbf{k})$,
$\mathbf{T}'(t) = (1 + t^2 + t^4)^{-1/2}(\mathbf{j} + 2t\mathbf{k}) - (t + 2t^3)(1 + t^2 + t^4)^{-3/2}(\mathbf{i} + t\mathbf{j} + t^2\mathbf{k})$,
$\mathbf{T}(0) = \mathbf{i}$, $\mathbf{T}'(0) = \mathbf{j} = \mathbf{N}(0)$.

12. $\mathbf{r}'(t) = \cos t\mathbf{i} - \sin t\mathbf{j} + t\mathbf{k}$, $\mathbf{T}(t) = (1 + t^2)^{-1/2}(\cos t\mathbf{i} - \sin t\mathbf{j} + t\mathbf{k})$,
$\mathbf{T}'(t) = (1 + t^2)^{-1/2}(-\sin t\mathbf{i} - \cos t\mathbf{j} + \mathbf{k}) - t(1 + t^2)^{-3/2}(\cos t\mathbf{i} - \sin t\mathbf{j} + t\mathbf{k})$,
$\mathbf{T}(0) = \mathbf{i}$, $\mathbf{T}'(0) = -\mathbf{j} + \mathbf{k}$, $\mathbf{N}(0) = -\dfrac{1}{\sqrt{2}}\mathbf{j} + \dfrac{1}{\sqrt{2}}\mathbf{k}$.

13. $\mathbf{r}'(t) = -3\sin t\mathbf{i} + 4\cos t\mathbf{j} + \mathbf{k}$, $\mathbf{T}(t) = (9\sin^2 t + 16\cos^2 t + 1)^{-1/2}(-3\sin t\mathbf{i} + 4\cos t\mathbf{j} + \mathbf{k})$,
$\mathbf{T}'(t) = (9\sin^2 t + 16\cos^2 t + 1)^{-1/2}(-3\cos t\mathbf{i} - 4\sin t\mathbf{j})$
$\qquad\qquad + 7\sin t\cos t(9\sin^2 t + 16\cos^2 +1)^{-3/2}(-3\sin t\mathbf{i} + 4\cos t\mathbf{j} + \mathbf{k})$,
$\mathbf{T}(\pi/2) = -\dfrac{3}{\sqrt{10}}\mathbf{i} + \dfrac{1}{\sqrt{10}}\mathbf{k}$, $\mathbf{T}'(\pi/2) = -\dfrac{4}{\sqrt{10}}\mathbf{j}$, $\mathbf{N}(\pi/2) = -\mathbf{j}$.

14. $\mathbf{r}'(t) = e^t[(\cos t - \sin t)\mathbf{i} + (\cos t + \sin t)\mathbf{j} + \mathbf{k}]$, $\mathbf{T}(t) = \dfrac{1}{\sqrt{3}}[(\cos t - \sin t)\mathbf{i} + (\cos t + \sin t)\mathbf{j} + \mathbf{k}]$,

$\mathbf{T}'(t) = \dfrac{1}{\sqrt{3}}[(-\sin t - \cos t)\mathbf{i} + (-\sin t + \cos t)\mathbf{j}]$,

$\mathbf{T}(0) = \dfrac{1}{\sqrt{3}}\mathbf{i} + \dfrac{1}{\sqrt{3}}\mathbf{j} + \dfrac{1}{\sqrt{3}}\mathbf{k}$, $\mathbf{T}'(0) = \dfrac{1}{\sqrt{3}}(-\mathbf{i} + \mathbf{j})$, $\mathbf{N}(0) = -\dfrac{1}{\sqrt{2}}\mathbf{i} + \dfrac{1}{\sqrt{2}}\mathbf{j}$.

15. $\mathbf{r}'(t) = \mathbf{j} + 2t\mathbf{k}$, $\mathbf{T}(t) = (1 + 4t^2)^{-1/2}(\mathbf{j} + 2t\mathbf{k})$,
$\mathbf{T}'(t) = (1 + 4t^2)^{-1/2}(2\mathbf{k}) - 4t(1 + 4t^2)^{-3/2}(\mathbf{j} + 2t\mathbf{k})$,
$\mathbf{T}(1) = \dfrac{1}{\sqrt{5}}\mathbf{j} + \dfrac{2}{\sqrt{5}}\mathbf{k}$, $\mathbf{T}'(1) = \dfrac{2}{5\sqrt{5}}(-2\mathbf{j} + \mathbf{k})$, $\mathbf{N}(1) = -\dfrac{2}{\sqrt{5}}\mathbf{j} + \dfrac{1}{\sqrt{5}}\mathbf{k}$.

16. $\mathbf{r}'(t) = \sinh t\mathbf{i} + \cosh t\mathbf{j} + \mathbf{k}$, $\|\mathbf{r}'(t)\| = \sqrt{\sinh^2 t + \cosh^2 t + 1} = \sqrt{2}\cosh t$,
$\mathbf{T}(t) = \dfrac{1}{\sqrt{2}}(\tanh t\mathbf{i} + \mathbf{j} + \operatorname{sech} t\mathbf{k})$, $\mathbf{T}'(t) = \dfrac{1}{\sqrt{2}}(\operatorname{sech}^2 t\mathbf{i} - \operatorname{sech} t\tanh t\mathbf{k})$, at $t = \ln 2$,

$\tanh(\ln 2) = \tfrac{3}{5}$ and $\operatorname{sech}(\ln 2) = \tfrac{4}{5}$ so $\mathbf{T}(\ln 2) = \dfrac{3}{5\sqrt{2}}\mathbf{i} + \dfrac{1}{\sqrt{2}}\mathbf{j} + \dfrac{4}{5\sqrt{2}}\mathbf{k}$,

$\mathbf{T}'(\ln 2) = \dfrac{4}{25\sqrt{2}}(4\mathbf{i} - 3\mathbf{k})$, $\mathbf{N}(\ln 2) = \dfrac{4}{5}\mathbf{i} - \dfrac{3}{5}\mathbf{k}$.

17. $\mathbf{r}(t) = a\cos t\mathbf{i} + a\sin t\mathbf{j} + ct\mathbf{k}$ where $a\cos t\mathbf{i} + a\sin t\mathbf{j}$ points from the z-axis to a point on the curve, but $\mathbf{N}$ is oppositely directed so $\mathbf{N}$ points directly toward the z-axis.

18. $\dfrac{d}{dt}\left[\dfrac{\mathbf{r}'}{\|\mathbf{r}'\|}\right] = \dfrac{d\mathbf{T}}{dt} = \dfrac{1}{\|\mathbf{r}'\|}\mathbf{r}'' - \dfrac{\mathbf{r}' \cdot \mathbf{r}''}{\|\mathbf{r}'\|^3}\mathbf{r}' = \dfrac{1}{\|\mathbf{r}'\|^3}[\|\mathbf{r}'\|^2\mathbf{r}'' - (\mathbf{r}' \cdot \mathbf{r}'')\mathbf{r}']$.

19. $\mathbf{r}'(t) = -5\sin t\mathbf{i} + 5\cos t\mathbf{j}$, $\mathbf{r}''(t) = -5\cos t\mathbf{i} - 5\sin t\mathbf{j}$,

$\mathbf{r}'(\pi/3) = -\dfrac{5\sqrt{3}}{2}\mathbf{i} + \dfrac{5}{2}\mathbf{j}$, $\mathbf{r}''(\pi/3) = -\dfrac{5}{2}\mathbf{i} - \dfrac{5\sqrt{3}}{2}\mathbf{j}$,

$\mathbf{u} = 25(-5/2\mathbf{i} - 5\sqrt{3}/2\mathbf{j}) - (0)\mathbf{r}' = \dfrac{125}{2}(-\mathbf{i} - \sqrt{3}\mathbf{j})$; $\mathbf{N} = -(1/2)\mathbf{i} - (\sqrt{3}/2)\mathbf{j}$.

20. $\mathbf{r}'(t) = 2\mathbf{i} + 8t\mathbf{j}$, $\mathbf{r}''(t) = 8\mathbf{j}$, $\mathbf{r}'(1) = 2\mathbf{i} + 8\mathbf{j}$, $\mathbf{r}''(1) = 8\mathbf{j}$,

$\mathbf{u} = 68(8\mathbf{j}) - 64(2\mathbf{i} + 8\mathbf{j}) = 32(-4\mathbf{i} + \mathbf{j})$; $\mathbf{N} = -(4/\sqrt{17})\mathbf{i} + (1/\sqrt{17})\mathbf{j}$.

21. $\mathbf{r}'(t) = 2t\mathbf{i} + \mathbf{j}$, $\mathbf{r}''(t) = 2\mathbf{i}$, $\mathbf{r}'(1) = 2\mathbf{i} + \mathbf{j}$, $\mathbf{r}''(1) = 2\mathbf{i}$,

$\mathbf{u} = 5(2\mathbf{i}) - (4)(2\mathbf{i} + \mathbf{j}) = 2(\mathbf{i} - 2\mathbf{j})$; $\mathbf{N} = (1/\sqrt{5})\mathbf{i} - (2/\sqrt{5})\mathbf{j}$.

22. $\mathbf{r}'(t) = e^t\mathbf{i} - e^{-t}\mathbf{j}$, $\mathbf{r}''(t) = e^t\mathbf{i} + e^{-t}\mathbf{j}$, $\mathbf{r}'(0) = \mathbf{i} - \mathbf{j}$, $\mathbf{r}''(0) = \mathbf{i} + \mathbf{j}$,

$\mathbf{u} = 2(\mathbf{i} + \mathbf{j}) - (0)\mathbf{r}' = 2(\mathbf{i} + \mathbf{j})$; $\mathbf{N} = (1/\sqrt{2})\mathbf{i} + (1/\sqrt{2})\mathbf{j}$.

23. $\mathbf{r}'(t) = -4\sin t\mathbf{i} + 4\cos t\mathbf{j} + \mathbf{k}$, $\mathbf{r}''(t) = -4\cos t\mathbf{i} - 4\sin t\mathbf{j}$,

$\mathbf{r}'(\pi/2) = -4\mathbf{i} + \mathbf{k}$, $\mathbf{r}''(\pi/2) = -4\mathbf{j}$, $\mathbf{u} = 17(-4\mathbf{j}) - (0)\mathbf{r}' = -68\mathbf{j}$; $\mathbf{N} = -\mathbf{j}$.

24. $\mathbf{r}'(t) = e^t\mathbf{i} - e^{-t}\mathbf{j} + \mathbf{k}$, $\mathbf{r}''(t) = e^t\mathbf{i} + e^{-t}\mathbf{j}$, $\mathbf{r}'(0) = \mathbf{i} - \mathbf{j} + \mathbf{k}$,

$\mathbf{r}''(0) = \mathbf{i} + \mathbf{j}$, $\mathbf{u} = 3(\mathbf{i} + \mathbf{j}) - (0)\mathbf{r}' = 3(\mathbf{i} + \mathbf{j})$; $\mathbf{N} = (1/\sqrt{2})\mathbf{i} + (1/\sqrt{2})\mathbf{j}$.

25. $\mathbf{r}'(t) = \mathbf{i} + t\mathbf{j} + t^2\mathbf{k}$, $\mathbf{r}''(t) = \mathbf{j} + 2t\mathbf{k}$, $\mathbf{r}'(0) = \mathbf{i}$, $\mathbf{r}''(0) = \mathbf{j}$, $\mathbf{u} = (1)(\mathbf{j}) - (0)\mathbf{r}' = \mathbf{j} = \mathbf{N}$.

26. $\mathbf{r}'(t) = \cos t\mathbf{i} - \sin t\mathbf{j} + t\mathbf{k}$, $\mathbf{r}''(t) = -\sin t\mathbf{i} - \cos t\mathbf{j} + \mathbf{k}$,

$\mathbf{r}'(0) = \mathbf{i}$, $\mathbf{r}''(0) = -\mathbf{j} + \mathbf{k}$, $\mathbf{u} = (1)(-\mathbf{j} + \mathbf{k}) - (0)\mathbf{r}' = -\mathbf{j} + \mathbf{k}$; $\mathbf{N} = -(1/\sqrt{2})\mathbf{j} + (1/\sqrt{2})\mathbf{k}$.

27. $\mathbf{T} = \dfrac{3}{5}\cos t\mathbf{i} - \dfrac{3}{5}\sin t\mathbf{j} + \dfrac{4}{5}\mathbf{k}$, $\mathbf{N} = -\sin t\mathbf{i} - \cos t\mathbf{j}$, $\mathbf{B} = \mathbf{T} \times \mathbf{N} = \dfrac{4}{5}\cos t\mathbf{i} - \dfrac{4}{5}\sin t\mathbf{j} - \dfrac{3}{5}\mathbf{k}$

28. $\mathbf{T} = (-a\sin t\mathbf{i} + a\cos t\mathbf{j} + b\mathbf{k})/\sqrt{a^2 + b^2}$, $\mathbf{N} = -\cos t\mathbf{i} - \sin t\mathbf{j}$,

$\mathbf{B} = \mathbf{T} \times \mathbf{N} = (b\sin t\mathbf{i} - b\cos t\mathbf{j} + a\mathbf{k})/\sqrt{a^2 + b^2}$

29. **(a)** $\mathbf{n}$ is perpendicular to S; if $\mathbf{r} = \mathbf{r}(t)$ lies in S, then $\mathbf{r} - \mathbf{r}_0$ is perpendicular to $\mathbf{n}$ so $\mathbf{n} \cdot (\mathbf{r} - \mathbf{r}_0) = 0$. If $\mathbf{n} \cdot (\mathbf{r} - \mathbf{r}_0) = 0$ then either $\mathbf{r} = \mathbf{r}_0$ or $\mathbf{r} - \mathbf{r}_0$ is perpendicular to $\mathbf{n}$ so $\mathbf{r} = \mathbf{r}(t)$ lies in S.

(b) Differentiate $\mathbf{n} \cdot (\mathbf{r} - \mathbf{r}_0)$ twice with respect to t to get $\mathbf{n} \cdot \mathbf{r}' = 0$ and $\mathbf{n} \cdot \mathbf{r}'' = 0$ so both $\mathbf{r}'$ and $\mathbf{r}''$ are perpendicular to $\mathbf{n}$ and thus in S, $\mathbf{T}$ is in the direction of $\mathbf{r}'$ so $\mathbf{T}$ is in S. From Exercise 18, $\mathbf{N}$ is in the direction of $\mathbf{u}$, but $\mathbf{n} \cdot \mathbf{u} = \|\mathbf{r}'\|^2\mathbf{n} \cdot \mathbf{r}'' - (\mathbf{r}' \cdot \mathbf{r}'')\mathbf{n} \cdot \mathbf{r}' = 0$ so $\mathbf{u}$, and hence $\mathbf{N}$, are perpendicular to $\mathbf{n}$ and thus in S.

EXERCISE SET 15.5

1. $\mathbf{r}'(t) = 2t\mathbf{i} + 3t^2\mathbf{j}$, $\mathbf{r}''(t) = 2\mathbf{i} + 6t\mathbf{j}$, $\mathbf{r}'(1/2) = \mathbf{i} + 3/4\mathbf{j}$,
   $\mathbf{r}''(1/2) = 2\mathbf{i} + 3\mathbf{j}$; $\kappa = \|3/2\mathbf{k}\|/\|\mathbf{i} + 3/4\mathbf{j}\|^3 = 96/125$.

2. $\mathbf{r}'(t) = -4\sin t\mathbf{i} + \cos t\mathbf{j}$, $\mathbf{r}''(t) = -4\cos t\mathbf{i} - \sin t\mathbf{j}$,
   $\mathbf{r}'(\pi/2) = -4\mathbf{i}$, $\mathbf{r}''(\pi/2) = -\mathbf{j}$; $\kappa = \|4\mathbf{k}\|/\| -4\mathbf{i}\|^3 = 1/16$.

3. $\mathbf{r}'(t) = 3e^{3t}\mathbf{i} - e^{-t}\mathbf{j}$, $\mathbf{r}''(t) = 9e^{3t}\mathbf{i} + e^{-t}\mathbf{j}$,
   $\mathbf{r}'(0) = 3\mathbf{i} - \mathbf{j}$, $\mathbf{r}''(0) = 9\mathbf{i} + \mathbf{j}$; $\kappa = \|12\mathbf{k}\|/\|3\mathbf{i} - \mathbf{j}\|^3 = 6/(5\sqrt{10})$.

4. $\mathbf{r}'(t) = -3t^2\mathbf{i} + (1 - 2t)\mathbf{j}$, $\mathbf{r}''(t) = -6t\mathbf{i} - 2\mathbf{j}$, $\mathbf{r}'(1) = -3\mathbf{i} - \mathbf{j}$, $\mathbf{r}''(1) = -6\mathbf{i} - 2\mathbf{j}$; $\kappa = 0$.

5. $\mathbf{r}'(t) = (\cos t - t\sin t)\mathbf{i} + (\sin t + t\cos t)\mathbf{j}$, $\mathbf{r}''(t) = -(2\sin t + t\cos t)\mathbf{i} + (2\cos t - t\sin t)\mathbf{j}$,
   $\|\mathbf{r}'(t) \times \mathbf{r}''(t)\| = 2 + t^2$, $\|\mathbf{r}'(t)\| = (1 + t^2)^{1/2}$; $\kappa(1) = 3/(2\sqrt{2})$.

6. $\mathbf{r}'(t) = 2ab\mathbf{i} + 2b^2t\mathbf{j}$, $\mathbf{r}''(t) = 2b^2\mathbf{j}$, $\mathbf{r}'(1) = 2ab\mathbf{i} + 2b^2\mathbf{j}$,
   $\mathbf{r}''(1) = 2b^2\mathbf{j}$; $\kappa = \|4ab^3\mathbf{k}\|/\|2ab\mathbf{i} + 2b^2\mathbf{j}\|^3 = a/[2(a^2 + b^2)^{3/2}]$.

7. $\mathbf{r}'(t) = -4\sin t\mathbf{i} + 4\cos t\mathbf{j} + \mathbf{k}$, $\mathbf{r}''(t) = -4\cos t\mathbf{i} - 4\sin t\mathbf{j}$,
   $\mathbf{r}'(\pi/2) = -4\mathbf{i} + \mathbf{k}$, $\mathbf{r}''(\pi/2) = -4\mathbf{j}$; $\kappa = \|4\mathbf{i} + 16\mathbf{k}\|/\| -4\mathbf{i} + \mathbf{k}\|^3 = 4/17$.

8. $\mathbf{r}'(t) = e^t\mathbf{i} - e^{-t}\mathbf{j} + \mathbf{k}$, $\mathbf{r}''(t) = e^t\mathbf{i} + e^{-t}\mathbf{j}$, $\mathbf{r}'(0) = \mathbf{i} - \mathbf{j} + \mathbf{k}$,
   $\mathbf{r}''(0) = \mathbf{i} + \mathbf{j}$, $\kappa = \| -\mathbf{i} + \mathbf{j} + 2\mathbf{k}\|/\|\mathbf{i} - \mathbf{j} + \mathbf{k}\|^3 = \sqrt{2}/3$.

9. $\mathbf{r}'(t) = \mathbf{i} + t\mathbf{j} + t^2\mathbf{k}$, $\mathbf{r}''(t) = \mathbf{j} + 2t\mathbf{k}$, $\mathbf{r}'(0) = \mathbf{i}$, $\mathbf{r}''(0) = \mathbf{j}$; $\kappa = \|\mathbf{k}\|/\|\mathbf{i}\|^3 = 1$.

10. $\mathbf{r}'(t) = \cos t\mathbf{i} - \sin t\mathbf{j} + t\mathbf{k}$, $\mathbf{r}''(t) = -\sin t\mathbf{i} - \cos t\mathbf{j} + \mathbf{k}$,
    $\mathbf{r}'(0) = \mathbf{i}$, $\mathbf{r}''(0) = -\mathbf{j} + \mathbf{k}$; $\kappa = \| -\mathbf{j} - \mathbf{k}\|/\|\mathbf{i}\|^3 = \sqrt{2}$.

11. $\mathbf{r}'(t) = -3\sin t\mathbf{i} + 4\cos t\mathbf{j} + \mathbf{k}$, $\mathbf{r}''(t) = -3\cos t\mathbf{i} - 4\sin t\mathbf{j}$,
    $\mathbf{r}'(\pi/2) = -3\mathbf{i} + \mathbf{k}$, $\mathbf{r}''(\pi/2) = -4\mathbf{j}$; $\kappa = \|4\mathbf{i} + 12\mathbf{k}\|/\| -3\mathbf{i} + \mathbf{k}\|^3 = 2/5$.

12. $\mathbf{r}'(t) = e^t(\cos t - \sin t)\mathbf{i} + e^t(\cos t + \sin t)\mathbf{j} + e^t\mathbf{k}$,
    $\mathbf{r}''(t) = -2e^t\sin t\mathbf{i} + 2e^t\cos t\mathbf{j} + e^t\mathbf{k}$, $\mathbf{r}'(0) = \mathbf{i} + \mathbf{j} + \mathbf{k}$,
    $\mathbf{r}''(0) = 2\mathbf{j} + \mathbf{k}$; $\kappa = \| -\mathbf{i} - \mathbf{j} + 2\mathbf{k}\|/\|\mathbf{i} + \mathbf{j} + \mathbf{k}\|^3 = \sqrt{2}/3$.

13. $\mathbf{r}'(t) = \mathbf{j} + 2t\mathbf{k}$, $\mathbf{r}''(t) = 2\mathbf{k}$, $\mathbf{r}'(1) = \mathbf{j} + 2\mathbf{k}$, $\mathbf{r}''(1) = 2\mathbf{k}$; $\kappa = \|2\mathbf{i}\|/\|\mathbf{j} + 2\mathbf{k}\|^3 = 2/(5\sqrt{5})$.

14. $\mathbf{r}'(t) = \sinh t\mathbf{i} + \cosh t\mathbf{j} + \mathbf{k}$, $\mathbf{r}''(t) = \cosh t\mathbf{i} + \sinh t\mathbf{j}$,
     $\sinh(\ln 2) = 3/4$, $\cosh(\ln 2) = 5/4$, $\mathbf{r}'(\ln 2) = (3/4)\mathbf{i} + (5/4)\mathbf{j} + \mathbf{k}$,
     $\mathbf{r}''(\ln 2) = (5/4)\mathbf{i} + (3/4)\mathbf{j}$; $\kappa = \|(-3/4)\mathbf{i} + (5/4)\mathbf{j} - \mathbf{k}\| / \|(3/4)\mathbf{i} + (5/4)\mathbf{j} + \mathbf{k}\|^3 = 8/25$.

15. $\mathbf{r}'(x) = \mathbf{i} + (dy/dx)\mathbf{j}$, $\mathbf{r}''(x) = (d^2y/dx^2)\mathbf{j}$;
     $\kappa(x) = \|(d^2y/dx^2)\mathbf{k}\|/\|\mathbf{i} + (dy/dx)\mathbf{j}\|^3 = |d^2y/dx^2|/[1 + (dy/dx)^2]^{3/2}$.

16. $\dfrac{dy}{dx} = \tan\phi$, $(1 + \tan^2\phi)^{3/2} = (\sec^2\phi)^{3/2} = |\sec\phi|^3$, $\kappa(x) = \dfrac{|y''|}{|\sec\phi|^3} = |y''\cos^3\phi|$.

17. $\kappa(x) = \dfrac{|\sin x|}{(1 + \cos^2 x)^{3/2}}$, $\kappa(\pi/2) = 1$ 18. $\kappa(x) = \dfrac{2|x|}{(1 + x^4)^{3/2}}$, $\kappa(0) = 0$

19. $\kappa(x) = \dfrac{2|x|^3}{(x^4 + 1)^{3/2}}$, $\kappa(1) = 1/\sqrt{2}$ 20. $\kappa(x) = \dfrac{e^{-x}}{(1 + e^{-2x})^{3/2}}$, $\kappa(1) = \dfrac{e^{-1}}{(1 + e^{-2})^{3/2}}$

21. $\kappa(x) = \dfrac{2\sec^2 x|\tan x|}{(1 + \sec^4 x)^{3/2}}$, $\kappa(\pi/4) = 4/(5\sqrt{5})$

22. By implicit differentiation, $dy/dx = 4x/y$, $d^2y/dx^2 = 36/y^3$ so $\kappa = \dfrac{36/|y|^3}{(1 + 16x^2/y^2)^{3/2}}$;

     if $(x, y) = (2, 5)$ then $\kappa = \dfrac{36/125}{(1 + 64/25)^{3/2}} = \dfrac{36}{89\sqrt{89}}$.

23. $\kappa(x) = \dfrac{\sec^2 x}{(1 + \tan^2 x)^{3/2}} = \cos x$; $\kappa(x)$ is maximum for $x = 0$.

24. $\mathbf{r}' = x'\mathbf{i} + y'\mathbf{j}$, $\mathbf{r}'' = x''\mathbf{i} + y''\mathbf{j}$; $\kappa = \dfrac{\|(x'y'' - y'x'')\mathbf{k}\|}{\|x'\mathbf{i} + y'\mathbf{k}\|} = \dfrac{|x'y'' - y'x''|}{(x'^2 + y'^2)^{3/2}}$

25. $x'(t) = 2t$, $y'(t) = 3t^2$, $x''(t) = 2$, $y''(t) = 6t$,
     $x'(1/2) = 1$, $y'(1/2) = 3/4$, $x''(1/2) = 2$, $y''(1/2) = 3$; $\kappa = 96/125$.

26. $x'(t) = -4\sin t$, $y'(t) = \cos t$, $x''(t) = -4\cos t$, $y''(t) = -\sin t$,
     $x'(\pi/2) = -4$, $y'(\pi/2) = 0$, $x''(\pi/2) = 0$, $y''(\pi/2) = -1$; $\kappa = 1/16$.

27. $x'(t) = 3e^{3t}$, $y'(t) = -e^{-t}$, $x''(t) = 9e^{3t}$, $y''(t) = e^{-t}$,
     $x'(0) = 3$, $y'(0) = -1$, $x''(0) = 9$, $y''(0) = 1$; $\kappa = 6/(5\sqrt{10})$.

28. $x'(t) = -3t^2$, $y'(t) = 1 - 2t$, $x''(t) = -6t$, $y''(t) = -2$,
     $x'(1) = -3$, $y'(1) = -1$, $x''(1) = -6$, $y''(1) = -2$; $\kappa = 0$.

29. $x'(t) = \cos t - t \sin t,\ y'(t) = \sin t + t \cos t,$
$x''(t) = -2\sin t - t\cos t,\ y''(t) = 2\cos t - t\sin t,$
$x'y'' - y'x'' = 2 + t^2,\ x'^2 + y'^2 = 1 + t^2;\ \kappa(1) = 3/(2\sqrt{2}).$

30. $x'(t) = 2ab,\ y'(t) = 2b^2 t,\ x''(t) = 0,\ y''(t) = 2b^2,$
$x'(1) = 2ab,\ y'(1) = 2b^2,\ x''(1) = 0,\ y''(1) = 2b^2;\ \kappa = \dfrac{a}{2(a^2 + b^2)^{3/2}}$

31. $x'(t) = -a\sin t,\ y'(t) = b\cos t,\ x''(t) = -a\cos t,\ y''(t) = -b\sin t;$
$\kappa(0) = a/b^2,\ \kappa(\pi/2) = b/a^2.$

32. $\mathbf{r}'(\theta) = \left(-r\sin\theta + \cos\theta\dfrac{dr}{d\theta}\right)\mathbf{i} + \left(r\cos\theta + \sin\theta\dfrac{dr}{d\theta}\right)\mathbf{j};$

$\mathbf{r}''(\theta) = \left(-r\cos\theta - 2\sin\theta\dfrac{dr}{d\theta} + \cos\theta\dfrac{d^2 r}{d\theta^2}\right)\mathbf{i} + \left(-r\sin\theta + 2\cos\theta\dfrac{dr}{d\theta} + \sin\theta\dfrac{d^2 r}{d\theta^2}\right)\mathbf{j};$

$\kappa = \dfrac{\left|r^2 + 2\left(\dfrac{dr}{d\theta}\right)^2 - r\dfrac{d^2 r}{d\theta^2}\right|}{\left[r^2 + \left(\dfrac{dr}{d\theta}\right)^2\right]^{3/2}}.$

33. $\kappa(\theta) = 1,\ \kappa(\pi/6) = 1$

34. $\kappa(\theta) = \dfrac{\theta^2 + 2}{(\theta^2 + 1)^{3/2}},\ \kappa(1) = \dfrac{3}{2\sqrt{2}}$

35. $\kappa(\theta) = \dfrac{3}{2\sqrt{2}a(1 + \cos\theta)^{1/2}},\ \kappa(\pi/2) = \dfrac{3}{2\sqrt{2}a}$

36. $\kappa(\theta) = \dfrac{1}{\sqrt{5}e^{2\theta}},\ \kappa(1) = \dfrac{1}{\sqrt{5}e^2}$

37. $x'(t) = a(1 - \cos t),\ y'(t) = a\sin t,$
$x''(t) = a\sin t,\ y''(t) = a\cos t;$
$\kappa(t) = \dfrac{a^2(1 - \cos t)}{[2a^2(1 - \cos t)]^{3/2}}$
$= \dfrac{1}{2\sqrt{2}a(1 - \cos t)^{1/2}},$
but $1 - \cos t = 2\sin^2(t/2)$ so
$\kappa(t) = \dfrac{1}{4a\sin(t/2)} = \dfrac{1}{4a}\csc(t/2).$

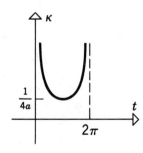

38. $x'(t) = -e^{-t}(\cos t + \sin t)$,

$y'(t) = e^{-t}(\cos t - \sin t)$,

$x''(t) = 2e^{-t}\sin t$,

$y''(t) = -2e^{-t}\cos t$;

using the formula of Exercise 24,

$\kappa = \dfrac{1}{\sqrt{2}}e^{t}.$

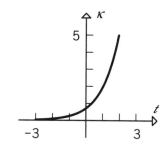

39. $\kappa(x) = \dfrac{|\sin x|}{(1 + \cos^2 x)^{3/2}}$,

$\kappa(\pi/2) = 1, \rho = 1/\kappa = 1$

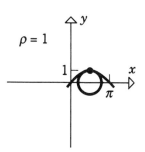

40. $\kappa(t) = \dfrac{2}{(1 + 4t^2)^{3/2}}$,

$\kappa(1) = 2/(5\sqrt{5}), \rho = 5\sqrt{5}/2$

41. $\kappa(x) = (1 + x^2)^{-3/2}$,

$\kappa(-1) = 2^{-3/2}, \rho = 2^{3/2} = 2\sqrt{2}$

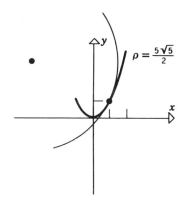

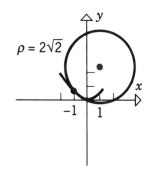

42. $\kappa(t) = \dfrac{2}{(4t+1)^{3/2}}$

$\kappa(2) = 2/27, \rho = 27/2$

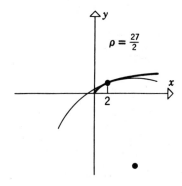

43. $\kappa(x) = \dfrac{|x|}{(x^2+1)^{3/2}}$,

$\kappa(1) = 2^{-3/2}, \rho = 2^{3/2} = 2\sqrt{2}$

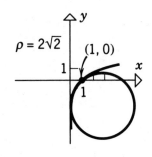

44. $\kappa(t) = \dfrac{16t^3}{8(t^4+4)^{3/2}}$

$\kappa(1) = 2/(5\sqrt{5}), \rho = 5\sqrt{5}/2$

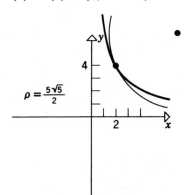

45. $\kappa(t) = \dfrac{|\cos t - 1|}{(2 - 2\cos t)^{3/2}}$,

$\kappa(\pi) = 1/4, \rho = 4$

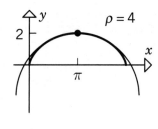

46. $\kappa(x) = \dfrac{|\cos x|}{(1 + \sin^2 x)^{3/2}}$,

$\rho(x) = \dfrac{(1 + \sin^2 x)^{3/2}}{|\cos x|}$

$\rho(0) = \rho(\pi) = 1.$

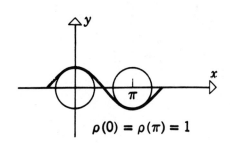

47. $\kappa(t) = \dfrac{2}{(4\sin^2 t + \cos^2 t)^{3/2}}$,

$\rho(t) = \dfrac{1}{2}(4\sin^2 t + \cos^2 t)^{3/2}$,

$\rho(0) = 1/2,\ \rho(\pi/2) = 4$

$\rho(0) = \dfrac{1}{2}$

$\rho\left(\dfrac{\pi}{2}\right) = 4$

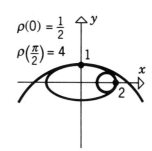

48. **(a)** The relative extrema occur at $(-1, -1)$, $(0, 0)$, and $(1, -1)$.

$\kappa(x) = \dfrac{|12x^2 - 4|}{[1 + (4x^3 - 4x)^2]^{3/2}}$, $\rho(x) = \dfrac{[1 + (4x^3 - 4x)^2]^{3/2}}{|12x^2 - 4|}$,

$\rho(-1) = \rho(1) = 1/8,\ \rho(0) = 1/4$.

(b)

$\rho(0) = \tfrac{1}{4}$

$\rho(-1) = \tfrac{1}{8}$ $\rho(1) = \tfrac{1}{8}$

49. Let $y = t$, then $x = \dfrac{t^2}{4p}$ and $\kappa(t) = \dfrac{1/|2p|}{[t^2/(4p^2) + 1]^{3/2}}$;

$t = 0$ when $(x, y) = (0, 0)$ so $\kappa(0) = 1/|2p|$, $\rho = 2|p|$.

50. $\kappa(x) = \dfrac{e^x}{(1 + e^{2x})^{3/2}}$, $\kappa'(x) = \dfrac{e^x(1 - 2e^{2x})}{(1 + e^{2x})^{5/2}}$; $\kappa'(x) = 0$ when $e^{2x} = 1/2$, $x = -(\ln 2)/2$. By the first derivative test, $\kappa(-\tfrac{1}{2}\ln 2)$ is maximum so the point is $(-\tfrac{1}{2}\ln 2, 1/\sqrt{2})$.

51. Let $x = 3\cos t$, $y = 2\sin t$ for $0 \le t < 2\pi$, $\kappa(t) = \dfrac{6}{(9\sin^2 t + 4\cos^2 t)^{3/2}}$ so

$\rho(t) = \dfrac{1}{6}(9\sin^2 t + 4\cos^2 t)^{3/2} = \dfrac{1}{6}(5\sin^2 t + 4)^{3/2}$ which, by inspection, is minimum when

$t = 0$ or π. The radius of curvature is minimum at $(3, 0)$ and $(-3, 0)$.

52. $\kappa(x) = \dfrac{6x}{(1+9x^4)^{3/2}}$ for $x > 0$, $\kappa'(x) = \dfrac{6(1-45x^4)}{(1+9x^4)^{5/2}}$; $\kappa'(x) = 0$ when $x = 45^{-1/4}$ which, by the first derivative test, yields the maximum.

53. $\mathbf{r}'(t) = -\sin t\mathbf{i} + \cos t\mathbf{j} - \sin t\mathbf{k}$, $\mathbf{r}''(t) = -\cos t\mathbf{i} - \sin t\mathbf{j} - \cos t\mathbf{k}$,
$\|\mathbf{r}'(t) \times \mathbf{r}''(t)\| = \|-\mathbf{i}+\mathbf{k}\| = \sqrt{2}$, $\|\mathbf{r}'(t)\| = (1+\sin^2 t)^{1/2}$; $\kappa(t) = \sqrt{2}/(1+\sin^2 t)^{3/2}$,
$\rho(t) = (1+\sin^2 t)^{3/2}/\sqrt{2}$. The minimum value of ρ is $1/\sqrt{2}$; the maximum value is 2.

54. $\mathbf{r}'(t) = e^t\mathbf{i} - e^{-t}\mathbf{j} + \sqrt{2}\mathbf{k}$, $\mathbf{r}''(t) = e^t\mathbf{i} + e^{-t}\mathbf{j}$;

$\kappa(t) = \dfrac{\sqrt{2}}{e^{2t} + e^{-2t} + 2}$, $\rho(t) = \dfrac{1}{\sqrt{2}}(e^t + e^{-t})^2 = 2\sqrt{2}\cosh^2 t$. The minimum value of ρ is $2\sqrt{2}$.

55. From Exercise 32: $dr/d\theta = ae^{a\theta} = ar$, $d^2r/d\theta^2 = a^2e^{a\theta} = a^2r$; $\kappa = 1/[\sqrt{1+a^2}\,r]$.

56. Use implicit differentiation on $r^2 = a^2\cos 2\theta$ to get $2r\dfrac{dr}{d\theta} = -2a^2\sin 2\theta$, $r\dfrac{dr}{d\theta} = -a^2\sin 2\theta$, and

again to get $r\dfrac{d^2r}{d\theta^2} + \left(\dfrac{dr}{d\theta}\right)^2 = -2a^2\cos 2\theta$ so $r\dfrac{d^2r}{d\theta^2} = -\left(\dfrac{dr}{d\theta}\right)^2 - 2a^2\cos 2\theta = -\left(\dfrac{dr}{d\theta}\right)^2 - 2r^2$,

thus $\left|r^2 + 2\left(\dfrac{dr}{d\theta}\right)^2 - r\dfrac{d^2r}{d\theta^2}\right| = 3\left[r^2 + \left(\dfrac{dr}{d\theta}\right)^2\right]$, $\kappa = \dfrac{3}{[r^2+(dr/d\theta)^2]^{1/2}}$; $\dfrac{dr}{d\theta} = -\dfrac{a^2\sin 2\theta}{r}$ so

$r^2 + \left(\dfrac{dr}{d\theta}\right)^2 = r^2 + \dfrac{a^4\sin^2 2\theta}{r^2} = \dfrac{r^4 + a^4\sin^2 2\theta}{r^2} = \dfrac{a^4\cos^2 2\theta + a^4\sin^2 2\theta}{r^2} = \dfrac{a^4}{r^2}$, hence $\kappa = \dfrac{3r}{a^2}$.

57. $|d\phi/ds| = \kappa = \|d\mathbf{T}/ds\| = 0.05$ radians/cm $= (9/\pi)^\circ$/cm $\approx 2.86^\circ$/cm.

58. $\kappa(x) = \dfrac{6|x|}{(1+9x^4)^{3/2}}$; at $x = 1$, $\left|\dfrac{d\phi}{ds}\right| = \kappa = \dfrac{3}{5\sqrt{10}}$ radians/in. $\approx 10.87^\circ$/in.

59. $\kappa = 0$ along $y = 0$; along $y = x^2$, $\kappa(x) = 2/(1+4x^2)^{3/2}$, $\kappa(0) = 2$. Along $y = x^3$,
$\kappa(x) = 6|x|/(1+9x^4)^{3/2}$, $\kappa(0) = 0$.

60. **(a)**

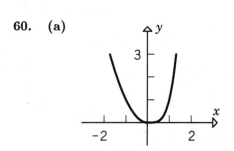

(b) For $y = x^2$, $\kappa(x) = \dfrac{2}{(1+4x^2)^{3/2}}$

so $\kappa(0) = 2$; for $y = x^4$,

$\kappa(x) = \dfrac{12x^2}{(1+16x^6)^{3/2}}$ so $\kappa(0) = 0$.

κ is not continuous at $x = 0$.

61. $\kappa = 1/r$ along the circle; along $y = ax^2$, $\kappa(x) = 2a/(1 + 4a^2x^2)^{3/2}$, $\kappa(0) = 2a$ so $2a = 1/r$, $a = 1/(2r)$.

62. $\kappa(x) = \dfrac{|y''|}{(1 + y'^2)^{3/2}}$ so the transition will be smooth if the values of y are equal, the values of y' are equal, and the values of y'' are equal at $x = 0$. If $y = e^x$, then $y' = y'' = e^x$; if $y = ax^2 + bx + c$, then $y' = 2ax + b$ and $y'' = 2a$. Equate y, y', and y'' at $x = 0$ to get $c = 1$, $b = 1$, and $a = 1/2$.

63. $\mathbf{r}'(t) = (1/t)\mathbf{i} + 2\mathbf{j} + 2t\mathbf{k}$

   (a) $\|\mathbf{r}'(t)\| = \sqrt{1/t^2 + 4 + 4t^2} = \sqrt{(2t + 1/t)^2} = 2t + 1/t$

   (b) $\dfrac{ds}{dt} = 2t + 1/t$ **(c)** $\displaystyle\int_1^3 (2t + 1/t)dt = 8 + \ln 3$

64. $\mathbf{r}(t) = \cos t\,\mathbf{i} + \sin t\,\mathbf{j} + t^{3/2}\mathbf{k}$, $\mathbf{r}'(t) = -\sin t\,\mathbf{i} + \cos t\,\mathbf{j} + \dfrac{3}{2}t^{1/2}\mathbf{k}$

   (a) $\|\mathbf{r}'(t)\| = \sqrt{\sin^2 t + \cos^2 t + 9t/4} = \dfrac{1}{2}\sqrt{4 + 9t}$

   (b) $\dfrac{ds}{dt} = \dfrac{1}{2}\sqrt{4 + 9t}$ **(c)** $\displaystyle\int_0^2 \dfrac{1}{2}\sqrt{4 + 9t}\,dt = \dfrac{2}{27}(11\sqrt{22} - 4)$

65.   **(a)** $\mathbf{r}(s) = (3s/5 + 1)\mathbf{i} + (4s/5 - 2)\mathbf{j}$,   **66.**   **(a)** $\mathbf{r}(s) = 2\cos(s/2)\mathbf{i} + 2\sin(s/2)\mathbf{j}$,
            $\mathbf{T} = d\mathbf{r}/ds = (3/5)\mathbf{i} + (4/5)\mathbf{j}$ $\mathbf{T} = d\mathbf{r}/ds = -\sin(s/2)\mathbf{i} + \cos(s/2)\mathbf{j}$,
   (b) $\mathbf{T}(5) = (3/5)\mathbf{i} + (4/5)\mathbf{j}$ $\mathbf{N} = -\cos(s/2)\mathbf{i} - \sin(s/2)\mathbf{j}$
            $\mathbf{r}(5) = 4\mathbf{i} + 2\mathbf{j}$ **(b)** $\mathbf{T}(\pi/2) = -(\sqrt{2}/2)\mathbf{i} + (\sqrt{2}/2)\mathbf{j}$
                                                                      $\mathbf{N}(\pi/2) = -(\sqrt{2}/2)\mathbf{i} - (\sqrt{2}/2)\mathbf{j}$
                                                                      $\mathbf{r}(\pi/2) = \sqrt{2}\mathbf{i} + \sqrt{2}\mathbf{j}$

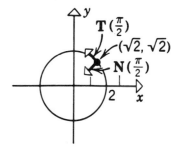

67.   **(a)** $\kappa = \dfrac{d\phi}{ds} = as$, $\phi = \dfrac{1}{2}as^2 + C$, but $\phi = 0$ when $s = 0$ so $C = 0$, $\phi = \dfrac{1}{2}as^2$.

(b) $\mathbf{T} = \dfrac{d\mathbf{r}}{ds} = \dfrac{dx}{ds}\mathbf{i} + \dfrac{dy}{ds}\mathbf{j}$ so $\dfrac{dx}{ds} = \cos\left(\frac{1}{2}as^2\right)$ and $\dfrac{dy}{ds} = \sin\left(\frac{1}{2}as^2\right)$, $x = \displaystyle\int_0^s \cos\left(\frac{1}{2}au^2\right) du$ and

$y = \displaystyle\int_0^s \left(\sin\frac{1}{2}au^2\right) du.$

68. (a) $\mathbf{B} \cdot \dfrac{d\mathbf{B}}{ds} = 0$ because $\|\mathbf{B}\| = 1$ so $\dfrac{d\mathbf{B}}{ds}$ is perpendicular to $\mathbf{B}$.

(b) $\mathbf{B} \cdot \mathbf{T} = 0$, $\mathbf{B} \cdot \dfrac{d\mathbf{T}}{ds} + \dfrac{d\mathbf{B}}{ds} \cdot \mathbf{T} = 0$, but $\dfrac{d\mathbf{T}}{ds} = \kappa\mathbf{N}$ so $\kappa\mathbf{B} \cdot \mathbf{N} + \dfrac{d\mathbf{B}}{ds} \cdot \mathbf{T} = 0$, $\dfrac{d\mathbf{B}}{ds} \cdot \mathbf{T} = 0$
because $\mathbf{B} \cdot \mathbf{N} = 0$ thus $\dfrac{d\mathbf{B}}{ds}$ is perpendicular to $\mathbf{T}$.

(c) $\dfrac{d\mathbf{B}}{ds}$ is perpendicular to both $\mathbf{B}$ and $\mathbf{T}$ but so is $\mathbf{N}$, thus $\dfrac{d\mathbf{B}}{ds}$ is parallel to $\mathbf{N}$ and hence a scalar multiple of $\mathbf{N}$.

(d) If C lies in a plane, then $\mathbf{T}$ and $\mathbf{N}$ also lie in the plane; $\mathbf{B} = \mathbf{T} \times \mathbf{N}$ so $\mathbf{B}$ is always perpendicular to the plane and hence $d\mathbf{B}/ds = \mathbf{0}$, thus $\tau = 0$.

69. $\dfrac{d\mathbf{N}}{ds} = \mathbf{B} \times \dfrac{d\mathbf{T}}{ds} + \dfrac{d\mathbf{B}}{ds} \times \mathbf{T} = \mathbf{B} \times (\kappa\mathbf{N}) + (-\tau\mathbf{N}) \times \mathbf{T} = \kappa\mathbf{B} \times \mathbf{N} - \tau\mathbf{N} \times \mathbf{T}$, but $\mathbf{B} \times \mathbf{N} = -\mathbf{T}$
and $\mathbf{N} \times \mathbf{T} = -\mathbf{B}$ so $\dfrac{d\mathbf{N}}{ds} = -\kappa\mathbf{T} + \tau\mathbf{B}$.

70. (a) If $\mathbf{r}'(s) = \mathbf{T}$, then $\mathbf{r}''(s) = d\mathbf{T}/ds = \kappa\mathbf{N}$ so $\|\mathbf{r}''(s)\| = \kappa\|\mathbf{N}\| = \kappa$,
$\mathbf{N} = \mathbf{r}''(s)/\kappa = \mathbf{r}''(s)/\|\mathbf{r}''(s)\|.$

(b) From part (a), $\mathbf{r}''(s) = \kappa\mathbf{N}$ so $\mathbf{r}'''(s) = \kappa d\mathbf{N}/ds + (d\kappa/ds)\mathbf{N}$ but $d\mathbf{N}/ds = -\kappa\mathbf{T} + \tau\mathbf{B}$
so $\mathbf{r}'''(s) = -\kappa^2\mathbf{T} + (d\kappa/ds)\mathbf{N} + \kappa\tau\mathbf{B}$, $\mathbf{r}'(s) \times \mathbf{r}''(s) = \mathbf{T} \times (\kappa\mathbf{N}) = \kappa\mathbf{T} \times \mathbf{N} = \kappa\mathbf{B}$,
$[\mathbf{r}'(s) \times \mathbf{r}''(s)] \cdot \mathbf{r}'''(s) = -\kappa^3\mathbf{B} \cdot \mathbf{T} + \kappa(d\kappa/ds)\mathbf{B} \cdot \mathbf{N} + \kappa^2\tau\mathbf{B} \cdot \mathbf{B} = \kappa^2\tau$,
$\tau = [\mathbf{r}'(s) \times \mathbf{r}''(s)] \cdot \mathbf{r}'''(s)/\kappa^2 = [\mathbf{r}'(s) \times \mathbf{r}''(s)] \cdot \mathbf{r}'''(s)/\|\mathbf{r}''(s)\|^2$ and
$\mathbf{B} = \mathbf{T} \times \mathbf{N} = [\mathbf{r}'(s) \times \mathbf{r}''(s)]/\|\mathbf{r}'(s)\|.$

71. $\mathbf{r} = a\cos(s/w)\mathbf{i} + a\sin(s/w)\mathbf{j} + (cs/w)\mathbf{k}$, $\mathbf{r}' = -(a/w)\sin(s/w)\mathbf{i} + (a/w)\cos(s/w)\mathbf{j} + (c/w)\mathbf{k}$,
$\mathbf{r}'' = -(a/w^2)\cos(s/w)\mathbf{i} - (a/w^2)\sin(s/w)\mathbf{j}$, $\mathbf{r}''' = (a/w^3)\sin(s/w)\mathbf{i} - (a/w^3)\cos(s/w)\mathbf{j}$,
$\mathbf{r}' \times \mathbf{r}'' = (ac/w^3)\sin(s/w)\mathbf{i} - (ac/w^3)\cos(s/w)\mathbf{j} + (a^2/w^3)\mathbf{k}$, $(\mathbf{r}' \times \mathbf{r}'') \cdot \mathbf{r}''' = a^2c/w^6$,
$\|\mathbf{r}''(s)\| = a/w^2$, so $\tau = c/w^2$ and $\mathbf{B} = (c/w)\sin(s/w)\mathbf{i} - (c/w)\cos(s/w)\mathbf{j} + (a/w)\mathbf{k}.$

72. (a) $\mathbf{T}' = \dfrac{d\mathbf{T}}{dt} = \dfrac{d\mathbf{T}}{ds}\dfrac{ds}{dt} = (\kappa\mathbf{N})s' = \kappa s'\mathbf{N}$,
$\mathbf{N}' = \dfrac{d\mathbf{N}}{dt} = \dfrac{d\mathbf{N}}{ds}\dfrac{ds}{dt} = (-\kappa\mathbf{T} + \tau\mathbf{B})s' = -\kappa s'\mathbf{T} + \tau s'\mathbf{B}.$

(b) $\|\mathbf{r}'(t)\| = s'$ so $\mathbf{r}'(t) = s'\mathbf{T}$ and $\mathbf{r}''(t) = s''\mathbf{T} + s'\mathbf{T}' = s''\mathbf{T} + s'(\kappa s'\mathbf{N}) = s''\mathbf{T} + \kappa(s')^2\mathbf{N}.$

(c) $\mathbf{r}'''(t) = s''\mathbf{T}' + s'''\mathbf{T} + \kappa(s')^2\mathbf{N}' + [2\kappa s's'' + \kappa'(s')^2]\mathbf{N}$
$\quad = s''(\kappa s'\mathbf{N}) + s'''\mathbf{T} + \kappa(s')^2(-\kappa s'\mathbf{T} + \tau s'\mathbf{B}) + [2\kappa s's'' + \kappa'(s')^2]\mathbf{N}$
$\quad = [s''' - \kappa^2(s')^3]\mathbf{T} + [3\kappa s's'' + \kappa'(s')^2]\mathbf{N} + \kappa\tau(s')^3\mathbf{B}.$

(d) $\mathbf{r}'(t) \times \mathbf{r}''(t) = s's''\mathbf{T} \times \mathbf{T} + \kappa(s')^3\mathbf{T} \times \mathbf{N} = \kappa(s')^3\mathbf{B}$, $[\mathbf{r}'(t) \times \mathbf{r}''(t)] \cdot \mathbf{r}'''(t) = \kappa^2\tau(s')^6$ so

$$\tau = \frac{[\mathbf{r}'(t) \times \mathbf{r}''(t)] \cdot \mathbf{r}'''(t)}{\kappa^2(s')^6} = \frac{[\mathbf{r}'(t) \times \mathbf{r}''(t)] \cdot \mathbf{r}'''(t)}{\|\mathbf{r}'(t) \times \mathbf{r}''(t)\|^2}.$$

73. $\mathbf{r}' = 2\mathbf{i} + 2t\mathbf{j} + t^2\mathbf{k}$, $\mathbf{r}'' = 2\mathbf{j} + 2t\mathbf{k}$, $\mathbf{r}''' = 2\mathbf{k}$, $\mathbf{r}' \times \mathbf{r}'' = 2t^2\mathbf{i} - 4t\mathbf{j} + 4\mathbf{k}$, $\|\mathbf{r}' \times \mathbf{r}''\| = 2(t^2 + 2)$,
$\tau = 8/[2(t^2 + 2)]^2 = 2/(t^2 + 2)^2.$

74. $\mathbf{r}' = -a\sin t\mathbf{i} + a\cos t\mathbf{j} + b\mathbf{k}$, $\mathbf{r}'' = -a\cos t\mathbf{i} - a\sin t\mathbf{j}$, $\mathbf{r}''' = a\sin t\mathbf{i} - a\cos t\mathbf{j}$,
$\mathbf{r}' \times \mathbf{r}'' = ab\sin t\mathbf{i} - ab\cos t\mathbf{j} + a^2\mathbf{k}$, $\|\mathbf{r}' \times \mathbf{r}''\| = \sqrt{a^2(a^2 + b^2)}$,
$\tau = a^2 b/[a^2(a^2 + b^2)] = b/(a^2 + b^2).$

75. $\mathbf{r}' = e^t\mathbf{i} - e^{-t}\mathbf{j} + \sqrt{2}\mathbf{k}$, $\mathbf{r}'' = e^t\mathbf{i} + e^{-t}\mathbf{j}$, $\mathbf{r}''' = e^t\mathbf{i} - e^{-t}\mathbf{j}$, $\mathbf{r}' \times \mathbf{r}'' = -\sqrt{2}e^{-t}\mathbf{i} + \sqrt{2}e^t\mathbf{j} + 2\mathbf{k}$,
$\|\mathbf{r}' \times \mathbf{r}''\| = \sqrt{2}(e^t + e^{-t})$, $\tau = (-2\sqrt{2})/[2(e^t + e^{-t})^2] = -\sqrt{2}/(e^t + e^{-t})^2.$

76. $\mathbf{r}' = (1 - \cos t)\mathbf{i} + \sin t\mathbf{j} + \mathbf{k}$, $\mathbf{r}'' = \sin t\mathbf{i} + \cos t\mathbf{j}$, $\mathbf{r}''' = \cos t\mathbf{i} - \sin t\mathbf{j}$,
$\mathbf{r}' \times \mathbf{r}'' = -\cos t\mathbf{i} + \sin t\mathbf{j} + (\cos t - 1)\mathbf{k}$,
$\|\mathbf{r}' \times \mathbf{r}''\| = \sqrt{\cos^2 t + \sin^2 t + (\cos t - 1)^2} = \sqrt{1 + 4\sin^4(t/2)}$, $\tau = -1/[1 + 4\sin^4(t/2)].$

EXERCISE SET 15.6

1. $\mathbf{v}(t) = -3\sin t\mathbf{i} + 3\cos t\mathbf{j}$

$\mathbf{a}(t) = -3\cos t\mathbf{i} - 3\sin t\mathbf{j}$

$\|\mathbf{v}(t)\| = \sqrt{9\sin^2 t + 9\cos^2 t} = 3$

$\mathbf{r}(\pi/3) = (3/2)\mathbf{i} + (3\sqrt{3}/2)\mathbf{j}$

$\mathbf{v}(\pi/3) = -(3\sqrt{3}/2)\mathbf{i} + (3/2)\mathbf{j}$

$\mathbf{a}(\pi/3) = -(3/2)\mathbf{i} - (3\sqrt{3}/2)\mathbf{j}$

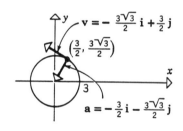

2. $\mathbf{v}(t) = \mathbf{i} + 2t\mathbf{j}$

$\mathbf{a}(t) = 2\mathbf{j}$

$\|\mathbf{v}(t)\| = \sqrt{1 + 4t^2}$

$\mathbf{r}(2) = 2\mathbf{i} + 4\mathbf{j}$

$\mathbf{v}(2) = \mathbf{i} + 4\mathbf{j}$

$\mathbf{a}(2) = 2\mathbf{j}$

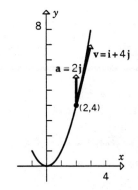

3. $\mathbf{v}(t) = e^t\mathbf{i} - e^{-t}\mathbf{j}$

$\mathbf{a}(t) = e^t\mathbf{i} + e^{-t}\mathbf{j}$

$\|\mathbf{v}(t)\| = \sqrt{e^{2t} + e^{-2t}}$

$\mathbf{r}(0) = \mathbf{i} + \mathbf{j}$

$\mathbf{v}(0) = \mathbf{i} - \mathbf{j}$

$\mathbf{a}(0) = \mathbf{i} + \mathbf{j}$

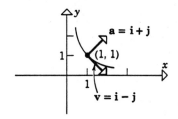

4. $\mathbf{v}(t) = 4\mathbf{i} - \mathbf{j}$

$\mathbf{a}(t) = 0$

$\|\mathbf{v}(t)\| = \sqrt{17}$

$\mathbf{r}(1) = 6\mathbf{i}$

$\mathbf{v}(1) = 4\mathbf{i} - \mathbf{j}$

$\mathbf{a}(1) = 0$

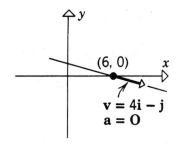

5. $\mathbf{v}(t) = \sinh t\mathbf{i} + \cosh t\mathbf{j}$

$\mathbf{a}(t) = \cosh t\mathbf{i} + \sinh t\mathbf{j}$

$\|\mathbf{v}(t)\| = \sqrt{\sinh^2 t + \cosh^2 t}$

$\mathbf{r}(\ln 2) = (5/4)\mathbf{i} + (3/4)\mathbf{j}$

$\mathbf{v}(\ln 2) = (3/4)\mathbf{i} + (5/4)\mathbf{j}$

$\mathbf{a}(\ln 2) = (5/4)\mathbf{i} + (3/4)\mathbf{j}$

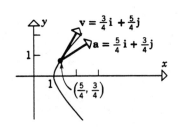

6. $\mathbf{v}(t) = -4\sin t\mathbf{i} + 9\cos t\mathbf{j}$
   $\mathbf{a}(t) = -4\cos t\mathbf{i} - 9\sin t\mathbf{j}$
   $\|\mathbf{v}(t)\| = \sqrt{16\sin^2 t + 81\cos^2 t}$
   $\mathbf{r}(\pi/2) = 9\mathbf{j}$
   $\mathbf{v}(\pi/2) = -4\mathbf{i}$
   $\mathbf{a}(\pi/2) = -9\mathbf{j}$

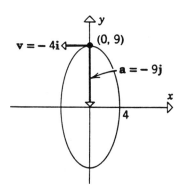

7. $\mathbf{v} = \mathbf{i} + t\mathbf{j} + t^2\mathbf{k}$, $\mathbf{a} = \mathbf{j} + 2t\mathbf{k}$; at $t = 1$, $\mathbf{v} = \mathbf{i} + \mathbf{j} + \mathbf{k}$, $\|\mathbf{v}\| = \sqrt{3}$, $\mathbf{a} = \mathbf{j} + 2\mathbf{k}$

8. $\mathbf{r} = (1 + 3t)\mathbf{i} + (2 - 4t)\mathbf{j} + (7 + t)\mathbf{k}$, $\mathbf{v} = 3\mathbf{i} - 4\mathbf{j} + \mathbf{k}$,
   $\mathbf{a} = 0$; at $t = 2$, $\mathbf{v} = 3\mathbf{i} - 4\mathbf{j} + \mathbf{k}$, $\|\mathbf{v}\| = \sqrt{26}$, $\mathbf{a} = 0$

9. $\mathbf{v} = -2\sin t\mathbf{i} + 2\cos t\mathbf{j} + \mathbf{k}$, $\mathbf{a} = -2\cos t\mathbf{i} - 2\sin t\mathbf{j}$;
   at $t = \pi/4$, $\mathbf{v} = -\sqrt{2}\mathbf{i} + \sqrt{2}\mathbf{j} + \mathbf{k}$, $\|\mathbf{v}\| = \sqrt{5}$, $\mathbf{a} = -\sqrt{2}\mathbf{i} - \sqrt{2}\mathbf{j}$

10. $\mathbf{v} = 3\mathbf{i} + 4t\mathbf{j} + (1/t)\mathbf{k}$, $\mathbf{a} = 4\mathbf{j} - (1/t^2)\mathbf{k}$; at $t = 1$, $\mathbf{v} = 3\mathbf{i} + 4\mathbf{j} + \mathbf{k}$, $\|\mathbf{v}\| = \sqrt{26}$, $\mathbf{a} = 4\mathbf{j} - \mathbf{k}$

11. $\mathbf{v} = e^t(\cos t + \sin t)\mathbf{i} + e^t(\cos t - \sin t)\mathbf{j} + \mathbf{k}$, $\mathbf{a} = 2e^t\cos t\mathbf{i} - 2e^t\sin t\mathbf{j}$; at $t = \pi/2$,
   $\mathbf{v} = e^{\pi/2}\mathbf{i} - e^{\pi/2}\mathbf{j} + \mathbf{k}$, $\|\mathbf{v}\| = (1 + 2e^\pi)^{1/2}$, $\mathbf{a} = -2e^{\pi/2}\mathbf{j}$

12. $\mathbf{v} = 2\mathbf{i} + 2t\mathbf{j} + (1/t)\mathbf{k}$, $\mathbf{a} = 2\mathbf{j} - (1/t^2)\mathbf{k}$; at $t = 2$,
   $\mathbf{v} = 2\mathbf{i} + 4\mathbf{j} + (1/2)\mathbf{k}$, $\|\mathbf{v}\| = 9/2$, $\mathbf{a} = 2\mathbf{j} - (1/4)\mathbf{k}$

13. $\mathbf{v} = (6/\sqrt{t})\mathbf{i} + (3/2)t^{1/2}\mathbf{j}$, $\|\mathbf{v}\| = \sqrt{36/t + 9t/4}$, $d\|\mathbf{v}\|/dt = (-36/t^2 + 9/4)/(2\sqrt{36/t + 9t/4}) = 0$
   if $t = 4$ which yields a minimum by the first derivative test. The minimum speed is $3\sqrt{2}$ when
   $\mathbf{r} = 24\mathbf{i} + 8\mathbf{j}$.

14. $\mathbf{v} = (1 - 2t)\mathbf{i} - 2t\mathbf{j}$, $\|\mathbf{v}\| = \sqrt{(1 - 2t)^2 + 4t^2} = \sqrt{8t^2 - 4t + 1}$,
   $$\frac{d}{dt}\|\mathbf{v}\| = \frac{8t - 2}{\sqrt{8t^2 - 4t + 1}} = 0 \text{ if } t = \frac{1}{4} \text{ which yields a minimum by the first derivative test. The}$$
   minimum speed is $1/\sqrt{2}$ when the particle is at $\mathbf{r} = \dfrac{3}{16}\mathbf{i} - \dfrac{1}{16}\mathbf{j}$.

15. $\mathbf{v} = 3\cos 3t\mathbf{i} + 6\sin 3t\mathbf{j}$, $\|\mathbf{v}\| = \sqrt{9\cos^2 3t + 36\sin^2 3t} = 3\sqrt{1 + 3\sin^2 3t}$; the maximum speed
   is 6, the minimum speed is 3.

16. $\mathbf{v} = -6\sin 2t\mathbf{i} + 2\cos 2t\mathbf{j} + 4\mathbf{k}$, $\|\mathbf{v}\| = \sqrt{36\sin^2 2t + 4\cos^2 2t + 16} = 2\sqrt{8\sin^2 t + 5}$;
the maximum speed is $2\sqrt{13}$, the minimum speed is $2\sqrt{5}$.

17. $\mathbf{v} = 3t^2\mathbf{i} + 2t\mathbf{j}$, $\mathbf{a} = 6t\mathbf{i} + 2\mathbf{j}$; $\mathbf{v} = 3\mathbf{i} + 2\mathbf{j}$ and $\mathbf{a} = 6\mathbf{i} + 2\mathbf{j}$ when $t = 1$ so
$\cos\theta = (\mathbf{v}\cdot\mathbf{a})/(\|\mathbf{v}\|\,\|\mathbf{a}\|) = 11/\sqrt{130}$, $\theta \approx 15°$.

18. $\mathbf{v} = e^t(\cos t - \sin t)\mathbf{i} + e^t(\cos t + \sin t)\mathbf{j}$, $\mathbf{a} = -2e^t\sin t\mathbf{i} + 2e^t\cos t\mathbf{j}$, $\mathbf{v}\cdot\mathbf{a} = 2e^{2t}$, $\|\mathbf{v}\| = \sqrt{2}e^t$,
$\|\mathbf{a}\| = 2e^t$, $\cos\theta = (\mathbf{v}\cdot\mathbf{a})/(\|\mathbf{v}\|\,\|\mathbf{a}\|) = 1/\sqrt{2}$, $\theta = 45°$.

19. $\mathbf{v} = (2t - 5)\mathbf{i} + 2\mathbf{j} + 6t\mathbf{k}$, $\mathbf{a} = 2\mathbf{i} + 6\mathbf{k}$;
$\mathbf{v}\cdot\mathbf{a} = 40t - 10 = 0$ if $t = 1/4$, $\mathbf{r} = -19/16\mathbf{i} + 3/2\mathbf{j} + 3/16\mathbf{k}$.

20. If $\|\mathbf{v}\|$ is constant then so is $\|\mathbf{v}\|^2$, but $\mathbf{v}\cdot\mathbf{v} = \|\mathbf{v}\|^2$ so $d(\mathbf{v}\cdot\mathbf{v})/dt = 0$,
$\mathbf{v}\cdot(d\mathbf{v}/dt) + (d\mathbf{v}/dt)\cdot\mathbf{v} = 0$, $2\mathbf{v}\cdot\mathbf{a} = 0$, $\mathbf{v}\cdot\mathbf{a} = 0$, $\mathbf{v}$ and $\mathbf{a}$ are orthogonal.

21. In both cases, the equation of the path in rectangular coordinates is $x^2 + y^2 = 4$, the particles
move counterclockwise around this circle; $\mathbf{v}_1 = -6\sin 3t\mathbf{i} + 6\cos 3t\mathbf{j}$ and
$\mathbf{v}_2 = -4t\sin(t^2)\mathbf{i} + 4t\cos(t^2)\mathbf{j}$ so $\|\mathbf{v}_1\| = 6$ and $\|\mathbf{v}_2\| = 4t$.

22. Let $u = 1 - t^3$ in $\mathbf{r}_2$ to get $\mathbf{r}_2(u) = (3 + 2u)\mathbf{i} + u\mathbf{j} + (1 - u)\mathbf{k}$ so both particles move along the
same line; $\mathbf{v}_1 = 2\mathbf{i} + \mathbf{j} - \mathbf{k}$ and $\mathbf{v}_2 = -6t^2\mathbf{i} - 3t^2\mathbf{j} + 3t^2\mathbf{k}$ so $\|\mathbf{v}_1\| = \sqrt{6}$ and $\|\mathbf{v}_2\| = 3\sqrt{6}t^2$.

23. $\mathbf{v}(t) = \int(-32\mathbf{j})dt = -32t\mathbf{j} + \mathbf{C}_1$, $\mathbf{v}(0) = \mathbf{C}_1 = 0$ so $\mathbf{v}(t) = -32t\mathbf{j}$;

$\mathbf{r}(t) = \int(-32t\mathbf{j})dt = -16t^2\mathbf{j} + \mathbf{C}_2$, $\mathbf{r}(0) = \mathbf{C}_2 = 0$ so $\mathbf{r}(t) = -16t^2\mathbf{j}$

24. $\mathbf{v}(t) = \int t\mathbf{j}\,dt = (t^2/2)\mathbf{j} + \mathbf{C}_1$, $\mathbf{v}(0) = \mathbf{C}_1 = \mathbf{i} + \mathbf{j}$ so $\mathbf{v}(t) = \mathbf{i} + (1 + t^2/2)\mathbf{j}$;

$\mathbf{r}(t) = \int[\mathbf{i} + (1 + t^2/2)\mathbf{j}]dt = t\mathbf{i} + (t + t^3/6)\mathbf{j} + \mathbf{C}_2$, $\mathbf{r}(0) = \mathbf{C}_2 = 0$ so $\mathbf{r}(t) = t\mathbf{i} + (t + t^3/6)\mathbf{j}$

25. $\mathbf{v}(t) = -\sin t\mathbf{i} + \cos t\mathbf{j} + \mathbf{C}_1$, $\mathbf{v}(0) = \mathbf{j} + \mathbf{C}_1 = \mathbf{i}$, $\mathbf{C}_1 = \mathbf{i} - \mathbf{j}$, $\mathbf{v}(t) = (1 - \sin t)\mathbf{i} + (\cos t - 1)\mathbf{j}$;
$\mathbf{r}(t) = (t + \cos t)\mathbf{i} + (\sin t - t)\mathbf{j} + \mathbf{C}_2$, $\mathbf{r}(0) = \mathbf{i} + \mathbf{C}_2 = \mathbf{j}$,
$\mathbf{C}_2 = -\mathbf{i} + \mathbf{j}$ so $\mathbf{r}(t) = (t + \cos t - 1)\mathbf{i} + (\sin t - t + 1)\mathbf{j}$

26. $\mathbf{v}(t) = t\mathbf{i} - e^{-t}\mathbf{j} + \mathbf{C}_1$, $\mathbf{v}(0) = -\mathbf{j} + \mathbf{C}_1 = 2\mathbf{i} + \mathbf{j}$; $\mathbf{C}_1 = 2\mathbf{i} + 2\mathbf{j}$ so
$\mathbf{v}(t) = (t + 2)\mathbf{i} + (2 - e^{-t})\mathbf{j}$; $\mathbf{r}(t) = (t^2/2 + 2t)\mathbf{i} + (2t + e^{-t})\mathbf{j} + \mathbf{C}_2$
$\mathbf{r}(0) = \mathbf{j} + \mathbf{C}_2 = \mathbf{i} - \mathbf{j}$, $\mathbf{C}_2 = \mathbf{i} - 2\mathbf{j}$ so $\mathbf{r}(t) = (t^2/2 + 2t + 1)\mathbf{i} + (2t + e^{-t} - 2)\mathbf{j}$

27. $\mathbf{v}(t) = \displaystyle\int (\mathbf{i} + t\mathbf{k})dt = t\mathbf{i} + \frac{1}{2}t^2\mathbf{k} + \mathbf{C}_1$, $\mathbf{v}(0) = \mathbf{C}_1 = 0$ so

$\mathbf{v}(t) = t\mathbf{i} + \frac{1}{2}t^2\mathbf{k}$; $\mathbf{r}(t) = \displaystyle\int \left(t\mathbf{i} + \frac{1}{2}t^2\mathbf{k}\right) dt = \frac{1}{2}t^2\mathbf{i} + \frac{1}{6}t^3\mathbf{k} + \mathbf{C}_2$,

$\mathbf{r}(0) = \mathbf{C}_2 = \mathbf{j}$ so $\mathbf{r}(t) = \frac{1}{2}t^2\mathbf{i} + \mathbf{j} + \frac{1}{6}t^3\mathbf{k}$.

28. $\mathbf{v}(t) = \displaystyle\int (\sin 2t\mathbf{j})dt = -\frac{1}{2}\cos 2t\mathbf{j} + \mathbf{C}_1$, $\mathbf{v}(0) = -\frac{1}{2}\mathbf{j} + \mathbf{C}_1 = \mathbf{i} - \mathbf{k}$ so

$\mathbf{C}_1 = \mathbf{i} + \frac{1}{2}\mathbf{j} - \mathbf{k}$, $\mathbf{v}(t) = \mathbf{i} + \left(\frac{1}{2} - \frac{1}{2}\cos 2t\right)\mathbf{j} - \mathbf{k}$; $\mathbf{r}(t) = t\mathbf{i} + \left(\frac{1}{2}t - \frac{1}{4}\sin 2t\right)\mathbf{j} - t\mathbf{k} + \mathbf{C}_2$,

$\mathbf{r}(0) = \mathbf{C}_2 = 0$ so $\mathbf{r}(t) = t\mathbf{i} + \left(\frac{1}{2}t - \frac{1}{4}\sin 2t\right)\mathbf{j} - t\mathbf{k}$.

29. $\mathbf{v}(t) = -\cos t\mathbf{i} + \sin t\mathbf{j} + e^t\mathbf{k} + \mathbf{C}_1$, $\mathbf{v}(0) = -\mathbf{i} + \mathbf{k} + \mathbf{C}_1 = \mathbf{k}$ so
$\mathbf{C}_1 = \mathbf{i}$, $\mathbf{v}(t) = (1 - \cos t)\mathbf{i} + \sin t\mathbf{j} + e^t\mathbf{k}$; $\mathbf{r}(t) = (t - \sin t)\mathbf{i} - \cos t\mathbf{j} + e^t\mathbf{k} + \mathbf{C}_2$,
$\mathbf{r}(0) = -\mathbf{j} + \mathbf{k} + \mathbf{C}_2 = -\mathbf{i} + \mathbf{k}$ so $\mathbf{C}_2 = -\mathbf{i} + \mathbf{j}$, $\mathbf{r}(t) = (t - \sin t - 1)\mathbf{i} + (1 - \cos t)\mathbf{j} + e^t\mathbf{k}$.

30. $\mathbf{v}(t) = -\dfrac{1}{t+1}\mathbf{j} + \dfrac{1}{2}e^{-2t}\mathbf{k} + \mathbf{C}_1$, $\mathbf{v}(0) = -\mathbf{j} + \frac{1}{2}\mathbf{k} + \mathbf{C}_1 = 3\mathbf{i} - \mathbf{j}$ so

$\mathbf{C}_1 = 3\mathbf{i} - \frac{1}{2}\mathbf{k}$, $\mathbf{v}(t) = 3\mathbf{i} - \dfrac{1}{t+1}\mathbf{j} + \left(\dfrac{1}{2}e^{-2t} - \dfrac{1}{2}\right)\mathbf{k}$;

$\mathbf{r}(t) = 3t\mathbf{i} - \ln(t+1)\mathbf{j} - \left(\dfrac{1}{4}e^{-2t} + \dfrac{1}{2}t\right)\mathbf{k} + \mathbf{C}_2$,

$\mathbf{r}(0) = -\dfrac{1}{4}\mathbf{k} + \mathbf{C}_2 = 2\mathbf{k}$ so $\mathbf{C}_2 = \dfrac{9}{4}\mathbf{k}$, $\mathbf{r}(t) = 3t\mathbf{i} - \ln(t+1)\mathbf{j} + \left(\dfrac{9}{4} - \dfrac{1}{4}e^{-2t} - \dfrac{1}{2}t\right)\mathbf{k}$.

31. $\mathbf{a} = \mathbf{r}''(t) = 0$, $\mathbf{r}'(t) = \langle b_1, b_2, b_3 \rangle$, $\mathbf{r}(t) = \langle b_1t + c_1, b_2t + c_2, b_3t + c_3 \rangle$ where $b_1, b_2, b_3, c_1, c_2,$ c_3 are constants so $x = b_1t + c_1$, $y = b_2t + c_2$, $z = b_3t + c_3$ which is a line.

32. $\displaystyle\int_{t_1}^{t_2} \mathbf{a}(t)dt = \mathbf{v}(t)\Big]_{t_1}^{t_2} = \mathbf{v}(t_2) - \mathbf{v}(t_1)$.

33. $\Delta\mathbf{r} = \mathbf{r}(3) - \mathbf{r}(1) = 8\mathbf{i} + 26/3\mathbf{j}$; $\mathbf{v} = 2t\mathbf{i} + t^2\mathbf{j}$, $L = \displaystyle\int_1^3 t\sqrt{4 + t^2}dt = (13\sqrt{13} - 5\sqrt{5})/3$.

34. $\Delta\mathbf{r} = \mathbf{r}(3\pi/2) - \mathbf{r}(0) = 3\mathbf{i} - 3\mathbf{j}$; $\mathbf{v} = 3\cos t\mathbf{i} - 3\sin t\mathbf{j}$, $L = \displaystyle\int_0^{3\pi/2} 3dt = 9\pi/2$.

35. $\Delta\mathbf{r} = \mathbf{r}(2\pi) - \mathbf{r}(0) = 0$; $\mathbf{v} = 6\cos 3t\mathbf{i} - 6\sin 3t\mathbf{j}$, $L = \displaystyle\int_0^{2\pi} 6dt = 12\pi$.

36. $\Delta r = r(3\pi/4) - r(0) = 3i + 3j + 6\pi k$; $v = 6\cos 2ti + 6\sin 2tj + 8k$, $L = \int_0^{3\pi/4} 10 dt = 15\pi/2$.

37. $\Delta r = r(\ln 3) - r(0) = 2i - 2/3j + \sqrt{2}\ln 3k$; $v = e^t i - e^{-t} j + \sqrt{2}k$, $L = \int_0^{\ln 3}(e^t + e^{-t})dt = 8/3$.

38. $\Delta r = r(\pi) - r(0) = 0$; $v = -2\sin 2ti + 2\sin 2tj - \sin 2tk$,

$\|v\| = 3|\sin 2t|$, $L = \int_0^{\pi} 3|\sin 2t|dt = 6\int_0^{\pi/2}\sin 2t\, dt = 6$.

39. $v = -2\sin ti + 2\cos tj$, $a = -2\cos ti - 2\sin tj$; when $t = \pi/3$, $v = -\sqrt{3}i + j$, $a = -i - \sqrt{3}j$, $\|v\| = 2$, $v \cdot a = 0$, $v \times a = 4k$ so $a_T = 0$, $a_N = 2$.

40. $v = i + 2tj$, $a = 2j$; when $t = 1$, $v = i + 2j$, $a = 2j$, $\|v\| = \sqrt{5}$, $v \cdot a = 4$, $v \times a = 2k$ so $a_T = 4/\sqrt{5}$, $a_N = 2/\sqrt{5}$.

41. $v = -e^{-t}i + e^t j$, $a = e^{-t}i + e^t j$; when $t = 0$, $v = -i + j$, $a = i + j$, $\|v\| = \sqrt{2}$, $v \cdot a = 0$, $v \times a = -2k$ so $a_T = 0$, $a_N = \sqrt{2}$.

42. $v = -2t\sin(t^2)i + 2t\cos(t^2)j$, $a = [-4t^2\cos(t^2) - 2\sin(t^2)]i + [-4t^2\sin(t^2) + 2\cos(t^2)]j$; when $t = \sqrt{\pi}/2$, $v = -\sqrt{\pi/2}i + \sqrt{\pi/2}j$, $a = (-\pi/\sqrt{2} - \sqrt{2})i + (-\pi/\sqrt{2} + \sqrt{2})j$, $\|v\| = \sqrt{\pi}$, $v \cdot a = 2\sqrt{\pi}$, $v \times a = \pi^{3/2}k$ so $a_T = 2$, $a_N = \pi$.

43. $v = (3t^2 - 2)i + 2tj$, $a = 6ti + 2j$; when $t = 1$, $v = i + 2j$, $a = 6i + 2j$, $\|v\| = \sqrt{5}$, $v \cdot a = 10$, $v \times a = -10k$ so $a_T = 2\sqrt{5}$, $a_N = 2\sqrt{5}$.

44. $v = e^t(-\sin t + \cos t)i + e^t(\cos t + \sin t)j$, $a = -2e^t\sin ti + 2e^t\cos tj$; when $t = \pi/4$, $v = \sqrt{2}e^{\pi/4}j$, $a = -\sqrt{2}e^{\pi/4}i + \sqrt{2}e^{\pi/4}j$, $\|v\| = \sqrt{2}e^{\pi/4}$, $v \cdot a = 2e^{\pi/2}$, $v \times a = 2e^{\pi/2}k$ so $a_T = \sqrt{2}e^{\pi/4}$, $a_N = \sqrt{2}e^{\pi/4}$.

45. $v = i + 2tj + 3t^2k$, $a = 2j + 6tk$; when $t = 1$, $v = i + 2j + 3k$, $a = 2j + 6k$, $\|v\| = \sqrt{14}$, $v \cdot a = 22$, $v \times a = 6i - 6j - 2k$ so $a_T = 22/\sqrt{14}$, $a_N = \sqrt{76}/\sqrt{14} = \sqrt{38/7}$.

46. $v = e^t i - 2e^{-2t}j + k$, $a = e^t i + 4e^{-2t}j$; when $t = 0$, $v = i - 2j + k$, $a = i + 4j$, $\|v\| = \sqrt{6}$, $v \cdot a = -7$, $v \times a = -4i + j + 6k$ so $a_T = -7/\sqrt{6}$, $a_N = \sqrt{53/6}$.

47. $v = 3\cos ti - 2\sin tj - 2\cos 2tk$, $a = -3\sin ti - 2\cos tj + 4\sin 2tk$; when $t = \pi/2$, $v = -2j + 2k$, $a = -3i$, $\|v\| = 2\sqrt{2}$, $v \cdot a = 0$, $v \times a = -6j - 6k$ so $a_T = 0$, $a_N = 3$.

48. $v = 3t^2 j - (16/t)k$, $a = 6tj + (16/t^2)k$; when $t = 1$, $v = 3j - 16k$, $a = 6j + 16k$, $\|v\| = \sqrt{265}$, $v \cdot a = -238$, $v \times a = 144i$ so $a_T = -238/\sqrt{265}$, $a_N = 144/\sqrt{265}$.

49. $\|v\| = 4$, $v \cdot a = -12$, $v \times a = 8k$ so $a_T = -3$, $a_N = 2$, $T = -j$, $N = (a - a_T T)/a_N = i$.

50. $\|\mathbf{v}\| = \sqrt{5}$, $\mathbf{v} \cdot \mathbf{a} = 3$, $\mathbf{v} \times \mathbf{a} = -6\mathbf{k}$ so $a_T = 3/\sqrt{5}$, $a_N = 6/\sqrt{5}$, $\mathbf{T} = (1/\sqrt{5})(\mathbf{i} + 2\mathbf{j})$, $\mathbf{N} = (\mathbf{a} - a_T\mathbf{T})/a_N = (1/\sqrt{5})(2\mathbf{i} - \mathbf{j})$.

51. $\|\mathbf{v}\| = 3$, $\mathbf{v} \cdot \mathbf{a} = 4$, $\mathbf{v} \times \mathbf{a} = 4\mathbf{i} - 3\mathbf{j} - 2\mathbf{k}$ so $a_T = 4/3$, $a_N = \sqrt{29}/3$, $\mathbf{T} = (1/3)(2\mathbf{i} + 2\mathbf{j} + \mathbf{k})$, $\mathbf{N} = (\mathbf{a} - a_T\mathbf{T})/a_N = (\mathbf{i} - 8\mathbf{j} + 14\mathbf{k})/(3\sqrt{29})$.

52. $\|\mathbf{v}\| = 5$, $\mathbf{v} \cdot \mathbf{a} = -5$, $\mathbf{v} \times \mathbf{a} = -4\mathbf{i} - 10\mathbf{j} - 3\mathbf{k}$ so $a_T = -1$, $a_N = \sqrt{5}$, $\mathbf{T} = (1/5)(3\mathbf{i} - 4\mathbf{k})$, $\mathbf{N} = (\mathbf{a} - a_T\mathbf{T})/a_N = (8\mathbf{i} - 5\mathbf{j} + 6\mathbf{k})/(5\sqrt{5})$.

53. $a_T = \dfrac{d^2s}{dt^2} = \dfrac{d}{dt}\sqrt{3t^2 + 4} = 3t/\sqrt{3t^2 + 4}$ so when $t = 2$, $a_T = 3/2$.

54. $a_T = \dfrac{d^2s}{dt^2} = \dfrac{d}{dt}\sqrt{t^2 + e^{-3t}} = (2t - 3e^{-3t})/[2\sqrt{t^2 + e^{-3t}}]$ so when $t = 0$, $a_T = -3/2$.

55. $a_T = \dfrac{d^2s}{dt^2} = \dfrac{d}{dt}\sqrt{(4t - 1)^2 + \cos^2 \pi t} = [4(t - 1) - \pi \cos \pi t \sin \pi t]/\sqrt{(4t - 1)^2 + \cos^2 \pi t}$ so when $t = 1/4$, $a_T = -\pi/\sqrt{2}$.

56. $a_T = \dfrac{d^2s}{dt^2} = \dfrac{d}{dt}\sqrt{t^4 + 5t^2 + 3} = (2t^3 + 5t)/\sqrt{t^4 + 5t^2 + 3}$ so when $t = 1$, $a_T = 7/3$

57. $\|\mathbf{v}\| = 4$, $\mathbf{v} \times \mathbf{a} = 8\mathbf{k}$ so $\kappa = \|\mathbf{v} \times \mathbf{a}\|/\|\mathbf{v}\|^3 = 1/8$.

58. $\|\mathbf{v}\| = \sqrt{5}$, $\mathbf{v} \times \mathbf{a} = -6\mathbf{k}$ so $\kappa = \|\mathbf{v} \times \mathbf{a}\|/\|\mathbf{v}\|^3 = 6/(5\sqrt{5})$.

59. $\|\mathbf{v}\| = 3$, $\mathbf{v} \times \mathbf{a} = 4\mathbf{i} - 3\mathbf{j} - 2\mathbf{k}$ so $\kappa = \|\mathbf{v} \times \mathbf{a}\|/\|\mathbf{v}\|^3 = \sqrt{29}/27$.

60. $\|\mathbf{v}\| = 5$, $\mathbf{v} \times \mathbf{a} = -4\mathbf{i} - 10\mathbf{j} - 3\mathbf{k}$ so $\kappa = \|\mathbf{v} \times \mathbf{a}\|/\|\mathbf{v}\|^3 = 1/(5\sqrt{5})$.

61. $a_N = \kappa(ds/dt)^2 = (1/\rho)(ds/dt)^2 = (1/1)(3 \times 10^5)^2 = 9 \times 10^{10}$ kilometers/sec^2

62. $\mathbf{a} = (d^2s/dt^2)\mathbf{T} + \kappa(ds/dt)^2\mathbf{N}$ where $\kappa = \dfrac{|d^2y/dx^2|}{[1 + (dy/dx)^2]^{3/2}}$. If $d^2y/dx^2 = 0$, then $\kappa = 0$ and $\mathbf{a} = (d^2s/dt^2)\mathbf{T}$ so $\mathbf{a}$ is tangent to the curve.

63. $a_N = \kappa(ds/dt)^2 = [2/(1 + 4x^2)^{3/2}](3)^2 = 18/(1 + 4x^2)^{3/2}$.

64. $a_N = \kappa(ds/dt)^2 = [e^x/(1 + e^{2x})^{3/2}](2)^2 = 4e^x/(1 + e^{2x})^{3/2}$.

65. **(a)** $v_0 = 320$, $\alpha = 60°$, $s_0 = 0$ so $x = 160t$, $y = 160\sqrt{3}t - 16t^2$.

　　(b) $dy/dt = 160\sqrt{3} - 32t$, $dy/dt = 0$ when $t = 5\sqrt{3}$ so
　　　　$y_{max} = 160\sqrt{3}(5\sqrt{3}) - 16(5\sqrt{3})^2 = 1200$ ft.

(c) $y = 16t(10\sqrt{3} - t)$, $y = 0$ when $t = 0$ or $10\sqrt{3}$ so $x_{max} = 160(10\sqrt{3}) = 1600\sqrt{3}$ ft.

(d) $v(t) = 160i + (160\sqrt{3} - 32t)j$, $v(10\sqrt{3}) = 160(i - \sqrt{3}j)$, $\|v(10\sqrt{3})\| = 320$ ft/sec.

66. (a) $v_0 = 980$, $\alpha = 45°$, $s_0 = 0$ so $x = 490\sqrt{2}t$, $y = 490\sqrt{2}t - 4.9t^2$

(b) $dy/dt = 490\sqrt{2} - 9.8t$, $dy/dt = 0$ when $t = 50\sqrt{2}$ so
$y_{max} = 490\sqrt{2}(50\sqrt{2}) - 4.9(50\sqrt{2})^2 = 24,500$ m.

(c) $y = 4.9t(100\sqrt{2} - t)$, $y = 0$ when $t = 0$ or $100\sqrt{2}$ so
$x_{max} = 490\sqrt{2}(100\sqrt{2}) = 98,000$ m.

(d) $v(t) = 490\sqrt{2}i + (490\sqrt{2} - 9.8t)j$, $v(100\sqrt{2}) = 490\sqrt{2}(i - j)$, $\|v(100\sqrt{2})\| = 980$ m/sec.

67. $v_0 = 80$, $\alpha = -60°$, $s_0 = 168$ so $x = 40t$, $y = 168 - 40\sqrt{3}t - 16t^2$; $y = 0$ when
$t = -7\sqrt{3}/2$ (invalid) or $t = \sqrt{3}$ so $x(\sqrt{3}) = 40\sqrt{3}$ ft.

68. $v_0 = 80$, $\alpha = 0°$, $s_0 = 168$ so $x = 80t$, $y = 168 - 16t^2$; $y = 0$ when $t = -\sqrt{42}/2$ (invalid) or
$t = \sqrt{42}/2$ so $x(\sqrt{42}/2) = 40\sqrt{42}$ ft.

69. $\alpha = 30°$, $s_0 = 0$ so $x = \sqrt{3}v_0t/2$, $y = v_0t/2 - 16t^2$; $dy/dt = v_0/2 - 32t$, $dy/dt = 0$ when
$t = v_0/64$ so $y_{max} = v_0^2/256 = 2500$, $v_0 = 800$ ft/sec.

70. $\alpha = 45°$, $s_0 = 0$ so $x = \sqrt{2}v_0t/2$, $y = \sqrt{2}v_0t/2 - 4.9t^2$; $y = 0$ when $t = 0$ or $\sqrt{2}v_0/9.8$ so
$x_{max} = v_0^2/9.8 = 24,500$, $v_0 = 490$ m/sec.

71. $v_0 = 800$, $s_0 = 0$ so $x = (800\cos\alpha)t$, $y = (800\sin\alpha)t - 16t^2 = 16t(50\sin\alpha - t)$; $y = 0$ when
$t = 0$ or $50\sin\alpha$ so $x_{max} = 40,000\sin\alpha\cos\alpha = 20,000\sin 2\alpha = 10,000$, $2\alpha = 30°$ or $150°$,
$\alpha = 15°$ or $75°$.

72. (a) $v_0 = 5$, $\alpha = 0°$, $s_0 = 4$ so $x = 5t$, $y = 4 - 16t^2$; $y = 0$ when $t = -1/2$ (invalid) or $1/2$ so
it takes the ball $1/2$ sec to hit the floor.

(b) $v(t) = 5i - 32tj$, $v(1/2) = 5i - 16j$, $\|v(1/2)\| = \sqrt{281}$ so the ball hits the floor with a
speed of $\sqrt{281}$ ft/sec.

(c) $v_0 = 0$, $\alpha = -90°$, $s_0 = 4$ so $x = 0$, $y = 4 - 16t^2$; $y = 0$ when $t = 1/2$ so both balls would
hit the ground at the same instant.

73. $s_0 = 0$ so $x = (v_0\cos\alpha)t$, $y = (v_0\sin\alpha)t - gt^2/2$

(a) $dy/dt = v_0\sin\alpha - gt$ so $dy/dt = 0$ when $t = (v_0\sin\alpha)/g$, $y_{max} = (v_0\sin\alpha)^2/(2g)$

(b) $y = 0$ when $t = 0$ or $(2v_0\sin\alpha)/g$, so $x = R = (2v_0^2\sin\alpha\cos\alpha)/g = (v_0^2\sin 2\alpha)/g$ when
$t = (2v_0\sin\alpha)/g$; R is maximum when $2\alpha = 90°$, $\alpha = 45°$, and the maximum value of R
is v_0^2/g.

74. The range is $(v_0^2 \sin 2\alpha)/g$ and the maximum range is v_0^2/g so $(v_0^2 \sin 2\alpha)/g = (3/4)v_0^2/g$,
$\sin 2\alpha = 3/4$, $\alpha = (1/2)\sin^{-1}(3/4) \approx 24.3°$ or $\alpha = (1/2)[180° - \sin^{-1}(3/4)] \approx 65.7°$.

75. $v_0 = 80$, $\alpha = 30°$, $s_0 = 5$ so $x = 40\sqrt{3}t$, $y = 5 + 40t - 16t^2$

    (a) $y = 0$ when $t = (-40 \pm \sqrt{(40)^2 - 4(-16)(5)})/(-32) = (5 \pm \sqrt{30})/4$, reject $(5 - \sqrt{30})/4$
    to get $t = (5 + \sqrt{30})/4 \approx 2.62$ sec.

    (b) $x \approx 40\sqrt{3}(2.62) \approx 181.5$ ft.

76. **(a)** $v_0 = v$, $s_0 = h$ so $x = (v \cos \alpha)t$, $y = h + (v \sin \alpha)t - \frac{1}{2}gt^2$. If $x = R$, then $(v \cos \alpha)t = R$,
    $t = \dfrac{R}{v \cos \alpha}$ but $y = 0$ for this value of t so $h + (v \sin \alpha)[R/(v \cos \alpha)] - \frac{1}{2}g[R/(v \cos \alpha)]^2 = 0$,
    $h + (\tan \alpha)R - g(\sec^2 \alpha)R^2/(2v^2) = 0$, $g(\sec^2 \alpha)R^2 - 2v^2(\tan \alpha)R - 2v^2h = 0$.

    (b) $2g \sec^2\alpha \tan \alpha R^2 + 2g \sec^2\alpha R\dfrac{dR}{d\alpha} - 2v^2 \sec^2\alpha R - 2v^2 \tan \alpha \dfrac{dR}{d\alpha} = 0$; if $\dfrac{dR}{d\alpha} = 0$ and $\alpha = \alpha_0$
    when $R = R_0$, then $2g \sec^2\alpha_0 \tan \alpha_0 R_0^2 - 2v^2 \sec^2\alpha_0 R_0 = 0$, $g \tan \alpha_0 R_0 - v^2 = 0$,
    $\tan \alpha_0 = v^2/(gR_0)$.

    (c) If $\alpha = \alpha_0$ and $R = R_0$, then from part (a)
    $g(\sec^2\alpha_0)R_0^2 - 2v^2(\tan \alpha_0)R_0 - 2v^2h = 0$, but from part (b) $\tan \alpha_0 = v^2/(gR_0)$ so
    $\sec^2\alpha_0 = 1 + \tan^2\alpha_0 = 1 + v^4/(gR_0)^2$ thus
    $g[1 + v^4/(gR_0)^2]R_0^2 - 2v^2[v^2/(gR_0)]R_0 - 2v^2h = 0$, $gR_0^2 - v^4/g - 2v^2h = 0$,
    $R_0^2 = v^2(v^2 + 2gh)/g^2$, $R_0 = (v/g)\sqrt{v^2 + 2gh}$ and
    $\tan \alpha_0 = v^2/(v\sqrt{v^2 + 2gh}) = v/\sqrt{v^2 + 2gh}$, $\alpha_0 = \tan^{-1}(v/\sqrt{v^2 + 2gh})$.

SUPPLEMENTARY EXERCISES CHAPTER 15

1. **(a)** $\mathbf{v} = \dfrac{1}{2}(t+4)^{-1/2}\mathbf{i} + 2\mathbf{j}$, $\mathbf{a} = -\dfrac{1}{4}(t+4)^{-3/2}\mathbf{i}$

    (b) $\mathbf{r}'(-3) = (1/2)\mathbf{i} + 2\mathbf{j}$, $\mathbf{r}''(-3) = -(1/4)\mathbf{i}$
    $\mathbf{r}'(0) = (1/4)\mathbf{i} + 2\mathbf{j}$, $\mathbf{r}''(0) = -(1/32)\mathbf{i}$

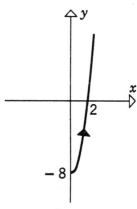

$y = 2x^2 - 8$, $x \geq 0$

2. (a) $\mathbf{v} = \langle \sinh t, -2 \cosh t \rangle$, $\mathbf{a} = \langle \cosh t, -2 \sinh t \rangle$

(b) $\mathbf{r}'(0) = \langle 0, -2 \rangle$

$\mathbf{r}''(0) = \langle 1, 0 \rangle$

$\mathbf{r}'(\ln 2) = \langle 3/4, -5/2 \rangle$

$\mathbf{r}''(\ln 2) = \langle 5/4, -3/2 \rangle$

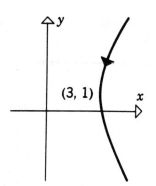

3. (a) $\mathbf{v} = \langle 6t^2, 3t^2 \rangle$, $\mathbf{a} = \langle 12t, 6t \rangle$

(b) $\mathbf{r}'(0) = \langle 0, 0 \rangle$, $\mathbf{r}''(0) = \langle 0, 0 \rangle$

$\mathbf{r}'(-1/2) = \langle 3/2, 3/4 \rangle$, $\mathbf{r}''(-1/2) = \langle -6, -3 \rangle$

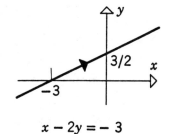

$x - 2y = -3$

4. (a) $\langle e + 2, 1 + e^2 \rangle$ (b) $(1/2)\mathbf{i} - (\pi/2)\mathbf{j}$

5. (a) $(k\mathbf{i} + m\mathbf{j})t + \mathbf{C}$

(b) $\langle e^{2t}/2, 2e^t \rangle \big]_0^{\ln 3} = \langle 9/2, 6 \rangle - \langle 1/2, 2 \rangle = \langle 4, 4 \rangle$

(c) $\displaystyle\int_0^2 dt = 2$ (d) $\sqrt{t^2 + 3}\,\mathbf{i} + \ln(\sin t)\mathbf{j} + \mathbf{C}$

6. (a) $ds/dt = \|\mathbf{r}'(t)\| = \|3e^t\mathbf{i} + e^t\mathbf{j}\| = \sqrt{10}\,e^t$

(b) $s = \displaystyle\int_0^t \sqrt{10}\,e^u\,du = \sqrt{10}(e^t - 1)$, $e^t = 1 + s/\sqrt{10}$, $x = 5 + 3s/\sqrt{10}$, $y = s/\sqrt{10}$

7. (a) $ds/dt = \|\mathbf{r}'(t)\| = \|\langle (t^2 - 1)/t^2, 2/t \rangle\| = 1 + 1/t^2$

(b) $s = \displaystyle\int_1^t (1 + 1/u^2)\,du = t - 1/t$, $t^2 - st - 1 = 0$, $t = (s \pm \sqrt{s^2 + 4})/2$, but $t \geq 0$

so $t = (s + \sqrt{s^2 + 4})/2$ and $x = \sqrt{s^2 + 4}$, $y = 2\ln[(s + \sqrt{s^2 + 4})/2]$.

8. (a) $ds/dt = \|\mathbf{r}'(t)\| = \|\langle 3t^2, 2t \rangle\| = t\sqrt{9t^2 + 4}$

(b) $s = \int_0^t u(9u^2 + 4)^{1/2}\,du = [(9t^2 + 4)^{3/2} - 8]/27,\ t = \frac{1}{3}[(27s + 8)^{2/3} - 4]^{1/2},$

$x = \frac{1}{27}[(27s + 8)^{2/3} - 4]^{3/2},\ y = \frac{1}{9}[(27s + 8)^{2/3} - 4]$

9.

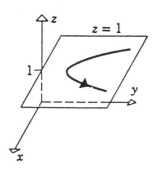

10.

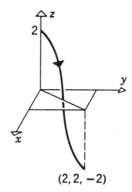

$(2, 2, -2)$

11. $\mathbf{r}(t) = a\sin t\mathbf{i} + a\cos t\mathbf{j} + a\ln(\cos t)\mathbf{k},\ \mathbf{v} = a\cos t\mathbf{i} - a\sin t\mathbf{j} - a\tan t\mathbf{k}$

$\|\mathbf{v}\| = a(\cos^2 t + \sin^2 t + \tan^2 t)^{1/2} = a(1 + \tan^2 t)^{1/2} = a\sec t$

$\mathbf{a} = -a\sin t\mathbf{i} - a\cos t\mathbf{j} - a\sec^2 t\mathbf{k},\ \mathbf{T} = \mathbf{v}/\|\mathbf{v}\| = \cos^2 t\mathbf{i} - \sin t\cos t\mathbf{j} - \sin t\mathbf{k}$

$d\mathbf{T}/dt = -2\sin t\cos t\mathbf{i} - (\cos^2 t - \sin^2 t)\mathbf{j} - \cos t\mathbf{k};\ \text{at } t = 0,\ \mathbf{v} = a\mathbf{i},\ \|\mathbf{v}\| = a,\ \mathbf{a} = -a(\mathbf{j} + \mathbf{k}),$

$\mathbf{T} = \mathbf{i},\ \mathbf{N} = (d\mathbf{T}/dt)/\|d\mathbf{T}/dt\| = (-\mathbf{j} - \mathbf{k})/\sqrt{2},\ \kappa = \|\mathbf{v} \times \mathbf{a}\|/\|\mathbf{v}\|^3 = \|a^2\mathbf{j} - a^2\mathbf{k}\|/a^3 = \sqrt{2}/a$

12. (a) $\mathbf{v} = 2\cos(2t)\mathbf{i} - 2\sin(2t)\mathbf{j} + 2e^t\mathbf{k},\ \|\mathbf{v}\| = 2(1 + e^{2t})^{1/2}$

$\mathbf{a} = -4\sin(2t)\mathbf{i} - 4\cos(2t)\mathbf{j} + 2e^t\mathbf{k}$

(b) When $t = 0,\ \mathbf{v} = 2\mathbf{i} + 2\mathbf{k},\ \mathbf{a} = -4\mathbf{j} + 2\mathbf{k},\ \|\mathbf{v}\| = 2\sqrt{2},\ \mathbf{v} \cdot \mathbf{a} = 4,\ \mathbf{v} \times \mathbf{a} = 8\mathbf{i} - 4\mathbf{j} - 8\mathbf{k}$ so

$a_T = (\mathbf{v} \cdot \mathbf{a})/\|\mathbf{v}\| = \sqrt{2},\ a_N = \|\mathbf{v} \times \mathbf{a}\|/\|\mathbf{v}\| = 12/(2\sqrt{2}) = 3\sqrt{2},$ and

$\kappa = \|\mathbf{v} \times \mathbf{a}\|/\|\mathbf{v}\|^3 = 3\sqrt{2}/8.$

13. $(dx/dt)^2 + (dy/dt)^2 + (dz/dt)^2 = 4 + 144\cos^2 3t + 144\sin^2 3t = 148,$

$L = \int_0^{2\pi} \sqrt{148}\,dt = 2\pi\sqrt{148} = 4\pi\sqrt{37}.$

14. $\mathbf{r}'(t) = \langle -e^{-t}, \sqrt{2}, e^t \rangle,\ \|\mathbf{r}'(t)\| = (e^{-2t} + 2 + e^{2t})^{1/2} = e^{-t} + e^t,\ L = \int_0^{\ln 2} (e^{-t} + e^t)\,dt = 3/2.$

15. $\mathbf{r}'(t) = \langle -e^{-t}, 2e^{2t}, 3t^2 \rangle,\ \mathbf{r}'(0) = \langle -1, 2, 0 \rangle$ is parallel to the tangent line to the curve at the tip of $\mathbf{r}(0) = \langle 1, 1, 1 \rangle$ so parametric equations of the tangent line are $x = 1 - t,\ y = 1 + 2t,\ z = 1.$

16. (a) $\mathbf{v} = 6\cos 2t\mathbf{i} + 6\sin 2t\mathbf{j} - 8\mathbf{k},\ \|\mathbf{v}\| = \sqrt{36\cos^2 2t + 36\sin^2 2t + 64} = \sqrt{100} = 10.$

(b) $\mathbf{a} = -12\sin 2t\mathbf{i} + 12\cos 2t\mathbf{j}$, $\mathbf{v} \cdot \mathbf{a} = 0$.

17. **(a)** $\displaystyle\int_0^3 \langle 2t, 3, -t^2\rangle dt = \langle t^2, 3t, -t^3/3\rangle\Big]_0^3 = \langle 9, 9, -9\rangle$

(b) $\mathbf{u} \times \mathbf{v} = \langle 3t + t^4, -2t^2, 2t^3\rangle$, $d(\mathbf{u} \times \mathbf{v})/dt = \langle 3 + 4t^3, -4t, 6t^2\rangle$.

18. $\mathbf{v} = \pi\langle -e^t\sin(\pi e^t), e^t\cos(\pi e^t), 1\rangle$,

$\mathbf{a} = \pi e^t\langle -\pi e^t\cos(\pi e^t) - \sin(\pi e^t), -\pi e^t\sin(\pi e^t) + \cos(\pi e^t), 0\rangle$; when $t = 0$, $\mathbf{v} = \pi\langle 0, -1, 1\rangle$,

$\mathbf{a} = \pi\langle \pi, -1, 0\rangle$, $\cos\theta = (\mathbf{v} \cdot \mathbf{a})/(\|\mathbf{v}\| \|\mathbf{a}\|) = 1/\sqrt{2\pi^2 + 2}$, $\theta = \cos^{-1}(1/\sqrt{2\pi^2 + 2}) \approx 78°$.

19. **(a)** $\mathbf{r}'(t) = 2t\mathbf{i} - (1/t^2)\mathbf{j}$, $t = 1$ at P_0 so $\mathbf{T} = \mathbf{r}'(1)/\|\mathbf{r}'(1)\| = (2\mathbf{i} - \mathbf{j})/\sqrt{5}$

(b) $\kappa(t) = \dfrac{6t^4}{(4t^6 + 1)^{3/2}}$ so $\kappa(1) = \dfrac{6}{5^{3/2}}$

20. **(a)** Let $x = t$, then $\mathbf{r}(t) = t\mathbf{i} + \ln t\mathbf{j}$, $\mathbf{r}'(t) = \mathbf{i} + (1/t)\mathbf{j}$,

$t = 1$ at P_0 so $\mathbf{T} = \mathbf{r}'(1)/\|\mathbf{r}'(1)\| = (\mathbf{i} + \mathbf{j})/\sqrt{2}$

(b) $\kappa(t) = \dfrac{t}{(t^2 + 1)^{3/2}}$, $\kappa(1) = \dfrac{1}{2^{3/2}}$

21. **(a)** Let $y = t$, then $\mathbf{r}(t) = (t - 1)^2\mathbf{i} + t\mathbf{j}$,

$\mathbf{r}'(t) = 2(t - 1)\mathbf{i} + \mathbf{j}$, $t = 1$ at P_0 so $\mathbf{T} = \mathbf{r}'(1)/\|\mathbf{r}'(1)\| = \mathbf{j}$

(b) $\kappa(t) = 2/[4(t - 1)^2 + 1]^{3/2}$, $\kappa(1) = 2$

22. Let $y = t$, then $x = 1/t^2$, $\kappa(t) = \dfrac{6|t|^5}{(4 + t^6)^{3/2}}$, $t = 1$ at P_0, $\kappa(1) = \dfrac{6}{5^{3/2}}$

23. $x = t + t^3$, $y = t + t^2$, $\kappa(t) = \dfrac{|2 - 6t - 6t^2|}{[(1 + 3t^2)^2 + (1 + 2t)^2]^{3/2}}$, $t = 1$ at P_0, $\kappa(1) = 2/25$

24. $\kappa(x) = \dfrac{\cosh(x/a)}{a[1 + \sinh^2(x/a)]^{3/2}} = \dfrac{1}{2}\operatorname{sech}^2(x/a)$, $\kappa(a) = \dfrac{1}{a}\operatorname{sech}^2 1$

25. Let $y = t$, then $x = \ln(\sec t)$, $\kappa(t) = |\cos t|$, $t = 0$ at P_0, $\kappa(0) = 1$

26. $\kappa(t) = \dfrac{2}{(e^{4t} + e^{-4t})^{3/2}}$, $\rho(t) = \dfrac{1}{2}(e^{4t} + e^{-4t})^{3/2} = \sqrt{2}(\cosh 4t)^{3/2}$, the smallest radius of curvature is $\rho(0) = \sqrt{2}$, it occurs at the point $(1, 1)$.

27. $\kappa(x) = \dfrac{2}{[1+4(x-1)^2]^{3/2}}$, $\kappa(1) = 2$, $\rho = 1/2$. The parabola opens upward and has its vertex at $(1,0)$ so the center of curvature is at $(1, 1/2)$ and the oscillating circle is $(x-1)^2 + (y-1/2)^2 = 1/4$. $y' = 0$ and $y'' = 2$ at $(1,0)$ for both the parabola and the circle.

28. $d\mathbf{r}/du = (d\mathbf{r}/dt)(dt/du) = \dfrac{1}{2}e^{u/2}\langle \cos t, -4\sin 2t\rangle = \langle (1/2)e^{u/2}\cos e^{u/2}, -2e^{u/2}\sin 2e^{u/2}\rangle$

29. $d\mathbf{r}/du = (d\mathbf{r}/dt)(dt/du) = (1/u)\langle e^t, 4e^{2t}\rangle = \langle 1, 4u\rangle$

30. $\mathbf{v} = \langle 2\sinh 2t, 2\cosh 2t\rangle$, $\mathbf{a} = \langle 4\cosh 2t, 4\sinh 2t\rangle$, $\|\mathbf{v}\| = 2\sqrt{\sinh^2 2t + \cosh^2 2t} = 2\sqrt{\cosh 4t}$, $\mathbf{v}\cdot\mathbf{a} = 16\sinh 2t\cosh 2t = 8\sinh 4t$, $\mathbf{v}\times\mathbf{a} = 8\mathbf{k}$ so $a_T = (4\sinh 4t)/\sqrt{\cosh 4t}$, $a_N = 4/\sqrt{\cosh 4t}$.

31. $\mathbf{v} = \langle t\sin t, t\cos t\rangle$, $\mathbf{a} = \langle \sin t + t\cos t, \cos t - t\sin t\rangle$, $\|\mathbf{v}\| = t$, $\mathbf{v}\cdot\mathbf{a} = t$, $\mathbf{v}\times\mathbf{a} = -t^2\mathbf{k}$ so $a_T = 1$, $a_N = t$.

32. **(a)** $\mathbf{v} = -2t\mathbf{i} + 2\mathbf{j}$, $\mathbf{a} = -2\mathbf{i}$; $t = 1$ at P_0 so $\mathbf{v} = -2\mathbf{i}+2\mathbf{j}$, $\mathbf{a} = -2\mathbf{i}$, $ds/dt = \|\mathbf{v}\| = 2\sqrt{2}$.

(b) $\mathbf{v}\times\mathbf{a} = 4\mathbf{k}$, $\kappa = \|\mathbf{v}\times\mathbf{a}\|/\|\mathbf{v}\|^3 = 1/(4\sqrt{2})$.

(c) $\mathbf{v}\cdot\mathbf{a} = 4$, $a_T = (\mathbf{v}\cdot\mathbf{a})/\|\mathbf{v}\| = \sqrt{2}$, $a_N = \|\mathbf{v}\times\mathbf{a}\|/\|\mathbf{v}\| = \sqrt{2}$.

(d) The trajectory is the parabola $x = 1 - y^2/4$, traced so that y increases with t.

(e) From part (b), the radius is $1/\kappa = 4\sqrt{2}$. If the center is (h, k), then $(x-h)^2 + (y-k)^2 = 32$ is an equation of the circle. The circle must be tangent to the curve at P_0 so $h^2 + (2-k)^2 = 32$ and, equating slopes, $h/(2-k) = -1$, $h = k - 2$ thus $h^2 + h^2 = 32$, $h^2 = 16$, $h = -4$ (because the center must be to the left of the vertex of the parabola), $k - 2 = -4$, $k = -2$. The center is at $(-4, -2)$.

33. **(a)** $\mathbf{v} = \langle -e^{-t}, e^t\rangle$, $\mathbf{a} = \langle e^{-t}, e^t\rangle$; $t = 0$ at P_0 so $\mathbf{v} = \langle -1, 1\rangle$, $\mathbf{a} = \langle 1, 1\rangle$, $ds/dt = \|\mathbf{v}\| = \sqrt{2}$

(b) $\mathbf{v}\times\mathbf{a} = -2\mathbf{k}$, $\kappa = \|\mathbf{v}\times\mathbf{a}\|/\|\mathbf{v}\|^3 = 1/\sqrt{2}$

(c) $\mathbf{v}\cdot\mathbf{a} = 0$, $a_T = (\mathbf{v}\cdot\mathbf{a})/\|\mathbf{v}\| = 0$, $a_N = \|\mathbf{v}\times\mathbf{a}\|/\|\mathbf{v}\| = \sqrt{2}$

(d) The trajectory is the branch of the hyperbola $y = 1/x$ in the first quadrant, traced so that y increases with t.

(e) The radius is $1/\kappa = \sqrt{2}$. If the center is (h, k), then $(x-h)^2 + (y-k)^2 = 2$ is an equation of the circle. The circle must be tangent to the curve at P_0 so $(1-h)^2 + (1-k)^2 = 2$ and, equating slopes, $-(1-h)/(1-k) = -1$, $1-h = 1-k$ thus $(1-h)^2 = 1$, $(1-h) = \pm 1$, $h = 0$ (reject, the center must be to the right of $x = 1$) or $h = 2$, $k = h = 2$. The center is at $(2, 2)$.

34. $\mathbf{r}(0) = (-2/m)\mathbf{i}$, $\mathbf{v}(0) = (2\mathbf{i} - 3\mathbf{j})/m$. Use $\mathbf{F} = m\mathbf{a}$ to get $\mathbf{a} = (2\cos t\mathbf{i} + 3\sin t\mathbf{j})/m$,
$\mathbf{v}(t) = \displaystyle\int \mathbf{a}\, dt = (2\sin t\mathbf{i} - 3\cos t\mathbf{j})/m + \mathbf{C}_1,$

$v(0) = (-3/m)j + C_1 = (2i - 3j)/m$, $C_1 = (2/m)i$ so $v(t) = [(2 + 2\sin t)i - 3\cos tj]/m$,

$r(t) = \displaystyle\int v\,dt = [(2t - 2\cos t)i - 3\sin tj]/m + C_2$,

$r(0) = (-2/m)i + C_2 = (-2/m)i$, $C_2 = 0$ so $r(t) = [2(t - \cos t)i - 3\sin tj]/m$

35. $r(0) = 0$, $v(0) = i + 2j$. Use $F = ma$ with $m = 1$ to get

$a = \sin ti + 4e^{2t}j$, $v(t) = \displaystyle\int a\,dt = -\cos ti + 2e^{2t}j + C_1$,

$v(0) = -i + 2j + C_1 = i + 2j$, $C_1 = 2i$ so, $v(t) = (2 - \cos t)i + 2e^{2t}j$,

$r(t) = \displaystyle\int v\,dt = (2t - \sin t)i + e^{2t}j + C_2$, $r(0) = j + C_2 = 0$ so $C_2 = -j$,

$r(t) = (2t - \sin t)i + (e^{2t} - 1)j$

36. $\kappa(y) = \dfrac{|d^2x/dy^2|}{[1 + (dx/dy)^2]^{3/2}} = \dfrac{1/50}{[1 + (y/50)^2]^{3/2}}$, $\kappa(0) = 1/50$, $a_N = \kappa(ds/dt)^2$ so

$ds/dt = (a_N/\kappa)^{1/2} \le [25/(1/50)]^{1/2} = 25\sqrt{2}$.

37. $dx/dt = 4$, by the chain rule $dy/dt = (2 - 2x)(dx/dt) = 8(1 - x)$,

$ds/dt = [(dx/dt)^2 + (dy/dt)^2]^{1/2} = 4[1 + 4(1 - x)^2]^{1/2}$,

$d^2s/dt^2 = 2[1 + 4(1 - x)^2]^{-1/2}[8(1 - x)](-dx/dt) = -64(1 - x)[1 + 4(1 - x)^2]^{-1/2}$

so $a_T = -64(1 - x)/\sqrt{1 + 4(1 - x)^2}$; $d^2x/dt^2 = 0$, $d^2y/dt^2 = -8dx/dt = -32$,

$\|a\|^2 = (d^2x/dt^2)^2 + (d^2y/dt^2)^2 = 0 + (-32)^2 = 1024$.

(a) $a_T = 0$, $a_N^2 = \|a\|^2 - a_T^2 = 1024$, $a_N = 32$

(b) $a_T = -64/\sqrt{5}$, $a_N^2 = 1024 - (64/\sqrt{5})^2 = 1024/5$, $a_N = 32/\sqrt{5}$

38. $a_T = d^2s/dt^2 = 0$, $a_N = \kappa(ds/dt)^2 = \dfrac{4}{(1 + 16x^2)^{3/2}}(10)^2 = 400/(1 + 16x^2)^{3/2}$

39. In one revolution the weight travels a distance that is equal to the circumference of a circle of radius 2 m so $ds/dt = 2\pi(2) = 4\pi$ m/sec, $a_T = d^2s/dt^2 = 0$,

$a_N = \kappa(ds/dt)^2 = (1/2)(4\pi)^2 = 8\pi^2$ m/sec^2.

40. (a) $r'(t) = \langle 2\cosh t, 2\sinh t \cosh t\rangle = 2\cosh t\langle 1, \sinh t\rangle$

$ds/dt = \|r'(t)\| = 2\cosh t(1 + \sinh^2 t)^{1/2} = 2\cosh^2 t$

(b) $L = \displaystyle\int_0^1 (ds/dt)dt = \int_0^1 2\cosh^2 t\,dt = \int_0^1 (\cosh 2t + 1)dt = 1 + \frac{1}{2}\sinh 2$

41. (a) $r'(t) = e^t\langle 2\cos 2t, -2\sin 2t\rangle + e^t\langle \sin 2t, \cos 2t\rangle = e^t\langle 2\cos 2t + \sin 2t, \cos 2t - 2\sin 2t\rangle$,

$ds/dt = \|r'(t)\| = e^t[(2\cos 2t + \sin 2t)^2 + (\cos 2t - 2\sin 2t)^2]^{1/2} = \sqrt{5}\,e^t$

(b) $L = \int_0^{\ln 3} (ds/dt)dt = \int_0^{\ln 3} \sqrt{5}\,e^t dt = 2\sqrt{5}.$

CHAPTER 16
Partial Derivatives

EXERCISE SET 16.1

1. (a) $f(2,1) = (2)^2(1) + 1 = 5$ (b) $f(1,2) = (1)^2(2) + 1 = 3$

     (c) $f(0,0) = (0)^2(0) + 1 = 1$ (d) $f(1,-3) = (1)^2(-3) + 1 = -2$

     (e) $f(3a,a) = (3a)^2(a) + 1 = 9a^3 + 1$

     (f) $f(ab, a-b) = (ab)^2(a-b) + 1 = a^3b^2 - a^2b^3 + 1$

2. (a) $2t$ (b) $2x$ (c) $2y^2 + 2y$

3. (a) $f(x+y, x-y) = (x+y)(x-y) + 3 = x^2 - y^2 + 3$

     (b) $f\left(xy, 3x^2y^3\right) = (xy)\left(3x^2y^3\right) + 3 = 3x^3y^4 + 3$

4. (a) $(x/y)\sin(x/y)$ (b) $xy\sin(xy)$ (c) $(x-y)\sin(x-y)$

5. $F(g(x), h(y)) = F\left(x^3, 3y+1\right) = x^3 e^{x^3(3y+1)}$

6. $g(u(x,y), v(x,y)) = g\left(x^2y^3, \pi xy\right) = \pi xy \sin\left[\left(x^2y^3\right)^2 (\pi xy)\right] = \pi xy \sin\left(\pi x^5 y^7\right)$

7. (a) $t^2 + 3t^{10}$ (b) 0 (c) 3076

8. $\sqrt{t}\, e^{-3\ln(t^2+1)} = \dfrac{\sqrt{t}}{\left(t^2 + 1\right)^3}$

9. (a) 19 (b) -9 (c) 3

     (d) $a^6 + 3$ (e) $-t^8 + 3$ (f) $(a+b)(a-b)^2 b^3 + 3$

10. (a) $x^2(x+y)(x-y) + (x+y) = x^2\left(x^2 - y^2\right) + (x+y) = x^4 - x^2 y^2 + x + y$

     (b) $(xz)(xy)(y/x) + xy = xy^2z + xy$

11. $F\left(x^2, y+1, z^2\right) = (y+1)e^{x^2(y+1)z^2}$ 12. $g\left(x^2z^3, \pi xyz, xy/z\right) = (xy/z)\sin\left(\pi x^3 yz^4\right)$

13. (a) t^{14} (b) 0 (c) $16,384$

14.

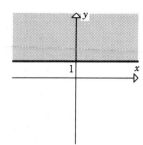

15.

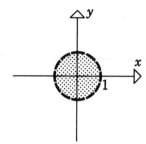

16.

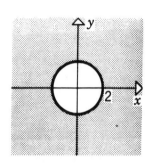

17.

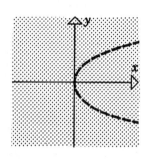

18.

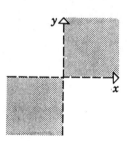

19.

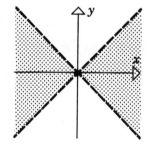

20. $-1 \leq x + y \leq 1$, $-1 - x \leq y \leq 1 - x$; all points on or between the parallel lines $y = 1 - x$, $y = -1 - x$.

21. all points above or on the line $y = -2$

22. all points on or between the vertical lines $x = \pm 2$.

23. all points above the line $y = 2x$

24. all points on or within the sphere $x^2 + y^2 + z^2 = 25$

25. all points not on the plane $x + y + z = 0$

26. all points in 3-space

27. all points inside the cylinder $x^2 + y^2 = 1$

28.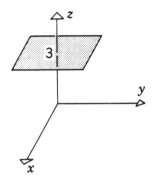

29.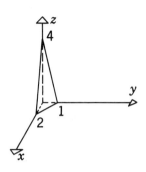

30.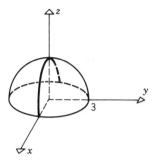

31.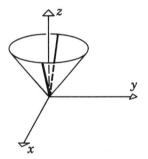

32.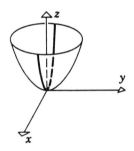

33.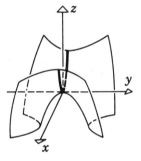

34.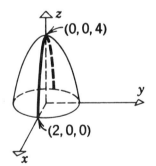

35.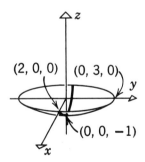

36.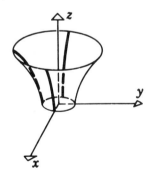

37.

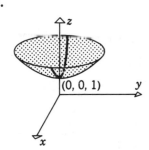

38.

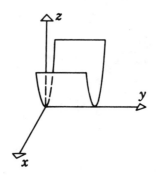

39.

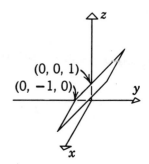

40.

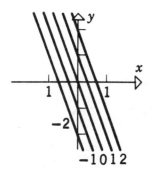

41.

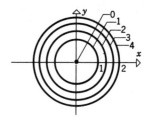

42.

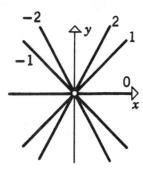

43.

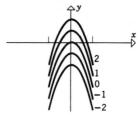

44.

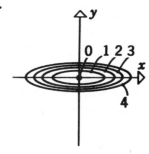

45.

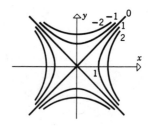

46.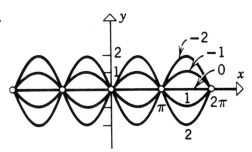

47.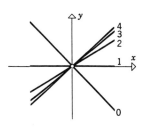

48.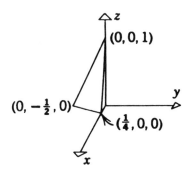

49.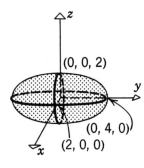

50.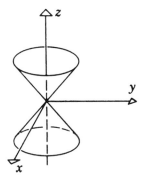

51.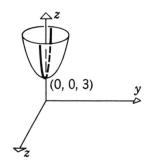

52. parallel planes, common normal $3\mathbf{i} - \mathbf{j} + 2\mathbf{k}$

53. concentric spheres, common center at $(2,0,0)$

54. Circular paraboloids, common axis the z-axis, all the same but with different vertices along z-axis.

55. concentric cylinders, common axis the y-axis

56. (a) $f(1,2) = 3$; $yx^2 + 1 = 3$, $yx^2 = 2$ (b) $f(-2,4) = 17$; $yx^2 + 1 = 17$, $yx^2 = 16$
    (c) $f(0,0) = 1$; $yx^2 + 1 = 1$, $yx^2 = 0$

57. (a) $f(-1,1) = 0$; $x^2 - 2x^3 + 3xy = 0$ (b) $f(0,0) = 0$; $x^2 - 2x^3 + 3xy = 0$
    (c) $f(2,-1) = -18$; $x^2 - 2x^3 + 3xy = -18$

58. (a) $f(\ln 2, 1) = 2$; $ye^x = 2$ (b) $f(0,3) = 3$; $ye^x = 3$
    (c) $f(1,-2) = -2e$; $ye^x = -2e$

59. (a) $f(1,-2,0) = 5$; $x^2 + y^2 - z = 5$ (b) $f(1,0,3) = -2$; $x^2 + y^2 - z = -2$
    (c) $f(0,0,0) = 0$; $x^2 + y^2 - z = 0$

60. (a) $f(1,0,2) = 3$; $xyz + 3 = 3$, $xyz = 0$ (b) $f(-2,4,1) = -5$;
    (c) $f(0,0,0) = 3$; $xyz = 0$ $xyz + 3 = -5$, $xyz = -8$

61. $V = 8/\sqrt{16 + x^2 + y^2}$
$\sqrt{16 + x^2 + y^2} = 8/V$
$x^2 + y^2 = 64/V^2 - 16$,
the equipotential curves are circles.

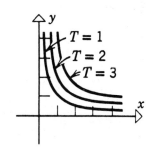

62. (a)

(b) At $(1,4)$ the temperature is
$T(1,4) = 4$ so the temperature
will remain constant along the
path $xy = 4$.

63. (a) A (b) B

64. (a) increase   (b) decrease   (c) decrease   (d) increase

65. (a) decrease   (b) increase   (c) increase   (d) decrease

66. (a) closed   (b) neither   (c) neither   (d) open

67. (a) open   (b) neither   (c) closed   (d) closed

68. (a) bounded   (b) unbounded   (c) unbounded   (d) unbounded

69. (a) bounded   (b) unbounded   (c) unbounded   (d) unbounded

EXERCISE SET 16.2

1.

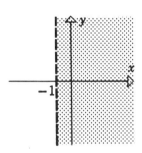

2.

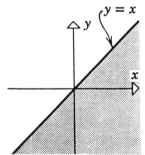

3.

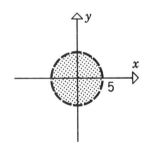

4.

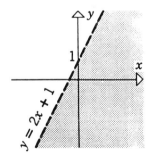

5.

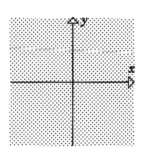

6.

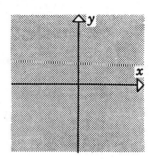

7.

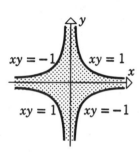

8.

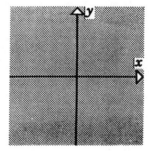

9.   all of 3-space

10.   all points inside the sphere with radius 2 and center at the origin

11.   all points not on the cylinder $x^2 + z^2 = 1$

12.   all of 3-space

13.   35   **14.** $\pi^2/2$ **15.** -8

16. e^{-7} **17.**   0   **18.**   0

19.   along $y = 0 : \lim\limits_{x \to 0} \dfrac{x}{x^2} = \lim\limits_{x \to 0} \dfrac{1}{x}$ does not exist because $\left| \dfrac{1}{x} \right| \to +\infty$ as $x \to 0$ so the original
limit does not exist.

20.   The limit does not exist because $\lim\limits_{(x,y) \to (0,0)} \dfrac{3}{x^2 + 2y^2} = +\infty$

21.   Let $z = x^2 + y^2$, then $\lim\limits_{(x,y) \to (0,0)} \dfrac{\sin\left(x^2 + y^2\right)}{x^2 + y^2} = \lim\limits_{z \to 0^+} \dfrac{\sin z}{z} = 1$

22. Let $z = x^2 + y^2$, then $\displaystyle\lim_{(x,y)\to(0,0)} \frac{1 - \cos\left(x^2 + y^2\right)}{x^2 + y^2} = \lim_{z\to 0+} \frac{1 - \cos z}{z} = \lim_{z\to 0+} \frac{\sin z}{1} = 0$

23. $\displaystyle\lim_{(x,y)\to(0,0)} \frac{\left(x^2 + y^2\right)\left(x^2 - y^2\right)}{x^2 + y^2} = \lim_{(x,y)\to(0,0)} \left(x^2 - y^2\right) = 0$

24. $\displaystyle\lim_{(x,y)\to(0,0)} \frac{\left(x^2 + 4y^2\right)\left(x^2 - 4y^2\right)}{x^2 + 4y^2} = \lim_{(x,y)\to(0,0)} \left(x^2 - 4y^2\right) = 0$

25. along $y = 0 : \displaystyle\lim_{x\to 0} \frac{0}{3x^2} = \lim_{x\to 0} 0 = 0$; along $y = x : \displaystyle\lim_{x\to 0} \frac{x^2}{5x^2} = \lim_{x\to 0} 1/5 = 1/5$
    so the limit does not exist.

26. Let $z = x^2 + y^2$, then $\displaystyle\lim_{(x,y)\to(0,0)} \frac{1 - x^2 - y^2}{x^2 + y^2} = \lim_{z\to 0+} \frac{1 - z^2}{z^2} = +\infty$ so the limit does not exist.

27. Let $z = x^2 + y^2$, then $\displaystyle\lim_{(x,y)\to(0,0)} e^{-1/\left(x^2 + y^2\right)} = \lim_{z\to 0+} e^{-1/z} = 0$

28. With $z = \dfrac{1}{\sqrt{x^2 + y^2}}$, $\displaystyle\lim_{z\to +\infty} ze^{-z} = \lim_{z\to +\infty} \frac{z}{e^z} = 0$

29. Use polar coordinates: $y = r\sin\theta$ and $x^2 + y^2 = r^2$ so
    $y\ln\left(x^2 + y^2\right) = r\sin\theta \ln r^2 = 2r\sin\theta \ln r$. But $|\sin\theta| \le 1$ so $|y\ln(x^2 + y^2)| \le |2r\ln r|$;
    $\displaystyle\lim_{r\to 0+} 2r\ln r = 0$ thus $\displaystyle\lim_{(x,y)\to(0,0)} y\ln\left(x^2 + y^2\right) = 0$

30. Using polar coordinates with $r > 0$, $x = r\cos\theta$ and $y = r\sin\theta$ so $|x| \le r$ and $|y| \le r$,
    $|x| + |y| \le 2r$, $|x\ln(|x| + |y|)| \le |r\ln 2r|$; $\displaystyle\lim_{r\to 0+} r\ln 2r = 0$ thus $\displaystyle\lim_{(x,y)\to(0,0)} x\ln(|x| + |y|) = 0$.

31. $8/3$ 32. $\ln 5$

33. Let $t = \sqrt{x^2 + y^2 + z^2}$, then $\displaystyle\lim_{(x,y)\to(0,0,0)} \frac{\sin\left(x^2 + y^2 + z^2\right)}{\sqrt{x^2 + y^2 + z^2}} = \lim_{t\to 0+} \frac{\sin\left(t^2\right)}{t} = 0$

34. With $t = \sqrt{x^2 + y^2 + z^2}$, $\displaystyle\lim_{t\to 0+} \frac{\sin t}{t^2} = \lim_{t\to 0+} \frac{\cos t}{2t} = +\infty$ so the limit does not exist.

35. along the z-axis: $\displaystyle\lim_{z\to 0} \left(0/z^2\right) = \lim_{z\to 0} 0 = 0$;

    along the line $x = t$, $y = t$, $z = t : \displaystyle\lim_{t\to 0} \frac{t^2}{3t^2} = \lim_{t\to 0} 1/3 = 1/3$ so the limit does not exist.

36. With $y = mx$, $\displaystyle\lim_{x \to 0} \frac{mx^2}{x^2 + m^2x^2} = \lim_{x \to 0} \frac{m}{1 + m^2} = \frac{m}{1 + m^2}$ which has a maximum value of 1/2 when $m = 1$, and a minimum value of $-1/2$ when $m = -1$.

37. **(a)** $\displaystyle\lim_{x \to 0} \frac{mx^3}{x^4 + m^2x^2} = \lim_{x \to 0} \frac{mx}{x^2 + m^2} = 0$ **(b)** $\displaystyle\lim_{x \to 0} \frac{x^4}{2x^4} = \lim_{x \to 0} 1/2 = 1/2$

38. **(a)** Along $y = mx$: $\displaystyle\lim_{x \to 0} \frac{mx^4}{2x^6 + m^2x^2} = \lim_{x \to 0} \frac{mx^2}{2x^4 + m^2} = 0$;

along $y = kx^2$: $\displaystyle\lim_{x \to 0} \frac{kx^5}{2x^6 + k^2x^4} = \lim_{x \to 0} \frac{kx}{2x^2 + k^2} = 0$.

(b) $\displaystyle\lim_{x \to 0} \frac{x^6}{2x^6 + x^6} = \lim_{x \to 0} \frac{1}{3} = \frac{1}{3} \neq 0$.

39. **(a)** $\displaystyle\lim_{t \to 0} \frac{abct^3}{a^2t^2 + b^4t^4 + c^4t^4} = \lim_{t \to 0} \frac{abct}{a^2 + b^4t^2 + c^4t^2} = 0$

(b) $\displaystyle\lim_{t \to 0} \frac{t^4}{t^4 + t^4 + t^4} = \lim_{t \to 0} 1/3 = 1/3$

40. $\pi/2$ because $\displaystyle\frac{x^2 + 1}{x^2 + (y-1)^2} \to +\infty$ as $(x, y) \to (0, 1)$.

41. $-\pi/2$ because $\displaystyle\frac{x^2 - 1}{x^2 + (y-1)^2} \to -\infty$ as $(x, y) \to (0, 1)$

42. with $z = x^2 + y^2$, $\displaystyle\lim_{z \to 0^+} \frac{\sin z}{z} = 1 = f(0, 0)$.

43. No, because $\displaystyle\lim_{(x,y) \to (0,0)} \frac{x^2}{x^2 + y^2}$ does not exist.

Along $x = 0$: $\displaystyle\lim_{y \to 0} (0/y^2) = \lim_{y \to 0} 0 = 0$; along $y = 0$: $\displaystyle\lim_{x \to 0} (x^2/x^2) = \lim_{x \to 0} 1 = 1$.

44. Using polar coordinates with $r > 0$, $xy = r^2 \sin\theta \cos\theta$ and $x^2 + y^2 = r^2$ so $|xy \ln(x^2 + y^2)| = |r^2 \sin\theta \cos\theta \ln r^2| \leq |2r^2 \ln r|$, but $\displaystyle\lim_{r \to 0^+} 2r^2 \ln r = 0$ thus $\displaystyle\lim_{(x,y) \to (0,0)} xy \ln(x^2 + y^2) = 0$; $f(x, y)$ will be continuous at $(0,0)$ if we define $f(0, 0) = 0$.

45. $x^2 + y^2 = r^2$, $|x^2 + y^2 - 0| = |r^2| = r^2 < \epsilon$ if $r < \sqrt{\epsilon}$; choose $\delta = \sqrt{\epsilon}$.

46. $x^2 + y^2 = r^2$ so $x^2 \le r^2$ and $y^2 \le r^2$, $\left| \dfrac{x^2 y^2}{\sqrt{x^2 + y^2}} - 0 \right| = \dfrac{x^2 y^2}{\sqrt{x^2 + y^2}} \le \dfrac{r^4}{r} = r^3 < \epsilon$ if $r < \epsilon^{1/3}$;

choose $\delta = \epsilon^{1/3}$.

47. $x^2 + y^2 + z^2 = \rho^2$, $|x^2 + y^2 + z^2 - 0| = |\rho^2| = \rho^2 < \epsilon$ if $\rho < \sqrt{\epsilon}$; choose $\delta = \sqrt{\epsilon}$.

48. $|e\sqrt{x^2 + y^2 + z^2} - 1| = |e^\rho - 1| = e^\rho - 1 < \epsilon$ if $e^\rho < 1 + \epsilon$, $\rho < \ln(1 + \epsilon)$; choose $\delta = \ln(1 + \epsilon)$.

EXERCISE SET 16.3

1. $\partial z / \partial x = 9x^2 y^2$, $\partial z / \partial y = 6x^3 y$

2. $\partial z / \partial x = 8x + 28x^3 y^5$, $\partial z / \partial y = -2 + 35x^4 y^4$

3. $\partial z / \partial x = 8xy^3 e^{x^2 y^3}$, $\partial z / \partial y = 12x^2 y^2 e^{x^2 y^3}$

4. $\partial z / \partial x = -5x^4 y^4 \sin(x^5 y^4)$, $\partial z / \partial y = -4x^5 y^3 \sin\left(x^5 y^4\right)$

5. $\partial z / \partial x = x^3 / (y^{3/5} + x) + 3x^2 \ln(1 + xy^{-3/5})$, $\partial z / \partial y = -(3/5)x^4 / (y^{8/5} + xy)$

6. $\partial z / \partial x = ye^{xy} \sin(4y^2)$, $\partial z / \partial y = 8ye^{xy} \cos(4y^2) + xe^{xy} \sin(4y^2)$

7. $f_x(x, y) = (3/2)x^2 y \left(5x^2 - 7\right) \left(3x^5 y - 7x^3 y\right)^{-1/2}$

$f_y(x, y) = (1/2)x^3 \left(3x^2 - 7\right) \left(3x^5 y - 7x^3 y\right)^{-1/2}$

8. $f_x(x, y) = -2y/(x - y)^2$, $f_y(x, y) = 2x/(x - y)^2$

9. $f_x(x, y) = \dfrac{y^{-1/2}}{y^2 + x^2}$, $f_y(x, y) = -\dfrac{xy^{-3/2}}{y^2 + x^2} - \dfrac{3}{2}y^{-5/2} \tan^{-1}(x/y)$

10. $f_x(x, y) = 3x^2 e^{-y} + (1/2)x^{-1/2} y^3 \sec \sqrt{x} \tan \sqrt{x}$, $f_y(x, y) = -x^3 e^{-y} + 3y^2 \sec \sqrt{x}$

11. $f_x(x, y) = -(4/3)y^2 \sec^2 x \left(y^2 \tan x\right)^{-7/3}$, $f_y(x, y) = -(8/3)y \tan x \left(y^2 \tan x\right)^{-7/3}$

12. $f_x(x, y) = 2y^2 \cosh \sqrt{x} \sinh \left(xy^2\right) \cosh \left(xy^2\right) + \dfrac{1}{2}x^{-1/2} \sinh \sqrt{x} \sinh^2 \left(xy^2\right)$

$f_y(x, y) = 4xy \cosh \sqrt{x} \sinh \left(xy^2\right) \cosh \left(xy^2\right)$

13. (a) $f_x(x, y) = -2x$, $f_x(3, 1) = -6$ (b) $f_y(x, y) = -21y^2$, $f_y(3, 1) = -21$

14. **(a)** $\partial f/\partial x = x^2 y^2 e^{xy} + 2xye^{xy}$, $\partial f/\partial x\,|_{(1,1)} = 3e$

     (b) $\partial f/\partial y = x^3 y e^{xy} + x^2 e^{xy}$, $\partial f/\partial y\,|_{(1,1)} = 2e$

15. **(a)** $\partial z/\partial x = x(x^2 + 4y^2)^{-1/2}$, $\partial z/\partial x\,|_{(1,2)} = 1/\sqrt{17}$

     (b) $\partial z/\partial y = 4y(x^2 + 4y^2)^{-1/2}$, $\partial z/\partial y\,|_{(1,2)} = 8/\sqrt{17}$

16. **(a)** $\partial w/\partial x = -x^2 y \sin xy + 2x \cos xy$, $\dfrac{\partial w}{\partial x}(1/2, \pi) = -\pi/4$

     (b) $\partial w/\partial y = -x^3 \sin xy$, $\dfrac{\partial w}{\partial y}(1/2, \pi) = -1/8$

17. $\dfrac{3}{2}(x^2 + y^2 + z^2)^{1/2}\left(2x + 2z\dfrac{\partial z}{\partial x}\right) = 0$, $\partial z/\partial x = -x/z$; similarly, $\partial z/\partial y = -y/z$

18. $\dfrac{4x - 3z^2(\partial z/\partial x)}{2x^2 + y - z^3} = 1$, $\dfrac{\partial z}{\partial x} = \dfrac{4x - 2x^2 - y + z^3}{3z^2}$; $\dfrac{1 - 3z^2(\partial z/\partial y)}{2x^2 + y - z^3} = 1$, $\dfrac{\partial z}{\partial y} = \dfrac{1 - 2x^2 - y + z^3}{3z^2}$

19. $2x + z\left(xy\dfrac{\partial z}{\partial x} + yz\right)\cos xyz + \dfrac{\partial z}{\partial x}\sin xyz = 0$, $\dfrac{\partial z}{\partial x} = -\dfrac{2x + yz^2 \cos xyz}{xyz \cos xyz + \sin xyz}$;

     $z\left(xy\dfrac{\partial z}{\partial y} + xz\right)\cos xyz + \dfrac{\partial z}{\partial y}\sin xyz = 0$, $\dfrac{\partial z}{\partial y} = -\dfrac{xz^2 \cos xyz}{xyz \cos xyz + \sin xyz}$

20. $e^{xy}(\cosh z)\dfrac{\partial z}{\partial x} + ye^{xy}\sinh z - z^2 - 2xz\dfrac{\partial z}{\partial x} = 0$, $\dfrac{\partial z}{\partial x} = \dfrac{z^2 - ye^{xy}\sinh z}{e^{xy}\cosh z - 2xz}$;

     $e^{xy}(\cosh z)\dfrac{\partial z}{\partial y} + xe^{xy}\sinh z - 2xz\dfrac{\partial z}{\partial y} = 0$, $\dfrac{\partial z}{\partial y} = -\dfrac{xe^{xy}\sinh z}{e^{xy}\cosh z - 2xz}$

21. $f_{xx} = 8$, $f_{yy} = -96xy^2 + 140y^3$, $f_{xy} = f_{yx} = -32y^3$

22. $f_{xx} = y^2(x^2 + y^2)^{-3/2}$, $f_{yy} = x^2(x^2 + y^2)^{-3/2}$, $f_{xy} = f_{yx} = -xy(x^2 + y^2)^{-3/2}$

23. $f_{xx} = e^x \cos y$, $f_{yy} = -e^x \cos y$, $f_{xy} = f_{yx} = -e^x \sin y$

24. $f_{xx} = e^{x-y^2}$, $f_{yy} = 2(2y^2 - 1)e^{x-y^2}$, $f_{xy} = f_{yx} = -2ye^{x-y^2}$

25. $f_{xx} = -16/(4x - 5y)^2$, $f_{yy} = -25/(4x - 5y)^2$, $f_{xy} = f_{yx} = 20/(4x - 5y)^2$

26. $f_{xx} = 4y^2(y^2 - 3x^2)/(x^2 + y^2)^3$, $f_{yy} = -4x^2(x^2 - 3y^2)/(x^2 + y^2)^3$,

     $f_{xy} = f_{yx} = 8xy(x^2 - y^2)/(x^2 + y^2)^3$

27. **(a)** $30xy^4 - 4$ **(b)** $60x^2 y^3$ **(c)** $60x^3 y^2$

28. (a) $120(2x - y)^2$ (b) $-240(2x - y)^2$ (c) $480(2x - y)$

29. (a) $f_{xyy} = -30ye^{-5x}$, $f_{xyy}(0,1) = -30$ (b) $f_{xxx} = -125y^3 e^{-5x}$, $f_{xxx}(0,1) = -125$
    (c) $f_{yyxx} = 150ye^{-5x}$, $f_{yyxx}(0,1) = 150$

30. (a) $\dfrac{\partial^3 w}{\partial y^2 \partial x} = -e^y \sin x$, $\dfrac{\partial^3 w}{\partial y^2 \partial x}\bigg|_{(\pi/4, 0)} = -1/\sqrt{2}$

    (b) $\dfrac{\partial^3 w}{\partial x^2 \partial y} = -e^y \cos x$, $\dfrac{\partial^3 w}{\partial x^2 \partial y}\bigg|_{(\pi/4, 0)} = -1/\sqrt{2}$

31. (a) $\dfrac{\partial^3 f}{\partial x^3}$ (b) $\dfrac{\partial^3 f}{\partial y^2 \partial x}$ (c) $\dfrac{\partial^4 f}{\partial x^2 \partial y^2}$ (d) $\dfrac{\partial^4 f}{\partial y^3 \partial x}$

32. (a) f_{xyy} (b) f_{xxxx} (c) f_{xxyy} (d) f_{yyyxx}

33. $\partial w/\partial x = 2xy^4 z^3 + y$, $\partial w/\partial y = 4x^2 y^3 z^3 + x$, $\partial w/\partial z = 3x^2 y^4 z^2 + 2z$

34. $\partial w/\partial x = ye^z \cos x$, $\partial w/\partial y = e^z \sin x$, $\partial w/\partial z = ye^z \sin x$

35. $\partial w/\partial x = 2x/\left(y^2 + z^2\right)$, $\partial w/\partial y = -2y\left(x^2 + z^2\right)/\left(y^2 + z^2\right)^2$, $\partial w/\partial z = 2z\left(y^2 - x^2\right)/\left(y^2 + z^2\right)^2$

36. $\partial w/\partial x = 2y^3 e^{2x+3z}$, $\partial w/\partial y = 3y^2 e^{2x+3z}$, $\partial w/\partial z = 3y^3 e^{2x+3z}$

37. $\partial w/\partial x = x/\sqrt{x^2 + y^2 + z^2}$, $\partial w/\partial y = y/\sqrt{x^2 + y^2 + z^2}$, $\partial w/\partial z = z/\sqrt{x^2 + y^2 + z^2}$

38. $f_x = 2z/x$, $f_y = z/y$, $f_z = \ln(x^2 y \cos z) - z \tan z$

39. $f_x = -y^2 z^3 / \left(1 + x^2 y^4 z^6\right)$, $f_y = -2xyz^3 / \left(1 + x^2 y^4 z^6\right)$, $f_z = -3xy^2 z^2 / \left(1 + x^2 y^4 z^6\right)$

40. $f_x = y^{-5/2} z \sec(xz/y) \tan(xz/y)$, $f_y = -xy^{-7/2} z \sec(xz/y) \tan(xz/y) - (3/2)y^{-5/2} \sec(xz/y)$,
    $f_z = xy^{-5/2} \sec(xz/y) \tan(xz/y)$

41. $f_x = 4xyz \cos h\sqrt{z} \sin h\left(x^2 yz\right) \cos h\left(x^2 yz\right)$, $f_y = 2x^2 z \cos h\sqrt{z} \sin h\left(x^2 yz\right) \cos h\left(x^2 yz\right)$,
    $f_z = 2x^2 y \cos h\sqrt{z} \sin h\left(x^2 yz\right) \cos h\left(x^2 yz\right) + (1/2)z^{-1/2} \sin h\sqrt{z} \sin h^2\left(x^2 yz\right)$

42. $f_x = -\dfrac{3}{4}\left(\dfrac{xz}{1 - z^2 - y^2}\right)^{-7/4} \dfrac{z}{1 - z^2 - y^2}$, $f_y = -\dfrac{3}{2}\left(\dfrac{xz}{1 - z^2 - y^2}\right)^{-7/4} \dfrac{xyz}{\left(1 - z^2 - y^2\right)^2}$,

    $f_z = -\dfrac{3}{4}\left(\dfrac{xz}{1 - z^2 - y^2}\right)^{-7/4} \dfrac{x\left(1 + z^2 - y^2\right)}{\left(1 - z^2 - y^2\right)^2}$

43. **(a)** -80 **(b)** 40 **(c)** -60

44. **(a)** e **(b)** $2e$ **(c)** e

45. **(a)** $2/\sqrt{7}$ **(b)** $4/\sqrt{7}$ **(c)** $1/\sqrt{7}$

46. **(a)** 1 **(b)** 0 **(c)** 0

47. $(3/2)\left(x^2 + y^2 + z^2 + w^2\right)^{1/2}\left(2x + 2w\dfrac{\partial w}{\partial x}\right) = 0$, $\partial w/\partial x = -x/w$; similarly, $\partial w/\partial y = -y/w$ and $\partial w/\partial z = -z/w$

48. $\partial w/\partial x = -4x/3$, $\partial w/\partial y = -1/3$, $\partial w/\partial z = (2x^2 + y - z^3 + 3z^2 + 3w)/3$

49. $\dfrac{\partial w}{\partial x} = -\dfrac{yzw\cos xyz}{2w + \sin xyz}$, $\dfrac{\partial w}{\partial y} = -\dfrac{xzw\cos xyz}{2w + \sin xyz}$, $\dfrac{\partial w}{\partial z} = -\dfrac{xyw\cos xyz}{2w + \sin xyz}$

50. $\dfrac{\partial w}{\partial x} = \dfrac{ye^{xy}\sinh w}{z^2 - e^{xy}\cosh w}$, $\dfrac{\partial w}{\partial y} = \dfrac{xe^{xy}\sinh w}{z^2 - e^{xy}\cosh w}$, $\dfrac{\partial w}{\partial z} = \dfrac{2zw}{e^{xy}\cosh w - z^2}$

51. **(a)** $f_{xy} = 15x^2y^4z^7 + 2y$ **(b)** $f_{yz} = 35x^3y^4z^6 + 3y^2$
(c) $f_{xz} = 21x^2y^5z^6$ **(d)** $f_{zz} = 42x^3y^5z^5$
(e) $f_{zyy} = 140x^3y^3z^6 + 6y$ **(f)** $f_{xxy} = 30xy^4z^7$
(g) $f_{zyx} = 105x^2y^4z^6$ **(h)** $f_{xxyz} = 210xy^4z^6$

52. **(a)** $160(4x - 3y + 2z)^3$ **(b)** $-1440(4x - 3y + 2z)^2$
(c) $-5760(4x - 3y + 2z)$

53. **(a)** $\partial^2 f/\partial x^2 = e^x\sin y - e^y\cos x = -\partial^2 f/\partial y^2$
(b) $\partial^2 f/\partial x^2 = 2(y^2 - x^2)/(x^2 + y^2)^2 = -\partial^2 f/\partial y^2$
(c) $\partial^2 f/\partial x^2 = 4xy/(x^2 + y^2)^2 = -\partial^2 f/\partial y^2$

54. **(a)** $\partial u/\partial x = \partial v/\partial y = 2x$, $\partial u/\partial y = -\partial v/\partial x = -2y$
(b) $\partial u/\partial x = \partial v/\partial y = e^x\cos y$, $\partial u/\partial y = -\partial v/\partial x = -e^x\sin y$
(c) $\partial u/\partial x = \partial v/\partial y = 2x/(x^2 + y^2)$, $\partial u/\partial y = -\partial v/\partial x = 2y/(x^2 + y^2)$

55. $\partial z/\partial y = 6y$, $\partial z/\partial y\big|_{(2,1)} = 6$

56. $\partial z/\partial x = -x\left(29 - x^2 - y^2\right)^{-1/2}$, $\partial z/\partial x\big|_{(4,3)} = -2$

57. (a) $\partial z/\partial y = 8y$, $\partial z/\partial y\,|_{(-1,1)} = 8$ (b) $\partial z/\partial x = 2x$, $\partial z/\partial x\,|_{(-1,1)} = -2$

58. Use implicit differentiation to get
(a) $\partial z/\partial y = -y/z$, $\partial z/\partial y = -1/2$ at $(2,1,2)$ (b) $\partial z/\partial x = -x/z$, $\partial z/\partial x = -1$ at $(2,1,2)$

59. (a) $\partial V/\partial r = 2\pi rh$ (b) $\partial V/\partial h = \pi r^2$
(c) $\partial V/\partial r\,|_{r=6,\,h=4} = 48\pi$ (d) $\partial V/\partial h\,|_{r=8,\,h=10} = 64\pi$

60. (a) $\partial V/\partial s = \dfrac{\pi sd^2}{6\sqrt{4s^2 - d^2}}$ (b) $\partial V/\partial d = \dfrac{\pi d(8s^2 - 3d^2)}{24\sqrt{4s^2 - d^2}}$
(c) $\partial V/\partial s\,|_{s=10,\,d=16} = 320\pi/9$ (d) $\partial V/\partial d\,|_{s=10,\,d=16} = 16\pi/9$

61. (a) $P = 10T/V$, $\partial P/\partial T = 10/V$, $\partial P/\partial T\,|_{T=80,\,V=50} = 1/5$
(b) $V = 10T/P$, $\partial V/\partial P = -10T/P^2$, if $V = 50$ and $T = 80$ then
$P = 10(80)/(50) = 16$, $\partial V/\partial P\,|_{T=80,\,P=16} = -25/8$

62. (a) $\partial z/\partial y = x^2$, $\partial z/\partial y\,|_{(1,3)} = 1$, $\mathbf{j} + \mathbf{k}$ is parallel to the tangent line so $x = 1$, $y = 3 + t$,
$z = 3 + t$
(b) $\partial z/\partial x = 2xy$, $\partial z/\partial x\,|_{(1,3)} = 6$, $\mathbf{i} + 6\mathbf{k}$ is parallel to the tangent line so $x = 1 + t$, $y = 3$,
$z = 3 + 6t$

63. $\left(1 + \dfrac{\partial z}{\partial x}\right)\cos(x + z) + \cos(x - y) = 0,\ \dfrac{\partial z}{\partial x} = -1 - \dfrac{\cos(x - y)}{\cos(x + z)};\ \dfrac{\partial z}{\partial y}\cos(x + z) - \cos(x - y) = 0,$
$\dfrac{\partial z}{\partial y} = \dfrac{\cos(x - y)}{\cos(x + z)};\ \dfrac{\partial^2 z}{\partial x \partial y} = \dfrac{-\cos(x + z)\sin(x - y) + \cos(x - y)\sin(x + z)(\partial z/\partial x)}{\cos^2(x + z)},$
substitute for $\partial z/\partial x$ and simplify to get
$\dfrac{\partial^2 z}{\partial x \partial y} = -\dfrac{\cos^2(x + z)\sin(x - y) + \cos^2(x - y)\sin(x + z) + \cos(x - y)\cos(x + z)\sin(x + z)}{\cos^3(x + z)}$

64. $\partial V/\partial r = \dfrac{2}{3}\pi rh = \dfrac{2}{r}\left(\dfrac{1}{3}\pi r^2 h\right) = 2V/r$

65. (a) $\partial T/\partial x = 3x^2 + 1$, $\partial T/\partial x\,|_{(1,2)} = 4$ (b) $\partial T/\partial y = 4y$, $\partial T/\partial y\,|_{(1,2)} = 8$

66. $\partial^2 R/\partial R_1^2 = -2R_2^2/(R_1 + R_2)^3$, $\partial^2 R/\partial R_2^2 = -2R_1^2/(R_1 + R_2)^3$,
$\left(\partial^2 R/\partial R_1^2\right)\left(\partial^2 R/\partial R_2^2\right) = 4R_1^2 R_2^2/(R_1 + R_2)^6$
$= \left[4/(R_1 + R_2)^4\right][R_1 R_2/(R_1 + R_2)]^2 = 4R^2/(R_1 + R_2)^4$

67. $\partial u/\partial x = \partial v/\partial y$ and $\partial u/\partial y = -\partial v/\partial x$ so $\partial^2 u/\partial x^2 = \partial^2 v/\partial x \partial y$, and $\partial^2 u/\partial y^2 = -\partial^2 v/\partial y \partial x$, $\partial^2 u/\partial x^2 + \partial^2 u/\partial y^2 = \partial^2 v/\partial x \partial y - \partial^2 v/\partial y \partial x$, if $\partial^2 v/\partial x \partial y = \partial^2 v/\partial y \partial x$ then

$\partial^2 u/\partial x^2 + \partial^2 u/\partial y^2 = 0$ thus u satisfies Laplace's equation. The proof that v satisfies Laplace's equation is similar.

68. $f_x(x,y) = \lim\limits_{h\to 0} \dfrac{f(x+h,y)-f(x,y)}{h}$, $f_y(x,y) = \lim\limits_{h\to 0} \dfrac{f(x,y+h)-f(x,y)}{h}$

69. **(a)** Both are positive; $\partial T/\partial x$ has the largest absolute value.

  (b) All are negative.

70. **(a)** $\dfrac{\partial T}{\partial x} > 0$, $\dfrac{\partial T}{\partial y} < 0$; $\dfrac{\partial T}{\partial x}$ has the largest absolute value.

  (b) $\dfrac{\partial^2 T}{\partial x^2} > 0$, $\dfrac{\partial^2 T}{\partial y^2} > 0$, both $\dfrac{\partial^2 T}{\partial y \partial x}$ and $\dfrac{\partial^2 T}{\partial x \partial y}$ are negative.

71. $f_x(x,y) = \dfrac{2}{3}(x^2+y^2)^{-1/3}(2x) = \dfrac{4x}{(x^2+y^2)^{1/3}}$, $(x,y) \neq (0,0)$;

$f_x(0,0) = \dfrac{d}{dx}[f(x,0)]\Big|_{x=0} = \dfrac{d}{dx}[x^{4/3}]\Big|_{x=0} = \dfrac{4}{3}x^{1/3}\Big|_{x=0} = 0$.

72. **(a)** $f_y(0,0) = \dfrac{d}{dy}[f(0,y)]\Big|_{y=0} = \dfrac{d}{dy}[y]\Big|_{y=0} = 1$

  (b) If $(x,y) \neq (0,0)$, then $f_y(x,y) = \dfrac{1}{3}(x^3+y^3)^{-2/3}(3y^2) = \dfrac{y^2}{(x^3+y^3)^{2/3}}$;

  $f_y(x,y)$ does not exist where $y = -x$, $x \neq 0$.

EXERCISE SET 16.4

1. $\Delta f = f(1.1,3.2) - f(1,3) = (1.1)^2(3.2) - (1)^2(3) = 0.872$

2. Let $f(x,y) = 3x^2 - 2y$ then
$\Delta z = f(-1.98,3.97) - f(-2,4) = [3(-1.98)^2 - 2(3.97)] - [3(-2)^2 - 2(4)] = -0.1788$

3. $\Delta f = f(3,1) - f(-1,2) = 3/1 - (-1)/2 = 7/2$

4. $\Delta g = g(4,-2) - g(0,1) = [2(4)(-2) - (-2)^3] - [2(0)(1) - (1)^3] = -7$

5. $f_x(x,y) = y$, $f_y(x,y) = x$,
$\Delta f = (x + \Delta x)(y + \Delta y) - xy = y\Delta x + x\Delta y + \Delta x\Delta y$
$= f_x(x,y)\Delta x + f_y(x,y)\Delta y + (0)\Delta x + (\Delta x)\Delta y$ where $\epsilon_1 = 0$ and $\epsilon_2 = \Delta x$.

6. $f_x(x,y) = 2x$, $f_y(x,y) = 2y$,
$\Delta f = (x + \Delta x)^2 + (y + \Delta y)^2 - (x^2 + y^2) = 2x\Delta x + (\Delta x)^2 + 2y\Delta y + (\Delta y)^2$
$= f_x(x,y)\Delta x + f_y(x,y)\Delta y + (\Delta x)\Delta x + (\Delta y)\Delta y$ where $\epsilon_1 = \Delta x$ and $\epsilon_2 = \Delta y$.

7. $f_x(x,y) = 2xy$, $f_y(x,y) = x^2$,
$\Delta f = (x + \Delta x)^2(y + \Delta y) - x^2 y = 2xy\Delta x + x^2\Delta y + y(\Delta x)^2 + (\Delta x)^2\Delta y + 2x\Delta x\Delta y$
$= f_x(x,y)\Delta x + f_y(x,y)\Delta y + (y\Delta x + \Delta x\Delta y)\Delta x + (2x\Delta x)\Delta y$
where $\epsilon_1 = y\Delta x + \Delta x\Delta y$ and $\epsilon_2 = 2x\Delta x$.

8. $f_x(x,y) = 3$, $f_y(x,y) = 2y$,
$\Delta f = 3(x + \Delta x) + (y + \Delta y)^2 - (3x - y^2) = 3\Delta x + 2y\Delta y + (\Delta y)^2$
$= f_x(x,y)\Delta x + f_y(x,y)\Delta y + (0)\Delta x + (\Delta y)\Delta y$ where $\epsilon_1 = 0$ and $\epsilon_2 = \Delta y$.

9. (a) $\lim\limits_{(x,y)\to(0,0)} f(x,y) = 0 = f(0,0)$

   (b) $\lim\limits_{h\to 0} \dfrac{f(0 + h, 0) - f(0,0)}{h} = \lim\limits_{h\to 0} \dfrac{f(h,0)}{h} = \lim\limits_{h\to 0} \dfrac{|h|}{h}$, which does not exist because
   $\lim\limits_{h\to 0+} |h|/h = 1$ and $\lim\limits_{h\to 0-} |h|/h = -1$.

10. $f_x(0,0) = \lim\limits_{h\to 0} \dfrac{f(h,0) - f(0,0)}{h} = \lim\limits_{h\to 0} \dfrac{-3h}{h} = -3$,
   $f_y(0,0) = \lim\limits_{h\to 0} \dfrac{f(0,h) - f(0,0)}{h} = \lim\limits_{h\to 0} \dfrac{-2h}{h} = -2$;
   $\lim\limits_{(x,y)\to(0,0)} f(x,y)$ does not exist because $f(x,y) \to 5$ if $(x,y) \to (0,0)$ where $x \geq 0$ or $y \geq 0$,
   but $f(x,y) \to 0$ if $(x,y) \to (0,0)$ where $x < 0$ and $y < 0$, so f is not continuous at $(0,0)$.

11. $f_x(0,0) = \lim\limits_{h\to 0} \dfrac{f(h,0) - f(0,0)}{h} = \lim\limits_{h\to 0} \dfrac{0 - 0}{h} = \lim\limits_{h\to 0} 0 = 0$
   $f_y(0,0) = \lim\limits_{h\to 0} \dfrac{f(0,h) - f(0,0)}{h} = \lim\limits_{h\to 0} \dfrac{0 - 0}{h} = 0$; along $y = 0$, $\lim\limits_{x\to 0} \dfrac{0}{x^2} = \lim\limits_{x\to 0} 0 = 0$
   along $y = x$, $\lim\limits_{x\to 0} \dfrac{x^2}{2x^2} = \lim\limits_{x\to 0} 1/2 = 1/2$ so $\lim\limits_{(x,y)\to(0,0)} f(x,y)$ does not exist

12. $f_{xy} = f_{yx} = 2$

13. $f_{xy} = f_{yx} = 12x^2 + 6x$

14. $f_{xy} = f_{yx} = -3x^2/y^2$

15. $f_{xy} = f_{yx} = -6xy^2 \sin(x^2 + y^3)$

16. $f_{xy} = f_{yx} = -xy\left(x^2 + y^2 - 1\right)^{-3/2}$

17. **(a)** $\quad 4: \quad f_{xxx}, f_{xxy} = f_{xyx} = f_{yxx}, f_{xyy} = f_{yxy} = f_{yyx}, f_{yyy}$

      (b) $\quad 5: \quad f_{xxxx}, f_{xxxy} = f_{xxyx} = f_{xyxx} = f_{yxxx},$

$$f_{xxyy} = f_{xyxy} = f_{xyyx} = f_{yxyx} = f_{yyxx} = f_{yxxy},$$

$$f_{xyyy} = f_{yxyy} = f_{yyxy} = f_{yyyx}, f_{yyyy}$$

18. $f_{xyx} = f_{xxy} = f_{yxx} = 2xy^5 e^{xy^2} + 4y^3 e^{xy^2}$

19. $42t^{13}$

20. $\dfrac{2(3 + t^{-1/3})}{3(2t + t^{2/3})}$

21. $3t^{-2}\sin(1/t)$

22. $\dfrac{1 - 2t^4 - 8t^4\ln t}{2t\sqrt{1 + \ln t - 2t^4\ln t}}$

23. $-\dfrac{10}{3}t^{7/3}e^{1 - t^{10/3}}$

24. $\quad (1 + t)e^t\cosh\left(te^t/2\right)\sinh\left(te^t/2\right)$

25. $\partial z/\partial u = 24u^2 v^2 - 16uv^3 - 2v + 3, \; \partial z/\partial v = 16u^3 v - 24u^2 v^2 - 2u - 3$

26. $\partial z/\partial u = 2u/v^2 - u^2 v\sec^2(u/v) - 2uv^2\tan(u/v)$

$\partial z/\partial v = -2u^2/v^3 + u^3\sec^2(u/v) - 2u^2 v\tan(u/v)$

27. $\partial z/\partial u = -\dfrac{2\sin u}{3\sin v}, \; \partial z/\partial v = -\dfrac{2\cos u\cos v}{3\sin^2 v}$

28. $\partial z/\partial u = 3 + 3v/u - 4u, \; \partial z/\partial v = 2 + 3\ln u + 2\ln v$

29. $\partial z/\partial u = e^u, \; \partial z/\partial v = 0$

30. $\partial z/\partial u = -\sin(u - v)\sin\left(u^2 + v^2\right) + 2u\cos(u - v)\cos\left(u^2 + v^2\right)$

$\partial z/\partial v = \sin(u - v)\sin\left(u^2 + v^2\right) + 2v\cos(u - v)\cos\left(u^2 + v^2\right)$

31. $\partial z/\partial u = 2e^{2u}/(1 + e^{4u}), \; \partial z/\partial v = 0$

32. $\partial w/\partial u = \dfrac{2v^2\left[u^2 v^2 - (u - 2v)^2\right]}{\left[u^2 v^2 + (u - 2v)^2\right]^2}, \; \partial w/\partial v = \dfrac{u^2\left[(u - 2v)^2 - u^2 v^2\right]}{\left[u^2 v^2 + (u - 2v)^2\right]^2}$

33. $\partial T/\partial r = 3r^2\sin\theta\cos^2\theta - 4r^3\sin^3\theta\cos\theta$

$\partial T/\partial\theta = -2r^3\sin^2\theta\cos\theta + r^4\sin^4\theta + r^3\cos^3\theta - 3r^4\sin^2\theta\cos^2\theta$

34. $dR/d\phi = 5e^{5\phi}$

35. $\partial t/\partial x = \left(x^2 + y^2\right) / \left(4x^2 y^3\right),\ \partial t/\partial y = \left(y^2 - 3x^2\right) / \left(4xy^4\right)$

36. 1161   **37.** $-\pi$

38. $351/2,\ -168$ **39.** $\sqrt{3}e^{\sqrt{3}},\ \left(2 - 4\sqrt{3}\right)e^{\sqrt{3}}$

40. $F(x,y) = x^2 y^3 + \cos y,\ \dfrac{dy}{dx} = -\dfrac{2xy^3}{3x^2 y^2 - \sin y}$

41. $F(x,y) = x^3 - 3xy^2 + y^3 - 5,\ \dfrac{dy}{dx} = -\dfrac{3x^2 - 3y^2}{-6xy + 3y^2} = \dfrac{x^2 - y^2}{2xy - y^2}$

42. $F(x,y) = e^{xy} + ye^y - 1,\ \dfrac{dy}{dx} = -\dfrac{ye^{xy}}{xe^{xy} + ye^y + e^y}$

43. $F(x,y) = x - (xy)^{1/2} + 3y - 4,\ \dfrac{dy}{dx} = -\dfrac{1 - (1/2)(xy)^{-1/2}y}{-(1/2)(xy)^{-1/2}x + 3} = \dfrac{2\sqrt{xy} - y}{x - 6\sqrt{xy}}$

44. $V = (\pi/4)D^2 h$ where D is the diameter and h is the height,

$dV/dt = (\pi/2)Dh(dD/dt) + (\pi/4)D^2(dh/dt),\ dD/dt = 3$ and $dh/dt = 24$ when $D = 30$ and $h = 240$ so $dV/dt = (\pi/2)(30)(240)(3) + (\pi/4)(30)^2(24) = 16,200\pi$ in^3/year.

45. $D = \left(x^2 + y^2\right)^{1/2}$ where x and y are the distances of cars A and B, respectively, from the intersection and D is the distance between them.

$dD/dt = \left[x/\left(x^2 + y^2\right)^{1/2}\right](dx/dt) + \left[y/\left(x^2 + y^2\right)^{1/2}\right](dy/dt),\ dx/dt = -25$ and $dy/dt = -30$ when $x = 0.3$ and $y = 0.4$ so $dD/dt = (0.3/0.5)(-25) + (0.4/0.5)(-30) = -39$ mph.

46. $T = (1/10)PV,\ dT/dt = (V/10)(dP/dt) + (P/10)(dV/dt),\ dV/dt = 4$ and $dP/dt = -1$ when $V = 200$ and $P = 5$ so $dT/dt = (20)(-1) + (1/2)(4) = -18$ degrees per second.

47. $A = \dfrac{1}{2}ab\sin\theta$ but $\theta = \pi/6$ when $a = 4$ and $b = 3$ so $A = \dfrac{1}{2}(4)(3)\sin(\pi/6) = 3$.

Solve $\dfrac{1}{2}ab\sin\theta = 3$ for θ to get $\theta = \sin^{-1}\left(\dfrac{6}{ab}\right),\ 0 \le \theta \le \pi/2$.

$$\frac{d\theta}{dt} = \frac{\partial\theta}{\partial a}\frac{da}{dt} + \frac{\partial\theta}{\partial b}\frac{db}{dt} = \frac{1}{\sqrt{1 - \dfrac{36}{a^2 b^2}}}\left(-\frac{6}{a^2 b}\right)\frac{da}{dt} + \frac{1}{\sqrt{1 - \dfrac{36}{a^2 b^2}}}\left(-\frac{6}{ab^2}\right)\frac{db}{dt}$$

$$= -\frac{6}{\sqrt{a^2 b^2 - 36}}\left(\frac{1}{a}\frac{da}{dt} + \frac{1}{b}\frac{db}{dt}\right), \frac{da}{dt} = 1 \text{ and } \frac{db}{dt} = 1$$

when $a = 4$ and $b = 3$ so $\dfrac{d\theta}{dt} = -\dfrac{6}{\sqrt{144 - 36}}\left(\dfrac{1}{4} + \dfrac{1}{3}\right) = -\dfrac{7}{12\sqrt{3}} = -\dfrac{7}{36}\sqrt{3}$ radians/sec

48. From the law of cosines, $c = \sqrt{a^2 + b^2 - 2ab\cos\theta}$ where c is the length of the third side. $\theta = \pi/3$ so $c = \sqrt{a^2 + b^2 - ab}$,

$$\frac{dc}{dt} = \frac{\partial c}{\partial a}\frac{da}{dt} + \frac{\partial c}{\partial b}\frac{db}{dt} = \frac{1}{2}(a^2 + b^2 - ab)^{-1/2}(2a - b)\frac{da}{dt} + \frac{1}{2}(a^2 + b^2 - ab)^{-1/2}(2b - a)\frac{db}{dt}$$

$$= \frac{1}{2\sqrt{a^2 + b^2 - ab}}\left[(2a - b)\frac{da}{dt} + (2b - a)\frac{db}{dt}\right], \frac{da}{dt} = 2 \text{ and } \frac{db}{dt} = 1 \text{ when } a = 5 \text{ and } b = 10 \text{ so}$$

$$\frac{dc}{dt} = \frac{1}{2\sqrt{75}}[(0)(2) + (15)(1)] = \sqrt{3}/2 \text{ cm/sec. The third side is increasing.}$$

49. $\dfrac{dT}{dt} = \dfrac{\partial T}{\partial x}\dfrac{dx}{dt} + \dfrac{\partial T}{\partial y}\dfrac{dy}{dt} = \dfrac{y^2}{x}\dfrac{dx}{dt} + 2y\ln x\dfrac{dy}{dt}$, $dx/dt = 1$ and $dy/dt = -4$ at $(3,2)$ so

$dT/dt = (4/3)(1) + (4\ln 3)(-4) = 4/3 - 16\ln 3°C/\text{sec}$.

50. $\dfrac{\partial z}{\partial x} = \dfrac{dz}{du}\dfrac{\partial u}{\partial x}, \dfrac{\partial z}{\partial y} = \dfrac{dz}{du}\dfrac{\partial u}{\partial y}$.

51. $z = f(u)$, $u = x^2 - y^2$; $\partial z/\partial x = (dz/du)(\partial u/\partial x) = 2x\,dz/du$,

$\partial z/\partial y = (dz/du)(\partial u/\partial y) = -2y\,dz/du$, $y\partial z/\partial x + x\partial z/\partial y = 2xy\,dz/du - 2xy\,dz/du = 0$.

52. $z = f(u)$, $u = xy$; $\dfrac{\partial z}{\partial x} = \dfrac{dz}{du}\dfrac{\partial u}{\partial x} = y\dfrac{dz}{du}, \dfrac{\partial z}{\partial y} = \dfrac{dz}{du}\dfrac{\partial u}{\partial y} = x\dfrac{dz}{du}, x\dfrac{\partial z}{\partial x} - y\dfrac{\partial z}{\partial y} = xy\dfrac{dz}{du} - xy\dfrac{dz}{du} = 0$.

53. (a) $\dfrac{\partial z}{\partial x} = \dfrac{dz}{du}\dfrac{\partial u}{\partial x}, \dfrac{\partial^2 z}{\partial x^2} = \dfrac{dz}{du}\dfrac{\partial^2 u}{\partial x^2} + \dfrac{\partial}{\partial x}\left(\dfrac{dz}{du}\right)\dfrac{\partial u}{\partial x} = \dfrac{dz}{du}\dfrac{\partial^2 u}{\partial x^2} + \dfrac{d^2 z}{du^2}\left(\dfrac{\partial u}{\partial x}\right)^2$; proceed in a similar fashion for $\partial^2 z/\partial y^2$.

(b) $\dfrac{\partial^2 z}{\partial y\partial x} = \dfrac{dz}{du}\dfrac{\partial^2 u}{\partial y\partial x} + \dfrac{\partial}{\partial y}\left(\dfrac{dz}{du}\right)\dfrac{\partial u}{\partial x} = \dfrac{dz}{du}\dfrac{\partial^2 u}{\partial y\partial x} + \dfrac{d^2 z}{du^2}\dfrac{\partial u}{\partial x}\dfrac{\partial u}{\partial y}$.

54. (a) $\dfrac{\partial r}{\partial x} = \dfrac{x}{\sqrt{x^2 + y^2}} = \dfrac{x}{r}$ 　　　　　　(b) $\dfrac{\partial r}{\partial y} = \dfrac{y}{\sqrt{x^2 + y^2}} = \dfrac{y}{r}$

(c) $\dfrac{\partial^2 r}{\partial x^2} = \dfrac{r - x\partial r/\partial x}{r^2} = \dfrac{r - x^2/r}{r^2} = \dfrac{r^2 - x^2}{r^3} = \dfrac{y^2}{r^3}$

(d) $\dfrac{\partial^2 r}{\partial y^2} = \dfrac{r - y\partial r/\partial y}{r^2} = \dfrac{r - y^2/r}{r^2} = \dfrac{r^2 - y^2}{r^3} = \dfrac{x^2}{r^3}$

55. (a) $\dfrac{\partial^2 z}{\partial x^2} + \dfrac{\partial^2 z}{\partial y^2} = \dfrac{dz}{dr}\dfrac{\partial^2 r}{\partial x^2} + \dfrac{d^2 z}{dr^2}\left(\dfrac{\partial r}{\partial x}\right)^2 + \dfrac{dz}{dr}\dfrac{\partial^2 r}{\partial y^2} + \dfrac{d^2 z}{dr^2}\left(\dfrac{\partial r}{\partial y}\right)^2$

$= \dfrac{dz}{dr}\dfrac{y^2}{r^3} + \dfrac{d^2 z}{dr^2}\dfrac{x^2}{r^2} + \dfrac{dz}{dr}\dfrac{x^2}{r^3} + \dfrac{d^2 z}{dr^2}\dfrac{y^2}{r^2} = \dfrac{d^2 z}{dr^2} + \dfrac{1}{r}\dfrac{dz}{dr} = 0$ so $r\dfrac{d^2 z}{dr^2} + \dfrac{dz}{dr} = 0.$

(b) $r\dfrac{d^2 z}{dr^2} + \dfrac{dz}{dr} = \dfrac{d}{dr}\left(r\dfrac{dz}{dr}\right) = 0,\ r\dfrac{dz}{dr} = C_1,\ \dfrac{dz}{dr} = C_1/r,\ z = C_1\ln r + C_2.$

56. $z = f(u,v)$ where $u = x - y$ and $v = y - x$,

$\dfrac{\partial z}{\partial x} = \dfrac{\partial z}{\partial u}\dfrac{\partial u}{\partial x} + \dfrac{\partial z}{\partial v}\dfrac{\partial v}{\partial x} = \dfrac{\partial z}{\partial u} - \dfrac{\partial z}{\partial v}$ and $\dfrac{\partial z}{\partial y} = \dfrac{\partial z}{\partial u}\dfrac{\partial u}{\partial y} + \dfrac{\partial z}{\partial v}\dfrac{\partial v}{\partial y} = -\dfrac{\partial z}{\partial u} + \dfrac{\partial z}{\partial v}$ so $\dfrac{\partial z}{\partial x} + \dfrac{\partial z}{\partial y} = 0$

57. $z = f(u) + g(v)$ where $u = y + cx$ and $v = y - cx$, $\dfrac{\partial z}{\partial x} = \dfrac{\partial z}{\partial u}\dfrac{\partial u}{\partial x} + \dfrac{\partial z}{\partial v}\dfrac{\partial v}{\partial x} = cf'(u) - cg'(v)$

and $\dfrac{\partial^2 z}{\partial x^2} = \dfrac{\partial}{\partial u}\left(\dfrac{\partial z}{\partial x}\right)\dfrac{\partial u}{\partial x} + \dfrac{\partial}{\partial v}\left(\dfrac{\partial z}{\partial x}\right)\dfrac{\partial v}{\partial x} = c^2 f''(u) + c^2 g''(v),$

similarly we find that $\dfrac{\partial^2 z}{\partial y^2} = f''(u) + g''(v)$ so $\dfrac{\partial^2 z}{\partial x^2} = c^2\dfrac{\partial^2 z}{\partial y^2}.$

58. (a) The results follow by a direct application of the chain rule.

(b) $\dfrac{dz}{dt} = \dfrac{\partial z}{\partial x}\dfrac{dx}{dt} + \dfrac{\partial z}{\partial y}\dfrac{dy}{dt},$

$\dfrac{d^2 z}{dt^2} = \dfrac{\partial z}{\partial x}\dfrac{d^2 x}{dt^2} + \dfrac{dx}{dt}\dfrac{d}{dt}\left(\dfrac{\partial z}{\partial x}\right) + \dfrac{\partial z}{\partial y}\dfrac{d^2 y}{dt^2} + \dfrac{dy}{dt}\dfrac{d}{dt}\left(\dfrac{\partial z}{\partial y}\right)$

$= \dfrac{\partial z}{\partial x}\dfrac{d^2 x}{dt^2} + \dfrac{\partial^2 z}{\partial x^2}\left(\dfrac{dx}{dt}\right)^2 + \dfrac{\partial z}{\partial y}\dfrac{d^2 y}{dt^2} + \dfrac{\partial^2 z}{\partial y^2}\left(\dfrac{dy}{dt}\right)^2 + 2\dfrac{\partial^2 z}{\partial y\partial x}\dfrac{dx}{dt}\dfrac{dy}{dt}.$

59. The result follows by a direct application of the chain rule.

60. $\dfrac{\partial z}{\partial u} = \dfrac{\partial z}{\partial x}\dfrac{\partial x}{\partial u} + \dfrac{\partial z}{\partial y}\dfrac{\partial y}{\partial u} = \dfrac{\partial z}{\partial x} + \dfrac{\partial z}{\partial y},\ \dfrac{\partial^2 z}{\partial v\partial u} = \dfrac{\partial^2 z}{\partial x^2}\dfrac{\partial x}{\partial v} + \dfrac{\partial^2 z}{\partial y\partial x}\dfrac{\partial y}{\partial v} + \dfrac{\partial^2 z}{\partial x\partial y}\dfrac{\partial x}{\partial v} + \dfrac{\partial^2 z}{\partial y^2}\dfrac{\partial y}{\partial v}$

$= \dfrac{\partial^2 z}{\partial x^2} - \dfrac{\partial^2 z}{\partial y\partial x} + \dfrac{\partial^2 z}{\partial x\partial y} - \dfrac{\partial^2 z}{\partial y^2} = \dfrac{\partial^2 z}{\partial x^2} - \dfrac{\partial^2 z}{\partial y^2}.$

61. (a) $1 = -r\sin\theta\dfrac{\partial\theta}{\partial x} + \cos\theta\dfrac{\partial r}{\partial x}$ and $0 = r\cos\theta\dfrac{\partial\theta}{\partial x} + \sin\theta\dfrac{\partial r}{\partial x}$; solve for $\partial r/\partial x$ and $\partial\theta/\partial x.$

(b) $0 = -r\sin\theta\dfrac{\partial\theta}{\partial y} + \cos\theta\dfrac{\partial r}{\partial y}$ and $1 = r\cos\theta\dfrac{\partial\theta}{\partial y} + \sin\theta\dfrac{\partial r}{\partial y}$; solve for $\partial r/\partial y$ and $\partial\theta/\partial y$.

62. **(a)** $\dfrac{\partial z}{\partial x} = \dfrac{\partial z}{\partial r}\dfrac{\partial r}{\partial x} + \dfrac{\partial z}{\partial\theta}\dfrac{\partial\theta}{\partial x} = \dfrac{\partial z}{\partial r}\cos\theta - \dfrac{1}{r}\dfrac{\partial z}{\partial\theta}\sin\theta.$

(b) $\dfrac{\partial z}{\partial y} = \dfrac{\partial z}{\partial r}\dfrac{\partial r}{\partial y} + \dfrac{\partial z}{\partial\theta}\dfrac{\partial\theta}{\partial y} = \dfrac{\partial z}{\partial r}\sin\theta + \dfrac{1}{r}\dfrac{\partial z}{\partial\theta}\cos\theta.$

63. Square and add the results of parts (a) and (b).

64. From part (a) of Exercise 62,

$$\frac{\partial^2 z}{\partial x^2} = \frac{\partial}{\partial r}\left(\frac{\partial z}{\partial r}\cos\theta - \frac{1}{r}\frac{\partial z}{\partial\theta}\sin\theta\right)\frac{\partial r}{\partial x} + \frac{\partial}{\partial\theta}\left(\frac{\partial z}{\partial r}\cos\theta - \frac{1}{r}\frac{\partial z}{\partial\theta}\sin\theta\right)\frac{\partial\theta}{\partial x}$$

$$= \left(\frac{\partial^2 z}{\partial r^2}\cos\theta + \frac{1}{r^2}\frac{\partial z}{\partial\theta}\sin\theta - \frac{1}{r}\frac{\partial^2 z}{\partial r\partial\theta}\sin\theta\right)\cos\theta$$

$$+ \left(\frac{\partial^2 z}{\partial\theta\partial r}\cos\theta - \frac{\partial z}{\partial r}\sin\theta - \frac{1}{r}\frac{\partial^2 z}{\partial\theta^2}\sin\theta - \frac{1}{r}\frac{\partial z}{\partial\theta}\cos\theta\right)\left(-\frac{\sin\theta}{r}\right)$$

$$= \frac{\partial^2 z}{\partial r^2}\cos^2\theta + \frac{2}{r^2}\frac{\partial z}{\partial\theta}\sin\theta\cos\theta - \frac{2}{r}\frac{\partial^2 z}{\partial\theta\partial r}\sin\theta\cos\theta + \frac{1}{r^2}\frac{\partial^2 z}{\partial\theta^2}\sin^2\theta + \frac{1}{r}\frac{\partial z}{\partial r}\sin^2\theta.$$

Similarly, from part (b) of Exercise 62,

$$\frac{\partial^2 z}{\partial y^2} = \frac{\partial^2 z}{\partial r^2}\sin^2\theta - \frac{2}{r^2}\frac{\partial z}{\partial\theta}\sin\theta\cos\theta + \frac{2}{r}\frac{\partial^2 z}{\partial\theta\partial r}\sin\theta\cos\theta + \frac{1}{r^2}\frac{\partial^2 z}{\partial\theta^2}\cos^2\theta + \frac{1}{r}\frac{\partial z}{\partial r}\cos^2\theta.$$

Add to get $\dfrac{\partial^2 z}{\partial x^2} + \dfrac{\partial^2 z}{\partial y^2} = \dfrac{\partial^2 z}{\partial r^2} + \dfrac{1}{r^2}\dfrac{\partial^2 z}{\partial\theta^2} + \dfrac{1}{r}\dfrac{\partial z}{\partial r}.$

65. **(a)** $f(tx, ty) = 3t^2 x^2 + t^2 y^2 = t^2 f(x, y); \ n = 2.$

(b) $f(tx, ty) = \sqrt{t^2 x^2 + t^2 y^2} = tf(x, y); \ n = 1.$

(c) $f(tx, ty) = t^3 x^2 y - 2t^3 y^3 = t^3 f(x, y); \ n = 3.$

(d) $f(tx, ty) = 5/\left(t^2 x^2 + 2t^2 y^2\right)^2 = t^{-4} f(x, y); \ n = -4.$

66. If $f(u, v) = t^n f(x, y)$, then $\dfrac{\partial f}{\partial u}\dfrac{du}{dt} + \dfrac{\partial f}{\partial v}\dfrac{dv}{dt} = nt^{n-1}f(x, y)$, $x\dfrac{\partial f}{\partial u} + y\dfrac{\partial f}{\partial v} = nt^{n-1}f(x, y)$;

let $t = 1$ to get $x\dfrac{\partial f}{\partial x} + y\dfrac{\partial f}{\partial y} = nf(x, y).$

67. **(a)** $\dfrac{\partial w}{\partial x} = \dfrac{\partial f}{\partial x} + \dfrac{\partial f}{\partial y}\dfrac{\partial y}{\partial x}$

(b) $\dfrac{\partial w}{\partial z} = \dfrac{\partial f}{\partial y}\dfrac{\partial y}{\delta z}$

68. By the chain rule, $\dfrac{\partial u}{\partial r} = \dfrac{\partial u}{\partial x}\cos\theta + \dfrac{\partial u}{\partial y}\sin\theta$ and $\dfrac{\partial v}{\partial\theta} = -\dfrac{\partial v}{\partial x}r\sin\theta + \dfrac{\partial v}{\partial y}r\cos\theta$, use the

Cauchy-Riemann conditions $\dfrac{\partial u}{\partial x} = \dfrac{\partial v}{\partial y}$ and $\dfrac{\partial u}{\partial y} = -\dfrac{\partial v}{\partial x}$ in the equation for $\dfrac{\partial u}{\partial r}$ to get

$\dfrac{\partial u}{\partial r} = \dfrac{\partial v}{\partial y}\cos\theta - \dfrac{\partial v}{\partial x}\sin\theta$ and compare to $\dfrac{\partial v}{\partial\theta}$ to see that $\dfrac{\partial u}{\partial r} = \dfrac{1}{r}\dfrac{\partial v}{\partial\theta}$. The result $\dfrac{\partial v}{\partial r} = -\dfrac{1}{r}\dfrac{\partial u}{\partial\theta}$

can be obtained by considering $\dfrac{\partial v}{\partial r}$ and $\dfrac{\partial u}{\partial\theta}$.

69. Represent the line segment C that joins A and B by $x = x_0 + (x_1 - x_0)t$, $y = y_0 + (y_1 - y_0)t$ for $0 \le t \le 1$. $f(x,y) = F(t)$ for (x,y) on C, moreover $f(x_1,y_1) - f(x_0,y_0) = F(1) - F(0)$. Apply the Mean Value Theorem to $F(t)$ on the interval $[0,1]$ to get $[F(1) - F(0)]/(1 - 0) = F'(t^*)$, $F(1) - F(0) = F'(t^*)$ for some t^* in $(0,1)$ so $f(x_1,y_1) - f(x_0,y_0) = F'(t^*)$. By the chain rule, $F'(t) = f_x(x,y)(dx/dt) + f_y(x,y)(dy/dt) = f_x(x,y)(x_1 - x_0) + f_y(x,y)(y_1 - y_0)$. Let (x^*,y^*) be the point on C for $t = t^*$ then
$f(x_1,y_1) - f(x_0,y_0) = F'(t^*) = f_x(x^*,y^*)(x_1 - x_0) + f_y(x^*,y^*)(y_1 - y_0)$.

70. Let (a,b) be any point in the region, if (x,y) is in the region then by the result of Exercise 69 $f(x,y) - f(a,b) = f_x(x^*,y^*)(x - a) + f_y(x^*,y^*)(y - b)$ where (x^*,y^*) is on the line segment joining (a,b) and (x,y). If $f_x(x,y) = f_y(x,y) = 0$ throughout the region then $f(x,y) - f(a,b) = (0)(x - a) + (0)(y - b) = 0$, $f(x,y) = f(a,b)$ so $f(x,y)$ is constant on the region.

EXERCISE SET 16.5

1. At P, $\partial z/\partial x = 48$ and $\partial z/\partial y = -14$, tangent plane $48x - 14y - z = 64$, normal line $x = 1 + 48t$, $y = -2 - 14t$, $z = 12 - t$.

2. At P, $\partial z/\partial x = 14$ and $\partial z/\partial y = -2$, tangent plane $14x - 2y - z = 16$, normal line $x = 2 + 14t$, $y = 4 - 2t$, $z = 4 - t$.

3. At P, $\partial z/\partial x = 1$ and $\partial z/\partial y = -1$, tangent plane $x - y - z = 0$, normal line $x = 1 + t$, $y = -t$, $z = 1 - t$.

4. At P, $\partial z/\partial x = -1$ and $\partial z/\partial y = 0$, tangent plane $x + z = -1$, normal line $x = -1 - t$, $y = 0$, $z = -t$.

5. At P, $\partial z/\partial x = 0$ and $\partial z/\partial y = 3$, tangent plane $3y - z = -1$, normal line $x = \pi/6$, $y = 3t$, $z = 1 - t$.

6. At P, $\partial z/\partial x = 1/4$ and $\partial z/\partial y = 1/6$, tangent plane $3x + 2y - 12z = -30$, normal line $x = 4 + t/4$, $y = 9 + t/6$, $z = 5 - t$.

7. By implicit differentiation $\partial z/\partial x = -x/z$, $\partial z/\partial y = -y/z$ so at P, $\partial z/\partial x = 3/4$ and $\partial z/\partial y = 0$, tangent plane $3x - 4z = -25$, normal line $x = -3 + 3t/4$, $y = 0$, $z = 4 - t$.

8. By implicit differentiation $\partial z/\partial x = (xy)/(4z)$, $\partial z/\partial y = x^2/(8z)$ so at P, $\partial z/\partial x = 3/8$ and $\partial z/\partial y = -9/16$, tangent plane $6x - 9y - 16z = 5$, normal line $x = -3 + 3t/8$, $y = 1 - 9t/16$, $z = -2 - t$.

9. $dz = 7dx - 2dy$

10. $dz = (10xy^5 - 2)dx + (25x^2y^4 + 4)dy$

11. $dz = \left[y/\left(1 + x^2y^2\right) \right] dx + \left[x/\left(1 + x^2y^2\right) \right] dy$

12. $dz = 2\sec^2(x - 3y)\tan(x - 3y)dx - 6\sec^2(x - 3y)\tan(x - 3y)dy$

13. $df = (2x + 2y - 4)dx + 2xdy$; $x = 1$, $y = 2$, $dx = 0.01$, $dy = 0.04$ so $df = 0.10$

14. $df = (1/3)x^{-2/3}y^{1/2}dx + (1/2)x^{1/3}y^{-1/2}dy$; $x = 8$, $y = 9$, $dx = -0.02$, $dy = 0.03$ so $df = 0.005$

15. $df = -x^{-2}dx - y^{-2}dy$; $x = -1$, $y = -2$, $dx = -0.02$, $dy = -0.04$ so $df = 0.03$

16. $df = \dfrac{y}{2(1 + xy)}dx + \dfrac{x}{2(1 + xy)}dy$; $x = 0$, $y = 2$, $dx = -0.09$, $dy = -0.02$ so $df = -0.09$

17. The tangent plane is horizontal if the normal $\partial z/\partial x\mathbf{i} + \partial z/\partial y\mathbf{j} - \mathbf{k}$ is parallel to $\mathbf{k}$ which occurs when $\partial z/\partial x = \partial z/\partial y = 0$.

(a) $\partial z/\partial x = 3x^2y^2$, $\partial z/\partial y = 2x^3y$; $3x^2y^2 = 0$ and $2x^3y = 0$ for all (x, y) on the x-axis or y-axis, and $z = 0$ for these points, the tangent plane is horizontal at all points on the x-axis or y-axis.

(b) $\partial z/\partial x = 2x - y - 2$, $\partial z/\partial y = -x + 2y + 4$; solve the system $2x - y - 2 = 0$, $-x + 2y + 4 = 0$, to get $x = 0$, $y = -2$. $z = -4$ at $(0, -2)$, the tangent plane is horizontal at $(0, -2, -4)$.

18. $\partial z/\partial x = 6x$, $\partial z/\partial y = -2y$, so $6x_0\mathbf{i} - 2y_0\mathbf{j} - \mathbf{k}$ is normal to the surface at a point (x_0, y_0, z_0) on the surface. $6\mathbf{i} + 4\mathbf{j} - \mathbf{k}$ is normal to the given plane. The tangent plane and the given plane are parallel if their normals are parallel so $6x_0 = 6$, $x_0 = 1$ and $-2y_0 = 4$, $y_0 = -2$. $z = -1$ at $(1, -2)$, the point on the surface is $(1, -2, -1)$.

19. $\partial z/\partial x = -6x$, $\partial z/\partial y = -4y$ so $-6x_0\mathbf{i} - 4y_0\mathbf{j} - \mathbf{k}$ is normal to the surface at a point (x_0, y_0, z_0) on the surface. This normal must be parallel to the given line and hence to the vector

$-3\mathbf{i} + 8\mathbf{j} - \mathbf{k}$ which is parallel to the line so $-6x_0 = -3$, $x_0 = 1/2$ and $-4y_0 = 8$, $y_0 = -2$. $z = -3/4$ at $(1/2, -2)$. The point on the surface is $(1/2, -2, -3/4)$.

20. $(3,4,5)$ is a point of intersection because it satisfies both equations. Both surfaces have $(3/5)\mathbf{i} + (4/5)\mathbf{j} - \mathbf{k}$ as a normal so they have a common tangent plane at $(3,4,5)$.

21. $(2, 2, 2\sqrt{2})$ satisfies both equations. $\mathbf{n}_1 = -\left(1/\sqrt{2}\right)\mathbf{i} - \left(1/\sqrt{2}\right)\mathbf{j} - \mathbf{k}$ and
$\mathbf{n}_2 = \left(1/\sqrt{2}\right)\mathbf{i} + \left(1/\sqrt{2}\right)\mathbf{j} - \mathbf{k}$ are normal, respectively, to each of the surfaces at $(2, 2, 2\sqrt{2})$.
$\mathbf{n}_1 \cdot \mathbf{n}_2 = 0$ so the normals are perpendicular and hence so are the tangent planes.

22. **(a)** $\partial z/\partial x = x/\sqrt{x^2 + y^2} = x/z$, $\partial z/\partial y = y/\sqrt{x^2 + y^2} = y/z$ so if (x_0, y_0, z_0) is on the cone
then the normal line is $x = x_0 + (x_0/z_0)\,t$, $y = y_0 + (y_0/z_0)\,t$, $z = z_0 - t$. If $t = -z_0$ then
$x = 0$, $y = 0$, $z = 2z_0$ which is a point on the z-axis.

(b) At (x_0, y_0, z_0) the tangent plane is $(x_0/z_0)\,x + (y_0/z_0)\,y - z = x_0^2/z_0 + y_0^2/z_0 - z_0$, or
$x_0 x + y_0 y - z_0 z = x_0^2 + y_0^2 - z_0^2 = 0$ (because $z_0^2 = x_0^2 + y_0^2$). The line through $(0,0,0)$ and
(x_0, y_0, z_0) is $x = x_0 t$, $y = y_0 t$, $z = z_0 t$ which, for $t \geq 0$, satisfies the equation of the cone
and the equation of the tangent plane so the tangent plane intersects the cone in a line
passing through the origin.

23. $z = \sqrt{x^2 + y^2}$, $dz = x\left(x^2 + y^2\right)^{-1/2} dx + y\left(x^2 + y^2\right)^{-1/2} dy$; $x = 3$, $y = 4$, $dx = 0.2$,
$dy = -0.04$ so $dz = 0.088$ cm.

24. $dV = (2/3)\pi rh\,dr + (1/3)\pi r^2 dh$; $r = 4$, $h = 20$, $dr = 0.05$, $dh = -0.05$ so $dV = 2.4\pi \approx 7.54$ in^3.

25. $A = xy$, $dA = y\,dx + x\,dy$, $dA/A = dx/x + dy/y$, $|dx/x| \leq 0.03$ and $|dy/y| \leq 0.05$,
$|dA/A| \leq |dx/x| + |dy/y| \leq 0.08 = 8\%$

26. $V = (1/3)\pi r^2 h$, $dV = (2/3)\pi rh\,dr + (1/3)\pi r^2 dh$, $dV/V = 2(dr/r) + dh/h$, $|dr/r| \leq 0.01$ and
$|dh/h| \leq 0.04$, $|dV/V| \leq 2|dr/r| + |dh/h| \leq 0.06 = 6\%$.

27. $z = \sqrt{x^2 + y^2}$, $dz = \dfrac{x}{\sqrt{x^2 + y^2}}dx + \dfrac{y}{\sqrt{x^2 + y^2}}dy$,

$\dfrac{dz}{z} = \dfrac{x}{x^2 + y^2}dx + \dfrac{y}{x^2 + y^2}dy = \dfrac{x^2}{x^2 + y^2}\left(\dfrac{dx}{x}\right) + \dfrac{y^2}{x^2 + y^2}\left(\dfrac{dy}{y}\right)$,

$\left|\dfrac{dz}{z}\right| \leq \dfrac{x^2}{x^2 + y^2}\left|\dfrac{dx}{x}\right| + \dfrac{y^2}{x^2 + y^2}\left|\dfrac{dy}{y}\right|$, if $\left|\dfrac{dx}{x}\right| \leq r/100$ and $\left|\dfrac{dy}{y}\right| \leq r/100$ then

$\left|\dfrac{dz}{z}\right| \leq \dfrac{x^2}{x^2 + y^2}(r/100) + \dfrac{y^2}{x^2 + y^2}(r/100) = \dfrac{r}{100}$ so the percentage error in z is at most $r\%$.

28. **(a)** $z = \sqrt{x^2 + y^2}$, $dz = x\left(x^2 + y^2\right)^{-1/2} dx + y\left(x^2 + y^2\right)^{-1/2} dy$,

$|dz| \leq x\left(x^2 + y^2\right)^{-1/2}|dx| + y\left(x^2 + y^2\right)^{-1/2}|dy|$; if $x = 3$, $y = 4$, $|dx| \leq 0.05$, and
$|dy| \leq 0.05$ then $|dz| \leq (3/5)(0.05) + (4/5)(0.05) = 0.07$ cm

(b) $A = (1/2)xy$, $dA = (1/2)y\,dx + (1/2)x\,dy$,
$|dA| \leq (1/2)y|dx| + (1/2)x|dy| \leq 2(0.05) + (3/2)(0.05) = 0.175$ cm^2.

29. $dR = \dfrac{R_2^2}{(R_1 + R_2)^2} dR_1 + \dfrac{R_1^2}{(R_1 + R_2)^2} dR_2, \ \dfrac{dR}{R} = \dfrac{R_2}{R_1 + R_2}\left(\dfrac{dR_1}{R_1}\right) + \dfrac{R_1}{R_1 + R_2}\left(\dfrac{dR_2}{R_2}\right),$

$\left|\dfrac{dR}{R}\right| \le \dfrac{R_2}{R_1 + R_2}\left|\dfrac{dR_1}{R_1}\right| + \dfrac{R_1}{R_1 + R_2}\left|\dfrac{dR_2}{R_2}\right|;$ if $R_1 = 200, \ R_2 = 400, \ |dR_1/R_1| \le 0.02,$ and

$|dR_2/R_2| \le 0.02$ then $|dR/R| \le (400/600)(0.02) + (200/600)(0.02) = 0.02 = 2\%.$

30. $dP = (k/V)dT - (kT/V^2)dV, \ dP/P = dT/T - dV/V;$ if $dT/T = 0.03$ and $dV/V = 0.05$ then
$dP/P = -0.02$ so there is about a 2% decrease in pressure.

31. $d\theta = \dfrac{1}{\sqrt{c^2 - a^2}}da - \dfrac{a}{c\sqrt{c^2 - a^2}}dc;$ if $a = 3, \ c = 5, \ |da| \le 0.01,$ and $|dc| \le 0.01$ then
$|d\theta| \le (1/4)(0.01) + (3/20)(0.01) = 0.004$ radians.

32. $V = \pi r^2 h, \ dV = 2\pi r h \, dr + \pi r^2 \, dh; \ r = 2, \ h = 5, \ dr = 0.01,$ and $dh = 0.01$ so
$dV = (20\pi)(0.01) + (4\pi)(0.01) = 0.24\pi,$ or about 0.754 cm^3.

33. $dT = \dfrac{\pi}{g\sqrt{L/g}}dL - \dfrac{\pi L}{g^2\sqrt{L/g}}dg, \ \dfrac{dT}{T} = \dfrac{1}{2}\dfrac{dL}{L} - \dfrac{1}{2}\dfrac{dg}{g}; \ |dL/L| \le 0.005$ and $|dg/g| \le 0.001$ so
$|dT/T| \le (1/2)(0.005) + (1/2)(0.001) = 0.003 = 0.3\%$

34. Let h be the height of the building, x the distance to the building, and θ the angle of elevation,
then $h = x\tan\theta, \ dh = \tan\theta \, dx + x\sec^2\theta \, d\theta;$ if $x = 100, \ \theta = 60°, \ |dx| \le 1/6$ ft, and
$|d\theta| \le (0.2)(\pi/180) = \pi/900$ radians, then $|dh| \le (\sqrt{3})(1/6) + (100)(4)(\pi/900) < 1.7$ ft.

35. **(a)** $z = xy, \ dz = y\,dx + x\,dy, \ dz/z = dx/x + dy/y; \ (r + s)\%.$

(b) $z = x/y, \ dz = dx/y - x\,dy/y^2, \ dz/z = dx/x - dy/y; \ (r + s)\%.$

(c) $z = x^2 y^3, \ dz = 2xy^3\,dx + 3x^2y^2\,dy, \ dz/z = 2dx/x + 3dy/y; \ (2r + 3s)\%.$

(d) $z = x^3 y^{1/2}, \ dz = 3x^2 y^{1/2}\,dx + x^3\,dy/(2y^{1/2}), \ dz/z = 3dx/x + (1/2)dy/y; \ (3r + s/2)\%.$

36. $z = \dfrac{k}{xy};$ at a point $\left(a, b, \dfrac{k}{ab}\right)$ on the surface, $\left\langle -\dfrac{k}{a^2 b}, -\dfrac{k}{ab^2}, -1 \right\rangle$ and hence $\langle bk, ak, a^2 b^2 \rangle$ is
normal to the surface so the tangent plane is $bkx + aky + a^2 b^2 z = 3abk.$ The plane cuts the
$x, \ y,$ and z-axes at the points $3a, \ 3b,$ and $\dfrac{3k}{ab},$ respectively, so the volume of the pyramid that
is formed is $V = \dfrac{1}{3}\left(\dfrac{3k}{ab}\right)\left[\dfrac{1}{2}(3a)(3b)\right] = \dfrac{9}{2}k,$ which does not depend on a and $b.$

37. **(a)** $2t + 7 = (-1 + t)^2 + (2 + t)^2, \ t^2 = 1, \ t = \pm 1$ so the points of intersection are $(-2, 1, 5)$
and $(0, 3, 9).$

(b) $\partial z/\partial x = 2x$, $\partial z/\partial y = 2y$ so at $(-2, 1, 5)$ the vector $\mathbf{n} = -4\mathbf{i} + 2\mathbf{j} - \mathbf{k}$ is normal to the surface. $\mathbf{v} = \mathbf{i} + \mathbf{j} + 2\mathbf{k}$ is parallel to the line; $\mathbf{n} \cdot \mathbf{v} = -4$ so the cosine of the acute angle is $[\mathbf{n} \cdot (-\mathbf{v})]/(\|\mathbf{n}\| \| -\mathbf{v}\|) = 4/(\sqrt{21}\sqrt{6}) = 4/(3\sqrt{14})$. Similarly, at $(0,3,9)$ the vector $\mathbf{n} = 6\mathbf{j} - \mathbf{k}$ is normal to the surface, $\mathbf{n} \cdot \mathbf{v} = 4$ so the cosine of the acute angle is $4/(\sqrt{37}\sqrt{6}) = 4/\sqrt{222}$.

38. $z = xf(u)$ where $u = x/y$, $\partial z/\partial x = xf'(u)\partial u/\partial x + f(u) = (x/y)f'(u) + f(u) = uf'(u) + f(u)$, $\partial z/\partial y = xf'(u)\partial u/\partial y = -(x^2/y^2)f'(u) = -u^2 f'(u)$. If (x_0, y_0, z_0) is on the surface then, with $u_0 = x_0/y_0$, $[u_0 f'(u_0) + f(u_0)]\mathbf{i} - u_0^2 f'(u_0)\mathbf{j} - \mathbf{k}$ is normal to the surface so the tangent plane is $[u_0 f'(u_0) + f(u_0)]x - u_0^2 f'(u_0)y - z = [u_0 f'(u_0) + f(u_0)]x_0 - u_0^2 f'(u_0)y_0 - z_0$

$$= \left[\frac{x_0}{y_0}f'(u_0) + f(u_0)\right]x_0 - \frac{x_0^2}{y_0^2}f'(u_0)y_0 - z_0$$
$$= x_0 f(u_0) - z_0 = 0$$

so all tangent planes pass through the origin.

39. Use implicit differentiation to get $\partial z/\partial x = -c^2 x/(a^2 z)$, $\partial z/\partial y = -c^2 y/(b^2 z)$. At (x_0, y_0, z_0), $z_0 \ne 0$, a normal to the surface is $-[c^2 x_0/(a^2 z_0)]\mathbf{i} - [c^2 y_0/(b^2 z_0)]\mathbf{j} - \mathbf{k}$ so the tangent

plane is $-\dfrac{c^2 x_0}{a^2 z_0}x - \dfrac{c^2 y_0}{b^2 z_0}y - z = -\dfrac{c^2 x_0^2}{a^2 z_0} - \dfrac{c^2 y_0^2}{b^2 z_0} - z_0$, $\dfrac{x_0 x}{a^2} + \dfrac{y_0 y}{b^2} - \dfrac{z_0 z}{c^2} = \dfrac{x_0^2}{a^2} + \dfrac{y_0^2}{b^2} + \dfrac{z_0^2}{c^2} = 1$

40. $\partial z/\partial x = 2x/a^2$, $\partial z/\partial y = 2y/b^2$. At (x_0, y_0, z_0) the vector $(2x_0/a^2)\mathbf{i} + (2y_0/b^2)\mathbf{j} - \mathbf{k}$ is normal to the surface so the tangent plane is $(2x_0/a^2)x + (2y_0/b^2)y - z = 2x_0^2/a^2 + 2y_0^2/b^2 - z_0$, but $z_0 = x_0^2/a^2 + y_0^2/b^2$ so $(2x_0/a^2)x + (2y_0/b^2)y - z = 2z_0 - z_0 = z_0$, $2x_0 x/a^2 + 2y_0 y/b^2 = z - z_0$

41. $\mathbf{n}_1 = f_x(x_0, y_0)\mathbf{i} + f_y(x_0, y_0)\mathbf{j} - \mathbf{k}$ and $\mathbf{n}_2 = g_x(x_0, y_0)\mathbf{i} + g_y(x_0, y_0)\mathbf{j} - \mathbf{k}$ are normal, respectively, to $z = f(x, y)$ and $z = g(x, y)$ at P; $\mathbf{n}_1$ and $\mathbf{n}_2$ are perpendicular if and only if $\mathbf{n}_1 \cdot \mathbf{n}_2 = 0$, $f_x(x_0, y_0)g_x(x_0, y_0) + f_y(x_0, y_0)g_y(x_0, y_0) + 1 = 0$, $f_x(x_0, y_0)g_x(x_0, y_0) + f_y(x_0, y_0)g_y(x_0, y_0) = -1$.

EXERCISE SET 16.6

1. $\nabla z = 4\mathbf{i} - 8\mathbf{j}$

2. $\nabla z = -4e^{-3y}\sin 4x\mathbf{i} - 3e^{-3y}\cos 4x\mathbf{j}$

3. $\nabla z = \dfrac{x}{x^2 + y^2}\mathbf{i} + \dfrac{y}{x^2 + y^2}\mathbf{j}$

4. $\nabla z = e^{-5x}\sec x^2 y\left[(2xy\tan x^2 y - 5)\mathbf{i} + x^2\tan x^2 y\mathbf{j}\right]$

5. $\nabla f(x, y) = 3(2x + y)(x^2 + xy)^2\mathbf{i} + 3x(x^2 + xy)^2\mathbf{j}$, $\nabla f(-1, -1) = -36\mathbf{i} - 12\mathbf{j}$

6. $\nabla f(x, y) = -x(x^2 + y^2)^{-3/2}\mathbf{i} - y(x^2 + y^2)^{-3/2}\mathbf{j}$, $\nabla f(3, 4) = -(3/125)\mathbf{i} - (4/125)\mathbf{j}$

7. $\nabla f(x,y) = [y/(x+y)]\mathbf{i} + [y/(x+y) + \ln(x+y)]\mathbf{j}$, $\nabla f(-3,4) = 4\mathbf{i} + 4\mathbf{j}$

8. $\nabla f(x,y) = 3y^2 \tan^2 x \sec^2 x\mathbf{i} + 2y \tan^3 x\mathbf{j}$, $\nabla f(\pi/4, -3) = 54\mathbf{i} - 6\mathbf{j}$

9. $\nabla f(x,y) = (3y/2)(1+xy)^{1/2}\mathbf{i} + (3x/2)(1+xy)^{1/2}\mathbf{j}$, $\nabla f(3,1) = 3\mathbf{i} + 9\mathbf{j}$,
$D_{\mathbf{u}}f = \nabla f \cdot \mathbf{u} = 12/\sqrt{2} = 6\sqrt{2}$

10. $\nabla f(x,y) = 2ye^{2xy}\mathbf{i} + 2xe^{2xy}\mathbf{j}$, $\nabla f(4,0) = 8\mathbf{j}$, $D_{\mathbf{u}}f = \nabla f \cdot \mathbf{u} = 32/5$

11. $\nabla f(x,y) = [2x/(1+x^2+y)]\mathbf{i} + [1/(1+x^2+y)]\mathbf{j}$, $\nabla f(0,0) = \mathbf{j}$, $D_{\mathbf{u}}f = -3/\sqrt{10}$

12. $\nabla f(x,y) = -[(c+d)y/(x-y)^2]\mathbf{i} + [(c+d)x/(x-y)^2]\mathbf{j}$, $\nabla f(3,4) = -4(c+d)\mathbf{i} + 3(c+d)\mathbf{j}$,
$D_{\mathbf{u}}f = -(7/5)(c+d)$

13. $\nabla f(x,y) = 12x^2y^2\mathbf{i} + 8x^3y\mathbf{j}$, $\nabla f(2,1) = 48\mathbf{i} + 64\mathbf{j}$, $\mathbf{u} = (4/5)\mathbf{i} - (3/5)\mathbf{j}$, $D_{\mathbf{u}}f = \nabla f \cdot \mathbf{u} = 0$

14. $\nabla f(x,y) = (2x-3y)\mathbf{i} + (-3x+12y^2)\mathbf{j}$, $\nabla f(-2,0) = -4\mathbf{i} + 6\mathbf{j}$, $\mathbf{u} = (\mathbf{i}+2\mathbf{j})/\sqrt{5}$, $D_{\mathbf{u}}f = 8/\sqrt{5}$

15. $\nabla f(x,y) = (y^2/x)\mathbf{i} + 2y \ln x\mathbf{j}$, $\nabla f(1,4) = 16\mathbf{i}$, $\mathbf{u} = (-\mathbf{i}+\mathbf{j})/\sqrt{2}$, $D_{\mathbf{u}}f = -8\sqrt{2}$

16. $\nabla f(x,y) = e^x \cos y\mathbf{i} - e^x \sin y\mathbf{j}$, $\nabla f(0, \pi/4) = (\mathbf{i} - \mathbf{j})/\sqrt{2}$, $\mathbf{u} = (5\mathbf{i} - 2\mathbf{j})/\sqrt{29}$, $D_{\mathbf{u}}f = 7/\sqrt{58}$

17. $\nabla f(x,y) = -[y/(x^2+y^2)]\mathbf{i} + [x/(x^2+y^2)]\mathbf{j}$, $\nabla f(-2,2) = -(\mathbf{i}+\mathbf{j})/4$, $\mathbf{u} = -(\mathbf{i}+\mathbf{j})/\sqrt{2}$,
$D_{\mathbf{u}}f = \sqrt{2}/4$

18. $\nabla f(x,y) = (e^y - ye^x)\mathbf{i} + (xe^y - e^x)\mathbf{j}$, $\nabla f(0,0) = \mathbf{i} - \mathbf{j}$, $\mathbf{u} = (5\mathbf{i} - 2\mathbf{j})/\sqrt{29}$, $D_{\mathbf{u}}f = 7/\sqrt{29}$

19. $\nabla f(x,y) = (y/2)(xy)^{-1/2}\mathbf{i} + (x/2)(xy)^{-1/2}\mathbf{j}$, $\nabla f(1,4) = \mathbf{i} + (1/4)\mathbf{j}$,
$\mathbf{u} = \cos \theta\mathbf{i} + \sin \theta\mathbf{j} = (1/2)\mathbf{i} + (\sqrt{3}/2)\mathbf{j}$, $D_{\mathbf{u}}f = 1/2 + \sqrt{3}/8$

20. $\nabla f(x,y) = [2y/(x+y)^2]\mathbf{i} - [2x/(x+y)^2]\mathbf{j}$, $\nabla f(-1,-2) = -(4/9)\mathbf{i} + (2/9)\mathbf{j}$, $\mathbf{u} = \mathbf{j}$, $D_{\mathbf{u}}f = 2/9$

21. $\nabla f(x,y) = 2\sec^2(2x+y)\mathbf{i} + \sec^2(2x+y)\mathbf{j}$, $\nabla f(\pi/6, \pi/3) = 8\mathbf{i} + 4\mathbf{j}$, $\mathbf{u} = (\mathbf{i} - \mathbf{j})/\sqrt{2}$, $D_{\mathbf{u}}f = 2\sqrt{2}$

22. $\nabla f(x,y) = \cosh x \cosh y\mathbf{i} + \sinh x \sinh y\mathbf{j}$, $\nabla f(0,0) = \mathbf{i}$, $\mathbf{u} = -\mathbf{i}$, $D_{\mathbf{u}}f = -1$

23. $f(1,2) = 3$, level curve
$4x - 2y + 3 = 3$,
$4x - 2y = 0$.
$\nabla f(x,y) = 4\mathbf{i} - 2\mathbf{j}$
$\nabla f(1,2) = 4\mathbf{i} - 2\mathbf{j}$

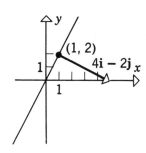

24. $f(-2,2) = 1/2$, level curve
$y/x^2 = 1/2$, $y = x^2/2$ for $x \neq 0$.
$\nabla f(x,y) = -\left(2y/x^3\right)\mathbf{i} + \left(1/x^2\right)\mathbf{j}$
$\nabla f(-2,2) = (1/2)\mathbf{i} + (1/4)\mathbf{j}$

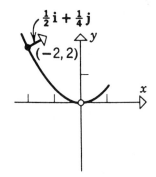

25. $f(-2,0) = 4$, level curve
$x^2 + 4y^2 = 4$, $x^2/4 + y^2 = 1$.
$\nabla f(x,y) = 2x\mathbf{i} + 8y\mathbf{j}$
$\nabla f(-2,0) = -4\mathbf{i}$

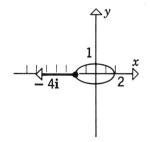

26. $f(2,-1) = 3$, level curve
$x^2 - y^2 = 3$.
$\nabla f(x,y) = 2x\mathbf{i} - 2y\mathbf{j}$
$\nabla f(2,-1) = 4\mathbf{i} + 2\mathbf{j}$

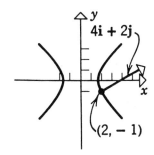

27. $\nabla f(x,y) = 12x^2y^2\mathbf{i} + 8x^3y\mathbf{j}$, $\nabla f(-1,1) = 12\mathbf{i} - 8\mathbf{j}$, $\mathbf{u} = (3\mathbf{i} - 2\mathbf{j})/\sqrt{13}$, $\|\nabla f(-1,1)\| = 4\sqrt{13}$

28. $\nabla f(x,y) = 3\mathbf{i}$ $(1/y)\mathbf{j}$, $\nabla f(2,4) - 3\mathbf{i} - (1/4)\mathbf{j}$, $\mathbf{u} = (12\mathbf{i} - \mathbf{j})/\sqrt{145}$, $\|\nabla f(2,4)\| = \sqrt{145}/4$

29. $\nabla f(x,y) = x\left(x^2 + y^2\right)^{-1/2}\mathbf{i} + y\left(x^2 + y^2\right)^{-1/2}\mathbf{j}$, $\nabla f(4,-3) = (4\mathbf{i} - 3\mathbf{j})/5$, $\mathbf{u} = (4\mathbf{i} - 3\mathbf{j})/5$, $\|\nabla f(4,-3)\| = 1$

30. $\nabla f(x,y) = y(x + y)^{-2}\mathbf{i} - x(x + y)^{-2}\mathbf{j}$, $\nabla f(0,2) = (1/2)\mathbf{i}$, $\mathbf{u} = \mathbf{i}$, $\|\nabla f(0,2)\| = 1/2$

31. $\nabla f(x,y) = -2x\mathbf{i} - 2y\mathbf{j}$, $\nabla f(-1,-3) = 2\mathbf{i} + 6\mathbf{j}$, $\mathbf{u} = -(\mathbf{i} + 3\mathbf{j})/\sqrt{10}$, $-\|\nabla f(-1,-3)\| = -2\sqrt{10}$

32. $\nabla f(x,y) = ye^{xy}\mathbf{i} + xe^{xy}\mathbf{j}$; $\nabla f(2,3) = e^6(3\mathbf{i} + 2\mathbf{j})$, $\mathbf{u} = -(3\mathbf{i} + 2\mathbf{j})/\sqrt{13}$, $-\|\nabla f(2,3)\| = -\sqrt{13}e^6$

33. $\nabla f(x,y) = -3\sin(3x - y)\mathbf{i} + \sin(3x - y)\mathbf{j}$, $\nabla f(\pi/6, \pi/4) = (-3\mathbf{i} + \mathbf{j})/\sqrt{2}$, $\mathbf{u} = (3\mathbf{i} - \mathbf{j})/\sqrt{10}$, $-\|\nabla f(\pi/6, \pi/4)\| = -\sqrt{5}$

34. $\nabla f(x,y) = \dfrac{y}{(x + y)^2}\sqrt{\dfrac{x + y}{x - y}}\mathbf{i} - \dfrac{x}{(x + y)^2}\sqrt{\dfrac{x + y}{x - y}}\mathbf{j}$, $\nabla f(3,1) = (\sqrt{2}/16)(\mathbf{i} - 3\mathbf{j})$,
    $\mathbf{u} = -(\mathbf{i} - 3\mathbf{j})/\sqrt{10}$, $-\|\nabla f(3,1)\| = -\sqrt{5}/8$

35. $\nabla f(x,y) = y(x + y)^{-2}\mathbf{i} - x(x + y)^{-2}\mathbf{j}$, $\nabla f(1,0) = -\mathbf{j}$, $\overrightarrow{PQ} = -2\mathbf{i} - \mathbf{j}$, $\mathbf{u} = (-2\mathbf{i} - \mathbf{j})/\sqrt{5}$, $D_\mathbf{u}f = 1/\sqrt{5}$

36. $\nabla f(x,y) = -e^{-x}\sec y\mathbf{i} + e^{-x}\sec y\tan y\mathbf{j}$, $\nabla f(0, \pi/4) = \sqrt{2}(-\mathbf{i} + \mathbf{j})$, $\overrightarrow{PO} = -(\pi/4)\mathbf{j}$, $\mathbf{u} = -\mathbf{j}$, $D_\mathbf{u}f = -\sqrt{2}$

37. $\nabla f(x,y) = \dfrac{ye^y}{2\sqrt{xy}}\mathbf{i} + \left(\sqrt{xy}e^y + \dfrac{xe^y}{2\sqrt{xy}}\right)\mathbf{j}$, $\nabla f(1,1) = (e/2)(\mathbf{i} + 3\mathbf{j})$, $\mathbf{u} = -\mathbf{j}$, $D_\mathbf{u}f = -3e/2$

38. $\nabla f(x,y) = -y(x + y)^{-2}\mathbf{i} + x(x + y)^{-2}\mathbf{j}$, $\nabla f(2,3) = (-3\mathbf{i} + 2\mathbf{j})/25$, if $D_\mathbf{u}f = 0$ then $\mathbf{u}$ and ∇f are perpendicular, by inspection $2\mathbf{i} + 3\mathbf{j}$ is perpendicular to $\nabla f(2,3)$ so $\mathbf{u} = \pm(2\mathbf{i} + 3\mathbf{j})/\sqrt{13}$.

39. $\nabla f(x,y) = 8xy\mathbf{i} + 4x^2\mathbf{j}$, $\nabla f(1,-2) = -16\mathbf{i} + 4\mathbf{j}$ is perpendicular to the level curve through P so $\mathbf{u} = \pm(-4\mathbf{i} + \mathbf{j})/\sqrt{17}$.

40. $\nabla f(x,y) = (6xy - y)\mathbf{i} + (3x^2 - x)\mathbf{j}$, $\nabla f(2,-3) = -33\mathbf{i} + 10\mathbf{j}$ is perpendicular to the level curve through P so $\mathbf{u} = \pm(-33\mathbf{i} + 10\mathbf{j})/\sqrt{1189}$.

41. Solve the system $(3/5)f_x(1,2) - (4/5)f_y(1,2) = -5$, $(4/5)f_x(1,2) + (3/5)f_y(1,2) = 10$ for $f_x(1,2)$ and $f_y(1,2)$ to get $f_x(1,2) = 5$, $f_y(1,2) = 10$. For (c), $\nabla f(1,2) = 5\mathbf{i} + 10\mathbf{j}$, $\mathbf{u} = (-\mathbf{i} - 2\mathbf{j})/\sqrt{5}$, $D_\mathbf{u}f = -5\sqrt{5}$.

42. $\nabla f(-5,1) = -3\mathbf{i} + 2\mathbf{j}$, $\overrightarrow{PQ} = \mathbf{i} + 2\mathbf{j}$, $\mathbf{u} = (\mathbf{i} + 2\mathbf{j})/\sqrt{5}$, $D_{\mathbf{u}}f = 1/\sqrt{5}$

43. $\nabla f(4,-5) = 2\mathbf{i} - \mathbf{j}$, $\mathbf{u} = (5\mathbf{i} + 2\mathbf{j})/\sqrt{29}$, $D_{\mathbf{u}}f = 8/\sqrt{29}$

44. Let $\mathbf{u} = u_1\mathbf{i} + u_2\mathbf{j}$ where $u_1^2 + u_2^2 = 1$, but $D_{\mathbf{u}}f = \nabla f \cdot \mathbf{u} = u_1 - 2u_2 = -2$ so $u_1 = 2u_2 - 2$, $(2u_2 - 2)^2 + u_2^2 = 1$, $5u_2^2 - 8u_2 + 3 = 0$, $u_2 = 1$ or $u_2 = 3/5$ thus $u_1 = 0$ or $u_1 = -4/5$; $\mathbf{u} = \mathbf{j}$ or $\mathbf{u} = -\frac{4}{5}\mathbf{i} + \frac{3}{5}\mathbf{j}$.

45. $\nabla z = 6x\mathbf{i} - 2y\mathbf{j}$, $\|\nabla z\| = \sqrt{36x^2 + 4y^2} = 6$ if $36x^2 + 4y^2 = 36$; all points on the ellipse $9x^2 + y^2 = 9$.

46. $\nabla z = 3\mathbf{i} + 2y\mathbf{j}$, $\|\nabla z\| = \sqrt{9 + 4y^2}$, but $\dfrac{d}{ds}(\|\nabla z\|)$ is just the directional derivative of $\|\nabla z\|$; $\nabla\|\nabla z\| = \dfrac{4y}{\sqrt{9 + 4y^2}}\mathbf{j}$, at $(5,2)$, $\nabla\|\nabla z\| = \dfrac{8}{5}\mathbf{j}$ so the maximum value of $\dfrac{d}{ds}(\|\nabla z\|)$ is $\dfrac{8}{5}$ and is attained in the direction of $\mathbf{u} = \mathbf{j}$.

47. $\mathbf{r} = t\mathbf{i} - t^2\mathbf{j}$, $d\mathbf{r}/dt = \mathbf{i} - 2t\mathbf{j} = \mathbf{i} - 4\mathbf{j}$ at the point $(2,-4)$, $\mathbf{u} = (\mathbf{i} - 4\mathbf{j})/\sqrt{17}$; $dz/ds = D_{\mathbf{u}}z = \nabla z \cdot \mathbf{u} = 36/\sqrt{17}$.

48. (a) $\nabla T(x,y) = \dfrac{y(1 - x^2 + y^2)}{(1 + x^2 + y^2)^2}\mathbf{i} + \dfrac{x(1 + x^2 - y^2)}{(1 + x^2 + y^2)^2}\mathbf{j}$, $\nabla T(1,1) = (\mathbf{i} + \mathbf{j})/9$, $\mathbf{u} = (2\mathbf{i} - \mathbf{j})/\sqrt{5}$, $D_{\mathbf{u}}T = 1/(9\sqrt{5})$

    (b) $\mathbf{u} = -(\mathbf{i} + \mathbf{j})/\sqrt{2}$, opposite to $\nabla T(1,1)$

49. (a) $\nabla V(x,y) = -2e^{-2x}\cos 2y\,\mathbf{i} - 2e^{-2x}\sin 2y\,\mathbf{j}$, $\mathbf{E} = -\nabla V(\pi/4, 0) = 2e^{-\pi/2}\mathbf{i}$

    (b) $V(x,y)$ decreases most rapidly in the direction of $-\nabla V(x,y)$ which is $\mathbf{E}$.

50. $\nabla z = -4x\mathbf{i} - 8y\mathbf{j}$, if $x = -20$ and $y = 5$ then $\nabla z = 80\mathbf{i} - 40\mathbf{j}$.

    (a) $\mathbf{u} = -\mathbf{i}$ points due west, $D_{\mathbf{u}}z = -80$, the climber will descend because z is decreasing.

    (b) $\mathbf{u} = (\mathbf{i} + \mathbf{j})/\sqrt{2}$ points northeast, $D_{\mathbf{u}}z = 20/\sqrt{2}$, the climber will ascend at the rate of $20\sqrt{2}$ ft per ft of travel in the xy-plane.

    (c) The climber will travel a level path in a direction perpendicular to $\nabla z = 80\mathbf{i} - 40\mathbf{j}$, by inspection $\pm(\mathbf{i} + 2\mathbf{j})/\sqrt{5}$ are unit vectors in these directions; $(\mathbf{i} + 2\mathbf{j})/\sqrt{5}$ makes an angle of $\cos^{-1}(2/\sqrt{5}) \approx 27°$ with the positive y-axis so $-(\mathbf{i}+2\mathbf{j})/\sqrt{5}$ makes the same angle with the negative y-axis. The compass direction should be N $27°$ E or S $27°$ W.

51. (a) $\nabla r = \dfrac{x}{\sqrt{x^2 + y^2}}\mathbf{i} + \dfrac{y}{\sqrt{x^2 + y^2}}\mathbf{j} = \mathbf{r}/r$

(b) $\nabla f(r) = \dfrac{\partial f(r)}{\partial x}\mathbf{i} + \dfrac{\partial f(r)}{\partial y}\mathbf{j} = f'(r)\dfrac{\partial r}{\partial x}\mathbf{i} + f'(r)\dfrac{\partial r}{\partial y}\mathbf{j} = f'(r)\nabla r$

52. (a) $\nabla\left(re^{-3r}\right) = \dfrac{(1-3r)}{r}e^{-3r}\mathbf{r}$

  (b) $3r^2\mathbf{r} = \dfrac{f'(r)}{r}\mathbf{r}$ so $f'(r) = 3r^3$, $f(r) = \dfrac{3}{4}r^4 + C$, $f(2) = 12 + C = 1$, $C = -11$;

  $f(r) = \dfrac{3}{4}r^4 - 11.$

53. $\mathbf{u}_r = \cos\theta\,\mathbf{i} + \sin\theta\,\mathbf{j}$, $\mathbf{u}_\theta = -\sin\theta\,\mathbf{i} + \cos\theta\,\mathbf{j}$,

$\nabla z = \dfrac{\partial z}{\partial x}\mathbf{i} + \dfrac{\partial z}{\partial y}\mathbf{j} = \left(\dfrac{\partial z}{\partial r}\cos\theta - \dfrac{1}{r}\dfrac{\partial z}{\partial \theta}\sin\theta\right)\mathbf{i} + \left(\dfrac{\partial z}{\partial r}\sin\theta + \dfrac{1}{r}\dfrac{\partial z}{\partial x}\cos\theta\right)\mathbf{j}$

$= \dfrac{\partial z}{\partial r}(\cos\theta\,\mathbf{i} + \sin\theta\,\mathbf{j}) + \dfrac{1}{r}\dfrac{\partial z}{\partial \theta}(-\sin\theta\,\mathbf{i} + \cos\theta\,\mathbf{j}) = \dfrac{\partial z}{\partial r}\mathbf{u}_r + \dfrac{1}{r}\dfrac{\partial z}{\partial \theta}\mathbf{u}_\theta$

54. (a) $\nabla(f+g) = (f_x + g_x)\mathbf{i} + (f_y + g_y)\mathbf{j} = (f_x\mathbf{i} + f_y\mathbf{j}) + (g_x\mathbf{i} + g_y\mathbf{j}) = \nabla f + \nabla g$

  (b) $\nabla(cf) = (cf_x)\mathbf{i} + (cf_y)\mathbf{j} = c\,(f_x\mathbf{i} + f_y\mathbf{j}) = c\nabla f$

  (c) $\nabla(fg) = (fg_x + gf_x)\mathbf{i} + (fg_y + gf_y)\mathbf{j} = f\,(g_x\mathbf{i} + g_y\mathbf{j}) + g\,(f_x\mathbf{i} + f_y\mathbf{j}) = f\nabla g + g\nabla f$

  (d) $\nabla(f/g) = \dfrac{gf_x - fg_x}{g^2}\mathbf{i} + \dfrac{gf_y - fg_y}{g^2}\mathbf{j} = \dfrac{g\,(f_x\mathbf{i} + f_y\mathbf{j}) - f\,(g_x\mathbf{i} + g_y\mathbf{j})}{g^2} = \dfrac{g\nabla f - f\nabla g}{g^2}$

  (e) $\nabla\left(f^p\right) = \left(pf^{p-1}f_x\right)\mathbf{i} + \left(pf^{p-1}f_y\right)\mathbf{j} = pf^{p-1}\,(f_x\mathbf{i} + f_y\mathbf{j}) = pf^{p-1}\nabla f$

55. $dz/dt = (\partial z/\partial x)(dx/dt) + (\partial z/\partial y)(dy/dt)$

  $= (\partial z/\partial x\,\mathbf{i} + \partial z/\partial y\,\mathbf{j})\cdot(dx/dt\,\mathbf{i} + dy/dt\,\mathbf{j}) = \nabla z\cdot\mathbf{r}'(t)$

56. $\nabla f(x,y) = f_x(x,y)\mathbf{i} + f_y(x,y)\mathbf{j}$, if $\nabla f(x,y) = 0$ throughout the region then

  $f_x(x,y) = f_y(x,y) = 0$ throughout the region, the result follows from Exercise 70, Section 16.4

57. Let $\mathbf{u}_1$ and $\mathbf{u}_2$ be nonparallel unit vectors for which the directional derivative is zero. Let $\mathbf{u}$ be any other unit vector, then $\mathbf{u} = c_1\mathbf{u}_1 + c_2\mathbf{u}_2$ for some choice of scalars c_1 and c_2;

  $D_{\mathbf{u}}f(x,y) = \nabla f(x,y)\cdot\mathbf{u} = c_1\nabla f(x,y)\cdot\mathbf{u}_1 + c_2\nabla f(x,y)\cdot\mathbf{u}_2$

  $= c_1 D_{\mathbf{u}_1}f(x,y) + c_2 D_{\mathbf{u}_2}f(x,y) = 0.$

EXERCISE SET 16.7

1. $165t^{32}$

2. $\dfrac{3 - (4/3)t^{-1/3} - 24t^{-7}}{3t - 2t^{2/3} + 4t^{-6}}$

3. $-2t \cos\left(t^2\right)$

4. $\dfrac{1 - 512t^5 - 2560t^5 \ln t}{2t\sqrt{1 + \ln t} - 512t^5 \ln t}$

5. 3264

6. 0

7. $\nabla f(x,y,z) = 20x^4 y^2 z^3 \mathbf{i} + 8x^5 yz^3 \mathbf{j} + 12x^5 y^2 z^2 \mathbf{k}$, $\nabla f(2,-1,1) = 320\mathbf{i} - 256\mathbf{j} + 384\mathbf{k}$, $D_{\mathbf{u}}f = -320$

8. $\nabla f(x,y,z) = yze^{xz}\mathbf{i} + e^{xz}\mathbf{j} + (xye^{xz} + 2z)\,\mathbf{k}$, $\nabla f(0,2,3) = 6\mathbf{i} + \mathbf{j} + 6k$, $D_{\mathbf{u}}f = 45/7$

9. $\nabla f(x,y,z) = \dfrac{2x}{x^2 + 2y^2 + 3z^2}\mathbf{i} + \dfrac{4y}{x^2 + 2y^2 + 3z^2}\mathbf{j} + \dfrac{6z}{x^2 + 2y^2 + 3z^2}\mathbf{k}$,
$\nabla f(-1,2,4) = (-2/57)\mathbf{i} + (8/57)\mathbf{j} + (24/57)\mathbf{k}$, $D_{\mathbf{u}}f = -314/741$

10. $\nabla f(x,y,z) = yz \cos xyz\,\mathbf{i} + xz \cos xyz\,\mathbf{j} + xy \cos xyz\,\mathbf{k}$,
$\nabla f(1/2, 1/3, \pi) = (\pi\sqrt{3}/6)\mathbf{i} + (\pi\sqrt{3}/4)\mathbf{j} + (\sqrt{3}/12)\mathbf{k}$, $D_{\mathbf{u}}f = (1 - \pi)/12$

11. $\nabla f(x,y,z) = \left(3x^2 z - 2xy\right)\mathbf{i} - x^2\mathbf{j} + \left(x^3 + 2z\right)\mathbf{k}$, $\nabla f(2,-1,1) = 16\mathbf{i} - 4\mathbf{j} + 10\mathbf{k}$,
$\mathbf{u} = (3\mathbf{i} - \mathbf{j} + 2\mathbf{k})/\sqrt{14}$, $D_{\mathbf{u}}f = 72/\sqrt{14}$

12. $\nabla f(x,y,z) = -x\left(x^2 + z^2\right)^{-1/2}\mathbf{i} + \mathbf{j} - z\left(x^2 + z^2\right)^{-1/2}\mathbf{k}$, $\nabla f(-3,1,4) = (3/5)\mathbf{i} + \mathbf{j} - (4/5)\mathbf{k}$,
$\mathbf{u} = (2\mathbf{i} - 2\mathbf{j} - \mathbf{k})/3$, $D_{\mathbf{u}}f = 0$

13. $\nabla f(x,y,z) = -\dfrac{1}{z+y}\mathbf{i} - \dfrac{z-x}{(z+y)^2}\mathbf{j} + \dfrac{y+x}{(z+y)^2}\mathbf{k}$, $\nabla f(1,0,-3) = (1/3)\mathbf{i} + (4/9)\mathbf{j} + (1/9)\mathbf{k}$,
$\mathbf{u} = (-6\mathbf{i} + 3\mathbf{j} - 2\mathbf{k})/7$, $D_{\mathbf{u}}f = -8/63$

14. $\nabla f(x,y,z) = e^{x+y+3z}(\mathbf{i} + \mathbf{j} + 3\mathbf{k})$, $\nabla f(-2,2,-1) = e^{-3}(\mathbf{i} + \mathbf{j} + 3\mathbf{k})$, $\mathbf{u} = (20\mathbf{i} - 4\mathbf{j} + 5\mathbf{k})/21$,
$D_{\mathbf{u}}f = (31/21)e^{-3}$

15. $\nabla f(1,1,-1) = 3\mathbf{i} - 3\mathbf{j}$, $\mathbf{u} = (\mathbf{i} - \mathbf{j})/\sqrt{2}$, $\|\nabla f(1,1,-1)\| = 3\sqrt{2}$

16. $\nabla f(0,-3,0) = (\mathbf{i} - 3\mathbf{j} + 4\mathbf{k})/6$, $\mathbf{u} = (\mathbf{i} - 3\mathbf{j} + 4\mathbf{k})/\sqrt{26}$, $\|\nabla f(0,-3,0)\| = \sqrt{26}/6$

17. $\nabla f(1,2,-2) = (-\mathbf{i} + \mathbf{j})/2$, $\mathbf{u} = (-\mathbf{i} + \mathbf{j})/\sqrt{2}$, $\|\nabla f(1,2,-2)\| = 1/\sqrt{2}$

18. $\nabla f(4,2,2) = (\mathbf{i} - \mathbf{j} - \mathbf{k})/8$, $\mathbf{u} = (\mathbf{i} - \mathbf{j} - \mathbf{k})/\sqrt{3}$, $\|\nabla f(4,2,2)\| = \sqrt{3}/8$

19. $\nabla f(5,7,6) = -\mathbf{i} + 11\mathbf{j} - 12\mathbf{k}$, $\mathbf{u} = (\mathbf{i} - 11\mathbf{j} + 12\mathbf{k})/\sqrt{266}$, $-\|\nabla f(5,7,6)\| = -\sqrt{266}$

20. $\nabla f(0,1,\pi/4) = 2\sqrt{2}(\mathbf{i} - \mathbf{k})$, $\mathbf{u} = -(\mathbf{i} - \mathbf{k})/\sqrt{2}$, $-\|\nabla f(0,1,\pi/4)\| = -4$

21. $\nabla f(2,1,-1) = -\mathbf{i}+\mathbf{j}-\mathbf{k}$. $\overrightarrow{PQ} = -3\mathbf{i}+\mathbf{j}+\mathbf{k}$, $\mathbf{u} = (-3\mathbf{i}+\mathbf{j}+\mathbf{k})/\sqrt{11}$, $D_{\mathbf{u}}f = 3/\sqrt{11}$

22. $\nabla f(-1,-2,1) = 13\mathbf{i}+5\mathbf{j}-20\mathbf{k}$, $\mathbf{u} = -\mathbf{k}$, $D_{\mathbf{u}}f = 20$

23.   Let $\mathbf{u}$ be the unit vector in the direction of $\mathbf{a}$, then

$D_{\mathbf{u}}f(3,-2,1) = \nabla f(3,-2,1)\cdot\mathbf{u} = \|\nabla f(3,-2,1)\|\cos\theta = 5\cos\theta = -5$, $\cos\theta = -1$, $\theta = \pi$ so $\nabla f(3,-2,1)$ is oppositely directed to $\mathbf{u}$; $\nabla f(3,-2,1) = -5\mathbf{u} = -10/3\mathbf{i}+5/3\mathbf{j}+10/3\mathbf{k}$.

24.   **(a)** $\nabla T(1,1,1) = (\mathbf{i}+\mathbf{j}+\mathbf{k})/8$, $\mathbf{u} = -(\mathbf{i}+\mathbf{j}+\mathbf{k})/\sqrt{3}$, $D_{\mathbf{u}}T = -\sqrt{3}/8$

      (b) $(\mathbf{i}+\mathbf{j}+\mathbf{k})/\sqrt{3}$ **(c)** $\sqrt{3}/8$

25. $f(x,y,z) = x^2+y^2+z^2$, $\nabla f(-3,2,-6) = -2(3\mathbf{i}-2\mathbf{j}+6\mathbf{k})$; tangent plane $3x-2y+6z = -49$; normal line $x = -3+3t$, $y = 2-2t$, $z = -6+6t$

26. $f(x,y,z) = xz - yz^3 + yz^2$, $\nabla f(2,-1,1) = \mathbf{i}+3\mathbf{k}$; tangent plane $x+3z = 5$; normal line $x = 2+t$, $y = -1$, $z = 1+3t$

27. $f(x,y,z) = \sqrt{\dfrac{z+x}{y-1}} - z^2$, $\nabla f(3,5,1) = (\mathbf{i}-\mathbf{j}-15\mathbf{k})/8$; tangent plane $x-y-15z = -17$; normal line $x = 3+t$, $y = 5-t$, $z = 1-15t$

28. $f(x,y,z) = \sin xz - 4\cos yz$, $\nabla f(\pi,\pi,1) = -\mathbf{i}-\pi\mathbf{k}$; tangent plane $x+\pi z = 2\pi$; normal line $x = \pi - t$, $y = \pi$, $z = 1 - \pi t$

29. $f(x,y,z) = x^2+y^2+z^2$, if (x_0,y_0,z_0) is on the sphere then $\nabla f(x_0,y_0,z_0) = 2(x_0\mathbf{i}+y_0\mathbf{j}+z_0\mathbf{k})$ is normal to the sphere at (x_0,y_0,z_0), the normal line is $x = x_0+x_0 t$, $y = y_0+y_0 t$, $z = z_0+z_0 t$ which passes through the origin when $t = -1$.

30. $f(x,y,z) = 2x^2+3y^2+4z^2$, if (x_0,y_0,z_0) is on the ellipsoid then

$\nabla f(x_0,y_0,z_0) = 2(2x_0\mathbf{i}+3y_0\mathbf{j}+4z_0\mathbf{k})$ is normal there and hence so is $\mathbf{n}_1 = 2x_0\mathbf{i}+3y_0\mathbf{j}+4z_0\mathbf{k}$; $\mathbf{n}_1$ must be parallel to $\mathbf{n}_2 = \mathbf{i}-2\mathbf{j}+3\mathbf{k}$ which is normal to the given plane so $\mathbf{n}_1 = c\mathbf{n}_2$ for some constant c. Equate corresponding components to get $x_0 = c/2$, $y_0 = -2c/3$, and $z_0 = 3c/4$ which when substituted into the equation of the ellipsoid yields

$2(c^2/4) + 3(4c^2/9) + 4(9c^2/16) = 9$, $c^2 = 108/49$, $c = \pm 6\sqrt{3}/7$. The points on the ellipsoid are $(3\sqrt{3}/7, -4\sqrt{3}/7, 9\sqrt{3}/14)$ and $(-3\sqrt{3}/7, 4\sqrt{3}/7, -9\sqrt{3}/14)$.

31. $f(x,y,z) = x^2+y^2-z^2$, if (x_0,y_0,z_0) is on the surface then $\nabla f(x_0,y_0,z_0) = 2(x_0\mathbf{i}+y_0\mathbf{j}-z_0\mathbf{k})$ is normal there and hence so is $\mathbf{n}_1 = x_0\mathbf{i}+y_0\mathbf{j}-z_0\mathbf{k}$; $\mathbf{n}_1$ must be parallel to $\overrightarrow{PQ} = 3\mathbf{i}+2\mathbf{j}-2\mathbf{k}$ so $\mathbf{n}_1 = c\,\overrightarrow{PQ}$ for some constant c. Equate components to get $x_0 = 3c$, $y_0 = 2c$ and $z_0 = 2c$ which when substituted into the equation of the surface yields $9c^2 + 4c^2 - 4c^2 = 1$, $c^2 = 1/9$, $c = \pm 1/3$ so the points are $(1,2/3,2/3)$ and $(-1,-2/3,-2/3)$.

32. $f_1(x, y, z) = 2x^2 + 3y^2 + z^2$, $f_2(x, y, z) = x^2 + y^2 + z^2 - 6x - 8y - 8z + 24$,

$\mathbf{n}_1 = \nabla f_1(1, 1, 2) = 4\mathbf{i} + 6\mathbf{j} + 4\mathbf{k}$, $\mathbf{n}_2 = \nabla f_2(1, 1, 2) = -4\mathbf{i} - 6\mathbf{j} - 4\mathbf{k}$,

$\mathbf{n}_1 = -\mathbf{n}_2$ so $\mathbf{n}_1$ and $\mathbf{n}_2$ are parallel.

33. $dw = 8dx - 3dy + 4dz$

34. $dw = \left(8xy^3z^7 - 3y\right) dx + \left(12x^2y^2z^7 - 3x\right) dy + \left(28x^2y^3z^6 + 1\right) dz$

35. $dw = \dfrac{yz}{1 + x^2y^2z^2}dx + \dfrac{xz}{1 + x^2y^2z^2}dy + \dfrac{xy}{1 + x^2y^2z^2}dz$

36. $dw = \dfrac{1}{2\sqrt{x}}dx + \dfrac{1}{2\sqrt{y}}dy + \dfrac{1}{2\sqrt{z}}dz$

37. $df = 2y^2z^3dx + 4xyz^3dy + 6xy^2z^2dz$

$\qquad = 2(-1)^2(2)^3(-0.01) + 4(1)(-1)(2)^3(-0.02) + 6(1)(-1)^2(2)^2(0.02) = 0.96$

38. $df = \dfrac{yz(y + z)}{(x + y + z)^2}dx + \dfrac{xz(x + z)}{(x + y + z)^2}dy + \dfrac{xy(x + y)}{(x + y + z)^2}dz$

$\qquad = (-16)(-0.04) + (-12)(0.02) + (-6)(-0.03) = 0.58$

39. $V = \ell h$, $dV = whd\ell + \ell hdw + \ell wdh$,

$|dV| \leq wh|d\ell| + \ell h|dw| + \ell w|dh| \leq (4)(5)(0.05) + (3)(5)(0.05) + (3)(4)(0.05) = 2.35$ cm^3

40. $R = 1/(1/R_1 + 1/R_2 + 1/R_3)$, $\partial R/\partial R_1 = \dfrac{1}{R_1^2(1/R_1 + 1/R_2 + 1/R_3)^2} = R^2/R_1^2$, similarly

$\partial R/\partial R_2 = R^2/R_2^2$ and $\partial R/\partial R_3 = R^2/R_3^2$ so $\dfrac{dR}{R} = (R/R_1)\dfrac{dR_1}{R_1} + (R/R_2)\dfrac{dR_2}{R_2} + (R/R_3)\dfrac{dR_3}{R_3}$,

$\left|\dfrac{dR}{R}\right| \leq (R/R_1)\left|\dfrac{dR_1}{R_1}\right| + (R/R_2)\left|\dfrac{dR_2}{R_2}\right| + (R/R_3)\left|\dfrac{dR_3}{R_3}\right|$

$\qquad \leq (R/R_1)(0.10) + (R/R_2)(0.10) + (R/R_3)(0.10)$

$\qquad = R(1/R_1 + 1/R_2 + 1/R_3)(0.10) = (1)(0.10) = 0.10 = 10\%$

41. $dA = \dfrac{1}{2}b \sin\theta da + \dfrac{1}{2}a \sin\theta db + \dfrac{1}{2}ab \cos\theta d\theta$,

$|dA| \leq \dfrac{1}{2}b \sin\theta |da| + \dfrac{1}{2}a \sin\theta |db| + \dfrac{1}{2}ab |\cos\theta||d\theta|$

$\qquad \leq \dfrac{1}{2}(50)(1/2)(1/2) + \dfrac{1}{2}(40)(1/2)(1/4) + \dfrac{1}{2}(40)(50)\left(\sqrt{3}/2\right)(\pi/90)$

$\qquad = 35/4 + 50\pi\sqrt{3}/9 \approx 39$ ft^2

42. $V = \ell wh$, $dV = whd\ell + \ell hdw + \ell wdh$, $|dV/V| \le |d\ell/\ell| + |dw/w| + |dh/h| \le 3(r/100) = 3r\%$

43. $dw = y^2 z^3 dx + 2xyz^3 dy + 3xy^2 z^2 dz$,
$|dw/w| \le |dx/x| + 2|dy/y| + 3|dz/z| \le (0.01) + 2(0.02) + 3(0.03) = 0.14 = 14\%$

44. $\nabla f = f_x \mathbf{i} + f_y \mathbf{j} + f_z \mathbf{k}$ and $\nabla g = g_x \mathbf{i} + g_y \mathbf{j} + g_z \mathbf{k}$ evaluated at (x_0, y_0, z_0) are normal, respectively, to the surfaces $f(x, y, z) = 0$ and $g(x, y, z) = 0$ at (x_0, y_0, z_0). The surfaces are orthogonal at (x_0, y_0, z_0) if and only if $\nabla f \cdot \nabla g = 0$ so $f_x g_x + f_y g_y + f_z g_z = 0$.

45. $f(x, y, z) = x^2 + y^2 + z^2 - a^2$, $g(x, y, z) = z^2 - x^2 - y^2$. If (x_0, y_0, z_0) is a point of intersection then $f_x g_x + f_y g_y + f_z g_z = (2x_0)(-2x_0) + (2y_0)(-2y_0) + (2z_0)(2z_0) = 4\left(z_0^2 - x_0^2 - y_0^2\right)$, but $z_0^2 - x_0^2 - y_0^2 = 0$ because (x_0, y_0, z_0) is on $z^2 = x^2 + y^2$.

EXERCISE SET 16.8

1. $\partial f / \partial v = 8vw^3 x^4 y^5$, $\partial f / \partial w = 12v^2 w^2 x^4 y^5$, $\partial f / \partial x = 16v^2 w^3 x^3 y^5$, $\partial f / \partial y = 20v^2 w^3 x^4 y^4$

2. $\partial w / \partial r = \cos st + ue^u \cos ur$, $\partial w / \partial s = -rt \sin st$,
$\partial w / \partial t = -rs \sin st$, $\partial w / \partial u = re^u \cos ur + e^u \sin ur$

3. $\partial f / \partial v_1 = 2v_1 / \left(v_3^2 + v_4^2\right)$, $\partial f / \partial v_2 = -2v_2 / \left(v_3^2 + v_4^2\right)$, $\partial f / \partial v_3 = -2v_3 \left(v_1^2 - v_2^2\right) / \left(v_3^2 + v_4^2\right)^2$,
$\partial f / \partial v_4 = -2v_4 \left(v_1^2 - v_2^2\right) / \left(v_3^2 + v_4^2\right)^2$

4. $V_x = 2xe^{2x-y} + e^{2x-y}$, $V_y = -xe^{2x-y} + w$, $V_z = w^2 e^{zw}$, $V_w = wze^{zw} + e^{zw} + y$

5. $128, -512, 32, 64/3$

6. (a) 0 \qquad\qquad (b) 0 \qquad\qquad (c) 0 \qquad\qquad (d) 0

(e) $2(yw + 1)e^{yw} \sin z \cos z$ \qquad\qquad (f) $2xw(yw + 2)e^{yw} \sin z \cos z$

7. $210t^{29}$

8. $\partial z / \partial x = (dz/du)(\partial u / \partial x) = 7u^6(10x) = 70x\left(5x^2 - 2y^3\right)^6$
$\partial z / \partial y = (dz/du)(\partial u / \partial y) = 7u^6(-6y^2) = -42y^2\left(5x^2 - 2y^3\right)^6$

9. $\partial z / \partial r = (dz/dx)(\partial x / \partial r) = 2r \cos^2 \theta / \left(r^2 \cos^2 \theta + 1\right)$,
$\partial z / \partial \theta = (dz/dx)(\partial x / \partial \theta) = -2r^2 \sin \theta \cos \theta / \left(r^2 \cos^2 \theta + 1\right)$

10. $\partial u/\partial x = (\partial u/\partial r)(dr/dx) + (\partial u/\partial t)(\partial t/\partial x)$

    $= \left(s^2 \ln t\right)(2x) + \left(rs^2/t\right)\left(y^3\right) = x(4y+1)^2 \left(1 + 2\ln xy^3\right)$

    $\partial u/\partial y = (\partial u/\partial s)(ds/dy) + (\partial u/\partial t)(\partial t/\partial y)$

    $= (2rs \ln t)(4) + \left(rs^2/t\right)\left(3xy^2\right) = 8x^2(4y+1)\ln xy^3 + 3x^2(4y+1)^2/y$

11. $\partial w/\partial \rho = 2\rho \left(4\sin^2 \phi + \cos^2 \phi\right),\ \partial w/\partial \phi = 6\rho^2 \sin\phi \cos\phi,\ \partial w/\partial\theta = 0$

12. $\dfrac{dw}{dx} = \dfrac{\partial w}{\partial x} + \dfrac{\partial w}{\partial y}\dfrac{dy}{dx} + \dfrac{\partial w}{\partial z}\dfrac{dz}{dx} = 3y^2z^3 + (6xyz^3)(6x) + 9xy^2z^2\left[\dfrac{1}{2}(x-1)^{-1/2}\right]$

13. $\dfrac{dw}{dy} = \dfrac{\partial w}{\partial x}\dfrac{dx}{dy} + \dfrac{\partial w}{\partial y} + \dfrac{\partial w}{\partial z}\dfrac{dz}{dy} = (-2\sin 2y \cos 2y + y + 1/2)/\sqrt{\cos^2 2y + y^2 + y}$

14. (a) $V = \ell w h,\ \dfrac{dV}{dt} = \dfrac{\partial V}{\partial \ell}\dfrac{d\ell}{dt} + \dfrac{\partial V}{\partial w}\dfrac{dw}{dt} + \dfrac{\partial V}{\partial h}\dfrac{dh}{dt} = wh\dfrac{d\ell}{dt} + \ell h\dfrac{dw}{dt} + \ell w\dfrac{dh}{dt}$

    $= (3)(6)(1) + (2)(6)(2) + (2)(3)(3) = 60\ \text{in}^3/\text{sec}$

    (b) $D = \sqrt{\ell^2 + w^2 + h^2};\ dD/dt = (\ell/D)d\ell/dt + (w/D)dw/dt + (h/D)dh/dt$

    $= (2/7)(1) + (3/7)(2) + (6/7)(3) = 26/7\ \text{in/sec}$

15. Let a, b, and c be the lengths of the sides opposite angles A, B, and C, respectively. By the law of cosines $a = \left(b^2 + c^2 - 2bc\cos A\right)^{1/2}$ so

    $\dfrac{da}{dt} = \dfrac{b - c\cos A}{a}\dfrac{db}{dt} + \dfrac{c - b\cos A}{a}\dfrac{dc}{dt} + \dfrac{bc\sin A}{a}\dfrac{dA}{dt} = \dfrac{10-10}{10\sqrt{3}}(4) + \dfrac{20-5}{10\sqrt{3}}(2) + \dfrac{100\sqrt{3}}{10\sqrt{3}}(\pi/60)$

    $= \sqrt{3} + \pi/6\ \text{cm/sec, increasing}$

16. (a) $\partial A/\partial a = (1/2)b\sin\theta = (1/2)(10)\left(\sqrt{3}/2\right) = 5\sqrt{3}/2$

    (b) $\partial A/\partial\theta = (1/2)ab\cos\theta = (1/2)(5)(10)(1/2) = 25/2$

    (c) $b = (2A\csc\theta)/a,\ \partial b/\partial a = -(2A\csc\theta)/a^2 = -b/a = -2$

17. $2x + 4x\partial z/\partial x + 4z + 2z\partial z/\partial x - 3y\partial z/\partial x = 0,\ \partial z/\partial x = -(2x+4z)/(4x+2z-3y);$

    $4x\partial z/\partial y + 2z\partial z/\partial y - 3y\partial z/\partial y - 3z = 0,\ \partial z/\partial y = 3z/(4x+2z-3y)$

18. $\dfrac{\partial z}{\partial x} = -\dfrac{ze^{yz}\cos xz - ye^{xy}\cos yz}{ye^{xy}\sin yz + xe^{yz}\cos xz + ye^{yz}\sin xz},\ \dfrac{\partial z}{\partial y} = -\dfrac{ze^{xy}\sin yz - xe^{xy}\cos yz + ze^{yz}\sin xz}{ye^{xy}\sin yz + xe^{yz}\cos xz + ye^{yz}\sin xz}$

19. $f_{ww} = 0,\ f_{xx} = -2wxyz/\left(x^2 + y^2\right)^2,\ f_{yy} = 2wxyz/\left(x^2 + y^2\right)^2,\ f_{zz} = 0$

20. Let $z = f(u)$ where $u = x + 2y$ then $\partial z/\partial x = (dz/du)(\partial u/\partial x) = dz/du,$

    $\partial z/\partial y = (dz/du)(\partial u/\partial y) = 2dz/du$ so $2\partial z/\partial x - \partial z/\partial y = 2dz/du - 2dz/du = 0$

21. Let $z = f(u)$ where $u = x^2 + y^2$ then $\partial z/\partial x = (dz/du)(\partial u/\partial x) = 2x\, dz/du$,

$\partial z/\partial y = (dz/du)(\partial u/\partial y) = 2y\,dz/du$ so $y\,\partial z/\partial x - x\partial z/\partial y = 2xy\,dz/du - 2xy\,dz/du = 0$

22. $\partial w/\partial x = (dw/d\rho)(\partial \rho/\partial x) = (x/\rho)dw/d\rho$, similarly $\partial w/\partial y = (y/\rho)dw/d\rho$ and

$\partial w/\partial z = (z/\rho)dw/d\rho$ so $(\partial w/\partial x)^2 + (\partial w/\partial y)^2 + (\partial w/\partial z)^2 = (dw/d\rho)^2$

23. Let $w = f(r, s, t)$ where $r = x - y$, $s = y - z$, $t = z - x$;

$\partial w/\partial x = (\partial w/\partial r)(\partial r/\partial x) + (\partial w/\partial t)(\partial t/\partial x) = \partial w/\partial r - \partial w/\partial t$, similarily

$\partial w/\partial y = -\partial w/\partial r + \partial w/\partial s$ and $\partial w/\partial z = -\partial w/\partial s + \partial w/\partial t$ so $\partial w/\partial x + \partial w/\partial y + \partial w/\partial z = 0$

24. $\partial w/\partial \rho = \sin\phi\cos\theta\,\partial w/\partial x + \sin\phi\sin\theta\,\partial w/\partial y + \cos\phi\,\partial w/\partial z$

$\partial w/\partial \phi = \rho\cos\phi\cos\theta\,\partial w/\partial x + \rho\cos\phi\sin\theta\,\partial w/\partial y - \rho\sin\phi\,\partial w/\partial z$

$\partial w/\partial \theta = -\rho\sin\phi\sin\theta\,\partial w/\partial x + \rho\sin\phi\cos\theta\,\partial w/\partial y$

25. $\dfrac{\partial F}{\partial x} + \dfrac{\partial F}{\partial z}\dfrac{\partial z}{\partial x} = 0$ so $\dfrac{\partial z}{\partial x} = -\dfrac{\partial F/\partial x}{\partial F/\partial z}$, $\dfrac{\partial F}{\partial y} + \dfrac{\partial F}{\partial z}\dfrac{\partial z}{\partial y} = 0$ so $\dfrac{\partial z}{\partial y} = -\dfrac{\partial F/\partial y}{\partial F/\partial z}$.

26. $\dfrac{\partial z}{\partial x} = \dfrac{2x + yz}{6yz - xy}$, $\dfrac{\partial z}{\partial y} = \dfrac{xz - 3z^2}{6yz - xy}$

27. $ye^x - 5\sin 3z - 3z = 0$; $\dfrac{\partial z}{\partial x} = -\dfrac{ye^x}{-15\cos 3z - 3} = \dfrac{ye^x}{15\cos 3z + 3}$, $\dfrac{\partial z}{\partial y} = \dfrac{e^x}{15\cos 3z + 3}$.

28. $\ln(1 + z) + xy^2 + z - 1 = 0$; $\dfrac{\partial z}{\partial x} = -\dfrac{y^2(1 + z)}{2 + z}$, $\dfrac{\partial z}{\partial y} = -\dfrac{2xy(1 + z)}{2 + z}$

29. $\nabla f(u, v, w) = \dfrac{\partial f}{\partial x}\mathbf{i} + \dfrac{\partial f}{\partial y}\mathbf{j} + \dfrac{\partial f}{\partial z}\mathbf{k}$

$= \left(\dfrac{\partial f}{\partial u}\dfrac{\partial u}{\partial x} + \dfrac{\partial f}{\partial v}\dfrac{\partial v}{\partial x} + \dfrac{\partial f}{\partial w}\dfrac{\partial w}{\partial x}\right)\mathbf{i} + \left(\dfrac{\partial f}{\partial u}\dfrac{\partial u}{\partial y} + \dfrac{\partial f}{\partial v}\dfrac{\partial v}{\partial y} + \dfrac{\partial f}{\partial w}\dfrac{\partial w}{\partial y}\right)\mathbf{j}$

$+ \left(\dfrac{\partial f}{\partial u}\dfrac{\partial u}{\partial z} + \dfrac{\partial f}{\partial v}\dfrac{\partial v}{\partial z} + \dfrac{\partial f}{\partial w}\dfrac{\partial w}{\partial z}\right)\mathbf{k} = \dfrac{\partial f}{\partial u}\nabla u + \dfrac{\partial f}{\partial v}\nabla v + \dfrac{\partial f}{\partial w}\nabla w$

30. **(a)** $\dfrac{\partial w}{\partial x} = \dfrac{\partial f}{\partial x} + \dfrac{\partial f}{\partial z}\dfrac{\partial z}{\partial x}$ **(b)** $\dfrac{\partial w}{\partial y} = \dfrac{\partial f}{\partial y} + \dfrac{\partial f}{\partial z}\dfrac{\partial z}{\partial y}$

31. $w_r = e^r/(e^r + e^s + e^t + e^u)$, $w_{rs} = -e^r e^s/(e^r + e^s + e^t + e^u)^2$,

$w_{rst} = 2e^r e^s e^t/(e^r + e^s + e^t + e^u)^3$,

$w_{rstu} = -6e^r e^s e^t e^u/(e^r + e^s + e^t + e^u)^4 = -6e^{r+s+t+u}/e^{4w} = -6e^{r+s+t+u-4w}$

32. $\partial w/\partial y_1 = a_1 \partial w/\partial x_1 + a_2 \partial w/\partial x_2 + a_3 \partial w/\partial x_3,$
$\partial w/\partial y_2 = b_1 \partial w/\partial x_1 + b_2 \partial w/\partial x_2 + b_3 \partial w/\partial x_3$

33. (a) $dw/dt = \displaystyle\sum_{i=1}^{4} (\partial w/\partial x_i)(dx_i/dt)$

     (b) $\partial w/\partial v_j = \displaystyle\sum_{i=1}^{4} (\partial w/\partial x_i)(\partial x_i/\partial v_j)$ for $j = 1, 2, 3$

34. Let $u = x_1^2 + x_2^2 + \ldots + x_n^2$ then $w = u^k$, $\partial w/\partial x_i = k u^{k-1}(2x_i) = 2k\, x_i u^{k-1}$,
$\partial^2 w/\partial x_i^2 = 2k(k-1)x_i u^{k-2}(2x_i) + 2k u^{k-1} = 4k(k-1)x_i^2 u^{k-2} + 2k u^{k-1}$ for $i = 1, 2, \ldots, n$

so $\displaystyle\sum_{i=1}^{4} \partial^2 w/\partial x_i^2 = 4k(k-1) u^{k-2} \sum_{i=1}^{n} x_i^2 + 2kn\, u^{k-1}$
$$= 4k(k-1)u^{k-2}u + 2kn\, u^{k-1} = 2k u^{k-1}[2(k-1) + n]$$
which is 0 if $k = 0$ or if $2(k-1) + n = 0$, $k = 1 - n/2$.

35. $dF/dx = (\partial F/\partial u)(du/dx) + (\partial F/\partial v)(dv/dx)$
$$= -f(u)a'(x) + f(v)b'(x) = f(b(x))b'(x) - f(a(x))a'(x)$$

36. (a) $2xe^{x^4} - e^{x^2}$ (b) $-\left(\cos^3 x + 2\right)^{2/3} \sin x - \left(\sin^3 x + 2\right)^{2/3} \cos x$
     (c) $3x^2 \sin^5(x^3) - 3\sin^5(3x)$ (d) $2e^{2x}(\ln e^{2x})^4 - e^x(\ln e^x)^4 = 32x^4 e^{2x} - x^4 e^x$

EXERCISE SET 16.9

1. $f_x = 6x + 2y = 0$, $f_y = 2x + 2y = 0$; critical point $(0,0)$; $D > 0$ and $f_{xx} > 0$ at $(0,0)$, relative minimum.

2. $f_x = 3x^2 - 3y = 0$, $f_y = -3x - 3y^2 = 0$; critical points $(0,0)$ and $(-1,1)$; $D < 0$ at $(0,0)$, saddle point; $D > 0$ and $f_{xx} < 0$ at $(-1,1)$, relative maximum.

3. $f_x = y + 2 = 0$, $f_y = 2y + x + 3 = 0$; critical point $(1,-2)$; $D < 0$ at $(1,-2)$, saddle point.

4. $f_x = 2x + y - 2 = 0$, $f_y = x - 2 = 0$; critical point $(2,-2)$; $D < 0$ at $(2,-2)$, saddle point.

5. $f_x = 2x + y - 3 = 0$, $f_y = x + 2y = 0$; critical point $(2,-1)$; $D > 0$ and $f_{xx} > 0$ at $(2,-1)$, relative minimum.

6. $f_x = y - 3x^2 = 0$, $f_y = x - 2y = 0$; critical points $(0,0)$ and $(1/6, 1/12)$; $D < 0$ at $(0,0)$, saddle point; $D > 0$ and $f_{xx} < 0$ at $(1/6, 1/12)$, relative maximum.

7. $f_x = 2x - 2xy = 0$, $f_y = 4y - x^2 = 0$; critical points $(0,0)$ and $(\pm 2, 1)$; $D > 0$ and $f_{xx} > 0$ at $(0,0)$, relative minimum; $D < 0$ at $(\pm 2, 1)$, saddle points.

8. $f_x = 4x - 4y = 0$, $f_y = -4x + 4y^3 = 0$; critical points $(0,0)$, $(-1,-1)$, and $(1,1)$; $D < 0$ at $(0,0)$, saddle point; $D > 0$ and $f_{xx} > 0$ at $(-1,-1)$ and $(1,1)$, relative minima.

9. $f_x = 2x - 2/(x^2 y) = 0$, $f_y = 2y - 2/(xy^2) = 0$; critical points $(-1,-1)$ and $(1,1)$; $D > 0$ and $f_{xx} > 0$ at $(-1,-1)$ and $(1,1)$, relative minima.

10. $f_x = 3x^2 - 3 = 0$, $f_y = 3y^2 - 3 = 0$; critical points $(-1, \pm 1)$ and $(1, \pm 1)$; $D < 0$ at $(-1,1)$ and $(1,-1)$, saddle points; $D > 0$ and $f_{xx} > 0$ at $(1,1)$, relative minimum; $D > 0$ and $f_{xx} < 0$ at $(-1,-1)$, relative maximum.

11. $f_x = 2x = 0$, $f_y = 1 - e^y = 0$; critical point $(0,0)$; $D < 0$ at $(0,0)$, saddle point.

12. $f_x = e^y = 0$ is impossible, no critical points.

13. $f_x = e^x \sin y = 0$, $f_y = e^x \cos y = 0$, $\sin y = \cos y = 0$ is impossible, no critical points.

14. $f_x = y - 2/x^2 = 0$, $f_y = x - 4/y^2 = 0$; critical point $(1,2)$; $D > 0$ and $f_{xx} > 0$ at $(1,2)$, relative minimum.

15. $f_x = 2y^2 - 2xy + 4y = 0$, $f_y = 4xy - x^2 + 4x = 0$; $2y(y - x + 2) = 0$ and $x(4y - x + 4) = 0$, critical points $(0,0)$, $(0,-2)$, $(4,0)$, and $(4/3, -2/3)$; $D < 0$ at $(0,0)$, $(0,-2)$, and $(4,0)$, saddle points; $D > 0$ and $f_{xx} > 0$ at $(4/3, -2/3)$, relative minimum.

16. $f_x = y \cos x = 0$, $f_y = \sin x = 0$; $\sin x = 0$ if $x = n\pi$ for $n = 0, \pm 1, \pm 2, ...$ and $\cos x \neq 0$ for these values of x so $y = 0$; critical points $(n\pi, 0)$ for $n = 0, \pm 1, \pm 2, ...$; $D < 0$ at $(n\pi, 0)$, saddle points.

17. $f_x = -2(x + 1)e^{-(x^2 + y^2 + 2x)} = 0$, $f_y = -2ye^{-(x^2 + y^2 + 2x)} = 0$; critical point $(-1,0)$; $D > 0$ and $f_{xx} < 0$ at $(-1,0)$, relative maximum.

18. $f_x = y - a^3/x^2 = 0$, $f_y = x - b^3/y^2 = 0$; critical point $(a^2/b, b^2/a)$; if $ab > 0$ then $D > 0$ and $f_{xx} > 0$ at $(a^2/b, b^2/a)$, relative minimum; if $ab < 0$ then $D > 0$ and $f_{xx} < 0$ at $(a^2/b, b^2/a)$, relative maximum.

19. $f_x = \cos x = 0$, $f_y = \cos y = 0$; critical point $(\pi/2, \pi/2)$; $D > 0$ and $f_{xx} < 0$ at $(\pi/2, \pi/2)$, relative maximum.

20. $f_x = \cos x + \cos(x+y) = 0$, $f_y = \cos y + \cos(x+y) = 0$; subtract equations to get

$\cos x - \cos y = 0$, $\cos y = \cos x$, $y = x$ because both x and y are between 0 and $\pi/2$, thus $\cos x + \cos 2x = 0$,

$2\cos^2 x + \cos x - 1 = 0$, $(2\cos x - 1)(\cos x + 1) = 0$ so $\cos x = -1$ (invalid) or $\cos x = 1/2$, $x = \pi/3$; critical point $(\pi/3, \pi/3)$; $D > 0$ and $f_{xx} < 0$ at $(\pi/3, \pi/3)$, relative maximum.

21.   **(a)**   critical point $(0,0)$; $D = 0$

       (b) $f(0,0) = 0$, $x^4 + y^4 \geq 0$ so $f(x,y) \geq f(0,0)$, relative minimum.

22.   **(a)**   critical point $(0,0)$; $D = 0$

       (b) $f(0,0) = 0$, inside any circle centered at $(0,0)$ there are points where $f(x,y) > 0$ (along the x-axis) and points where $f(x,y) < 0$ (along the y-axis) so $(0,0)$ is a saddle point.

23.   **(a)** $f_x = 3e^y - 3x^2 = 3\left(e^y - x^2\right) = 0$, $f_y = 3xe^y - 3e^{3y} = 3e^y\left(x - e^{2y}\right) = 0$, $e^y = x^2$ and $e^{2y} = x$, $x^4 = x$, $x\left(x^3 - 1\right) = 0$ so $x = 0, 1$; critical point $(1,0)$; $D > 0$ and $f_{xx} < 0$ at $(1,0)$, relative maximum.

       (b) $\lim\limits_{x \to -\infty} f(x,0) = \lim\limits_{x \to -\infty} \left(3x - x^3 - 1\right) = +\infty$ so no absolute maximum.

24.   **(a)** $f_x = 8xe^y - 8x^3 = 8x(e^y - x^2) = 0$, $f_y = 4x^2e^y - 4e^{4y} = 4e^y(x^2 - e^{3y}) = 0$, $x^2 = e^y$ and $x^2 = e^{3y}$, $e^{3y} = e^y$, $e^{2y} = 1$, so $y = 0$ and $x = \pm 1$; critical points $(1,0)$ and $(-1,0)$. $D > 0$ and $f_{xx} < 0$ at both points so a relative maximum occurs at each one.

       (b)   Along $x = e^{2y}$, $f(e^{2y}, y) = 4e^{5y} - 3e^{4y} = e^{4y}\left(4e^y - 3\right)$, $\lim\limits_{y \to +\infty} = +\infty$.

25. $f_x = y - 1 = 0$, $f_y = x - 3 = 0$; critical point $(3,1)$.

           Along $y = 0$: $u(x) = -x$; no critical points,

           along $x = 0$: $v(y) = -3y$; no critical points,

       along $y = -\dfrac{4}{5}x + 4$: $w(x) = -\dfrac{4}{5}x^2 + \dfrac{27}{5}x - 12$; critical point $(27/8, 13/10)$.

(x,y)	$(3,1)$	$(0,0)$	$(5,0)$	$(0,4)$	$(27/8, 13/10)$
$f(x,y)$	-3	0	-5	-12	$-231/80$

Absolute maxium value is 0, absolute minimum value is -12.

26. $f_x = y - 2 = 0$, $f_y = x = 0$; critical point $(0,2)$, but $(0,2)$ is not in the interior of R.

           Along $y = 0$: $u(x) = -2x$; no critical points,

           along $x = 0$: $v(y) = 0$; no critical points,

       along $y = 4 - x$: $w(x) = 2x - x^2$; critical point $(1, 3)$.

(x,y)	$(0,0)$	$(0,4)$	$(4,0)$	$(1,3)$
$f(x,y)$	0	0	-8	1

Absolute maximum value is 1, absolute minimum value is -8.

27. $f_x = 2x - 2 = 0$, $f_y = -6y + 6 = 0$; critical point $(1,1)$.

Along $y = 0$: $u_1(x) = x^2 - 2x$; critical point $(1, 0)$,
along $y = 2$: $u_2(x) = x^2 - 2x$; critical point $(1, 2)$
along $x = 0$: $v_1(y) = -3y^2 + 6y$; critical point $(0, 1)$,
along $x = 2$: $v_2(y) = -3y^2 + 6y$; critical point $(2, 1)$

(x, y)	$(1, 1)$	$(1, 0)$	$(1, 2)$	$(0, 1)$	$(2, 1)$	$(0, 0)$	$(0, 2)$	$(2, 0)$	$(2, 2)$
$f(x, y)$	2	-1	-1	3	3	0	0	0	0

Absolute maxium value is 3, absolute minimum value is -1.

28. $f_x = e^y - 2x = 0$, $f_y = xe^y - e^y = e^y(x - 1) = 0$; critical point $(1, \ln 2)$.

Along $y = 0$: $u_1(x) = x - x^2 - 1$; critical point $(1/2, 0)$,
along $y = 1$: $u_2(x) = ex - x^2 - e$; critical point $(e/2, 1)$,
along $x = 0$: $v_1(y) = -e^y$; no critical points,
along $x = 2$: $v_2(y) = e^y - 4$; no critical points for $0 < y < 1$.

(x, y)	$(0, 0)$	$(0, 1)$	$(2, 1)$	$(2, 0)$	$(1, \ln 2)$	$(1/2, 0)$	$(e/2, 1)$
$f(x, y)$	-1	$-e$	$e - 4$	-3	-1	$-3/4$	$e(e - 4)/4 \approx -0.87$

Absolute maximum value is $-3/4$, absolute minimim value is -3.

29. $f_x = 2x - 1 = 0$, $f_y = 4y = 0$; critical point $(1/2, 0)$.

Along $x^2 + y^2 = 4$: $y^2 = 4 - x^2$, $u(x) = 8 - x - x^2$ for $-2 \le x \le 2$; critical points $(-1/2, \pm\sqrt{15}/2)$.

(x, y)	$(1/2, 0)$	$(-1/2, \sqrt{15}/2)$	$(-1/2, -\sqrt{15}/2)$	$(-2, 0)$	$(2, 0)$
$f(x, y)$	$-1/4$	$33/4$	$33/4$	6	2

Absolute maximum value is $33/4$, absolute minimum value is $-1/4$.

30. $f_x = y^2 = 0$, $f_y = 2xy = 0$; no critical points in the interior of R.

Along $y = 0$: $u(x) = 0$; no critical points,
along $x = 0$: $v(y) = 0$; no critical points
along $x^2 + y^2 = 1$: $w(x) = x - x^3$ for $0 \le x \le 1$; critical point $\left(1/\sqrt{3}, \sqrt{2/3}\right)$.

(x, y)	$(0, 0)$	$(0, 1)$	$(1, 0)$	$\left(1/\sqrt{3}, \sqrt{2/3}\right)$
$f(x, y)$	0	0	0	$2\sqrt{3}/9$

Absolute maximum value is $\dfrac{2}{9}\sqrt{3}$, absolute minimum value is 0.

31. $f(x, y) = (y - x)^2$; if (x_0, y_0) is on the line $y = x$ then $f(x_0, y_0) = 0$, but $(y - x)^2 \ge 0$ so $f(x, y) \ge f(x_0, y_0)$ for all points (x, y) thus f has an absolute minimum at (x_0, y_0).

32. Maximize $P = xyz$ subject to $x + y + z = 48$, $x > 0$, $y > 0$, $z > 0$. $z = 48 - x - y$ so $P = xy(48 - x - y) = 48xy - x^2y - xy^2$, $P_x = 48y - 2xy - y^2 = 0$, $P_y = 48x - x^2 - 2xy = 0$. But $x \neq 0$ and $y \neq 0$ so $48 - 2x - y = 0$ and $48 - x - 2y = 0$; critical point $(16,16)$. $P_{xx}P_{yy} - P_{xy}^2 > 0$ and $P_{xx} < 0$ at $(16,16)$, relative maximum. $z = 16$ when $x = y = 16$, the product is maximum for the numbers $16,16,16$.

33. Minimize $S = x^2 + y^2 + z^2$ subject to $x + y + z = 27$, $x > 0$, $y > 0$, $z > 0$. $z = 27 - x - y$ so $S = x^2 + y^2 + (27 - x - y)^2$, $S_x = 4x + 2y - 54 = 0$, $S_y = 2x + 4y - 54 = 0$; critical point $(9,9)$; $S_{xx}S_{yy} - S_{xy}^2 > 0$ and $S_{xx} > 0$ at $(9,9)$, relative minimum. $z = 9$ when $x = y = 9$, the sum of the squares is minimum for the numbers $9,9,9$.

34. Maximize $w = xy^2z^2$ subject to $x + y + z = 5$, $x > 0$, $y > 0$, $z > 0$. $x = 5 - y - z$ so $w = (5 - y - z)y^2z^2 = 5y^2z^2 - y^3z^2 - y^2z^3$, $w_y = 10yz^2 - 3y^2z^2 - 2yz^3 = yz^2(10 - 3y - 2z) = 0$, $w_z = 10y^2z - 2y^3z - 3y^2z^2 = y^2z(10 - 2y - 3z) = 0$, $10 - 3y - 2z = 0$ and $10 - 2y - 3z = 0$; critical point when $y = z = 2$; $w_{yy}w_{zz} - w_{yz}^2 > 0$ and $w_{yy} < 0$ when $y = z = 2$, relative maximum. $x = 1$ when $y = z = 2$, xy^2z^2 is maximum at $(1,2,2)$.

35. Minimize $w = D^2 = x^2 + y^2 + z^2$ subject to $x^2 - yz = 5$. $x^2 = 5 + yz$ so $w = 5 + yz + y^2 + z^2$, $w_y = z + 2y = 0$, $w_z = y + 2z = 0$; critical point when $y = z = 0$; $w_{yy}w_{zz} - w_{yz}^2 > 0$ and $w_{yy} > 0$ when $y = z = 0$, relative minimum. $x^2 = 5$, $x = \pm\sqrt{5}$ when $y = z = 0$. The points $\left(\pm\sqrt{5}, 0, 0\right)$ are closest to the origin.

36. The diagonal of the box must equal the diameter of the sphere so maximize $V = xyz$ or, for convenience, $w = V^2 = x^2y^2z^2$ subject to $x^2 + y^2 + z^2 = 4a^2$, $x > 0$, $y > 0$, $z > 0$. $z^2 = 4a^2 - x^2 - y^2$ so $w = 4a^2x^2y^2 - x^4y^2 - x^2y^4$, $w_x = 2xy^2(4a^2 - 2x^2 - y^2) = 0$, $w_y = 2x^2y\left(4a^2 - x^2 - 2y^2\right) = 0$, $4a^2 - 2x^2 - y^2 = 0$ and $4a^2 - x^2 - 2y^2 = 0$; critical point $\left(2a/\sqrt{3}, 2a/\sqrt{3}\right)$; $w_{xx}w_{yy} - w_{xy}^2 > 0$ and $w_{xx} < 0$ at $\left(2a/\sqrt{3}, 2a/\sqrt{3}\right)$, relative maximum. $z = 2a/\sqrt{3}$ when $x = y = 2a/\sqrt{3}$, the dimensions of the box of maximum volume are $2a/\sqrt{3}, 2a/\sqrt{3}, 2a/\sqrt{3}$.

37. Maximize $V = xyz$ subject to $x + y + z = 1$, $x > 0$, $y > 0$, $z > 0$. $z = 1 - x - y$ so $V = xy - x^2y - xy^2$, $V_x = y(1 - 2x - y) = 0$, $V_y = x(1 - x - 2y) = 0$, $1 - 2x - y = 0$ and $1 - x - 2y = 0$; critical point $(1/3, 1/3)$; $V_{xx}V_{yy} - V_{xy}^2 > 0$ and $V_{xx} < 0$ at $(1/3, 1/3)$, relative maximum. The maximum volume is $V = (1/3)(1/3)(1/3) = 1/27$.

38. Maximize the profit $P = 500(y - x)(x - 40) + [45,000 + 500(x - 2y)](y - 60)$
$$= 500(-x^2 - 2y^2 + 2xy - 20x + 170y - 5400).$$
$P_x = 1000(-x + y - 10) = 0$, $P_y = 1000(-2y + x + 85) = 0$; critical point $(65,75)$; $P_{xx}P_{yy} - P_{xy}^2 > 0$ and $P_{xx} < 0$ at $(65,75)$, relative maximum. The profit will be maximum when $x = 65$ and $y = 75$.

39. Let x, y, and z be, respectively, the length, width, and height of the box. Minimize $C = 10(2xy) + 5(2xz + 2yz) = 10(2xy + xz + yz)$ subject to $xyz = 16$. $z = 16/(xy)$ so $C = 20(xy + 8/y + 8/x)$, $C_x = 20(y - 8/x^2) = 0$, $C_y = 20(x - 8/y^2) = 0$; critical point $(2,2)$;

$C_{xx}C_{yy} - C_{xy}^2 > 0$ and $C_{xx} > 0$ at $(2,2)$, relative minimum. $z = 4$ when $x = y = 2$. The cost of materials is minimum if the length and width are 2 ft and the height is 4 ft.

40. Using s and t as independent parameters, minimize
$w = D^2 = (3s-2t)^2+(2s-2t-3)^2+(s-2t)^2$. $w_s = 4(7s-6t-3) = 0$, $w_t = 12(-2s+2t+1) = 0$; critical point $s = 0$, $t = -1/2$; $w_{ss}w_{tt} - w_{st}^2 > 0$ and $w_{ss} > 0$ when $s = 0$ and $t = -1/2$, relative minimum. $w = 6$ when $s = 0$ and $t = -1/2$ so the distance between the lines is $\sqrt{6}$.

41. Minimize $w = D^2 = (x+1)^2 + (y-3)^2 + (z-2)^2$ subject to $x - 2y + z = 4$. $z = 4 - x + 2y$ so $w = (x+1)^2 + (y-3)^2 + (2 - x + 2y)^2$, $w_x = 2(2x - 2y - 1) = 0$, $w_y = 2(-2x + 5y + 1) = 0$; critical point $(1/2, 0)$; $w_{xx}w_{yy} - w_{xy}^2 > 0$ and $w_{xx} > 0$ at $(1/2, 0)$, relative minimum. $w = 27/2$, $D = \sqrt{w} = 3\sqrt{6}/2$ is the minimum distance.

42. Maximize $A = ab \sin \alpha$ subject to $2a + 2b = \ell$, $a > 0$, $b > 0$, $0 < \alpha < \pi$. $b = (\ell - 2a)/2$ so $A = (1/2)(\ell a - 2a^2) \sin \alpha$, $A_a = (1/2)(\ell - 4a) \sin \alpha$, $A_\alpha = (a/2)(\ell - 2a) \cos \alpha$; $\sin \alpha \neq 0$ so from $A_a = 0$ we get $a = \ell/4$ and then from $A_\alpha = 0$ we get $\cos \alpha = 0$, $\alpha = \pi/2$. $A_{aa}A_{\alpha\alpha} - A_{a\alpha}^2 > 0$ and $A_{aa} < 0$ when $a = \ell/4$ and $\alpha = \pi/2$, the area is maximum.

43. Minimize $S = xy + 2xz + 2yz$ subject to $xyz = V$, $x > 0$, $y > 0$, $z > 0$ where x, y, and z are, respectively, the length, width, and height of the box. $z = V/(xy)$ so $S = xy + 2V/y + 2V/x$, $S_x = y - 2V/x^2 = 0$, $S_y = x - 2V/y^2 = 0$; critical point $(\sqrt[3]{2V}, \sqrt[3]{2V})$; $S_{xx}S_{yy} - S_{xy}^2 > 0$ and $S_{xx} > 0$ at this point so there is a relative minimum there. The length and width are each $\sqrt[3]{2V}$, the height is $z = \sqrt[3]{2V}/2$.

44. The altitude of the trapezoid is $x \sin \phi$ and the lengths of the lower and upper bases are, respectively, $27 - 2x$ and $27 - 2x + 2x \cos \phi$ so we want to maximize
$A = (1/2)(x \sin \phi)[(27 - 2x) + (27 - 2x + 2x \cos \phi)] = 27x \sin \phi - 2x^2 \sin \phi + x^2 \sin \phi \cos \phi$.
$A_x = \sin \phi(27 - 4x + 2x \cos \phi)$,
$A_\phi = x(27 \cos \phi - 2x \cos \phi - x \sin^2 \phi + x \cos^2 \phi) = x(27 \cos \phi - 2x \cos \phi + 2x \cos^2 \phi - x)$.
$\sin \phi \neq 0$ so from $A_x = 0$ we get $\cos \phi = (4x - 27)/(2x)$, $x \neq 0$ so from $A_\phi = 0$ we get $(27 - 2x + 2x \cos \phi) \cos \phi - x = 0$ which, for $\cos \phi = (4x - 27)/(2x)$, yields $4x - 27 - x = 0$, $x = 9$. If $x = 9$ then $\cos \phi = 1/2$, $\phi = \pi/3$. The critical point occurs when $x = 9$ and $\phi = \pi/3$; $A_{xx}A_{\phi\phi} - A_{x\phi}^2 > 0$ and $A_{xx} < 0$ there, the area is maximum when $x = 9$ and $\phi = \pi/3$.

45. (a) $\dfrac{\partial f}{\partial a} = \Sigma 2 (ax_k + b - y_k) x_k = 2\left(a\Sigma x_k^2 + b\Sigma x_k - \Sigma x_k y_k\right) = 0$ if

$\left(\Sigma x_k^2\right) a + \left(\Sigma x_k\right)b = \Sigma x_k y_k$, $\dfrac{\partial f}{\partial b} = \Sigma 2 (ax_k + b - y_k) = 2\left(a\Sigma x_k + bn - \Sigma y_k\right) = 0$ if
$\left(\Sigma x_k\right) a + nb = \Sigma y_k$.

46. **(a)** $\Sigma (x_k - \bar{x})^2 = \Sigma (x_k^2 - 2\bar{x}x_k + \bar{x}^2) = \Sigma x_k^2 - 2\bar{x}\Sigma x_k + n\bar{x}^2 = \Sigma x_k^2 - \dfrac{2}{n}(\Sigma x_k)^2 + \dfrac{1}{n}(\Sigma x_k)^2$

$$= \Sigma x_k^2 - \dfrac{1}{n}(\Sigma x_k)^2 > 0 \text{ so } n\Sigma x_k^2 - (\Sigma x_k)^2 > 0.$$

(b) $f_{aa} = 2\Sigma x_k^2,\ f_{bb} = 2n,\ f_{ab} = 2\Sigma x_k.$

(c) $D = f_{aa}f_{bb} - f_{ab}^2 = 4[n\Sigma x_k^2 - (\Sigma x_k)^2] > 0$ and $f_{aa} > 0.$

(d) $f(a, b)$ is of the second-degree in a and b so the graph of $z = f(a, b)$ is a quadric surface. The only quadric surface of this form having a relative minimum is a paraboloid that opens upward where the relative minimum is also the absolute minimum.

47. $\Sigma x_k = 10,\ \Sigma y_k = 8.2,\ \Sigma x_k^2 = 30,\ \Sigma x_k y_k = 23,\ n = 4;\ a = 0.5,\ b = 0.8,\ y = 0.5x + 0.8.$

48. $f(x_0, y_0) \geq f(x, y)$ for all (x, y) inside a circle centered at (x_0, y_0) by virtue of Definition 16.9.1. If r is the radius of the circle, then in particular $f(x_0, y_0) \geq f(x, y_0)$ for all x satisfying $|x - x_0| < r$ so $f(x, y_0)$ has a relative maximum at x_0 (Definition 4.3.1). The proof is similar for the function $f(x_0, y)$.

49. For example, for $0 \leq x \leq 1$ let $z = \begin{cases} y & \text{if } 0 < y < 1 \\ 1/2 & \text{if } y = 0 \text{ or } y = 1 \end{cases}$; let $z = y$ for $-\infty < x < +\infty$, $y > 0$.

EXERCISE SET 16.10

1. $y = 8x\lambda,\ x = 16y\lambda;\ y/(8x) = x/(16y),\ x^2 = 2y^2$ so $4(2y^2) + 8y^2 = 16,\ y^2 = 1,\ y = \pm 1$. Test $(\pm\sqrt{2}, -1)$ and $(\pm\sqrt{2}, 1)$. $f(-\sqrt{2}, -1) = f(\sqrt{2}, 1) = \sqrt{2},\ f(-\sqrt{2}, 1) = f(\sqrt{2}, -1) = -\sqrt{2}$. Maximum $\sqrt{2}$ at $(-\sqrt{2}, -1)$ and $(\sqrt{2}, 1)$, minimum $-\sqrt{2}$ at $(-\sqrt{2}, 1)$ and $(\sqrt{2}, -1)$.

2. $2x = 2x\lambda,\ -1 = 2y\lambda$. If $x \neq 0$ then $\lambda = 1$ and $y = -1/2$ so $x^2 + (-1/2)^2 = 25$, $x^2 = 99/4,\ x = \pm 3\sqrt{11}/2$. If $x = 0$ then $0^2 + y^2 = 25,\ y = \pm 5$. Test $(\pm 3\sqrt{11}/2, -1/2)$ and $(0, \pm 5)$. $f(\pm 3\sqrt{11}/2, -1/2) = 101/4,\ f(0, -5) = 5,\ f(0, 5) = -5$. Maximum $101/4$ at $(\pm 3\sqrt{11}/2, -1/2)$, minimum -5 at $(0, 5)$.

3. $12x^2 = 4x\lambda,\ 2y = 2y\lambda$. If $y \neq 0$ then $\lambda = 1$ and $12x^2 = 4x,\ 12x(x - 1/3) = 0,\ x = 0$ or $x = 1/3$ so from $2x^2 + y^2 = 1$ we find that $y = \pm 1$ when $x = 0,\ y = \pm\sqrt{7}/3$ when $x = 1/3$. If $y = 0$ then $2x^2 + (0)^2 = 1,\ x = \pm 1/\sqrt{2}$. Test $(0, \pm 1),\ (1/3, \pm\sqrt{7}/3)$, and $(\pm 1/\sqrt{2}, 0)$. $f(0, \pm 1) = 1,\ f(1/3, \pm\sqrt{7}/3) = 25/27,\ f(1/\sqrt{2}, 0) = \sqrt{2},\ f(-1/\sqrt{2}, 0) = -\sqrt{2}$. Maximum $\sqrt{2}$ at $(1/\sqrt{2}, 0)$, minimum $-\sqrt{2}$ at $(-1/\sqrt{2}, 0)$.

4. $1 = 2x\lambda$, $-3 = 6y\lambda$; $1/(2x) = -1/(2y)$, $y = -x$ so $x^2 + 3(-x)^2 = 16$, $x = \pm 2$. Test $(-2, 2)$ and $(2, -2)$. $f(-2, 2) = -9$, $f(2, -2) = 7$. Maximum 7 at $(2, -2)$, minimum -9 at $(-2, 2)$.

5. $2 = 2x\lambda$, $1 = 2y\lambda$, $-2 = 2z\lambda$; $1/x = 1/(2y) = -1/z$ thus $x = 2y$, $z = -2y$ so $(2y)^2 + y^2 + (-2y)^2 = 4$, $y^2 = 4/9$, $y = \pm 2/3$. Test $(-4/3, -2/3, 4/3)$ and $(4/3, 2/3, -4/3)$. $f(-4/3, -2/3, 4/3) = -6$, $f(4/3, 2/3, -4/3) = 6$. Maximum 6 at $(4/3, 2/3, -4/3)$, minimum -6 at $(-4/3, -2/3, 4/3)$.

6. $3 = 4x\lambda$, $6 = 8y\lambda$, $2 = 2z\lambda$; $3/(4x) = 3/(4y) = 1/z$ thus $y = x$, $z = 4x/3$, so $2x^2 + 4(x)^2 + (4x/3)^2 = 70$, $x^2 = 9$, $x = \pm 3$. Test $(-3, -3, -4)$ and $(3,3,4)$. $f(-3, -3, -4) = -35$, $f(3, 3, 4) = 35$. Maximum 35 at $(3, 3, 4)$, minimum -35 at $(-3, -3, -4)$.

7. $yz = 2x\lambda$, $xz = 2y\lambda$, $xy = 2z\lambda$; $yz/(2x) = xz/(2y) = xy/(2z)$ thus $y^2 = x^2$, $z^2 = x^2$ so $x^2 + x^2 + x^2 = 1$, $x = \pm 1/\sqrt{3}$. Test the eight possibilities with $x = \pm 1/\sqrt{3}$, $y = \pm 1/\sqrt{3}$, and $z = \pm 1/\sqrt{3}$ to find the maximum is $1/\left(3\sqrt{3}\right)$ at $(1/\sqrt{3}, 1/\sqrt{3}, 1/\sqrt{3})$, $(1/\sqrt{3}, -1/\sqrt{3}, -1/\sqrt{3})$, $(-1/\sqrt{3}, 1/\sqrt{3}, -1/\sqrt{3})$, and $(-1/\sqrt{3}, -1/\sqrt{3}, 1/\sqrt{3})$; the minimum is $-1/\left(3\sqrt{3}\right)$ at $(1/\sqrt{3}, 1/\sqrt{3}, -1/\sqrt{3})$, $(1/\sqrt{3}, -1/\sqrt{3}, 1/\sqrt{3})$, $(-1/\sqrt{3}, 1/\sqrt{3}, 1/\sqrt{3})$, and $(-1/\sqrt{3}, -1/\sqrt{3}, -1/\sqrt{3})$.

8. $f(x, y) = x^2 + y^2$; $2x = 2\lambda$, $2y = -4\lambda$; $y = -2x$ so $2x - 4(-2x) = 3$, $x = 3/10$. The point is $(3/10, -3/5)$.

9. $f(x, y) = (x - 4)^2 + (y - 2)^2$, $g(x, y) = y - 2x$; $2(x - 4) = -2\lambda$, $2(y - 2) = \lambda$; $x - 4 = -2(y - 2)$, $x = -2y + 8$ so $y = 2(-2y + 8) + 3$, $y = 19/5$. The point is $(2/5, 19/5)$.

10. $f(x, y, z) = x^2 + y^2 + z^2$; $2x = \lambda$, $2y = 2\lambda$, $2z = \lambda$; $y = 2x$, $z = x$ so $x + 2(2x) + x = 1$, $x = 1/6$. The point is $(1/6, 1/3, 1/6)$.

11. $f(x, y, z) = (x - 1)^2 + (y + 1)^2 + (z - 1)^2$; $2(x - 1) = 4\lambda$, $2(y + 1) = 3\lambda$, $2(z - 1) = \lambda$; $x = 4z - 3$, $y = 3z - 4$ so $4(4z - 3) + 3(3z - 4) + z = 2$, $z = 1$. The point is $(1, -1, 1)$.

12. $f(x, y, z) = x^2 + y^2 + z^2$; $2x = y\lambda$, $2y = x\lambda$, $2z = -2z\lambda$. If $z \neq 0$ then $\lambda = -1$ so $2x = -y$ and $2y = -x$, $x = y = 0$; substitute into $xy - z^2 = 1$ to get $z^2 = -1$ which has no real solution. If $z = 0$ then $xy - (0)^2 = 1$, $y = 1/x$, and also (from $2x = y\lambda$ and $2y = x\lambda$)$2x/y = 2y/x$, $y^2 = x^2$ so $(1/x)^2 = x^2$, $x^4 = 1$, $x = \pm 1$. Test $(1,1,0)$ and $(-1, -1, 0)$ to see that they are both closest to the origin.

13. $f(x, y) = \sin x \sin y$; $x + y = \pi/2$; $\cos x \sin y = \lambda$, $\sin x \cos y = \lambda$; $\cos x \sin y = \sin x \cos y$ but $\cos x \neq 0$ and $\cos y \neq 0$ thus $\tan y = \tan x$, $y = x$ so $x + x = \pi/2$, $x = \pi/4$. The maximum value of $f(x, y)$ is $f(\pi/4, \pi/4) = 1/2$.

14. $f(x,y,z) = x + y + z$, $x^2 + y^2 + z^2 = 25$ where x, y, and z are the components of the vector; $1 = 2x\lambda$, $1 = 2y\lambda$, $1 = 2z\lambda$; $1/(2x) = 1/(2y) = 1/(2z)$; $y = x$, $z = x$ so $x^2 + x^2 + x^2 = 25$, $x = \pm 5/\sqrt{3}$. $f\left(-5/\sqrt{3}, -5/\sqrt{3}, -5/\sqrt{3}\right) = -5/\sqrt{3}$ and $f\left(5/\sqrt{3}, 5/\sqrt{3}, 5/\sqrt{3}\right) = 5/\sqrt{3}$ so the vector is $5(\mathbf{i} + \mathbf{j} + \mathbf{k})/\sqrt{3}$.

15. $f(x,y) = (x-1)^2 + (y-2)^2$; $2(x-1) = 2x\lambda$, $2(y-2) = 2y\lambda$; $(x-1)/x = (y-2)/y$, $y = 2x$ so $x^2 + (2x)^2 = 45$, $x = \pm 3$. $f(-3,-6) = 80$ and $f(3,6) = 20$ so $(3,6)$ is closest and $(-3,-6)$ is farthest.

16. $x^2 + y^2 = 25$ is the constraint; $8x - 4y = 2x\lambda$, $-4x + 2y = 2y\lambda$; $(4x - 2y)/x = (-2x + y)/y$, $2x^2 + 3xy - 2y^2 = 0$, $(2x - y)(x + 2y) = 0$, $y = 2x$ or $x = -2y$. If $y = 2x$ then $x^2 + (2x)^2 = 25$, $x = \pm\sqrt{5}$. If $x = -2y$ then $(-2y^2) + y^2 = 25$, $y = \pm\sqrt{5}$. $T\left(-\sqrt{5}, -2\sqrt{5}\right) = T\left(\sqrt{5}, 2\sqrt{5}\right) = 0$ and $T\left(2\sqrt{5}, -\sqrt{5}\right) = T\left(-2\sqrt{5}, \sqrt{5}\right) = 125$. The highest temperature is 125 and the lowest is 0.

17. $f(x,y,z) = x^2 + y^2 + z^2$, $x + y + z = 27$; $2x = \lambda$, $2y = \lambda$, $2z = \lambda$, $y = x$, $z = x$ so $x + x + x = 27$, $x = 9$. The numbers are 9,9,9.

18. $y^2 z^2 = \lambda$, $2xyz^2 = \lambda$, $2xy^2 z = \lambda$; $y = 2x$, $z = 2x$ so $x + 2x + 2x = 5$, $x = 1$. The point is $(1,2,2)$.

19. $f(x,y,z) = x^2 + y^2 + z^2$; $2x = 2x\lambda$, $2y = -z\lambda$, $2z = -y\lambda$. If $x \neq 0$ then $\lambda = 1$ thus $2y = -z$ and $2z = -y$ so $y = z = 0$; use $x^2 - yz = 5$ to get $x = \pm\sqrt{5}$. If $x = 0$ then $(0)^2 - yz = 5$, $y = -5/z$ and also (from $2y = -z\lambda$, $2z = -y\lambda)y^2 = z^2$ so $(-5/z)^2 = z^2$, $z^4 = 25$, $z = \pm\sqrt{5}$. $f\left(\pm\sqrt{5}, 0, 0\right) = 5$ and $f\left(0, \sqrt{5}, -\sqrt{5}\right) = f\left(0, -\sqrt{5}, \sqrt{5}\right) = 10$ so $\left(\pm\sqrt{5}, 0, 0\right)$ are closest to the origin.

20. $f(x,y,z) = xyz$, $x^2 + y^2 + z^2 = 4a^2$; $yz = 2x\lambda$, $xz = 2y\lambda$, $xy = 2z\lambda$;

$yz/(2x) = xz/(2y) = xy/(2z)$; $y^2 = x^2$, $z^2 = x^2$ so $x^2 + x^2 + x^2 = 4a^2$, $x = -2a/\sqrt{3}$ (invalid) or $x = 2a/\sqrt{3}$. The dimensions of the box are $2a/\sqrt{3}$, $2a/\sqrt{3}$, $2a/\sqrt{3}$.

21. $f(x,y,z) = 20xy + 10xz + 10yz$, $xyz = 16$; $20y + 10z = yz\lambda$, $20x + 10z = xz\lambda$, $10x + 10y = xy\lambda$; $(20y + 10z)/(yz) = (20x + 10z)/(xz) = (10x + 10y)/(xy)$; $y = x$, $z = 2x$ so $x(x)(2x) = 16$, $x = 2$. The length and width are each 2 ft and the height is 4 ft.

22. $f(x,y,z) = (x+1)^2 + (y-3)^2 + (z-2)^2$, $x - 2y + z = 4$; $2(x+1) = \lambda$, $2(y-3) = -2\lambda$, $2(z-2) = \lambda$; $y = -2x + 1$, $z = x + 3$ so $x - 2(-2x + 1) + (x + 3) = 4$, $x = 1/2$. $(1/2, 0, 7/2)$ is closest to the plane and the distance is $\sqrt{f(1/2, 0, 7/2)} = \sqrt{27/2} = 3\sqrt{6}/2$.

23. $f(a,b,\alpha) = ab\sin\alpha$, $2a + 2b = \ell$; $b\sin\alpha = 2\lambda$, $a\sin\alpha = 2\lambda$, $ab\cos\alpha = 0$; $\cos\alpha = 0$, $\alpha = \pi/2$ and $a = b$ so $2b + 2b = \ell$, $b = \ell/4$.

24. $f(x,y,z) = xy + 2xz + 2yz$, $xyz = V$; $y + 2z = yz\lambda$, $x + 2z = xz\lambda$, $2x + 2y = xy\lambda$;
$(y + 2z)/(yz) = (x + 2z)/(xz) = (2x + 2y)/(xy)$; $y = x$, $z = x/2$ so $x(x)(x/2) = V$, $x = \sqrt[3]{2V}$.
The length and width are each $\sqrt[3]{2V}$ and the height is $\sqrt[3]{2V}/2$.

SUPPLEMENTARY EXERCISES CHAPTER 16

1. (a) 1

(b) xy

(c) $e^{r+s} \ln rs$

2. (a)

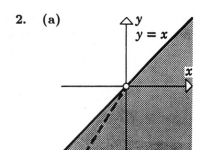

(b)

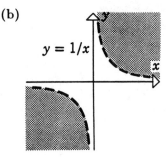

(c)

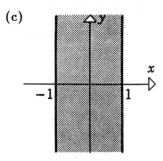

3. (a) upper half of the elliptic cone $z^2 = x^2 + 4y^2$

(b) the plane with x, y, and z intercepts of 1, a, and b.

4. $f_x = 2x/(y^2 + z^2)$, $f_y = -2x^2y/(y^2 + z^2)^2$, $f_z = -2x^2z/(y^2 + z^2)^2$

5. $1/(x \sin yz) - 3y(\csc yz \cot yz) \ln xy$

6. $\partial f/\partial x = -e^{yz}/x^2 - 1/(u - x)$, $\partial f/\partial y = ze^{yz}/x$, $\partial f/\partial u = 1/(u - x)$

7. $\pi/2, 0, 1, -\pi^2/4$

8. $1 + e^3, 2$

9. 2

10. $s^2(\cos y + y \cos x) - x \sin y + \sin x$

11. $(2x - 2y + 4r)/(x^2 + y^2 + 2z) = \dfrac{2}{r + s}$

12. $w_{xy} = w_{yx} = 8xy \sec^2(x^2 + y^2) \tan(x^2 + y^2) + (1/2)y^{-1/2}$

13. $\partial^2 w/\partial x^2 = \partial^2 w/\partial y^2 = -(x - y)^{-2} - \cos(x + y)$

14. $F_{xx} = F_{yy} = -6z$, $F_{zz} = 12z$

15. $f_{xyzx} = f_{zxxy} = 0$

16.   (a) $\partial z/\partial y = -2y$, slope $= -2(-2) = 4$ (b) $\partial z/\partial x = -8x$, slope $= -8(1) = -8$

17.   (a) $dP/dt = (\partial P/\partial T)(dT/dt) = (10/V)(dT/dt) = (10/2.5)(3) = 12$ newtons/m^2/min
        (b) $dP/dt = (\partial P/\partial V)(dV/dt) = - \left(10T/V^2\right)(dV/dt)$
$$= -(500/6.25)(-3) = 240 \text{ newtons/m}^2/\text{min}$$

18.   (a) $\displaystyle\lim_{(x,y)\to(0,0)} \frac{(x-y)\left(x^3-1\right)}{(x-y)} = \lim_{(x,y)\to(0,0)} \left(x^3-1\right) = -1$
        (b) not continuous at $(0,0)$ because $f(0,0)$ is not defined

19.   (a) $\displaystyle\lim_{(x,y)\to(0,0)} \frac{\left(x^2-y^2\right)\left(x^2+y^2\right)}{x^2+y^2} = \lim_{(x,y)\to(0,0)} \left(x^2-y^2\right) = 0$
        (b) continuous at $(0,0)$ because $\displaystyle\lim_{(x,y)\to(0,0)} f(x,y) = f(0,0)$

20.   (a) $(y\cos xy + y/x)e^t + 2t(x\cos xy + \ln xz)$ (b) $(1/2)(y\cos t + 3x + e^z\sin t)/\sqrt{xy - e^z}$

21.   (a) $-(6x - 5y + y\sec^2 xy)/\left(-5x + x\sec^2 xy\right)$ (b) $-[\ln y + \cos(x-y)]/[x/y - \cos(x-y)]$

22. $dy/dx = -F_x/F_y$; $d^2y/dx^2 = -(F_y dF_x/dx - F_x dF_y/dx)/F_y^2$
$$= -(F_y[F_{xx} + F_{xy}\,dy/dx] - F_x[F_{yx} + F_{yy}\,dy/dx])/F_y^2,$$
        replace dy/dx by $-F_x/F_y$ and assume that $F_{xy} = F_{yx}$ to get
        $d^2y/dx^2 = -\left(F_y^2 F_{xx} - 2F_x F_y F_{xy} + F_x^2 F_{yy}\right)/F_y^3$

23. $dV/dt = (\partial V/\partial E)(dE/dt) + (\partial V/\partial r)(dr/dt) = \dfrac{R}{r+R}\dfrac{dE}{dt} - \dfrac{RE}{(r+R)^2}\dfrac{dr}{dt}$

24.   (a) all (x, y, z) not on the elliptic paraboloid $z = x^2 + 4y^2$
        (b) $1/(z - x^2 - 4y^2) = 2$, $z - x^2 - 4y^2 = 1/2$, $z = 1/2 + x^2 + 4y^2$ which is an elliptic paraboloid
        (c) $1/\left(e^{3t} - 9t^2 - 4u^2 v^2\right)$

25.   (a) $\nabla f(3,1) = \langle 6, 45\rangle$
        (b) $\overrightarrow{P_0 P_1} = \langle 1, -4\rangle$, $\mathbf{u} = \langle 1, -4\rangle/\sqrt{17}$, $D_{\mathbf{u}}f = -174/\sqrt{17}$

26.   (a) $\nabla f(\ln 2, 2, \pi/4) = \sqrt{2}\,\langle 2, 1, 2\rangle$ (b) $\mathbf{u} = \langle 1, -2, 2\rangle/3$, $D_{\mathbf{u}}f = 4\sqrt{2}/3$

27.   (a) $\nabla f(3, 2, 6) = \langle 1/3, 1/2, 1/6\rangle$ (b) $D_{\mathbf{u}}f = \sqrt{3}/9$

28.   (a) $\nabla f(1, 2) = \langle 12, 9\rangle$ (b) $\mathbf{u} = \langle 1/2, \sqrt{3}/2\rangle$, $D_{\mathbf{u}}f = 6 + 9\sqrt{3}/2$

29. (a) $\nabla f(1, -1, 2) = \langle 1, 3, 0 \rangle$

   (b) $\overrightarrow{P_0 P_1} = \langle 10, 11, -2 \rangle$, $\mathbf{u} = \langle 10, 11, -2 \rangle / 15$, $D_{\mathbf{u}} f = 43/15$

30. $\nabla f(2, -1, 2) = 2\langle 5, 2, 5 \rangle$, $\|\nabla f(2, -1, 2)\| = 6\sqrt{6}$, the maximum rate of decrease is $6\sqrt{6}$ in the direction of $-\langle 5, 2, 5 \rangle$.

31. (a) $\nabla f(1, -1) = 2(-\mathbf{i} + \mathbf{j})$, $D_{\mathbf{u}} f = 0$ if $\mathbf{u}$ is normal to ∇f so $\mathbf{u} = \pm (\mathbf{i} + \mathbf{j})/\sqrt{2}$

   (b) $\nabla f(-2, 0) = \mathbf{i} - 2\mathbf{j}$, $\mathbf{u} = \pm (2\mathbf{i} + \mathbf{j})/\sqrt{5}$

32. $\nabla f(x_0, y_0) = a\mathbf{i} + b\mathbf{j}$. $D_{\mathbf{u}} f = 2$ when $\mathbf{u} = (\sqrt{3}\mathbf{i} + \mathbf{j})/2$ and $D_{\mathbf{u}} f = 8$ when $\mathbf{u} = (-\sqrt{3}\mathbf{i} + \mathbf{j})/2$ so $(\sqrt{3}a + b)/2 = 2$ and $(-\sqrt{3}a + b)/2 = 8$, solve for a and b to get $a = -2\sqrt{3}$, $b = 10$. If $\mathbf{u} = (\sqrt{3}\mathbf{i} + 2\mathbf{j})/\sqrt{7}$ then $D_{\mathbf{u}} f = (-2\sqrt{3}\mathbf{i} + 10\mathbf{j}) \cdot (\sqrt{3}\mathbf{i} + 2\mathbf{j})/\sqrt{7} = 2\sqrt{7}$.

33. $\nabla f(1, 2) = a\mathbf{i} + b\mathbf{j}$; $D_{\mathbf{u}} f = 2\sqrt{2}$ when $\mathbf{u} = (\mathbf{i} + \mathbf{j})/\sqrt{2}$ and $D_{\mathbf{u}} f = -3$ when $\mathbf{u} = -\mathbf{j}$ so $(a + b)/\sqrt{2} = 2\sqrt{2}$ and $-b = -3$, $a = 1$, $b = 3$. If $\mathbf{u} = -(\mathbf{i} + 2\mathbf{j})/\sqrt{5}$ then $D_{\mathbf{u}} f = -7/\sqrt{5}$.

34. (a) $\langle f_x(1, 2), f_y(1, 2), -1 \rangle = \langle 8, 4, -1 \rangle = \mathbf{N}$ (b) $8x + 4y - z = 7$

35. (a) $\langle f_x(4, -3), f_y(4, -3), -1 \rangle = \langle 8/5, -6/5, -1 \rangle$, let $\mathbf{N} = \langle 8, -6, -5 \rangle$

   (b) $8x - 6y - 5z = 0$

36. (a) $f(x, y, z) = z - x^2 e^{2y}$, $\nabla f(1, \ln 2, 4) = \langle -8, -8, 1 \rangle$, $\mathbf{n} = \langle 8, 8, -1 \rangle$; tangent plane $8x + 8y - z = 4 + 8\ln 2$; normal line $x = 1 + 8t$, $y = \ln 2 + 8t$, $z = 4 - t$.

   (b) $f(x, y, z) = x^2 y^3 z^4 + xyz$, $\nabla f(2, 1, -1) = \langle 3, 10, -14 \rangle = \mathbf{n}$; tangent plane $3x + 10y - 14z = 30$; normal line $x = 2 + 3t$, $y = 1 + 10t$, $z = -1 - 14t$.

37. Let $f(x, y, z) = z + xy$; $\nabla f(x_0, y_0, z_0) = \langle y_0, x_0, 1 \rangle$ is normal to the surface at $P_0 (x_0, y_0, z_0)$. The normal line passes through the origin when $\langle x_0, y_0, z_0 \rangle$ and $\langle y_0, x_0, 1 \rangle$ are parallel so $\langle x_0, y_0, z_0 \rangle = k \langle y_0, x_0, 1 \rangle = \langle k y_0, k x_0, k \rangle$ for some value of k. Equate the third component of these vectors to find that $k = z_0$ so $x_0 = y_0 z_0$ and $y_0 = x_0 z_0$, eliminate y_0 to get $x_0 = x_0 z_0^2$, $x_0 (1 - z_0^2) = 0$, $x_0 = 0$ or $z_0 = \pm 1$. If $x_0 = 0$ then $y_0 = (0)z_0 = 0$ and, from the equation of the surface, $z_0 = 2 - (0)(0) = 2$ so $(0, 0, 2)$ is one of the points. If $z_0 = 1$ then $y_0 = x_0$ so $1 = 2 - x_0^2$, $x_0^2 = 1$, $x_0 = \pm 1$ so $(1, 1, 1)$ and $(-1, -1, 1)$ are also points where the normal line passes through the origin. If $z_0 = -1$ then $y_0 = -x_0$ so $-1 = 2 + x_0^2$, $x_0^2 = -3$ which has no real solution.

38. Let $P_0 (x_0, y_0, z_0)$ be a point on the surface then if $x_0 \neq 0$, $y_0 \neq 0$, and $z_0 \neq 0$ the vector $\langle x_0^{-1/3}, y_0^{-1/3}, z_0^{-1/3} \rangle$ is normal to the surface at P_0 and the tangent plane is
$x_0^{-1/3} x + y_0^{-1/3} y + z_0^{-1/3} z = x_0^{2/3} + y_0^{2/3} + z_0^{2/3} = 1$, the x, y and z intercepts are $x_0^{1/3}$, $y_0^{1/3}$, $z_0^{1/3}$, the sum of the squares is $x_0^{2/3} + y_0^{2/3} + z_0^{2/3} = 1$ because (x_0, y_0, z_0) is on the surface.

39. $\langle 18x_0, 8y_0, -1 \rangle$ is normal to the surface at a point (x_0, y_0, z_0). $\overrightarrow{PQ} = \langle -6, -4, -1 \rangle$ so the normal line is parallel to $\overrightarrow{PQ}$ if $\langle 18x_0, 8y_0, -1 \rangle = k\langle -6, -4, -1 \rangle$ for some value of k. By inspection $k = 1$ so $18x_0 = -6$ and $8y_0 = -4$, $x_0 = -1/3$ and $y_0 = -1/2$ thus $z_0 = 2$. The only point is $(-1/3, -1/2, 2)$.

40. Let $f(x, y) = w$ then $\Delta w = f(1.1, -0.1) - f(1, 0) = 0.11$,

$dw = (2xy - 2y + y^2)\, dx + (x^2 - 2x + 2yx)\, dy = (0)(0.1) + (-1)(-0.1) = 0.1$

41. $dV = (2/3)xh\,dx + (1/3)x^2\,dh = (2/3)(1)(2)(-0.1) + (1/3)(1)^2(0.2) = -0.2/3 \approx -0.067$ m^3
$\Delta V = (1/3)(0.9)^2(2.2) - (1/3)(1)^2(2) = -0.218/3 \approx -0.073$ m^3

42. $df = \left[2xy^4/\left(1 + z^2\right)\right] dx + \left[4x^2y^3/\left(1 + z^2\right)\right] dy - \left[2x^2y^4z/\left(1 + z^2\right)^2\right] dz$

$\quad = (10/5)(-0.004) + (100/5)(0.003) - (100/25)(-0.005) = 0.072$

$f(4.996, 1.003, 1.995) \approx f(5, 1, 2) + df = 5 + 0.072 = 5.072$

43. $f_x = 2x + 3y - 6 = 0$, $f_y = 3x + 6y + 3 = 0$; critical point $(15, -8)$; $f_{xx}f_{yy} - f_{xy}^2 > 0$ and $f_{xx} > 0$ at $(15, -8)$, relative minimum.

44. $f_x = 2xy - 6x = 0$, $f_y = x^2 - 12y = 0$; critical points $(0,0)$ and $(\pm 6, 3)$; $D > 0$ and $f_{xx} < 0$ at $(0,0)$, relative maximum; $D < 0$ at $(\pm 6, 3)$, saddle points.

45. $f_x = 3x^2 - 3y = 0$, $f_y = -3x + y = 0$; critical points $(0,0)$ and $(3,9)$; $D < 0$ at $(0,0)$, saddle point; $D > 0$ and $f_{xx} > 0$ at $(3,9)$, relative minimum.

46. **(a)** $w = x^2y^2$; $y^2 = 8 - 4x^2$ so $w = 8x^2 - 4x^4$ for $-\sqrt{2} \le x \le \sqrt{2}$. $dw/dx = 16x\left(1 - x^2\right) = 0$ if $x = 0, \pm 1$. If $x = 0$ then $y = \pm 2\sqrt{2}$ and $d^2w/dx^2 > 0$ so relative minima occur at $(0, \pm 2\sqrt{2})$. If $x = -1$ or 1 then $y = \pm 2$ and $d^2w/dx^2 < 0$ so relative maxima occur at $(-1, \pm 2)$ and $(1, \pm 2)$. At the endpoints $x = \pm\sqrt{2}$ we find that $y = 0$ thus $w = \left(\pm\sqrt{2}\right)(0) = 0$ so relative minima occur at $(\pm\sqrt{2}, 0)$ because $w = x^2y^2 \ge 0$ everywhere.

(b) $2xy^2 = 8x\lambda$, $2x^2y = 2y\lambda$. If $x \ne 0$ then $\lambda = y^2/4$ and thus $2x^2y = y^3/2$, $4x^2y - y^3 = 0$, $y\left(4x^2 - y^2\right) = 0$, $y = 0$ or $y^2 = 4x^2$; if $y = 0$ then $4x^2 + (0)^2 = 8$ so $x = \pm\sqrt{2}$, if $y^2 = 4x^2$ then $4x^2 + 4x^2 = 8$ so $x = \pm 1$. If $x = 0$ then $4(0)^2 + y^2 = 8$ so $y = \pm 2\sqrt{2}$. Test $(\pm\sqrt{2}, 0)$, $(1, \pm 2)$, $(-1, \pm 2)$ and $(0, \pm 2\sqrt{2})$. $w = 0$ at $(\pm\sqrt{2}, 0)$ and $(0, \pm 2\sqrt{2})$, $w = 4$ at $(1, \pm 2)$ and $(-1, \pm 2)$. The maximum value occurs at $(1, \pm 2)$ and $(-1, \pm 2)$, the minumum value at $(\pm\sqrt{2}, 0)$ and $(0, \pm 2\sqrt{2})$.

47. **(a)** Let (x, y, z) be a point on the portion of the ellipsoid that is in the first octant then $V = (2x)(2y)(2z) = 8xyz$. For convenience introduce the new variables $u = x/a$, $v = y/b$, and $w = z/c$ so $V = (8abc)uvw$ where $u^2 + v^2 + w^2 = 1$. Also for convenience we will maximize $S = u^2v^2w^2$ instead of V. $w^2 = 1 - u^2 - v^2$ so $S = u^2v^2 - u^4v^2 - u^2v^4$,

$S_u = 2uv^2(1 - 2u^2 - v^2) = 0$, $S_v = 2vu^2\left(1 - u^2 - 2v^2\right) = 0$; critical point $(1/\sqrt{3}, 1/\sqrt{3})$; $S_{uu}S_{vv} - S_{uv}^2 > 0$ and $S_{uu} < 0$ at this point so a relative maximum occurs there. If $u = v = 1/\sqrt{3}$ then $w = 1/\sqrt{3}$ so $x = a/\sqrt{3}$, $y = b/\sqrt{3}$, and $z = c/\sqrt{3}$. The dimensions of the box are $2a/\sqrt{3}$, $2b/\sqrt{3}$, and $2c/\sqrt{3}$.

(b) $f(x, y, z) = 8xyz$, $(x/a)^2 + (y/b)^2 + (z/c)^2 = 1$; $8yz = (2x/a^2)\lambda$, $8xz = (2y/b^2)\lambda$, $8xy = (2z/c^2)\lambda$; $4a^2yz/x = 4b^2xz/y = 4c^2xy/z$, $y^2/b^2 = x^2/a^2$ and $z^2/c^2 = x^2/a^2$ so $3\left(x^2/a^2\right) = 1$, $x = a/\sqrt{3}$ and therefore $y = b/\sqrt{3}$ and $z = c/\sqrt{3}$. The dimensions agree with those in part (a).

48. $f(x, y) = x^2 + y^2$; $2x = (10x - 6y)\lambda$; $2y = (-6x + 10y)\lambda$. If $10x - 6y \neq 0$ and $-6x + 10y \neq 0$ then $x/(5x - 3y) = y/(-3x + 5y)$, $y^2 = x^2$, $y = \pm x$; if $y = x$ then $5x^2 - 6x^2 + 5x^2 = 8$ so $x = \pm\sqrt{2}$, if $y = -x$ then $5x^2 + 6x^2 + 5x^2 = 8$ so $x = \pm 1/\sqrt{2}$. If $10x - 6y = 0$ or $-6x + 10y = 0$ then $x = y = 0$, which does not satisfy the equation of the curve. The test points are $(\sqrt{2}, \sqrt{2})$, $(-\sqrt{2}, -\sqrt{2})$, $(1/\sqrt{2}, -1/\sqrt{2})$, and $(-1/\sqrt{2}, 1/\sqrt{2})$. $f(\sqrt{2}, \sqrt{2}) = f(-\sqrt{2}, -\sqrt{2}) = 4$, $f(1/\sqrt{2}, -1/\sqrt{2}) = f(-1/\sqrt{2}, 1/\sqrt{2}) = 1$ so the distance from the origin is minimum at $(1/\sqrt{2}, -1/\sqrt{2})$ and $(-1/\sqrt{2}, 1/\sqrt{2})$, maximum at $(\sqrt{2}, \sqrt{2})$ and $(-\sqrt{2}, -\sqrt{2})$.

49. $f(I_1, I_2, I_3) = I_1^2 R_1 + I_2^2 R_2 + I_3^2 R_3$, $I_1 + I_2 + I_3 = I$. $2I_1 R_1 = \lambda$, $2I_2 R_2 = \lambda$, $2I_3 R_3 = \lambda$; $2I_1 R_1 = 2I_2 R_2 = 2I_3 R_3$, $I_1/I_2 = R_2/R_1 = R_1^{-1}/R_2^{-1}$ and $I_2/I_3 = R_2^{-1}/R_3^{-1}$ so $I_1 : I_2 : I_3 = R_1^{-1} : R_2^{-1} : R_3^{-1}$.

CHAPTER 17
Multiple Integrals

EXERCISE SET 17.1

1. $\displaystyle\int_0^1 \int_0^2 (x+3)\,dy\,dx = \int_0^1 (2x+6)\,dx = 7$

2. $\displaystyle\int_1^3 \int_{-1}^1 (2x-4y)\,dy\,dx = \int_1^3 4x\,dx = 16$

3. $\displaystyle\int_2^4 \int_0^1 x^2 y\,dx\,dy = \int_2^4 \frac{1}{3}y\,dy = 2$

4. $\displaystyle\int_{-2}^0 \int_{-1}^2 (x^2+y^2)\,dx\,dy = \int_{-2}^0 (3+3y^2)\,dy = 14$

5. $\displaystyle\int_0^{\ln 3} \int_0^{\ln 2} e^{x+y}\,dy\,dx = \int_0^{\ln 3} e^x\,dx = 2$

6. $\displaystyle\int_0^2 \int_0^1 y\sin x\,dy\,dx = \int_0^2 \frac{1}{2}\sin x\,dx = (1-\cos 2)/2$

7. $\displaystyle\int_0^3 \int_0^1 x(x^2+y)^{1/2}\,dx\,dy = \int_0^3 \frac{1}{3}[(1+y)^{3/2}-y^{3/2}]\,dy = 2(31-9\sqrt{3})/15$

8. $\displaystyle\int_{-1}^2 \int_2^4 (2x^2 y + 3xy^2)\,dx\,dy = \int_{-1}^2 \left(\frac{112}{3}y + 18y^2\right)dy = 110$

9. $\displaystyle\int_{-1}^0 \int_2^5 dx\,dy = \int_{-1}^0 3\,dy = 3$ **10.** $\displaystyle\int_4^6 \int_{-3}^7 dy\,dx = \int_4^6 10\,dx = 20$

11. $\displaystyle\int_0^1 \int_0^1 \frac{x}{(xy+1)^2}\,dy\,dx = \int_0^1 \left(1-\frac{1}{x+1}\right)dx = 1-\ln 2$

12. $\displaystyle\int_{\pi/2}^{\pi} \int_1^2 x\cos xy\,dy\,dx = \int_{\pi/2}^{\pi} (\sin 2x - \sin x)\,dx = -2$

13. $\displaystyle\int_0^{\ln 2} \int_0^1 xy\,e^{y^2 x}\,dy\,dx = \int_0^{\ln 2} \frac{1}{2}(e^x - 1)\,dx = (1-\ln 2)/2$

14. $\displaystyle\int_3^4 \int_1^2 \frac{1}{(x+y)^2} dy\, dx = \int_3^4 \left(\frac{1}{x+1} - \frac{1}{x+2}\right) dx = \ln(25/24)$

15. $\displaystyle\int_{-1}^1 \int_{-2}^2 4xy^3 dy\, dx = \int_{-1}^1 0\, dx = 0$

16. $\displaystyle\int_0^1 \int_0^1 \frac{xy}{\sqrt{x^2+y^2+1}} dy\, dx = \int_0^1 [x(x^2+2)^{1/2} - x(x^2+1)^{1/2}]dx = (3\sqrt{3} - 4\sqrt{2} + 1)/3$

17. $\displaystyle\int_0^1 \int_2^3 x\sqrt{1-x^2}\, dy\, dx = \int_0^1 x(1-x^2)^{1/2} dx = 1/3$

18. $\displaystyle\int_0^{\pi/2} \int_0^{\pi/3} (x\sin y - y\sin x)dy\, dx = \int_0^{\pi/2} \left(\frac{x}{2} - \frac{\pi^2}{18}\sin x\right) dx = \pi^2/144$

19. $\displaystyle\int_{-\pi/4}^{\pi/4} \int_0^{\pi/4} \cos(x+y)dy\, dx = \int_{-\pi/4}^{\pi/4} [\sin(x+\pi/4) - \sin x]dx = 1$

20.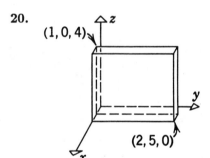

21.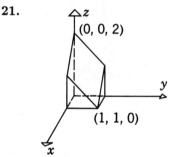

22.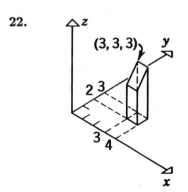

23.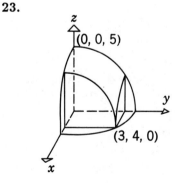

24.

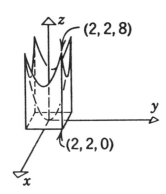

25.

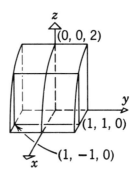

26. $V = \int_3^5 \int_1^2 (2x + y) dy\, dx = \int_3^5 (2x + 3/2) dx = 19$

27. $V = \int_1^3 \int_0^2 (3x^3 + 3x^2 y) dy\, dx = \int_1^3 (6x^3 + 6x^2) dx = 172$

28. $V = \int_0^3 \int_0^4 5(1 - x/3) dy\, dx = \int_0^3 5(4 - 4x/3) dx = 30$

29. $V = \int_0^2 \int_0^3 x^2 dy\, dx = \int_0^2 3x^2 dx = 8$

30. $V = \int_0^5 \int_0^2 y\, dy\, dx + \int_0^5 \int_2^3 (6 - 2y) dy\, dx$

$= \int_0^5 2\, dx + \int_0^5 dx = 15$

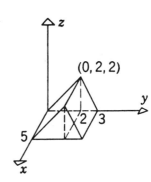

31. $\displaystyle\iint\limits_{R} f(x,y)dA = \int_a^b \left[\int_c^d g(x)h(y)dy\right]dx = \int_a^b g(x)\left[\int_c^d h(y)dy\right]dx$

$\displaystyle\qquad = \left[\int_a^b g(x)dx\right]\left[\int_c^d h(y)dy\right]$

32. $\displaystyle\int_0^{1/2}\int_0^{\pi} x\cos xy\cos^2 \pi x\, dy\, dx = \int_0^{1/2}\sin \pi x\cos^2 \pi x\, dx = 1/(3\pi)$

EXERCISE SET 17.2

1. $\displaystyle\int_0^1\int_{x^2}^x xy^2\, dy\, dx = \int_0^1 \frac{1}{3}(x^4 - x^7)dx = 1/40$

2. $\displaystyle\int_1^2\int_y^{3-y} y\, dx\, dy = \int_1^2 (3y - 2y^2)dy = -1/6$

3. $\displaystyle\int_0^3\int_0^{\sqrt{9-y^2}} y\, dx\, dy = \int_0^3 y\sqrt{9-y^2}\, dy = 9$

4. $\displaystyle\int_{1/4}^1\int_{x^2}^x \sqrt{x/y}\, dy\, dx = \int_{1/4}^1\int_{x^2}^x x^{1/2}y^{-1/2}dy\, dx = \int_{1/4}^1 2(x - x^{3/2})dx = 13/80$

5. $\displaystyle\int_{\sqrt{\pi}}^{\sqrt{2\pi}}\int_0^{x^3} \sin(y/x)dy\, dx = \int_{\sqrt{\pi}}^{\sqrt{2\pi}} [-x\cos(x^2) + x]dx = \pi/2$

6. $\displaystyle\int_{-1}^1\int_{-x^2}^{x^2} (x^2 - y)dy\, dx = \int_{-1}^1 2x^4 dx = 4/5$

7. $\displaystyle\int_{\pi/2}^{\pi}\int_0^{x^2} \frac{1}{x}\cos(y/x)dy\, dx = \int_{\pi/2}^{\pi}\sin x\, dx = 1$

8. $\displaystyle\int_0^{\pi/2}\int_0^{\sin y} e^x \cos y\, dx\, dy = \int_0^{\pi/2} (e^{\sin y}\cos y - \cos y)dy = e - 2$

9. $\displaystyle\int_0^a\int_0^{\sqrt{a^2-x^2}} (x + y)dy\, dx = \int_0^a [x\sqrt{a^2 - x^2} + (a^2 - x^2)/2]dx = 2a^3/3$

10. $\displaystyle\int_1^2 \int_0^{y^2} e^{x/y^2}\,dx\,dy = \int_1^2 (e-1)y^2\,dy = 7(e-1)/3$

11. $\displaystyle\int_0^1 \int_0^x y\sqrt{x^2-y^2}\,dy\,dx = \int_0^1 \frac{1}{3}x^3\,dx = 1/12$

12. $\displaystyle\int_0^1 \int_0^x e^{x^2}\,dy\,dx = \int_0^1 xe^{x^2}\,dx = (e-1)/2$

13. $\displaystyle\int_0^2 \int_0^{x^2} 6xy\,dy\,dx = \int_0^2 3x^5\,dx = 32$

14. $\displaystyle\int_1^3 \int_{-(y-5)/2}^{(y+7)/2} xy\,dx\,dy = \int_1^3 (3y^2 + 3y)\,dy = 38$

15. $\displaystyle\int_1^2 \int_{\pi/2}^{2\pi/x} x\cos xy\,dy\,dx = -\int_1^2 \sin(\pi x/2)\,dx = -2/\pi$

16. $\displaystyle\int_0^1 \int_{x^2}^{\sqrt{x}} (x+y)\,dy\,dx = \int_0^1 (x^{3/2} + x/2 - x^3 - x^4/2)\,dx = 3/10$

17. $\displaystyle\int_4^8 \int_{16/x}^{x} x^2\,dy\,dx = \int_4^8 (x^3 - 16x)\,dx = 576$

18. $\displaystyle\int_1^2 \int_0^y xy^2\,dx\,dy = \int_1^2 \frac{1}{2}y^4\,dy = 31/10$

19. $\displaystyle\int_0^4 \int_0^{\sqrt{y}} x(1+y^2)^{-1/2}\,dx\,dy = \int_0^4 \frac{1}{2}y(1+y^2)^{-1/2}\,dy = (\sqrt{17}-1)/2$

20. $\displaystyle\int_0^\pi \int_0^x x\cos y\,dy\,dx = \int_0^\pi x\sin x\,dx = \pi$

21. $\displaystyle\int_{-1}^1 \int_{-\sqrt{1-x^2}}^{\sqrt{1-x^2}} (3x - 2y)\,dy\,dx = \int_{-1}^1 6x\sqrt{1-x^2}\,dx = 0$

22. $\displaystyle\int_0^5 \int_{5-x}^{\sqrt{25-x^2}} y\,dy\,dx = \int_0^5 (5x - x^2)\,dx = 125/6$

23. $\displaystyle\int_0^1 \int_x^1 \frac{1}{1+x^2}\,dy\,dx = \int_0^1 \left[\frac{1}{1+x^2} - \frac{x}{1+x^2}\right]\,dx = \frac{\pi}{4} - \frac{1}{2}\ln 2$

24. $\displaystyle\int_0^2 \int_x^{3x-x^2} (x^2 - xy)dy\,dx = \int_0^2 (-2x^3 + 2x^4 - x^5/2)dx = -8/15$

25. $\displaystyle\int_0^3 \int_{y^2}^{6-y} xy\,dx\,dy = \int_0^2 \frac{1}{2}(36y - 12y^2 + y^3 - y^5)dy = 50/3$

26. $\displaystyle\int_0^{\pi/4} \int_{\sin y}^{1/\sqrt{2}} x\,dx\,dy = \int_0^{\pi/4} \frac{1}{4}\cos 2y\,dy = 1/8$

27. $\displaystyle\int_{-1}^0 \int_x^{x^3} (x-1)dy\,dx + \int_0^1 \int_{x^3}^x (x-1)dy\,dx$

$\displaystyle = \int_{-1}^0 (x^4 - x^3 - x^2 + x)dx + \int_0^1 (-x^4 + x^3 + x^2 - x)dx = -1/2$

28. $\displaystyle\int_0^{1/\sqrt{2}} \int_x^{2x} x^2 dy\,dx + \int_{1/\sqrt{2}}^1 \int_x^{1/x} x^2 dy\,dx = \int_0^{1/\sqrt{2}} x^3 dx + \int_{1/\sqrt{2}}^1 (x - x^3)dx = 1/8$

29. $\displaystyle A = \int_0^5 \int_0^{5-x} dy\,dx = \int_0^5 (5-x)dx = 25/2$

30. $\displaystyle A = \int_0^4 \int_{x^2}^{4x} dy\,dx = \int_0^4 (4x - x^2)dx = 32/3$

31. $\displaystyle A = \int_0^{\pi/4} \int_{\sin x}^{\cos x} dy\,dx = \int_0^{\pi/4} (\cos x - \sin x)dx = \sqrt{2} - 1$

32. $\displaystyle A = \int_{-4}^1 \int_{3y-4}^{-y^2} dx\,dy = \int_{-4}^1 (-y^2 - 3y + 4)dy = 125/6$

33. $\displaystyle A = \int_{-3}^3 \int_{1-y^2/9}^{9-y^2} dx\,dy = \int_{-3}^3 8(1 - y^2/9)dy = 32$

34. $\displaystyle A = \int_0^1 \int_{\sinh x}^{\cosh x} dy\,dx = \int_0^1 (\cosh x - \sinh x)dx = 1 - e^{-1}$

35. $\displaystyle V = \int_0^{5/2} \int_0^{5-2x} (5 - 2x - y)dy\,dx = \int_0^{5/2} \frac{1}{2}(5 - 2x)^2 dx = 125/12$

36. $\displaystyle V = \int_{-3}^3 \int_{-\sqrt{9-x^2}}^{\sqrt{9-x^2}} (3 - x)dy\,dx = \int_{-3}^3 (6\sqrt{9-x^2} - 2x\sqrt{9-x^2})dx = 27\pi$

37. $V = \int_{-1}^{1} \int_{0}^{1-x^2} (x + 2y + 2)dy\,dx = \int_{-1}^{1} (x^4 - x^3 - 4x^2 + x + 3)dx = 56/15$

38. $V = \int_{0}^{1} \int_{x^2}^{x} (x^2 + 3y^2)dy\,dx = \int_{0}^{1} (2x^3 - x^4 - x^6)dx = 11/70$

39. $V = \int_{0}^{3} \int_{0}^{2} (9x^2 + y^2)dy\,dx = \int_{0}^{3} (18x^2 + 8/3)dx = 170$

40. $V = \int_{-1}^{1} \int_{y^2}^{1} (1 - x)dx\,dy = \int_{-1}^{1} (1/2 - y^2 + y^4/2)dy = 8/15$

41. $V = \int_{-3/2}^{3/2} \int_{-\sqrt{9-4x^2}}^{\sqrt{9-4x^2}} (y + 3)dy\,dx = \int_{-3/2}^{3/2} 6\sqrt{9 - 4x^2}\,dx = 27\pi/2$

42. $V = \int_{0}^{3} \int_{y^2/3}^{3} (9 - x^2)dx\,dy = \int_{0}^{3} (18 - 3y^2 + y^6/81)dy = 216/7$

43. $V = \int_{0}^{4} \int_{0}^{2-x/2} (x/4 + 2y)dy\,dx = \int_{0}^{4} (x^2/8 - 3x/2 + 4)dx = 20/3$

44. $V = \int_{0}^{1} \int_{0}^{1-x} e^{y-x}dy\,dx = \int_{0}^{1} (e^{1-2x} - e^{-x})dx = (e^{-1} + e - 2)/2$

45. $V = 4\int_{0}^{1} \int_{0}^{\sqrt{1-x^2}} (1 - x^2 - y^2)dy\,dx = \frac{8}{3}\int_{0}^{1} (1 - x^2)^{3/2}dx = \pi/2$

46. $V = \int_{0}^{2} \int_{0}^{\sqrt{4-x^2}} (x^2 + y^2)dy\,dx = \int_{0}^{2} \left[x^2\sqrt{4 - x^2} + \frac{1}{3}(4 - x^2)^{3/2} \right] dx = 2\pi$

47. $V = 8\int_{0}^{5} \int_{0}^{\sqrt{25-x^2}} \sqrt{25 - x^2}dy\,dx = 8\int_{0}^{5} (25 - x^2)dx = 2000/3$

48. $V = 2\int_{0}^{2} \int_{0}^{\sqrt{1-(y-1)^2}} (x^2 + y^2)dx\,dy = 2\int_{0}^{2} \left(\frac{1}{3}[1 - (y - 1)^2]^{3/2} + y^2[1 - (y - 1)^2]^{1/2} \right) dy,$

let $y - 1 = \sin\theta$ to get $V = 2\int_{-\pi/2}^{\pi/2} \left[\frac{1}{3}\cos^3\theta + (1 + \sin\theta)^2\cos\theta \right] \cos\theta\,d\theta$ which eventually

yields $V = 3\pi/2$

49. $\displaystyle\int_0^{\sqrt{2}}\int_{y^2}^2 f(x,y)dx\,dy$

50. $\displaystyle\int_0^8\int_0^{x/2} f(x,y)dy\,dx$

51. $\displaystyle\int_1^{e^2}\int_{\ln x}^2 f(x,y)dy\,dx$

52. $\displaystyle\int_0^1\int_{e^y}^e f(x,y)dx\,dy$

53. $\displaystyle\int_{-1}^1\int_{-2\sqrt{1-y^2}}^{2\sqrt{1-y^2}} f(x,y)dx\,dy$

54. $\displaystyle\int_0^1\int_{x^2}^{\sqrt{x}} f(x,y)dy\,dx$

55. $\displaystyle\int_0^{\pi/2}\int_0^{\sin x} f(x,y)dy\,dx$

56. $\displaystyle\int_{-9}^7\int_{(y-3)/4}^{-3+\sqrt{9+y}} f(x,y)dx\,dy$

57. $\displaystyle\int_0^4\int_0^{y/4} e^{-y^2}dx\,dy = \int_0^4 \frac{1}{4}ye^{-y^2}dy = (1-e^{-16})/8$

58. $\displaystyle\int_0^1\int_0^{2x} \cos(x^2)dy\,dx = \int_0^1 2x\cos(x^2)dx = \sin 1$

59. $\displaystyle\int_0^2\int_0^{x^2} e^{x^3}dy\,dx = \int_0^2 x^2 e^{x^3}dx = (e^8-1)/3$

60. $\displaystyle\int_0^{\ln 3}\int_{e^y}^3 x\,dx\,dy = \frac{1}{2}\int_0^{\ln 3}(9-e^{2y})dy = \frac{1}{2}(9\ln 3 - 4)$

61. $\displaystyle\int_0^{\pi/2}\int_0^{\cos y} x\,dx\,dy = \frac{1}{2}\int_0^{\pi/2}\cos^2 y\,dy = \pi/8$

62. $\displaystyle\int_0^{\pi/2}\int_0^{\sin x} \sec^2(\cos x)dy\,dx = \int_0^{\pi/2}\sec^2(\cos x)\sin x\,dx = \tan 1$

63. $\displaystyle\int_0^2\int_0^{y^2} \sin(y^3)dx\,dy = \int_0^2 y^2\sin(y^3)dy = (1-\cos 8)/3$

64. $\displaystyle\int_0^1\int_{e^x}^e x\,dy\,dx = \int_0^1 (ex - xe^x)dx = e/2 - 1$

65. **(a)** $\displaystyle \int_{-2}^{-1}\int_0^2 xy^2\,dy\,dx + \int_{-1}^1\int_1^2 xy^2\,dy\,dx + \int_1^2\int_0^2 xy^2\,dy\,dx$

$$= \int_{-2}^{-1}\frac{8}{3}x\,dx + \int_{-1}^1\frac{7}{3}x\,dx + \int_1^2\frac{8}{3}x\,dx = 0$$

(b) $\displaystyle \int_1^4\int_{-\sqrt{y}}^{2-y} xy^2\,dx\,dy + \int_{1/2}^1\int_{-\sqrt{y}}^{\sqrt{y}} xy^2\,dx\,dy$

$$= \int_1^4\frac{1}{2}(4y^2 - 5y^3 + y^4)\,dy + \int_{1/2}^1(0)\,dy = -603/40$$

66. **(a)** 6 **(b)** 0

67. $\displaystyle 2\int_{-1}^1\int_0^{\sqrt{1-x^2}} dy\,dx + \int_{-1}^1\int_0^{\sqrt{1-x^2}} x\sqrt{9-y^2}\,dy\,dx = 2\cdot\frac{1}{2}\pi(1)^2 + 0 = \pi$ because the first integral gives the area of a semicircle of radius 1, and with $f(x,y) = x\sqrt{9-y^2}$, $f(-x,y) = -f(x,y)$ so the second integral evaluates to 0.

68. The region is symmetric with respect to the x-axis and $f(x,-y) = -f(x,y)$ where
$f(x,y) = \sin(xy^3)$ so $\displaystyle \int_0^2\int_{x-2}^{2-x}\sin(xy^3)\,dy\,dx = 0$.

69. $f(x,y) = x^3y$, $f(-x,y) = -f(x,y)$ so $\displaystyle \iint_R x^3y\,dA = 0$

EXERCISE SET 17.3

1. $\displaystyle \int_0^{\pi/2}\int_0^{\sin\theta} r\cos\theta\,dr\,d\theta = \int_0^{\pi/2}\frac{1}{2}\sin^2\theta\cos\theta\,d\theta = 1/6$

2. $\displaystyle \int_0^{\pi}\int_0^{1+\cos\theta} r\,dr\,d\theta = \int_0^{\pi}\frac{1}{2}(1+\cos\theta)^2\,d\theta = 3\pi/4$

3. $\displaystyle \int_{-\pi/2}^{\pi/2}\int_0^{a\sin\theta} r^2\,dr\,d\theta = \int_{-\pi/2}^{\pi/2}\frac{a^3}{3}\sin^3\theta\,d\theta = 0$

4. $\displaystyle \int_0^{\pi/3}\int_0^{\cos3\theta} r\,dr\,d\theta = \int_0^{\pi/3}\frac{1}{2}\cos^2 3\theta\,d\theta = \pi/12$

5. $\displaystyle\int_0^\pi \int_0^{1-\sin\theta} r^2 \cos\theta \, dr \, d\theta = \int_0^\pi \frac{1}{3}(1-\sin\theta)^3 \cos\theta \, d\theta = 0$

6. $\displaystyle\int_0^\pi \int_0^{\cos\theta} r^3 dr \, d\theta = \int_0^\pi \frac{1}{4}\cos^4\theta \, d\theta = 3\pi/32$

7. $\displaystyle A = \int_0^{2\pi} \int_0^{1-\cos\theta} r \, dr \, d\theta = \int_0^{2\pi} \frac{1}{2}(1-\cos\theta)^2 d\theta = 3\pi/2$

8. $\displaystyle A = 4\int_0^{\pi/2} \int_0^{\sin 2\theta} r \, dr \, d\theta = 2\int_0^{\pi/2} \sin^2 2\theta \, d\theta = \pi/2$

9. $\displaystyle A = \int_{\pi/4}^{\pi/2} \int_{\sin 2\theta}^1 r \, dr \, d\theta = \int_{\pi/4}^{\pi/2} \frac{1}{2}(1-\sin^2 2\theta)d\theta = \pi/16$

10. $\displaystyle A = 2\int_0^{\pi/3} \int_{\sec\theta}^2 r \, dr \, d\theta = \int_0^{\pi/3} (4-\sec^2\theta)d\theta = 4\pi/3 - \sqrt{3}$

11. $\displaystyle A = 2\int_{\pi/6}^{\pi/2} \int_2^{4\sin\theta} r \, dr \, d\theta = \int_{\pi/6}^{\pi/2} (16\sin^2\theta - 4)d\theta = 4\pi/3 + 2\sqrt{3}$

12. $\displaystyle A = 2\int_{\pi/2}^\pi \int_{1+\cos\theta}^1 r \, dr \, d\theta = \int_{\pi/2}^\pi (-2\cos\theta - \cos^2\theta)d\theta = 2 - \pi/4$

13. $\displaystyle V = 8\int_0^{\pi/2} \int_0^1 r\sqrt{9-r^2} \, dr \, d\theta = \frac{8}{3}(27 - 16\sqrt{2})\int_0^{\pi/2} d\theta = 4(27 - 16\sqrt{2})\pi/3$

14. $\displaystyle V = 4\int_0^{\pi/2} \int_0^{2\cos\theta} r\sqrt{4-r^2} \, dr \, d\theta = \frac{32}{3}\int_0^{\pi/2} (1-\sin^3\theta)d\theta = \frac{32}{9}(3\pi - 4)$

15. $\displaystyle V = 2\int_0^{\pi/2} \int_0^{2\sin\theta} r^2 dr \, d\theta = \frac{16}{3}\int_0^{\pi/2} \sin^3\theta \, d\theta = 32/9$

16. $\displaystyle V = 4\int_0^{\pi/2} \int_1^3 dr \, d\theta = 8\int_0^{\pi/2} d\theta = 4\pi$

17. $\displaystyle V = 2\int_0^{\pi/2} \int_0^{\cos\theta} (1-r^2)r \, dr \, d\theta = \frac{1}{2}\int_0^{\pi/2} (1-\sin^4\theta)d\theta = 5\pi/32$

18. $\displaystyle V = \int_0^{\pi/2} \int_0^{3\sin\theta} r^2 \sin\theta \, dr \, d\theta = 9\int_0^{\pi/2} \sin^4\theta \, d\theta = 27\pi/16$

19. $\displaystyle\int_0^{2\pi}\int_0^1 e^{-r^2}r\,dr\,d\theta = \frac{1}{2}(1-e^{-1})\int_0^{2\pi}d\theta = (1-e^{-1})\pi$

20. $\displaystyle\int_0^{\pi/2}\int_0^3 r\sqrt{9-r^2}\,dr\,d\theta = 9\int_0^{\pi/2}d\theta = 9\pi/2$

21. $\displaystyle\int_0^{\pi/4}\int_0^2 \frac{1}{1+r^2}r\,dr\,d\theta = \frac{1}{2}\ln 5\int_0^{\pi/4}d\theta = \frac{\pi}{8}\ln 5$

22. $\displaystyle\int_{\pi/4}^{\pi/2}\int_0^{2\cos\theta} 2r^2\sin\theta\,dr\,d\theta = \frac{16}{3}\int_{\pi/4}^{\pi/2}\cos^3\theta\sin\theta\,d\theta = 1/3$

23. $\displaystyle\int_0^{\pi/2}\int_0^1 r^3\,dr\,d\theta = \frac{1}{4}\int_0^{\pi/2}d\theta = \pi/8$

24. $\displaystyle\int_0^{2\pi}\int_0^2 e^{-r^2}r\,dr\,d\theta = \frac{1}{2}(1-e^{-4})\int_0^{2\pi}d\theta = (1-e^{-4})\pi$

25. $\displaystyle\int_0^{\pi/2}\int_0^{2\cos\theta} r^2\,dr\,d\theta = \frac{8}{3}\int_0^{\pi/2}\cos^3\theta\,d\theta = 16/9$

26. $\displaystyle\int_0^{\pi/2}\int_0^1 \cos(r^2)r\,dr\,d\theta = \frac{1}{2}\sin 1\int_0^{\pi/2}d\theta = \frac{\pi}{4}\sin 1$

27. $\displaystyle\int_0^{\pi/2}\int_0^a \frac{r}{(1+r^2)^{3/2}}\,dr\,d\theta = \frac{\pi}{2}(1-1/\sqrt{1+a^2})$

28. $\displaystyle\int_0^{\pi/4}\int_0^{\sec\theta\tan\theta} r^2\,dr\,d\theta = \frac{1}{3}\int_0^{\pi/4}\sec^3\theta\tan^3\theta\,d\theta = 2(\sqrt{2}+1)/45$

29. $\displaystyle\int_0^{\pi/4}\int_0^2 \frac{r}{\sqrt{1+r^2}}\,dr\,d\theta = \frac{\pi}{4}(\sqrt{5}-1)$

30. $\displaystyle\int_{\tan^{-1}(3/4)}^{\pi/2}\int_{3\csc\theta}^5 r\,dr\,d\theta = \frac{1}{2}\int_{\tan^{-1}(3/4)}^{\pi/2}(25-9\csc^2\theta)\,d\theta$

$$= \frac{25}{2}\left[\frac{\pi}{2}-\tan^{-1}(3/4)\right]-6 = \frac{25}{2}\tan^{-1}(4/3)-6$$

31. $\displaystyle V = 2\int_0^{\pi/2}\int_0^{a\sin\theta} \frac{c}{a}(a^2-r^2)^{1/2}r\,dr\,d\theta = \frac{2}{3}a^2c\int_0^{\pi/2}(1-\cos^3\theta)\,d\theta = (3\pi-4)a^2c/9$

32. $A = 4 \displaystyle\int_0^{\pi/4} \int_0^{a\sqrt{2\cos 2\theta}} r\, dr\, d\theta = 4a^2 \int_0^{\pi/4} \cos 2\theta\, d\theta = 2a^2$

33. $A = \displaystyle\int_{\pi/6}^{\pi/4} \int_{\sqrt{8\cos 2\theta}}^{4\sin\theta} r\, dr\, d\theta + \int_{\pi/4}^{\pi/2} \int_0^{4\sin\theta} r\, dr\, d\theta$

$\qquad = \displaystyle\int_{\pi/6}^{\pi/4} (8\sin^2\theta - 4\cos 2\theta)d\theta + \int_{\pi/4}^{\pi/2} 8\sin^2\theta\, d\theta = 4\pi/3 + 2\sqrt{3} - 2$

34. $A = \displaystyle\int_0^\phi \int_0^{2a\sin\theta} r\, dr\, d\theta = 2a^2 \int_0^\phi \sin^2\theta\, d\theta = a^2\phi - \frac{1}{2}a^2 \sin 2\phi.$

35. **(a)** $I^2 = \left[\displaystyle\int_0^{+\infty} e^{-x^2}\, dx\right]\left[\int_0^{+\infty} e^{-y^2}\, dy\right] = \int_0^{+\infty} \left[\int_0^{+\infty} e^{-x^2}\, dx\right] e^{-y^2}\, dy$

$\qquad = \displaystyle\int_0^{+\infty} \int_0^{+\infty} e^{-x^2} e^{-y^2}\, dx\, dy = \int_0^{+\infty} \int_0^{+\infty} e^{-(x^2+y^2)}\, dx\, dy$

$\qquad$ **(b)** $I^2 = \displaystyle\int_0^{\pi/2} \int_0^{+\infty} e^{-r^2} r\, dr\, d\theta = \frac{1}{2}\int_0^{\pi/2} d\theta = \pi/4$

$\qquad$ **(c)** $I = \sqrt{\pi}/2$

36. **(a)** $\displaystyle\int_0^{\pi/2} \int_1^3 r^3 \cos^2\theta\, dr\, d\theta = 20\int_0^{\pi/2} \cos^2\theta\, d\theta = 5\pi$

$\qquad$ **(b)** $\displaystyle\int_{\tan^{-1}(1/3)}^{\tan^{-1}(2)} \int_0^2 r^3 \cos^2\theta\, dr\, d\theta = 4\int_{\tan^{-1}(1/3)}^{\tan^{-1}(2)} \cos^2\theta\, d\theta = \frac{1}{5} + 2[\tan^{-1}(2) - \tan^{-1}(1/3)]$

EXERCISE SET 17.4

1. $z = \sqrt{9 - y^2}$, $z_x = 0$, $z_y = -y/\sqrt{9 - y^2}$, $z_x^2 + z_y^2 + 1 = 9/(9 - y^2)$,

$\qquad S = \displaystyle\int_0^2 \int_{-3}^3 \frac{3}{\sqrt{9 - y^2}}\, dy\, dx = \int_0^2 3\pi\, dx = 6\pi$

2. $z = 8 - 2x - 2y$, $z_x^2 + z_y^2 + 1 = 4 + 4 + 1 = 9$, $S = \displaystyle\int_0^4 \int_0^{4-x} 3\, dy\, dx = \int_0^4 3(4 - x)dx = 24$

3. $z^2 = 4x^2 + 4y^2$, $2zz_x = 8x$ so $z_x = 4x/z$, similarly $z_y = 4y/z$ thus

$\qquad z_x^2 + z_y^2 + 1 = (16x^2 + 16y^2)/z^2 + 1 = 5$, $S = \displaystyle\int_0^1 \int_{x^2}^x \sqrt{5}\, dy\, dx = \sqrt{5}\int_0^1 (x - x^2)dx = \sqrt{5}/6$

4. $z^2 = x^2 + y^2$, $z_x = x/z$, $z_y = y/z$, $z_x^2 + z_y^2 + 1 = (z^2 + y^2)/z^2 + 1 = 2$,

$$S = \iint_R \sqrt{2}\,dA = 2\int_0^{\pi/2}\int_0^{2\cos\theta} \sqrt{2}\,r\,dr\,d\theta = 4\sqrt{2}\int_0^{\pi/2}\cos^2\theta\,d\theta = \sqrt{2}\pi$$

5. $z_x = -2x$, $z_y = -2y$, $z_x^2 + z_y^2 + 1 = 4x^2 + 4y^2 + 1$,

$$S = \iint_R \sqrt{4x^2 + 4y^2 + 1}\,dA = \int_0^{2\pi}\int_0^1 r\sqrt{4r^2 + 1}\,dr\,d\theta$$

$$= \frac{1}{12}(5\sqrt{5} - 1)\int_0^{2\pi} d\theta = (5\sqrt{5} - 1)\pi/6$$

6. $z_x = 2$, $z_y = 2y$, $z_x^2 + z_y^2 + 1 = 5 + 4y^2$,

$$S = \int_0^1\int_0^y \sqrt{5 + 4y^2}\,dx\,dy = \int_0^1 y\sqrt{5 + 4y^2}\,dy = (27 - 5\sqrt{5})/12$$

7. $z_x = y$, $z_y = x$, $z_x^2 + z_y^2 + 1 = x^2 + y^2 + 1$,

$$S = \iint_R \sqrt{x^2 + y^2 + 1}\,dA = \int_0^{\pi/6}\int_0^3 r\sqrt{r^2 + 1}\,dr\,d\theta$$

$$= \frac{1}{3}(10\sqrt{10} - 1)\int_0^{\pi/6} d\theta = (10\sqrt{10} - 1)\pi/18$$

8. $z_x = x$, $z_y = y$, $z_x^2 + z_y^2 + 1 = x^2 + y^2 + 1$,

$$S = \iint_R \sqrt{x^2 + y^2 + 1}\,dA = \int_0^{2\pi}\int_0^{\sqrt{8}} r\sqrt{r^2 + 1}\,dr\,d\theta = \frac{26}{3}\int_0^{2\pi} d\theta = 52\pi/3$$

9. On the sphere, $z_x = -x/z$ and $z_y = -y/z$ so
$z_x^2 + z_y^2 + 1 = (x^2 + y^2 + z^2)/z^2 = 16/(16 - x^2 - y^2)$; the planes $z = 1$ and $z = 2$ intersect the sphere along the circles $x^2 + y^2 = 15$ and $x^2 + y^2 = 12$;

$$S = \iint_R \frac{4}{\sqrt{16 - x^2 - y^2}}\,dA = \int_0^{2\pi}\int_{\sqrt{12}}^{\sqrt{15}} \frac{4r}{\sqrt{16 - r^2}}\,dr\,d\theta = 4\int_0^{2\pi} d\theta = 8\pi$$

10. On the sphere, $z_x = -x/z$ and $z_y = -y/z$ so
$z_x^2 + z_y^2 + 1 = (x^2 + y^2 + z^2)/z^2 = 8/(8 - x^2 - y^2)$; the cone cuts the sphere in the circle

$$x^2 + y^2 = 4; \quad S = \int_0^{2\pi}\int_0^2 \frac{2\sqrt{2}r}{\sqrt{8 - r^2}}\,dr\,d\theta = (8 - 4\sqrt{2})\int_0^{2\pi} d\theta = 8(2 - \sqrt{2})\pi$$

11. On both upper and lower halves of the sphere, $z_x = -x/z$ and $z_y = -y/z$ so

$$z_x^2 + z_y^2 + 1 = (x^2 + y^2 + z^2)/z^2 = a^2/(a^2 - x^2 - y^2),$$

$$S = (2)(2) \int_0^{\pi/2} \int_0^{a\sin\theta} \frac{ar}{\sqrt{a^2 - r^2}} dr\, d\theta = 4a^2 \int_0^{\pi/2} (1 - \cos\theta) d\theta = 2(\pi - 2)a^2$$

12. $x^2 + y^2 + z^2 = a^2$, $z_x = -x/z$, $z_y = -y/z$

$z_x^2 + z_y^2 + 1 = (x^2 + y^2 + z^2)/z^2 = a^2/(a^2 - x^2 - y^2)$, by symmetry

$$S = 8 \int_0^{\pi/2} \int_0^a \frac{ar}{\sqrt{a^2 - r^2}} dr\, d\theta = 8a^2 \int_0^{\pi/2} d\theta = 4\pi a^2$$

13. $z_x = -x/z$ and $z_y = 0$ on $x^2 + z^2 = 16$ so $z_x^2 + z_y^2 + 1 = (x^2 + z^2)/z^2 = 16/(16 - x^2)$,

$$S = 8 \int_0^4 \int_0^{\sqrt{16-x^2}} \frac{4}{\sqrt{16 - x^2}} dy\, dx = 32 \int_0^4 dx = 128$$

14. On the cylinder, $z_x = (5 - 2x)/(2z)$ and $z_y = 0$ so

$z_x^2 + z_y^2 + 1 = [(5 - 2x)^2 + 4z^2]/(4z^2) = [25 - 20x + 4x^2 + 20x - 4x^2]/(4z^2) = 25/[4(5x - x^2)]$,

combine the equations of the cylinder and sphere to eliminate z to get $y^2 = 25 - 5x$ which for $0 \le x \le 5$ is the projection onto the xy-plane of the curve of intersection of the surfaces so, using symmetry,

$$S = 4 \int_0^5 \int_0^{\sqrt{25-5x}} \frac{5}{2\sqrt{5x - x^2}} dy\, dx = 10 \int_0^5 \frac{\sqrt{25 - 5x}}{\sqrt{5x - x^2}} dx = 10 \int_0^5 \frac{\sqrt{5}}{\sqrt{x}} dx = 100$$

15. $z_x = \dfrac{h}{a} \dfrac{x}{\sqrt{x^2 + y^2}}$, $z_y = \dfrac{h}{a} \dfrac{y}{\sqrt{x^2 + y^2}}$, $z_x^2 + z_y^2 + 1 = \dfrac{h^2 x^2 + h^2 y^2}{a^2(x^2 + y^2)} + 1 = (a^2 + h^2)/a^2$,

$$S = \int_0^{2\pi} \int_0^a \frac{\sqrt{a^2 + h^2}}{a} r\, dr\, d\theta = \frac{1}{2} a\sqrt{a^2 + h^2} \int_0^{2\pi} d\theta = \pi a\sqrt{a^2 + h^2}$$

EXERCISE SET 17.5

1. $\displaystyle \int_{-1}^1 \int_0^2 \int_0^1 (x^2 + y^2 + z^2) dx\, dy\, dz = \int_{-1}^1 \int_0^2 (1/3 + y^2 + z^2) dy\, dz = \int_{-1}^1 (10/3 + 2z^2) dz = 8$

2. $\displaystyle \int_{1/3}^{1/2} \int_0^\pi \int_0^1 zx \sin xy\, dz\, dy\, dx = \int_{1/3}^{1/2} \int_0^\pi \frac{1}{2} x \sin xy\, dy\, dx$

$$= \int_{1/3}^{1/2} \frac{1}{2}(1 - \cos\pi x) dx = \frac{1}{12} + \frac{\sqrt{3} - 2}{4\pi}$$

3. $\displaystyle\int_0^2 \int_{-1}^{y^2} \int_1^z yz\,dx\,dz\,dy = \int_0^2 \int_{-1}^{y^2} (yz^2 - yz)dz\,dy = \int_0^2 \left(\frac{1}{3}y^7 - \frac{1}{2}y^5 + \frac{5}{6}y\right)dy = 7$

4. $\displaystyle\int_0^{\pi/4} \int_0^1 \int_0^{x^2} x\cos y\,dz\,dx\,dy = \int_0^{\pi/4} \int_0^1 x^3\cos y\,dx\,dy = \int_0^{\pi/4} \frac{1}{4}\cos y\,dy = \sqrt{2}/8$

5. $\displaystyle\int_0^3 \int_0^{\sqrt{9-z^2}} \int_0^x xy\,dy\,dx\,dz = \int_0^3 \int_0^{\sqrt{9-z^2}} \frac{1}{2}x^3 dx\,dz = \int_0^3 \frac{1}{8}(81 - 18z^2 + z^4)dz = 81/5$

6. $\displaystyle\int_1^3 \int_x^{x^2} \int_0^{\ln z} xe^y\,dy\,dz\,dx = \int_1^3 \int_x^{x^2} (xz - x)dz\,dx = \int_1^3 \left(\frac{1}{2}x^5 - \frac{3}{2}x^3 + x^2\right)dx = 118/3$

7. $\displaystyle\int_0^2 \int_0^{\sqrt{4-x^2}} \int_{-5+x^2+y^2}^{3-x^2-y^2} x\,dz\,dy\,dx = \int_0^2 \int_0^{\sqrt{4-x^2}} [2x(4 - x^2) - 2xy^2]dy\,dx$

$$= \int_0^2 \frac{4}{3}x(4 - x^2)^{3/2}dx = 128/15$$

8. $\displaystyle\int_1^2 \int_z^2 \int_0^{\sqrt{3}y} \frac{y}{x^2 + y^2}dx\,dy\,dz = \int_1^2 \int_z^2 \frac{\pi}{3}dy\,dz = \int_1^2 \frac{\pi}{3}(2 - z)dz = \pi/6$

9. $\displaystyle\int_0^{\pi} \int_0^1 \int_0^{\pi/6} xy\sin yz\,dz\,dy\,dx = \int_0^{\pi} \int_0^1 x[1 - \cos(\pi y/6)]dy\,dx$

$$= \int_0^{\pi} (1 - 3/\pi)x\,dx = \pi(\pi - 3)/2$$

10. $\displaystyle\int_{-1}^1 \int_0^{1-x^2} \int_0^y y\,dz\,dy\,dx = \int_{-1}^1 \int_0^{1-x^2} y^2\,dy\,dx = \int_{-1}^1 \frac{1}{3}(1 - x^2)^3 dx = 32/105$

11. $\displaystyle\int_0^{\sqrt{2}} \int_0^x \int_0^{2-x^2} xyz\,dz\,dy\,dx = \int_0^{\sqrt{2}} \int_0^x \frac{1}{2}xy(2 - x^2)^2 dy\,dx = \int_0^{\sqrt{2}} \frac{1}{4}x^3(2 - x^2)^2 dx = 1/6$

12. $\displaystyle\int_{\pi/6}^{\pi/2} \int_y^{\pi/2} \int_0^{xy} \cos(z/y)dz\,dx\,dy = \int_{\pi/6}^{\pi/2} \int_y^{\pi/2} y\sin x\,dx\,dy$

$$= \int_{\pi/6}^{\pi/2} y\cos y\,dy = (5\pi - 6\sqrt{3})/12$$

13. $V = \displaystyle\int_0^4 \int_0^{(4-x)/2} \int_0^{(12-3x-6y)/4} dz\,dy\,dx$

$= \displaystyle\int_0^4 \int_0^{(4-x)/2} \frac{1}{4}(12 - 3x - 6y)dy\,dx = \int_0^4 \frac{3}{16}(4-x)^2 dx = 4$

14. $V = \displaystyle\int_0^1 \int_0^{1-x} \int_0^{\sqrt{y}} dz\,dy\,dx = \int_0^1 \int_0^{1-x} \sqrt{y}\,dy\,dx = \int_0^1 \frac{2}{3}(1-x)^{3/2}dx = 4/15$

15. $V = 2\displaystyle\int_0^2 \int_{x^2}^4 \int_0^{4-y} dz\,dy\,dx = 2\int_0^2 \int_{x^2}^4 (4-y)dy\,dx = 2\int_0^2 \left(8 - 4x^2 + \frac{1}{2}x^4\right)dx = 256/15$

16. $V = \displaystyle\int_0^1 \int_0^y \int_0^{\sqrt{1-y^2}} dz\,dx\,dy = \int_0^1 \int_0^y \sqrt{1-y^2}\,dx\,dy = \int_0^1 y\sqrt{1-y^2}\,dy = 1/3$

17. $V = 2\displaystyle\int_{-3}^3 \int_0^{\sqrt{9-x^2}/3} \int_0^{x+3} dz\,dy\,dx = 2\int_{-3}^3 \int_0^{\sqrt{9-x^2}/3} (x+3)dy\,dx$

$= 2\displaystyle\int_{-3}^3 \frac{1}{3}(x+3)\sqrt{9-x^2}\,dx = 9\pi$

18. $V = 8\displaystyle\int_0^1 \int_0^{\sqrt{1-x^2}} \int_0^{\sqrt{1-x^2}} dz\,dy\,dx = 8\int_0^1 \int_0^{\sqrt{1-x^2}} \sqrt{1-x^2}\,dy\,dx = 8\int_0^1 (1-x^2)dx = 16/3$

19.   The projection of the curve of intersection onto the xy-plane is $x^2 + y^2 = 1$,

$V = 4\displaystyle\int_0^1 \int_0^{\sqrt{1-x^2}} \int_{4x^2+y^2}^{4-3y^2} dz\,dy\,dx = 16\int_0^1 \int_0^{\sqrt{1-x^2}} (1 - x^2 - y^2)dy\,dx$

$= \dfrac{32}{3}\displaystyle\int_0^1 (1-x^2)^{3/2}dx = 2\pi$

20.   The projection of the curve of intersection onto the xy-plane is $2x^2 + y^2 = 4$,

$V = 4\displaystyle\int_0^{\sqrt{2}} \int_0^{\sqrt{4-2x^2}} \int_{3x^2+y^2}^{8-x^2-y^2} dz\,dy\,dx = 8\int_0^{\sqrt{2}} \int_0^{\sqrt{4-2x^2}} (4 - 2x^2 - y^2)dy\,dx$

$= \dfrac{16}{3}\displaystyle\int_0^{\sqrt{2}} (4 - 2x^2)^{3/2}dx = 8\sqrt{2}\pi$

21. The projection of the curve of intersection onto the xy-plane is $x^2 + y^2 = a^2$,

$$V = 4 \int_0^a \int_0^{\sqrt{a^2-x^2}} \int_{(x^2+y^2)/a}^{\sqrt{2a^2-x^2-y^2}} dz\, dy\, dx$$

$$= 4 \int_0^a \int_0^{\sqrt{a^2-x^2}} \left[\sqrt{2a^2 - x^2 - y^2} - \frac{1}{a}(x^2 + y^2) \right] dy\, dx$$

$$= 4 \int_0^{\pi/2} \int_0^a \left(r\sqrt{2a^2 - r^2} - \frac{1}{a}r^3 \right) dr\, d\theta = 4 \int_0^{\pi/2} \frac{1}{12}(8\sqrt{2} - 7)a^3\, d\theta = (8\sqrt{2} - 7)\pi a^3/6$$

22. **(a)**

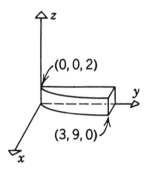

(b)

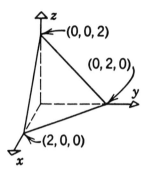

23. **(a)**

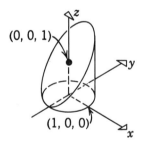

(b)

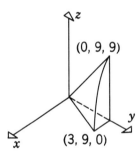

24. **(a)**

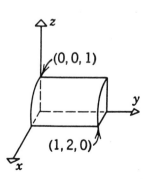

(b)

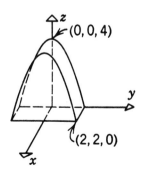

25. **(a)** $\int_0^a \int_0^{b(1-x/a)} \int_0^{c(1-x/a-y/b)} dz\,dy\,dx,$ $\int_0^b \int_0^{a(1-y/b)} \int_0^{c(1-x/a-y/b)} dz\,dx\,dy,$

$\int_0^c \int_0^{a(1-z/c)} \int_0^{b(1-x/a-z/c)} dy\,dx\,dz,$ $\int_0^a \int_0^{c(1-x/a)} \int_0^{b(1-x/a-z/c)} dy\,dz\,dx,$

$\int_0^c \int_0^{b(1-z/c)} \int_0^{a(1-y/b-z/c)} dx\,dy\,dz,$ $\int_0^b \int_0^{c(1-y/b)} \int_0^{a(1-y/b-z/c)} dx\,dz\,dy$

(b) Use the first integral in part (a) to get

$$\int_0^a \int_0^{b(1-x/a)} c\left(1 - \frac{x}{a} - \frac{y}{b}\right) dy\,dx = \int_0^a \frac{1}{2}bc\left(1 - \frac{x}{a}\right)^2 dx = \frac{1}{6}abc$$

26. **(a)** $\int_0^3 \int_0^{\sqrt{9-x^2}} \int_0^{\sqrt{9-x^2-y^2}} f(x,y,z)dz\,dy\,dx$

(b) $\int_0^4 \int_0^{x/2} \int_0^2 f(x,y,z)dz\,dy\,dx$ **(c)** $\int_0^2 \int_0^{4-x^2} \int_{x^2}^{4-y} f(x,y,z)dz\,dy\,dx$

27. $V = \int_0^a \int_0^x \int_0^{x-y} dz\,dy\,dx = \int_0^a \int_0^x (x-y)dy\,dx = \int_0^a \frac{1}{2}x^2 dx = a^3/6$

28. $\int_a^b \int_c^d \int_k^\ell f(x)g(y)h(z)dz\,dy\,dx = \int_a^b \int_c^d f(x)g(y)\left[\int_k^\ell h(z)dz\right]dy\,dx$

$$= \left[\int_a^b f(x)\left[\int_c^d g(y)dy\right]dx\right]\left[\int_k^\ell h(z)dz\right]$$

$$= \left[\int_a^b f(x)dx\right]\left[\int_c^d g(y)dy\right]\left[\int_k^\ell h(z)dz\right]$$

29. **(a)** $\left[\int_{-1}^1 x\,dx\right]\left[\int_0^1 y^2 dy\right]\left[\int_0^{\pi/2} \sin z\,dz\right] = (0)(1/3)(1) = 0$

(b) $\left[\int_0^1 e^{2x} dx\right]\left[\int_0^{\ln 3} e^y dy\right]\left[\int_0^{\ln 2} e^{-z} dz\right] = [(e^2-1)/2](2)(1/2) = (e^2-1)/2$

30. $V = 8 \int_0^a \int_0^{b\sqrt{1-x^2/a^2}} \int_0^{c\sqrt{1-x^2/a^2-y^2/b^2}} dz\,dy\,dx$

$$= 8 \int_0^a \int_0^{b\sqrt{1-x^2/a^2}} c\sqrt{1 - x^2/a^2 - y^2/b^2}\,dy\,dx$$

to perform the y-integration let $k^2 = 1 - x^2/a^2$ and $u = y/b$ then $du = (1/b)dy$ and

$$\int_0^{b\sqrt{1-x^2/a^2}} \sqrt{1 - x^2/a^2 - y^2/b^2}\, dy = b \int_0^k \sqrt{k^2 - u^2}\, du = \frac{1}{4}\pi bk^2$$

so $V = 8 \int_0^a \frac{1}{4}\pi bc \left(1 - \frac{x^2}{a^2}\right) dx = \frac{4}{3}\pi abc$

31. **(a)** 10 **(b)** 0

32. G is the region bounded by the xz-plane and the hemisphere $y = \sqrt{4 - x^2 - z^2}$, and

$$\iiint_G [z^3 \cos(xyz) - 3]dV = \iiint_G z^3 \cos(xyz)dV - 3 \iiint_G dV. \text{ If } f(x,y,z) = z^3 \cos(xyz), \text{ then}$$

$f(x, y, -z) = -f(x, y, z)$ so $\displaystyle\iiint_G z^3 \cos(xyz)dV = 0$ because G is symmetric with respect to

the xy-plane, hence $\displaystyle\iiint_G [z^3 \cos(xyz) - 3]dV = -3 \iiint_G dV = -3 \cdot \frac{1}{2}\frac{4}{3}\pi(2)^3 = -16\pi.$

33. The region is symmetric with respect to the xz-plane, and for $f(x, y, z) = x^2 y^3 e^z$,
$f(x, -y, z) = -f(x, y, z)$ so the integral evaluates to 0.

34. G is symmetric with respect to the xy-pane, and $f(x, y, -z) = -f(x, y, z)$ where
$f(x, y, z) = e^{xy} \sin z$ so $\displaystyle\iiint_G e^{xy} \sin z \, dV = 0.$

EXERCISE SET 17.6

1. Introduce an x-axis with origin at m_1, let a be the unknown coordinate of the fulcrum then the total moment about the fulcrum is $5(0 - a) + 10(5 - a) + 20(15 - a) = 350 - 35a$ so for equilibrium $350 - 35a = 0$, $a = 10$. The fulcrum should be placed 10 ft to the right of m_1.

2. $M = \displaystyle\int_0^3 \int_0^2 xy^2 dy\, dx = 12, \quad M_x = \int_0^3 \int_0^2 xy^3 dy\, dx = 18, \quad M_y = \int_0^3 \int_0^2 x^2 y^2 dy\, dx = 24,$
$\bar{x} = M_y/M = 2, \bar{y} = M_x/M = 3/2$; the mass is 12 and the center of gravity is at $(2, 3/2)$.

3. $M = \displaystyle\int_0^1 \int_0^{\sqrt{x}} (x+y) dy\, dx = 13/20$, $M_x = \displaystyle\int_0^1 \int_0^{\sqrt{x}} (x+y)y\, dy\, dx = 3/10$,

$M_y = \displaystyle\int_0^1 \int_0^{\sqrt{x}} (x+y)x\, dy\, dx = 19/42$, $\bar{x} = M_y/M = 190/273$, $\bar{y} = M_x/M = 0/13$,

the mass is $13/30$ and the center of gravity is at $(190/273, 6/13)$.

4. $M = \displaystyle\int_0^\pi \int_0^{\sin x} y\, dy\, dx = \pi/4$, $\bar{x} = \pi/2$ from the symmetry of the density and the region,

$M_x = \displaystyle\int_0^\pi \int_0^{\sin x} y^2 dy\, dx = 4/9$, $\bar{y} = M_x/M = \dfrac{16}{9\pi}$; mass $\pi/4$, center of gravity $\left(\dfrac{\pi}{2}, \dfrac{16}{9\pi}\right)$.

5. $M = \displaystyle\int_0^{\pi/2} \int_0^a r^3 \sin\theta \cos\theta\, dr\, d\theta = a^4/8$, $\bar{x} = \bar{y}$ from the symmetry of the density and the

region, $M_y = \displaystyle\int_0^{\pi/2} \int_0^a r^4 \sin\theta \cos^2\theta\, dr\, d\theta = a^5/15$, $\bar{x} = 8a/15$; mass $a^4/8$, center of gravity

$(8a/15, 8a/15)$.

6. $M = \displaystyle\int_0^\pi \int_0^1 r^3 dr\, d\theta = \pi/4$, $\bar{x} = 0$ from the symmetry of density and region,

$M_x = \displaystyle\int_0^\pi \int_0^1 r^4 \sin\theta\, dr\, d\theta = 2/5$, $\bar{y} = \dfrac{8}{5\pi}$; mass $\pi/4$, center of gravity $\left(0, \dfrac{8}{5\pi}\right)$.

7. $A = 1/2$, $\displaystyle\iint_R x\, dA = \int_0^1 \int_0^x x\, dy\, dx = 1/3$, $\displaystyle\iint_R y\, dA = \int_0^1 \int_0^x y\, dy\, dx = 1/6$;

centroid $(2/3, 1/3)$

8. $A = \displaystyle\int_0^1 \int_0^{x^2} dy\, dx = 1/3$, $\displaystyle\iint_R x\, dA = \int_0^1 \int_0^{x^2} x\, dy\, dx = 1/4$,

$\displaystyle\iint_R y\, dA = \int_0^1 \int_0^{x^2} y\, dy\, dx = 1/10$; centroid $(3/4, 3/10)$

9. $A = \displaystyle\int_{-2}^1 \int_x^{2-x^2} dy\, dx = 9/2$, $\displaystyle\iint_R x\, dA = \int_{-2}^1 \int_x^{2-x^2} x\, dy\, dx = -9/4$,

$\displaystyle\iint_R y\, dA = \int_{-2}^1 \int_x^{2-x^2} y\, dy\, dx = 9/5$; centroid $(-1/2, 2/5)$

10. $\bar{y} = 1$ from the symmetry of the region,

$$A = \int_0^2 \int_{3y^2-6y}^{2y-y^2} dx\, dy = 16/3, \quad \iint_R x\, dA = -64/15; \text{ centroid } (-4/5, 1)$$

11. $\bar{x} = 0$ from the symmetry of the region,

$$A = \frac{1}{2}\pi(b^2 - a^2), \quad \iint_R y\, dA = \int_0^\pi \int_a^b r^2 \sin\theta\, dr\, d\theta = \frac{2}{3}(b^3 - a^3);$$

centroid $\bar{x} = 0$, $\bar{y} = \dfrac{4(b^3 - a^3)}{3\pi(b^2 - a^2)}$.

12. $\bar{y} = 0$ from the symmetry of the region, $A = \pi a^2/2$,

$$\iint_R x\, dA = \int_{-\pi/2}^{\pi/2} \int_0^a r^2 \cos\theta\, dr\, d\theta = 2a^3/3; \text{ centroid } \left(\frac{4a}{3\pi}, 0\right)$$

13. $\bar{x} = 0$ from the symmetry of the region, $A = 16$,

$$\iint_R y\, dA = \int_{-4}^4 \int_{|x|}^4 y\, dy\, dx = 128/3; \text{ centroid } (0, 8/3)$$

14. $M = \displaystyle\int_0^1 \int_0^1 \int_0^1 3xyz\, dz\, dy\, dx = 3/8$, $\bar{x} = \bar{y} = \bar{z}$ from the symmetry of density and region,

$$\bar{x} = \frac{1}{M} \int_0^1 \int_0^1 \int_0^1 3x^2 yz\, dz\, dy\, dx = (8/3)(1/4) = 2/3; \text{ mass } 3/8,$$

center of gravity $(2/3, 2/3, 2/3)$

15. $M = \displaystyle\int_0^a \int_0^a \int_0^a (a - x)dz\, dy\, dx = a^4/2$, $\bar{y} = \bar{z} = a/2$ from the symmetry of density and

region, $\bar{x} = \dfrac{1}{M} \displaystyle\int_0^a \int_0^a \int_0^a x(a - x)dz\, dy\, dx = (2/a^4)(a^5/6) = a/3$; mass $a^4/2$, center of

gravity $(a/3, a/2, a/2)$

16. $M = \displaystyle\int_{-a}^a \int_{-\sqrt{a^2-x^2}}^{\sqrt{a^2-x^2}} \int_0^h (h - z)dz\, dy\, dx = \frac{1}{2}\pi a^2 h^2$, $\bar{x} = \bar{y} = 0$ from the symmetry of density

and region, $\bar{z} = \dfrac{1}{M} \displaystyle\iiint_G z(h - z)dV = \frac{2}{\pi a^2 h^2}(\pi a^2 h^3/6) = h/3$; mass $\pi a^2 h^2/2$,

center of gravity $(0, 0, h/3)$

17. $M = \int_{-1}^{1} \int_{0}^{1} \int_{0}^{1-y^2} yz\, dz\, dy\, dx = 1/6$, $\bar{x} = 0$ by the symmetry of density and region,

$$\bar{y} = \frac{1}{M} \iiint_G y^2 z\, dV = (6)(8/105) = 16/35, \ z = \frac{1}{M} \iiint_G yz^2 dV = (0)(1/12) - 1/2;$$

mass $1/6$, center of gravity $(0, 16/35, 1/2)$

18. $M = \int_{0}^{3} \int_{0}^{9-x^2} \int_{0}^{1} xz\, dz\, dy\, dx = 81/8$, $\bar{x} = \frac{1}{M} \iiint_G x^2 z\, dV = (8/81)(81/5) = 8/5,$

$$\bar{y} = \frac{1}{M} \iiint_G xyz\, dV = (8/81)(243/8) = 3, \ \bar{z} = \frac{1}{M} \iiint_G xz^2 dV = (8/81)(27/4) = 2/3;$$

mass $81/8$, center of gravity $(8/5, 3, 2/3)$

19. $\bar{x} = \bar{y} = \bar{z}$ from the symmetry of the region, $V = 1/6$,

$$\bar{x} = \frac{1}{V} \int_{0}^{1} \int_{0}^{1-x} \int_{0}^{1-x-y} x\, dz\, dy\, dx = (6)(1/24) = 1/4; \text{ centroid } (1/4, 1/4, 1/4)$$

20. $\bar{x} = \bar{y} = 0$ from the symmetry of the region, $V = 2\pi a^3/3$

$$\bar{z} = \frac{1}{V} \int_{-a}^{a} \int_{\sqrt{a^2-x^2}}^{-\sqrt{a^2-x^2}} \int_{0}^{\sqrt{a^2-x^2-y^2}} z\, dz\, dy\, dx = \frac{1}{V} \int_{-a}^{a} \int_{-\sqrt{a^2-x^2}}^{\sqrt{a^2-x^2}} \frac{1}{2}(a^2 - x^2 - y^2) dy\, dx$$

$$= \frac{1}{V} \int_{0}^{2\pi} \int_{0}^{a} \frac{1}{2}(a^2 - r^2) r\, dr\, d\theta = \frac{3}{2\pi a^3}(\pi a^4/4) = 3a/8; \text{ centroid } (0, 0, 3a/8)$$

21. $\bar{x} = 1/2$ and $\bar{y} = 0$ from the symmetry of the region,

$$V = \int_{0}^{1} \int_{-1}^{1} \int_{y^2}^{1} dz\, dy\, dx = 4/3, \ \bar{z} = \frac{1}{V} \iiint_G z\, dV = (3/4)(4/5) = 3/5;$$

centroid $(1/2, 0, 3/5)$

22. $\bar{x} = \bar{y}$ from the symmetry of the region,

$$V = \int_{0}^{2} \int_{0}^{2} \int_{0}^{xy} dz\, dy\, dx = 4, \ \bar{x} = \frac{1}{V} \iiint_G x\, dV = (1/4)(16/3) = 4/3,$$

$$\bar{z} = \frac{1}{V} \iiint_G z\, dV = (1/4)(32/9) = 8/9; \text{ centroid } (4/3, 4/3, 8/9)$$

23. $\bar{x} = \bar{y} = \bar{z}$ from the symmetry of the region, $V = \pi a^3/6$,

$$\bar{x} = \frac{1}{V}\int_0^a \int_0^{\sqrt{a^2-x^2}} \int_0^{\sqrt{a^2-x^2-y^2}} x\, dz\, dy\, dx = \frac{1}{V}\int_0^a \int_0^{\sqrt{a^2-x^2}} x\sqrt{a^2 - x^2 - y^2}\, dy\, dx$$

$$= \frac{1}{V}\int_0^{\pi/2}\int_0^a r^2\sqrt{a^2 - r^2}\cos\theta\, dr\, d\theta = \frac{6}{\pi a^3}(\pi a^4/16) = 3a/8; \text{ centroid } (3a/8, 3a/8, 3a/8)$$

24.   **(a)** $M = \displaystyle\int_0^1 \int_0^1 k(x^2 + y^2)dy\, dx = 2k/3$, $\bar{x} = \bar{y}$ from the symmetry of density and region,

$$\bar{x} = \frac{1}{M}\iint_R kx(x^2 + y^2)dA = \frac{3}{2k}(5k/12) = 5/8; \text{ center of gravity } (5/8, 5/8)$$

   (b) $\bar{y} = 1/2$ from the symmetry of density and region,

$$M = \int_0^1 \int_0^1 kx\, dy\, dx = k/2, \quad \bar{x} = \frac{1}{M}\iint_R kx^2 dA = (2/k)(k/3) = 2/3,$$

   center of gravity $(2/3, 1/2)$

25. $M = \displaystyle\iint_R k\sqrt{x^2 + y^2}dA = \int_0^{2\pi}\int_0^a kr^2 dr\, d\theta = \frac{2}{3}\pi k a^3$

26.   **(a)** $\bar{x} = \bar{y} = \bar{z}$ from the symmetry of density and region,

$$M = \int_0^1 \int_0^1 \int_0^1 k(x^2 + y^2 + z^2)dz\, dy\, dx = k,$$

$$\bar{x} = \frac{1}{M}\iiint_G kx(x^2+y^2+z^2)dV = (1/k)(7k/12) = 7/12; \text{ center of gravity } (7/12, 7/12, 7/12)$$

   (b) $\bar{x} = \bar{y} = \bar{z}$ from the symmetry of density and region,

$$M = \int_0^1 \int_0^1 \int_0^1 k(x + y + z)dz\, dy\, dx = 3k/2,$$

$$\bar{x} = \frac{1}{M}\iiint_G kx(x + y + z)dV = \frac{2}{3k}(5k/6) = 5/9; \text{ center of gravity } (5/9, 5/9, 5/9)$$

27.   Let $x = r\cos\theta$, $y = r\sin\theta$, and $dA = r\, dr\, d\theta$ in formulas (15a) and (15b).

28. $\bar{x} = 0$ from the symmetry of the region, $A = \displaystyle\int_0^{2\pi}\int_0^{a(1+\sin\theta)} r\, dr\, d\theta = 3\pi a^2/2$,

$$\bar{y} = \frac{1}{A}\int_0^{2\pi}\int_0^{a(1+\sin\theta)} r^2\sin\theta\, dr\, d\theta = \frac{2}{3\pi a^2}(5\pi a^3/4) = 5a/6; \text{ centroid } (0, 5a/6)$$

29. $\bar{x} = \bar{y}$ from the symmetry of the region, $A = \displaystyle\int_0^{\pi/2}\int_0^{\sin 2\theta} r\,dr\,d\theta = \pi/8,$

$$\bar{x} = \frac{1}{A}\int_0^{\pi/2}\int_0^{\sin 2\theta} r^2\cos\theta\,dr\,d\theta = (8/\pi)(16/105) = \frac{128}{105\pi};\ \text{centroid}\ \left(\frac{128}{105\pi},\frac{128}{105\pi}\right)$$

30. $\bar{x} = 3/2$ and $\bar{y} = 1$ from the symmetry of the region,

$$\iint_R x\,dA = \bar{x}A = (3/2)(6) = 9,\quad \iint_R y\,dA = \bar{y}A = (1)(6) = 6$$

31. $\bar{x} = 0$ from the symmetry of the region, $\pi a^2/2$ is the area of the semicircle, $2\pi\bar{y}$ is the distance traveled by the centroid to generate the sphere so $4\pi a^3/3 = (\pi a^2/2)(2\pi\bar{y})$, $\bar{y} = 4a/(3\pi)$

32. (a) $V = \left[\dfrac{1}{2}\pi a^2\right]\left[2\pi\left(a + \dfrac{4a}{3\pi}\right)\right] = \dfrac{1}{3}\pi(3\pi + 4)a^3$

(b) the distance between the centroid and the line is $\dfrac{\sqrt{2}}{2}\left(a + \dfrac{4a}{3\pi}\right)$ so

$$V = \left[\frac{1}{2}\pi a^2\right]\left[2\pi\frac{\sqrt{2}}{2}\left(a + \frac{4a}{3\pi}\right)\right] = \frac{1}{6}\sqrt{2}\pi(3\pi + 4)a^3$$

33. $\bar{x} = k$ so $V = (\pi ab)(2\pi k) = 2\pi^2 abk$

34. $\bar{y} = 4$ from the symmetry of the region,

$$A = \int_{-2}^{2}\int_{x^2}^{8-x^2} dy\,dx = 64/3 \text{ so } V = (64/3)[2\pi(4)] = 512\pi/3$$

35. The region generates a cone of volume $\dfrac{1}{3}\pi ab^2$ when it is revolved about the x-axis, the area of the region is $\dfrac{1}{2}ab$ so $\dfrac{1}{3}\pi ab^2 = \left(\dfrac{1}{2}ab\right)(2\pi\bar{y})$, $\bar{y} = b/3$. A cone of volume $\dfrac{1}{3}\pi a^2 b$ is generated when the region is revolved about the y-axis so $\dfrac{1}{3}\pi a^2 b = \left(\dfrac{1}{2}ab\right)(2\pi\bar{x})$, $\bar{x} = a/3$. The centroid is $(a/3, b/3)$.

36. $M = \delta ab,\ I_x = \displaystyle\int_0^a\int_0^b y^2\delta\,dy\,dx = \frac{1}{3}\delta ab^3 = \frac{1}{3}Mb^2,$

$$I_y = \int_0^a\int_0^b x^2\delta\,dy\,dx = \frac{1}{3}\delta a^3 b = \frac{1}{3}Ma^2,\ I_z = \int_0^a\int_0^b (x^2 + y^2)\delta\,dy\,dx = \frac{1}{3}M(a^2 + b^2)$$

37. $I_z = \int_{-a/2}^{a/2} \int_{-b/2}^{b/2} (x^2 + y^2)\delta \, dy \, dx = 4\delta \int_0^{a/2} \int_0^{b/2} (x^2 + y^2) dy \, dx$

$\quad = \delta ab(a^2 + b^2)/12; M = \delta ab$ so $I_z = M(a^2 + b^2)/12.$

38. $I_x = \int_{-a/2}^{a/2} \int_{-b/2}^{b/2} y^2 \delta \, dy \, dx = 4\delta \int_0^{a/2} \int_0^{b/2} y^2 dy \, dx = \frac{1}{12}\delta ab^3; M = \delta ab$ so $I_x = \frac{1}{12}Mb^2.$

39. $I_y = \int_0^{2\pi} \int_0^R r^3 \cos^2 \theta \, \delta \, dr \, d\theta = \delta \pi R^4/4; M = \delta \pi R^2$ so $I_y = MR^2/4.$

40. $I_z = \int_0^{2\pi} \int_0^R r^3 \delta \, dr \, d\theta = \frac{1}{2}\delta \pi R^4; M = \delta \pi R^2$ so $I_z = \frac{1}{2}MR^2.$

41. $I_z = \int_0^\pi \int_0^{2R\sin\theta} r^3 \delta \, dr \, d\theta = 3\delta \pi R^4/2; M = \delta \pi R^2$ so $I_z = 3MR^2/2.$

42. $I_y = \int_0^1 \int_0^{2-2x} x^2 \delta \, dy \, dx = \frac{1}{6}\delta; M = \delta$ so $I_y = \frac{1}{6}M.$

43. $I_z = \int_0^a \int_0^a \int_0^a (x^2 + y^2)\delta \, dz \, dy \, dx = 2\delta a^5/3; M = \delta a^3$ so $I_z = 2Ma^2/3.$

44. $I_x = \int_0^a \int_{-b/2}^{b/2} \int_{-c/2}^{c/2} (y^2 + z^2)\delta \, dz \, dy \, dx = 4\delta \int_0^a \int_0^{b/2} \int_0^{c/2} (y^2 + z^2)dz \, dy \, dx = \frac{1}{12}\delta abc(b^2 + c^2);$

$\quad M = \delta abc$ so $I_x = \frac{1}{12}M(b^2 + c^2).$

EXERCISE SET 17.7

1. $\int_0^{2\pi} \int_0^1 \int_0^{\sqrt{1-r^2}} zr \, dz \, dr \, d\theta = \int_0^{2\pi} \int_0^1 \frac{1}{2}(1 - r^2)r \, dr \, d\theta = \int_0^{2\pi} \frac{1}{8} d\theta = \pi/4$

2. $\int_0^{\pi/2} \int_0^{\cos\theta} \int_0^{r^2} r \sin\theta \, dz \, dr \, d\theta = \int_0^{\pi/2} \int_0^{\cos\theta} r^3 \sin\theta \, dr \, d\theta = \int_0^{\pi/2} \frac{1}{4} \cos^4 \theta \sin\theta \, d\theta = 1/20$

3. $\int_0^{\pi/2} \int_0^{\pi/2} \int_0^1 \rho^3 \sin\phi \cos\phi \, d\rho \, d\phi \, d\theta = \int_0^{\pi/2} \int_0^{\pi/2} \frac{1}{4} \sin\phi \cos\phi \, d\phi \, d\theta = \int_0^{\pi/2} \frac{1}{8} d\theta = \pi/16$

4. $\displaystyle\int_0^{2\pi}\int_0^{\pi/4}\int_0^{a\sec\phi}\rho^2\sin\phi\,d\rho\,d\phi\,d\theta=\int_0^{2\pi}\int_0^{\pi/4}\frac{1}{3}a^3\cos^{-3}\phi\sin\phi\,d\phi\,d\theta=\int_0^{2\pi}\frac{1}{6}a^3d\theta=\pi a^3/3$

5. $\displaystyle V=\int_0^{2\pi}\int_0^3\int_{r^2}^9 r\,dz\,dr\,d\theta=\int_0^{2\pi}\int_0^3 r(9-r^2)dr\,d\theta=\int_0^{2\pi}\frac{81}{4}d\theta=81\pi/2$

6. $\displaystyle V=2\int_0^{2\pi}\int_0^2\int_0^{\sqrt{9-r^2}}r\,dz\,dr\,d\theta=2\int_0^{2\pi}\int_0^2 r\sqrt{9-r^2}dr\,d\theta$

$$=\frac{2}{3}(27-5\sqrt5)\int_0^{2\pi}d\theta=4(27-5\sqrt5)\pi/3$$

7. $r^2+z^2=20$ intersects $z=r^2$ in a circle of radius 2,

$$V=\int_0^{2\pi}\int_0^2\int_{r^2}^{\sqrt{20-r^2}}r\,dz\,dr\,d\theta=\int_0^{2\pi}\int_0^2(r\sqrt{20-r^2}-r^3)dr\,d\theta$$

$$=\frac{4}{3}(10\sqrt5-19)\int_0^{2\pi}d\theta=8(10\sqrt5-19)\pi/3$$

8. $z=hr/a$ intersects $z=h$ in a circle of radius a,

$$V=\int_0^{2\pi}\int_0^a\int_{hr/a}^h r\,dz\,dr\,d\theta=\int_0^{2\pi}\int_0^a\frac{h}{a}(ar-r^2)dr\,d\theta=\int_0^{2\pi}\frac{1}{6}a^2h\,d\theta=\pi a^2h/3$$

9. $x^2+y^2=4x$ becomes $r=4\cos\theta$ in cylindrical coordinates,

$$V=\int_0^{\pi/2}\int_0^{4\cos\theta}\int_0^{\sqrt{16-r^2}}r\,dz\,dr\,d\theta=\int_0^{\pi/2}\int_0^{4\cos\theta}r\sqrt{16-r^2}\,dr\,d\theta$$

$$=\int_0^{\pi/2}\frac{64}{3}(1-\sin^3\theta)d\theta=32(3\pi-4)/9$$

10. $\displaystyle V=\int_0^{2\pi}\int_0^{\pi/3}\int_0^4\rho^2\sin\phi\,d\rho\,d\phi\,d\theta=\int_0^{2\pi}\int_0^{\pi/3}\frac{64}{3}\sin\phi\,d\phi\,d\theta=\frac{32}{3}\int_0^{2\pi}d\theta=64\pi/3$

11. $\displaystyle V=\int_0^{\pi/2}\int_{\pi/6}^{\pi/3}\int_0^2\rho^2\sin\phi\,d\rho\,d\phi\,d\theta=\int_0^{\pi/2}\int_{\pi/6}^{\pi/3}\frac{8}{3}\sin\phi\,d\phi\,d\theta$

$$=\frac{4}{3}(\sqrt3-1)\int_0^{\pi/2}d\theta=2(\sqrt3-1)\pi/3$$

12. $\displaystyle V = \int_0^{2\pi} \int_0^{\pi/4} \int_1^2 \rho^2 \sin\phi \, d\rho \, d\phi \, d\theta = \int_0^{2\pi} \int_0^{\pi/4} \frac{7}{3}\sin\phi \, d\phi \, d\theta$

$\displaystyle \qquad\qquad = \frac{7}{6}(2 - \sqrt{2}) \int_0^{2\pi} d\theta = 7(2 - \sqrt{2})\pi/3$

13. $\displaystyle V = \int_0^{2\pi} \int_{\pi/4}^{\pi/2} \int_0^3 \rho^2 \sin\phi \, d\rho \, d\phi \, d\theta = \int_0^{2\pi} \int_{\pi/4}^{\pi/2} 9\sin\phi \, d\phi \, d\theta = \frac{9\sqrt{2}}{2} \int_0^{2\pi} d\theta = 9\sqrt{2}\pi$

14. In spherical coordinates the sphere and the plane $z = a$ are $\rho = 2a$ and $\rho = a \sec\phi$, respectively. They intersect at $\phi = \pi/3$,

$\displaystyle V = \int_0^{2\pi} \int_0^{\pi/3} \int_0^{a\sec\phi} \rho^2 \sin\phi \, d\rho \, d\phi \, d\theta + \int_0^{2\pi} \int_{\pi/3}^{\pi/2} \int_0^{2a} \rho^2 \sin\phi \, d\rho \, d\phi \, d\theta$

$\displaystyle \quad = \int_0^{2\pi} \int_0^{\pi/3} \frac{1}{3}a^3 \sec^3\phi \sin\phi \, d\phi \, d\theta + \int_0^{2\pi} \int_{\pi/3}^{\pi/2} \frac{8}{3}a^3 \sin\phi \, d\phi \, d\theta$

$\displaystyle \quad = \frac{1}{2}a^3 \int_0^{2\pi} d\theta + \frac{4}{3}a^3 \int_0^{2\pi} d\theta = 11\pi a^3/3$

15. (a) $\displaystyle V = 2\int_0^{2\pi} \int_0^a \int_0^{\sqrt{a^2-r^2}} r \, dz \, dr \, d\theta = 4\pi a^3/3$

(b) $\displaystyle V = \int_0^{2\pi} \int_0^\pi \int_0^a \rho^2 \sin\phi \, d\rho \, d\phi \, d\theta = 4\pi a^3/3$

16. $\displaystyle M = \int_0^{2\pi} \int_0^3 \int_r^3 (3 - z)r \, dz \, dr \, d\theta = \int_0^{2\pi} \int_0^3 \frac{1}{2}r(3 - r)^2 dr \, d\theta = \frac{27}{8}\int_0^{2\pi} d\theta = 27\pi/4$

17. $\displaystyle M = \int_0^{\pi/2} \int_0^{2\cos\theta} \int_0^{4-r^2} zr \, dz \, dr \, d\theta = \int_0^{\pi/2} \int_0^{2\cos\theta} \frac{1}{2}r(4 - r^2)^2 dr \, d\theta$

$\displaystyle \quad = \frac{16}{3}\int_0^{\pi/2} (1 - \sin^6\theta)d\theta = (16/3)(11\pi/32) = 11\pi/6$

18. $\displaystyle M = \int_0^{2\pi} \int_0^a \int_0^h k \, zr \, dz \, dr \, d\theta = \int_0^{2\pi} \int_0^a \frac{1}{2}kh^2 r \, dr \, d\theta = \frac{1}{4}ka^2h^2 \int_0^{2\pi} d\theta = \pi ka^2h^2/2$

19. $\displaystyle M = \int_0^{2\pi} \int_0^{\pi/4} \int_0^1 \rho^3 \sin\phi \, d\rho \, d\phi \, d\theta = \int_0^{2\pi} \int_0^{\pi/4} \frac{1}{4}\sin\phi \, d\phi \, d\theta$

$\displaystyle \qquad\qquad = \frac{1}{8}(2 - \sqrt{2}) \int_0^{2\pi} d\theta = (2 - \sqrt{2})\pi/4$

20. $M = \int_0^{2\pi} \int_0^{\pi} \int_1^2 \rho \sin\phi \, d\rho \, d\phi \, d\theta = \int_0^{2\pi} \int_0^{\pi} \frac{3}{2} \sin\phi \, d\phi \, d\theta = 3 \int_0^{2\pi} d\theta = 6\pi$

21. $M = \int_0^{2\pi} \int_0^{\pi} \int_0^a k\rho^3 \sin\phi \, d\rho \, d\phi \, d\theta = \int_0^{2\pi} \int_0^{\pi} \frac{1}{4} ka^4 \sin\phi \, d\phi \, d\theta = \frac{1}{2} ka^4 \int_0^{2\pi} d\theta = \pi ka^4$

22. $\bar{x} = \bar{y} = 0$ from the symmetry of the region, $V = 8\pi/3$,

$\bar{z} = \frac{1}{V} \int_0^{2\pi} \int_0^2 \int_r^2 zr \, dz \, dr \, d\theta = \frac{3}{8\pi}(4\pi) = 3/2$; centroid $(0, 0, 3/2)$

23. $\bar{x} = \bar{y} = 0$ from the symmetry of the region,

$V = \int_0^{2\pi} \int_0^1 \int_{r^2}^{\sqrt{2-r^2}} r \, dz \, dr \, d\theta = \int_0^{2\pi} \int_0^1 (r\sqrt{2-r^2} - r^3) dr \, d\theta = (8\sqrt{2} - 7)\pi/6$,

$\bar{z} = \frac{1}{V} \int_0^{2\pi} \int_0^1 \int_{r^2}^{\sqrt{2-r^2}} zr \, dz \, dr \, d\theta = \frac{6}{(8\sqrt{2} - 7)\pi}(7\pi/12) = 7/(16\sqrt{2} - 14)$;

centroid $\left(0, 0, \dfrac{7}{16\sqrt{2} - 14}\right)$

24. $\bar{y} = 0$ from the symmetry of the region, $V = 2\int_0^{\pi/2} \int_0^{2\cos\theta} \int_0^{r^2} r \, dz \, dr \, d\theta = 3\pi/2$,

$\bar{x} = \frac{2}{V} \int_0^{\pi/2} \int_0^{2\cos\theta} \int_0^{r^2} r^2 \cos\theta \, dz \, dr \, d\theta = \frac{4}{3\pi}(\pi) = 4/3$,

$\bar{z} = \frac{2}{V} \int_0^{\pi/2} \int_0^{2\cos\theta} \int_0^{r^2} rz \, dz \, dr \, d\theta = \frac{4}{3\pi}(5\pi/6) = 10/9$; centroid $(4/3, 0, 10/9)$

25. $\bar{x} = \bar{y} = \bar{z}$ from the symmetry of the region, $V = \pi a^3/6$,

$\bar{z} = \frac{1}{V} \int_0^{\pi/2} \int_0^{\pi/2} \int_0^a \rho^3 \cos\phi \sin\phi \, d\rho \, d\phi \, d\theta = \frac{6}{\pi a^3}(\pi a^4/16) = 3a/8$;

centroid $(3a/8, 3a/8, 3a/8)$

26. $\bar{x} = \bar{y} = 0$ from the symmetry of the region, $V = \int_0^{2\pi} \int_0^{\pi/3} \int_0^4 \rho^2 \sin\phi \, d\rho \, d\phi \, d\theta = 64\pi/3$,

$\bar{z} = \frac{1}{V} \int_0^{2\pi} \int_0^{\pi/3} \int_0^4 \rho^3 \cos\phi \sin\phi \, d\rho \, d\phi \, d\theta = \frac{3}{64\pi}(48\pi) = 9/4$; centroid $(0, 0, 9/4)$

27. $\bar{x} = \bar{z} = 0$ from the symmetry of the region, $V = 54\pi/3 - 16\pi/3 = 38\pi/3$,

$$\bar{y} = \frac{1}{V}\int_0^\pi \int_0^\pi \int_2^3 \rho^3 \sin^2\phi\sin\theta\,d\rho\,d\phi\,d\theta = \frac{1}{V}\int_0^\pi \int_0^\pi \frac{65}{4}\sin^2\phi\sin\theta\,d\phi\,d\theta$$

$$= \frac{1}{V}\int_0^\pi \frac{65\pi}{8}\sin\theta\,d\theta = \frac{3}{38\pi}(65\pi/4) = 195/152;\ \ \text{centroid } (0, 195/152, 0)$$

28. $\displaystyle\int_0^{\pi/2}\int_0^a\int_0^{a^2-r^2} r^3\cos^2\theta\,dz\,dr\,d\theta = \int_0^{\pi/2}\int_0^a (a^2 r^3 - r^5)\cos^2\theta\,dr\,d\theta$

$$= \frac{1}{12}a^6\int_0^{\pi/2}\cos^2\theta\,d\theta = \pi a^6/48$$

29. $\displaystyle\int_0^\pi\int_0^{\pi/2}\int_0^1 e^{-\rho^3}\rho^2\sin\phi\,d\rho\,d\phi\,d\theta = \frac{1}{3}(1-e^{-1})\int_0^\pi\int_0^{\pi/2}\sin\phi\,d\phi\,d\theta = (1-e^{-1})\pi/3$

30. $\displaystyle\int_0^{\pi/2}\int_0^{\pi/4}\int_0^{\sqrt{8}} \rho^4\cos^2\phi\sin\phi\,d\rho\,d\phi\,d\theta = 32(2\sqrt{2}-1)\pi/15$

31. $\displaystyle\int_0^{2\pi}\int_0^\pi\int_0^3 \rho^3\sin\phi\,d\rho\,d\phi\,d\theta = 81\pi$

32. (a) $\displaystyle\int_0^2\int_0^{\sqrt{4-x^2}}\int_0^{\sqrt{4-x^2-y^2}} xyz\,dz\,dy\,dx$

$$= \int_0^2\int_0^{\sqrt{4-x^2}} \frac{1}{2}xy(4-x^2-y^2)\,dy\,dx = \frac{1}{8}\int_0^2 x(4-x^2)^2\,dx = 4/3$$

(b) $\displaystyle\int_0^{\pi/2}\int_0^2\int_0^{\sqrt{4-r^2}} r^3 z\sin\theta\cos\theta\,dz\,dr\,d\theta$

$$= \int_0^{\pi/2}\int_0^2 \frac{1}{2}(4r^3 - r^5)\sin\theta\cos\theta\,dr\,d\theta = \frac{8}{3}\int_0^{\pi/2}\sin\theta\cos\theta\,d\theta = 4/3$$

(c) $\displaystyle\int_0^{\pi/2}\int_0^{\pi/2}\int_0^2 \rho^5\sin^3\phi\cos\phi\sin\theta\cos\theta\,d\rho\,d\phi\,d\theta$

$$= \int_0^{\pi/2}\int_0^{\pi/2} \frac{32}{3}\sin^3\phi\cos\phi\sin\theta\cos\theta\,d\phi\,d\theta = \frac{8}{3}\int_0^{\pi/2}\sin\theta\cos\theta\,d\theta = 4/3$$

33. $\bar{x} = \bar{y} = 0$ from the symmetry of density and region,

$$M = \int_0^{2\pi}\int_0^{\pi/2}\int_0^a k\rho^3\sin\phi\,d\rho\,d\phi\,d\theta = \pi ka^4/2,$$

$$\bar{z} = \frac{1}{M} \int_0^{2\pi} \int_0^{\pi/2} \int_0^a k\rho^4 \sin\phi \cos\phi \, d\rho \, d\phi \, d\theta = \frac{2}{\pi k a^4}(\pi k a^5/5) = 2a/5;$$

center of gravity $(0, 0, 2a/5)$

34. $\bar{x} = \bar{y}$ from the symmetry of density and region,

$$M = \int_0^{\pi/2} \int_0^a \int_0^a r^3 z \sin\theta \cos\theta \, dz \, dr \, d\theta = a^6/16,$$

$$\bar{x} = \frac{1}{M} \int_0^{\pi/2} \int_0^a \int_0^a r^4 z \sin\theta \cos^2\theta \, dz \, dr \, d\theta = (16/a^6)(a^7/30) = 8a/15,$$

$$\bar{z} = \frac{1}{M} \int_0^{\pi/2} \int_0^a \int_0^a r^3 z^2 \sin\theta \cos\theta \, dz \, dr \, d\theta = (16/a^6)(a^7/24) = 2a/3;$$

center of gravity $(8a/15, 8a/15, 2a/3)$

35. $\bar{x} = \bar{y} = 0$ from the symmetry of density and region,

$$M = \int_0^{2\pi} \int_0^1 \int_0^{1-r^2} (r^2 + z^2) r \, dz \, dr \, d\theta = \pi/4,$$

$$\bar{z} = \frac{1}{M} \int_0^{2\pi} \int_0^1 \int_0^{1-r^2} z(r^2 + z^2) r \, dz \, dr \, d\theta = (4/\pi)(11\pi/120) = 11/30;$$

center of gravity $(0, 0, 11/30)$

36. $\bar{x} = \bar{y} = 0$ from the symmetry of density and region, $M = \int_0^{2\pi} \int_0^1 \int_0^r zr \, dz \, dr \, d\theta = \pi/4,$

$$\bar{z} = \frac{1}{M} \int_0^{2\pi} \int_0^1 \int_0^r z^2 r \, dz \, dr \, d\theta = (4/\pi)(2\pi/15) = 8/15;$$ center of gravity $(0, 0, 8/15)$

37. In spherical coordinates the spheres are $\rho = 3$ and $\rho = 4\cos\phi$, respectively. They intersect when $\phi = \cos^{-1}(3/4)$ so

$$V = \int_0^{2\pi} \int_0^{\cos^{-1}(3/4)} \int_0^3 \rho^2 \sin\phi \, d\rho \, d\phi \, d\theta + \int_0^{2\pi} \int_{\cos^{-1}(3/4)}^{\pi/2} \int_0^{4\cos\phi} \rho^2 \sin\phi \, d\rho \, d\phi \, d\theta$$

$$= \int_0^{2\pi} \int_0^{\cos^{-1}(3/4)} 9 \sin\phi \, d\phi \, d\theta + \int_0^{2\pi} \int_{\cos^{-1}(3/4)}^{\pi/2} \frac{64}{3} \sin\phi \cos^3\phi \, d\phi \, d\theta$$

$$= \frac{9}{4} \int_0^{2\pi} d\theta + \frac{27}{16} \int_0^{2\pi} d\theta = 63\pi/8$$

38. $M = \int_0^{2\pi} \int_0^\pi \int_0^R \delta_0 e^{[(\rho/R)^3-1]}\rho^2 \sin\phi \, d\rho \, d\phi \, d\theta$

$= \int_0^{2\pi} \int_0^\pi \frac{1}{3}(1 - e^{-1})R^3\delta_0 \sin\phi \, d\phi \, d\theta = \frac{4}{3}\pi(1 - e^{-1})\delta_0 R^3$

39. **(a)** The sphere and cone intersect in a circle of radius $\rho_0 \sin\phi_0$,

$V = \int_{\theta_1}^{\theta_2} \int_0^{\rho_0 \sin\phi_0} \int_{r\cot\phi_0}^{\sqrt{\rho_0^2-r^2}} r \, dz \, dr \, d\theta = \int_{\theta_1}^{\theta_2} \int_0^{\rho_0 \sin\phi_0} \left(r\sqrt{\rho_0^2 - r^2} - r^2\cot\phi_0 \right) dr \, d\theta$

$= \int_{\theta_1}^{\theta_2} \frac{1}{3}\rho_0^3(1 - \cos^3\phi_0 - \sin^3\phi_0 \cot\phi_0)d\theta = \frac{1}{3}\rho_0^3(1 - \cos^3\phi_0 - \sin^2\phi_0 \cos\phi_0)(\theta_2 - \theta_1)$

$= \frac{1}{3}\rho_0^3(1 - \cos\phi_0)(\theta_2 - \theta_1).$

(b) From part (a), the volume of the solid bounded by $\theta = \theta_1$, $\theta = \theta_2$, $\phi = \phi_1$, $\phi = \phi_2$, and $\rho = \rho_0$ is

$\frac{1}{3}\rho_0^3(1 - \cos\phi_2)(\theta_2 - \theta_1) - \frac{1}{3}\rho_0^3(1 - \cos\phi_1)(\theta_2 - \theta_1) = \frac{1}{3}\rho_0^3(\cos\phi_1 - \cos\phi_2)(\theta_2 - \theta_1)$

so the volume of the spherical wedge between $\rho = \rho_1$ and $\rho = \rho_2$ is

$\Delta V = \frac{1}{3}\rho_2^3(\cos\phi_1 - \cos\phi_2)(\theta_2 - \theta_1) - \frac{1}{3}\rho_1^3(\cos\phi_1 - \cos\phi_2)(\theta_2 - \theta_1)$

$= \frac{1}{3}(\rho_2^3 - \rho_1^3)(\cos\phi_1 - \cos\phi_2)(\theta_2 - \theta_1)$

(c) $\frac{d}{d\phi}\cos\phi = -\sin\phi$ so from the Mean-Value Theorem $\cos\phi_2 - \cos\phi_1 = -\sin\phi^*(\phi_2 - \phi_1)$

where ϕ^* is between ϕ_1 and ϕ_2. Similarly $\frac{d}{d\rho}\rho^3 = 3\rho^2$ so $\rho_2^3 - \rho_1^3 = 3\rho^{*2}(\rho_2 - \rho_1)$ where ρ^* is between ρ_1 and ρ_2. Thus $\cos\phi_1 - \cos\phi_2 = \sin\phi^*\Delta\phi$ and $\rho_2^3 - \rho_1^3 = 3\rho^{*2}\Delta\rho$ so $\Delta V = \rho^{*2}\sin\phi^*\Delta\rho\Delta\phi\Delta\theta$.

40. $I_z = \int_0^{2\pi} \int_0^R \int_0^h r^2\delta r \, dz \, dr \, d\theta = \delta \int_0^{2\pi} \int_0^R \int_0^h r^3 dz \, dr \, d\theta = \frac{1}{2}\delta\pi R^4 h;$

$M = \delta\pi R^2 h$ so $I_z = \frac{1}{2}MR^2.$

41. $I_y = \int_0^{2\pi} \int_0^R \int_0^h (r^2\cos^2\theta + z^2)\delta r \, dz \, dr \, d\theta = \delta \int_0^{2\pi} \int_0^R (hr^3\cos^2\theta + \frac{1}{3}h^3 r)dr \, d\theta$

$= \delta \int_0^{2\pi} \left(\frac{1}{4}R^4 h\cos^2\theta + \frac{1}{6}R^2 h^3 \right) d\theta = \delta \left(\frac{\pi}{4}R^4 h + \frac{\pi}{3}R^2 h^3 \right);$

$M = \delta\pi R^2 h$ so $I_y = M(R^2/4 + h^2/3).$

42. $I_z = \int_0^{2\pi} \int_{R_1}^{R_2} \int_0^h r^2 \delta r \, dz \, dr \, d\theta = \delta \int_0^{2\pi} \int_{R_1}^{R_2} \int_0^h r^3 \, dz \, dr \, d\theta = \frac{1}{2} \delta \pi (R_2^4 - R_1^4) h;$

$M = \delta \pi \left(R_2^2 - R_1^2 \right) h$ so $I_z = \frac{1}{2} \delta \pi \left(R_2^2 - R_1^2 \right) \left(R_2^2 + R_1^2 \right) h - \frac{1}{2} M \left(R_1^2 + R_2^2 \right),$

43. $I_z = \int_0^{2\pi} \int_0^{\pi} \int_0^R (\rho^2 \sin^2 \phi) \delta \, \rho^2 \sin \phi \, d\rho \, d\phi \, d\theta$

$= \delta \int_0^{2\pi} \int_0^{\pi} \int_0^R \rho^4 \sin^3 \phi \, d\rho \, d\phi \, d\theta = \frac{8}{15} \delta \pi R^5; M = \frac{4}{3} \delta \pi R^3$ so $I_z = \frac{2}{5} M R^2.$

44. $I_z = \int_0^{2\pi} \int_0^R \int_{hr/R}^h r^2 \delta r \, dz \, dr \, d\theta = \delta \int_0^{2\pi} \int_0^R h \left(r^3 - \frac{r^4}{R} \right) dr \, d\theta = \frac{1}{10} \delta \pi R^4 h;$

$M = \frac{1}{3} \delta \pi R^2 h$ so $I_z = \frac{3}{10} M R^2.$

45. **(a)** $\rho = \sqrt{r^2 + z^2}, \cos \phi = z/\rho = z/\sqrt{r^2 + z^2},$

$F_z = \int_0^{2\pi} \int_0^R \int_a^{a+h} \frac{k \delta z r}{(r^2 + z^2)^{3/2}} dz \, dr \, d\theta$

$= k\delta \int_0^{2\pi} \int_0^R \left[\frac{r}{\sqrt{r^2 + a^2}} - \frac{r}{\sqrt{r^2 + (a+h)^2}} \right] dr \, d\theta$

$= 2\pi k\delta (\sqrt{R^2 + a^2} - \sqrt{R^2 + (a+h)^2} + h).$

(b) The components of the force in the x and y directions are zero because of the symmetry of the solid with respect to the yz and xz planes.

46. $\cos \phi = \frac{a}{\rho}, \rho = \sqrt{a^2 + r^2}$ so $F_z = \int_0^{2\pi} \int_0^R \frac{k \delta a r}{(a^2 + r^2)^{3/2}} dr \, d\theta = 2\pi k\delta \left(1 - \frac{a}{\sqrt{a^2 + R^2}} \right).$

47. In spherical coordinates the plane $z = h$ is $\rho \cos \phi = h$ so $\rho = h/\cos \phi,$

$F_z = \int_0^{2\pi} \int_0^{\tan^{-1}(R/h)} \int_0^{h/\cos \phi} \frac{k \delta \cos \phi}{\rho^2} \rho^2 \sin \phi \, d\rho \, d\phi \, d\theta$

$= k\delta \int_0^{2\pi} \int_0^{\tan^{-1}(R/h)} \int_0^{h/\cos \phi} \sin \phi \cos \phi \, d\rho \, d\phi \, d\theta$

$= 2\pi k\delta h \left[1 - \cos \left(\tan^{-1} \frac{R}{h} \right) \right] = 2\pi k\delta h (1 - h/\sqrt{R^2 + h^2}).$

48. In spherical coordinates the sphere
$x^2 + y^2 + (z - a)^2 = R^2$ is $\rho^2 \sin^2 \phi + (\rho \cos \phi - a)^2 = R^2,$

$$\rho^2 \sin^2 \phi + \rho^2 \cos^2 \phi - 2a\rho \cos \phi + a^2 = R^2, \; \rho^2 - 2a\rho \cos \phi + a^2 \cos^2 \phi = R^2 - a^2 + a^2 \cos^2 \phi,$$

$$(\rho - a \cos \phi)^2 = R^2 - a^2 \sin^2 \phi, \; \rho = a \cos \phi \pm \sqrt{R^2 - a^2 \sin^2 \phi} \text{ for } 0 \le \phi \le \sin^{-1} \frac{R}{a}.$$

Let $\alpha = \sin^{-1} \dfrac{R}{a}$, $\rho_1 = a \cos \phi - \sqrt{R^2 - a^2 \sin^2 \phi}$, and $\rho_2 = a \cos \phi + \sqrt{R^2 - a^2 \sin^2 \phi}$. Then

$$F_z = k\delta \int_0^{2\pi} \int_0^\alpha \int_{\rho_1}^{\rho_2} \sin \phi \cos \phi \, d\rho \, d\phi \, d\theta = k\delta \int_0^{2\pi} \int_0^\alpha (\rho_2 - \rho_1) \sin \phi \cos \phi \, d\phi \, d\theta$$

$$= 2k\delta \int_0^{2\pi} \int_0^\alpha \sqrt{R^2 - a^2 \sin^2 \phi} \sin \phi \cos \phi \, d\phi \, d\theta$$

$$= -\frac{2k\delta}{3a^2} \int_0^{2\pi} [(R^2 - a^2 \sin^2 \alpha)^{3/2} - R^3] d\theta = \frac{2k\delta R^3}{3a^2} \int_0^{2\pi} d\theta = \frac{4k\delta\pi R^3}{3a^2},$$

but the mass of the sphere is $M = \dfrac{4}{3}\delta\pi R^3$ so $F_z = k\dfrac{M}{a^2}$ which is the same as the force of attraction on a point mass of mass M located at $x = 0, \, y = 0, \, z = a$.

SUPPLEMENTARY EXERCISES CHAPTER 17

1. $\displaystyle\int_{1/2}^1 \int_0^{2x} \cos(\pi x^2) dy \, dx = \int_{1/2}^1 2x \cos(\pi x^2) dx = -1/(\sqrt{2}\pi)$

2. $\displaystyle\int_0^2 \int_{-y}^{2y} xe^{y^3} dx \, dy = \int_0^2 \frac{3}{2} y^2 e^{y^3} dy = (e^8 - 1)/2$

3. $\displaystyle\int_{-1}^0 \int_0^{y^2} \int_{xy}^1 2y \, dz \, dx \, dy = \int_{-1}^0 \int_0^{y^2} (2y - 2xy^2) dx \, dy = \int_{-1}^0 (2y^3 - y^6) dy = -9/14$

4. $\displaystyle\int_0^1 \int_0^z \int_0^{\sqrt{yz}} x \, dx \, dy \, dz = \int_0^1 \int_0^z \frac{1}{2} yz \, dy \, dz = \int_0^1 \frac{1}{4} z^3 dz = 1/16$

5. $\displaystyle\int_0^1 \int_{2y}^2 e^x e^y \, dx \, dy$ 6. $\displaystyle\int_0^\pi \int_0^x \frac{\sin x}{x} dy \, dx$

7. $A = \displaystyle\int_0^1 \int_0^{2x^3} dy \, dx + \int_1^2 \int_0^{4-2x} dy \, dx = 1/2 + 1 = 3/2$

8. $A = \displaystyle\int_0^2 \int_{y^2}^{4y-y^2} dx \, dy = 8/3$

9.　(a)

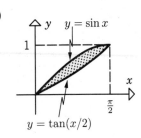

(b)

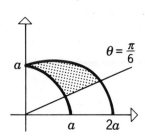

10. $\displaystyle\int_0^1\int_{\sqrt{x}}^{2-\sqrt{x}} xy\,dy\,dx = \int_0^1 (2-2\sqrt{x})dx = 2/3$

11. $\displaystyle\int_0^8\int_{-\sqrt[3]{y}}^{\sqrt[3]{y}} x^2\sin(y^2)dx\,dy = \int_0^8 \frac{2}{3}y\sin(y^2)dy = (1-\cos 64)/3$

12. $\displaystyle\int_0^{\pi/2}\int_0^2 (4-r^2)r\,dr\,d\theta = 2\pi$

13. $V = \displaystyle\int_0^2\int_0^{(6-3x)/2} (6-3x-2y)dy\,dx = \int_0^2 \frac{1}{4}(6-3x)^2 dx = 6$

14. $V = \displaystyle\int_{-1}^4\int_{x^2}^{3x+4} \sqrt{y}\,dy\,dx = \int_{-1}^4 \frac{2}{3}[(3x+4)^{3/2}-x^3]dx = 1453/30$

15. $V = \displaystyle\int_0^{2\pi}\int_{\sqrt{2}}^2 \frac{1}{r^3}dr\,d\theta = \int_0^{2\pi}\frac{1}{8}d\theta = \pi/4$

16. $\displaystyle\int_{\pi/4}^{\pi/2}\int_0^2 4r^3\cos\theta\sin\theta\,dr\,d\theta = 4$

17. $\displaystyle\int_0^{2a}\int_0^{\sqrt{2ay-y^2}} \frac{2xy}{x^2+y^2}dx\,dy = \int_0^{2a}(y\ln 2a - y\ln y)dy = a^2$

18. $A = 4\displaystyle\int_0^{\pi/6}\int_{\sqrt{2a}}^{2a\sqrt{\cos 2\theta}} r\,dr\,d\theta = 4a^2\int_0^{\pi/6}(2\cos 2\theta - 1)d\theta = \frac{2}{3}(3\sqrt{3}-\pi)a^2$

19. $A = 6\displaystyle\int_0^{\pi/6}\int_0^{\cos 3\theta} r\,dr\,d\theta = 3\int_0^{\pi/6}\cos^2 3\theta\,d\theta = \pi/4$

20. $A = 2 \int_{\pi/3}^{\pi/2} \int_{3}^{2\sqrt{3}\sin\theta} r\, dr\, d\theta = \int_{\pi/3}^{\pi/2} (12\sin^2\theta - 9)d\theta = (3\sqrt{3} - \pi)/2$

21. $z_x = 6x,\ z_y = 6y,\ z_x^2 + z_y^2 + 1 = 36(x^2 + y^2) + 1;$

$S = \int_{0}^{2\pi} \int_{0}^{1} r\sqrt{36r^2 + 1}\, dr\, d\theta = (37\sqrt{37} - 1)\pi/54$

22. $z_x^2 + z_y^2 + 1 = 9;\ S = \int_{0}^{7/2} \int_{0}^{7/2-x} 3\, dy\, dx = 147/8$

23. $z_x = x/z,\ z_y = y/z,\ z_x^2 + z_y^2 + 1 = 2;\ S = \int_{0}^{2\pi} \int_{1}^{4} \sqrt{2}\, r\, dr\, d\theta = 15\sqrt{2}\pi$

24. $\displaystyle\int_{0}^{2} \int_{-x}^{x^2} \int_{0}^{x+y} x^2 yz\, dz\, dy\, dx = \int_{0}^{2} \int_{-x}^{x^2} \frac{1}{2}x^2(x^2 y + 2xy^2 + y^3)dy\, dx$

$= \int_{0}^{2} \left(\frac{1}{4}x^8 + \frac{1}{3}x^9 + \frac{1}{8}x^{10} - \frac{1}{24}x^6\right) dx = \dfrac{245,552}{3465}$

25. $\displaystyle\int_{0}^{2\pi} \int_{0}^{4} \int_{0}^{4-r\sin\theta} r^2\, dz\, dr\, d\theta = \int_{0}^{2\pi} \int_{0}^{4} (4r^2 - r^3\sin\theta)dr\, d\theta$

$= \int_{0}^{2\pi} \frac{64}{3}(4 - 3\sin\theta)d\theta = 512\pi/3$

26. $z = x^2 + y^2$ and $z = 4x$ intersect in the curve whose projection onto the xy-plane is $x^2 + y^2 = 4x$ or, in polar coordinates, $r = 4\cos\theta$.

(a) $\displaystyle\int_{0}^{4} \int_{-\sqrt{4x-x^2}}^{\sqrt{4x-x^2}} \int_{x^2+y^2}^{4x} dz\, dy\, dx$ **(b)** $\displaystyle\int_{-\pi/2}^{\pi/2} \int_{0}^{4\cos\theta} \int_{r^2}^{4r\cos\theta} r\, dz\, dr\, d\theta$

27. **(a)** G is the region in the first octant bounded by the coordinate planes and the plane $z = 1 - x - 2y$; the integral is $\displaystyle\int_{0}^{1/2} \int_{0}^{1-2y} \int_{0}^{1-2y-z} z\, dx\, dz\, dy$

(b) G is the region in the first octant bounded by the planes $x = 0$, $z = 0$, $z = 4 - y$, and the parabolic cylinder $y = x^2$; the integral is $\displaystyle\int_{0}^{4} \int_{0}^{4-y} \int_{0}^{\sqrt{y}} 3\, dx\, dz\, dy$

28. **(a)** $\displaystyle\int_{0}^{2\pi} \int_{0}^{2} \int_{r^4}^{16} r^3\cos^2\theta\, dz\, dr\, d\theta = \int_{0}^{2\pi} \int_{0}^{2} (16r^3 - r^7)\cos^2\theta\, dr\, d\theta = 32\int_{0}^{2\pi} \cos^2\theta\, d\theta = 32\pi$

(b) $\displaystyle\int_0^{\pi/2}\int_0^{\pi/2}\int_0^1 \frac{\rho^2\sin\phi}{1+\rho^2}\,d\rho\,d\phi\,d\theta = (1-\pi/4)\int_0^{\pi/2}\int_0^{\pi/2}\sin\phi\,d\phi\,d\theta = \pi(4-\pi)/8$

29. **(a)** $\displaystyle\int_0^{2\pi}\int_0^{\pi/3}\int_0^a \rho^4\sin^3\phi\,d\rho\,d\phi\,d\theta$ **(b)** $\displaystyle\int_0^{2\pi}\int_0^{\sqrt{3}a/2}\int_{r/\sqrt{3}}^{\sqrt{a^2-r^2}} r^3\,dz\,dr\,d\theta$

(c) $\displaystyle\int_{-\sqrt{3}a/2}^{\sqrt{3}a/2}\int_{-\sqrt{3a^2/4-x^2}}^{\sqrt{3a^2/4-x^2}}\int_{\sqrt{x^2+y^2}/\sqrt{3}}^{\sqrt{a^2-x^2-y^2}} (x^2+y^2)\,dz\,dy\,dx$

30. $\displaystyle V = \int_0^\pi\int_0^{2\sin\theta}\int_0^{r\sin\theta} r\,dz\,dr\,d\theta = \int_0^\pi\int_0^{2\sin\theta} r^2\sin\theta\,dr\,d\theta = \frac{8}{3}\int_0^\pi \sin^4\theta\,d\theta = \pi$

31. $\displaystyle V = \int_0^{2\pi}\int_0^\pi\int_0^{a(1+\cos\phi)} \rho^2\sin\phi\,d\rho\,d\phi\,d\theta = \int_0^{2\pi}\int_0^\pi \frac{1}{3}a^3(1+\cos\phi)^3\sin\phi\,d\phi\,d\theta$

$$= \frac{4}{3}a^3\int_0^{2\pi} d\theta = 8\pi a^3/3$$

32. $x = y^2 + z^2$ and $x = 1 - y^2$ intersect in the curve whose projection onto the yz-plane is the ellipse $2y^2 + z^2 = 1$,

$$V = 4\int_0^{1/\sqrt{2}}\int_0^{\sqrt{1-2y^2}}\int_{y^2+z^2}^{1-y^2} dx\,dz\,dy$$

$$= 4\int_0^{1/\sqrt{2}}\int_0^{\sqrt{1-2y^2}} (1-2y^2-z^2)\,dz\,dy = \frac{8}{3}\int_0^{1/\sqrt{2}} (1-2y^2)^{3/2}\,dy = \sqrt{2}\pi/4$$

33. $\displaystyle V = \int_0^{2\pi}\int_0^{a/\sqrt{3}}\int_{\sqrt{3}r}^a r\,dz\,dr\,d\theta = \int_0^{2\pi}\int_0^{a/\sqrt{3}} (ar - \sqrt{3}r^2)\,dr\,d\theta = \frac{1}{18}a^3\int_0^{2\pi} d\theta = \pi a^3/9$

34. $\bar{x} = 0$ from the symmetry of the region, $A = \pi ab/2$,

$$\bar{y} = \frac{1}{A}\int_{-a}^a\int_0^{b\sqrt{1-(x/a)^2}} y\,dy\,dx = \frac{2}{\pi ab}(2ab^2/3) = 4b/(3\pi);\ \text{centroid } \left(0, \frac{4b}{3\pi}\right)$$

35. $\bar{x} = 0$ from the symmetry of the region,

$$A = \int_0^{2\pi}\int_0^{a(1+\sin\theta)} r\,dr\,d\theta = 3\pi a^2/2,$$

$$\bar{y} = \frac{1}{A}\int_0^{2\pi}\int_0^{a(1+\sin\theta)} r^2\sin\theta\,dr\,d\theta = \frac{1}{A}\int_0^{2\pi}\frac{1}{3}a^3(1+\sin\theta)^3\sin\theta\,d\theta\ \text{but}$$

$$(1 + \sin\theta)^3 \sin\theta = \sin\theta + 3\sin^2\theta + 3\sin^3\theta + \sin^4\theta \text{ and } \int_0^{2\pi} \sin\theta\, d\theta = \int_0^{2\pi} 3\sin^3\theta\, d\theta = 0$$

$$\text{so } \bar{y} = \frac{1}{A}\int_0^{2\pi} \frac{1}{3}a^3(3\sin^2\theta + \sin^4\theta)d\theta = \frac{2}{3\pi a^2}(5\pi a^3/4) = 5a/6; \text{ centroid } (0, 5a/6)$$

36. $\bar{y} = 0$ from the symmetry of the region, $A = 2\int_0^4 \int_{y^2/4}^{y^2/8+2} dx\, dy = 32/3,$

$$\bar{x} = \frac{2}{A}\int_0^4 \int_{y^2/4}^{y^2/8+2} x\, dx\, dy = (3/16)(128/15) = 8/5; \text{ centroid } (8/5, 0)$$

37. $\bar{x} = 0$ from the symmetry of density and region, $M = 2\int_0^a \int_0^{b(1-x/a)} kx\, dy\, dx = ka^2b/3,$

$$\bar{y} = \frac{2}{M}\int_0^a \int_0^{b(1-x/a)} k\, xy\, dy\, dx = \frac{6}{ka^2b}(ka^2b^2/24) = b/4; \text{ center of gravity } (0, b/4)$$

38. $\bar{y} = 0$ from the symmetry of density and region,

$$M = 2\int_0^{\pi/3} \int_{1+\cos\theta}^{3\cos\theta} kr^2 \sin\theta\, dr\, d\theta = 115k/48,$$

$$\bar{x} = \frac{2}{M}\int_0^{\pi/3} \int_{1+\cos\theta}^{3\cos\theta} kr^3 \cos\theta \sin\theta\, dr\, d\theta = \frac{2}{M}\int_0^{\pi/3} \frac{k}{4}[81\cos^4\theta - (1+\cos\theta)^4]\cos\theta \sin\theta\, d\theta$$

$$= \frac{k}{2M}\left[\int_0^{\pi/3} 81\cos^5\theta \sin\theta\, d\theta - \int_0^{\pi/3} (1+\cos\theta)^4 \cos\theta \sin\theta\, d\theta\right]$$

and with $u = \cos\theta$, $v = 1 + \cos\theta$

$$\bar{x} = \frac{k}{2M}\left[-\int_1^{1/2} 81u^5 du + \int_2^{3/2} v^4(v-1)dv\right]$$

$$= (24/115)(1701/128 - 7463/1920) = 4513/2300; \text{ center of gravity } (4513/2300, 0)$$

39. $M = \int_0^a \int_0^{b(1-x/a)} \int_0^{c(1-x/a-y/b)} kz\, dz\, dy\, dx = \frac{1}{2}kc^2\int_0^a \int_0^{b(1-x/a)} (1 - x/a - y/b)^2 dy\, dx$

$$= \frac{1}{6}kbc^2\int_0^a (1 - x/a)^3 dx = \frac{1}{24}kabc^2$$

40. $M = \int_0^{2\pi} \int_0^\pi \int_0^a 2\rho^3 \sin\phi\, d\rho\, d\phi\, d\theta = 2\pi a^4$

41. $\bar{x} = 0$ from the symmetry of the region, $V = 2 \displaystyle\int_0^2 \int_{x^2}^4 \int_0^{4-y} dz\, dy\, dx = 256/15$,

$$\bar{y} = \frac{2}{V} \int_0^2 \int_{x^2}^4 \int_0^{4-y} y\, dz\, dy\, dx = (15/128)(512/35) = 12/7,$$

$$\bar{z} = \frac{2}{V} \int_0^2 \int_{x^2}^4 \int_0^{4-y} z\, dz\, dy\, dx = (15/128)(1024/105) = 8/7; \text{ centroid } (0, 12/7, 8/7)$$

42. $\bar{x} = \bar{y} = 0$ from the symmetry of the region,

$$V = \int_0^{2\pi} \int_0^{\phi_0} \int_0^a \rho^2 \sin\phi\, d\rho\, d\phi\, d\theta = \frac{2}{3}\pi a^3 (1 - \cos\phi_0),$$

$$\bar{z} = \frac{1}{V} \int_0^{2\pi} \int_0^{\phi_0} \int_0^a \rho^3 \cos\phi \sin\phi\, d\rho\, d\phi\, d\theta = \frac{\pi a^4 (1 - \cos^2 \phi_0)/4}{2\pi a^3 (1 - \cos\phi_0)/3} = \frac{3}{8}a(1 + \cos\phi_0);$$

$$\text{centroid } \left(0, 0, \frac{3}{8}a(1 + \cos\phi_0)\right)$$

43. $\bar{x} = \bar{y} = 0$ from the symmetry of the region, $V = \pi R^2 h/3$,

$$\bar{z} = \frac{1}{V} \int_0^{2\pi} \int_0^R \int_0^{h(1-r/R)} zr\, dz\, dr\, d\theta = \frac{3}{\pi R^2 h}(\pi R^2 h^2/12) = h/4; \text{ centroid } (0, 0, h/4)$$

CHAPTER 18
Topics In Vector Calculus

EXERCISE SET 18.1

1. (a) $\int_0^1 (2t + t^2)dt = 4/3$ (b) $\int_0^1 (t^2 - t^2)2t\, dt = 0$

   (c) $\int_C (2x + y)dx + \int_C (x^2 - y)dy = 4/3 + 0 = 4/3$

2. (a) $C : x = t,\ y = t,\ 0 \le t \le 1;\ F = 5t\mathbf{i} + t\mathbf{j},\ d\mathbf{r}/dt = \mathbf{i} + \mathbf{j},\ \int_C \mathbf{F} \cdot d\mathbf{r} = \int_0^1 6t\, dt = 3$

   (b) $C : x = t,\ y = t^2,\ 0 \le t \le 1;\ \mathbf{F} = (3t + 2t^2)\mathbf{i} + (2t - t^2)\mathbf{j},$

        $d\mathbf{r}/dt = \mathbf{i} + 2t\mathbf{j},\ \int_C \mathbf{F} \cdot d\mathbf{r} = \int_0^1 (3t + 6t^2 - 2t^3)dt = 3$

   (c) $C : x = t,\ y = \sin(\pi t/2),\ 0 \le t \le 1;$

        $\mathbf{F} = [3t + 2\sin(\pi t/2)]\mathbf{i} + [2t - \sin(\pi t/2)]\mathbf{j},\ d\mathbf{r}/dt = \mathbf{i} + (\pi/2)\cos(\pi t/2)\mathbf{j},$

        $\int_C \mathbf{F} \cdot d\mathbf{r} = \int_0^1 [3t + 2\sin(\pi t/2) + \pi t\cos(\pi t/2) - (\pi/2)\sin(\pi t/2)\cos(\pi t/2)]dt = 3$

   (d) $C : x = t^3,\ y = t,\ 0 \le t \le 1;\ \mathbf{F} = (3t^3 + 2t)\mathbf{i} + (2t^3 - t)\mathbf{j},\ d\mathbf{r}/dt = 3t^2\mathbf{i} + \mathbf{j},$

        $\int_C \mathbf{F} \cdot d\mathbf{r} = \int_0^1 (9t^5 + 8t^3 - t)dt = 3$

3. $\int_0^2 (t^2/2 - t^3)dt = -8/3$

4. $\int_0^1 (e^{1-2t} + t^2 - t - 6)dt = (e - e^{-1})/2 - 37/6$

5. $\int_0^{\pi/4} (8\cos^2 t - 16\sin^2 t - 20\sin t\cos t)dt = 1 - \pi$

6. $\int_{-1}^1 \left(\frac{2}{3}t - \frac{2}{3}t^{5/3} + t^{2/3}\right)dt = 6/5$

7. $C : x = (3 - t)^2/3,\ y = 3 - t,\ 0 \le t \le 3;\ \int_0^3 \frac{1}{3}(3 - t)^2 dt = 3$

8. $C : x = t^{2/3}, y = t, -1 \le t \le 1;$ $\int_{-1}^{1} \left(\frac{2}{3} t^{2/3} - \frac{2}{3} t^{1/3} + t^{7/3} \right) dt = 4/5$

9. $C : x = \cos t, y = \sin t, 0 \le t \le \pi/2;$ $\int_{0}^{\pi/2} (-\sin t - \cos^2 t) dt = -1 - \pi/4$

10. $C : x = 3 - t, y = 4 - 3t, 0 \le t \le 1;$ $\int_{0}^{1} (-37 + 41t - 9t^2) dt = -39/2$

11. $\int_{0}^{\pi} (0) dt = 0$

12. $\int_{0}^{1} (e^{2t} - 4e^{-t}) dt = e^2/2 + 4e^{-1} - 9/2$

13. $\int_{0}^{1} e^{-t} dt = 1 - e^{-1}$

14. **(a)** $C_1 : (0,0)$ to $(1,0); x = t, y = 0, 0 \le t \le 1$
$C_2 : (1,0)$ to $(0,1); x = 1 - t, y = t, 0 \le t \le 1$
$C_3 : (0,1)$ to $(0,0); x = 0, y = 1 - t, 0 \le t \le 1$

$$\int_{0}^{1} (0) dt + \int_{0}^{1} (-1) dt + \int_{0}^{1} (0) dt = -1$$

(b) $C_1 : (0,0)$ to $(1,0); x = t, y = 0, 0 \le t \le 1$
$C_2 : (1,0)$ to $(1,1); x = 1, y = t, 0 \le t \le 1$
$C_3 : (1,1)$ to $(0,1); x = 1 - t, y = 1, 0 \le t \le 1$
$C_4 : (0,1)$ to $(0,0); x = 0, y = 1 - t, 0 \le t \le 1$

$$\int_{0}^{1} (0) dt + \int_{0}^{1} (-1) dt + \int_{0}^{1} (-1) dt + \int_{0}^{1} (0) dt = -2$$

(c) $C_1 : (0,0)$ to $(1,1); x = t, y = t, 0 \le t \le 1$
$C_2 : (1,1)$ to $(2,0); x = 1 + t, y = 1 - t, 0 \le t \le 1$
$C_3 : (2,0)$ to $(0,0); x = 2 - 2t, y = 0, 0 \le t \le 1$

$$\int_{0}^{1} (0) dt + \int_{0}^{1} 2 dt + \int_{0}^{1} (0) dt = 2$$

(d) $C_1 : (-5,0)$ to $(5,0); x = -5 + 10t, y = 0, 0 \le t \le 1$
$C_2 : x = 5 \cos t, y = 5 \sin t, 0 \le t \le \pi$

$$\int_{0}^{1} (0) dt + \int_{0}^{\pi} (-25) dt = -25\pi$$

15. $\int_{0}^{1} (-3) e^{3t} dt = 1 - e^3$

16. $C : x = 1 - 4t, \; y = 1 + t, \; z = 1 - t, \; 0 \le t \le 1; \; \displaystyle\int_0^1 (-2 - 9t)dt = -13/2$

17. $\displaystyle\int_0^{\pi/2} (7 \sin^2 t \cos t + 3 \sin t \cos t)dt = 23/6$

18. $C_1 : (0,0,0)$ to $(1,1,0); \; x = t, y = t, z = 0, 0 \le t \le 1$
$C_2 : (1,1,0)$ to $(1,1,1); \; x = 1, y = 1, z = t, 0 \le t \le 1$
$C_3 : (1,1,1)$ to $(0,0,0); \; x = 1 - t, y = 1 - t, z = 1 - t, 0 \le t \le 1$
$$\int_0^1 (-t^3)dt + \int_0^1 3t \, dt + \int_0^1 (-3)(1 - t)^2 dt = 1/4$$

19. $C : x = t^2, \; y = t, \; 0 \le t \le 1; \; W = \displaystyle\int_0^1 3t^4 dt = 3/5$

20. $W = \displaystyle\int_1^3 (t^2 + 1 - 1/t^3 + 1/t)dt = 92/9 + \ln 3$

21. **(a)** $C_1 : (1,1)$ to $(2,2); \; x = 1 + t, y = 1 + t, 0 \le t \le 1$
$C_2 : (2,2)$ to $(4,2); \; x = 2 + 2t, y = 2, 0 \le t \le 1$
$$\int_0^1 \frac{5/2}{(1+t)^2} dt + \int_0^1 \frac{1/2}{1 + (1+t)^2} dt = 5/4 - \pi/8 + \frac{1}{2} \tan^{-1} 2$$

(b) $C_1 : (0,3)$ to $(6,3); \; x = 6t, y = 3, 0 \le t \le 1$
$C_2 : (6,3)$ to $(6,0); \; x = 6, y = 3 - 3t, 0 \le t \le 1$
$$\int_0^1 \frac{6}{36t^2 + 9} dt + \int_0^1 \frac{-12}{36 + 9(1-t)^2} dt = \frac{1}{3} \tan^{-1} 2 - \frac{2}{3} \tan^{-1}(1/2)$$

(c) $C : x = 4 \cos t, y = 4 \sin t, 0 \le t \le \pi/2$
$$\int_0^{\pi/2} \left(-\frac{1}{4} \sin t + \cos t \right) dt = 3/4$$

22. $W = \displaystyle\int_0^1 (t^3 + 5t^6)dt = 27/28$

23. $C_1 : (0,0,0)$ to $(1,3,1); \; x = t, \; y = 3t, \; z = t, \; 0 \le t \le 1$
$C_2 : (1,3,1)$ to $(2,-1,4); \; x = 1 + t, \; y = 3 - 4t, \; z = 1 + 3t, \; 0 \le t \le 1$
$$W = \int_0^1 (4t + 8t^2)dt + \int_0^1 (-11 - 17t - 11t^2)dt = -37/2$$

24. $C : x = a \cos t, y = a \sin t, 0 \le t \le 2\pi, \; \displaystyle\int_{-C} dt = - \int_C dt = - \int_0^{2\pi} dt = -2\pi$

25. $W = \int_0^1 \lambda[(1-\lambda)t + (3\lambda - 1)t^2 - (1 + 2\lambda)t^3]dt = -\lambda/12, \; W = 1$ when $\lambda = -12$

26. (a) $x = x_0, \; y = y_0 + (y_1 - y_0)t, \; 0 \le t \le 1$ for C from (x_0, y_0) to (x_0, y_1) so
$$\int_C f(x, y)dx = \int_0^1 (0)dt = 0$$
(b) similar to part (a) with $x = x_0 + (x_1 - x_0)t, \; y = y_0$ for C from (x_0, y_0) to (x_1, y_0)

27. $C : x = a\cos t, \; y = a\sin t, \; 0 \le t \le \pi;$
$$\mathbf{F} = \frac{k(x\mathbf{i} + y\mathbf{j})}{(x^2 + y^2)^{3/2}} = \frac{k}{a^2}(\cos t\mathbf{i} + \sin t\mathbf{j}), \; d\mathbf{r}/dt = a(-\sin t\mathbf{i} + \cos t\mathbf{j}), \; W = \int_0^\pi (0)dt = 0$$

28. Let t be the amount of rotation, in radians. The farmer climbs 60 ft in 8π radians so the elevation increases at the rate of $60/(8\pi) = 15/(2\pi)$ ft/radian. Represent the helical path by $x = 25\cos t, \; y = 25\sin t, \; z = \dfrac{15}{2\pi}t$. The force exerted by the farmer on the sack is
$$\mathbf{F} = \left(20 - \frac{1}{10}z\right)\mathbf{k} = \left(20 - \frac{3}{4\pi}t\right)\mathbf{k} \text{ so the work done is } W = \int_0^{8\pi} \frac{15}{2\pi}\left(20 - \frac{3}{4\pi}t\right)dt = 1020$$
ft · lb.

EXERCISE SET 18.2

1. $\partial x/\partial y = 0 = \partial y/\partial x$, conservative so $\partial \phi/\partial x = x$ and $\partial \phi/\partial y = y, \; \phi = x^2/2 + k(y), \; k'(y) = y,$
$k(y) = y^2/2 + K, \; \phi = x^2/2 + y^2/2 + K$

2. $\partial(3y^2)/\partial y = 6y = \partial(6xy)/\partial x$, conservative so $\partial \phi/\partial x = 3y^2$ and $\partial \phi/\partial y = 6xy,$
$\phi = 3xy^2 + k(y), \; 6xy + k'(y) = 6xy, \; k'(y) = 0, \; k(y) = K, \; \phi = 3xy^2 + K$

3. $\partial(x^2 y)/\partial y = x^2$ and $\partial(5xy^2)/\partial x = 5y^2$, not conservative

4. $\partial(e^x \cos y)/\partial y = -e^x \sin y = \partial(-e^x \sin y)/\partial x$, conservative so $\partial \phi/\partial x = e^x \cos y$ and
$\partial \phi/\partial y = -e^x \sin y, \; \phi = e^x \cos y + k(y), \; -e^x \sin y + k'(y) = -e^x \sin y,$
$k'(y) = 0, \; k(y) = K, \; \phi = e^x \cos y + K$

5. $\partial(\cos y + y\cos x)/\partial y = -\sin y + \cos x = \partial(\sin x - x\sin y)/\partial x$, conservative so
$\partial \phi/\partial x = \cos y + y\cos x$ and $\partial \phi/\partial y = \sin x - x\sin y, \; \phi = x\cos y + y\sin x + k(y),$
$-x\sin y + \sin x + k'(y) = \sin x - x\sin y, \; k'(y) = 0, \; k(y) = K, \; \phi = x\cos y + y\sin x + K$

6. $\partial(x\ln y)/\partial y = x/y$ and $\partial(y\ln x)/\partial x = y/x$, not conservative

7. $\partial(y^2)/\partial y = 2y = \partial(2xy)/\partial x$, independent of path

     (a) $\partial\phi/\partial x = y^2$ and $\partial\phi/\partial y = 2xy$, $\phi = xy^2 + k(y)$, $2xy + k'(y) = 2xy$, $k'(y) = 0$, $k(y) = K$, $\phi = xy^2 + K$. Let $K = 0$ to get $\phi(1,3) - \phi(-1,2) = 9 - (-4) = 13$

     (b) $C : x = -1 + 2t, \; y = 2 + t, \; 0 \le t \le 1$; $\displaystyle\int_0^1 (4 + 14t + 6t^2)dt = 13$

8. $\partial(y \sin x)/\partial y = \sin x = \partial(-\cos x)/\partial x$, independent of path

     (a) $\partial\phi/\partial x = y \sin x$ and $\partial\phi/\partial y = -\cos x$, $\phi = -y \cos x + k(y)$, $-\cos x + k'(y) = -\cos x$, $k'(y) = 0$, $k(y) = K$, $\phi = -y \cos x + K$. Let $K = 0$ to get $\phi(\pi, -1) - \phi(0, 1) = (-1) - (-1) = 0$

     (b) $C : x = \pi t, \; y = 1 - 2t, \; 0 \le t \le 1$; $\displaystyle\int_0^1 (\pi \sin \pi t - 2\pi t \sin \pi t + 2 \cos \pi t)dt = 0$

9. $\partial(3y)/\partial y = 3 = \partial(3x)/\partial x$, $\phi = 3xy$, $\phi(4,0) - \phi(1,2) = -6$

10. $\partial(e^x \sin y)/\partial y = e^x \cos y = \partial(e^x \cos y)/\partial x$, $\phi = e^x \sin y$, $\phi(1, \pi/2) - \phi(0,0) = e$

11. $\partial(2xe^y)/\partial y = 2xe^y = \partial(x^2 e^y)/\partial x$, $\phi = x^2 e^y$, $\phi(3, 2) - \phi(0,0) = 9e^2$

12. $\partial(3x - y + 1)/\partial y = -1 = \partial[-(x + 4y + 2)]/\partial x$,
     $\phi = 3x^2/2 - xy + x - 2y^2 - 2y$, $\phi(0, 1) - \phi(-1, 2) = 11/2$

13. $\partial(2xy^3)/\partial y = 6xy^2 = \partial(3x^2y^2)/\partial x$, $\phi = x^2y^3$, $\phi(-1, 0) - \phi(2, -2) = 32$

14. $\partial(e^x \ln y - e^y/x)/\partial y = e^x/y - e^y/x = \partial(e^x/y - e^y \ln x)/\partial x$,
     $\phi = e^x \ln y - e^y \ln x$, $\phi(3, 3) - \phi(1, 1) = 0$

15. $\phi = x^2y^2/2$, $W = \phi(0,0) - \phi(1,1) = -1/2$

16. $\phi = e^{xy}$, $W = \phi(2, 0) - \phi(-1, 1) = 1 - e^{-1}$

17. $\phi = \tan^{-1}(x/y)$, $W = \phi(3, 3) - \phi(0, 2) = \pi/4$

18. $\phi = e^{-y} \sin x$, $W = \phi(-\pi/2, 0) - \phi(\pi/2, 1) = -1 - e^{-1}$

19. $\partial(e^y + ye^x)/\partial y = e^y + e^x = \partial(xe^y + e^x)/\partial x$ so $\mathbf{F}$ is conservative, $\phi = xe^y + ye^x$ so the work done in parts (a), (b), and (c) is $\phi(-a, 0) - \phi(a, 0) = -2a$. From Theorem 18.2.2 the work done in part (d) is 0.

20. $(\sin y \sinh x + \cos y \cosh x)\mathbf{i} + (\cos y \cosh x - \sin y \sinh x)\mathbf{j}$ is conservative,

$\phi = \sin y \cosh x + \cos y \sinh x$, the line segment extends from $(1,0)$ to $(2, \pi/2)$ so the value of the integral is $\phi(2, \pi/2) - \phi(1, 0) = \cosh 2 - \sinh 1$

21. $\mathbf{F} = \dfrac{kx}{(x^2 + y^2)^{3/2}}\mathbf{i} + \dfrac{ky}{(x^2 + y^2)^{3/2}}\mathbf{j}$, $\dfrac{\partial}{\partial y}\dfrac{kx}{(x^2 + y^2)^{3/2}} = -\dfrac{3kxy}{(x^2 + y^2)^{5/2}} = \dfrac{\partial}{\partial x}\dfrac{ky}{(x^2 + y^2)^{3/2}}$

so $\mathbf{F}$ is conservative

22. $\dfrac{\partial}{\partial y}(h(x)[x \sin y + y \cos y]) = h(x)[x \cos y - y \sin y + \cos y]$

$\dfrac{\partial}{\partial x}(h(x)[x \cos y - y \sin y]) = h(x) \cos y + h'(x)[x \cos y - y \sin y]$,

equate these two partial derivatives to get $(x \cos y - y \sin y)(h'(x) - h(x)) = 0$ which holds for all x and y if $h'(x) = h(x)$, $h(x) = Ce^x$ where C is an arbitrary constant.

23. **(a)** If $\mathbf{F}$ is conservative then $\mathbf{F} = (\partial\phi/\partial x)\mathbf{i} + (\partial\phi/\partial y)\mathbf{j}$ for some function ϕ so $f(x, y) = \partial\phi/\partial x$ and $g(x, y) = \partial\phi/\partial y$. But $d\phi = (\partial\phi/\partial x)dx + (\partial\phi/\partial y)dy$ so $d\phi = f(x, y)dx + g(x, y)dy$. If ϕ is such that $d\phi = f(x, y)dx + g(x, y)dy$ then $f(x, y) = \partial\phi/\partial x$ and $g(x, y) = \partial\phi/\partial y$ so $\mathbf{F} = \nabla\phi$ and hence $\mathbf{F}$ is conservative.

(b) $\displaystyle\int_{(x_0,y_0)}^{(x_1,y_1)} d\phi = \int_{(x_0,y_0)}^{(x_1,y_1)} f(x, y)dx + g(x, y)dy = \phi(x_1, y_1) - \phi(x_0, y_0)$

24. If C is composed of smooth curves $C_1, C_2, \ldots, C_n$ and curve C_i extends from (x_{i-1}, y_{i-1}) to (x_i, y_i) then $\displaystyle\int_C \mathbf{F} \cdot d\mathbf{r} = \sum_{i=1}^{n} \int_{C_i} \mathbf{F} \cdot d\mathbf{r} = \sum_{i=1}^{n}[\phi(x_i, y_i) - \phi(x_{i-1}, y_{i-1})] = \phi(x_n, y_n) - \phi(x_0, y_0)$

where (x_0, y_0) and (x_n, y_n) are the endpoints of C.

EXERCISE SET 18.3

1. $\displaystyle\iint\limits_{R} (2x - 2y)dA = \int_0^1 \int_0^1 (2x - 2y)dy\, dx = 0$

2. $\displaystyle\iint\limits_{R} (1 - 1)dA = 0$

3. $\displaystyle\int_{-2}^{4} \int_1^2 (2y - 3x)dy\, dx = 0$

4. $\displaystyle\int_0^{2\pi} \int_0^3 (1 + 2r \sin\theta)r\, dr\, d\theta = 9\pi$

5. $\displaystyle\int_0^{\pi/2} \int_0^{\pi/2} (-y \cos x + x \sin y)dy\, dx = 0$

6. $\displaystyle\iint\limits_{R}(\sec^2 x - \tan^2 x)dA = \iint\limits_{R} dA = \pi$ **7.** $\displaystyle\iint\limits_{R}[1-(-1)]dA = 2\iint\limits_{R} dA = 8\pi$

8. $\displaystyle\int_0^1 \int_{x^2}^x (2x - 2y)dy\,dx = 1/30$

9. $\displaystyle\iint\limits_{R}\left(-\frac{y}{1+y} - \frac{1}{1+y}\right)dA = -\iint\limits_{R} dA = -4$

10. $\displaystyle\int_0^{\pi/2}\int_0^4 (-r^2)r\,dr\,d\theta = -32\pi$

11. $\displaystyle\iint\limits_{R}\left(-\frac{y^2}{1+y^2} - \frac{1}{1+y^2}\right)dA = -\iint\limits_{R} dA = -1$

12. $\displaystyle\iint\limits_{R}(\cos x \cos y - \cos x \cos y)dA = 0$ **13.** $\displaystyle\int_0^1 \int_{x^2}^{\sqrt{x}}(y^2 - x^2)dy\,dx = 0$

14. **(a)** $\displaystyle\int_0^2 \int_{x^2}^{2x}(-6x + 2y)dy\,dx = -56/15$ **(b)** $\displaystyle\int_0^2 \int_{x^2}^{2x} 6y\,dy\,dx = 64/5$

15. **(a)** $\displaystyle\int_C x\,dy = \int_0^{2\pi} ab\cos^2 t\,dt = \pi ab$ **(b)** $\displaystyle\int_C -y\,dx = \int_0^{2\pi} ab\sin^2 t\,dt = \pi ab$

16. $\displaystyle A = \frac{1}{2}\int_C -y\,dx + x\,dy = \frac{1}{2}\int_0^{2\pi}(3a^2\sin^4 t\cos^2 t + 3a^2\cos^4 t\sin^2 t)dt$

$$= \frac{3}{2}a^2\int_0^{2\pi}\sin^2 t\cos^2 t\,dt = \frac{3}{8}a^2\int_0^{2\pi}\sin^2 2t\,dt = 3\pi a^2/8$$

17. $C_1 : (0,0)$ to $(a,0); x = at, \quad y = 0, \quad\quad 0 \le t \le 1$
$C_2 : (a,0)$ to $(0,b); x = a - at, y = bt, \quad\quad 0 \le t \le 1$
$C_3 : (0,b)$ to $(0,0); x = 0, \quad\quad y = b - bt, 0 \le t \le 1$

$$A = \int_C x\,dy = \int_0^1 (0)dt + \int_0^1 ab(1 - t)dt + \int_0^1 (0)dt = \frac{1}{2}ab$$

18. $C_1 : (0,0)$ to $(3, 1/3); x = 3t, y = t/3, 0 \le t \le 1$
$C_2 : (3, 1/3)$ to $(1/1)$ along $y = 1/x; x = 3 - t, y = 1/(3 - t), 0 \le t \le 2$

$C_3 : (1,1)$ to $(0,0)$; $x = 1 - t$, $y = 1 - t$, $0 \le t \le 1$

$$A = \int_C x \, dy = \int_0^1 t \, dt + \int_0^2 \frac{1}{3-t} dt + \int_0^1 (t-1) dt = \ln 3$$

19. $\quad W = \iint\limits_R y \, dA = \int_0^\pi \int_0^5 r^2 \sin\theta \, dr \, d\theta = 250/3$

20. $\quad W = \int_0^2 \int_0^{x^3/4} \left(\frac{1}{2} x^{-1/2} - \frac{1}{2} y^{-1/2} \right) dy \, dx = -18\sqrt{2}/35$

21. **(a)** $\bar{x} = \frac{1}{A} \iint\limits_R x \, dA$, but $\int_C \frac{1}{2} x^2 dy = \iint\limits_R x \, dA$ from Green's Theorem so

$\bar{x} = \frac{1}{A} \int_C \frac{1}{2} x^2 dy = \frac{1}{2A} \int_C x^2 dy$. Similarly, $\bar{y} = -\frac{1}{2A} \int_C y^2 dx$.

(b) $\bar{x} = 0$ from the symmetry of the region,

$C_1 : (a,0)$ to $(-a,0)$ along $y = \sqrt{a^2 - x^2}$; $x = a\cos t$, $y = a\sin t$, $0 \le t \le \pi$

$C_2 : (-a,0)$ to $(a,0)$; $x = -a + 2at$, $y = 0$, $0 \le t \le 1$

$$A = \pi a^2/2, \quad \bar{y} = -\frac{1}{2A} \left[\int_0^\pi -a^3 \sin^3 t \, dt + \int_0^1 (0) dt \right]$$

$$= -\frac{1}{\pi a^2} \left(-\frac{4a^3}{3} \right) = \frac{4a}{3\pi}; \text{ centroid } \left(0, \frac{4a}{3\pi} \right)$$

22. $\quad \int_C y \, dx - x \, dy = \iint\limits_R (-2) dA = -2 \int_0^{2\pi} \int_0^{a(1+\cos\theta)} r \, dr \, d\theta = -3\pi a^2$

23. **(a)** $C : x = a + (c-a)t$, $y = b + (d-b)t$, $0 \le t \le 1$

$$\int_C x \, dy - y \, dx = \int_0^1 (ad - bc) dt = ad - bc$$

(b) Let C_1, C_2, and C_3 be the line segments from (x_1, y_1) to (x_2, y_2), (x_2, y_2) to (x_3, y_3), and (x_3, y_3) to (x_1, y_1), then from (4c)

$$A = \sum_{i=1}^3 \frac{1}{2} \int_{C_i} x \, dy - y \, dx \text{ and from the result of part (a)}$$

$$A = \frac{1}{2} [(x_1 y_2 - x_2 y_1) + (x_2 y_3 - x_3 y_2) + (x_3 y_1 - x_1 y_3)]$$

(c) $A = \frac{1}{2} [(x_1 y_2 - x_2 y_1) + (x_2 y_3 - x_3 y_2) + \cdots + (x_n y_1 - x_1 y_n)]$

(d) $A = \frac{1}{2} [(0 - 0) + (6 + 8) + (0 + 2) + (0 - 0)] = 8$

24. From Green's Theorem, the given integral equals $\displaystyle\iint_R (1 - x^2 - y^2)dA$ where R is the region

enclosed by C. The value of this integral is maximum if the integration extends over the largest region for which the integrand $1 - x^2 - y^2$ is nonnegative so we want $1 - x^2 - y^2 \geq 0$, $x^2 + y^2 \leq 1$. The largest region is that bounded by the circle $x^2 + y^2 = 1$ which is the desired curve C.

25. (a) $\displaystyle\int_0^{2\pi} (\sin^2 t + \cos^2 t)dt = \int_0^{2\pi} dt = 2\pi$

(b) $\partial g/\partial x = \dfrac{y^2 - x^2}{(x^2 + y^2)^2} = \partial f/\partial y$

(c) f and g do not have continuous first partial derivatives at the point $(0,0)$ in R so Green's Theorem is not applicable.

EXERCISE SET 18.4

1. R is the circular region enclosed by $x^2 + y^2 = 1$;

$$\iint_\sigma \delta_0 dS = \delta_0 \iint_R \sqrt{4x^2 + 4y^2 + 1}\, dA = \delta_0 \int_0^{2\pi} \int_0^1 \sqrt{4r^2 + 1}\, r\, dr\, d\theta$$

$$= \frac{1}{12}(5\sqrt{5} - 1)\delta_0 \int_0^{2\pi} d\theta = \frac{\pi}{6}(5\sqrt{5} - 1)\delta_0.$$

2. $z = 8 - 2x - 2y$, R is the triangular region enclosed by $x + y = 4$, $x = 0$ and $y = 0$;

$$\iint_\sigma \delta_0 dS = \delta_0 \iint_R \sqrt{9}\, dA = 3\delta_0 \iint_R dA, \text{ but } \iint_R dA \text{ is the area of a right triangle with altitude}$$

and base each 4, so $\displaystyle\iint_R dA = \frac{1}{2}(4)(4) = 8$ and $\displaystyle\iint_\sigma \delta_0 dS = 3\delta_0(8) = 24\delta_0.$

3. $z = \sqrt{4 - x^2}$, $\dfrac{\partial z}{\partial x} = -\dfrac{x}{\sqrt{4 - x^2}}$, $\dfrac{\partial z}{\partial y} = 0$;

$$\iint_\sigma \delta_0 dS = \delta_0 \iint_R \sqrt{\frac{x^2}{4 - x^2} + 1}\, dA = 2\delta_0 \int_0^4 \int_0^1 \frac{1}{\sqrt{4 - x^2}}\, dx\, dy = \frac{4}{3}\pi\delta_0.$$

4. $z = \dfrac{1}{2}(x^2 + y^2)$, R is the circular region enclosed by $x^2 + y^2 = 8$;

$$\iint_\sigma \delta_0 dS = \delta_0 \iint_R \sqrt{x^2 + y^2 + 1}\, dA = \delta_0 \int_0^{2\pi} \int_0^{\sqrt{8}} \sqrt{r^2 + 1}\, r\, dr\, d\theta = \frac{52}{3}\pi\delta_0.$$

5. R is the annular region between $x^2 + y^2 = 1$ and $x^2 + y^2 = 4$;

$$\iint_\sigma z^2 dS = \iint_R (x^2+y^2)\sqrt{\frac{x^2}{x^2+y^2} + \frac{y^2}{x^2+y^2} + 1}\, dA$$

$$= \sqrt{2} \iint_R (x^2+y^2)\, dA = \sqrt{2} \int_0^{2\pi} \int_1^2 r^3 dr\, d\theta = \frac{15}{2}\pi\sqrt{2}.$$

6. $z = 1 - x - y$, R is the triangular region enclosed by $x + y = 1$, $x = 0$ and $y = 0$;

$$\iint_\sigma xyz\, dS = \iint_R xy(1 - x - y)\sqrt{3}\, dA = \sqrt{3} \int_0^1 \int_0^{1-x} (xy - x^2 y - xy^2)\, dy\, dx = \frac{\sqrt{3}}{120}.$$

7. $z = \sqrt{1 - x^2}$, R is the rectangular region enclosed by $x = -1$, $x = 1$, $y = 0$ and $y = 1$; $\partial z / \partial x = -x/\sqrt{1-x^2}$ which does not exist along the boundaries $x = \pm 1$. We avoid them by using $x = \pm x_0$ as boundaries where x_0 is slightly smaller than 1 and then let x_0 approach 1. By the symmetry of the surface and the integrand we can integrate over the region R' enclosed by $x = 0$, $x = x_0$, $y = 0$ and $y = 1$ and double the result so

$$\iint_\sigma x^2 y\, dS = \lim_{x_0 \to 1^-} 2\iint_{R'} x^2 y\sqrt{\frac{x^2}{1-x^2} + 1}\, dA = \lim_{x_0 \to 1^-} 2\int_0^{x_0} \int_0^1 \frac{x^2 y}{\sqrt{1-x^2}}\, dy\, dx$$

$$= \lim_{x_0 \to 1^-} \int_0^{x_0} \frac{x^2}{\sqrt{1-x^2}}\, dx; \text{ use } x = \sin\theta \text{ to get}$$

$$\iint_\sigma x^2 y\, dS = \lim_{\theta_0 \to \pi/2^-} \int_0^{\theta_0} \sin^2\theta\, d\theta \quad (\theta_0 = \sin^{-1} x_0)$$

$$= \lim_{\theta_0 \to \pi/2^-} \left(\frac{1}{2}\theta_0 - \frac{1}{4}\sin 2\theta_0 \right) = \frac{\pi}{4}.$$

8. $z = \sqrt{4 - x^2 - y^2}$, R is the circular region enclosed by $x^2 + y^2 = 3$;

$$\iint_\sigma (x^2+y^2)z\, dS = \iint_R (x^2+y^2)\sqrt{4-x^2-y^2}\sqrt{\frac{x^2}{4-x^2-y^2} + \frac{y^2}{4-x^2-y^2} + 1}\, dA$$

$$= \iint_R 2(x^2+y^2)\, dA = 2\int_0^{2\pi} \int_0^{\sqrt{3}} r^3 dr\, d\theta = 9\pi.$$

9. If we use the projection of σ onto the xz-plane then $y = 1 - x$ and R is the rectangular region in the xz-plane enclosed by $x = 0$, $x = 1$, $z = 0$ and $z = 1$;

$$\iint_\sigma (x+y+z)\, dS = \iint_R (1+z)\sqrt{2}\, dA = \sqrt{2}\int_0^1 \int_0^1 (1+z)\, dz\, dx = \frac{3\sqrt{2}}{2}.$$

10. R is the triangular region enclosed by $2x + 3y = 6$, $x = 0$, and $y = 0$;

$$\iint_\sigma (x+y)dS = \iint_R (x+y)\sqrt{14}\,dA = \sqrt{14}\int_0^3 \int_0^{(6-2x)/3} (x+y)dy\,dx = 5\sqrt{14}.$$

11. There are six surfaces:

$\sigma_1 : z = 0;\ 0 \le x \le 1,\ 0 \le y \le 1$ (project onto xy-plane),

$\sigma_2 : x = 0;\ 0 \le y \le 1,\ 0 \le z \le 1$ (project onto yz-plane),

$\sigma_3 : y = 0;\ 0 \le x \le 1,\ 0 \le z \le 1$ (project onto xz-plane),

$\sigma_4 : z = 1;\ 0 \le x \le 1,\ 0 \le y \le 1$ (project onto xy-plane),

$\sigma_5 : x = 1;\ 0 \le y \le 1,\ 0 \le z \le 1$ (project onto yz-plane),

$\sigma_6 : y = 1;\ 0 \le x \le 1,\ 0 \le z \le 1$ (project onto xz-plane), so

$$\iint_{\sigma_1} (x+y+z)dS = \int_0^1 \int_0^1 (x+y)dx\,dy = 1,\quad \iint_{\sigma_2} (x+y+z)dS = \int_0^1 \int_0^1 (y+z)dy\,dz = 1,$$

$$\iint_{\sigma_3} (x+y+z)dS = \int_0^1 \int_0^1 (x+z)dx\,dz = 1,$$

$$\iint_{\sigma_4} (x+y+z)dS = \int_0^1 \int_0^1 (x+y+1)dx\,dy = 2,$$

$$\iint_{\sigma_5} (x+y+z)dS = \int_0^1 \int_0^1 (1+y+z)dy\,dz = 2,$$

$$\iint_{\sigma_6} (x+y+z)dS = \int_0^1 \int_0^1 (x+1+z)dx\,dz = 2,$$

thus, $\displaystyle\iint_\sigma (x+y+z)dS = 1+1+1+2+2+2 = 9.$

12. Use $y = \sqrt{1-x^2}$ and let R be the rectangular region in the xz-plane enclosed by $x = 0$, $x = 1$, $z = 0$ and $z = 1$. Then by the symmetry of the surface and the integrand

$$\iint_\sigma zx^2\,dS = 4\iint_R zx^2\sqrt{\frac{x^2}{1-x^2}+1}\,dA = 4\iint_R \frac{x^2 z}{\sqrt{1-x^2}}\,dA,$$

but the integrand is not defined along the boundary $x = 1$ so we use $x = x_0$ where x_0 is slightly less than 1 and then let x_0 approach 1,

$$\iint_\sigma zx^2\,dS = \lim_{x_0\to 1^-} 4\int_0^{x_0} \int_0^1 \frac{x^2 z}{\sqrt{1-x^2}}\,dz\,dx = \frac{\pi}{2}\ \text{(See solution of Exercise 7 for details.)}$$

13. R is the circular region enclosed by $x^2 + y^2 = 1$;

$$\iint_\sigma \sqrt{x^2 + y^2 + z^2}\, dS = \iint_R \sqrt{2(x^2+y^2)}\sqrt{\frac{x^2}{x^2+y^2} + \frac{y^2}{x^2+y^2} + 1}\, dA$$

$$= \lim_{r_0 \to 0^+} 2 \iint_{R'} \sqrt{x^2 + y^2}\, dA$$

where R' is the annular region enclosed by $x^2 + y^2 = 1$ and $x^2 + y^2 = r_0^2$ with r_0 slightly larger than 0 because $\sqrt{\dfrac{x^2}{x^2+y^2} + \dfrac{y^2}{x^2+y^2} + 1}$ is not defined for $x^2 + y^2 = 0$, so

$$\iint_\sigma \sqrt{x^2 + y^2 + z^2}\, dS = \lim_{r_0 \to 0^+} 2 \int_0^{2\pi} \int_{r_0}^1 r^2\, dr\, d\theta = \lim_{r_0 \to 0^+} \frac{4\pi}{3}(1 - r_0^3) = \frac{4\pi}{3}.$$

14. R is the circular region enclosed by $x^2 + y^2 = 1$;

$$\iint_\sigma (z+1)\, dS = \iint_R (\sqrt{1 - x^2 - y^2} + 1)\sqrt{\frac{x^2}{1 - x^2 - y^2} + \frac{y^2}{1 - x^2 - y^2} + 1}\, dA$$

$$= \iint_R \frac{\sqrt{1 - x^2 - y^2} + 1}{\sqrt{1 - x^2 - y^2}}\, dA$$

$$= \lim_{r_0 \to 1^-} \int_0^{2\pi} \int_0^{r_0} \left(1 + \frac{1}{\sqrt{1 - r^2}}\right) r\, dr\, d\theta$$

$$= \lim_{r_0 \to 1^-} 2\pi \left(\frac{1}{2}r_0^2 - \sqrt{1 - r_0^2} + 1\right) = 3\pi.$$

15. Use $z = \sqrt{a^2 - x^2 - y^2}$ and let R be the circular region enclosed by $x^2 + y^2 = a^2$, $x = 0$, and $y = 0$ then by symmetry of the surface and the integrand

$$\iint_\sigma (x^2 + y^2)\, dS = 2 \iint_R (x^2 + y^2)\sqrt{\frac{x^2}{a^2 - x^2 - y^2} + \frac{y^2}{a^2 - x^2 - y^2} + 1}\, dA$$

$$= 2a \iint_R \frac{x^2 + y^2}{\sqrt{a^2 - x^2 - y^2}}\, dA,$$

but the integrand is not defined along the boundary $x^2 + y^2 = a^2$ so

$$\iint_\sigma (x^2 + y^2)\, dS = \lim_{r_0 \to a^-} 2a \int_0^{2\pi} \int_0^{r_0} \frac{r^3}{\sqrt{a^2 - r^2}}\, dr\, d\theta$$

$$= \lim_{r_0 \to a^-} 4\pi a \left[\frac{2}{3}a^3 + \frac{1}{3}(a^2 - r_0^2)^{3/2} - a^2\sqrt{a^2 - r_0^2}\right] = \frac{8\pi}{3}a^4.$$

16. R is the annular region enclosed by $x^2 + y^2 = 1$ and $x^2 + y^2 = 16$;

$$\iint_\sigma x^2 z \, dS = \iint_R x^2 \sqrt{x^2 + y^2} \sqrt{\frac{x^2}{x^2 + y^2} + \frac{y^2}{x^2 + y^2} + 1} \, dA$$

$$= \sqrt{2} \iint_R x^2 \sqrt{x^2 + y^2} \, dA = \sqrt{2} \int_0^{2\pi} \int_1^4 r^4 \cos^2 \theta \, dr \, d\theta = \frac{1023\sqrt{2}}{5} \pi.$$

17. $z = 4 - y^2$, R is the rectangular region enclosed by $x = 0$, $x = 3$, $y = 0$ and $y = 3$;

$$\iint_\sigma y \, dS = \iint_R y\sqrt{4y^2 + 1} \, dA = \int_0^3 \int_0^3 y\sqrt{4y^2 + 1} \, dy \, dx = \frac{1}{4}(37\sqrt{37} - 1).$$

18. R is the circular region enclosed by $x^2 + y^2 = 1$;

$$\iint_\sigma \sqrt{x^2 + y^2} \, dS = \iint_R \sqrt{x^2 + y^2} \sqrt{4x^2 + 4y^2 + 1} \, dA = \int_0^{2\pi} \int_0^1 r^2 \sqrt{4r^2 + 1} \, dr \, d\theta$$

$$= \frac{\pi}{32}[18\sqrt{5} - \ln(2 + \sqrt{5})].$$

19. **(a)** $\dfrac{\sqrt{29}}{16} \displaystyle\int_0^6 \int_0^{(12-2x)/3} xy(12 - 2x - 3y) dy \, dx$

(b) $\dfrac{\sqrt{29}}{4} \displaystyle\int_0^3 \int_0^{(12-4z)/3} yz(12 - 3y - 4z) dy \, dz$

(c) $\dfrac{\sqrt{29}}{9} \displaystyle\int_0^3 \int_0^{6-2z} xz(12 - 2x - 4z) dx \, dz$

20. **(a)** $a \displaystyle\int_0^a \int_0^{\sqrt{a^2 - x^2}} x \, dy \, dx$ **(b)** $a \displaystyle\int_0^a \int_0^{\sqrt{a^2 - z^2}} z \, dy \, dz$

(c) $a \displaystyle\int_0^a \int_0^{\sqrt{a^2 - z^2}} \frac{xz}{\sqrt{a^2 - x^2 - z^2}} dx \, dz$

21. $\displaystyle\int_0^4 \int_1^2 y^3 z \sqrt{4y^2 + 1} \, dy \, dz; \quad \frac{1}{2} \int_0^4 \int_1^4 xz\sqrt{1 + 4x} \, dx \, dz$

22. $a \displaystyle\int_0^9 \int_{a/\sqrt{5}}^{a/\sqrt{2}} \frac{x^2 y}{\sqrt{a^2 - y^2}} dy \, dx, \quad a \int_{a/\sqrt{2}}^{2a/\sqrt{5}} \int_0^9 x^2 dx \, dz$

23. $M = \displaystyle\iint_\sigma \delta(x, y, z) dS = \iint_\sigma \delta_0 dS = \delta_0 \iint_\sigma dS = \delta_0 S$

24. $\delta(x,y,z) = |z|$; use $z = \sqrt{a^2 - x^2 - y^2}$ and let R be the circular region enclosed by $x^2 + y^2 = a^2$. By the symmetry of both the surface and the density function with respect to the xy-plane we have

$$M = 2\iint_\sigma z\,dS = 2\iint_R \sqrt{a^2 - x^2 - y^2}\sqrt{\frac{x^2}{a^2 - x^2 - y^2} + \frac{y^2}{a^2 - x^2 - y^2} + 1}\,dA$$

$$= \lim_{r_0 \to a^-} 2a\iint_{R_{r_0}} dA$$

where R_{r_0} is the circular region with radius r_0 that is slightly less than a. But $\iint_{R_{r_0}} dA$ is

simply the area of the circle with radius r_0 so $M = \lim_{r_0 \to a^-} 2a(\pi r_0^2) = 2\pi a^3$.

EXERCISE SET 18.5

1. From the orientation of the plane surface we see that upward, right, and forward unit normals should be used; in each case the result is $\dfrac{2}{\sqrt{29}}\mathbf{i} + \dfrac{3}{\sqrt{29}}\mathbf{j} + \dfrac{4}{\sqrt{29}}\mathbf{k}$.

2. With $z = -\sqrt{9 - x^2 - y^2}$, $y = \sqrt{9 - x^2 - z^2}$, or $x = \sqrt{9 - y^2 - z^2}$ we see that downward, right, and forward unit normals should be used; in each case the result is $\dfrac{2}{3}\mathbf{i} + \dfrac{1}{3}\mathbf{j} - \dfrac{2}{3}\mathbf{k}$.

3. **(a)** Use an upward unit normal to get $\mathbf{n} = -\dfrac{2}{\sqrt{21}}\mathbf{i} - \dfrac{4}{\sqrt{21}}\mathbf{j} + \dfrac{1}{\sqrt{21}}\mathbf{k}$.

   (b) Use an upward unit normal to get $\mathbf{n} = \dfrac{3}{5\sqrt{2}}\mathbf{i} - \dfrac{4}{5\sqrt{2}}\mathbf{j} + \dfrac{1}{\sqrt{2}}\mathbf{k}$.

   (c) Use a downward unit normal with $z = -\sqrt{25 - x^2}$ to get $\mathbf{n} = \dfrac{3}{5}\mathbf{i} - \dfrac{4}{5}\mathbf{k}$.

4. **(a)** Use a forward unit normal with $x = y^2$ to get $\mathbf{n} = \dfrac{1}{\sqrt{5}}\mathbf{i} - \dfrac{2}{\sqrt{5}}\mathbf{j}$.

   (b) Use a backward unit normal with $x = \sqrt{z^2 - y}$ to get $\mathbf{n} = -\dfrac{2}{\sqrt{21}}\mathbf{i} - \dfrac{1}{\sqrt{21}}\mathbf{j} + \dfrac{4}{\sqrt{21}}\mathbf{k}$.

   (c) Use a downward unit normal with $z = -\sqrt{x^2 - y^2}$ to get $\mathbf{n} = -\dfrac{\sqrt{2}}{2}\mathbf{i} - \dfrac{1}{2}\mathbf{j} - \dfrac{1}{2}\mathbf{k}$.

5. R is the circular region enclosed by $x^2 + y^2 = 1$;

$$\iint\limits_{\sigma} \mathbf{F} \cdot \mathbf{n}\, dS = \iint\limits_{R} (2x^2 + 2y^2 + 2z)dA = 2\iint\limits_{R} dA = (2)(\text{area of } R) = 2\pi.$$

6. With $z = 1 - x - y$, R is the triangular region enclosed by $x + y = 1$, $x = 0$ and $y = 0$; use upward normals to get

$$\iint\limits_{\sigma} \mathbf{F} \cdot \mathbf{n}\, dS = 2\iint\limits_{R} (x + y + z)dA = 2\iint\limits_{R} dA = (2)(\text{area of } R) = 1.$$

7. R is the circular region enclosed by $x^2 + y^2 = 1$;

$$\iint\limits_{\sigma} \mathbf{F} \cdot \mathbf{n}\, dS\ \lim_{r_0 \to 1^-} \iint\limits_{R_{r_0}} z^2\, dA = \lim_{r_0 \to 1^-} \iint\limits_{R_{r_0}} (1 - x^2 - y^2)dA$$

where R_{r_0} is the region enclosed by $x^2 + y^2 = r_0^2$ with r_0 slightly less than 1 because

$-\dfrac{\partial z}{\partial x}\mathbf{i} - \dfrac{\partial z}{\partial y}\mathbf{j} + \mathbf{k}$ is not defined along the boundary $x^2 + y^2 = 1$, so

$$\iint\limits_{\sigma} \mathbf{F} \cdot \mathbf{n}\, dS\ \lim_{r_0 \to 1^-} \int_0^{2\pi} \int_0^{r_0} (1 - r^2)r\, dr\, d\theta = \lim_{r_0 \to 1^-} 2\pi \left(\frac{1}{2}r_0^2 - \frac{1}{4}r_0^4\right) = \frac{\pi}{2}.$$

8. With $z = \dfrac{1}{2}(6 - 6x - 3y)$, R is the triangular region enclosed by $2x + y = 2$, $x = 0$, and $y = 0$;

$$\iint\limits_{\sigma} \mathbf{F} \cdot \mathbf{n}\, dS = \iint\limits_{R} \left(3x^2 + \frac{3}{2}yx + zx\right) dA = 3\iint\limits_{R} x\, dA = 3\int_0^1 \int_0^{2-2x} x\, dy\, dx = 1.$$

9. R is the circular region enclosed by $x^2 + y^2 = 9$;

$$\iint\limits_{\sigma} \mathbf{F} \cdot \mathbf{n}\, dS = \iint\limits_{R} \left(\frac{x^2}{\sqrt{9 - x^2 - y^2}} + \frac{y^2}{\sqrt{9 - x^2 - y^2}} + z\right) dA$$

$$= 9\iint\limits_{R} \frac{1}{\sqrt{9 - x^2 - y^2}} dA = \lim_{r_0 \to 3^-} 9 \int_0^{2\pi} \int_0^{r_0} \frac{r}{\sqrt{9 - r^2}} dr\, d\theta$$

$$= \lim_{r_0 \to 3^-} 18\pi(3 - \sqrt{9 - r_0^2}) = 54\pi.$$

10. R is the circular region enclosed by $x^2 + y^2 = 1$;

$$\iint_\sigma \mathbf{F} \cdot \mathbf{n}\, dS = \iint_R \left(\frac{x}{\sqrt{x^2+y^2}} + \frac{y}{\sqrt{x^2+y^2}} - 1 \right) dA$$

$$= \iint_R \frac{x + y - \sqrt{x^2+y^2}}{\sqrt{x^2+y^2}}\, dA$$

$$= \lim_{r_0 \to 0+} \int_0^{2\pi} \int_{r_0}^1 (r\cos\theta + r\sin\theta - r)\, dr\, d\theta = \lim_{r_0 \to 0+} \pi(r_0^2 - 1) = -\pi.$$

11. R is the annular region enclosed by $x^2 + y^2 = 1$ and $x^2 + y^2 = 4$;

$$\iint_\sigma \mathbf{F} \cdot \mathbf{n}\, dS = \iint_R \left(-\frac{x^2}{\sqrt{x^2+y^2}} - \frac{y^2}{\sqrt{x^2+y^2}} + 2z \right) dA$$

$$= \iint_R \sqrt{x^2+y^2}\, dA = \int_0^{2\pi} \int_1^2 r^2\, dr\, d\theta = \frac{14\pi}{3}.$$

12. R is the circular region enclosed by $x^2 + y^2 = 4$;

$$\iint_\sigma \mathbf{F} \cdot \mathbf{n}\, dS = \iint_R (2y^2 - 1)\, dA = \int_0^{2\pi} \int_0^2 (2r^2 \sin^2\theta - 1)\, r\, dr\, d\theta = 4\pi.$$

13. R is the circular region enclosed by $x^2 + y^2 - y = 0$; $\displaystyle\iint_\sigma \mathbf{F} \cdot \mathbf{n}\, dS = \iint_R (-x)\, dA$, but in polar

coordinates the boundary $x^2 + y^2 - y = 0$ is $r = \sin\theta$, so

$$\iint_\sigma \mathbf{F} \cdot \mathbf{n}\, dS = -\int_0^\pi \int_0^{\sin\theta} r^2 \cos\theta\, dr\, d\theta = 0.$$

14. Divide the surface into two parts σ_1 and σ_2 corresponding to $z = \sqrt{1 - x^2}$ and $z = -\sqrt{1 - x^2}$, respectively. For each part R is the rectangular region enclosed by $x = -1$, $x = 1$, $y = 1$, and $y = -1$; σ_1 is oriented by upward normals and σ_2 by downward normals so

$$\iint_{\sigma_1} \mathbf{F} \cdot \mathbf{n}\, dS = \iint_R \left(\frac{x^2}{\sqrt{1-x^2}} + z \right) dA = \iint_R \frac{1}{\sqrt{1-x^2}}\, dA$$

and, using the symmetry of R and the integrand,

$$\iint_{\sigma_1} \mathbf{F} \cdot \mathbf{n}\, dS = \lim_{x_0 \to 1-} 2\int_0^{x_0} \int_{-2}^1 \frac{1}{\sqrt{1-x^2}}\, dy\, dx = \lim_{x_0 \to 1-} 6\sin^{-1}(x_0) = 3\pi;$$

similarly $\displaystyle\iint_{\sigma_2} \mathbf{F} \cdot \mathbf{n}\, dS = \iint_R \frac{1}{\sqrt{1-x^2}}\, dA = 3\pi$ so $\displaystyle\iint_\sigma \mathbf{F} \cdot \mathbf{n}\, dS = 3\pi + 3\pi = 6\pi.$

15. Divide the surface into two parts σ_1 and σ_2 corresponding to $z = \sqrt{a^2 - x^2 - y^2}$ and $z = -\sqrt{a^2 - x^2 - y^2}$, respectively. For each part R is the circular region enclosed by $x^2 + y^2 = a^2$; σ_1 is oriented by upward normals and σ_2 by downward normals so

$$\iint_{\sigma_1} \mathbf{F} \cdot \mathbf{n}\, dS = \iint_R \left(\frac{x^2}{\sqrt{a^2 - x^2 - y^2}} + \frac{y^2}{\sqrt{a^2 - x^2 - y^2}} + z \right) dA$$

$$= a^2 \iint_R \frac{1}{\sqrt{a^2 - x^2 - y^2}}\, dA = \lim_{r_0 \to a^-} a^2 \int_0^{2\pi} \int_0^{r_0} \frac{r}{\sqrt{a^2 - r^2}}\, dr\, d\theta$$

$$= \lim_{r_0 \to a^-} 2\pi a^2 (a - \sqrt{a^2 - r_0^2}) = 2\pi a^3;$$

similarly $\displaystyle \iint_{\sigma_2} \mathbf{F} \cdot \mathbf{n}\, dS = a^2 \iint_R \frac{1}{\sqrt{a^2 - x^2 - y^2}}\, dA = 2\pi a^3$ so

$$\iint_{\sigma} \mathbf{F} \cdot \mathbf{n}\, dS = 2\pi a^3 + 2\pi a^3 = 4\pi a^3.$$

16. In each part, divide σ into the six surfaces

$\sigma_1 : x = -1$ with $|y| \le 1$, $|z| \le 1$, and $\mathbf{n} = -\mathbf{i}$, $\sigma_2 : x = 1$ with $|y| \le 1$, $|z| \le 1$, and $\mathbf{n} = \mathbf{i}$,

$\sigma_3 : y = -1$ with $|x| \le 1$, $|z| \le 1$, and $\mathbf{n} = -\mathbf{j}$, $\sigma_4 : y = 1$ with $|x| \le 1$, $|z| \le 1$, and $\mathbf{n} = \mathbf{j}$,

$\sigma_5 : z = -1$ with $|x| \le 1$, $|y| \le 1$, and $\mathbf{n} = -\mathbf{k}$, $\sigma_6 : z = 1$ with $|x| \le 1$, $|y| \le 1$, and $\mathbf{n} = \mathbf{k}$,

(a) $\displaystyle \iint_{\sigma_1} \mathbf{F} \cdot \mathbf{n}\, dS = \iint_{\sigma_1} dS = 4$, $\displaystyle \iint_{\sigma_2} \mathbf{F} \cdot \mathbf{n}\, dS = \iint_{\sigma_2} dS = 4$, and $\displaystyle \iint_{\sigma_i} \mathbf{F} \cdot \mathbf{n}\, dS = 0$ for

$i = 3, 4, 5, 6$ so $\displaystyle \iint_{\sigma} \mathbf{F} \cdot \mathbf{n}\, dS = 4 + 4 + 0 + 0 + 0 + 0 = 8.$

(b) $\displaystyle \iint_{\sigma_1} \mathbf{F} \cdot \mathbf{n}\, dS = \iint_{\sigma_1} dS = 4$, similarly $\displaystyle \iint_{\sigma_i} \mathbf{F} \cdot \mathbf{n}\, dS = 4$ for $i = 2, 3, 4, 5, 6$ so

$$\iint_{\sigma} \mathbf{F} \cdot \mathbf{n}\, dS = 4 + 4 + 4 + 4 + 4 + 4 = 24.$$

(c) $\displaystyle \iint_{\sigma_1} \mathbf{F} \cdot \mathbf{n}\, dS = -\iint_{\sigma_1} dS = -4$, $\displaystyle \iint_{\sigma_2} \mathbf{F} \cdot \mathbf{n}\, dS = 4$, similarly $\displaystyle \iint_{\sigma_i} \mathbf{F} \cdot \mathbf{n}\, dS = -4$ for

$i = 3, 5$ and $\displaystyle \iint_{\sigma_i} \mathbf{F} \cdot \mathbf{n}\, dS = 4$ for $i = 4, 6$ so

$$\iint_{\sigma} \mathbf{F} \cdot \mathbf{n}\, dS = (-4) + (4) + (-4) + (4) + (-4) + (4) = 0.$$

17. Replace $\mathbf{n}$ by $-\mathbf{n}$ to reverse the orientation of σ, so $\iint_\sigma \mathbf{F} \cdot (-\mathbf{n}) dS = - \iint_\sigma \mathbf{F} \cdot \mathbf{n} \, dS.$

18. The derivation of (6) is the same as for (5) except that it is done with the general equation $z = z(x,y)$ in mind. For (7), we use the downward normal so

$$\iint_\sigma \mathbf{F} \cdot \mathbf{n} \, dS = \iint_R \mathbf{F} \cdot \left[\frac{\frac{\partial z}{\partial x}\mathbf{i} + \frac{\partial z}{\partial y}\mathbf{j} - \mathbf{k}}{\sqrt{\left(\frac{\partial z}{\partial x}\right)^2 + \left(\frac{\partial z}{\partial y}\right)^2 + 1}} \right] \sqrt{\left(\frac{\partial z}{\partial x}\right)^2 + \left(\frac{\partial z}{\partial x}\right)^2 + 1} \, dA$$

$$= \iint_R \mathbf{F} \cdot \left(\frac{\partial z}{\partial x}\mathbf{i} + \frac{\partial z}{\partial y}\mathbf{j} - \mathbf{k} \right) dA.$$

19. (a) $\iint_R \mathbf{F} \cdot \left(\mathbf{i} - \frac{\partial x}{\partial y}\mathbf{j} - \frac{\partial x}{\partial z}\mathbf{k} \right) dA$, σ oriented by forward normals, and

$\iint_R \mathbf{F} \cdot \left(-\mathbf{i} + \frac{\partial x}{\partial y}\mathbf{j} + \frac{\partial x}{\partial z}\mathbf{k} \right) dA$, σ oriented by backward normals where R is the projection of σ onto the yz-plane.

(b) $\iint_R \mathbf{F} \cdot \left(-\frac{\partial y}{\partial x}\mathbf{i} + \mathbf{j} - \frac{\partial y}{\partial z}\mathbf{k} \right) dA$, σ oriented by right normals, and

$\iint_R \mathbf{F} \cdot \left(\frac{\partial y}{\partial x}\mathbf{i} - \mathbf{j} + \frac{\partial y}{\partial z}\mathbf{k} \right) dA$, σ oriented by left normals, where R is the projection of σ onto the xz-plane.

20. R is the semicircular region in the yz-plane enclosed by $z = \sqrt{1 - y^2}$ and $z = 0$;

$$\iint_\sigma \mathbf{F} \cdot \mathbf{n} \, dS = \iint_R (-y - 2yz + 16z) dA = \int_{-1}^{1} \int_0^{\sqrt{1-y^2}} (-y - 2yz + 16z) dz \, dy = \frac{32}{3}.$$

21. R is the circular region in the xz-plane enclosed by $x^2 + z^2 = 1$;

$$\iint_\sigma \mathbf{F} \cdot \mathbf{n} \, dS = \iint_R \left(\frac{x^2}{\sqrt{1 - x^2 - z^2}} + y + \frac{z^2}{\sqrt{1 - x^2 - z^2}} \right) dA = \iint_R \frac{1}{\sqrt{1 - x^2 - z^2}} dA,$$

use polar coordinates in the xz-plane with $x = r\cos\theta$ and $z = r\sin\theta$ to get

$$\iint_\sigma \mathbf{F} \cdot \mathbf{n} \, dS = \lim_{r_0 \to 1^-} \int_0^{2\pi} \int_0^{r_0} \frac{r}{\sqrt{1 - r^2}} dr \, d\theta = \lim_{r_0 \to 1^-} 2\pi(1 - \sqrt{1 - r_0^2}) = 2\pi$$

22. **(a)** The vectors do not vary continuously along the curve because there is an abrupt change in direciton of the vectors as we cross the vertical line.

(b) Any attempt to construct an orientation results in vectors that do not vary continuously along the curve.

EXERCISE SET 18.6

1. $\operatorname{div} \mathbf{F} = z^3 + 8y^3 x^2 + 10zy$

2. $\operatorname{div} \mathbf{F} = 0$

3. $\operatorname{div} \mathbf{F} = ye^{xy} + \sin y + 2\sin z \cos z$

4. $\operatorname{div} \mathbf{F} = \dfrac{2}{\sqrt{x^2 + y^2 + z^2}}$

5. $\operatorname{div} \mathbf{F} = \dfrac{1}{x} + xze^{xyz} + \dfrac{x}{x^2 + z^2}$

6. G is the spherical solid enclosed by σ;

$$\iiint\limits_{G} \operatorname{div} \mathbf{F}\, dV = 6 \iiint\limits_{G} dV = (6)(\text{volume of sphere}) = 6\left[\frac{4}{3}\pi(3)^3\right] = 216\pi.$$

7. G is the cube; $\displaystyle\iiint\limits_{G} \operatorname{div} \mathbf{F}\, dV = 8 \iiint\limits_{G} dV = (8)(\text{volume of cube}) = (8)(1) = 8.$

8. G is the spherical solid enclosed by σ; $\displaystyle\iiint\limits_{G} \operatorname{div} \mathbf{F}\, dV = \iiint\limits_{G} 0\, dV = 0 \iiint\limits_{G} dV = 0.$

9. G is the cylindrical solid;

$$\iiint\limits_{G} \operatorname{div} \mathbf{F}\, dV = 3 \iiint\limits_{G} dV = (3)(\text{volume of cylinder}) = (3)[\pi a^2(1)] = 3\pi a^2.$$

10. G is the solid bounded by $z = 1 - x^2 - y^2$ and the xy-plane;

$$\iiint\limits_{G} \operatorname{div} \mathbf{F}\, dV = 3 \iiint\limits_{G} dV = 3 \int_0^{2\pi} \int_0^1 \int_0^{1-r^2} r\, dz\, dr\, d\theta = \frac{3\pi}{2}.$$

11. G is the cylindrical solid;

$$\iiint\limits_{G} \operatorname{div} \mathbf{F}\, dV = 3 \iiint\limits_{G} (x^2 + y^2 + z^2)dV = 3 \int_0^{2\pi} \int_0^2 \int_0^3 (r^2 + z^2)r\, dz\, dr\, d\theta = 180\pi.$$

12. G is the hemispherical solid bounded by $z = \sqrt{4 - x^2 - y^2}$ and the xy-plane;

$$\iiint\limits_G \operatorname{div} \mathbf{F}\, dV = 3 \iiint\limits_G (x^2 + y^2 + z^2)\,dV = 3 \int_0^{2\pi} \int_0^{\pi/2} \int_0^2 \rho^4 \sin\phi\, d\rho\, d\phi\, d\theta = \frac{192\pi}{5}.$$

13. G is the tetrahedron; $\displaystyle \iiint\limits_G \operatorname{div} \mathbf{F}\, dV = \iiint\limits_G x\, dV = \int_0^1 \int_0^{1-x} \int_0^{1-x-y} x\, dz\, dy\, dx = \frac{1}{24}.$

14. G is the hemispherical solid;

$$\iiint\limits_G \operatorname{div} \mathbf{F}\, dV = 5 \iiint\limits_G z\, dV = 5 \int_0^{2\pi} \int_0^{\pi/2} \int_0^a \rho^3 \sin\phi \cos\phi\, d\rho\, d\phi\, d\theta = \frac{5\pi a^4}{4}.$$

15. G is the conical solid;

$$\iiint\limits_G \operatorname{div} \mathbf{F}\, dV = 2 \iiint\limits_G (x + y + z)\,dV = 2 \int_0^{2\pi} \int_0^1 \int_r^1 (r\cos\theta + r\sin\theta + z)r\, dz\, dr\, d\theta = \frac{\pi}{2}.$$

16. G is the solid bounded by $z = 2x$ and $z = x^2 + y^2$;

$$\iiint\limits_G \operatorname{div} \mathbf{F}\, dV = \iiint\limits_G dV = 2 \int_0^{\pi/2} \int_0^{2\cos\theta} \int_{r^2}^{2r\cos\theta} r\, dz\, dr\, d\theta = \frac{\pi}{2}.$$

17. G is the solid bounded by $z = 4 - x^2$, $y + z = 5$, and the coordinate planes;

$$\iiint\limits_G \operatorname{div} \mathbf{F}\, dV = 4 \iiint\limits_G x^2\, dV = 4 \int_{-2}^2 \int_0^{4-x^2} \int_0^{5-z} x^2\, dy\, dz\, dx = \frac{4608}{35}.$$

18. Divide σ into six parts;

$\sigma_1 : x = 0$ with $0 \le y \le 1, 0 \le z \le 1$, and $\mathbf{n} = -\mathbf{i}$,

$\sigma_2 : x = 1$ with $0 \le y \le 1, 0 \le z \le 1$, and $\mathbf{n} = \mathbf{i}$,

$\sigma_3 : y = 0$ with $0 \le x \le 1, 0 \le z \le 1$, and $\mathbf{n} = -\mathbf{j}$,

$\sigma_4 : y = 1$ with $0 \le x \le 1, 0 \le z \le 1$, and $\mathbf{n} = \mathbf{j}$,

$\sigma_5 : z = 0$ with $0 \le x \le 1, 0 \le y \le 1$, and $\mathbf{n} = -\mathbf{k}$,

$\sigma_6 : z = 1$ with $0 \le x \le 1, 0 \le y \le 1$, and $\mathbf{n} = \mathbf{k}$,

$\displaystyle \iint\limits_{\sigma_i} \mathbf{F} \cdot \mathbf{n}\, dS = 0$ for $i = 1, 3, 5$ and $\displaystyle \iint\limits_{\sigma_i} \mathbf{F} \cdot \mathbf{n}\, dS = 1$ for $i = 2, 4, 6$ so

$$\iint\limits_{\sigma} \mathbf{F} \cdot \mathbf{n} \, dS = 0 + 1 + 0 + 1 + 0 + 1 = 3;$$

$$\iiint\limits_{G} \text{div } \mathbf{F} \, dV = 2 \iiint\limits_{G} (x + y + z) dV = 2 \int_0^1 \int_0^1 \int_0^1 (x + y + z) dz \, dy \, dx = 3.$$

19. Refer to Exercise 15 in 18.5 where it is shown that $\iint\limits_{\sigma} \mathbf{F} \cdot \mathbf{n} \, dS = 4\pi a^3$;

$$\iiint\limits_{G} \text{div } \mathbf{F} \, dV = 3 \iiint\limits_{G} dV = (3)(\text{volume of sphere}) = (3)\left(\frac{4}{3}\pi a^3\right) = 4\pi a^3.$$

20. Divide σ into four parts;

$\sigma_1 : z = 0$ with $x^2 + y^2 \leq 9$ and $\mathbf{n} = -\mathbf{k}$, $\sigma_2 : z = 5$ with $x^2 + y^2 \leq 9$ and $\mathbf{n} = \mathbf{k}$,

$\sigma_3 : y = \sqrt{9 - x^2}$ and $\sigma_4 : y = -\sqrt{9 - x^2}$, both with $0 \leq z \leq 5$.

$$\iint\limits_{\sigma_1} \mathbf{F} \cdot \mathbf{n} \, dS = \iint\limits_{\sigma_1} (-x) dS = -\int_0^{2\pi} \int_0^3 r^2 \cos\theta \, dr \, d\theta = 0,$$

$$\iint\limits_{\sigma_2} \mathbf{F} \cdot \mathbf{n} \, dS = \iint\limits_{\sigma_2} (5 + x) dS = \int_0^{2\pi} \int_0^3 (5 + r\cos\theta) r \, dr \, d\theta = 45\pi,$$

$$\iint\limits_{\sigma_3} \mathbf{F} \cdot \mathbf{n} \, dS = \iint\limits_{R} \left(\frac{9}{\sqrt{9 - x^2}} + x + z\right) dA = \lim_{x_0 \to 3^-} \int_0^5 \int_{-x_0}^{x_0} \left(\frac{9}{\sqrt{9 - x^2}} + x + z\right) dx \, dz$$

$$= 45\pi + 75,$$

similarly $\iint\limits_{\sigma_4} \mathbf{F} \cdot \mathbf{n} \, dS = \iint\limits_{R} \left(\frac{9}{\sqrt{9 - x^2}} - x - z\right) dA = 45\pi - 75$

so $\iint\limits_{\sigma} \mathbf{F} \cdot \mathbf{n} \, dS = (0) + (45\pi) + (45\pi + 75) + (45\pi - 75) = 135\pi;$

$$\iiint\limits_{G} \text{div } \mathbf{F} \, dV = 3 \iiint\limits_{G} dV = (3)(\text{volume of cylinder}) = (3)[\pi(3)^2(5)] = 135\pi.$$

21. **(a)** Let $\mathbf{F} = f_1\mathbf{i} + g_1\mathbf{j} + h_1\mathbf{k}$ and $\mathbf{G} = f_2\mathbf{i} + g_2\mathbf{j} + h_2\mathbf{k}$ then

$\mathbf{F} + \mathbf{G} = (f_1 + f_2)\mathbf{i} + (g_1 + g_2)\mathbf{j} + (h_1 + h_2)\mathbf{k}$ and

$$\text{div } (\mathbf{F} + \mathbf{G}) = \frac{\partial}{\partial x}(f_1 + f_2) + \frac{\partial}{\partial y}(g_1 + g_2) + \frac{\partial}{\partial z}(h_1 + h_2)$$

$$= \frac{\partial f_1}{\partial x} + \frac{\partial f_2}{\partial x} + \frac{\partial g_1}{\partial y} + \frac{\partial g_2}{\partial y} + \frac{\partial h_1}{\partial z} + \frac{\partial h_2}{\partial z}$$

$$= \left(\frac{\partial f_1}{\partial x} + \frac{\partial g_1}{\partial y} + \frac{\partial h_1}{\partial z}\right) + \left(\frac{\partial f_2}{\partial x} + \frac{\partial g_2}{\partial y} + \frac{\partial h_2}{\partial z}\right) = \text{div } \mathbf{F} + \text{div } \mathbf{G}$$

(b) Let $\mathbf{F} = f_1\mathbf{i} + g_1\mathbf{j} + h_1\mathbf{k}$ then $f\mathbf{F} = ff_1\mathbf{i} + fg_1\mathbf{j} + fh_1\mathbf{k}$ and

$$\text{div } (f\mathbf{F}) = \frac{\partial}{\partial x}(ff_1) + \frac{\partial}{\partial y}(fg_1) + \frac{\partial}{\partial z}(fh_1)$$

$$= f\frac{\partial f_1}{\partial x} + \frac{\partial f}{\partial x}f_1 + f\frac{\partial g_1}{\partial y} + \frac{\partial f}{\partial y}g_1 + f\frac{\partial h_1}{\partial z} + \frac{\partial f}{\partial z}h_1$$

$$= f\left(\frac{\partial f_1}{\partial x} + \frac{\partial g_1}{\partial y} + \frac{\partial h_1}{\partial z}\right) + \left(\frac{\partial f}{\partial x}f_1 + \frac{\partial f}{\partial y}g_1 + \frac{\partial f}{\partial z}h_1\right) = f \text{ div } \mathbf{F} + (\nabla f) \cdot \mathbf{F}.$$

22. $\iint\limits_{\sigma} \mathbf{F} \cdot \mathbf{n}\, dS = \iiint\limits_{G} \text{div } \mathbf{F}\, dV = 3\iiint\limits_{G} dV = 3\, \text{vol}(G)$ so $\text{vol}(G) = \dfrac{1}{3}\iint\limits_{\sigma} \mathbf{F} \cdot \mathbf{n}\, dS.$

23. Let σ be the surface of the cylindrical solid G bounded by $x^2 + y^2 = a^2$, $z = 0$ and $z = h$. Divide σ into four parts;

$\sigma_1 : z = 0$ with $x^2 + y^2 \leq a^2$ and $\mathbf{n} = -\mathbf{k}$, $\sigma_2 : z = h$ with $x^2 + y^2 \leq a^2$ and $\mathbf{n} = \mathbf{k}$,

$\sigma_3 : y = \sqrt{a^2 - x^2}$ and $\sigma_4 : y = -\sqrt{a^2 - x^2}$, both with $0 \leq z \leq h$.

$$\iint\limits_{\sigma_1} \mathbf{F} \cdot \mathbf{n}\, dS = \iint\limits_{\sigma_1} 0\, dS = 0, \quad \iint\limits_{\sigma_2} \mathbf{F} \cdot \mathbf{n}\, dS = h\iint\limits_{\sigma_2} dS = \pi a^2 h,$$

$$\iint\limits_{\sigma_3} \mathbf{F} \cdot \mathbf{n}\, dS = \iint\limits_{\sigma_4} \mathbf{F} \cdot \mathbf{n}\, dS = a^2\iint\limits_{R} \frac{1}{\sqrt{a^2 - x^2}}\, dA$$

$$= \lim_{x_0 \to a^-} a^2\int_0^h\int_{-x_0}^{x_0} \frac{1}{\sqrt{a^2 - x^2}}\, dx\, dz = \lim_{x_0 \to a^-}\left(2a^2 h \sin^{-1}\frac{x_0}{a}\right) = \pi a^2 h \text{ so}$$

$$\iint\limits_{\sigma} \mathbf{F} \cdot \mathbf{n}\, dS = 0 + \pi a^2 h + \pi a^2 h + \pi a^2 h = 3\pi a^2 h \text{ and } \text{vol}(G) = \frac{1}{3}(3\pi a^2 h) = \pi a^2 h.$$

24. $\iint\limits_{\sigma} \mathbf{F} \cdot \mathbf{n}\, dS = \iiint\limits_{G} \text{div } \mathbf{F}\, dV = \iiint\limits_{G} 0\, dV = 0$

EXERCISE SET 18.7

1. $\operatorname{curl} \mathbf{F} = 0$

2. $\operatorname{curl} \mathbf{F} = 5z^2\mathbf{i} + 3xz^2\mathbf{j} + 4xy^4\mathbf{k}$

3. $\operatorname{curl} \mathbf{F} = -xe^{xy}\mathbf{k}$

4. $\operatorname{curl} \mathbf{F} = (40x^2z^4 - 12xy^3)\mathbf{i} + (14y^3z + 3y^4)\mathbf{j} - (16xz^5 + 21y^2z^2)\mathbf{k}$

5. $\operatorname{curl} \mathbf{F} = -xye^{xyz}\mathbf{i} + \dfrac{z}{x^2 + z^2}\mathbf{j} + yze^{xyz}\mathbf{k}$

6. $\operatorname{curl} \mathbf{F} = x\mathbf{i} + (x - y)\mathbf{j} + 6xy^2\mathbf{k}$;

$$\iint_\sigma (\operatorname{curl} \mathbf{F}) \cdot \mathbf{n}\, dS = \iint_R (x - y - 6xy^2)dA = \int_0^1 \int_0^3 (x - y - 6xy^2)dy\, dx = -30.$$

7. $\operatorname{curl} \mathbf{F} = 2\mathbf{i} + 3\mathbf{j} + 4\mathbf{k}$;

$$\iint_\sigma (\operatorname{curl} \mathbf{F}) \cdot \mathbf{n}\, dS = \iint_R (4x + 6y + 4)dA = \int_0^{2\pi} \int_0^2 (4r\cos\theta + 6r\sin\theta + 4)r\, dr\, d\theta = 16\pi.$$

8. $\operatorname{curl} \mathbf{F} = -4\mathbf{i} - 6\mathbf{j} + 6y\mathbf{k}$, $z = y/2$ oriented with upward normals, R is the triangular region in the xy-plane enclosed by $x + y = 2$, $x = 0$, and $y = 0$;

$$\iint_\sigma (\operatorname{curl} \mathbf{F}) \cdot \mathbf{n}\, dS = \iint_R (3 + 6y)dA = \int_0^2 \int_0^{2-x} (3 + 6y)dy\, dx = 14.$$

9. $\operatorname{curl} \mathbf{F} = x\mathbf{k}$, take σ as part of the plane $z = y$ oriented with upward normals, R is the circular region in the xy-plane enclosed by $x^2 + y^2 - y = 0$;

$$\iint_\sigma (\operatorname{curl} \mathbf{F}) \cdot \mathbf{n}\, dS = \iint_R x\, dA = \int_0^\pi \int_0^{\sin\theta} r^2 \cos\theta\, dr\, d\theta = 0.$$

10. $\operatorname{curl} \mathbf{F} = -y\mathbf{i} - z\mathbf{j} - x\mathbf{k}$, $z = 1 - x - y$ oriented with upward normals, R is the triangular region in the xy-plane enclosed by $x + y = 1$, $x = 0$ and $y = 0$;

$$\iint_\sigma (\operatorname{curl} \mathbf{F}) \cdot \mathbf{n}\, dS = \iint_R (-y - z - x)dA = -\iint_R dA = -\frac{1}{2}(1)(1) = -\frac{1}{2}.$$

11. $\operatorname{curl} \mathbf{F} = \mathbf{i} + \mathbf{j} + \mathbf{k}$, take σ as part of the plane $z = 0$ with $x^2 + y^2 \le a^2$ and $\mathbf{n} = \mathbf{k}$;

$$\iint_\sigma (\operatorname{curl} \mathbf{F}) \cdot \mathbf{n}\, dS = \iint_\sigma dS = \text{ area of circle } = \pi a^2.$$

12. curl $\mathbf{F} = \mathbf{i} + \mathbf{j} + \mathbf{k}$, take σ as part of the plane $z = 1/\sqrt{2}$ with $x^2 + y^2 \leq 1/2$ and $\mathbf{n} = \mathbf{k}$.

$$\iint_\sigma (\text{curl } \mathbf{F}) \cdot \mathbf{n}\, dS = \iint_\sigma dS = \text{ area of circle } = \frac{\pi}{2}.$$

13. If σ is oriented with upward normals then C consists of three parts parametrized as
$C_1 : \mathbf{r}(t) = (1-t)\mathbf{i} + t\mathbf{j}$ for $0 \leq t \leq 1$, $C_2 : \mathbf{r}(t) = (1-t)\mathbf{j} + t\mathbf{k}$ for $0 \leq t \leq 1$,
$C_3 : \mathbf{r}(t) = t\mathbf{i} + (1-t)\mathbf{k}$ for $0 \leq t \leq 1$.

$$\int_{C_1} \mathbf{F} \cdot d\mathbf{r} = \int_{C_2} \mathbf{F} \cdot d\mathbf{r} = \int_{C_3} \mathbf{F} \cdot d\mathbf{r} = \int_0^1 (3t-1)dt = \frac{1}{2} \text{ so}$$

$$\int_C \mathbf{F} \cdot d\mathbf{r} = \frac{1}{2} + \frac{1}{2} + \frac{1}{2} = \frac{3}{2}. \text{ curl } \mathbf{F} = \mathbf{i} + \mathbf{j} + \mathbf{k}, \ z = 1 - x - y, \ R \text{ is the triangular region in}$$
the xy-plane enclosed by $x + y = 1$, $x = 0$, and $y = 0$;

$$\iint_\sigma (\text{curl } \mathbf{F}) \cdot \mathbf{n}\, dS = 3 \iint_R dA = (3)(\text{area of } R) = (3)\left[\frac{1}{2}(1)(1)\right] = \frac{3}{2}.$$

14. If σ is oriented with upward normals then C can be parametrized as $\mathbf{r}(t) = \cos t\, \mathbf{i} + \sin t\, \mathbf{j} + \mathbf{k}$
for $0 \leq t \leq 2\pi$.

$$\int_C \mathbf{F} \cdot d\mathbf{r} = \int_0^{2\pi} (\sin^2 t \cos t - \cos^2 t \sin t)dt = 0;$$

$$\text{curl } \mathbf{F} = 0 \text{ so } \iint_\sigma (\text{curl } \mathbf{F}) \cdot \mathbf{n}\, dS = \iint_\sigma 0\, dS = 0.$$

15. If σ is oriented with upward normals then C can be parametrized as $\mathbf{r}(t) = a\cos t\, \mathbf{i} + a\sin t\, \mathbf{j}$
for $0 \leq t \leq 2\pi$.

$$\int_C \mathbf{F} \cdot d\mathbf{r} = \int_0^{2\pi} 0\, dt = 0; \text{ curl } \mathbf{F} = 0 \text{ so } \iint_\sigma (\text{curl } \mathbf{F}) \cdot \mathbf{n}\, dS = \iint_\sigma 0\, dS = 0.$$

16. If σ is oriented with upward normals then C can be parametrized as $\mathbf{r}(t) = 3\cos t\, \mathbf{i} + 3\sin t\, \mathbf{j}$
for $0 \leq t \leq 2\pi$.

$$\int_C \mathbf{F} \cdot d\mathbf{r} = \int_0^{2\pi} (9\sin^2 t + 9\cos^2 t)dt = 9\int_0^{2\pi} dt = 18\pi.$$

curl $\mathbf{F} = -2\mathbf{i} + 2\mathbf{j} + 2\mathbf{k}$, R is the circular region in the xy-plane enclosed by $x^2 + y^2 = 9$;

$$\iint_\sigma (\text{curl } \mathbf{F}) \cdot \mathbf{n}\, dS = \iint_R (-4x + 4y + 2)dA = \int_0^{2\pi}\int_0^3 (-4r\cos\theta + 4r\sin\theta + 2)r\, dr\, d\theta = 18\pi.$$

17. Take σ as part of the plane $z = 0$ for $x^2 + y^2 \leq 1$ with $\mathbf{n} = \mathbf{k}$; $\mathbf{F} = z^2\mathbf{i} + 2x\mathbf{j} - y^3\mathbf{k}$,

curl $\mathbf{F} = -3y^2\mathbf{i} + 2z\mathbf{j} + 2\mathbf{k}$,

$$\iint_\sigma (\text{curl } \mathbf{F}) \cdot \mathbf{n}\, dS = 2 \iint_\sigma dS = (2)(\text{area of circle}) = (2)[\pi(1)^2] = 2\pi.$$

18. Take σ as part of the plane $x + y + z = a$ in the first octant, oriented with upward normals; $\mathbf{F} = y^2\mathbf{i} + z^2\mathbf{j} + x^2\mathbf{k}$, curl $\mathbf{F} = -2z\mathbf{i} - 2x\mathbf{j} - 2y\mathbf{k}$, R is the triangular region in the xy-plane enclosed by $x + y = a$, $x = 0$, and $y = 0$, so

$$\iint_\sigma (\text{curl } \mathbf{F}) \cdot \mathbf{n}\, dS = -2 \iint_R (x + y + z)dA = -2a \iint_R dA = (-2a)(\text{area of } R) = -a^3.$$

19. Let $\mathbf{F} = f\mathbf{i} + g\mathbf{j} + h\mathbf{k}$ then

$$\text{curl } \mathbf{F} = \left(\frac{\partial h}{\partial y} - \frac{\partial g}{\partial z}\right)\mathbf{i} + \left(\frac{\partial f}{\partial z} - \frac{\partial h}{\partial x}\right)\mathbf{j} + \left(\frac{\partial g}{\partial x} - \frac{\partial f}{\partial y}\right)\mathbf{k},$$

$$\text{div(curl } \mathbf{F}) = \frac{\partial^2 h}{\partial x \partial y} - \frac{\partial^2 g}{\partial x \partial z} + \frac{\partial^2 f}{\partial y \partial z} - \frac{\partial^2 h}{\partial y \partial x} + \frac{\partial^2 g}{\partial z \partial x} - \frac{\partial^2 f}{\partial z \partial y}$$

$$= \left(\frac{\partial^2 f}{\partial y \partial z} - \frac{\partial^2 f}{\partial z \partial y}\right) + \left(\frac{\partial^2 g}{\partial z \partial x} - \frac{\partial^2 g}{\partial x \partial z}\right) + \left(\frac{\partial^2 h}{\partial x \partial y} - \frac{\partial^2 h}{\partial y \partial x}\right)$$

but $\dfrac{\partial^2 f}{\partial y \partial z} = \dfrac{\partial^2 f}{\partial z \partial y}$, $\dfrac{\partial^2 g}{\partial z \partial x} = \dfrac{\partial^2 g}{\partial x \partial z}$, and $\dfrac{\partial^2 h}{\partial x \partial y} = \dfrac{\partial^2 h}{\partial y \partial x}$

because of the continuity assumptions so div(curl $\mathbf{F}$) = 0.

20. Let G be the spherical solid bounded by σ then by the Divergence Theorem

$$\iint_\sigma (\text{curl } \mathbf{F}) \cdot \mathbf{n}\, dS = \iiint_G \text{div(curl } \mathbf{F})dV = \iiint_G 0\, dV = 0.$$

21. **(a)** $\nabla f = \dfrac{\partial f}{\partial x}\mathbf{i} + \dfrac{\partial f}{\partial y}\mathbf{j} + \dfrac{\partial f}{\partial z}\mathbf{k}$,

$$\text{curl } (\nabla f) = \left(\frac{\partial^2 f}{\partial y \partial z} - \frac{\partial^2 f}{\partial z \partial y}\right)\mathbf{i} + \left(\frac{\partial^2 f}{\partial z \partial x} - \frac{\partial^2 f}{\partial x \partial z}\right)\mathbf{j} + \left(\frac{\partial^2 f}{\partial x \partial y} - \frac{\partial^2 f}{\partial y \partial x}\right)\mathbf{k}$$

but the continuity conditions imply equality of mixed second partial derivatives so curl $(\nabla f) = \mathbf{0}$.

(b) curl $(\nabla f + \text{curl } \mathbf{F}) = \text{curl } (\nabla f) + \text{curl(curl } \mathbf{F}) = \text{curl(curl } \mathbf{F})$ because curl $(\nabla f) = \mathbf{0}$ from part (a).

22. **(a)** By Stokes' Theorem $\displaystyle\iint_{\sigma_1} (\text{curl } \mathbf{F}) \cdot \mathbf{n}\, dS = \int_C \mathbf{F} \cdot d\mathbf{r}$ and $\displaystyle\iint_{\sigma_2} (\text{curl } \mathbf{F}) \cdot \mathbf{n}\, dS = \int_C \mathbf{F} \cdot d\mathbf{r}$

so the surface integrals are equal.

(b) C is the circle $x^2 + y^2 = a^2$ in the xy-plane with a counterclockwise orientation looking down the positive z-axis. Let σ_2 be the circular disk $x^2 + y^2 \le a^2$ in the xy-plane oriented with upward normals then, from the result in part (a),

$$\iint\limits_{\sigma} (\text{curl } \mathbf{F}) \cdot \mathbf{n}\, dS = \iint\limits_{\sigma_2} (\text{curl } \mathbf{F}) \cdot \mathbf{n}\, dS.$$

$\text{curl } \mathbf{F} = xz^2 e^{xy}\mathbf{i} - yz^2 e^{xy}\mathbf{j} = 0$ on σ_2 because $z = 0$ so

$$\iint\limits_{\sigma_2} (\text{curl } \mathbf{F}) \cdot \mathbf{n}\, dS = \iint\limits_{\sigma_2} 0\, dS = 0.$$

23. Let σ_1 and σ_2 be the upper and lower hemispheres oriented, respectively, by upward and downward normals so

$$\iint\limits_{\sigma} (\text{curl } \mathbf{F}) \cdot \mathbf{n}\, dS = \iint\limits_{\sigma_1} (\text{curl } \mathbf{F}) \cdot \mathbf{n}\, dS + \iint\limits_{\sigma_2} (\text{curl } \mathbf{F}) \cdot \mathbf{n}\, dS.$$

Let C be the boundary shared by σ_1 and σ_2 and suppose that C is positively oriented with respect to σ_1 and hence negatively oriented with respect to σ_2. Then by Stokes' Theorem

$$\iint\limits_{\sigma_1} (\text{curl } \mathbf{F}) \cdot \mathbf{n}\, dS = \int_C \mathbf{F} \cdot d\mathbf{r} \text{ and } \iint\limits_{\sigma_2} (\text{curl } \mathbf{F}) \cdot \mathbf{n}\, dS = -\int_C \mathbf{F} \cdot d\mathbf{r} \text{ so}$$

$$\iint\limits_{\sigma} (\text{curl } \mathbf{F}) \cdot \mathbf{n}\, dS = \int_C \mathbf{F} \cdot d\mathbf{r} - \int_C \mathbf{F} \cdot d\mathbf{r} = 0.$$

EXERCISE SET 18.8

1. $\displaystyle \iint\limits_{\sigma} \mathbf{F} \cdot \mathbf{n}\, dS = 2 \iint\limits_{R} (x^2 + y^2 + z)\, dA = 2 \iint\limits_{R} dA = (2)(\text{area of } R) = 2\pi$

2. $\displaystyle \iint\limits_{\sigma} \mathbf{F} \cdot \mathbf{n}\, dS = \iint\limits_{R} \left(3x^2 + \frac{3}{2}xy + xz \right) dA = \iint\limits_{R} 3x\, dA = 3 \int_0^1 \int_0^{2-2x} x\, dy\, dx = 1$

3. $\displaystyle \iint\limits_{\sigma} \mathbf{F} \cdot \mathbf{n}\, dS = \iint\limits_{R} \left(x + y + \frac{9 + xy}{\sqrt{9 - x^2 - y^2}} \right) dA$

$$= \lim_{r_0 \to 3^-} \int_0^{2\pi} \int_0^{r_0} \left(r\cos\theta + r\sin\theta + \frac{9 + r^2\sin\theta\cos\theta}{\sqrt{9 - r^2}} \right) r\, dr\, d\theta$$

$$= \lim_{r_0 \to 3^-} \int_0^{2\pi} \int_0^{r_0} \left(r^2 \cos\theta + r^2 \sin\theta + \frac{9r}{\sqrt{9-r^2}} + \frac{r^3}{\sqrt{9-r^2}} \sin\theta \cos\theta \right) dr \, d\theta$$

$$= \lim_{r_0 \to 3^-} 18\pi(3 - \sqrt{9-r_0^2}) = 54\pi.$$

4. $\displaystyle\iint_\sigma \mathbf{F} \cdot \mathbf{n} \, dS = \iint_R \sqrt{x^2 + y^2} \, dA = \int_0^{2\pi} \int_1^2 r^2 \, dr \, d\theta = \frac{14\pi}{3}$

5. $\displaystyle\iint_\sigma \mathbf{F} \cdot \mathbf{n} \, dS = \iiint_G \operatorname{div} \mathbf{F} \, dV = 3 \iiint_G dV = (3)(\text{volume of sphere}) = 4\pi a^3$

6. $\displaystyle\iint_\sigma \mathbf{F} \cdot \mathbf{n} \, dS = \iiint_G \operatorname{div} \mathbf{F} \, dV = \iiint_G (y + z + x) dV = \int_0^2 \int_0^2 \int_0^2 (x + y + z) dz \, dy \, dx = 24$

7. $\displaystyle\iint_\sigma \mathbf{F} \cdot \mathbf{n} \, dS = \iiint_G \operatorname{div} \mathbf{F} \, dV = 3 \iiint_G (x^2 + y^2 + z^2) dV$

$$= 3 \int_0^{2\pi} \int_0^2 \int_0^3 (r^2 + z^2) r \, dz \, dr \, d\theta = 180\pi$$

8. $\displaystyle\iint_\sigma \mathbf{F} \cdot \mathbf{n} \, dS = \iiint_G \operatorname{div} \mathbf{F} \, dV = \iiint_G x \, dV = \int_0^1 \int_0^{1-x} \int_0^{1-x-y} x \, dz \, dy \, dx = \frac{1}{24}$

9. $\operatorname{div} \mathbf{F} = 0$; no sources or sinks.

10. $\operatorname{div} \mathbf{F} = y - x$; sources where $y > x$, sinks where $y < x$.

11. $\operatorname{div} \mathbf{F} = 3x^2 + 3y^2 + 3z^2$; sources at all points except the origin, no sinks.

12. $\operatorname{div} \mathbf{F} = 3(x^2 + y^2 + z^2 - 1)$; sources outside the sphere $x^2 + y^2 + z^2 = 1$, sinks inside the sphere $x^2 + y^2 + z^2 = 1$.

13. **(a)** Take σ as the part of the plane $2x + y + 2z = 2$ in the first octant, oriented with downward normals; $\operatorname{curl} \mathbf{F} = -x\mathbf{i} + (y - 1)\mathbf{j} - \mathbf{k}$,

$$\int_C \mathbf{F} \cdot \mathbf{T} \, ds = \iint_\sigma (\operatorname{curl} \mathbf{F}) \cdot \mathbf{n} \, dS$$

$$= \iint_R \left(x - \frac{1}{2}y + \frac{3}{2} \right) dA = \int_0^1 \int_0^{2-2x} \left(x - \frac{1}{2}y + \frac{3}{2} \right) dy \, dx = \frac{3}{2}.$$

(b) At the origin $\operatorname{curl} \mathbf{F} = -\mathbf{j} - \mathbf{k}$ and with $\mathbf{n} = \mathbf{k}$, $\operatorname{curl} \mathbf{F}(0,0,0) \cdot \mathbf{n} = (-\mathbf{j} - \mathbf{k}) \cdot \mathbf{k} = -1$.

(c) The rotation of **F** has its maximum value at the origin about the unit vector in the same direction as curl $\mathbf{F}(0,0,0)$ so $\mathbf{n} = -\dfrac{1}{\sqrt{2}}\mathbf{j} - \dfrac{1}{\sqrt{2}}\mathbf{k}$.

SUPPLEMENTARY EXERCISES CHAPTER 18

1. $x = t,\ y = \sin t,\ 0 \le t \le \pi;\ \displaystyle\int_0^\pi (2\sin t + 3\cos t)dt = 4$

2. $\displaystyle\int_1^2 8/t^4\,dt = 7/3$

3. $x = t,\ y = \ln t,\ 1 \le t \le 3;\ \displaystyle\int_1^3 (2t - 1)dt = 6$

4. $\displaystyle\int_0^2 (4 - 3t^2)dt = 0$

5. $x = t,\ y = 2t,\ z = 3t,\ 0 \le t \le 1;\ \displaystyle\int_0^1 4t\,dt = 2$

6. $x = t,\ y = \pi t,\ 0 \le t \le 1;\ \displaystyle\int_0^1 (1 - \pi^2)t\sin(\pi t^2)dt = (1 - \pi^2)/\pi$

7. $\partial(y\sin xy)/\partial y = xy\cos xy + \sin xy,\ \partial(-x\cos xy)/\partial x = xy\sin xy - \cos xy$, not conservative.

8. $\partial[2x(\ln y - 1)]/\partial y = 2x/y = \partial(x^2/y - 3y^2)/\partial x$, conservative so $\partial\phi/\partial x = 2x(\ln y - 1)$ and $\partial\phi/\partial y = x^2/y - 3y^2,\ \phi = x^2(\ln y - 1) + k(y),\ x^2/y + k'(y) = x^2/y - 3y^2,\ k'(y) = -3y^2,$ $k(y) = -y^3 + K,\ \phi = x^2(\ln y - 1) - y^3 + K.$

9. $\partial(3x^2 - y^2/x^2)/\partial y = -2y/x^2 = \partial(2y/x + 4y)/\partial x$, conservative so $\partial\phi/\partial x = 3x^2 - y^2/x^2$ and $\partial\phi/\partial y = 2y/x + 4y,\ \phi = x^3 + y^2/x + k(y),\ 2y/x + k'(y) = 2y/x + 4y,\ k'(y) = 4y,\ k(y) = 2y^2 + K,$ $\phi = x^3 + y^2/x + 2y^2 + K.$

10. $h(x)F(x,y)$ is conservative if $\partial[yh(x)]/\partial y = \partial[-2xh(x)]/\partial x,\ h(x) = -2xh'(x) - 2h(x),$ $2xh'(x) + 3h(x) = 0$ which is both separable and first-order-linear; the solution is $h(x) = C|x|^{-3/2}.\ g(y)F(x,y)$ is conservative if $\partial[yg(y)]/\partial y = \partial[-2xg(y)]/\partial x,$ $yg'(y) + g(y) = -2g(y),\ yg'(y) + 3g(y) = 0$ so $g(y) = Cy^{-3}.$

11. $\partial(\cos 2y - 3x^2y^2)/\partial y = -2\sin 2y - 6x^2y$ and $\partial(\cos 2y - 2x\sin 2y - 2x^3y)/\partial x = -2\sin 2y - 6x^2y$ so it is independent of path. The line segment from $(1, \pi/4)$ to $(2, \pi/4)$ is $x = 1 + t$, $y = \pi/4$, $0 \le t \le 1$; the line integral along this path is

$$-\int_0^1 3(\pi/4)^2(1+t)^3 dt = -7\pi^2/16.$$

12. $\partial(x^2y^4)/\partial y = 4x^2y^3$, $\partial(y^2x^4)/\partial x = 4y^2x^3$, not independent of path

13. $\partial(1/y)/\partial y = -1/y^2 = \partial(-x/y^2)/\partial x$, independent of path;
$\phi = x/y$, $\phi(2,1) - \phi(1,2) = 2 - 1/2 = 3/2$

14. $\partial(ye^{xy} - 1)/\partial y = xye^{xy} + e^{xy} = \partial(xe^{xy})/\partial x$, independent of path;
$\phi = e^{xy} - x$, $\phi(1,0) - \phi(0,1) = 0 - 1 = -1$

15. $\displaystyle\int_0^2\int_0^{2x}(y^2 - 2x)dy\,dx = 0$ **16.** $\displaystyle\iint\limits_R -7dA = -7(\pi) = -7\pi$

17. $\displaystyle\int_{-2}^2\int_0^{4-y^2}3\,dx\,dy = 32$ **18.** $\displaystyle\int_0^2\int_{x^2}^{2x}(3x^2 - 5x)dy\,dx = -28/15$

19. $\displaystyle\iint\limits_R(-3x^2 - 3y^2)dA = -3\int_0^\pi\int_1^2 r^3 dr\,d\theta = -45\pi/4$

20. $x = r\cos\theta = 2\cos^2\theta = 1 + \cos 2\theta$, $y = r\sin\theta = 2\sin\theta\cos\theta = \sin 2\theta$;
$$A = \frac{1}{2}\int_C x\,dy - y\,dx = \int_0^\pi(\cos 2\theta + 1)d\theta = \pi$$

21. $C: x = t, y = t^2, 0 \le t \le 1$; $\displaystyle W = \int_C \mathbf{F}\cdot d\mathbf{r} = \int_0^1(2t + 3t^2 + 2t^4)dt = 12/5$

22. $\partial(3x^2y^3)/\partial y = 9x^2y^2 = \partial(3x^3y^2)/\partial x$ so $\mathbf{F}$ is conservative and $W = \int_C \mathbf{F}\cdot d\mathbf{r} = 0$ because C is closed

23. $C: x = t, y = 2t, z = 3t, 0 \le t \le 1$; $\displaystyle W = \int_C \mathbf{F}\cdot d\mathbf{r} = \int_0^1 4t\,dt = 2$

24. **(a)** $\nabla\phi = \phi_x\mathbf{i} + \phi_y\mathbf{j}$; curl $(\nabla\phi) = (\phi_{yx} - \phi_{xy})\mathbf{k} = 0$ because $\phi_{yx} = \phi_{xy}$.
   (b) div $(\nabla\phi) = \phi_{xx} + \phi_{yy}$

25. By symmetry $\bar{x} = \bar{y} = 0$.

$$\iint_\sigma dS = \iint_R \sqrt{x^2 + y^2 + 1}\, dA = \int_0^{2\pi}\int_0^{\sqrt{8}} \sqrt{r^2 + 1}\, r\, dr\, d\theta = \frac{52\pi}{3},$$

$$\iint_\sigma z\, dS = \iint_R z\sqrt{x^2 + y^2 + 1}\, dA = \frac{1}{2}\iint_R (x^2 + y^2)\sqrt{x^2 + y^2 + 1}\, dA$$

$$= \frac{1}{2}\int_0^{2\pi}\int_0^{\sqrt{8}} r^3\sqrt{r^2 + 1}\, dr\, d\theta = \frac{596\pi}{15}$$

so $\bar{z} = \dfrac{596\pi/15}{52\pi/3} = \dfrac{149}{65}$. The centroid is $(\bar{x}, \bar{y}, \bar{z}) = (0, 0, 149/65)$.

26. By symmetry $\bar{x} = \bar{y} = 0$.

$$\iint_\sigma dS = \iint_R \frac{2}{\sqrt{4 - x^2 - y^2}}\, dA = 2\int_0^{2\pi}\int_0^{\sqrt{3}} \frac{r}{\sqrt{4 - r^2}}\, dr\, d\theta = 4\pi,$$

$$\iint_\sigma z\, dS = \iint_R 2\, dA = (2)(\text{area of circle of radius } \sqrt{3}) = 6\pi$$

so $\bar{z} = \dfrac{6\pi}{4\pi} = \dfrac{3}{2}$. The centroid is $(\bar{x}, \bar{y}, \bar{z}) = (0, 0, 3/2)$.

27. $\nabla f = \dfrac{x}{x^2 + y^2 + z^2}\mathbf{i} + \dfrac{y}{x^2 + y^2 + z^2}\mathbf{j} + \dfrac{z}{x^2 + y^2 + z^2}\mathbf{k}$; on σ, $\nabla f = x\mathbf{i} + y\mathbf{j} + z\mathbf{k}$ because $x^2 + y^2 + z^2 = 1$. $D_\mathbf{n}f = \nabla f \cdot \mathbf{n}$ so

$$\iint_\sigma D_\mathbf{n}f\, dS = \iint_\sigma \nabla f \cdot \mathbf{n}\, dS = \iint_R \frac{1}{\sqrt{1 - x^2 - y^2}}\, dA$$

$$= \lim_{r_0 \to 1^-} \int_0^{\pi/2}\int_0^{r_0} \frac{r}{\sqrt{1 - r^2}}\, dr\, d\theta = \lim_{r_0 \to 1^-} \frac{\pi}{2}(1 - \sqrt{1 - r_0^2}) = \frac{\pi}{2}.$$

28. $D_\mathbf{n}f = \nabla f \cdot \mathbf{n}$ so $\displaystyle\iint_\sigma D_\mathbf{n}f\, dS = \iint_\sigma \nabla f \cdot \mathbf{n}\, dS = -\iiint_G \text{div}\,(\nabla f)\, dV$ by the Divergence

Theorem. $\nabla f = 2x\mathbf{i} + 2y\mathbf{j} + 2z\mathbf{k}$; $\text{div}\,(\nabla f) = 6$ so

$$\iint_\sigma D_\mathbf{n}f\, dS = -6\iiint_G dV = -6\left[\frac{4}{3}\pi(1)^3\right] = -8\pi.$$

29. $D_{\mathbf{n}}\phi = \nabla\phi \cdot \mathbf{n}$ so $\displaystyle\iint_\sigma D_{\mathbf{n}}\phi\, dS = \iint_\sigma \nabla\phi \cdot \mathbf{n}\, dS = \iiint_G$ div $(\nabla\phi)dV$ by the Divergence

Theorem. $\nabla\phi = \dfrac{\partial\phi}{\partial x}\mathbf{i} + \dfrac{\partial\phi}{\partial y}\mathbf{j} + \dfrac{\partial\phi}{\partial z}\mathbf{k}$ so div $(\nabla\phi) = \dfrac{\partial^2\phi}{\partial x^2} + \dfrac{\partial^2\phi}{\partial y^2} + \dfrac{\partial^2\phi}{\partial z^2}$ and

$$\iint_\sigma D_{\mathbf{n}}\phi\, dS = \iiint_G \left(\dfrac{\partial^2\phi}{\partial x^2} + \dfrac{\partial^2\phi}{\partial y^2} + \dfrac{\partial^2\phi}{\partial z^2}\right) dV.$$

30. curl $\mathbf{F} = \left(\dfrac{\partial g}{\partial x} - \dfrac{\partial f}{\partial y}\right)\mathbf{k}$. If σ is the region in the xy-plane oriented by $\mathbf{n} = \mathbf{k}$ and enclosed by

a curve C then by Stokes' Theorem $\displaystyle\int_C \mathbf{F} \cdot d\mathbf{r} = \iint_\sigma (\text{curl } \mathbf{F}) \cdot \mathbf{n}\, dS = \iint_\sigma \left(\dfrac{\partial g}{\partial x} - \dfrac{\partial f}{\partial y}\right) dS$ or

equivalently, $\displaystyle\int_C f\, dx + g\, dy = \iint_\sigma \left(\dfrac{\partial g}{\partial x} - \dfrac{\partial f}{\partial y}\right) dS$ which is Green's Theorem.

CHAPTER 19
Second-Order Differential Equations

EXERCISE SET 19.1

1. **(a)** $y = e^{2x}, y' = 2e^{2x}, y'' = 4e^{2x}; y'' - y' - 2y = 0$
   $y = e^{-x}, y' = -e^{-x}, y'' = e^{-x}; y'' - y' - 2y = 0.$

   (b) $y = c_1 e^{2x} + c_2 e^{-x}, y' = 2c_1 e^{2x} - c_2 e^{-x}, y'' = 4c_1 e^{2x} + c_2 e^{-x}; y'' - y' - 2y = 0$

2. **(a)** $y = e^{-2x}, y' = -2e^{-2x}, y'' = 4e^{-2x}; y'' + 4y' + 4y = 0$
   $y = xe^{-2x}, y' = (1 - 2x)e^{-2x}, y'' = (4x - 4)e^{-2x}; y'' + 4y' + 4y = 0.$

   (b) $y = c_1 e^{-2x} + c_2 xe^{-2x}, y' = -2c_1 e^{-2x} + c_2(1 - 2x)e^{-2x},$
   $y'' = 4c_1 e^{-2x} + c_2(4x - 4)e^{-2x}; y'' + 4y' + 4y = 0.$

3. $m^2 + 3m - 4 = 0, (m - 1)(m + 4) = 0; m = 1, -4$ so $y = c_1 e^x + c_2 e^{-4x}.$

4. $m^2 + 6m + 5 = 0, (m + 1)(m + 5) = 0; m = -1, -5$ so $y = c_1 e^{-x} + c_2 e^{-5x}.$

5. $m^2 - 2m + 1 = 0, (m - 1)^2 = 0; m = 1,$ so $y = c_1 e^x + c_2 xe^x.$

6. $m^2 + 6m + 9 = 0, (m + 3)^2 = 0; m = -3$ so $y = c_1 e^{-3x} + c_2 xe^{-3x}.$

7. $m^2 + 5 = 0, m = \pm\sqrt{5}\,i$ so $y = c_1 \cos\sqrt{5}\,x + c_2 \sin\sqrt{5}\,x.$

8. $m^2 + 1 = 0, m = \pm i$ so $y = c_1 \cos x + c_2 \sin x.$

9. $m^2 - m = 0, m(m - 1) = 0; m = 0, 1$ so $y = c_1 + c_2 e^x.$

10. $m^2 + 3m = 0, m(m + 3) = 0; m = 0, -3$ so $y = c_1 + c_2 e^{-3x}.$

11. $m^2 + 4m + 4 = 0, (m + 2)^2 = 0; m = -2$ so $y = c_1 e^{-2t} + c_2 te^{-2t}.$

12. $m^2 - 10m + 25 = 0, (m - 5)^2 = 0; m = 5$ so $y = c_1 e^{5t} + c_2 te^{5t}.$

13. $m^2 - 4m + 13 = 0, m = 2 \pm 3i$ so $y = e^{2x}(c_1 \cos 3x + c_2 \sin 3x).$

14. $m^2 - 6m + 25 = 0, m = 3 \pm 4i$ so $y = e^{3x}(c_1 \cos 4x + c_2 \sin 4x).$

15. $8m^2 - 2m - 1 = 0, (4m + 1)(2m - 1) = 0; m = -1/4, 1/2$ so $y = c_1 e^{-x/4} + c_2 e^{x/2}.$

16. $9m^2 - 6m + 1 = 0, (3m - 1)^2 = 0; m = 1/3$ so $y = c_1 e^{x/3} + c_2 xe^{x/3}.$

17. $m^2 + 2m - 3 = 0$, $(m+3)(m-1) = 0$; $m = -3, 1$ so $y = c_1 e^{-3x} + c_2 e^x$ and $y' = -3c_1 e^{-3x} + c_2 e^x$.
    Solve the system $c_1 + c_2 = 1$, $-3c_1 + c_2 = 5$ to get $c_1 = -1$, $c_2 = 2$ so $y = -e^{-3x} + 2e^x$.

18. $m^2 - 6m - 7 = 0$, $(m+1)(m-7) = 0$; $m = -1, 7$ so $y = c_1 e^{-x} + c_2 e^{7x}$, $y' = -c_1 e^{-x} + 7c_2 e^{7x}$.
    Solve the system $c_1 + c_2 = 5$, $-c_1 + 7c_2 = 3$ to get $c_1 = 4$, $c_2 = 1$ so $y = 4e^{-x} + e^{7x}$.

19. $m^2 - 6m + 9 = 0$, $(m-3)^2 = 0$; $m = 3$ so $y = (c_1 + c_2 x)e^{3x}$ and $y' = (3c_1 + c_2 + 3c_2 x)e^{3x}$.
    Solve the system $c_1 = 2$, $3c_1 + c_2 = 1$ to get $c_1 = 2$, $c_2 = -5$ so $y = (2 - 5x)e^{3x}$.

20. $m^2 + 4m + 1 = 0$, $m = -2 \pm \sqrt{3}$ so $y = c_1 e^{(-2+\sqrt{3})x} + c_2 e^{(-2-\sqrt{3})x}$,
    $y' = (-2 + \sqrt{3})c_1 e^{(-2+\sqrt{3})x} + (-2 - \sqrt{3})c_2 e^{(-2-\sqrt{3})x}$. Solve the system $c_1 + c_2 = 5$,
    $(-2 + \sqrt{3})c_1 + (-2 - \sqrt{3})c_2 = 4$ to get $c_1 = \frac{5}{2} + \frac{7}{3}\sqrt{3}$, $c_2 = \frac{5}{2} - \frac{7}{3}\sqrt{3}$ so
    $y = \left(\frac{5}{2} + \frac{7}{3}\sqrt{3}\right) e^{(-2+\sqrt{3})x} + \left(\frac{5}{2} - \frac{7}{3}\sqrt{3}\right) e^{(-2-\sqrt{3})x}$.

21. $m^2 + 4m + 5 = 0$, $m = -2 \pm i$ so $y = e^{-2x}(c_1 \cos x + c_2 \sin x)$,
    $y' = e^{-2x}[(c_2 - 2c_1) \cos x - (c_1 + 2c_2) \sin x]$. Solve the system $c_1 = -3$, $c_2 - 2c_1 = 0$
    to get $c_1 = -3$, $c_2 = -6$ so $y = -e^{-2x}(3 \cos x + 6 \sin x)$.

22. $m^2 - 6m + 13 = 0$, $m = 3 \pm 2i$ so $y = e^{3x}(c_1 \cos 2x + c_2 \sin 2x)$,
    $y' = e^{3x}[(3c_1 + 2c_2) \cos 2x - (2c_1 - 3c_2) \sin 2x]$. Solve the system $c_1 = -1$, $3c_1 + 2c_2 = 1$
    to get $c_1 = -1$, $c_2 = 2$ so $y = e^{3x}(- \cos 2x + 2 \sin 2x)$.

23. (a) $m = 5, -2$ so $(m-5)(m+2) = 0$, $m^2 - 3m - 10 = 0$; $y'' - 3y' - 10y = 0$.
    (b) $m = 4, 4$ so $(m-4)^2 = 0$, $m^2 - 8m + 16 = 0$; $y'' - 8y' + 16y = 0$.
    (c) $m = -1 \pm 4i$ so $(m+1-4i)(m+1+4i) = 0$, $m^2 + 2m + 17 = 0$; $y'' + 2y' + 17y = 0$.

24. $c_1 e^x + c_2 e^{-x}$ is the general solution, but $\cosh x = \frac{1}{2}e^x + \frac{1}{2}e^{-x}$ and $\sinh x = \frac{1}{2}e^x - \frac{1}{2}e^{-x}$
    so $\cosh x$ and $\sinh x$ are also solutions.

25. $m^2 + km + k = 0$, $m = \left(-k \pm \sqrt{k^2 - 4k}\right)/2$
    (a) $k^2 - 4k > 0$, $k(k-4) > 0$; $k < 0$ or $k > 4$
    (b) $k^2 - 4k = 0$; $k = 0, 4$ (c) $k^2 - 4k < 0$, $k(k-4) < 0$; $0 < k < 4$

26. $z = \ln x$; $\dfrac{dy}{dx} = \dfrac{dy}{dz}\dfrac{dz}{dx} = \dfrac{1}{x}\dfrac{dy}{dz}$ and

    $\dfrac{d^2 y}{dx^2} = \dfrac{d}{dx}\left(\dfrac{dy}{dx}\right) = \dfrac{d}{dx}\left(\dfrac{1}{x}\dfrac{dy}{dz}\right) = \dfrac{1}{x}\dfrac{d^2 y}{dz^2}\dfrac{dz}{dx} - \dfrac{1}{x^2}\dfrac{dy}{dz} = \dfrac{1}{x^2}\dfrac{d^2 y}{dz^2} - \dfrac{1}{x^2}\dfrac{dy}{dz}$,

    substitute into the original equation to get $\dfrac{d^2 y}{dz^2} + (p - 1)\dfrac{dy}{dz} + qy = 0$.

27. **(a)** $\dfrac{d^2y}{dz^2} + 2\dfrac{dy}{dz} + 2y = 0$, $m^2 + 2m + 2 = 0$; $m = -1 \pm i$ so

$$y = e^{-z}(c_1 \cos z + c_2 \sin z) = \frac{1}{x}[c_1 \cos(\ln x) + c_2 \sin(\ln x)].$$

(b) $\dfrac{d^2y}{dz^2} - 2\dfrac{dy}{dz} - 2y = 0$, $m^2 - 2m - 2 = 0$; $m = 1 \pm \sqrt{3}$ so

$$y = c_1 e^{(1+\sqrt{3})z} + c_2 e^{(1-\sqrt{3})z} = c_1 x^{1+\sqrt{3}} + c_2 x^{1-\sqrt{3}}$$

28. $m^2 + pm + q = 0$, $m = \frac{1}{2}(-p \pm \sqrt{p^2 - 4q})$. If $0 < q < p^2/4$ then $y = c_1 e^{m_1 x} + c_2 e^{m_2 x}$ where $m_1 < 0$ and $m_2 < 0$, if $q = p^2/4$ then $y = c_1 e^{-p/2} + c_2 x e^{-p/2}$, if $q > p^2/4$ then $y = e^{-p/2}(c_1 \cos kx + c_2 \sin kx)$ where $k = \frac{1}{2}\sqrt{4q - p^2}$. In all cases $\lim\limits_{x \to +\infty} y(x) = 0$.

29. **(a)** $W(x) = \begin{vmatrix} e^{m_1 x} & e^{m_2 x} \\ m_1 e^{m_1 x} & m_2 e^{m_2 x} \end{vmatrix} = m_2 e^{(m_1 + m_2)x} - m_1 e^{(m_1 + m_2)x}$

$$= (m_2 - m_1)e^{(m_1 + m_2)x} \neq 0 \text{ if } m_1 \neq m_2.$$

(b) $W(x) = \begin{vmatrix} e^{mx} & x e^{mx} \\ m e^{mx} & (mx + 1)e^{mx} \end{vmatrix} = e^{2mx} \neq 0.$

30. $y_1 = e^{ax} \cos bx$, $y_1' = e^{ax}(a \cos bx - b \sin bx)$, $y_1'' = e^{ax}[(a^2 - b^2) \cos bx - 2ab \sin bx]$ so

$y_1'' + py_1' + qy_1 = e^{ax}[(a^2 - b^2 + ap + q) \cos bx - (2ab + bp) \sin bx]$. But $a = -\frac{1}{2}p$ and $b = \frac{1}{2}\sqrt{4q - p^2}$ so $a^2 - b^2 + ap + q = 0$ and $2ab + bp = 0$ thus $y_1'' + py_1' + qy_1 = 0$. Similarly, $y_2 = e^{ax} \sin bx$ is also a solution. From Exercise 29, $W(y_1, y_2) = y_1 y_2' - y_1' y_2 = be^{2ax} \neq 0$ because $b \neq 0$, so y_1 and y_2 are linearly independent and hence the general solution is $y(x) = e^{ax}(c_1 \cos bx + c_2 \sin bx)$.

31. **(a)** The general solution is $c_1 e^{\mu x} + c_2 e^{mx}$; let $c_1 = 1/(\mu - m)$, $c_2 = -1/(\mu - m)$.

(b) $\lim\limits_{\mu \to m} \dfrac{e^{\mu x} - e^{mx}}{\mu - m} = \lim\limits_{\mu \to m} x e^{\mu x} = x e^{mx}.$

32. **(a)** If $\lambda = 0$, then $y'' = 0$, $y = c_1 + c_2 x$. Use $y(0) = 0$ and $y(\pi) = 0$ to get $c_1 = c_2 = 0$. If $\lambda < 0$, then let $\lambda = -a^2$ where $a > 0$ so $y'' - a^2 y = 0$, $y = c_1 e^{ax} + c_2 e^{-ax}$. Use $y(0) = 0$ and $y(\pi) = 0$ to get $c_1 = c_2 = 0$.

(b) If $\lambda > 0$, then $m^2 + \lambda = 0$, $m^2 = -\lambda = \lambda i^2$, $m = \pm\sqrt{\lambda}i$, $y = c_1 \cos \sqrt{\lambda}x + c_2 \sin \sqrt{\lambda}x$. If $y(0) = 0$ and $y(\pi) = 0$, then $c_1 = 0$ and $c_1 \cos \pi\sqrt{\lambda} + c_2 \sin \pi\sqrt{\lambda} = 0$ so $c_2 \sin \pi\sqrt{\lambda} = 0$. But $c_2 \sin \pi\sqrt{\lambda} = 0$ for arbitrary values of c_2 if $\sin \pi\sqrt{\lambda} = 0$, $\pi\sqrt{\lambda} = n\pi$, $\lambda = n^2$ for $n = 1, 2, 3, \ldots$, otherwise $c_2 = 0$.

EXERCISE SET 19.2

1. $m^2 + 6m + 5 = 0$, $(m+1)(m+5) = 0$; $m = -1, -5$ so $y_c = c_1 e^{-x} + c_2 e^{-5x}$. Let
    $y_p = Ae^{3x}$, then $y_p' = 3Ae^{3x}$, $y_p'' = 9Ae^{3x}$, $(9A + 18A + 5A)e^{3x} = 32Ae^{3x} = 2e^{3x}$,
    $A = 1/16$; $y = c_1 e^{-x} + c_2 e^{-5x} + \frac{1}{16} e^{3x}$.

2. $m^2 + 3m - 4 = 0$, $(m-1)(m+4) = 0$; $m = 1, -4$ so $y_c = c_1 e^x + c_2 e^{-4x}$. Let $y_p = Ae^{7x}$, then
    $y_p' = 7Ae^{7x}$, $y_p'' = 49Ae^{7x}$, $(49A + 21A - 4A)e^{7x} = 66Ae^{7x} = 5e^{7x}$, $A = 5/66$;
    $y = c_1 e^x + c_2 e^{-4x} + \frac{5}{66} e^{7x}$.

3. $m^2 - 9m + 20 = 0$, $(m-4)(m-5) = 0$; $m = 4, 5$ so $y_c = c_1 e^{4x} + c_2 e^{5x}$. Let $y_p = Axe^{5x}$,
    then $y_p' = (5Ax + A)e^{5x}$, $y_p'' = (25Ax + 10A)e^{5x}$,
    $(25Ax + 10A - 45Ax - 9A + 20Ax)e^{5x} = Ae^{5x} = -3e^{5x}$, $A = -3$; $y = c_1 e^{4x} + c_2 e^{5x} - 3xe^{5x}$.

4. $m^2 + 7m - 8 = (m-1)(m+8) = 0$; $m = 1, -8$ so $y_c = c_1 e^x + c_2 e^{-8x}$. Let $y_p = Axe^x$, then
    $y_p' = (Ax + A)e^x$, $y_p'' = (Ax + 2A)e^x$, $(Ax + 2A + 7Ax + 7A - 8Ax)e^x = 9Ae^x = 7e^x$, $A = 7/9$;
    $y = c_1 e^x + c_2 e^{-8x} + \frac{7}{9} xe^x$.

5. $m^2 + 2m + 1 = 0$, $(m+1)^2 = 0$; $m = -1$ so $y_c = (c_1 + c_2 x)e^{-x}$. Let $y_p = Ax^2 e^{-x}$,
    then $y_p' = (-Ax^2 + 2Ax)e^{-x}$, $y_p'' = (Ax^2 - 4Ax + 2A)e^{-x}$,
    $(Ax^2 - 4Ax + 2A - 2Ax^2 + 4Ax + Ax^2)e^{-x} = 2Ae^{-x} = e^{-x}$, $A = 1/2$; $y = (c_1 + c_2 x)e^{-x} + \frac{1}{2} x^2 e^{-x}$.

6. $m^2 + 4m + 4 = 0$, $(m+2)^2 = 0$; $m = -2$ so $y_c = (c_1 + c_2 x)e^{-2x}$. Let $y_p = Ax^2 e^{-2x}$,
    then $y_p' = (-2Ax^2 + 2Ax)e^{-2x}$, $y_p'' = (4Ax^2 - 8Ax + 2A)e^{-2x}$,
    $(4Ax^2 - 8Ax + 2A - 8Ax^2 + 8Ax + 4Ax^2)e^{-2x} = 2Ae^{-2x} = 4e^{-2x}$, $A = 2$;
    $y = (c_1 + c_2 x)e^{-2x} + 2x^2 e^{-2x}$.

7. $m^2 + m - 12 = 0$, $(m-3)(m+4) = 0$; $m = 3, -4$ so $y_c = c_1 e^{3x} + c_2 e^{-4x}$. Let
    $y_p = A_0 + A_1 x + A_2 x^2$, then $y_p' = A_1 + 2A_2 x$, $y_p'' = 2A_2$,
    $2A_2 + A_1 + 2A_2 x - 12A_0 - 12A_1 x - 12A_2 x^2$
    $= (-12A_0 + A_1 + 2A_2) + 2(-6A_1 + A_2)x - 12A_2 x^2 = 4x^2$;
    solve the system $-12A_0 + A_1 + 2A_2 = 0$, $-6A_1 + A_2 = 0$, $-12A_2 = 4$ to get
    $A_0 = -13/216$, $A_1 = -1/18$, $A_2 = -1/3$ so $y = c_1 e^{3x} + c_2 e^{-4x} - \frac{13}{216} - \frac{1}{18} x - \frac{1}{3} x^2$.

8. $m^2 - 4m - 5 = 0$, $(m-5)(m+1) = 0$; $m = 5, -1$ so $y_c = c_1 e^{5x} + c_2 e^{-x}$. Let $y_p = A_0 + A_1 x + A_2 x^2$,
    then $y_p' = A_1 + 2A_2 x$, $y_p'' = 2A_2$,
    $2A_2 - 4A_1 - 8A_2 x - 5A_0 - 5A_1 x - 5A_2 x^2 = (-5A_0 - 4A_1 + 2A_2) + (-5A_1 - 8A_2)x - 5A_2 x^2 = -6x^2$;

solve the system $-5A_0 - 4A_1 + 2A_2 = 0$, $-5A_1 - 8A_2 = 0$, $-5A_2 = -6$ to get
$A_0 = 252/125$, $A_1 = -48/25$, $A_2 = 6/5$ so $y = c_1 e^{5x} + c_2 e^{-x} + \frac{252}{125} - \frac{48}{25}x + \frac{6}{5}x^2$.

9. $m^2 - 6m = 0$; $m = 0, 6$ so $y_c = c_1 + c_2 e^{6x}$. Let $y_p = A_0 x + A_1 x^2$, then $y_p' = A_0 + 2A_1 x$, $y_p'' = 2A_1$,
$2A_1 - 6A_0 - 12A_1 x = (-6A_0 + 2A_1) - 12A_1 x = x - 1$; solve the system $-6A_0 + 2A_1 = -1$,
$-12A_1 = 1$ to get $A_0 = 5/36$, $A_1 = -1/12$, so $y = c_1 + c_2 e^{6x} + \frac{5}{36}x - \frac{1}{12}x^2$.

10. $m^2 + 3m = 0$; $m = 0, -3$ so $y = c_1 + c_2 e^{-3x}$. Let $y_p = A_0 x + A_1 x^2$, then $y_p' = A_0 + 2A_1 x$,
$y_p'' = 2A_1$, $2A_1 + 3A_0 + 6A_1 x = (3A_0 + 2A_1) + 6A_1 x = 2x + 2$; solve the system $3A_0 + 2A_1 = 2$,
$6A_1 = 2$ to get $A_0 = 4/9$, $A_1 = 1/3$ so $y = c_1 + c_2 e^{-3x} + \frac{4}{9}x + \frac{1}{3}x^2$.

11. $m^2 = 0$, $m = 0$ so $y_c = c_1 + c_2 x$. Let $y_p = A_0 x^2 + A_1 x^3 + A_2 x^4 + A_3 x^5$,
then $y_p' = 2A_0 x + 3A_1 x^2 + 4A_2 x^3 + 5A_3 x^4$, $y_p'' = 2A_0 + 6A_1 x + 12A_2 x^2 + 20A_3 x^3$;
$A_0 = -1/2$, $A_1 = 0$, $A_2 = 0$, $A_3 = 1/20$ so $y = c_1 + c_2 x - x^2/2 + x^5/20$.

12. $m^2 = 0$; $m = 0$ so $y_c = c_1 + c_2 x$. Let $y_p = A_0 x^2 + A_1 x^3 + A_2 x^4 + A_3 x^5$,
then $y_p' = 2A_0 x + 3A_1 x^2 + 4A_2 x^3 + 5A_3 x^4$, $y_p'' = 2A_0 + 6A_1 x + 12A_2 x^2 + 20A_3 x^3$;
$A_0 = 0$, $A_1 = -1/6$, $A_2 = 0$, $A_3 = -3/20$ so $y = c_1 + c_2 x - \frac{1}{6}x^3 - \frac{3}{20}x^5$.

13. $m^2 - m - 2 = 0$, $(m+1)(m-2) = 0$; $m = -1, 2$ so $y_c = c_1 e^{-x} + c_2 e^{2x}$. Let
$y_p = A_1 \cos x + A_2 \sin x$, then $y_p' = -A_1 \sin x + A_2 \cos x$, $y_p'' = -A_1 \cos x - A_2 \sin x$,
$-A_1 \cos x - A_2 \sin x + A_1 \sin x - A_2 \cos x - 2A_1 \cos x - 2A_2 \sin x$
$\quad = (-3A_1 - A_2) \cos x + (A_1 - 3A_2) \sin x = 10 \cos x$; solve the system $-3A_1 - A_2 = 10$,
$A_1 - 3A_2 = 0$ to get $A_1 = -3$, $A_2 = -1$ so $y = c_1 e^{-x} + c_2 e^{2x} - 3\cos x - \sin x$.

14. $m^2 - 3m - 4 = 0$, $(m-4)(m+1) = 0$; $m = 4, -1$ so $y_c = c_1 e^{4x} + c_2 e^{-x}$. Let
$y_p = A_1 \cos x + A_2 \sin x$, then $y_p' = -A_1 \sin x + A_2 \cos x$, $y_p'' = -A_1 \cos x - A_2 \sin x$,
$-A_1 \cos x - A_2 \sin x + 3A_1 \sin x - 3A_2 \cos x - 4A_1 \cos x - 4A_2 \sin x$
$\quad = (-5A_1 - 3A_2) \cos x + (3A_1 - 5A_2) \sin x = 2 \sin x$;
solve the system $-5A_1 - 3A_2 = 0$, $3A_1 - 5A_2 = 2$ to get $A_1 = 3/17$, $A_2 = -5/17$ so
$y = c_1 e^{4x} + c_2 e^{-x} + \frac{3}{17} \cos x - \frac{5}{17} \sin x$.

15. $m^2 - 4 = 0$; $m = \pm 2$ so $y_c = c_1 e^{-2x} + c_2 e^{2x}$. Let $y_p = A_1 \cos 2x + A_2 \sin 2x$,
then $y_p' = -2A_1 \sin 2x + 2A_2 \cos 2x$, $y_p'' = -4A_1 \cos 2x - 4A_2 \sin 2x$,
$-8A_1 \cos 2x - 8A_2 \sin 2x = 2 \sin 2x + 3 \cos 2x$, $A_1 = -3/8$, $A_2 = -1/4$;
$y = c_1 e^{-2x} + c_2 e^{2x} - \frac{3}{8} \cos 2x - \frac{1}{4} \sin 2x$.

16. $m^2 - 9 = 0$; $m = \pm 3$ so $y_c = c_1 e^{-3x} + c_2 e^{3x}$. Let $y_p = A_1 \cos 3x + A_2 \sin 3x$,

    then $y_p' = -3A_1 \sin 3x + 3A_2 \cos 3x$, $y_p'' = -9A_1 \cos 3x - 9A_2 \sin 3x$,

    $-18A_1 \cos 3x - 18A_2 \sin 3x = \cos 3x - \sin 3x$, $A_1 = -1/18$, $A_2 = 1/18$;

    $y = c_1 e^{-3x} + c_2 e^{3x} - \frac{1}{18} \cos 3x + \frac{1}{18} \sin 3x$.

17. $m^2 + 1 = 0$; $m = \pm i$ so $y_c = c_1 \cos x + c_2 \sin x$. Let $y_p = A_1 x \cos x + A_2 x \sin x$,

    then $y_p' = (A_1 + A_2 x) \cos x + (A_2 - A_1 x) \sin x$, $y_p'' = (2A_2 - A_1 x) \cos x - (2A_1 + A_2 x) \sin x$,

    $2A_2 \cos x - 2A_1 \sin x = \sin x$, $A_1 = -1/2$, $A_2 = 0$; $y = c_1 \cos x + c_2 \sin x - \frac{1}{2} x \cos x$.

18. $m^2 + 4 = 0$; $m = \pm 2i$ so $y_c = c_1 \cos 2x + c_2 \sin 2x$. Let $y_p = A_1 x \cos 2x + A_2 x \sin 2x$, then

    $y_p' = (A_1 + 2A_2 x) \cos 2x + (A_2 - 2A_1 x) \sin 2x$, $y_p'' = (4A_2 - 4A_1 x) \cos 2x - (4A_1 + 4A_2 x) \sin 2x$,

    $4A_2 \cos 2x - 4A_1 \sin 2x = \cos 2x$, $A_1 = 0$, $A_2 = 1/4$; $y = c_1 \cos 2x + c_2 \sin 2x + \frac{1}{4} x \sin 2x$.

19. $m^2 - 3m + 2 = 0$, $(m - 1)(m - 2) = 0$; $m = 1, 2$ so $y_c = c_1 e^x + c_2 e^{2x}$. Let $y_p = A_0 + A_1 x$,

    then $y_p' = A_1$, $y_p'' = 0$; solve the system $2A_0 - 3A_1 = 0$, $2A_1 = 1$ to get $A_0 = 3/4$, $A_1 = 1/2$;

    $y = c_1 e^x + c_2 e^{2x} + 3/4 + x/2$.

20. $m^2 + 4m + 4 = 0$, $(m + 2)^2 = 0$; $m = -2$ so $y_c = (c_1 + c_2 x) e^{-2x}$. Let $y_p = A_0 + A_1 x$, then

    $y_p' = A_1$, $y_p'' = 0$, $(4A_0 + 4A_1) + 4A_1 x = 3x + 3$, $A_0 = 0$, $A_1 = 3/4$; $y = (c_1 + c_2 x) e^{-2x} + \frac{3}{4} x$.

21. $m^2 + 4m + 9 = 0$; $m = -2 \pm \sqrt{5} i$ so $y_c = e^{-2x}(c_1 \cos \sqrt{5} x + c_2 \sin \sqrt{5} x)$.

    Let $y_p = A_0 + A_1 x + A_2 x^2$, then $y_p' = A_1 + 2A_2 x$, $y_p'' = 2A_2$; solve the system

    $9A_0 + 4A_1 + 2A_2 = 0$, $9A_1 + 8A_2 = 3$, $9A_2 = 1$, to get $A_0 = -94/729$, $A_1 = 19/81$, $A_2 = 1/9$

    so $y = e^{-2x}(c_1 \cos \sqrt{5} x + c_2 \sin \sqrt{5} x) - 94/729 + 19x/81 + x^2/9$.

22. $m^2 - 1 = 0$; $m = \pm 1$ so $y_c = c_1 e^{-x} + c_2 e^x$. Let $y_p = A_0 + A_1 x + A_2 x^2$, then $y_p' = A_1 + 2A_2 x$,

    $y_p'' = 2A_2$, $(2A_2 - A_0) - A_1 x - A_2 x^2 = 1 + x + x^2$, $A_0 = -3$, $A_1 = -1$, $A_2 = -1$;

    $y = c_1 e^{-x} + c_2 e^x - 3 - x - x^2$.

23. $m^2 + 4 = 0$; $m = \pm 2i$ so $y_c = c_1 \cos 2x + c_2 \sin 2x$; $\sin x \cos x = \frac{1}{2} \sin 2x$,

    let $y_p = A_1 x \cos 2x + A_2 x \sin 2x$, then $y_p' = (A_1 + 2A_2 x) \cos 2x + (A_2 - 2A_1 x) \sin 2x$,

    $y_p'' = (4A_2 - 4A_1 x) \cos 2x - (4A_1 + 4A_2 x) \sin 2x$, $4A_2 \cos 2x - 4A_1 \sin 2x = \frac{1}{2} \sin 2x$,

    $A_1 = -1/8$, $A_2 = 0$; $y = c_1 \cos 2x + c_2 \sin 2x - \frac{1}{8} x \cos 2x$.

24. $m^2 + 4 = 0$; $m = \pm 2i$ so $y_c = c_1 \cos 2x + c_2 \sin 2x$. $\cos^2 x - \sin^2 x = \cos 2x$,

    let $y_p = A_1 x \cos 2x + A_2 x \sin 2x$, then $y_p' = (A_1 + 2A_2 x) \cos 2x + (A_2 - 2A_1 x) \sin 2x$,

    $y_p'' = (4A_2 - 4A_1 x) \cos 2x - (4A_1 + 4A_2 x) \sin 2x$, $4A_2 \cos 2x - 4A_1 \sin 2x = \cos 2x$,

    $A_1 = 0$, $A_2 = 1/4$; $y = c_1 \cos 2x + c_2 \sin 2x + \frac{1}{4} x \sin 2x$.

25. **(a)** Let $y = y_1 + y_2$, then $y' = y_1' + y_2'$, $y'' = y_1'' + y_2''$ so
$$y'' + p(x)y' + q(x)y = [y_1'' + p(x)y_1' + q(x)y_1] + [y_2'' + p(x)y_2' + q(x)y_2] = r_1(x) + r_2(x).$$

(b) $m^2 + 3m - 4 = 0$, $(m-1)(m+4) = 0$; $m = 1, -4$ so $y_c = c_1 e^x + c_2 e^{-4x}$. For $y'' + 3y' - 4y = x$ let $y_1 = A_0 + A_1 x$, then $y_1' = A_1$, $y_1'' = 0$; $-4A_0 + 3A_1 = 0$ and $-4A_1 = 1$ so $A_0 = -3/16$, $A_1 = -1/4$; $y_1 = -3/16 - x/4$, for $y'' + 3y' - 4y = e^x$ let $y_2 = Axe^x$, then $y_2' = (Ax + A)e^x$, $y_2'' = (Ax + 2A)e^x$, $5A = 1$, $A = 1/5$; $y_2 = \frac{1}{5}xe^x$ thus $y_1 + y_2 = -\frac{3}{16} - \frac{1}{4}x + \frac{1}{5}xe^x$ is a particular solution.

(c) If $y_i(x)$ is a solution of $y'' + p(x)y' + q(x)y = r_i(x)$ for $i = 1, 2, \cdots, n$ then $y_1(x) + y_2(x) + \cdots + y_n(x)$ is a solution of
$$y'' + p(x)y' + q(x)y = r_1(x) + r_2(x) + \cdots + r_n(x).$$

26. $m^2 - m - 2 = 0$, $(m+1)(m-2) = 0$; $m = -1, 2$ so $y_c = c_1 e^{-x} + c_2 e^{2x}$. Let $r_1(x) = x$ and $r_2(x) = e^{-x}$, then $y_1 = A_0 + A_1 x$, $y_1' = A_1$, $y_1'' = 0$, $(-A_1 - 2A_0) - 2A_1 x = x$, $A_0 = 1/4$, $A_1 = -1/2$; $y_2 = Axe^{-x}$, $y_2' = (A - Ax)e^{-x}$, $y_2'' = (-2A + Ax)e^{-x}$, $-3Ae^{-x} = e^{-x}$, $A = -1/3$ so $y = c_1 e^{-x} + c_2 e^{2x} + \frac{1}{4} - \frac{1}{2}x - \frac{1}{3}xe^{-x}$.

27. $m^2 - 1 = 0$; $m = \pm 1$ so $y_c = c_1 e^{-x} + c_2 e^x$. Let $r_1(x) = 1$ and $r_2(x) = e^x$, then $y_1 = A_0$, $y_1' = y_1'' = 0$, $A_0 = -1$; $y_2 = Axe^x$, $y_2' = (Ax + A)e^x$, $y_2'' = (Ax + 2A)e^x$, $2A = 1$, $A = 1/2$ so $y = c_1 e^{-x} + c_2 e^x - 1 + \frac{1}{2}xe^x$.

28. $m^2 - 4m + 3 = 0$, $(m-1)(m-3) = 0$; $m = 1, 3$ so $y_c = c_1 e^x + c_2 e^{3x}$. Let $r_1(x) = 2\cos x$ and $r_2(x) = 4\sin x$, then $y_1 = A_1 \cos x + A_2 \sin x$, $y_1' = -A_1 \sin x + A_2 \cos x$, $y_1'' = -A_1 \cos x - A_2 \sin x$, $(2A_1 - 4A_2)\cos x + (4A_1 + 2A_2)\sin x = 2\cos x$, $A_1 = 1/5$, $A_2 = -2/5$; let $y_2 = B_1 \cos x + B_2 \sin x$ to get $B_1 = 4/5$, $B_2 = 2/5$ so $y = c_1 e^x + c_2 e^{3x} + \cos x$.

29. $m^2 + 4 = 0$; $m = \pm 2i$ so $y_c = c_1 \cos 2x + c_2 \sin 2x$. Let $r_1(x) = 1 + x$ and $r_2(x) = \sin x$, then $y_1 = A_0 + A_1 x$, $y_1' = A_1$, $y_1'' = 0$, $4A_0 = 1$, and $4A_1 = 1$ so $A_0 = A_1 = 1/4$; $y_2 = B_1 \cos x + B_2 \sin x$, $y_2' = -B_1 \sin x + B_2 \cos x$, $y_2'' = -B_1 \cos x - B_2 \sin x$, $3B_1 = 0$ and $3B_2 = 1$ so $B_1 = 0$, $B_2 = 1/3$; $y = c_1 \cos 2x + c_2 \sin 2x + \frac{1}{4} + \frac{1}{4}x + \frac{1}{3}\sin x$.

30. $m^2 + 2m + 1 = 0$, $(m+1)^2 = 0$; $m = -1$ so $y_c = (c_1 + c_2 x)e^{-x}$. Let $r_1(x) = 2 + 3x$, $r_2(x) = 3e^x$, and $r_3(x) = 2\cos 2x$, then $y_1 = A_0 + A_1 x$, $y_1' = A_1$, $y_1'' = 0$, $(A_0 + 2A_1) + A_1 x = 2 + 3x$, $A_0 = -4$, $A_1 = 3$. Let $y_2 = Ae^x$, then $y_2' = y_2'' = Ae^x$, $4Ae^x = 3e^x$, $A = 3/4$. Let $y_3 = B_1 \cos 2x + B_2 \sin 2x$, $y_3' = -2B_1 \sin 2x + 2B_2 \cos 2x$, $y_3'' = -4B_1 \cos 2x - 4B_2 \sin 2x$, $(-3B_1 + 4B_2)\cos 2x - (4B_1 + 3B_2)\sin 2x = 2\cos 2x$, $B_1 = -6/25$, $B_2 = 8/25$ so $y = (c_1 + c_2 x)e^{-x} - 4 + 3x + \frac{3}{4}e^x - \frac{6}{25}\cos 2x + \frac{8}{25}\sin 2x$.

31. $m^2 - 2m + 1 = 0$, $(m-1)^2 = 0$; $m = 1$ so $y_c = (c_1 + c_2 x)e^x$. Let
$r_1(x) = \frac{1}{2}e^x$ and $r_2(x) = -\frac{1}{2}e^{-x}$, then $y_1 = Ax^2 e^x$, $y_1' = (Ax^2 + 2Ax)e^x$
$y_1'' = (Ax^2 + 4Ax + 2A)e^x$, $2A = 1/2$, $A = 1/4$; $y_2 = Be^{-x}$, $y_2' = -Be^{-x}$,
$y_2'' = Be^{-x}$, $4B = 1/2$, $D = 1/8$; $y = (c_1 + c_2 x)e^x + \frac{1}{4}x^2 e^x + \frac{1}{8}e^{-x}$.

32. $m^2 + 4m - 5 = 0$, $(m+5)(m-1) = 0$; $m = -5, 1$ so $y_c = c_1 e^{-5x} + c_2 e^x$. Let $r_1(x) = \frac{1}{2}e^x$ and
$r_2(x) = \frac{1}{2}e^{-x}$, then $y_1 = Axe^x$, $y_1' = (A + Ax)e^x$, $y_1'' = (2A + Ax)e^x$, $6Ae^x = \frac{1}{2}e^x$,
$A = \frac{1}{12}$; $y_2 = Be^{-x}$, $y_2' = -Be^{-x}$, $y_2'' = Be^{-x}$, $-8Be^{-x} = \frac{1}{2}e^{-x}$, $B = -\frac{1}{16}$
so $y = c_1 e^{-5x} + c_2 e^x + \frac{1}{12}xe^x - \frac{1}{16}e^{-x}$.

33. $m^2 + 1 = 0$; $m = \pm i$ so $y_c = c_1 \cos x + c_2 \sin x$. Let $r_1(x) = 6$ and
$r_2(x) = 6\cos 2x$, then $y_1 = A_0$, $y_1' = y_1'' = 0$, $A_0 = 6$; $y_2 = A_1 \cos 2x + A_2 \sin 2x$,
$y_2' = -2A_1 \sin 2x + 2A_2 \cos 2x$, $y_2'' = -4A_1 \cos 2x - 4A_2 \sin 2x$, $-3A_1 = 6$ and $-3A_2 = 0$
so $A_1 = -2$, $A_2 = 0$; $y = c_1 \cos x + c_2 \sin x + 6 - 2\cos 2x$.

34. $m^2 + 2m + 1 = 0$, $(m+1)^2 = 0$; $m = -1$ so $y_c = (c_1 + c_2 x)e^{-x}$. Let
$r_1(x) = \frac{1}{2}$ and $r_2(x) = -\frac{1}{2}\cos 2x$, then $y_1 = A$, $y_1' = y_1'' = 0$, $A = \frac{1}{2}$;
$y_2 = A_1 \cos 2x + A_2 \sin 2x$, $y_2' = -2A_1 \sin 2x + 2A_2 \cos 2x$, $y_2'' = -4A_1 \cos 2x - 4A_2 \sin 2x$,
$(4A_2 - 3A_1)\cos 2x - (4A_1 + 3A_2)\sin 2x = -\frac{1}{2}\cos 2x$, $A_1 = \frac{3}{50}$, $A_2 = -\frac{2}{25}$ so
$y = (c_1 + c_2 x)e^{-x} + \frac{1}{2} + \frac{3}{50}\cos 2x - \frac{2}{25}\sin 2x$.

35. **(a)** $m^2 + \mu^2 = 0$; $m = \pm\mu i$ so $y_c = c_1 \cos \mu x + c_2 \sin \mu x$. Let $y_p = A_1 \cos bx + A_2 \sin bx$,
then $y_p' = -bA_1 \sin bx + bA_2 \cos bx$, $y_p'' = -b^2 A_1 \cos bx - b^2 A_2 \sin bx$,
$A_1 = 0$, $A_2 = a/(\mu^2 - b^2)$; $y = c_1 \cos \mu x + c_2 \sin \mu x + \dfrac{a}{\mu^2 - b^2}\sin bx$.

(b) $y = c_1 \cos \mu x + c_2 \sin \mu x + \displaystyle\sum_{k=1}^{n} \dfrac{a_k}{\mu^2 - k^2\pi^2}\sin k\pi x$.

36. $m^2 + \lambda^2 = 0$; $m = \pm\lambda i$ so $y_c = c_1 \cos \lambda x + c_2 \sin \lambda x$. Let $r_k(x) = a_k \cos k\pi x$ for $k = 1, 2, 3, \ldots, n$,
then $y_k = A_1 \cos k\pi x + A_2 \sin k\pi x$,
$y_k' = -k\pi A_1 \sin k\pi x + k\pi A_2 \cos k\pi x$, $y_k'' = -k^2\pi^2 A_1 \cos k\pi x - k^2\pi^2 A_2 \sin k\pi x$,
$(\lambda^2 - k^2\pi^2)A_1 \cos k\pi x + (\lambda^2 - k^2\pi^2)A_2 \sin k\pi x = a_k \cos k\pi x$, $A_1 = \dfrac{a_k}{\lambda^2 - k^2\pi^2}$, $A_2 = 0$ so
$y = c_1 \cos \lambda x + c_2 \sin \lambda x + \displaystyle\sum_{k=1}^{n} \dfrac{a_k}{\lambda^2 - k^2\pi^2}\cos k\pi x$.

37. $m^2 - m = 0$; $m = 0, 1$ so $y_c = c_1 + c_2 e^x$. Let $y_p = A_0 x + A_1 x^2$, then
$y_p' = A_0 + 2A_1 x$, $y_p'' = 2A_1$; $A_0 = 0$, $A_1 = 2$, $y = c_1 + c_2 e^x + 2x^2$. If $y'(x_0) = y''(x_0) = 0$,

then $4 - 4x_0 = 0$, $x_0 = 1$ so $y'(1) = 0$ and $y''(1) = 0$; $y' = c_2 e^x + 4x$, $y'' = c_2 e^x + 4$,
$y'(1) = c_2 e + 4 = y''(1) = 0$ if $c_2 = -4/e$ so $y = c_1 - 4e^{x-1} + 2x^2$, or simply
$y = c - 4e^{x-1} + 2x^2$ where c is an arbitrary constant.

EXERCISE SET 19.3

1. $m^2 + 1 = 0$; $m = \pm i$ so $y_c = c_1 \cos x + c_2 \sin x$. $u' \cos x + v' \sin x = 0$ and $-u' \sin x + v' \cos x = x^2$;
$u' = -x^2 \sin x$, $v' = x^2 \cos x$ so $u = x^2 \cos x - 2x \sin x - 2 \cos x$, $v = x^2 \sin x + 2x \cos x - 2 \sin x$,
$y_p = u \cos x + v \sin x = x^2 - 2$, $y = c_1 \cos x + c_2 \sin x + x^2 - 2$.

2. $m^2 + 9 = 0$; $m = \pm 3i$ so $y_c = c_1 \cos 3x + c_2 \sin 3x$. $u' \cos 3x + v' \sin 3x = 0$ and
$-3u' \sin 3x + 3v' \cos 3x = 3x$; $u' = -x \sin 3x$, $v' = x \cos 3x$ so $u = \frac{1}{3}x \cos 3x - \frac{1}{9} \sin 3x$,
$v = \frac{1}{3}x \sin 3x + \frac{1}{9} \cos 3x$, $y_p = u \cos 3x + v \sin 3x = \frac{1}{3}x$, $y = c_1 \cos 3x + c_2 \sin 3x + \frac{1}{3}x$.

3. $m^2 + m - 2 = 0$, $(m-1)(m+2) = 0$; $m = 1, -2$ so $y_c = c_1 e^x + c_2 e^{-2x}$.
$u' e^x + v' e^{-2x} = 0$ and $u' e^x - 2v' e^{-2x} = 2e^x$;
$u' = \frac{2}{3}$, $v' = -\frac{2}{3}e^{3x}$ so $u = \frac{2}{3}x$, $v = -\frac{2}{9}e^{3x}$, $y_p = ue^x + ve^{-2x} = \frac{2}{3}xe^x - \frac{2}{9}e^x$.
But $-\frac{2}{9}e^x$ satisfies the complementary equation so $y = c_1 e^x + c_2 e^{-2x} + \frac{2}{3}xe^x$.

4. $m^2 + 5m + 6 = 0$, $(m+2)(m+3) = 0$, $m = -2, -3$ so $y_c = c_1 e^{-2x} + c_2 e^{-3x}$.
$u' e^{-2x} + v' e^{-3x} = 0$ and $-2u' e^{-2x} - 3v' e^{-3x} = e^{-x}$; $u' = e^x$, $v' = -e^{2x}$ so $u = e^x$, $v = -\frac{1}{2}e^{2x}$,
$y_p = ue^{-2x} + ve^{-3x} = \frac{1}{2}e^{-x}$, $y = c_1 e^{-2x} + c_2 e^{-3x} + \frac{1}{2}e^{-x}$.

5. $m^2 + 4 = 0$; $m = \pm 2i$ so $y_c = c_1 \cos 2x + c_2 \sin 2x$. $u' \cos 2x + v' \sin 2x = 0$ and
$-2u' \sin 2x + v' \cos 2x = \sin 2x$; $u' = -\frac{1}{2} \sin^2 2x$, $v' = \frac{1}{2} \sin 2x \cos 2x$ so
$u = -\frac{1}{4}x + \frac{1}{16} \sin 4x = -\frac{1}{4}x + \frac{1}{8} \sin 2x \cos 2x$, $v = -\frac{1}{8} \cos^2 2x$,
$y_p = u \cos 2x + v \sin 2x = -\frac{1}{4}x \cos 2x$, $y = c_1 \cos 2x + c_2 \sin 2x - \frac{1}{4}x \cos 2x$.

6. $m^2 + 9 = 0$; $m = \pm 3i$ so $y_c = c_1 \cos 3x + c_2 \sin 3x$. $u' \cos 3x + v' \sin 3x = 0$ and
$-3u' \sin 3x + 3v' \cos 3x = \cos 3x$; $u' = -\frac{1}{3} \sin 3x \cos 3x$, $v' = \frac{1}{3} \cos^2 3x$ so
$u = -\frac{1}{18} \sin^2 3x$, $v = \frac{1}{6}x + \frac{1}{36} \sin 6x = \frac{1}{6}x + \frac{1}{18} \sin 3x \cos 3x$,
$y_p = u \cos 3x + v \sin 3x = \frac{1}{6}x \sin 3x$, $y = c_1 \cos 3x + c_2 \sin 3x + \frac{1}{6}x \sin 3x$.

7. $m^2 + 1 = 0$; $m = \pm i$ so $y_c = c_1 \cos x + c_2 \sin x$. $u' \cos x + v' \sin x = 0$ and
$-u' \sin x + v' \cos x = \tan x$; $u' = -\tan x \sin x = \cos x - \sec x$, $v' = \tan x \cos x = \sin x$
so $u = \sin x - \ln|\sec x + \tan x|$, $v = -\cos x$, $y_p = u \cos x + v \sin x = -\cos x \ln|\sec x + \tan x|$,
$y = c_1 \cos x + c_2 \sin x - \cos x \ln|\sec x + \tan x|$.

8. $m^2 + 1 = 0$; $m = \pm i$ so $y_c = c_1 \cos x + c_2 \sin x$. $u' \cos x + v' \sin x = 0$ and
$-u' \sin x + v' \cos x = \cot x$; $u' = -\cos x$, $v' = \csc x - \sin x$ so $u = -\sin x$,
$v = \ln|\csc x - \cot x| + \cos x$, $y_p = u \cos x + v \sin x = \sin x \ln|\csc x - \cot x|$,
$y = c_1 \cos x + c_2 \sin x + \sin x \ln|\csc x - \cot x|$.

9. $m^2 - 2m + 1 = 0$, $(m-1)^2 = 0$; $m = 1$ so $y_c = c_1 e^x + c_2 x e^x$. $u' e^x + v' x e^x = 0$ and
$u' e^x + v'(x+1)e^x = e^x/x$; $u' = -1$, $v' = 1/x$ so $u = -x$, $v = \ln|x|$,
$y_p = u e^x + v x e^x = -x e^x + x e^x \ln|x|$. But $-x e^x$ satisfies the complementary equation so
$y = c_1 e^x + c_2 x e^x + x e^x \ln|x|$.

10. $m^2 - 4m + 4 = 0$, $(m-2)^2 = 0$; $m = 2$ so $y_c = c_1 e^{2x} + c_2 x e^{2x}$. $u' e^{2x} + v' x e^{2x} = 0$ and
$2u' e^{2x} + v'(2x+1)e^{2x} = e^{2x}/x$; $u' = -1$, $v' = 1/x$ so $u = -x$, $v = \ln|x|$,
$y_p = u e^{2x} + v x e^{2x} = -x e^{2x} + x e^{2x} \ln|x|$. But $-x e^{2x}$ satisfies the complementary equation
so $y = c_1 e^{2x} + c_2 x e^{2x} + x e^{2x} \ln|x|$.

11. $m^2 + 1 = 0$; $m = \pm i$ so $y_c = c_1 \cos x + c_2 \sin x$. $u' \cos x + v' \sin x = 0$ and
$-u' \sin x + v' \cos x = 3 \sin^2 x$; $u' = -3 \sin^3 x$, $v' = 3 \sin^2 x \cos x$ so $u = 3 \cos x - \cos^3 x$,
$v = \sin^3 x$, $y_p = u \cos x + v \sin x = 3 \cos^2 x - \cos^4 x + \sin^4 x = 3 \cos^2 x - (\cos^4 x - \sin^4 x)$
                $= \frac{3}{2}(1 + \cos 2x) - (\cos^2 x - \sin^2 x)(\cos^2 x + \sin^2 x) = \frac{3}{2} + \frac{1}{2} \cos 2x$,
$y = c_1 \cos x + c_2 \sin x + \frac{3}{2} + \frac{1}{2} \cos 2x$.

12. $m^2 + 1 = 0$; $m = \pm i$ so $y_c = c_1 \cos x + c_2 \sin x$. $u' \cos x + v' \sin x = 0$ and
$-u' \sin x + v' \cos x = 6 \cos^2 x$; $u' = -6 \cos^2 x \sin x$, $v' = 6 \cos^3 x$ so $u = 2 \cos^3 x$,
$v = 6 \sin x - 2 \sin^3 x$,
$y_p = u \cos x + v \sin x = 2 \cos^4 x + 6 \sin^2 x - 2 \sin^4 x = 2(\cos^4 x - \sin^4 x) + 6 \sin^2 x$
                $= 2(\cos^2 x - \sin^2 x)(\cos^2 x + \sin^2 x) + 3(1 - \cos 2x) = 3 - \cos 2x$,
$y = c_1 \cos x + c_2 \sin x + 3 - \cos 2x$.

13. $m^2 + 1 = 0$; $m = \pm i$ so $y_c = c_1 \cos x + c_2 \sin x$. $u' \cos x + v' \sin x = 0$ and
$-u' \sin x + v' \cos x = \csc x$; $u' = -1$, $v' = \cos x \csc x = \cot x$ so $u = -x$,
$v = \ln|\sin x|$, $y_p = u \cos x + v \sin x = -x \cos x + \sin x \ln|\sin x|$,
$y = c_1 \cos x + c_2 \sin x - x \cos x + \sin x \ln|\sin x|$.

14. $m^2 + 9 = 0$; $m = \pm 3i$ so $y_c = c_1 \cos 3x + c_2 \sin 3x$. $u' \cos 3x + v' \sin 3x = 0$ and
$-3u' \sin 3x + 3v' \cos 3x = 6 \sec 3x$; $u' = -2 \tan 3x$, $v' = 2$ so $u = \frac{2}{3} \ln|\cos 3x|$, $v = 2x$,
$y_p = u \cos 3x + v \sin 3x = \frac{2}{3} \cos 3x \ln|\cos 3x| + 2x \sin 3x$,
$y = c_1 \cos 3x + c_2 \sin 3x + \frac{2}{3} \cos 3x \ln|\cos 3x| + 2x \sin 3x$.

15. $m^2 + 1 = 0$; $m = \pm i$ so $y_c = c_1 \cos x + c_2 \sin x$. $u' \cos x + v' \sin x = 0$ and

$-u' \sin x + v' \cos x = \sec x \tan x$; $u' = -\tan^2 x$, $v' = \tan x$ so $u = x - \tan x$,

$v = -\ln|\cos x|$, $y_p = u \cos x + v \sin x = x \cos x - \sin x - \sin x \ln|\cos x|$. But $-\sin x$ satisfies
the complementary equation so $y = c_1 \cos x + c_2 \sin x + x \cos x - \sin x \ln|\cos x|$.

16. $m^2 + 1 = 0$; $m = \pm i$ so $y_c = c_1 \cos x + c_2 \sin x$. $u' \cos x + v' \sin x = 0$ and

$-u' \sin x + v' \cos x = \csc x \cot x$; $u' = -\cot x$, $v' = \cot^2 x$ so $u = -\ln|\sin x|$,

$v = -\cot x - x$, $y_p = u \cos x + v \sin x = -\cos x \ln|\sin x| - \cos x - x \sin x$. But $-\cos x$ satisfies
the complementary equation so $y = c_1 \cos x + c_2 \sin x - \cos x \ln|\sin x| - x \sin x$.

17. $m^2 + 2m + 1 = 0$, $(m+1)^2 = 0$; $m = -1$ so $y_c = c_1 e^{-x} + c_2 x e^{-x}$. $u' e^{-x} + v' x e^{-x} = 0$
and $-u' e^{-x} + v'(1-x)e^{-x} = e^{-x}/x^2$; $u' = -1/x$, $v' = 1/x^2$ so $u = -\ln|x|$, $v = -1/x$,
$y_p = u e^{-x} + v x e^{-x} = -e^{-x} \ln|x| - e^{-x}$. But $-e^{-x}$ satisfies the complementary equation so
$y = c_1 e^{-x} + c_2 x e^{-x} - e^{-x} \ln|x|$.

18. $m^2 - 1 = 0$; $m = \pm 1$ so $y_c = c_1 e^{-x} + c_2 e^{x}$. $u' e^{-x} + v' e^{x} = 0$ and

$-u' e^{-x} + v' e^{x} = x^2 e^{x}$; $u' = -\frac{1}{2} x^2 e^{2x}$, $v' = \frac{1}{2} x^2$ so $u = \left(-\frac{1}{4} x^2 + \frac{1}{4} x - \frac{1}{8}\right) e^{2x}$,

$v = \frac{1}{6} x^3$, $y_p = u e^{-x} + v e^{x} = -\frac{1}{4} x^2 e^{x} + \frac{1}{4} x e^{x} - \frac{1}{8} e^{x} + \frac{1}{6} x^3 e^{x}$. But $-\frac{1}{8} e^{x}$ satisfies the complementary equation so $y = c_1 e^{-x} + c_2 e^{x} + \frac{1}{6} x^3 e^{x} - \frac{1}{4} x^2 e^{x} + \frac{1}{4} x e^{x}$.

19. $m^2 + 4m + 4 = 0$, $(m+2)^2 = 0$; $m = -2$ so $y_c = c_1 e^{-2x} + c_2 x e^{-2x}$. $u' e^{-2x} + v' x e^{-2x} = 0$
and $-2u' e^{-2x} + v'(1-2x)e^{-2x} = x e^{-x}$; $u' = -x^2 e^{x}$, $v' = x e^{x}$ so $u = (-x^2 + 2x - 2)e^{x}$,
$v = (x-1)e^{x}$, $y_p = u e^{-2x} + v x e^{-2x} = (x-2)e^{-x}$, $y = c_1 e^{-2x} + c_2 x e^{-2x} + (x-2)e^{-x}$.

20. $m^2 + 4m + 4 = 0$, $(m+2)^2 = 0$; $m = -2$ so $y_c = c_1 e^{-2x} + c_2 x e^{-2x}$. $u' e^{-2x} + v' x e^{-2x} = 0$
and $-2u' e^{-2x} + v'(1-2x)e^{-2x} = x e^{2x}$; $u' = -x^2 e^{4x}$, $v' = x e^{4x}$ so $u = \left(-\frac{1}{4} x^2 + \frac{1}{8} x - \frac{1}{32}\right) e^{4x}$,
$v = \left(\frac{1}{4} x - \frac{1}{16}\right) e^{4x}$, $y_p = u e^{-2x} + v x e^{-2x} = \frac{1}{16} x e^{2x} - \frac{1}{32} e^{2x}$,
$y = c_1 e^{-2x} + c_2 x e^{-2x} + \frac{1}{16} x e^{2x} - \frac{1}{32} e^{2x}$.

21. $m^2 + 1 = 0$; $m = \pm i$ so $y_c = c_1 \cos x + c_2 \sin x$. $u' \cos x + v' \sin x = 0$ and

$-u' \sin x + v' \cos x = \sec^2 x$; $u' = -\sec x \tan x$, $v' = \sec x$ so $u = -\sec x$,

$v = \ln|\sec x + \tan x|$, $y_p = u \cos x + v \sin x = -1 + \sin x \ln|\sec x + \tan x|$,

$y = c_1 \cos x + c_2 \sin x - 1 + \sin x \ln|\sec x + \tan x|$.

22. $m^2 + 1 = 0$; $m = \pm i$ so $y_c = c_1 \cos x + c_2 \sin x$. $u' \cos x + v' \sin x = 0$ and

$-u' \sin x + v' \cos x = \sec^3 x$; $u' = -\tan x \sec^2 x$, $v' = \sec^2 x$ so $u = -\frac{1}{2} \tan^2 x$,

$v = \tan x$, $y_p = u \cos x + v \sin x = \frac{1}{2} \sec x - \frac{1}{2} \cos x$. But $-\frac{1}{2} \cos x$ satisfies the complementary
equation so $y = c_1 \cos x + c_2 \sin x + \frac{1}{2} \sec x$.

23. $m^2 - 2m + 1 = 0$, $(m-1)^2 = 0$; $m = 1$ so $y_c = c_1 e^x + c_2 x e^x$. $u' e^x + v' x e^x = 0$ and
$u' e^x + v'(x+1)e^x = e^x/x^2$; $u' = -1/x$, $v' = 1/x^2$ so $u = -\ln|x|$, $v = -1/x$,
$y_p = u e^x + v x e^x = -e^x \ln|x| - e^x$. But $-e^x$ satisfies the complementary equation so
$y = c_1 e^x + c_2 x e^x - e^x \ln|x|$.

24. $m^2 - 2m + 1 = 0$, $(m-1)^2 = 0$; $m = 1$ so $y_c = c_1 e^x + c_2 x e^x$. $u' e^x + v' x e^x = 0$ and
$u' e^x + v'(x+1)e^x = x^3 e^x$; $u' = -x^4$, $v' = x^3$ so $u = -\frac{1}{5}x^5$, $v = \frac{1}{4}x^4$,
$y_p = u e^x + v x e^x = -\frac{1}{5}x^5 e^x + \frac{1}{4}x^5 e^x = \frac{1}{20}x^5 e^x$, $y = c_1 e^x + c_2 x e^x + \frac{1}{20}x^5 e^x$.

25. $m^2 - 1 = 0$; $m = \pm 1$ so $y_c = c_1 e^x + c_2 e^{-x}$. $u' e^x + v' e^{-x} = 0$ and $u' e^x - v' e^{-x} = e^x \cos x$;
$u' = \frac{1}{2}\cos x$, $v' = -\frac{1}{2}e^{2x}\cos x$ so $u = \frac{1}{2}\sin x$, $v = -\frac{1}{10}e^{2x}(2\cos x + \sin x)$,
$y_p = u e^x + v e^{-x} = \frac{1}{2}e^x \sin x - \frac{1}{10}e^x(2\cos x + \sin x) = \frac{1}{5}e^x(2\sin x - \cos x)$,
$y = c_1 e^x + c_2 e^{-x} + \frac{1}{5}e^x(2\sin x - \cos x)$.

26. $m^2 - 2m + 2 = 0$; $m = 1 \pm i$ so $y_c = c_1 e^x \cos x + c_2 e^x \sin x$.
$u' e^x \cos x + v' e^x \sin x = 0$ and $u' e^x(\cos x - \sin x) + v' e^x(\cos x + \sin x) = e^{2x}\sin x$;
$u' = -e^x \sin^2 x = \frac{1}{2}e^x \cos 2x - \frac{1}{2}e^x$, $v' = e^x \sin x \cos x = \frac{1}{2}e^x \sin 2x$ so
$u = \frac{1}{10}e^x(\cos 2x + 2\sin 2x) - \frac{1}{2}e^x$, $v = \frac{1}{10}e^x(\sin 2x - 2\cos 2x)$,
$y_p = u e^x \cos x + v e^x \sin x = \frac{1}{5}e^{2x}(\sin x - 2\cos x)$, $y = e^x(c_1 \cos x + c_2 \sin x) + \frac{1}{5}e^{2x}(\sin x - 2\cos x)$.

27. $m^2 + 2m + 1 = 0$, $(m+1)^2 = 0$; $m = -1$ so $y_c = c_1 e^{-x} + c_2 x e^{-x}$. $u' e^{-x} + v' x e^{-x} = 0$
and $-u' e^{-x} + v'(1-x)e^{-x} = e^{-x}\ln|x|$; $u' = -x\ln|x|$, $v' = \ln|x|$ so $u = -\frac{1}{2}x^2\ln|x| + \frac{1}{4}x^2$,
$v = x\ln|x| - x$,
$y_p = u e^{-x} + v x e^{-x} = -\frac{1}{2}x^2 e^{-x}\ln|x| + \frac{1}{4}x^2 e^{-x} + x^2 e^{-x}\ln|x| - x^2 e^{-x} = \frac{1}{2}x^2 e^{-x}\ln|x| - \frac{3}{4}x^2 e^{-x}$,
$y = c_1 e^{-x} + c_2 x e^{-x} + \frac{1}{2}x^2 e^{-x}\ln|x| - \frac{3}{4}x^2 e^{-x}$.

28. $m^2 - 3m + 2 = 0$, $(m-1)(m-2) = 0$; $m = 1, 2$ so $y_c = c_1 e^x + c_2 e^{2x}$. $u' e^x + v' e^{2x} = 0$ and
$u' e^x + 2v' e^{2x} = \dfrac{e^x}{1+e^x}$; $u' = -\dfrac{1}{1+e^x} = -\dfrac{e^{-x}}{e^{-x}+1}$,
$v' = \dfrac{e^{-x}}{1+e^x} = e^{-x} - \dfrac{1}{1+e^x} = e^{-x} - \dfrac{e^{-x}}{e^{-x}+1}$ so $u = \ln(e^{-x}+1)$,
$v = -e^{-x} + \ln(e^{-x}+1)$, $y_p = u e^x + v e^{2x} = -e^x + (e^x + e^{2x})\ln(e^{-x}+1)$. But $-e^x$ satisfies the
complementary equation so $y = c_1 e^x + c_2 e^{2x} + (e^x + e^{2x})\ln(e^{-x}+1)$.

29. $m^2 + 1 = 0$; $m = \pm i$ so $y_c = c_1 \cos x + c_2 \sin x$. $u' \cos x + v' \sin x = 0$, $-u' \sin x + v' \cos x = r(x)$;
$u' = -r(x)\sin x$, $v' = r(x)\cos x$ so $u = -\displaystyle\int r(x)\sin x\, dx$,
$v = \displaystyle\int r(x)\cos x\, dx$, $y = c_1 \cos x + c_2 \sin x - \left[\displaystyle\int r(x)\sin x\, dx\right]\cos x + \left[\displaystyle\int r(x)\cos x\, dx\right]\sin x$.

30. $y_c = c_1 y_1 + c_2 y_2$. $u'y_1 + v'y_2 = 0$ and $u'y_1' + v'y_2' = r(x)$; $u' = -\dfrac{y_2 r}{W}$, $v' = \dfrac{y_1 r}{W}$ so

$$u = -\int \frac{y_2 r}{W}\,dx, \quad v = \int \frac{y_1 r}{W}\,dx, \quad y_p = uy_1 + vy_2 = -y_1\int \frac{y_2 r}{W}\,dx + y_2\int \frac{y_1 r}{W}\,dx.$$

EXERCISE SET 19.4

1. (a) $M = w/g = 64/32 = 2$, $k/M = 8/2 = 4$; $y'' + 4y = 0$, $y(0) = 1$, $y'(0) = 0$.

(b) $m^2 + 4 = 0$; $m = \pm 2i$ so $y = c_1 \cos 2t + c_2 \sin 2t$, $y' = -2c_1 \sin 2t + 2c_2 \cos 2t$, $c_1 = 1$ and $c_2 = 0$, $y = \cos 2t$.

2. (a) $M = 1000$, $\dfrac{k}{M} = \dfrac{25}{1000} = \dfrac{1}{40}$; $y'' + \dfrac{1}{40}y = 0$, $y(0) = 50$, $y'(0) = 0$.

(b) $m^2 + \dfrac{1}{40} = 0$; $m = \pm\dfrac{1}{2\sqrt{10}}i$ so $y = c_1 \cos\dfrac{t}{2\sqrt{10}} + c_2 \sin\dfrac{t}{2\sqrt{10}}$,

$y' = -\dfrac{1}{2\sqrt{10}}c_1 \sin\dfrac{t}{2\sqrt{10}} + \dfrac{1}{2\sqrt{10}}c_2 \cos\dfrac{t}{2\sqrt{10}}$, $c_1 = 50$ and $c_2 = 0$, $y = 50\cos\dfrac{t}{2\sqrt{10}}$.

3. (a) $k/M = g/\ell = 980/5 = 196$; $y'' + 196y = 0$, $y(0) = -10$, $y'(0) = 0$.

(b) $m = \pm 14i$ so $y = c_1 \cos 14t + c_2 \sin 14t$, $y' = -14c_1 \sin 14t + 14c_2 \cos 14t$, $c_1 = -10$ and $c_2 = 0$, $y = -10\cos 14t$.

4. (a) $k/M = g/\ell = 32/2 = 16$; $y'' + 16y = 0$, $y(0) = -4$, $y'(0) = 0$.

(b) $m^2 + 16 = 0$; $m = \pm 4i$ so $y = c_1 \cos 4t + c_2 \sin 4t$, $y' = -4c_1 \sin 4t + 4c_2 \cos 4t$, $c_1 = -4$ and $c_2 = 0$, $y = -4\cos 4t$.

5. (a) $M = w/g = (1/2)/32 = 1/64$, $k/M = 64$, $y_0 = 2$; $y = 2\cos 8t$.

(b) $|y_0| = 2$ (c) $T = \pi/4$ (d) $f = 4/\pi$

6. (a) $M = 2$, $k/M = 4/2 = 2$, $y_0 = 1$; $y = \cos\sqrt{2}\,t$.

(b) $|y_0| = 1$ (c) $T = \sqrt{2}\,\pi$ (d) $f = \dfrac{1}{\sqrt{2}\,\pi}$

7. (a) $y = -\dfrac{1}{4}\cos 8\sqrt{6}\,t$.

(b) $|y_0| = 1/4$ ft.   (c) $T = \pi/(4\sqrt{6})$ (d) $f = 4\sqrt{6}/\pi$

8. **(a)** $k/M = g/\ell = 9.8/8 = 1.225$, $y_0 = -2$; $y = -2\cos\sqrt{1.225}\,t$.

  (b) $|y_0| = 2$ **(c)** $T = \dfrac{2\pi}{\sqrt{1.225}}$ **(d)** $f = \dfrac{\sqrt{1.225}}{2\pi}$

9. **(a)** $M = w/g = 32/32 = 1$, $k/M = 8$; $y'' + 4y' + 8y - 0$, $y(0) - -3$, $y'(0) = 0$.

  (b) $m^2 + 4m + 8 = 0$; $m = -2 \pm 2i$ so $y = e^{-2t}(c_1\cos 2t + c_2\sin 2t)$,

    $y' = 2e^{-2t}[(c_2 - c_1)\cos 2t - (c_1 + c_2)\sin 2t]$, $c_1 = c_2 = -3$, $y = -3e^{-2t}(\cos 2t + \sin 2t)$.

  (d) $\alpha = \beta = 2$, $\omega = \tan^{-1}(\alpha/\beta) = \tan^{-1}1 = \pi/4$; $y = -3\sqrt{2}\,e^{-2t}\cos(2t - \pi/4)$.

  (e) $T = \pi$ **(f)** $f = 1/\pi$

10. **(a)** $M = 3$, $k/M = 9/3 = 3$; $y'' + 2y' + 3y = 0$, $y(0) = -1$, $y'(0) = 0$.

  (b) $m^2 + 2m + 3 = 0$; $m = -1 \pm \sqrt{2}\,i$ so $y = e^{-t}(c_1\cos\sqrt{2}\,t + c_2\sin\sqrt{2}\,t)$,

    $y' = e^{-t}[(\sqrt{2}\,c_2 - c_1)\cos\sqrt{2}\,t - (\sqrt{2}\,c_1 + c_2)\sin\sqrt{2}\,t]$, $c_1 = -1$,

    $c_2 = -1/\sqrt{2}$, $y = -\dfrac{1}{\sqrt{2}}e^{-t}(\sqrt{2}\cos\sqrt{2}\,t + \sin\sqrt{2}\,t)$.

  (d) $\alpha = 1$, $\beta = \sqrt{2}$, $\omega = \tan^{-1}(1/\sqrt{2})$; $y = -\sqrt{\dfrac{3}{2}}e^{-t}\cos[\sqrt{2}\,t - \tan^{-1}(1/\sqrt{2})]$.

  (e) $T = \sqrt{2}\pi$ **(f)** $f = \dfrac{1}{\sqrt{2}\,\pi}$

11. **(a)** $\alpha = 1/5$, $\beta = \sqrt{2}/5$; $y = \dfrac{5}{2}\sqrt{6}e^{-t/5}\cos[\sqrt{2}t/5 - \tan^{-1}(1/\sqrt{2})]$.

  (b) $T = 10\pi/\sqrt{2}$ **(c)** $\sqrt{2}/(10\pi)$

12. **(a)** $\alpha = 1/7$, $\beta = \sqrt{3}/7$, $\omega = \tan^{-1}(1/\sqrt{3}) = \pi/6$; $y = \dfrac{40}{\sqrt{3}}e^{-t/7}\cos\left(\dfrac{\sqrt{3}}{7}t - \dfrac{\pi}{6}\right)$.

  (b) $T = \dfrac{14\pi}{\sqrt{3}}$ **(c)** $f = \dfrac{\sqrt{3}}{14\pi}$

13. **(a)** $y'' + 64y = 0$, $y(0) = 0$, $y'(0) = -2$. $y = c_1\cos 8t + c_2\sin 8t$, $y' = -8c_1\sin 8t + 8c_2\cos 8t$,

    $c_1 = 0$ and $c_2 = -1/4$; $y = -\dfrac{1}{4}\sin 8t$.

  (b) $|y_0| = 1/4$ **(c)** $T = \pi/4$ **(d)** $f = 4/\pi$

14. **(a)** $y'' + 256y = 0$, $y(0) = -1/3$, $y'(0) = -8$. $y = c_1\cos 16t + c_2\sin 16t$,

    $y' = -16c_1\sin 16t + 16c_2\cos 16t$, $c_1 = -1/3$ and $c_2 = -1/2$; $y = -\dfrac{1}{3}\cos 16t - \dfrac{1}{2}\sin 16t$.

(b) $y = -\dfrac{1}{6}(2\cos 16t + 3\sin 16t) = -\dfrac{\sqrt{13}}{6}\left(\dfrac{2}{\sqrt{13}}\cos 16t + \dfrac{3}{\sqrt{13}}\sin 16t\right)$, let $\omega = \tan^{-1}(3/2)$,

then $\sin\omega = 3/\sqrt{13}$ and $\cos\omega = 2/\sqrt{13}$ so

$$y = -\dfrac{\sqrt{13}}{6}(\cos 16t\cos\omega + \sin 16t\sin\omega) = -\dfrac{\sqrt{13}}{6}\cos(16t - \omega);\ \text{the amplitude is } \sqrt{13}/6.$$

(c) $T = \pi/8$ **(d)** $f = 8/\pi$

15. $M = w/g = 1/8$, $k/M = 50$; $y'' + 2y' + 50y = 0$, $y(0) = 1/3$, $y'(0) = -5$.

   $m^2 + 2m + 50 = 0$; $m = -1 \pm 7i$ so $y = e^{-t}(c_1\cos 7t + c_2\sin 7t)$,

   $y' = e^{-t}[(7c_2 - c_1)\cos 7t - (7c_1 + c_2)\sin 7t]$, $c_1 = 1/3$ and $c_2 = -2/3$,

   $y = \dfrac{1}{3}e^{-t}(\cos 7t - 2\sin 7t)$.

16. $M = w/g = 1/20$, $k/M = 5$; $y'' + 4y' + 5y = 0$, $y(0) = 1$, $y'(0) = 2$.

   $m^2 + 4m + 5 = 0$; $m = -2 \pm i$ so $y = e^{-2t}(c_1\cos t + c_2\sin t)$,

   $y' = e^{-2t}[(c_2 - 2c_1)\cos t - (c_1 + 2c_2)\sin t]$, $c_1 = 1$, $c_2 = 4$, $y = e^{-2t}(\cos t + 4\sin t)$.

17. $T = 2\pi\sqrt{M/k} = 2\pi\sqrt{w/(kg)}$, $T^2 = 4\pi^2 w/(32k)$, $\pi^2 w = 8T^2 k$; for w and $w + 4$, $\pi^2 w = 72k$ and $\pi^2(w + 4) = 200k$. Solve this system of equations to get

   (a) $k = \pi^2/32$ **(b)** $w = 9/4$

18. **(a)** $x'' + \dfrac{k}{M}x = 0$ **(b)** $x'' + \dfrac{c}{M}x' + \dfrac{k}{M}x = 0$

19. Let ℓ be the depth to which the cylinder is submerged in the water at equilibrium, then $\rho\pi r^2\ell = \delta\pi r^2 h$ so $\ell = \delta h/\rho$, $M/k = \ell/g = \delta h/(\rho g)$, $T = 2\pi\sqrt{\delta h/(\rho g)}$.

20. $y'' + (k/M)y = 0$, $y(0) = y_0$, $y'(0) = v_0$; $y = c_1\cos\sqrt{k/M}\,t + c_2\sin\sqrt{k/M}\,t$,

   $y' = -c_1\sqrt{k/M}\sin\sqrt{k/M}\,t + c_2\sqrt{k/M}\cos\sqrt{k/M}\,t$, $c_1 = y_0$, $c_2 = v_0\sqrt{M/k}$ so

   $y = y_0\cos\sqrt{k/M}\,t + v_0\sqrt{M/k}\sin\sqrt{k/M}\,t$.

21. **(a)** $y = y_0\cos(\sqrt{k/M}\,t)$, $y' = -y_0\sqrt{k/M}\sin(\sqrt{k/M}\,t)$; when $\sin(\sqrt{k/M}t)$ is 1 or -1, $\cos(\sqrt{k/M}\,t)$ is 0 so $y = 0$ when $|y'| = |y_0|\sqrt{k/M} = 2\pi|y_0|/T$.

   (b) $y'' = -y_0(k/M)\cos(\sqrt{k/M}\,t)$; $|y''|$ is maximum when $\cos(\sqrt{k/M}\,t)$ is 1 or -1, and hence $|y|$ is maximum. The maximum value of $|y''|$ is $|y_0|k/M = 4\pi^2|y_0|/T^2$.

22. $Mm^2 + cm + k = 0$, $m = \dfrac{-c \pm \sqrt{c^2 - 4kM}}{2M}$ so it follows that the roots are distinct and real, equal and real, or complex according to whether $c^2 > 4kM$, $c^2 = 4kM$, or $c^2 < 4kM$.

23. Let $\omega = \tan^{-1}(\alpha/\beta)$, then $\cos\omega = \beta/\sqrt{\alpha^2 + \beta^2}$ and $\sin\omega = \alpha/\sqrt{\alpha^2 + \beta^2}$,

    $\beta\cos\beta t + \alpha\sin\beta t = \sqrt{\alpha^2 + \beta^2}(\cos\beta t\cos\omega + \sin\beta t\sin\omega) = \sqrt{\alpha^2 + \beta^2}\cos(\beta t - \omega)$

    so $y(t) - \dfrac{y_0\sqrt{\alpha^2 + \beta^2}}{\beta}e^{-\alpha t}\cos(\beta t - \omega)$.

24. **(a)** Let m_1 and m_2 be the distinct real roots of $m^2 + \dfrac{c}{M}m + \dfrac{k}{M} = 0$, then $y = c_1 e^{m_1 t} + c_2 e^{m_2 t}$,

    $y' = c_1 m_1 e^{m_1 t} + c_2 m_2 e^{m_2 t}$. Solve $c_1 + c_2 = y_0$ and $m_1 c_1 + m_2 c_2 = 0$ to get $c_1 = \dfrac{m_2 y_0}{m_2 - m_1}$,

    $c_2 = -\dfrac{m_1 y_0}{m_2 - m_1}$, so $y = \dfrac{y_0}{m_2 - m_1}(m_2 e^{m_1 t} - m_1 e^{m_2 t})$.

    (b) The roots are $\dfrac{-c \pm \sqrt{c^2 - 4kM}}{2M}$, but $0 < \sqrt{c^2 - 4kM} < c$ so both m_1 and m_2 are negative

    and hence $\lim\limits_{t \to +\infty} e^{m_1 t} = \lim\limits_{t \to +\infty} e^{m_2 t} = 0$, thus $\lim\limits_{t \to +\infty} y = 0$.

25. **(a)** $m = -\dfrac{c}{2M} = -\alpha$ so $y = (c_1 + c_2 t)e^{-\alpha t}$, $y' = (c_2 - \alpha c_1 - \alpha c_2 t)e^{-\alpha t}$, $c_1 = y_0$ and $c_2 = \alpha y_0$;

    $y = y_0(1 + \alpha t)e^{-\alpha t}$.

    (b) $\lim\limits_{t \to +\infty} y_0(1 + \alpha t)e^{-\alpha t} = \lim\limits_{t \to +\infty} \dfrac{y_0(1 + \alpha t)}{e^{\alpha t}} = \lim\limits_{t \to +\infty} \dfrac{y_0}{e^{\alpha t}} = 0$.

    (c) $\alpha > 0$ so $y_0(1 + \alpha t)e^{-\alpha t} \neq 0$ for $t > 0$.

APPENDIX B
Trigonometry Review

EXERCISES, TRIGONOMETRIC FUNCTIONS AND IDENTITIES

1. (a) $5\pi/12$ (b) $13\pi/6$ (c) $\pi/9$ (d) $23\pi/30$

2. (a) $7\pi/3$ (b) $\pi/12$ (c) $5\pi/4$ (d) $11\pi/12$

3. (a) $12°$ (b) $(270/\pi)°$ (c) $288°$ (d) $540°$

4. (a) $18°$ (b) $(360/\pi)°$ (c) $72°$ (d) $210°$

5. (a)

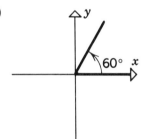

    (b)

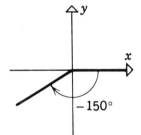

    (c)

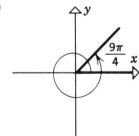

    (d)

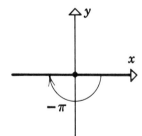

6. Replace θ by $\pi\theta/180$ in the formulas for s and A:

    (a) $s = \dfrac{\pi}{180}r\theta$ (b) $A = \dfrac{\pi}{360}r^2\theta$

7. $150° = 5\pi/6$ rad so

    (a) $s = 4(5\pi/6) = 10\pi/3$ cm   (b) $A = \dfrac{1}{2}(4)^2(5\pi/6) = 20\pi/3$ cm^2

8. $\theta = s/r$ so $A = \frac{1}{2}r^2\theta = \frac{1}{2}r^2(s/r) = \frac{1}{2}rs$

9.   **(a)** $2\pi r = R(2\pi - \theta)$, $r = \dfrac{2\pi - \theta}{2\pi}R$

       (b) $h = \sqrt{R^2 - r^2} = \sqrt{R^2 - (2\pi - \theta)^2 R^2/(4\pi^2)} = \dfrac{\sqrt{4\pi\theta - \theta^2}}{2\pi}R$

10.   The circumference of the circular base is $2\pi r$. When cut and flattened, the cone becomes a circular sector of radius L. If θ is the central angle that subtends the arc of length $2\pi r$, then $\theta = (2\pi r)/L$ so the area S of the sector is $S = (1/2)L^2(2\pi r/L) = \pi r L$ which is the lateral surface area of the cone.

11. $\sin\theta = \sqrt{21}/5$, $\tan\theta = \sqrt{21}/2$ **12.** $\cos\theta = \sqrt{7}/4$, $\tan\theta = 3/\sqrt{7}$

13. $\sin\theta = 5/\sqrt{34}$, $\cos\theta = 3/\sqrt{34}$ **14.** $\csc\theta = 3/\sqrt{8}$, $\cot\theta = 1/\sqrt{8}$

15. $\sin\theta = 3/\sqrt{10}$, $\cos\theta = 1/\sqrt{10}$ **16.** $\sin\theta = \sqrt{5}/3$, $\tan\theta = \sqrt{5}/2$

17. $\tan\theta = \sqrt{21}/2$, $\csc\theta = 5/\sqrt{21}$ **18.** $\cot\theta = \sqrt{15}$, $\sec\theta = 4/\sqrt{15}$

19.   Let x be the length of the side adjacent to θ, then $\cos\theta = x/6 = 0.3$, $x = 1.8$.

20.   Let x be the length of the side opposite θ, then $\cot\theta = 15.6/x = 5.2$, $x = 15.6/5.2 = 3$.

21.   Let x be the length of the hypotenuse, then $\sin\theta = 2.4/x = 0.8$, $x = 2.4/0.8 = 3$.

22.   Let x be the length of the hypotenuse, then $\cos\theta = 1.5/x = 0.6$, $x = 1.5/0.6 = 2.5$.

23.

	$\sin\theta$	$\cos\theta$	$\tan\theta$	$\csc\theta$	$\sec\theta$	$\cot\theta$
(a)	$a/3$	$\sqrt{9-a^2}/3$	$a/\sqrt{9-a^2}$	$3/a$	$3/\sqrt{9-a^2}$	$\sqrt{9-a^2}/a$
(b)	$a/\sqrt{a^2+25}$	$5/\sqrt{a^2+25}$	$a/5$	$\sqrt{a^2+25}/a$	$\sqrt{a^2+25}/5$	$5/a$
(c)	$\sqrt{a^2-1}/a$	$1/a$	$\sqrt{a^2-1}$	$a/\sqrt{a^2-1}$	a	$1/\sqrt{a^2-1}$

24.   Construct a right triangle with one angle equal to $17°$, measure the lengths of the sides and hypotenuse and use formulas (4) and (5) to approximate $\sin 17°$ and $\cos 17°$.

25.   Let h be the altitude as shown in the figure, then $h = 3\sin 60° = 3\sqrt{3}/2$

       so $A = \dfrac{1}{2}(3\sqrt{3}/2)(7) = 21\sqrt{3}/4$.

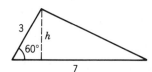

26.   Draw the perpendicular from vertex C
as shown in the figure, then

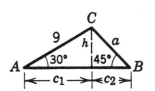

$h = 9 \sin 30° = 9/2$, $a = h/\sin 45° = 9\sqrt{2}/2$,

$c_1 = 9 \cos 30° = 9\sqrt{3}/2$, $c_2 = a \cos 45° = 9/2$,

$c_1 + c_2 = 9(\sqrt{3}+1)/2$, angle $C = 180° - (30° + 45°) = 105°$

27.   Let x be the distance above the ground, then $x = 10 \sin 67° \approx 9.2$ ft.

28.   Let x be the height of the building, then $x = 120 \tan 76° \approx 481$ ft.

29.   From the figure, $h = x - y$
but $x = d \tan \beta$, $y = d \tan \alpha$
so $h = d(\tan \beta - \tan \alpha)$.

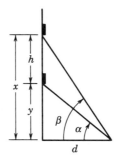

30.   From the figure, $d = x - y$
but $x = h \cot \alpha$, $y = h \cot \beta$
so $d = h(\cot \alpha - \cot \beta)$,

$h = \dfrac{d}{\cot \alpha - \cot \beta}.$

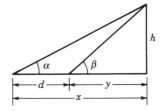

31.   From the figure, area $= \dfrac{1}{2} hc$ but $h = b \sin A$

so area $= \dfrac{1}{2} bc \sin A$. The formulas

area $= \dfrac{1}{2} ac \sin B$ and area $= \dfrac{1}{2} ab \sin C$

follow by drawing altitudes from

vertices B and C, respectively.

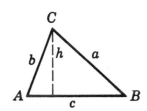

32. From right triangles ADC and BDC,

$h_1 = b\sin A = a\sin B$ so $a/\sin A = b/\sin B$.

From right triangles AEB and CEB,

$h_2 = c\sin A = a\sin C$ so $a/\sin A = c/\sin C$

thus $a/\sin A = b/\sin B = c/\sin C$.

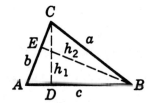

33.

	θ	$\sin\theta$	$\cos\theta$	$\tan\theta$	$\csc\theta$	$\sec\theta$	$\cot\theta$
(a)	$225°$	$-1/\sqrt{2}$	$-1/\sqrt{2}$	1	$-\sqrt{2}$	$-\sqrt{2}$	1
(b)	$-210°$	$1/2$	$-\sqrt{3}/2$	$-1/\sqrt{3}$	2	$-2/\sqrt{3}$	$-\sqrt{3}$
(c)	$5\pi/3$	$-\sqrt{3}/2$	$1/2$	$-\sqrt{3}$	$-2/\sqrt{3}$	2	$-1/\sqrt{3}$
(d)	$-3\pi/2$	1	0	—	1	—	0

34.

	θ	$\sin\theta$	$\cos\theta$	$\tan\theta$	$\csc\theta$	$\sec\theta$	$\cot\theta$
(a)	$330°$	$-1/2$	$\sqrt{3}/2$	$-1/\sqrt{3}$	-2	$2/\sqrt{3}$	$-\sqrt{3}$
(b)	$-120°$	$-\sqrt{3}/2$	$-1/2$	$\sqrt{3}$	$-2/\sqrt{3}$	-2	$1/\sqrt{3}$
(c)	$9\pi/4$	$1/\sqrt{2}$	$1/\sqrt{2}$	1	$\sqrt{2}$	$\sqrt{2}$	1
(d)	-3π	0	-1	0	—	-1	—

35. $\sin\theta = -3/5$, $\cos\theta = -4/5$, $\tan\theta = 3/4$, $\csc\theta = -5/3$, $\sec\theta = -5/4$, $\cot\theta = 4/3$

36. $\sin\theta = 2/5$, $\cos\theta = -\sqrt{21}/5$, $\tan\theta = -2/\sqrt{21}$, $\csc\theta = 5/2$ $\sec\theta = -5/\sqrt{21}$, $\cot\theta = -\sqrt{21}/2$

37. **(a)** from identity (23b) with $\alpha = 45°$ and $\beta = 30°$,

$\cos 15° = \cos(45° - 30°) = \cos 45° \cos 30° + \sin 45° \sin 30°$

$= (1/\sqrt{2})(\sqrt{3}/2) + (1/\sqrt{2})(1/2) = (\sqrt{6} + \sqrt{2})/4$, or from (27a) with $\alpha = 30°$,

$\cos^2 15° = \cos^2(30°/2) = (1 + \cos 30°)/2 = (2 + \sqrt{3})/4$ so $\cos 15° = \dfrac{1}{2}\sqrt{2 + \sqrt{3}}$

(b) from (27b) with $\alpha = 45°$, $\sin^2 22.5° = \sin^2(45°/2) = (1 - \cos 45°)/2 = (2 - \sqrt{2})/4$

so $\sin 22.5° = \dfrac{1}{2}\sqrt{2 - \sqrt{2}}$

(c) from (27a) with $\alpha = 150°$, $\cos^2 75° = \cos^2(150°/2) = (1 + \cos 150°)/2 = (2 - \sqrt{3})/4$

so $\cos 75° = \dfrac{1}{2}\sqrt{2 - \sqrt{3}}$;

from (27b) with $\alpha = 75°$, $\sin^2 37.5° = \sin^2(75°/2) = (1 - \cos 75°)/2 = (2 - \sqrt{2 - \sqrt{3}})/4$

so $\sin 37.5° = \dfrac{1}{2}\sqrt{2 - \sqrt{2 - \sqrt{3}}}$

38. **(a)** from (22a) with $\alpha = 30°$ and $\beta = 45°$,

$\sin 75° = \sin(30° + 45°) = \sin 30° \cos 45° + \cos 30° \sin 45°$

$\quad = (1/2)(1/\sqrt{2}) + (\sqrt{3}/2)(1/\sqrt{2}) = (\sqrt{2} + \sqrt{6})/4$

(b) from (24a) with $\alpha = 30°$ and $\beta = 45°$,

$\tan 75° = \tan(30° + 45°) = \dfrac{\tan 30° + \tan 45°}{1 - \tan 30° \tan 45°} = \dfrac{1/\sqrt{3} + 1}{1 - (1/\sqrt{3})(1)} = 2 + \sqrt{3}$

39. **(a)** $\sin 2\theta = 2\sin\theta\cos\theta = 2(\sqrt{5}/3)(2/3) = 4\sqrt{5}/9$

(b) $\cos 2\theta = 2\cos^2\theta - 1 = 2(2/3)^2 - 1 = -1/9$

40. **(a)** $\sin(\alpha - \beta) = \sin\alpha\cos\beta - \cos\alpha\sin\beta = (3/5)(1/\sqrt{5}) - (4/5)(2/\sqrt{5}) = -1/\sqrt{5}$

(b) $\cos(\alpha + \beta) = \cos\alpha\cos\beta - \sin\alpha\sin\beta = (4/5)(1/\sqrt{5}) - (3/5)(2/\sqrt{5}) = -2/(5\sqrt{5})$

41. **(a)** $\sin(\pi/2 + \theta) = \sin(\pi/2)\cos\theta + \cos(\pi/2)\sin\theta = (1)\cos\theta + (0)\sin\theta = \cos\theta$

(b) $\cos(\pi/2 + \theta) = \cos(\pi/2)\cos\theta - \sin(\pi/2)\sin\theta = (0)\cos\theta - (1)\sin\theta = -\sin\theta$

(c) $\sin(3\pi/2 - \theta) = \sin(3\pi/2)\cos\theta - \cos(3\pi/2)\sin\theta = (-1)\cos\theta - (0)\sin\theta = -\cos\theta$

(d) $\cos(3\pi/2 + \theta) = \cos(3\pi/2)\cos\theta - \sin(3\pi/2)\sin\theta = (0)\cos\theta - (-1)\sin\theta = \sin\theta$

42. $\tan(\alpha + \beta) = \dfrac{\sin(\alpha + \beta)}{\cos(\alpha + \beta)} = \dfrac{\sin\alpha\cos\beta + \cos\alpha\sin\beta}{\cos\alpha\cos\beta - \sin\alpha\sin\beta}$, divide numerator and denominator by

$\cos\alpha\cos\beta$ and use $\tan\alpha = \dfrac{\sin\alpha}{\cos\alpha}$ and $\tan\beta = \dfrac{\sin\beta}{\cos\beta}$ to get (24a);

$\tan(\alpha - \beta) = \tan(\alpha + (-\beta)) = \dfrac{\tan\alpha + \tan(-\beta)}{1 - \tan\alpha\tan(-\beta)} = \dfrac{\tan\alpha - \tan\beta}{1 + \tan\alpha\tan\beta}$ because

$\tan(-\beta) = -\tan\beta$.

43. **(a)** Add (22a) and (23a) to get $\sin(\alpha - \beta) + \sin(\alpha + \beta) = 2\sin\alpha\cos\beta$ so

$\sin\alpha\cos\beta = (1/2)[\sin(\alpha - \beta) + \sin(\alpha + \beta)]$.

(b) Subtract (22b) from (23b).   **(c)** Add (22b) and (23b).

44. **(a)** From (28a), $\sin\dfrac{A + B}{2}\cos\dfrac{A - B}{2} = \dfrac{1}{2}(\sin B + \sin A)$ so

$\sin A + \sin B = 2\sin\dfrac{A + B}{2}\cos\dfrac{A - B}{2}$.

(b) Use (28c)   **(c)** Use (28b)

45. $\sin \alpha + \sin(-\beta) = 2 \sin \dfrac{\alpha - \beta}{2} \cos \dfrac{\alpha + \beta}{2}$, but $\sin(-\beta) = -\sin \beta$ so

$\sin \alpha - \sin \beta = 2 \cos \dfrac{\alpha + \beta}{2} \sin \dfrac{\alpha - \beta}{2}.$

46. $\dfrac{\cos \theta \sec \theta}{1 + \tan^2 \theta} = \dfrac{\cos \theta \sec \theta}{\sec^2 \theta} = \dfrac{\cos \theta}{\sec \theta} = \dfrac{\cos \theta}{(1/\cos \theta)} = \cos^2 \theta$

47. $\dfrac{\cos \theta \tan \theta + \sin \theta}{\tan \theta} = \dfrac{\cos \theta (\sin \theta / \cos \theta) + \sin \theta}{\sin \theta / \cos \theta} = 2 \cos \theta$

48. $2 \csc 2\theta = \dfrac{2}{\sin 2\theta} = \dfrac{2}{2 \sin \theta \cos \theta} = \left(\dfrac{1}{\sin \theta} \right) \left(\dfrac{1}{\cos \theta} \right) = \csc \theta \sec \theta$

49. $\tan \theta + \cot \theta = \dfrac{\sin \theta}{\cos \theta} + \dfrac{\cos \theta}{\sin \theta} = \dfrac{\sin^2 \theta + \cos^2 \theta}{\sin \theta \cos \theta} = \dfrac{1}{\sin \theta \cos \theta} = \dfrac{2}{2 \sin \theta \cos \theta} = \dfrac{2}{\sin 2\theta} = 2 \csc 2\theta$

50. $\dfrac{\sin 2\theta}{\sin \theta} - \dfrac{\cos 2\theta}{\cos \theta} = \dfrac{\sin 2\theta \cos \theta - \cos 2\theta \sin \theta}{\sin \theta \cos \theta} = \dfrac{\sin \theta}{\sin \theta \cos \theta} = \sec \theta$

51. $\dfrac{\sin \theta + \cos 2\theta - 1}{\cos \theta - \sin 2\theta} = \dfrac{\sin \theta + (1 - 2 \sin^2 \theta) - 1}{\cos \theta - 2 \sin \theta \cos \theta} = \dfrac{\sin \theta (1 - 2 \sin \theta)}{\cos \theta (1 - 2 \sin \theta)} = \tan \theta$

52. Using (28a), $2 \sin 2\theta \cos \theta = 2(1/2)(\sin \theta + \sin 3\theta) = \sin \theta + \sin 3\theta$

53. Using (28a), $2 \cos 2\theta \sin \theta = 2(1/2)[\sin(-\theta) + \sin 3\theta] = \sin 3\theta - \sin \theta$

54. $\tan(\theta/2) = \dfrac{\sin(\theta/2)}{\cos(\theta/2)} = \dfrac{2 \sin^2(\theta/2)}{2 \sin(\theta/2) \cos(\theta/2)} = \dfrac{1 - \cos \theta}{\sin \theta}$

55. $\tan(\theta/2) = \dfrac{\sin(\theta/2)}{\cos(\theta/2)} = \dfrac{2 \sin(\theta/2) \cos(\theta/2)}{2 \cos^2(\theta/2)} = \dfrac{\sin \theta}{1 + \cos \theta}$

56. From (29c), $\cos(\pi/3 + \theta) + \cos(\pi/3 - \theta) = 2 \cos(\pi/3) \cos \theta = 2(1/2) \cos \theta = \cos \theta$

57. $\sin 3\theta = \sin(2\theta + \theta) = \sin 2\theta \cos \theta + \cos 2\theta \sin \theta = (2 \sin \theta \cos \theta) \cos \theta + (\cos^2 \theta - \sin^2 \theta) \sin \theta$
$\qquad = 2 \sin \theta \cos^2 \theta + \sin \theta \cos^2 \theta - \sin^3 \theta = 3 \sin \theta \cos^2 \theta - \sin^3 \theta;$

similarly, $\cos 3\theta = \cos^3 \theta - 3 \sin^2 \theta \cos \theta$

58. **(a)** From (22a), $C \sin(\alpha + \phi) = C \sin \alpha \cos \phi + C \cos \alpha \sin \phi$ so $C \cos \phi = 3$ and
$C \sin \phi = 5$, square and add to get $C^2(\cos^2 \phi + \sin^2 \phi) = 9 + 25$, $C^2 = 34$. If
$C = \sqrt{34}$ then $\cos \phi = 3/\sqrt{34}$ and $\sin \phi = 5/\sqrt{34}$ so ϕ is the first-quadrant angle for
which $\tan \phi = 5/3$. $3 \sin \alpha + 5 \cos \alpha = \sqrt{34} \sin(\alpha + \phi)$.

(b) Follow the procedure of part (a) to get $C \cos \phi = A$ and $C \sin \phi = B$, $C = \sqrt{A^2 + B^2}$, $\tan \phi = B/A$ where the quadrant in which ϕ lies is determined by the signs of A and B because $\cos \phi = A/C$ and $\sin \phi = B/C$, so $A \sin \alpha + B \cos \alpha = \sqrt{A^2 + B^2} \sin(\alpha + \phi)$.

59. Consider the triangle having a, b, and d as sides. The angle formed by sides a and b is $\pi - \theta$ so from the law of cosines, $d^2 = a^2 + b^2 - 2ab \cos(\pi - \theta) = a^2 + b^2 + 2ab \cos \theta$, $d = \sqrt{a^2 + b^2 + 2ab \cos \theta}$.

60. (a) $\theta = \pi/2 \pm 2n\pi$, $n = 0, 1, 2, \ldots$
    (c) $\theta = \pi/4 \pm n\pi$, $n = 0, 1, 2, \ldots$
    (e) $\theta = \pm 2n\pi$, $n = 0, 1, 2, \ldots$
    (b) $\theta = \pm 2n\pi$, $n = 0, 1, 2, \ldots$
    (d) $\theta = \pi/2 \pm 2n\pi$, $n = 0, 1, 2, \ldots$
    (f) $\theta = \pi/4 \pm n\pi$, $n = 0, 1, 2, \ldots$

61. (a) $\theta = \pm n\pi$, $n = 0, 1, 2, \ldots$
    (c) $\theta = \pm n\pi$, $n = 0, 1, 2, \ldots$
    (e) $\theta = \pi/2 \pm n\pi$, $n = 0, 1, 2, \ldots$
    (b) $\theta = \pi/2 \pm n\pi$, $n = 0, 1, 2, \ldots$
    (d) $\theta = \pm n\pi$, $n = 0, 1, 2, \ldots$
    (f) $\theta = \pm n\pi$, $n = 0, 1, 2, \ldots$

62. $\theta = 3\pi/4 \pm 2n\pi$ and $\theta = 5\pi/4 \pm 2n\pi$, $n = 0, 1, 2, \ldots$

63. $\theta = 5\pi/4 \pm 2n\pi$ and $\theta = 7\pi/4 \pm 2n\pi$, $n = 0, 1, 2, \ldots$

64. $\theta = 3\pi/4 \pm n\pi$, $n = 0, 1, 2, \ldots$

65. $\theta = \pi/3 \pm 2n\pi$ and $\theta = 5\pi/3 \pm 2n\pi$, $n = 0, 1, 2, \ldots$

66. $\theta = 7\pi/6 \pm 2n\pi$ and $\theta = 11\pi/6 \pm 2n\pi$, $n = 0, 1, 2, \ldots$

67. $\theta = \pi/3 \pm n\pi$, $n = 0, 1, 2, \ldots$ 68. $\theta = \pi/6 \pm n\pi$, $n = 0, 1, 2, \ldots$

69. $\theta = 4\pi/3 \pm 2n\pi$ and $\theta = 5\pi/3 \pm 2n\pi$, $n = 0, 1, 2, \ldots$

70. $\theta = 3\pi/2 \pm n\pi$, $n = 0, 1, 2, \ldots$ 71. $\theta = \pi \pm 2n\pi$, $n = 0, 1, 2, \ldots$

72. $\theta = 3\pi/4 \pm n\pi$, $n = 0, 1, 2, \ldots$ 73. $\theta = \pi/6 \pm n\pi$, $n = 0, 1, 2, \ldots$

74. $\theta = 2\pi/3 \pm 2n\pi$ and $\theta = 4\pi/3 \pm 2n\pi$, $n = 0, 1, 2, \ldots$

75. $\theta = 7\pi/6 \pm 2n\pi$ and $\theta = 11\pi/6 \pm 2n\pi$, $n = 0, 1, 2, \ldots$

76. $\theta = \pi/3 \pm 2n\pi$ and $\theta = 2\pi/3 \pm 2n\pi$, $n = 0, 1, 2, \ldots$

77. $\theta = \pi/6 \pm 2n\pi$ and $\theta = 11\pi/6 \pm 2n\pi$, $n = 0, 1, 2, \ldots$

EXERCISES, GRAPHS OF TRIGONOMETRIC FUNCTIONS

1.   **(a)** $2\pi/5$ **(b)** 6π **(c)** 8π **(d)** $\pi/7$
         (e) 2   **(f)** 10   **(g)** 1   **(h)** $2k\pi$

2.   **(a)** 4   **(b)** 8   **(c)** 1/2   **(d)** 1/8

3.   **(a)** 5   **(b)** 1/3   **(c)** 1/2   **(d)** 1

4.

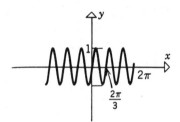

5.

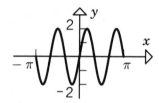

6.

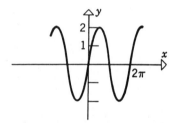

7.

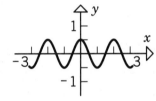

8.

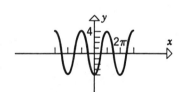

9.

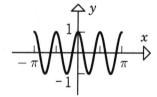

10.

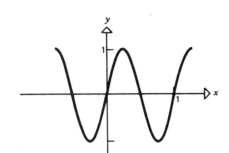

11.

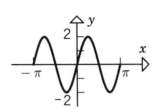

12. (a) They are the same because $\cos(-x) = \cos x$.

(b) They are mirror images of one another with respect to the x-axis because $\sin(-x) = -\sin x$.

13. **(a)**

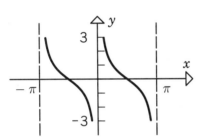

(b)

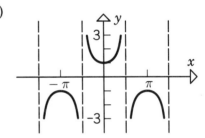

(c)

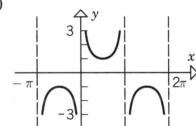

14.

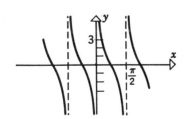

15.

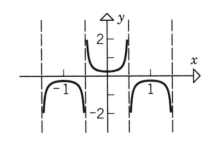

16.

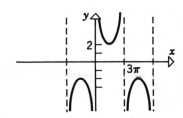

17.

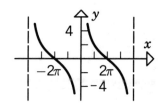

18.

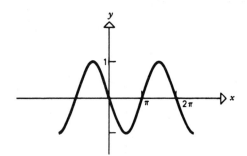

19.

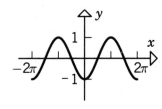

20.

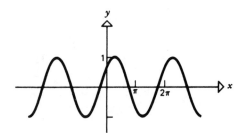

21.

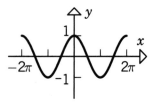

22.

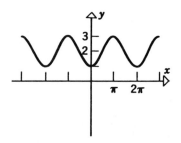

23.

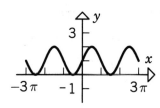

24.

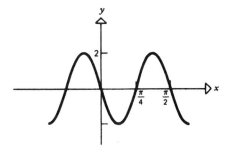

25.

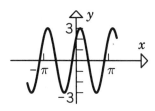

26.

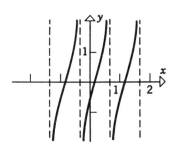

27.

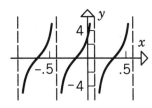

28.

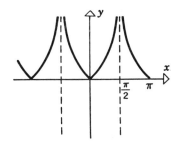

29.

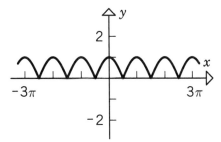

30.

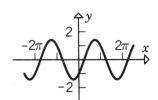

31.

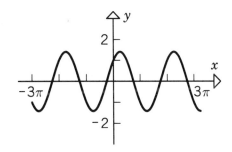

32.

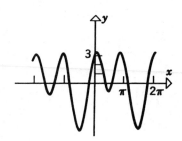

33. (a) odd (b) even (c) odd (d) even

(e) even (f) even (g) odd (h) even

34. area $OAP <$ area $OBP <$ area OBQ, $\dfrac{1}{2}\sin x < \dfrac{1}{2}x < \dfrac{1}{2}\tan x$, $\sin x < x < \tan x$ if $0 < x < \pi/2$.

35. If $|x| \geq \pi/2$ then $|\sin x| \leq |x|$ because $|\sin x| \leq 1 < \pi/2$ for all x. If $x = 0$ then $\sin x = 0$ so $|\sin x| \leq |x|$. If $0 < |x| < \pi/2$ then, from Exercise 34, $\sin|x| \leq |x|$. But $\sin|x| = |\sin x|$ if $0 < |x| < \pi/2$ so $|\sin x| \leq |x|$.

36. Both $a\sin bx$ and $a\cos bx$ repeat when bx changes by 2π or equivalently when x changes by $2\pi/b$ so the fundamental period is $2\pi/|b|$. Both $\sin bx$ and $\cos bx$ oscillate between -1 and 1 so $a\sin bx$ and $a\cos bx$ both oscillate between $-a$ and a.

37. $\tan bx$ repeats when bx changes by π or equivalently when x changes by π/b so the fundamental period is $\pi/|b|$.

APPENDIX C

Supplementary Material

EXERCISES, ONE-SIDED AND INFINITE LIMITS

1. If $x > 2$ then $|(x+1) - 3| = |x - 2| = x - 2 < \epsilon$ when $x < 2 + \epsilon$; take $\delta = \epsilon$.

2. If $x < 1$ then $|(3x+2) - 5| = 3|x - 1| = -3(x - 1) < \epsilon$ when $x - 1 > -\epsilon/3$, $x > 1 - \epsilon/3$; take $\delta = \epsilon/3$.

3. If $x > 4$ then $|\sqrt{x-4} - 0| = \sqrt{x-4} < \epsilon$ when $x - 4 < \epsilon^2$, $x < 4 + \epsilon^2$; take $\delta = \epsilon^2$.

4. If $x < 0$ then $|\sqrt{-x} - 0| = \sqrt{-x} < \epsilon$ when $-x < \epsilon^2$, $x > -\epsilon^2 = 0 - \epsilon^2$; take $\delta = \epsilon^2$.

5. If $x > 2$ then $|f(x) - 2| = |x - 2| = x - 2 < \epsilon$ when $x < 2 + \epsilon$; take $\delta = \epsilon$.

6. If $x < 2$ then $|f(x) - 6| = |3x - 6| = 3|x - 2| = -3(x - 2) < \epsilon$ when $x - 2 > -\epsilon/3$, $x > 2 - \epsilon/3$; take $\delta = \epsilon/3$.

7. If $x > 0$ then $|1/x^2 - 0| = 1/x^2 < \epsilon$ when $x^2 > 1/\epsilon$, $x > 1/\sqrt{\epsilon}$; take $N = 1/\sqrt{\epsilon}$.

8. If $x < 0$ then $|1/x - 0| = |1/x| = -1/x < \epsilon$ when $x < -1/\epsilon$; take $N = -1/\epsilon$.

9. If $x < -2$ then $|1/(x+2) - 0| = 1/|x+2| = -1/(x+2) < \epsilon$ when $x + 2 < -1/\epsilon$, $x < -2 - 1/\epsilon$; take $N = -2 - 1/\epsilon$.

10. If $x > -2$ then $|1/(x+2) - 0| = 1/(x+2) < \epsilon$ when $x + 2 > 1/\epsilon$, $x > -2 + 1/\epsilon$; take $N = 1/\epsilon$.

11. If $x > -1$ then $|x/(x+1) - 1| = |-1/(x+1)| = 1/(x+1) < \epsilon$ when $x + 1 > 1/\epsilon$, $x > -1 + 1/\epsilon$; take $N = 1/\epsilon$.

12. If $x < -1$ then $|x/(x+1) - 1| = 1/|x+1| = -1/(x+1) < \epsilon$ when $x + 1 < -1/\epsilon$, $x < -1 - 1/\epsilon$; take $N = -1 - 1/\epsilon$.

13. If $x < -5/2$ then $\left| \dfrac{4x-1}{2x+5} - 2 \right| = \left| \dfrac{-11}{2x+5} \right| = \dfrac{11}{|2x+5|} = -\dfrac{11}{2x+5} < \epsilon$ when $2x + 5 < -\dfrac{11}{\epsilon}$, $x < -\dfrac{5}{2} - \dfrac{11}{2\epsilon}$; take $N = -\dfrac{5}{2} - \dfrac{11}{2\epsilon}$.

14. If $x > -5/2$ then $\left| \dfrac{4x-1}{2x+5} - 2 \right| = \dfrac{11}{2x+5} < \epsilon$ when $2x + 5 > \dfrac{11}{\epsilon}$, $x > -\dfrac{5}{2} + \dfrac{11}{2\epsilon}$; take $N = \dfrac{11}{2\epsilon}$.

15. If $x \neq 3$ and $N > 0$ then $1/(x-3)^2 > N$ when $(x-3)^2 < 1/N$, $|x-3| < 1/\sqrt{N}$; take $\delta = 1/\sqrt{N}$.

16. If $x \neq 3$ and $N < 0$ then $-1/(x-3)^2 < N$ when $(x-3)^2 < -1/N = 1/|N|$, $|x-3| < 1/\sqrt{|N|}$; take $\delta = 1/\sqrt{|N|}$.

17. If $x \neq 0$ and $N > 0$ then $1/|x| > N$ when $|x| < 1/N$; take $\delta = 1/N$.

18. If $x \neq 1$ and $N > 0$ then $1/|x-1| > N$ when $|x-1| < 1/N$; take $\delta = 1/N$.

19. If $x \neq 0$ and $N < 0$ then $-1/x^4 < N$ when $x^4 < -1/N = 1/|N|$, $x < 1/\sqrt[4]{|N|}$; take $\delta = 1/\sqrt[4]{|N|}$.

20. If $x \neq 0$ and $N > 0$ then $1/x^4 > N$ when $x^4 < 1/N$, $x < 1/\sqrt[4]{N}$; take $\delta = 1/\sqrt[4]{N}$.

21. (15): Let f be defined on some open interval extending to the right from a. We will write $\lim\limits_{x \to a^+} f(x) = +\infty \ (-\infty)$ if given any positive (negative) number N we can find a number $\delta > 0$ such that $f(x)$ satisfies $f(x) > N \ (f(x) < N)$ whenever x satisfies $a < x < a + \delta$.

(16): Similar to (15) with "right" replaced by "left", a^+ replaced by a^-, and $a < x < a + \delta$ replaced by $a - \delta < x < a$.

22. (a) If $x > 0$ and $N > 0$ then $1/x > N$ when $x < 1/N$; take $\delta = 1/N$.

(b) If $x < 0$ and $N < 0$ then $1/x < N$ when $x > 1/N = -1/|N|$; take $\delta = 1/|N|$.

23. (a) If $x > 1$ and $N < 0$ then $1/(1-x) < N$ when $1-x > 1/N = -1/|N|$, $x < 1 + 1/|N|$; take $\delta = 1/|N|$.

(b) If $x < 1$ and $N > 0$ then $1/(1-x) > N$ when $1-x < 1/N$, $x > 1 - 1/N$; take $\delta = 1/N$.

24. (17): Let f be defined on some infinite open interval $(x_0, +\infty)$. We will write $\lim\limits_{x \to +\infty} f(x) = +\infty \ (-\infty)$ if given any positive (negative) number M there corresponds a positive number N such that $f(x) > M \ (f(x) < M)$ whenever x satisfies $x > N$.

(18): Similar to (17) with $(x_0, +\infty)$ replaced by $(-\infty, x_0)$, $x \to +\infty$ replaced by $x \to -\infty$, and $x > N$ replaced by $x < N$ where $N < 0$.

25. (a) If $M > 0$ then $x + 1 > M$ when $x > M - 1$; take $N = M$

(b) If $M < 0$ then $x + 1 < M$ when $x < M - 1$; take $N = M - 1$.

26. (a) If $x > 0$ and $M > 0$ then $x^2 - 3 > M$ when $x^2 > M + 3$, $x > \sqrt{M+3}$; take $N = \sqrt{M+3}$.

(b) If $M < 0$ then $x^3 + 5 < M$ when $x^3 < M - 5$, $x < \sqrt[3]{M-5}$; take $N = \sqrt[3]{M-5}$.

EXERCISES, PROOFS OF LIMIT THEOREMS

1. $|k - k| = |0| = 0 < \epsilon$ when $x > N$ for any $N > 0$.

2. $|k - k| = 0 < \epsilon$ when $x < N$ for any $N < 0$.

3. $|[f(x) + g(x)] - [L_1 + L_2]| = |[f(x) - L_1] + [g(x) - L_2]| \leq |f(x) - L_1| + |g(x) - L_2|$.

   Given $\epsilon > 0$, there exist negative numbers N_1 and N_2 such that $|f(x) - L_1| < \epsilon/2$ and $|g(x) - L_2| < \epsilon/2$ whenever $x < N_1$ and $x < N_2$, respectively. Let $N = \min(N_1, N_2)$, if $x < N$ then $|f(x) - L_1| + |g(x) - L_2| < \epsilon/2 + \epsilon/2 = \epsilon$ so $|[f(x) + g(x)] - [L_1 + L_2]| < \epsilon$.

4. Similar to Exercise 3, replace $x < N_1$ and $x < N_2$ by $x > N_1$ and $x > N_2$ where N_1 and N_2 are positive numbers, let $N = \max(N_1, N_2)$, and replace $x < N$ by $x > N$.

5. From Theorem 8, $\lim_{x \to a}(-1) = -1$ so from Theorem 10,

   $$\lim_{x \to a}[(-1)g(x)] = \lim_{x \to a}(-1) \lim_{x \to a} g(x) = (-1)L_2 = -L_2 \text{ thus, using Theorem 9,}$$

   $$\lim_{x \to a}[f(x) - g(x)] = \lim_{x \to a}[f(x) + (-g(x))] = \lim_{x \to a} f(x) + \lim_{x \to a}[-g(x)] = L_1 + (-L_2) = L_1 - L_2$$

6. (a) Given $N > 0$, there exist numbers $\delta_1 > 0$ and $\delta_2 > 0$ such that $f(x) > N/2$ and $g(x) > N/2$ whenever $0 < |x - a| < \delta_1$ and $0 < |x - a| < \delta_2$, respectively. Let $\delta = \min(\delta_1, \delta_2)$ then $f(x) > N/2$ and $g(x) > N/2$ whenever $0 < |x - a| < \delta$ so $f(x) + g(x) > N/2 + N/2 = N$.

   (b) No, for example $\lim_{x \to 0}(1/x^4 - 1/x^2) = \lim_{x \to 0}[(1 - x^2)/x^4] = +\infty$

7. (a) Given $N < 0$, there exist numbers $\delta_1 > 0$ and $\delta_2 > 0$ such that $f(x) < N/2$ and $g(x) > -N/2$ whenever $0 < |x - a| < \delta_1$ and $0 < |x - a| < \delta_2$, respectively. Let $\delta = \min(\delta_1, \delta_2)$ then $f(x) < N/2$ and $-g(x) < N/2$ whenever $0 < |x - a| < \delta$ so $f(x) - g(x) < N/2 + N/2 = N$.

   (b) No, for example $\lim_{x \to 0}[(-1/x^2) + (1/x^4)] = \lim_{x \to 0}[(1 - x^2)/x^4] = +\infty$

8. From Theorem 8, $\lim_{x \to a} k = k$ so from Theorem 10, $\lim_{x \to a}[k \, f(x)] = \left[\lim_{x \to a} k\right]\left[\lim_{x \to a} f(x)\right] = kL$.

9. If $\lim_{x \to a} f(x) = L$ then given $\epsilon > 0$, there exists a $\delta > 0$ such that $|f(x) - L| < \epsilon$ whenever $0 < |x - a| < \delta$. But $|f(x) - L| = |[f(x) - L] - 0| < \epsilon$ whenever $0 < |x - a| < \delta$ so $\lim_{x \to a}[f(x) - L] = 0$. If $\lim_{x \to a}[f(x) - L] = 0$ then given $\epsilon > 0$, there exists a $\delta > 0$ such that $|[f(x) - L] - 0| < \epsilon$ whenever $0 < |x - a| < \delta$, but $|[f(x) - L] - 0| = |f(x) - L| < \epsilon$ whenever $0 < |x - a| < \delta$ so $\lim_{x \to a} f(x) = L$.

10. Given $\epsilon > 0$, there exists a $\delta > 0$ such that $|f(x) - L| < \epsilon$ whenever $0 < |x - a| < \delta$. But $||f(x)| - |L|| \le |f(x) - L|$ (Section 1.2, Exercise 53) so $||f(x)| - |L|| < \epsilon$ whenever $0 < |x - a| < \delta$ thus $\lim\limits_{x \to a} |f(x)| = |L|$.

11. If $\lim\limits_{x \to a} f(x) = L$ then given $\epsilon > 0$ there exists a $\delta > 0$ such that $|f(x) - L| < \epsilon$ whenever $0 < |x - a| < \delta$ or equivalently whenever $a < x < a + \delta$ or $a - \delta < x < a$ so
$$\lim\limits_{x \to a^+} f(x) = \lim\limits_{x \to a^-} f(x) = L.$$

EXERCISES, PROOFS OF KEY RESULTS

1. **(a)** In the proof of part (a), interchange the words "increasing" and "decreasing", and reverse the order of the inequality symbols.

   (b) If $f'(x)$ has the same sign on the intervals (a, x_0) and (x_0, b), then f is increasing on (a, b) or decreasing on (a, b) so f does not have a relative extremum at x_0.

2. Proceed as in part (a) using $f''(x_0) < 0$ and $\epsilon = \dfrac{1}{2}|f''(x_0)| = -\dfrac{1}{2}f''(x_0)$ to show that $f'(x) < 0$ for all x in $(x_0, x_0 + \delta)$, and $f'(x) > 0$ for all x in $(x_0 - \delta, x_0)$.

3. **(a)** 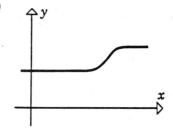   **(b)**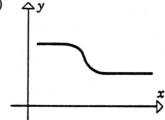

4. **(a)** Let $x_2 > x_1$, where x_1 and x_2 are points in (a, b). f is continuous on $[x_1, x_2]$ and differentiable on (x_1, x_2) so $[f(x_2) - f(x_1)]/(x_2 - x_1) = f'(c)$, c in (x_1, x_2), $f(x_2) - f(x_1) = (x_2 - x_1)f'(c) \ge 0$ because $x_2 - x_1 > 0$ and $f'(x) \ge 0$, thus $f(x_2) \ge f(x_1)$ so f is nondecreasing on (a, b).

   (b) Proof similar to that in part (a).

5. Let $h(x) = f(x) - g(x)$, then $h'(x) = f'(x) - g'(x) < 0$ thus h is decreasing on (a, b), that is $h(x_2) < h(x_1)$ if $x_2 > x_1$ so $f(x_2) - g(x_2) < f(x_1) - g(x_1)$, $f(x_2) - f(x_1) < g(x_2) - g(x_1)$.

6. (a) $\lim_{x \to 0} f'(x) = f'(x_0)$ from the assumption of continuity of $f'(x)$ at x_0 so that we can use

$\epsilon = \dfrac{1}{2}f'(x_0)$ in the definition of limit and deduce that there exists a $\delta > 0$ for which

$|f'(x) - f'(x_0)| < \dfrac{1}{2}f'(x_0)$ (i) whenever x is in the open interval $I = (x_0 - \delta, \, x_0 + \delta)$.

From (i), $-\dfrac{1}{2}f'(x_0) < f'(x) - f'(x_0) < \dfrac{1}{2}f'(x_0)$ thus $\dfrac{1}{2}f'(x_0) < f'(x) < \dfrac{3}{2}f'(x_0)$ (ii)

But $\dfrac{1}{2}f'(x_0) > 0$ because $f'(x_0) > 0$ so from the left hand inequality in (ii) we conclude that $f'(x) > 0$ for all x in I. It follows that f is increasing on I.

(b) Similar to the proof in part (a); use $\epsilon = -\dfrac{1}{2}f'(x_0)$ to show that $f'(x) < 0$ on I.

7. (a) From Exercise 6(a) it follows that $f'(x)$ is increasing on some open interval I containing x_0 so f is concave up on I.

(b) Similar to the proof in part (a).

8. f is continuous on $[a, b]$ because f is differentiable there, so f has both a maximum value and a minimum value on $[a, b]$. If $f'(a)f'(b) < 0$ then either Case 1: $f'(a) > 0$ and $f'(b) < 0$ or Case 2: $f'(a) < 0$ and $f'(b) > 0$ holds. Suppose (1) is true, then from Exercise 6 there is an open interval containing a on which f is increasing, and an open interval containing b on which f is decreasing so f does not attain its maximum value at either a or b (there are values of x to the right of a where $f(x) > f(a)$ because f is increasing in some open interval containing a; similarly there are values of x to the left of b where $f(x) > f(b)$ because f is decreasing in some open interval containing b). The maximum must occur at some point c in (a, b). Because f is differentiable at c it follows that $f'(c) = 0$. The proof for case 2 is similar to that for case 1; consider the minimum value of f on $[a, b]$.

EXERCISES, CRAMER'S RULE

1. $\begin{vmatrix} 3 & -4 \\ 2 & 1 \end{vmatrix} = 11, \quad \begin{vmatrix} -5 & -4 \\ 4 & 1 \end{vmatrix} = 11, \quad \begin{vmatrix} 3 & -5 \\ 2 & 4 \end{vmatrix} = 22; \; x = 1, \, y = 2$

2. $\begin{vmatrix} -1 & 3 \\ 2 & 5 \end{vmatrix} = -11, \quad \begin{vmatrix} 8 & 3 \\ 7 & 5 \end{vmatrix} = 19, \quad \begin{vmatrix} -1 & 8 \\ 2 & 7 \end{vmatrix} = -23; \; x = -19/11, \, y = 23/11$

3. $\begin{vmatrix} 2 & -5 \\ 4 & 6 \end{vmatrix} = 32, \quad \begin{vmatrix} -2 & -5 \\ 1 & 6 \end{vmatrix} = -7, \quad \begin{vmatrix} 2 & -2 \\ 4 & 1 \end{vmatrix} = 10; \; x_1 = -7/32, \, x_2 = 5/16$

4. $\begin{vmatrix} 3 & 2 \\ -1 & 1 \end{vmatrix} = 5, \quad \begin{vmatrix} 4 & 2 \\ 7 & 1 \end{vmatrix} = -10, \quad \begin{vmatrix} 3 & 4 \\ -1 & 7 \end{vmatrix} = 25; \; a = -2, \, b = 5$

5. $\begin{vmatrix} 1 & 2 & 1 \\ 2 & 1 & -1 \\ 1 & -1 & 1 \end{vmatrix} = -9, \quad \begin{vmatrix} 3 & 2 & 1 \\ 0 & 1 & -1 \\ 6 & -1 & 1 \end{vmatrix} = -18, \quad \begin{vmatrix} 1 & 3 & 1 \\ 2 & 0 & -1 \\ 1 & 6 & 1 \end{vmatrix} = 9, \quad \begin{vmatrix} 1 & 2 & 3 \\ 2 & 1 & 0 \\ 1 & -1 & 6 \end{vmatrix} = -27;$

$x = 2, \, y = -1, \, z = 3$

6. $\begin{vmatrix} 1 & -3 & 1 \\ 2 & -1 & 0 \\ 4 & 0 & -3 \end{vmatrix} = -11, \quad \begin{vmatrix} 4 & -3 & 1 \\ -2 & -1 & 0 \\ 0 & 0 & -3 \end{vmatrix} = 30, \quad \begin{vmatrix} 1 & 4 & 1 \\ 2 & -2 & 0 \\ 4 & 0 & -3 \end{vmatrix} = 39, \quad \begin{vmatrix} 1 & -3 & 4 \\ 2 & -1 & -2 \\ 4 & 0 & 0 \end{vmatrix} = 40;$

$x = -30/11, \, y = -38/11, \, z = -40/11$

7. $\begin{vmatrix} 1 & 1 & -2 \\ 2 & -1 & 1 \\ 1 & -2 & -4 \end{vmatrix} = 21, \quad \begin{vmatrix} 1 & 1 & -2 \\ 2 & -1 & 1 \\ -4 & -2 & -4 \end{vmatrix} = 26, \quad \begin{vmatrix} 1 & 1 & -2 \\ 2 & 2 & 1 \\ 1 & -4 & -4 \end{vmatrix} = 25, \quad \begin{vmatrix} 1 & 1 & 1 \\ 2 & -1 & 2 \\ 1 & -2 & -4 \end{vmatrix} = 15;$

$x_1 = 26/21, \, x_2 = 25/21, \, x_3 = 5/7$

8. $\begin{vmatrix} 1 & 1 & 1 \\ 1 & -1 & -2 \\ -1 & 2 & 1 \end{vmatrix} = 5, \quad \begin{vmatrix} 2 & 1 & 1 \\ 0 & -1 & -2 \\ 4 & 2 & 1 \end{vmatrix} = 2, \quad \begin{vmatrix} 1 & 2 & 1 \\ 1 & 0 & -2 \\ -1 & 4 & 1 \end{vmatrix} = 14, \quad \begin{vmatrix} 1 & 1 & 2 \\ 1 & -1 & 0 \\ -1 & 2 & 4 \end{vmatrix} = -6;$

$r = 2/5, \, s = 14/5, \, t = -6/5$

9. $\begin{vmatrix} \cos\theta & -\sin\theta \\ \sin\theta & \cos\theta \end{vmatrix} = 1, \quad \begin{vmatrix} x & -\sin\theta \\ y & \cos\theta \end{vmatrix} = x\cos\theta + y\sin\theta, \quad \begin{vmatrix} \cos\theta & x \\ \sin\theta & y \end{vmatrix} = y\cos\theta - x\sin\theta;$

$x' = x\cos\theta + y\sin\theta, \, y' = -x\sin\theta + y\cos\theta$

10. $\begin{vmatrix} 2 & -1 & 3 \\ 4 & 2 & -2 \\ 6 & -3 & 1 \end{vmatrix} = -64, \quad \begin{vmatrix} 3 & -1 & 3 \\ 2 & 2 & -2 \\ 9 & -3 & 1 \end{vmatrix} = -64, \quad \begin{vmatrix} 2 & 3 & 3 \\ 4 & 2 & -2 \\ 6 & 9 & 1 \end{vmatrix} = 64, \quad \begin{vmatrix} 2 & -1 & 3 \\ 4 & 2 & 2 \\ 6 & -3 & 9 \end{vmatrix} = 0;$

$\sin\alpha = 1, \, \cos\beta = -1, \, \tan\gamma = 0 \text{ so } \alpha = \pi/2, \, \beta = \pi, \, \gamma = 0$